AN INTRODUCTION
TO ELECTROOPTIC DEVICES

AN INTRODUCTION TO ELECTROOPTIC DEVICES

SELECTED REPRINTS AND INTRODUCTORY TEXT BY

IVAN P. KAMINOW

Bell Telephone Laboratories, Inc.
Crawford Hill Laboratory
Holmdel, New Jersey

ACADEMIC PRESS, INC.

(Harcourt Brace Jovanovich, Publishers)

Orlando San Diego San Francisco New York London
Toronto Montreal Sydney Tokyo São Paulo

ACADEMIC PRESS, INC.
Orlando, Florida 32887

United Kingdom Edition published by
ACADEMIC PRESS, INC. (LONDON) LTD.
24/28 Oval Road, London NW1 7DX

Library of Congress Cataloging in Publication Data

Kaminow, Ivan P Date comp.
An introduction to electrooptic devices.

Includes bibliographical references.
1. Electrooptical devices. 2. Crystal optics.
3. Dielectrics. I. Title.
TA1770.K35 621.38′0414 73-793
ISBN 0-12-395050-3

PRINTED IN THE UNITED STATES OF AMERICA

84 85 86 87 9 8 7 6 5 4 3 2

For Florence

CONTENTS

CHAPTER II **Nonlinear Dielectric Effects**

CHAPTER III **Reprints**

3. Lumped Electrooptic Modulators

4. Traveling Wave Electrooptic Modulators

PREFACE

The term *electrooptic effect* as it is employed here refers to a change in the refractive index of a transparent substance induced by an applied electric field, usually at a frequency below the optic vibrational resonance of the lattice or molecule involved. The linear and quadratic electrooptic effects are known as the Pockels and Kerr effects, respectively. Devices based on these phenomena have been used for the control of light for nearly a century, but it was the discovery of the laser in 1960 that stimulated most of the recent study and application of these effects. It is the purpose of this monograph to present an introduction to the electrooptic effect and to summarize recent work on devices employing the electrooptic effect.

Chapter I provides the necessary background in classical crystal optics. The topics covered include crystal symmetry, the tensor description of linear dielectric properties, propagation in anisotropic media, and passive crystal optic devices. Chapter II introduces the phenomenological description of tensor nonlinear dielectric properties of crystals. Although the emphasis is on the electrooptic effect, an effort is made to show its relationship to more general nonlinear optical phenomena.

The remainder of the book consists of selected reprints that treat various aspects of the materials and device problem in detail. Two review papers give a survey of device design and application. A third contains a thorough listing of linear electrooptic coefficients for various substances. A table of quadratic coefficients can be found elsewhere.*

*S. H. Wemple and M. DiDomenico, Jr., *Appl. Solid State Sci.* **3** (1972).

Techniques for measuring and characterizing the electrooptic properties of crystals are covered by several recent reprints. Also included is a translation by Mrs. A. Werner of Bell Laboratories of the chapter on electrooptic effects in the 1906 edition of "Lehrbuch der Kristalloptic" by F. Pockels. He introduces the mathematical description of the electrooptic effect used today. He also describes his experiments to prove to the skeptics of the day that a "true" linear electrooptic effect, independent of strain, does in fact exist.

Device configurations that have been employed to modulate and deflect laser beams are covered by other groups of reprints. Some very recent work on producing these devices in thin film or integrated optics configurations is also included.

Experimental work exploring the physics of the electrooptic effect is treated briefly. However, theoretical studies of the physical origin of the electrooptic effect is not included as it is still imperfectly understood. The present theoretical situation has been reviewed thoroughly by Wemple and DiDomenico.*

Several experiments have demonstrated picture display devices employing electrooptic crystals† or ceramic materials.‡ Unfortunately, space limitations do not permit their inclusion.

Internal modulation of lasers for Q-switching, mode-locking, and coupling modulation is chiefly a laser problem and is not covered here.

The first two chapters are taken from notes prepared for courses on nonlinear optics given at Princeton University in 1968, at UCLA in the summer of 1970, and at Bell Laboratories in 1972. I am grateful to Professor M. E. Van Valkenburg, Dr. Harold Lyons, Dr. L. K. Anderson, and the students at the respective institutions for providing the opportunity to organize this material.

I am also grateful to the authors and publishers who have generously allowed their work to be reproduced here.

*See footnote on page xiii.

†See for example: C. J. Salvo, *IEEE Trans. Electron. Devices* **ED-18,** 748 (1971); M. Grenot, J. Pergale, J. Donjon, and G. Marie, *Appl. Phys. Lett.* **21,** 83 (1972).

‡See for example: J. R. Maldanado and A. H. Meitzler, *Proc. IEEE* **59,** 368 (1971).

CHAPTER I

CRYSTAL OPTICS

For the most part, electrooptic materials are employed in the form of single crystals. In order to characterize these materials it will be necessary to introduce some of the nomenclature of crystallography. The physical properties of anisotropic media are described by tensors and these tensors can be greatly simplified by taking account of crystal symmetry.

Methods have been developed to describe the propagation of electromagnetic waves in crystals and are discussed briefly in this chapter.

A more thorough discussion of crystal optics is given in books by Nye,[1] Landau and Lifshitz,[2] and Born and Wolf.[3] A concise discussion of elementary crystallography is given by Kittel.[4]

1. Crystallography

1.1 *Bravais Lattice*

A crystal is a periodic array of atoms in three dimensions. The periodic building block is the *unit cell.* Typical unit cell dimensions in inorganic materials are ~10 Å = 10^{-9} m. Hence, any crystal of macroscopic size (~1 cm) may be regarded as infinite in extent on the scale of unit cell dimensions. There are only seven shapes that a unit cell may have and still fill all space. These shapes define a set of crystallographic *systems*, which are listed in Table 1.1. The shapes of the three-dimensional cells belonging to each system are shown in Fig. 1.1. The simplest cell in each system is the *primitive cell P* and it contains *one atom*. There are 8 atoms at the corners of the cell but each atom is shared by 8 other cells. One can also form *body centered* cells *I* which contain 2 atoms; *face centered* cells *F* with 4 atoms; and *partially face centered* cells *C* with 2 atoms. There is also a *rhombohedral* cell *R* which is obtained from a cubic cell by stretching along a body diagonal.

The edges of the cells define a three-dimensional coordinate system with *base vectors* **a**, **b**, **c** which need not be orthogonal. The angles between **a** and **b**, **b** and **c**, **c** and **a** are γ, α, and β, respectively. When unit cells of one kind are stacked to fill all space, the atomic positions form an array of *lattice points*, or simply a *lattice*. The space lattices formed from the 14 elementary cells in Fig. 1.1 are called *Bravais lattices*. Certain *elemental* crystals are formed by placing identical atoms at the lattice points. For example,

TABLE 1.1
The Fourteen Lattice Types in Three Dimensions[a]

System	Number of lattices in system	Lattice symbols	Restrictions on conventional unit-cell axes and angles
Triclinic	1	P	$a \neq b \neq c$ $\alpha \neq \beta \neq \gamma$
Monoclinic	2	P, C	$a \neq b \neq c$ $\alpha = \gamma = 90° \neq \beta$
Orthorhombic	4	P, C, I, F	$a \neq b \neq c$ $\alpha = \beta = \gamma = 90°$
Tetragonal	2	P, I	$a = b \neq c$ $\alpha = \beta = \gamma = 90°$
Cubic	3	P or sc I or bcc F or fcc	$a = b = c$ $\alpha = \beta = \gamma = 90°$
Trigonal	1	R	$a = b = c$ $\alpha = \beta = \gamma < 120°$, $\neq 90°$
Hexagonal	1	P	$a = b \neq c$ $\alpha = \beta = 90°$ $\gamma = 120°$

[a] After C. Kittel "Introduction to Solid State Physics," 4th ed. Wiley, New York, 1971. Copyright © 1971 by John Wiley and Sons, Inc. Used with permission of the publisher.

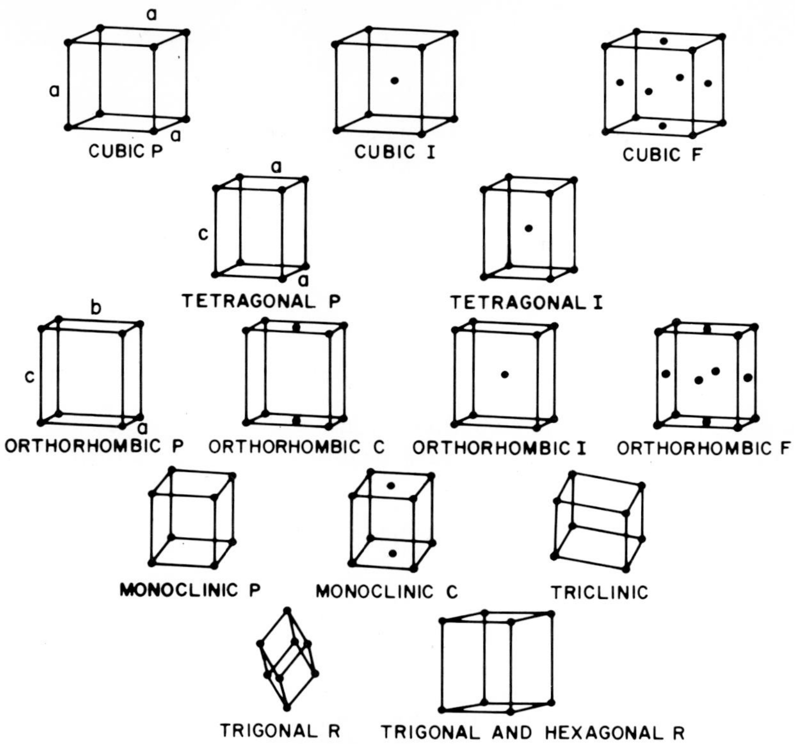

Fig. 1.1 Unit cells of the fourteen Bravais lattices (After C. Kittel, "Introduction to Solid State Physics," 4th ed., Wiley, New York, 1971. Copyright © 1971 by John Wiley and Sons, Inc. Used with permission of the publisher.)

aluminum is face centered cubic (fcc); and iron is body centered cubic (bcc).

Distances in the lattice can be measured in terms of the *lattice constants* a, b, c. If the origin is taken at a lattice point, the radius vector to any other lattice point is

$$\mathbf{r} = h\mathbf{a} + k\mathbf{b} + l\mathbf{c} \tag{1}$$

where h, k, l are integers. A particular direction can be specified by the set of integers $[hkl]$ defining **r**. Thus, [1 0 0], [0 1 0], and [0 0 1] point along the coordinate axes **a**, **b**, and **c**, respectively; and $[\bar{1}\ 0\ 0]$, $[0\ \bar{1}\ 0]$, $[0\ 0\ \bar{1}]$ point in the opposite directions. It is conventional to use square brackets for this set. In the cubic system all three directions **a**, **b**, **c** are equivalent and one speaks of "the set of $\langle 100 \rangle$ directions." Specific directions are given in square brackets and a set of equivalent directions in angular brackets.

A *primitive cell* containing only one lattice point may be defined for any Bravais lattice. However, the primitive cells may not exhibit the symmetry

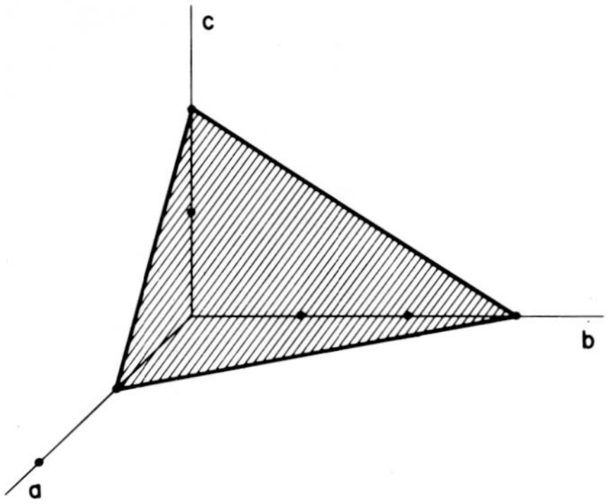

Fig. 1.2 The (623) plane.

of the appropriate system as well as the unit cells in Fig. 1.1. For example, in the fcc lattice with unit cell base vectors **a, b, c** of equal length a, the primitive cell base vectors are

$$\mathbf{a}' = \tfrac{1}{2}(\mathbf{a} + \mathbf{b}), \qquad \mathbf{b}' = \tfrac{1}{2}(\mathbf{b} + \mathbf{c}), \qquad \mathbf{c}' = \tfrac{1}{2}(\mathbf{a} + \mathbf{c}) \tag{2}$$

and the primitive cell volume V'

$$V' = (\mathbf{a}' \times \mathbf{b}') \cdot \mathbf{c}' = \tfrac{1}{4}a^3 = \tfrac{1}{4}V. \tag{3}$$

Thus, the primitive cell has a curious shape containing one-fourth the volume of the cubic unit cell. (See Fig. 1.6.)

Planes of lattice points can be specified by a set of *Miller indices* as follows: (a) Write the set of numbers giving the intercepts of the plane on **a, b, c** in units of lattice constants a, b, c. In Fig. 1.2 the intercepts are 1, 3, 2. (b) Take the reciprocals, 1/1, 1/3, 1/2. (c) Multiply by the smallest number that will make each reciprocal an integer, i.e., $6(1/1, 1/3, 1/2) = (6, 2, 3)$. The integers are enclosed in parentheses and the plane is called the (623) plane. Other planes in the cubic system are shown in Fig. 1.3. The bar over a number, e.g., $(\bar{1}00)$, means a *negative* intercept. The planes need not pass through lattice points, e.g., (200) is midway between lattice point planes. Equivalent sets of planes are enclosed in braces; e.g., in the cubic system (100), (010), and (001) are {100} planes.

In the cubic system the plane (hkl) is perpendicular to the direction $[hkl]$. In the tetragonal system only $(hk0)$ planes are perpendicular to $[hk0]$ directions; in the orthorhombic system only $(h00)$ planes and $[h00]$ directions are perpendicular.

1.2 *Symmetry Operations of Point Groups*

In order to reduce tensor quantities that describe the physical properties of a Bravais lattice, it will be necessary to know what symmetry operations leave the lattice invariant. These same operations must also leave any mathematical description of a physical property of the lattice invariant.

Of course, any translation

$$\mathbf{t} = h\mathbf{a} + k\mathbf{b} + l\mathbf{c},$$

with h, k, l integers, is a symmetry operation. However, this operation will not simplify a tensor that describes a *macroscopic* property—i.e., one that treats many cells identically. Typical optical wavelengths of 10,000 Å extend over ~1000 cells, and radio frequency wavelengths are at least 10^3 greater. Hence, displacements of an infinite lattice by a few lattice constants does not change the physical or mathematical situation significantly. Only if wavelengths comparable to lattice spacing (e.g. X rays) are used must the translational variation of the field be considered. For our purposes, we may ignore translations much shorter than an optical wavelength and, in particular, translations on the order of a, b, or c. We may, therefore, refer all symmetry operations to a convenient point in a cell through which all symmetry elements pass. We then speak of the *point symmetry* properties of the lattice.

The allowed symmetry elements for a Bravais lattice are limited as follows. The *identity* operation E corresponds to a rotation of 0 or 2π about any axis and is an element of every lattice. An *n-fold rotation* C_n corresponds to a rotation of $p(2\pi/n)$ about an axis, where p and n are integers. Only two-, three-, four-, and sixfold axes are consistent with an infinite lattice. In a *cubic lattice*, $2C_3$ rotations of $2\pi/3$ and $4\pi/3$ about the [111] axis are symmetry operations, as are similar rotations about $[\bar{1}\bar{1}1]$, $[1\bar{1}1]$, and $[\bar{1}11]$—there are $8C_3$ operations. Rotations of π about [110] and the five other equivalent directions make up $6C_2$ operations. Rotations of π

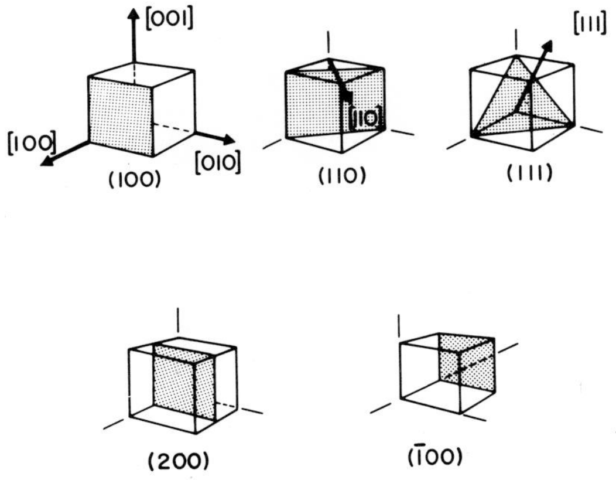

Fig. 1.3 Principal planes in the cubic system (After C. Kittel, "Introduction to Solid State Physics," 4th ed., Wiley, New York, 1971. Copyright © 1971 by John Wiley and Sons, Inc. Used with permission of the publisher.)

about the [100] directions account for $3C_2$ operations and rotations of $\pi/2$ and $3\pi/2$ about these axes constitute $6C_4$ operations.

Every Bravais lattice has an *inversion center* I as a symmetry operation. The lattice is also said to be *centrosymmetric* or *centric*. The inversion is performed by transforming every point at radius $\mathbf{r}$ with respect to the inversion center to the position $-\mathbf{r}$. Reflection in a *mirror plane* σ is identical

TABLE 1.2
Point Groups[a]

Crystal system	Class symbol: International	Class symbol: Schönflies	Elements of symmetry
Triclinic	1	C_1	E
	$\bar{1}$	C_i	EI
Monoclinic	m	C_3	$E\sigma_h$
	2	C_2	EC_2
	$2/m$	C_{2h}	$EC_2 I\sigma_h$
Orthorhombic	$2mm$	C_{2v}	$EC_2 \sigma'_v \sigma''_v$
	222	D_2	$EC_2 C'_2 C''_2$
	mmm	D_{2h}	$EC_2 C'_2 C''_2 I\sigma_h \sigma'_v \sigma''_v$
Tetragonal	4	C_4	$E2C_4 C_2$
	$\bar{4}$	S_4	$E2S_4 C_2$
	$4/m$	C_{4h}	$E2C_4 C_2 I2S_4 \sigma_h$
	$4mm$	C_{4v}	$E2C_4 C_2 2\sigma'_v 2\sigma''_v$
	$\bar{4}2m$	D_{2d}	$EC_2 C'_2 C''_2 \sigma'_v 2S_4 \sigma''_v$
	422	D_4	$E2C_4 C_2 2C'_2 2C''_2$
	$4/mmm$	D_{4h}	$E2C_4 C_2 2C'_2 2C''_2 I2S_4 \sigma_h 2\sigma'_v 2\sigma''_v$
Trigonal	3	C_3	$E2C_3$
	$\bar{3}$	C_{3i}	$E2C_3 I2S_3$
	$3m$	C_{3v}	$E2C_3 3\sigma_v$
	32	D_3	$E2C_3 3C_2$
	$\bar{3}m$	D_{3d}	$E2C_3 3C_2 I2S_3 3\sigma_v$
Hexagonal	6	C_6	$E2C_6 2C_3 C_2$
	$\bar{6}$	C_{3h}	$E2C_3 \sigma_h 2S_6$
	$6/m$	C_{6h}	$E2C_6 2C_3 C_2 I2S_3 2S_6 \sigma_h$
	$\bar{6}m2$	D_{3h}	$E2C_3 3C_2 \sigma_h 2S_6 3\sigma_v$
	$6mm$	C_{6v}	$E2C_6 2C_3 C_2 3\sigma'_v 3\sigma''$
	622	D_6	$E2C_6 2C_3 C_2 3C'_2 3C''_2$
	$6/mmm$	D_{6h}	$E2C_6 2C_3 C_2 3C'_2 3C''_2 I2S_3 2S_6 \sigma_h 2\sigma'_v 3\sigma''_v$
Cubic	23	T	$E8C_3 3C_2$
	$m3$	T_h	$E8C_3 3C_2 I8S_3 3\sigma$
	$\bar{4}3m$	T_d	$E8C_3 3C_2 6\sigma 6S_4$
	432	O	$E8C_3 3C_2 6C_2 6C_4$
	$m3m$	O_h	$E8C_3 3C_2 6C_2 6C_4 I8S_3 3\sigma 6\sigma 6S_4$

[a] After S. Bhagavantam "*Crystal Symmetry and Physical Properties.*" Academic Press, New York, 1966.

to reflection in a real mirror where the transformed lattice corresponds to the mirror image. In the cubic lattice the {100} planes account for 3σ operations and the {110} planes account for 6σ operations. A mirror normal to a symmetry axis is denoted by σ_h while a mirror containing the axis is σ_v. The final type of symmetry element is a *rotation-inversion* axis S_n. This operation is a rotation C_n followed by an inversion I through a point on the rotation axis. The operations involving σ, I, or S_n take a right-handed coordinate frame into a left-handed frame and vice versa, while E and C_n leave the handedness unchanged. The latter operations are said to be *proper rotations*, while the former are *improper rotations*. In the cubic Bravais lattice a rotation of $\pi/3$ or $5\pi/3$ about the eight $\langle 111 \rangle$ directions followed by I make up $8S_3$ operations. There are also $6S_4$ operations about the $\langle 100 \rangle$ directions.

These 48 operations or symmetry elements: E, $8C_3$, $3C_2$, $6C_2$, $6C_4$, I, $8S_3$, 3σ, 6σ, and $6S_4$ make up the *point group* of the cubic Bravais lattices. The elements form a mathematical group because, among other things, the product of two or more operations is another member of the group. *Further, all the elements pass through a common lattice point which remains fixed under these operations.*

More complicated crystal structures—including those containing several different kinds of atoms—may be developed from a Bravais lattice as follows: Consider a cluster of two or more atoms, called a *basis*, which is referred to some arbitrary origin. There will be a group of operations centered at the origin that transform the cluster into itself. A crystal may be formed by placing the origin of the basis at each lattice point of a Bravais lattice. Each atom of the basis will then form a *sublattice* displaced from but otherwise identical with the fundamental Bravais lattice. In general, the basis will lower the symmetry—i.e., will eliminate some symmetry elements. The number of *point groups* that can be formed from the 14 Bravais lattices in this way is 32. The elements of these groups are summarized in Table 1.2. Primes on C_n and σ_v indicate distinct elements and numerical prefixes indicate equivalent elements or multiple operations of the same element. The last group in each system has the greatest number of elements and is appropriate to the Bravais lattices. These latter groups are said to possess *holohedral symmetry* for the system. Each point group is denoted by an *international* and a *Schönflies* symbol. The orientations of the symmetry elements for each group are shown in a three-dimensional figure and a stereogram in Fig. 1.4, taken from the very useful book by Wood.[5] The development of the stereographic projection is illustrated in Fig. 1.5.

The open and closed circles (○, ●) on the stereograms in Fig. 1.4 have the following significance. Consider a point at a general position in space—not on a mirror plane, rotation axis, or center of inversion. Each symmetry operation of the point group will generate another point above (●) or below (○) the equatorial plane. The set of points so generated exhibit the point

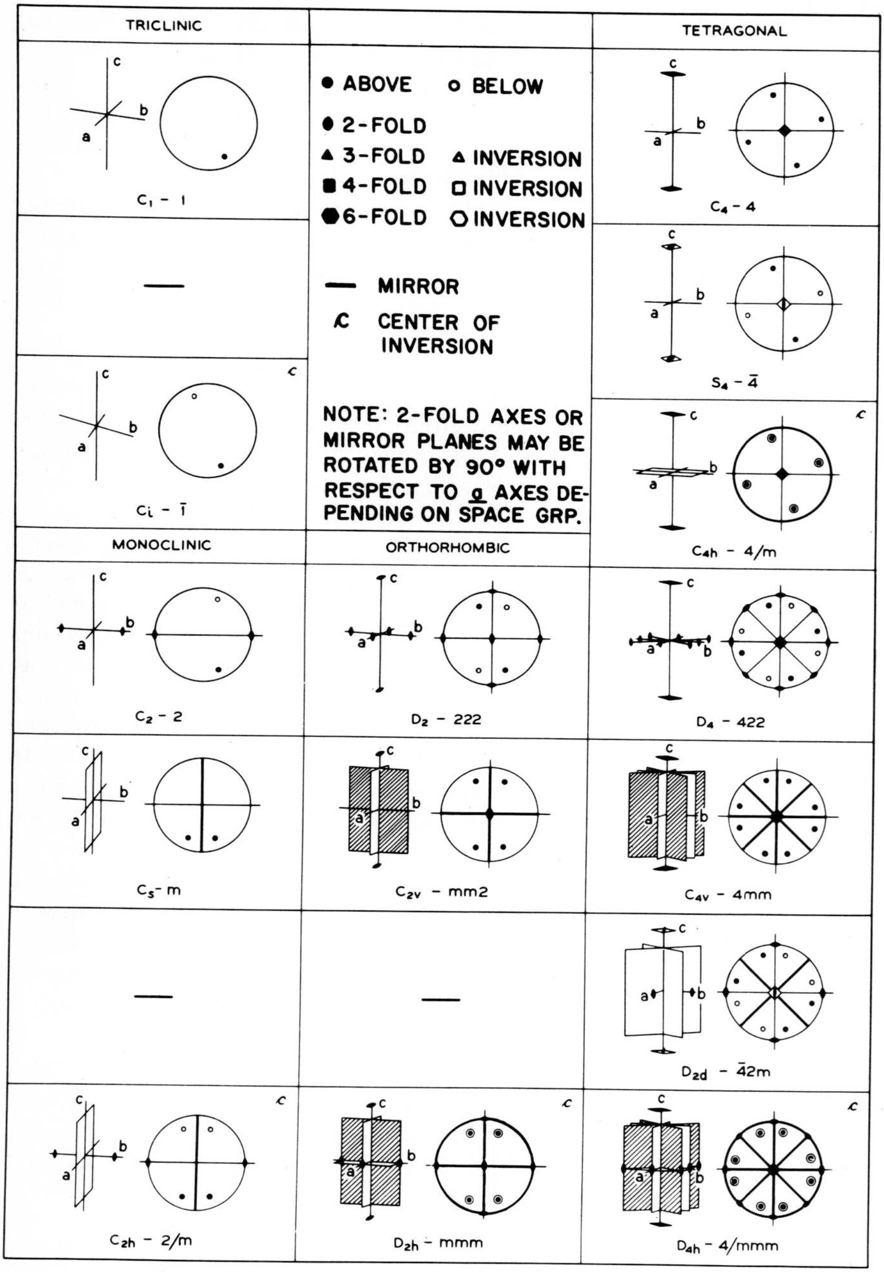

Fig. 1.4 Symmetries of the 32 point groups (after Wood[5]).

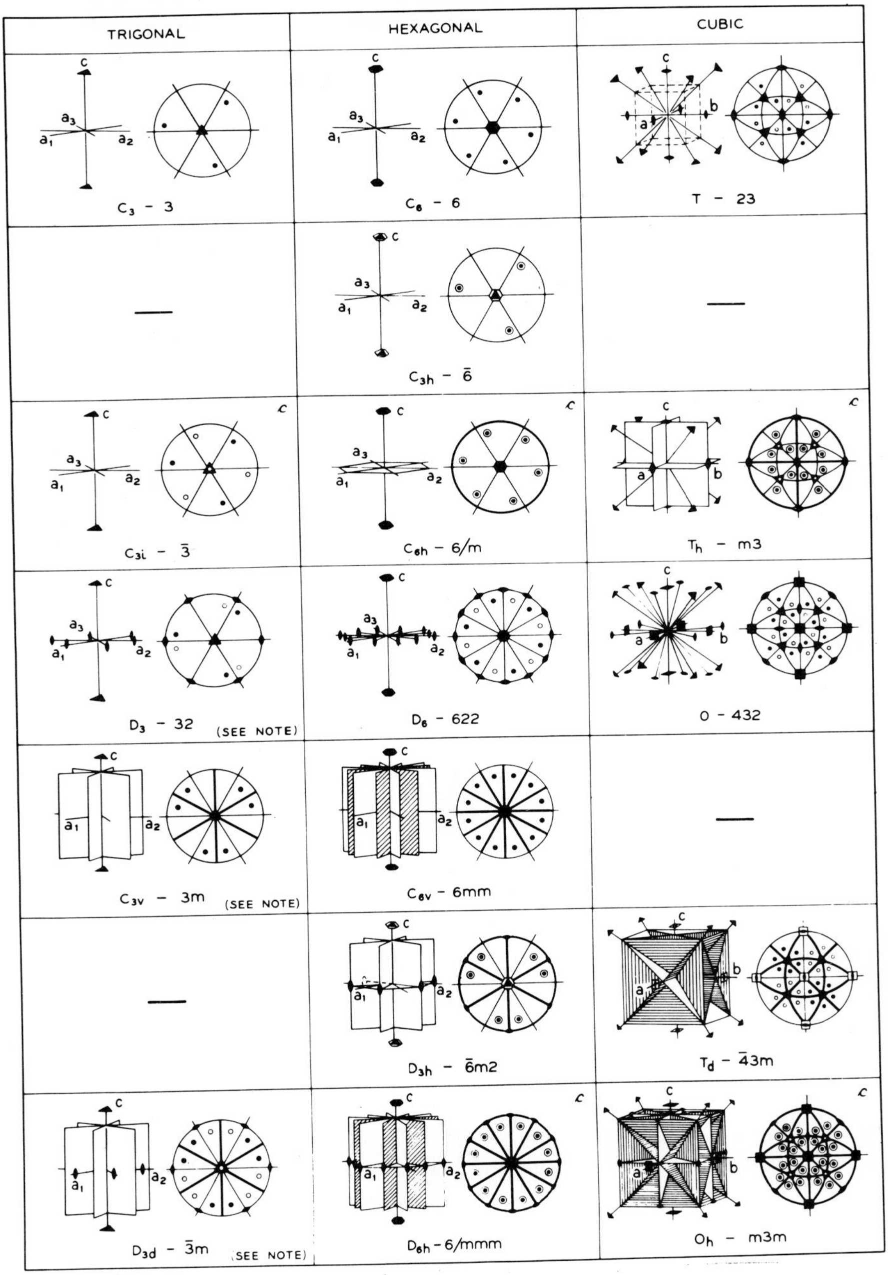

Fig. 1.4 *(continued)*

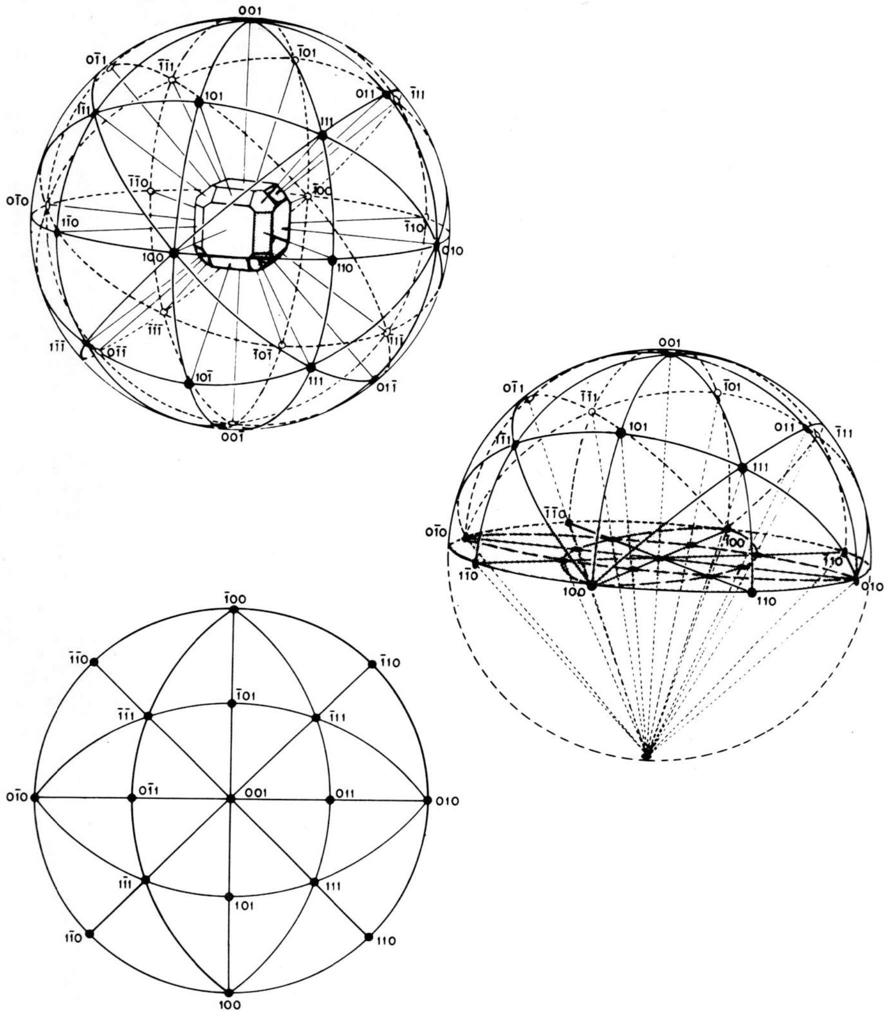

Fig. 1.5 Development of the stereographic projection (after Wood[5]).

group symmetry. If the starting point is located on a symmetry element (a special position), fewer points will be generated. For example, in the *tetrahedral group* T_d, if the starting point has coordinates (1, 1, 1), it is on one of the 6σ planes and one of the $8C_3$ axes. A point group element transforms a point on the element into itself; i.e., it does not generate a new point. The identity element E also does not generate a new point. The $3C_2$ elements generate points at $(1, 1, 1)$, $(\bar{1}, \bar{1}, \bar{1})$, $(1, \bar{1}, \bar{1})$, $(\bar{1}, 1, \bar{1})$ which are at the corners of a tetrahedron. The $6S_4$ elements about $\langle 100 \rangle$ directions generate the same set of points.

Four examples of cubic crystal lattices are given in Fig. 1.6. The Bravais lattice for NaCl is fcc and the basis consists of a Na and a Cl atom separated by half the lattice constant $a/2$ along a cube edge. The NaCl *rocksalt* lattice is thus made up of two fcc *sublattices*. The point group is O_h or $m3m$. *Diamond* is made up of two fcc carbon sublattices displaced along the unit cell body diagonal by 1/4 the length of the diagonal, $\sqrt{3}a/4$. The point group is also O_h. GaAs has the *zinc blende* structure, which is similar to that of diamond except that the two sublattices contain different atoms; the basis no longer has a center of inversion midway between the atoms. The symmetry is lowered by the basis and the point group is $T_d - \bar{4}3m$. Unlike O_h, T_d has no inversion center, which we will see has an important effect on the properties of crystals with this symmetry.

The point groups are those groups of point symmetry elements which when applied to an infinite three-dimensional crystal structure leave one point unmoved. Only 32 such groups are possible. A crystal structure that transforms according to a particular group of elements (i.e., is left invariant by the operations of the group) is said to belong to the corresponding *crystal class*, e.g., T_d, O_h, etc. The point group requirement must be relaxed in order to account for all real crystal structures. In particular, two new elements that do not leave any point unmoved must be added. The first is a *glide plane*, which is a mirror reflection followed by a translation parallel to the plane by a fraction of a lattice constant. The second is a *screw axis*, which is a proper rotation followed by a displacement along the axis by a fraction of a lattice constant. With these new elements, there are 230 ways of combining the symmetry elements into groups, called *space groups*.

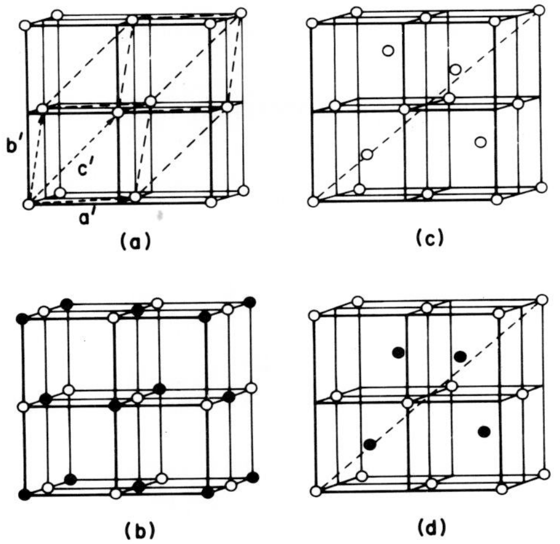

Fig. 1.6 Cubic lattices: (a) face centered cubic, showing the primitive cell, (b) rock salt, (c) diamond, and (d) zinc blende. (After M. Born and K. Huang, "*Dynamical Theory of Crystal Lattices*," Oxford Univ. Press, London and New York, 1966.)

Furthermore, these elements need not pass through a common point in the unit cell.

The displacements involved in the space groups, having dimensions on the order of a lattice constant, can have no influence on *macroscopic* properties, which by definition are uniform over many unit cells. Hence for optical problems it is sufficient to describe all crystal structures in terms of an equivalent point group, which is derived from the space group by replacing glide planes and screw axes by ordinary mirror planes and rotation axes. Any translation of magnitude comparable to a lattice constant may be employed to bring the structure back into position after an operation. *Macroscopic symmetry is described by the equivalent point groups.* A crystal with the equivalent point group symmetry is said to belong to one of the 32 classes. Each of the 230 space groups is defined and locations of symmetry elements are prescribed in the "International Tables for X-ray Crystallography."[6]

The fourfold axis of diamond, Fig. 1.6c, is a screw axis—90° rotation plus translation of a/2—passing through a carbon atom parallel to $\langle 100 \rangle$. The threefold axis is not a screw axis and passes through a carbon atom parallel to $\langle 111 \rangle$. The inversion center is at the midpoint of the bond between carbon sublattices—$\sqrt{3}\,a/8$ from a carbon atom along the body diagonal. The inversion center is absent in GaAs because it would transform a Ga into an As, which would not leave the lattice invariant.

2. Tensor Properties

2.1 *Dielectric Description*

The electric field **E**, dielectric displacement **D**, and polarization **P** are *vector* quantities that describe the fields in a dielectric medium. For an *isotropic* medium such as glass, these vectors are related by a *scalar dielectric constant* K or *susceptibility* χ. In MKS units

$$\mathbf{D} = \varepsilon_0 K \mathbf{E} \tag{1}$$

$$\mathbf{P} = \varepsilon_0 (K - 1)\mathbf{E} = \varepsilon_0 \chi \mathbf{E} \tag{2}$$

where

$$\varepsilon_0 = 10^{-9}/36\pi \text{ F/m} = 8.842 \quad \text{pF/m} \tag{3}$$

is the permittivity of vacuum. The vectors **E**, **D**, and **P** are all parallel.

In an anisotropic medium such as a crystal, the dielectric constant and susceptibility are *second-rank* tensors with components K_{ij} and χ_{ij}. The components of the fields along the coordinates x_1, x_2, x_3 are given by

$$D_i = \varepsilon_0 K_{ij} E_j \tag{4}$$

$$P_i = \varepsilon_0 (K_{ij} - 1) E_j = \varepsilon_0 \chi_{ij} E_j. \tag{5}$$

It will always be understood in what follows that each term is to be summed over all repeated indices $j = 1, 2, 3$ (Einstein sum convention). Thus, (4) consists of three equations, the first of which is

$$D_1 = \varepsilon_0 [K_{11} E_1 + K_{12} E_2 + K_{13} E_3]. \tag{6}$$

2.2 *Coordinate Transformation*

It will often be necessary to rotate the coordinate frame, as illustrated in Fig. 2.1a. Scalar quantities are unchanged by such a rotation but the components A_i of a vector quantity $\mathbf{A}$ in the old frame become A'_i in the new frame

$$A'_i = a_{ij} A_j \tag{1}$$

where $a_{ij} = \cos \theta_{ij}$ is the *direction cosine* of the angle between the new x'_i and old x_j axes. The elements a_{ij} make up the *transformation matrix*. For a

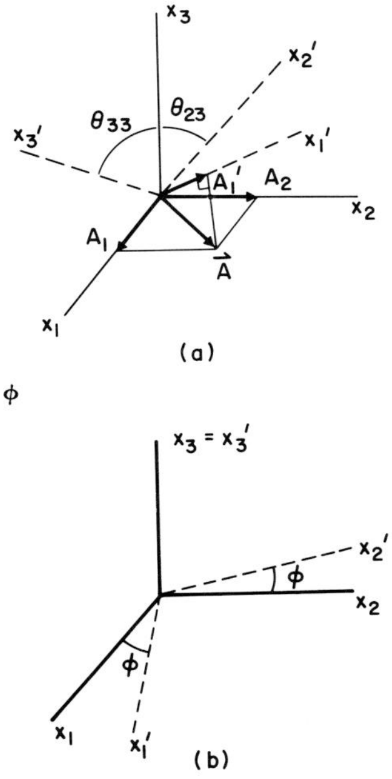

Fig. 2.1 Rotation of axes: (a) general, (b) rotation ϕ about x_3.

rotation of ϕ about the x_3 axis, for example,

$$a_{ij}(\phi) = \begin{bmatrix} \cos\phi & \sin\phi & 0 \\ -\sin\phi & \cos\phi & 0 \\ 0 & 0 & 1 \end{bmatrix}. \tag{2}$$

In order to transform in the reverse direction, from new to old, we use the *inverse transformation* a_{ij}^{-1} which is given by the *transpose matrix* $\tilde{a}_{ij} \equiv a_{ji} = a_{ij}^{-1}$ for rotations,

$$A_i = \tilde{a}_{ij} A'_j = a_{ji} A'_j. \tag{3}$$

In this case, for a rotation ϕ about x'_3,

$$\tilde{a}_{ij}(\phi) = a_{ji}(\phi) = \begin{bmatrix} \cos\phi & -\sin\phi & 0 \\ \sin\phi & \cos\phi & 0 \\ 0 & 0 & 1 \end{bmatrix}. \tag{4}$$

The transpose matrix corresponds to the direct matrix for a rotation $-\phi$.

Equation (1) holds for any vector **A** and in particular it holds for the radial vector **r** from the origin to a point (x_1, x_2, x_3). Thus, the coordinates of this point in the new frame are

$$x'_i = a_{ij} x_j. \tag{7}$$

We say that a vector transforms like the coordinates of a point. For example, (a) a rotation of $\pi/2$ about x_3 transforms to coordinates

$$x'_1 = x_2, \qquad x'_2 = -x_1, \qquad x'_3 = x_3; \tag{8}$$

a point with coordinates (x_1, x_2, x_3) in the old frame has coordinates $(x_2, -x_1, x_3)$ in the rotated frame. (b) A rotation of $\pi/4$ about x_3 transforms to coordinates

$$x'_1 = 2^{-1/2}(x_1 + x_2), \qquad x'_2 = 2^{-1/2}(-x_1 + x_2), \qquad x'_3 = x_3. \tag{9}$$

Similar transformations hold for the components of any vector

$$(a) \quad A'_1 = A_2, \qquad A'_2 = -A_1, \qquad A'_3 = A_3;$$

$$(b) \quad A'_1 = 2^{-1/2}(A_1 + A_2), \qquad A'_2 = 2^{-1/2}(-A_1 + A_2), \qquad A'_3 = A_3.$$

The transformation matrix d for a sequence of operations abc is obtained by matrix multiplication in the proper sequence (right to left)

$$c_{ij} b_{jk} a_{kl} = d_{il} \tag{5}$$

where the Einstein sum convention over j and k is understood. A simple chain rule applies: adjacent indices of successive elements are identical (jj), (kk), and the unrepeated indices (il) appear on the product element.

The product of the direct and transpose matrices, representing a rotation and its inverse, is the *identity transformation E*, which is represented by the *unit matrix* δ_{ik}

$$\tilde{a}_{ij} a_{jk} = a_{ji} a_{jk} = \delta_{ik} \tag{6}$$

where $\delta_{ik} = 1$ for $i = k$ and $\delta_{ik} = 0$ for $i \neq k$. The *inversion transformation* I is given by $-\delta_{ik}$, and a *reflection* in a mirror normal to x_3, $\sigma(x_3)$, is given by σ_{ij} with $\sigma_{11} = \sigma_{22} = 1$, $\sigma_{33} = -1$, and $\sigma_{ij} = 0$ for $i \neq j$.

2.3 Transformation of Higher-Rank Tensors

A scalar is a *zero-rank tensor* and a vector a *first-rank tensor*. The dielectric constant K_{ij} is a *second-rank tensor*. Like the vector, it represents a physical quantity independent of coordinate frame. For a particular choice of axes, the tensor quantity is represented by a set of elements or components. If the axes are rotated, the elements—but not the physical quantity—change. A second-rank tensor has nine elements T_{ij} which may be put into a 3 × 3 array. Thus, it looks like the coordinate transformation matrix a_{ij} but has entirely different mathematical and physical properties. For example, its inverse is not given by the transpose matrix. However, the matrix multiplication rule (2.2.5) also holds for tensors.

A second-rank tensor couples two vectors:

$$A_k = T_{kl} B_l. \tag{1}$$

A coordinate transformation gives, with (2.2.3),

$$A'_i = a_{ik} A_k = a_{ik} T_{kl} B_l = a_{ik} T_{kl} a_{jl} B'_l. \tag{2}$$

But we define T_{ij} in the new coordinate frame so that

$$A'_i = T'_{ij} B'_j \tag{3}$$

and, comparing (2) and (3), we see that the tensor components in the new frame are

$$T'_{ij} = a_{ik} a_{jl} T_{kl}. \tag{4}$$

A *third-rank tensor* couples a product of two vectors and another vector, or a second-rank tensor and a vector:

$$A_l = T_{lmn} B_m C_n \tag{5}$$

or

$$T_{lm} = T_{lmn} A_n . \tag{6}$$

A *fourth-rank tensor* couples a product of three vectors and another vector, or two second-rank tensors, or a second-rank tensor and product of two vectors:

$$A_m = T_{mnop} B_n C_o D_p \tag{7}$$

or

$$T_{mn} = T_{mnop} T_{op} \tag{8}$$

or

$$T_{mn} = T_{mnop} A_o B_p . \tag{9}$$

The transformation rules can be shown, as in (2) and (3), to be

$$T'_{ijk} = a_{il} a_{jm} a_{kn} T_{lmn} \tag{10}$$

and

$$T'_{ijkl} = a_{im} a_{jn} a_{ko} a_{lp} T_{mnop} . \tag{11}$$

The symmetrical disposition of indices in (4), (10), and (11) is easy to see. The inverse transformation simply requires a transposition of indices:

$$T_{ij} = a_{ki} a_{lj} T'_{k1} \tag{12}$$

$$T_{ijk} = a_{li} a_{mj} a_{nk} T'_{lmn} \tag{13}$$

and

$$T_{ijkl} = a_{mi} a_{nj} a_{ok} a_{pl} T'_{mnop} . \tag{14}$$

The transformation of tensor components can be greatly simplified by the recognition of another simple rule[1]: *n-rank tensor components transform like corresponding n-order products of the coordinates of a point*; A_i transforms like x_i, T_{ij} like $x_i x_j$, T_{ijk} like $x_i x_j x_k$, T_{ijk1} like $x_i x_j x_k x_l$, etc. where the sequence of indices must be preserved. Thus, for example, the third-order product $(x_l x_m x_n)$ clearly transforms like T_{lmn};

$$(x'_i x'_j x'_k) = a_{il} x_l a_{jm} x_m a_{kn} x_n = a_{il} a_{jm} a_{kn} (x_l x_m x_n). \tag{15}$$

We can illustrate the application of this rule to the dielectric constant tensor K_{ij}. Suppose that K_{ij} is *diagonal*, i.e., $K_{ij} = 0$ for $i \neq j$, and that $K_{11} = K_1$, $K_{22} = K_2$, and $K_{33} = K_3$ in a given frame. Apply the transformations noted in (2.2.8) and (2.2.9): (a) a rotation of $\pi/2$ about x_3 transforms

$$x'_1 x'_1 = x_2 x_2 \quad \text{or} \quad K'_{11} = K_2, \qquad x'_2 x'_2 = x_1 x_1 \quad \text{or} \quad K'_{22} = K_1,$$
$$x'_3 x'_3 = x_3 x_3 \quad \text{or} \quad K'_{33} = K_3, \qquad x'_1 x'_2 = -x_2 x_1 \quad \text{or} \quad K'_{12} = -K_{21} = 0,$$
$$x'_2 x'_1 = -x_1 x_2 \quad \text{or} \quad K'_{21} = -K_{12} = 0, \qquad \text{and similarly all } K'_{ij} = 0$$
$$\text{for} \quad i \neq j; \qquad (16)$$

(b) a rotation of $\pi/4$ about x_3 transforms

$$x'_1 x'_1 = \tfrac{1}{2}(x_1 x_1 + x_1 x_2 + x_2 x_1 + x_2 x_2) \quad \text{or} \quad K'_{11} = \tfrac{1}{2}[K_1 + K_2]$$
$$\text{and similarly} \quad K'_{22} = \tfrac{1}{2}[K_1 + K_2],\ K'_{33} = K_3;$$
$$x'_1 x'_2 = \tfrac{1}{2}[-x_1 x_1 + x_1 x_2 - x_2 x_1 + x_2 x_2] \quad \text{or} \quad K'_{12} = \tfrac{1}{2}[-K_1 + K_2]$$
$$\text{and similarly} \quad K'_{21} = \tfrac{1}{2}[-K_1 + K_2];$$
$$x'_1 x'_3 = 2^{-1/2}[x_1 x_3 + x_2 x_3] \quad \text{or} \quad K'_{13} = 0$$
$$\text{and similarly} \quad K'_{31} = K'_{23} = K'_{32} = 0. \qquad (17)$$

In the first example (a), the dielectric tensor remains diagonal after transformation but in the second example (b), it does not. Any frame in which K_{ij} is diagonal is a *principal axis system.* As we shall show, the dielectric constant tensor K_{ij} must be *symmetrical*, i.e., $K_{ij} = K_{ji}$. And it can be shown[1] that any symmetrical second-rank tensor can always be diagonalized by suitable rotation of axes to the principal axis system.

We show that $K_{ij} = K_{ji}$ as follows: The differential Helmoltz free energy per unit volume of a dielectric is

$$dF = -S\,dT - D_i dE_i = -S\,dT - K_{ij} E_j dE_i \qquad (18)$$

where S and T are the entropy and temperature, respectively. Since

$$D_i = \partial F/\partial E_i \qquad \text{and} \qquad K_{ij} = \partial D_i/\partial E_j,$$

then at constant T,

$$K_{ij} = -(\partial^2 F/\partial E_i \partial E_j)_T. \qquad (19)$$

But dF is a total differential (i.e., its value depends only on the end points and not the path of the process), so that the partial differential in (19) must be independent of the sequence of differentiation. Therefore,

$$K_{ji} = -(\partial^2 F/\partial E_j \partial E_i)_T = K_{ij}. \qquad (20)$$

This thermodynamic proof[2] is strictly valid only for lossless dielectrics at zero frequency. However, it can be shown in general that K_{ij}, χ_{ij}, and all other second-rank tensors to be considered here are indeed symmetrical.[2]

2.4 Reduction of the Dielectric Tensor by Crystal Symmetry

A general second-rank tensor contains nine components. We have noted that $K_{ij} = K_{ji}$, which reduces the number of independent elements to six; and further that one can always find a principal axis system for which the dielectric tensor contains only three independent diagonal elements K_1, K_2, and K_3. This number can be reduced still further by taking crystal symmetry into account.

The dielectric tensor for a crystal is simply a mathematical representation of a physical property. *If a crystal is invariant under a group of symmetry operations, then any tensor representing a physical property of the crystal must be invariant under these operations.* We have seen how to rotate a coordinate frame with respect to a tensor property; rotating the tensor with respect to the frame is just the inverse operation. If the x_3 axis is a fourfold axis of a crystal, for example, then a rotation of the dielectric tensor by $\pm\pi/2$ or $\pm\pi$ must leave the dielectric tensor invariant. Thus,

$$K_{ij}(C_4) = K_{ij}(E), \tag{1}$$

which means that the tensor components having indices (ij) before rotation (identity operation E) must be identical with the components having indices (ij) after the symmetry operation C_4. From (2.3.16) we find

$$K_{11}(C_4) = K'_{11} = K_2, \tag{2}$$

but (1) requires that

$$K_{11}(C_4) = K_{11}(E) = K_1. \tag{3}$$

Thus, symmetry requires $K_1 = K_2$ for all crystals with a C_4 axis along x_3. An S_4 axis gives the same result because the inversion operation I does not interchange x_1 and x_2. Thus, the dielectric constant in the tetragonal system, which is characterized by a C_4 or an S_4 axis, is described by only two components $K_1 = K_2$ and K_3. It can also be shown that the same result obtains in the trigonal and hexagonal systems, which have three- and sixfold axes along x_3. The tetragonal, trigonal, and hexagonal systems are called *axial* or *uniaxial* systems. No simplification can be effected in the orthorhombic, monoclinic, and triclinic systems, which all require three independent components.

In the cubic system, the four threefold axes along $\langle 111 \rangle$ directions reduce the number of independent components to one, $K_1 = K_2 = K_3 = K$. The coordinate transformation under such a threefold rotation gives

$$x'_1 = x_2, \qquad x'_2 = x_3, \qquad x'_3 = x_1. \tag{4}$$

Then the transformed tensor components are

$$K_{11}(C_3) = K'_{11} = K_2, \qquad K_{22}(C_3) = K'_{22} = K_3, \qquad K_{33}(C_3) = K'_{33} = K_1. \tag{5}$$

But symmetry requires

$$K_{11}(C_3) = K_{11} = K_1, \qquad K_{22}(C_3) = K_{22} = K_2, \qquad K_{33}(C_3) = K_{33} = K_3, \tag{6}$$

which is consistent with (5) only if $K_1 = K_2 = K_3$. Thus, as far as second-rank tensor properties are concerned, a cubic crystal behaves as if it were *isotropic*.

Later, we will make use of the symmetry rule illustrated above to reduce higher-rank tensors. Mathematically the rule requires that

$$T_{ijk}(R) = T_{ijk}(E) \tag{7}$$

and

$$T_{ijkl}(R) = T_{ijkl}(E) \tag{8}$$

for third- and fourth-rank tensors where R is any symmetry operation of the point group and E is the identity operation.

3. Light Propagation in Anisotropic Crystals

3.1 *Normal Modes of Propagation*

In order to take advantage of the nonlinear properties of crystals it is necessary to understand a few of the subtle differences between propagation of plane waves in linear isotropic and anisotropic dielectrics. We will see that in an anisotropic medium propagation along a particular direction can be described in terms of two normal modes associated with two orthogonal directions of polarization. We will also see that wavefronts need not be normal to the direction of propagation.

The *normal modes* we seek are infinite plane wave solutions of Maxwell's equations in an anisotropic dielectric medium with

$$D_i = \varepsilon_0 K_{ij} E_j. \tag{1}$$

An essential characteristic of a normal mode is that it retains the same form as it propagates throughout a uniform medium. Assume all fields vary as unattenuated plane waves, $\exp[-i(\omega t - \mathbf{k} \cdot \mathbf{r})]$, with ω the *radian frequency*.

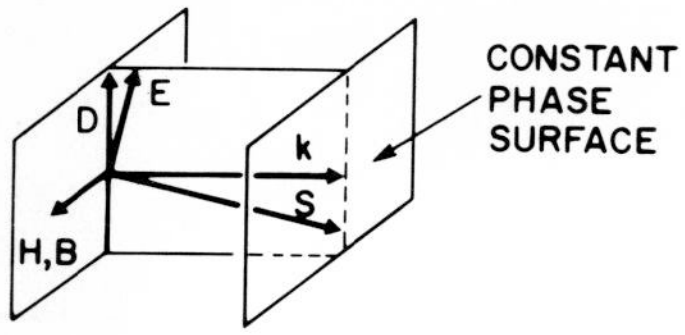

Fig. 3.1 Orientation of fields in anisotropic crystals (after Nye[1]).

The *wave vector* **k** defines the direction normal to surfaces of constant phase; i.e., surfaces on which $\mathbf{k} \cdot \mathbf{r}$ is a constant. The medium is taken to be a perfect insulator: K_{ij} real, conduction current $\mathbf{J} \equiv 0$; and nonmagnetic: $\mathbf{B} = \mu_0 \mathbf{H}$. Then Maxwell's equations are

$$\dot{\mathbf{D}} = -i\omega\mathbf{D} = \nabla \times \mathbf{H} = i\mathbf{k} \times \mathbf{H} \tag{2}$$

$$-\dot{\mathbf{B}} = i\omega\mu_0\mathbf{H} = \nabla \times \mathbf{E} = i\mathbf{k} \times \mathbf{E}. \tag{3}$$

The final equalities above are derived from the identity

$$\nabla \times (a\mathbf{A}) \equiv a\nabla \times \mathbf{A} + \nabla a \times \mathbf{A}. \tag{4}$$

It is clear from (2) that **D** is normal to **k** and **H**, and from (3) that **H** is normal to **k** and **E**. Hence, **D**, **k**, and **H** are mutually orthogonal, as in Fig. 3.1. The dielectric displacement **D** vibrates in a plane normal to **k**. The wave vector **k** is normal to the constant phase surfaces or *wavefronts* and **k** points in the *wave normal direction*. Wavefronts travel in the wave normal direction with *phase velocity* $v_p = \omega/k$.

The direction of power transmission is given by the Poynting vector **S**

$$\mathbf{S} = \mathbf{E} \times \mathbf{H} = \{|E|^2\mathbf{k} - (\mathbf{E} \cdot \mathbf{k})\mathbf{E}\}1/\omega\mu_0, \tag{5}$$

which is normal to **E** and **H**. The Poynting vector points in the *ray direction*. A packet of optical energy—an optical disturbance—travels in the ray direction at the *group velocity*. The second form of (5), obtained by substituting for **H** from (3) and using the identity

$$\mathbf{A} \times (\mathbf{B} \times \mathbf{C}) = (\mathbf{A} \cdot \mathbf{C})\mathbf{B} - (\mathbf{A} \cdot \mathbf{B})\mathbf{C} \tag{6}$$

gives the relative orientation of ray and wave normal directions.

Normal mode solutions for fields at frequency ω are characterized by particular values of k. These may be found by inserting (3) into (2) and using (6) to obtain

$$\omega^2\mu_0\mathbf{D} = \mathbf{k} \times (\mathbf{E} \times \mathbf{k}) = k^2\mathbf{E} - (\mathbf{k} \cdot \mathbf{E})\mathbf{k}. \tag{7}$$

Then insertion of the components for D from (1) gives

$$(\omega/c)^2 D_i/\varepsilon_0 = (\omega/c)^2 K_{ij} E_j = k^2 E_i - k_j E_j k_i \tag{8}$$

where $c = (\mu_0 \varepsilon_0)^{-1/2}$ is the velocity of light in vacuum. Rearranging (8) yields three homogeneous equations for $i = 1, 2, 3$.

$$(k^2 \delta_{ij} - k_i k_j - k_0^2 K_{ij}) E_j = 0 \tag{9}$$

where $k_0 = \omega/c$ and δ_{ij} is the unit matrix with $\delta_{ii} = 1$, $\delta_{ij} = 0$ for $i \neq j$. The equations have a consistent solution only when their determinant vanishes. In a principal axis system, K_{ij} is diagonal, i.e.

$$K_{ij} = K_{ii} \delta_{ij}, \tag{10}$$

and we require

$$\det |(k^2 - k_0^2 K_{ii}) \delta_{ij} - k_i k_j| = 0. \tag{11}$$

Expanding the determinant yields *Fresnel's equation*

$$k^2(K_{11} k_1^2 + K_{22} k_2^2 + K_{33} k_3^2) - [K_{11} k_1^2 (K_{22} + K_{33}) + K_{22} k_2^2 (K_{11} + K_{33}) + K_{33} k_3^2 (K_{11} + K_{22})] k_0^2 + K_{11} K_{22} K_{33} k_0^4 = 0. \tag{12}$$

Once the wave normal direction is specified by the components k_i/k, (11) becomes a fourth-order equation for the *wave number* k, which is the *magnitude* of the wave vector. Two solutions, with $k > 0$, correspond to orthogonal normal modes propagating in the +**r** (forward) direction, and two solutions, with the signs of the wave number reversed, correspond to propagation in the -**r** (backward) direction. The frequency ω appears explicitly in (12) and is also contained implicitly in the dispersion of K_{ij}. Hence, the dispersion of k, $k(\omega)$, can be determined from (12) if $K_{ii}(\omega)$ is known.

3.2 *Wave Vector Surfaces*

Equation (3.1.12) defines a fourth-order surface in k space. The surface is difficult to visualize in general but for a *uniaxial crystal* (i.e., a member of the tetragonal, trigonal (rhombohedral), or hexagonal systems) $K_{11} = K_{22}$ and (3.1.12) becomes

$$[k^2 - k_0^2 K_{11}][K_{11}(k_1^2 + k_2^2) + K_{33} k_3^2 - K_{11} K_{33} k_0^2] = 0. \tag{1}$$

(It is conventional to take x_3 as the symmetrical axis in uniaxial crystals.) The fourth-order Fresnel equation thus factors into two quadratic equations defining a sphere of radius $k_0(K_{11})^{1/2}$

$$k^2 = k_0^2 K_{11} \tag{2}$$

and an ellipsoid of revolution about k_3

$$[(k_1^2 + k_2^2)/K_{33}] + k_3^2/K_{11} = k_0^2. \tag{3}$$

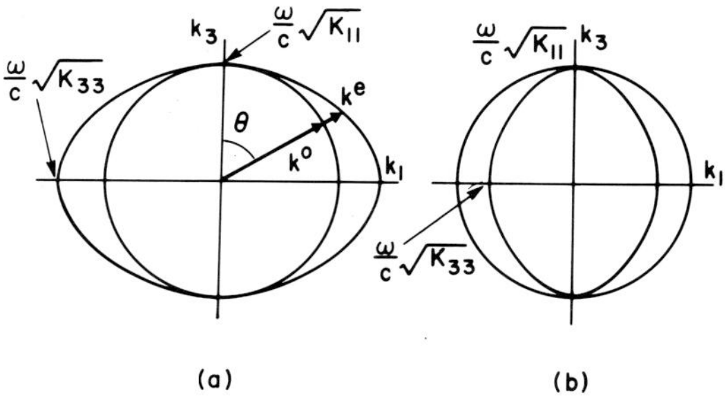

Fig. 3.2 Wave surfaces of (a) positive and (b) negative uniaxial crystals.

Since the crystal is axially symmetric about the x_3 axis, we can take $\mathbf{k}$ to be in the $x_1 x_3$ plane without loss of generality. Then (k_1, k_2, k_3) becomes $(k \sin \theta, 0, k \cos \theta)$ where θ is the angle between k and the x_3 axis, and (3) can be written

$$k^2[(\sin^2\theta/K_{33}) + (\cos^2\theta/K_{11})] = k_0^2. \tag{4}$$

Cross-sectional views of the surfaces, called *wave vector surfaces*, are shown in Fig. 3.2 for the cases of (a) a *positive* ($K_{33} > K_{11}$) and (b) a *negative* ($K_{33} < K_{11}$) *uniaxial* crystal. The solution corresponding to the spherical surface is the *ordinary wave*, and the other solution the *extraordinary wave*. The wave vectors making an angle θ with the x_3 axis of the crystal are just the radius vectors to each surface. For $\mathbf{k}$ parallel to $\hat{x}_3$, $\theta = 0$, the solutions are doubly degenerate with $k = (\omega/c)(K_{11})^{1/2}$. The x_3 direction is known as the *optic axis*. For $\mathbf{k}$ normal to the optic axis, the ordinary and extraordinary wave numbers are $k_0(K_{11})^{1/2}$ and $k_0(K_{33})^{1/2}$. At optical frequencies, it is usual to define *refractive indices*

$$n_{11} = (K_{11})^{1/2}, \qquad n_{22} = (K_{22})^{1/2}, \qquad n_{33} = (K_{33})^{1/2} \tag{5}$$

that are proportional to the major and minor radii of the wave surfaces.

The corresponding wave number and phase velocity for optical fields polarized along the principal x_i axes are then given by

$$k = k_0 n_{ii} \tag{6}$$

and

$$v_p = c/n_{ii}. \tag{7}$$

Having found the two wave vectors that satisfy the determinantal equation (3.1.11), we can insert the values into (3.1.8) to find the fields that correspond to the normal mode solutions. In a uniaxial crystal, the ordinary and extraordinary wave vectors are specified by (3.2.2) and (3.2.4). For the *ordinary wave* mode, $E_1 = E_3 = 0$, $D_1 = D_3 = 0$, and

$$D_2 = \varepsilon_0 K_{11} E_2 \tag{8}$$

in order that (3.1.8) and (3.2.2) hold for all θ. Thus, **D** is normal to both **k** and the optic axis, and **D** and **E** are parallel, as in an isotropic (ordinary) medium.

For the extraordinary wave mode, (3.1.8) and (3.2.4) can be satisfied for all θ only if $E_2 = D_2 = 0$. Thus, **D** for the extraordinary wave is normal to both **k** and **D** for the ordinary wave. However, $D_3 \neq 0$.

3.3 *Optical Indicatrix*

The normal mode solutions derived in the preceding section can be conveniently obtained by a simple geometrical construction called variously the *optical indicatrix*, *index ellipsoid*, or *ellipsoid of wave normals*.

The energy stored in a unit volume of dielectric is

$$W = \tfrac{1}{2}\mathbf{E} \cdot \mathbf{D} = (1/2\varepsilon_0)[(D_1^2/K_{11}) + (D_2^2/K_{22}) + (D_3^2/K_{33})] \tag{1}$$

in a principal axis system. The positive scalar energy W is represented by an ellipsoid in D space that must reflect the symmetry of the crystal. It is conventional to normalize (1) in x space so that

$$(x_1^2/K_{11}) + (x_2^2/K_{22}) + (x_3^2/K_{33}) = 1 \tag{2}$$

defines the general optical indicatrix, which is a triaxial ellipsoid having semiprincipal axes (radii) of length equal to the principal refractive indices; and

$$[(x_1^2 + x_2^2)/K_{11}] + (x_3^2/K_{33}) = 1 \tag{3}$$

defines the uniaxial indicatrix, which is an ellipsoid of revolution about the x_3 axis. Compare (3) with (3.2.3).

Consider a section through the origin of the uniaxial ellipsoid that is normal to a wave vector in the x_1x_3 plane making an angle θ with the x_3

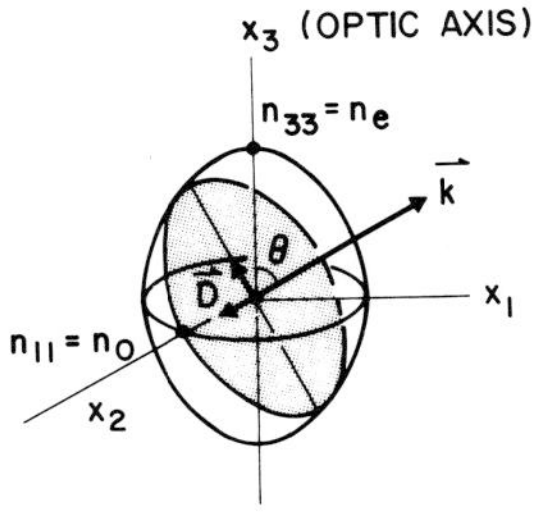

Fig. 3.3 Optical indicatrix for a positive uniaxial crystal.

axis as in Fig. 3.3. The equation of this plane is

$$x_1 \sin\theta + x_3 \cos\theta = 0. \tag{4}$$

The intersection of the plane and ellipsoid is an ellipse with principal axes along and normal to the x_2 axis. The respective lengths of these semiaxes are given by

$$r^2 = K_{11} \qquad (r = x_2) \tag{5}$$

and

$$r^2[(\sin^2\theta/K_{33}) + (\cos^2\theta/K_{11})] = 1 \qquad (r^2 = x_1^2 + x_3^2). \tag{6}$$

It may be seen that (5) and (6) are identical with (3.2.2) and (3.2.4) when r^2 is replaced by $(k/k_0)^2$. Further, the orientations of the semiaxes of the elliptical section correspond to the polarizations of the D vectors for the ordinary and extraordinary waves obtained in the previous section. *Thus a normal mode propagating in a specified direction in a uniaxial crystal may have either of two different wave numbers (or phase velocities) whose values are given by the lengths of the semiprincipal axes of the elliptical section normal to the wave vector, with the polarization of its* **D** *vector given by the corresponding direction of the principal axis.* If a wave is excited with a polarization other than a principal polarization, it will be decomposed into normal mode components polarized along the principal axes of the ellipse and traveling with the normal mode velocities. For a wave propagating along x_3, the axis of revolution, the elliptical section is a circle, and the two normal mode velocities are identical and their polarization arbitrary. This special direction of propagation is called the *optic axis.* (The optic axis is also called the *c axis* because crystallographers traditionally label the major symmetry axis of a unit cell as *c* and the others as *a* and *b* in uniaxial crystals.) The ordinary wave is always polarized normal to the optic axis, and the extraordinary wave is polarized in the plane containing the optic axis and **k**. For propagation normal to the optic axis, the ellipticity of the cross section is maximum and $k/k_0 = n_{11}$ for the ordinary wave and $k/k_0 = n_{33}$ for the extraordinary wave.

Although the correspondence between the indicatrix construction and normal mode solutions has been demonstrated only for the uniaxial case, it can be shown rigorously[3] that the correspondence also holds for the general ellipsoid of (1). The chief difference is that a general ellipsoid has two circular sections and the directions normal to these sections are each optic axes. Hence, crystals belonging to the triclinic, monoclinic, or orthorhombic systems, which are represented by a general ellipsoid, are said to be *biaxial,* while the tetragonal, trigonal, and hexagonal crystals are uniaxial. The index ellipsoid for cubic crystals is a sphere and these crystals behave as if they were isotropic for wave propagation.

Finally, we introduce some more notation to describe the indicatrix. We write (1) as

$$B_{11} x_1^2 + B_{22} x_2^2 + B_3 x_3^2 = 1 \tag{7}$$

in a principal axis system or, using the sum convention,

$$B_{ij} x_i x_j = 1 \tag{8}$$

in a general coordinate frame. Here B_{ij} is the *relative dielectric impermeability* tensor, which is the inverse of the dielectric constant tensor:

$$B_{ij} K_{jk} = \delta_{ik} . \tag{9}$$

Only in the principal axis system are the tensor elements themselves reciprocals,

$$B_{ii} = 1/K_{ii} . \tag{10}$$

The B_{ij} tensor is symmetric, just as K_{ij} is, so that (8) can be written

$$B_1 x_1^2 + B_2 x_2^2 + B_3 x_3^2 + 2 B_4 x_2 x_3 + 2 B_5 x_1 x_3 + 2 B_6 x_1 x_2 = 1 \tag{11}$$

where we have introduced the *contracted indices*: (11)→1, (22)→2, (33) → 3, (23) → 4, (13) → 5, (12) → 6.

3.4 *Birefringence*

As noted in Section 3.1 and Fig. 3.1, the Poynting vector **S** and wave vector **k** are not parallel in general. We shall show that the direction of **S** can be readily obtained as the normal to the wave vector surface at **k.**

Following Landau and Lifshitz,[2] differentiate (3.1.2) and (3.1.3) at constant ω,

$$\omega\, \delta\mathbf{D} = \delta\mathbf{H} \times \mathbf{k} + \mathbf{H} \times \delta\mathbf{k} \tag{1}$$

$$\omega\mu_0\, \delta\mathbf{H} = \delta\mathbf{k} \times E + \mathbf{k} \times \delta\mathbf{E} \tag{2}$$

and, with the identity

$$\mathbf{A} \cdot (\mathbf{B} \times \mathbf{C}) = (\mathbf{A} \times \mathbf{B}) \cdot \mathbf{C}, \tag{3}$$

obtain

$$\omega\mathbf{E} \cdot \delta\mathbf{D} = \omega\mu_0 \mathbf{H} \cdot \delta\mathbf{H} + (\mathbf{E} \times \mathbf{H}) \cdot \delta\mathbf{k} \tag{4}$$

$$\omega\mu_0 \mathbf{H} \cdot \delta\mathbf{H} = (\mathbf{E} \times \mathbf{H}) \cdot \delta\mathbf{k} + \omega\mathbf{D} \cdot \delta\mathbf{E}. \tag{5}$$

Since K_{ij} is symmetric,

$$\mathbf{D} \cdot \delta\mathbf{E} = \varepsilon_0 K_{ij} E_j \delta E_i = \mathbf{E} \cdot \delta\mathbf{D} \tag{6}$$

and (4) and (5) give

$$(\mathbf{E} \times \mathbf{H}) \cdot \delta\mathbf{k} = \mathbf{S} \cdot \delta\mathbf{k} = 0. \tag{7}$$

Since all **k** terminate on the wave vector surface, $\delta\mathbf{k}$ must lie in the surface and by (7) **S** must therefore be the normal to the surface at the point specified by **k**.

A light beam of finite diameter—a ray—travels in the direction of energy flow specified by **S**. Using the wave vector surface, we can determine the refraction of a ray entering an anisotropic medium from an isotropic medium. For the sake of simplicity, consider a (positive) uniaxial medium. Let the interface be the xy plane as shown in Fig. 3.4. The optic axis lies in the xz plane and makes an angle α with the z axis. The incident wave vector **k** in the isotropic medium lies in the xz plane and makes an angle β with z, and the refracted ordinary and extraordinary wave vectors $\mathbf{k}^{\mathrm{o}}$ and $\mathbf{k}^{\mathrm{e}}$ make angles of β^{o} and β^{e} with z. Continuity of fields across the boundary requires that the spatial periodicity along the boundary be the same in both media, i.e.,

$$k \sin\beta = k^{\mathrm{o}} \sin\beta^{\mathrm{o}} = k^{\mathrm{e}} \sin\beta^{\mathrm{e}}, \tag{8}$$

while the symmetry of the problem ensures that $\mathbf{k}^{\mathrm{o}}$ and $\mathbf{k}^{\mathrm{e}}$ also lie in the xz plane. The ordinary wave is polarized along x_2, which is parallel to y, and $k^{\mathrm{o}} = n_{11} k_0$ independent of β^{o}. Thus, (8) gives the ordinary refraction formula

$$\sin\beta / \sin\beta^{\mathrm{o}} = k^{\mathrm{o}}/k = n_{11}/n, \tag{9}$$

with n the refractive index of the isotropic medium. On the other hand, the wave number for the extraordinary wave, given by (3.2.4), is a function of β^{e},

$$\sin\beta / \sin\beta^{\mathrm{e}} = k^{\mathrm{e}}(\beta^{\mathrm{e}})/k. \tag{10}$$

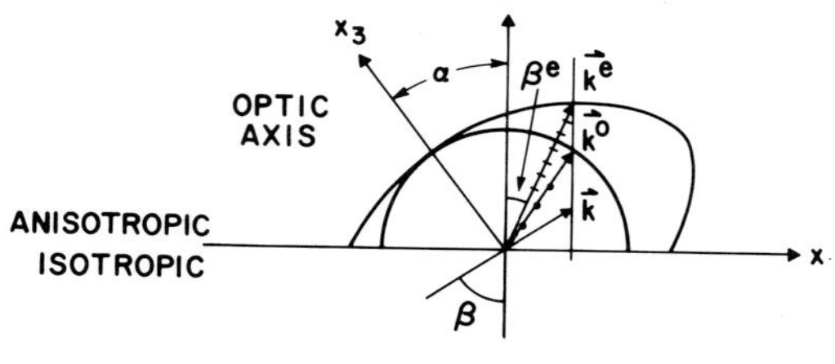

Fig. 3.4 Refraction at a boundary between an isotropic and an anisotropic medium.

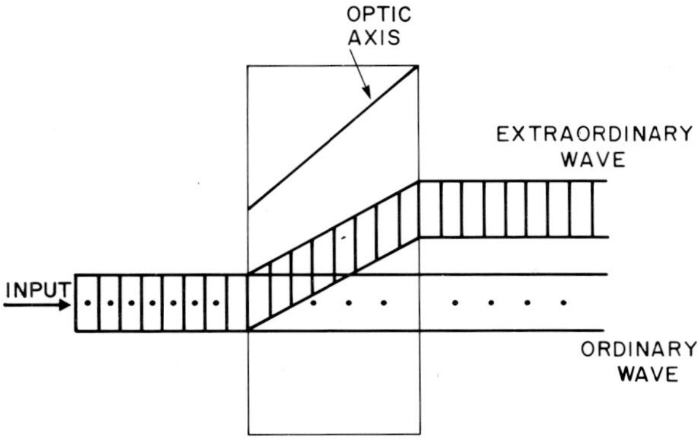

Fig. 3.5 Double refraction.

Figure 3.4 shows that $\mathbf{k}^e$ and $\mathbf{k}^o$ are parallel only for normal incidence, $\beta = 0$, or for $\mathbf{k}$ along the optic axis.

The directions of the ordinary and extraordinary rays are the normals to the surfaces in Fig. 3.4 at $\mathbf{k}^o$ and $\mathbf{k}^e$, respectively. $\mathbf{S}^o$ and $\mathbf{k}^o$ are always parallel but $\mathbf{S}^e$ and $\mathbf{k}^e$ are parallel only when $\mathbf{k}^e$ is parallel or perpendicular to the optic axis. Since there are in general two angles of refraction, an optically anisotropic medium is said to be *doubly refracting* or *birefringent*. The difference betwen principal indices $(n_{33} - n_{11})$ is the *birefringence*.

A sufficiently thick slab of birefringent crystal can be employed to separate a beam with arbitrary polarization into two orthogonally polarized beams as illustrated in Fig. 3.5. This technique has some important device applications.

3.5 *Wave Plates*

Birefringent plates can be employed to transform linearly polarized light into elliptically polarized light. Because light propagation in dielectric crystals is reciprocal, the same plates will transform elliptically polarized light back to linear polarization.

Consider a plate of thickness L fabricated from a uniaxial crystal with its optic axis in the plane of the plate. Let the optic axis be parallel to the x axis of the laboratory coordinate frame and let light be normally incident on the plate in the z direction as indicated in Fig. 3.6. A plane wave polarized along the optic axis with amplitude D_x will propagate with wave number $k_x = \omega n_{33}/c$ and phase velocity c/n_{33}, while a wave polarized along y with amplitude D_y has wave number $k_y = n_{11}/c$ and velocity c/n_{11}. For a positive uniaxial crystal, y and x are the *slow* and *fast axes*, respectively. An

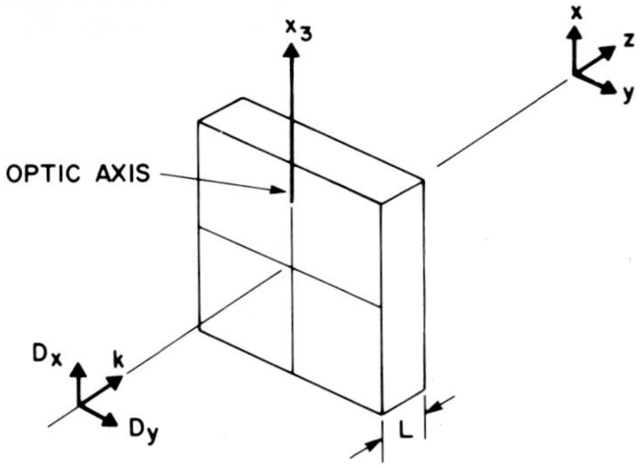

Fig. 3.6 Birefringent wave plate.

arbitrarily polarized wave can be resolved into principal components with fields

$$\begin{aligned} \mathbf{D}_x &= \{\tfrac{1}{2}D_x(0)\exp i\phi \exp[i(k_x z - \omega t)] + \text{c.c.}\}\hat{x} \\ \mathbf{D}_y &= \{\tfrac{1}{2}D_y(0)\exp i\phi \exp[i(k_y z - \omega t)] + \text{c.c.}\}\hat{y} \end{aligned} \tag{1}$$

where $\hat{x}$ and $\hat{y}$ are unit vectors, $D_x(0)$ and $D_y(0)$ are amplitudes at $t = 0$, $z = 0$, ϕ is an arbitrary phase factor, and c.c. denotes the complex conjugate. If the incident polarization $\mathbf{D}(0)$ is at 45° to $\hat{x}$ and $\hat{y}$, $D_x(0) = D_y(0) = D(0)/\sqrt{2}$ at $z = 0$, and, at $z = L$,

$$\mathbf{D}(L) = [D(0)/2\sqrt{2}]\exp[-i(\omega t - \phi)][\exp(ik_x L)\hat{x} + \exp(ik_y L)\hat{y}] + \text{c.c.} \tag{2}$$

We choose $2\phi = -(k_x + k_y)L$ for convenience and define the *phase retardation* Γ as

$$\Gamma = (k_x - k_y)L = 2\pi L(n_{33} - n_{11})/\lambda. \tag{3}$$

Then

$$\mathbf{D}(L) = [D(0)/\sqrt{2}][\cos(\omega t - \Gamma/2)\hat{x} + \cos(\omega t + \Gamma/2)\hat{y}], \tag{4}$$

which represents an elliptical wave with principal axes at ±45° to $\hat{x}$ and $\hat{y}$. In general, the principal axes of the wave will be along and normal to $\mathbf{D}(0)$ for any orientation of incident polarization.

The ellipticity is readily apparent in a coordinate system x', y' along the principal axes of the ellipse

$$\sqrt{2}\hat{x} = \hat{x}' - \hat{y}' \qquad \sqrt{2}\hat{y} = \hat{x}' + \hat{y}'. \tag{5}$$

In this system, (4) becomes

$$\mathbf{D}(L) = D(0)[\cos(\Gamma/2)\cos\omega t\,\hat{x}' - \sin(\Gamma/2)\sin\omega t\,\hat{y}']. \tag{6}$$

During one optical cycle, the vector $\mathbf{D}(L)$ traces out an ellipse with radii $\cos(\Gamma/2)$ and $\sin(\Gamma/2)$. The sense of rotation of $\mathbf{D}(L)$ reverses when the sign of Γ changes and the wave is *right-* or *left-handed*, according to which hand must be used in order that the thumb point along $\mathbf{k}$ and the fingers curl with the rotation of $\mathbf{D}(L)$.

When $\Gamma = \pi/2$, $\mathbf{D}(L)$ is circularly polarized and

$$(n_{33} - n_{11})L = \lambda/4. \tag{7}$$

The plate is called a *quarter-wave plate*. When $\Gamma = \pi$, $\mathbf{D}(L)$ is linearly polarized but is orthogonal to $\mathbf{D}(0)$, and

$$(n_{33} - n_{11})L = \lambda/2. \tag{8}$$

The plate is a *half-wave plate*. It can easily be shown that if $\mathbf{D}(0)$ makes an angle α with the fast axis of a half-wave plate, then the linearly polarized $\mathbf{D}(L)$ will make an angle $-\alpha$ with the fast axis. If the plate is rotated and $\mathbf{D}(0)$ held fixed, $\mathbf{D}(L)$ will rotate twice as fast as the plate.

If a wave plate is inserted between crossed polarizers with their axes oriented along $\hat{x}'$ and $\hat{y}'$, the intensity I of light transmitted through the combination will be periodic in Γ with period π,

$$I/I_0 = \sin^2(\Gamma/2); \tag{9}$$

and if the polarizers are parallel,

$$I/I_0 = \cos^2(\Gamma/2) \tag{10}$$

where I_0 is the maximum intensity transmitted by the combination.

Typical values of birefringence $(n_{33} - n_{11})$ are $+0.009$ for quartz, -0.04 for KH_2PO_4, and -0.172 for calcite. For propagation normal to a sheet of mica, which is biaxial, $n_{33} - n_{22} = 0.004$. At a wavelength of $0.5\ \mu m$, a quartz half-wave plate would be only $28\ \mu m$ thick, and would be difficult to fabricate and handle. A p half-wave plate, with p an odd integer, would be easier to manage but would be unnecessarily sensitive to variations in wavelength, temperature, and orientation of the plate. A more rugged element is obtained by cementing together two quartz plates whose thicknesses differ by a half-wave, with their optic axes at right angles.

Such a combination gives a half-wave retardation at only one wavelength. As noted by Bond[7], a more broadband device can be obtained by using two or more plates cut from different materials, thereby achieving a half-wave at two or more discrete wavelengths. For example, for two crystals a and b, thicknesses L_a and L_b can be chosen so that

$$[(n_{33}^a - n_{11}^a)L_a \pm (n_{33}^b - n_{11}^b)L_b] = \lambda/2 \tag{11}$$

is satisfied at two wavelengths. In (11) the upper sign holds for a positive and a negative crystal with axes parallel, and the lower sign for crystals of same sign oriented with axes orthogonal. The method depends on the availability of materials whose birefringence varies with wavelength in a manner that gives positive solutions for L_a and L_b.

3.6 *Compensators*

It is often desirable to have an adjustable wave plate or *compensator*. Such a device can be employed to produce a wave plate at any wavelength, to compensate (i.e., cancel) the natural birefringence of an element, to introduce a fixed retardation bias in an optical device, or, when calibrated, to measure the retardation of an unknown wave plate.

The *Babinet–Soleil compensator* is comprised of two quartz wedges, which can be displaced with respect to each other to give a plate of variable thickness, and a quartz plate with its optic axis orthogonal to that of the wedges, as shown in Fig. 3.7. By adjusting the thickness, it is possible to obtain positive, zero, and negative retardations.

The *Berek compensator*, shown in Fig. 3.8, consists of a plate of calcite that can be rotated about a normal to the optic axis, which is perpendicular to the plate. The retardation is zero for normal incidence. As the angle of incidence α is increased, both the birefringence and path length difference for ordinary and extraordinary rays change so as to give a variable retardation.

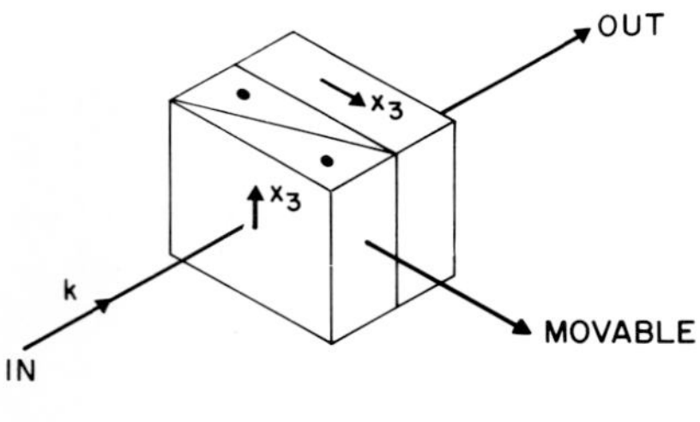

Fig. 3.7 Babinet–Soleil compensator.

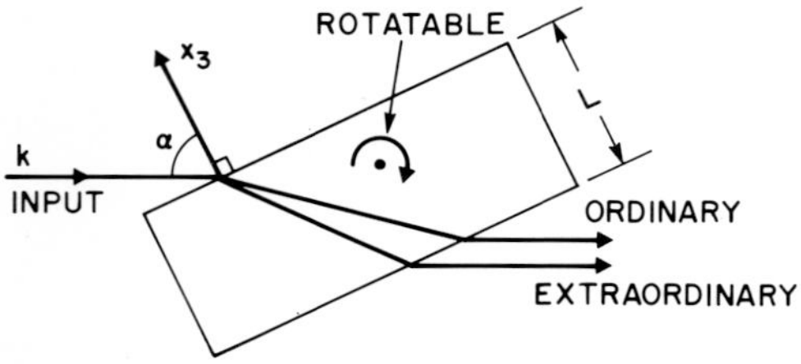

Fig. 3.8 Berek compensator.

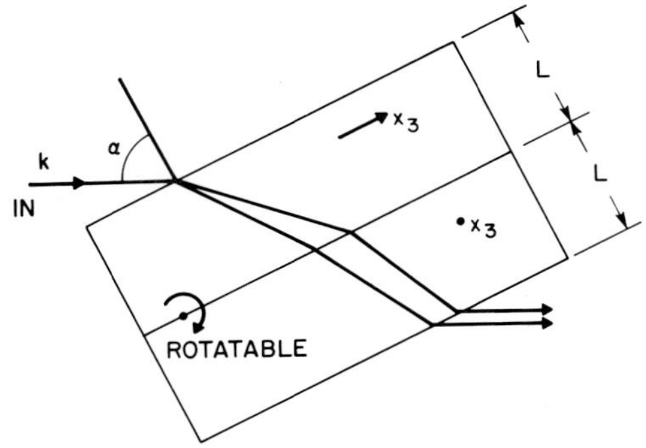

Fig. 3.9 Ehringhaus compensator.

The *Ehringhaus compensator* consists of two identical uniaxial plates with optic axes orthogonal, as in Fig. 3.9. The combination can be rotated about the optic axis of one of the plates. At normal incidence, there is no retardation, but as α increases, both birefringence and path length differences contribute to the retardation. Bond[7] has shown that the Berek and Ehringhaus compensators exhibit similar variation of Γ with α. For the Ehringhaus compensator he finds

$$\Gamma = (L/\lambda)[(n_{33}/n_{11})(n_{11}^2 - \sin^2\alpha)^{1/2} - (n_{33}^2 - \sin^2\alpha)^{1/2}], \qquad (1)$$

and for the Berek compensator he finds the same relation but with n_{33} and n_{11} interchanged.

A Babinet–Soleil compensator can be calibrated at a particular wavelength by inserting it between crossed polarizers with its principal axes at 45° to those of the polarizers. Extinction of the monochromatic beam transmitted through the combination occurs periodically as the compensator retardation is adjusted through multiples of π. The retardation is directly proportional to the displacement of the wedge. White light is extinguished only for $\Gamma = 0$. Calibration of the Berek and Ehringhaus compensators is more difficult because of the nonlinear relation (1).

The unknown retardation of a plate can be found by inserting it in series with a calibrated compensator with its principal axes parallel to those of the compensator. If the compensator was previously set for extinction, then the retardation that must be subtracted to give extinction with the unknown present is the unknown retardation to within an additive constant $p\pi$, which can usually be determined by crude estimate.

A simple and inexpensive arrangement for measuring an unknown Γ is the *Senarmont compensator* shown in Fig. 3.10. The axes of the quarter-wave plate are oriented at 45° from those of the unknown. The analyzer is

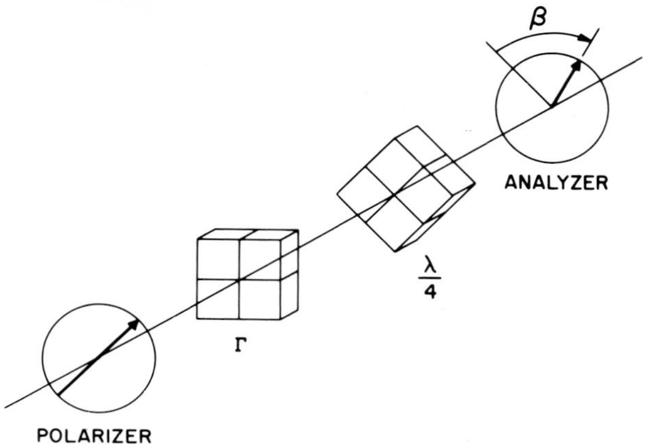

Fig. 3.10 Senarmont compensator.

rotated to give extinction. It can easily be shown that Γ can be obtained from the orientation of the analyzer as $\Gamma = \beta$.

3.7 *Group Velocity and Dispersion*

The phase $(\omega t - \mathbf{k} \cdot \mathbf{r})$ of a uniform plane wave component $\exp[i(\omega t - \mathbf{k} \cdot \mathbf{r})]$ is constant for an observer moving in the wave normal direction along **k** at the phase velocity

$$v_{\mathrm{p}} = \omega/k = \omega/nk_0 = c/n. \tag{1}$$

An observer moving in another direction must travel faster than v_p to keep up with the wave.

An optical disturbance, such as a pulse of light, can be represented by a Fourier superposition of plane waves, and if v_p is constant for all the component waves the disturbance will maintain its identity as it travels at velocity v_p. In general, however, the refractive index of a medium will be a function of frequency, and the component waves traveling at different velocities will produce a distortion of the optical disturbance after propagating some distance. A variation in phase velocity with frequency is known as *dispersion.* If the medium is sufficiently dispersive over the group of component waves, then the disturbance will soon lose its identity and it will not be possible to define a velocity. However, if the range in **k** and ω required to represent the disturbance is sufficiently small with respect to dispersion, then the disturbance will maintain its identity but will travel at the *group velocity* v_g of the component waves.

To choose a simple example, take the sum of two waves $(\omega_a, \mathbf{k}_a)$ and $(\omega_a + \Delta\omega, \mathbf{k}_a + \Delta\mathbf{k})$ as the group. The real wave amplitude is

$$\begin{aligned}
&\exp[-i(\omega_a t - \mathbf{k}_a \cdot \mathbf{r})] + \exp[-i[(\omega_a + \Delta\omega)t - (\mathbf{k}_a + \Delta\mathbf{k}) \cdot \mathbf{r}]] + \text{c.c.} \\
&\quad = \{1 + \exp[-i(\Delta\omega t - \Delta\mathbf{k} \cdot \mathbf{r})]\}\exp[-i(\omega_a t - \mathbf{k}_a \cdot \mathbf{r})] + \text{c.c.}
\end{aligned} \tag{2}$$

where c.c. denotes the complex conjugate. The envelope factor travels along $\Delta\mathbf{k}$ with velocity $v_g = \Delta\omega/\Delta k$. Now add a third wave $(\omega_a - \Delta\omega, \mathbf{k}_a + \Delta\mathbf{k}')$. If $\Delta k' = -\Delta\omega/v_g$, i.e., if $\omega(k)$ is linear near k_a, then the envelope of the three-wave field

$$\begin{aligned}
&\{1 + \exp[-i(\Delta\omega t - \Delta\mathbf{k} \cdot \mathbf{r})] + \exp[i(\Delta\omega t - \Delta\mathbf{k} \cdot \mathbf{r})]\}\exp[-i(\omega_a t - \mathbf{k}_a \cdot \mathbf{r})] \\
&\quad + \text{c.c.}
\end{aligned} \tag{3}$$

will travel at v_g. Otherwise, the shape of the envelope will become distorted. Hence, we may define a group velocity only if

$$\Delta\omega/\Delta\mathbf{k} = d\omega/d\mathbf{k} = \mathbf{v}_g \tag{4}$$

at the mean $(\omega_a, \mathbf{k}_a)$ over the range $(\Delta\omega, \Delta\mathbf{k})$ required to represent the disturbance.

Dielectric dispersion is due to lattice and electronic resonances in the medium which give rise to a complex frequency-dependent dielectric constant

$$K(\omega) = 1 + \sum_{\text{elect}} \frac{\Delta K_i \omega_i^2}{\omega_i^2 - \omega^2 + i\omega\gamma_i} + \sum_{\text{lattice}} \frac{\Delta K_j \omega_j^2}{\omega_j^2 - \omega^2 + i\omega\gamma_j} \tag{5}$$

where $\omega_{i,j}$ are the resonant frequencies, $\gamma_{i,j}$ the damping factors, $\Delta K_{i,j}$ the contributions of the resonant modes to $K(0)$, and i, j refer to electronic and lattice resonances, respectively. At frequencies well below the electronic resonances, $\omega \ll \omega_i$, but well above lattice resonances, $\omega \gg \omega_j$, $K(\omega)$ is the *electronic dielectric constant*

$$K(\infty) = 1 + \sum_{\text{elect}} \Delta K_i, \tag{6}$$

and at very low frequencies, $\omega \ll \omega_j$, $K(\omega)$ is the dc dielectric constant

$$K(0) = K(\infty) + \sum_{\text{lattice}} \Delta K_j. \tag{7}$$

The dispersion curve given by

$$K(\omega) = (kc/\omega)^2 = (k/k_0)^2 \tag{8}$$

is plotted in Fig. 3.11 for the case of a single lattice resonance and a band of electronic resonances.

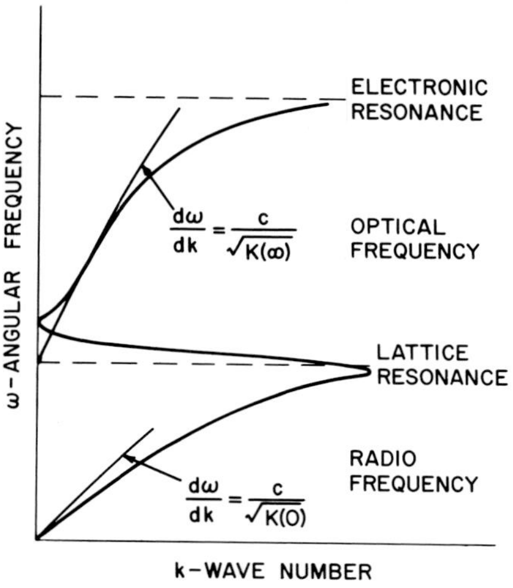

Fig. 3.11 Dispersion diagram.

The nondispersive region corresponding to $K(0)$ occurs at radio frequencies. Strong dispersion occurs as one approaches the lattice resonance at infrared frequencies. The dispersion is *normal* when $dv_p/d\omega < 0$ and *anomalous* in the highly absorbing region near resonance where $dv_p/d\omega > 0$. At higher frequency one enters another region of normal dispersion, then a nondispersive region corresponding to $K(\infty)$ in the visible region, and then a region of normal dispersion toward the ultraviolet where the electronic band edge absorption occurs. For materials that are not transparent in the visible, the frequency scale in Fig. 3.11 is compressed.

From (1) and (4), phase and group velocity are related by

$$v_g = v_p/[1 - (\omega/v_p)(dv_p/d\omega)]. \qquad (9)$$

For normal dispersion, v_g and v_p have the same sign and $v_g < v_p$. In the anomalous region the two velocities may have opposite signs—the wave is then called a *backward wave*—and v_g may approach ∞.

If we consider a well-defined pulse traveling over a substantial distance, it is intuitively clear that the group velocity and energy propagation velocity are the same. It can be shown[8] that these velocities are equivalent for normal dispersion but in general are not equivalent for anomalous dispersion since energy cannot travel faster than c. In addition it can be shown[3] that $\mathbf{S}$ and $\mathbf{v}_g$ are parallel. Thus, for normal dispersion,

$$\mathbf{S} = W_E \mathbf{v}_g = \tfrac{1}{2}(\mathbf{E} \cdot \mathbf{D})\mathbf{v}_g \qquad (10)$$

where W_E is the dielectric energy density.

3.8 *Optical Activity*

We have so far assumed the dielectric medium to be anisotropic but invariant under translation; that is, the point group elements give an adequate description of the medium. The normal modes of propagation are then linearly polarized plane waves.

Certain crystals have a structure characterized by an array of atoms that lie on a helix with pitch equal to the length of the unit cell. Quartz (SiO_2), which belongs to trigonal point group 32, is the best known example.[9,10] The unit cell of length c contains three equally spaced silicon layers in planes normal to the optic axis. Each plane can be derived from the one below it by a rotation of 120° about the c axis. Two different crystal forms occur: one for clockwise and the other for counterclockwise rotations of the planes as they are stacked. A projection on the plane normal to the optic axis is shown in Fig. 3.12, where the points with different shading connected by the equilateral triangles are separated vertically by $c/3$. These points lie on a helix which is right-handed when the white point lies above the black one and left-handed when the black point is above the white one.

Crystals that occur in right- and left-handed forms are called *enantiomorphic*. Since a center of inversion, a rotation-inversion axis, or a mirror plane change the hand of a structure, all point groups with these elements are nonenantiomorphic. The eleven enantiomorphous point groups are 1, 2, 222, 4, 422, 3, 32, 6, 622, 23, and 432. Crystals having structures belonging to these point groups *may* have space groups containing screw axes of only one hand.

When the screw axis and the optic axis are parallel, as in quartz, the symmetry of the medium prescribes normal modes of propagation that are right- and left-circularly polarized waves.[1] Because of the handedness of the

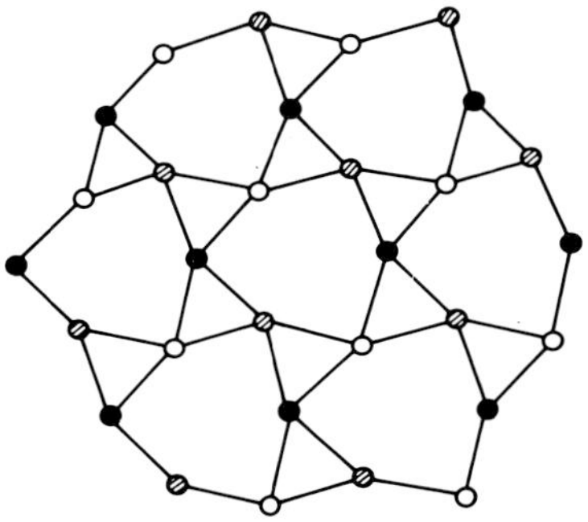

Fig. 3.12 Projection on a plane perpendicular to the optic axis of the lattice of β quartz. Points of different shading are separated by $c/3$. (After W. G. Cady, "Piezoelectricity," Vol. 2. Dover, New York, 1964.)

helical structure, the velocities, c/n_R and c/n_L, of the right- and left-handed waves may be different. At a given instant, the angle through which displacement **D** rotates over path length L for the respective waves is $2\pi n_L L/\lambda$ and $2\pi n_R L/\lambda$. Thus, a linearly polarized wave, which can be resolved into right- and left-circularly polarized waves, will experience a net rotation ϕ in its plane of polarization given by

$$\phi = \pi L(n_L - n_R)/\lambda = \rho L \tag{1}$$

when the waves are recombined, where ρ is the *rotatory power*. A substance that can rotate the plane of polarizaton in this way is *optically active*. The rotation is reciprocal; that is, a rotation induced by propagation through the crystal is undone by reflecting the wave back through the crystal. The value of ρ for quartz is 47 deg/mm at 0.41 μm, 22 deg/mm at 0.589 μm, and 14 deg/mm at 0.73 μm. The intermediate value corresponds to a difference in refractive indices $(n_L - n_R) = 7 \times 10^{-5}$, which is considerably smaller than typical index differences $(n_{33} - n_{11})$ encountered in birefringent crystals.

If an elliptically polarized wave is normally incident on a quartz plate cut normal to the optic axis, the two linear components into which the elliptic wave may be resolved will each be rotated through the same angle. Hence, the ellipticity (ratio of minor to major axis) will not be altered but the axes of the elliptical wave will be rotated through $\phi = \rho L$ by the plate.

For propagation along directions other than the optic axis, the two normal modes are elliptical waves of opposite sense but equal ellipticity. Since $(n_{33} - n_{11}) \gg (n_L - n_R)$ for quartz, the ellipticity is very small for off-axis angles greater han a few degrees and optical activity can usually be ignored.[1]

In principle, optical activity is also allowed in four nonenantiomorphic classes: m, $mm2$, $\bar{4}$, and $\bar{4}2m$. These substances must contain both right- and left-handed screw axes generated by the mirror plane but the axes need not be parallel to each other.[5] The same crystal then exhibits right-handed rotations along one axis and left-handed rotations along the other.

Since the sense of a screw is independent of orientation, optical activity is also observed in liquids containing enantiomorphic molecules of one hand.

REFERENCES

1. J. F. Nye, "Physical Properties of Crystals." Oxford Univ. Press, London, 1964.
2. L. D. Landau and E. M. Lifshitz, "Electrodynamics of Continuous Media." Addison-Wesley, Reading, Massachusetts, 1960.
3. M. Born and E. Wolf, "Principles of Optics." Macmillan, New York, 1959.
4. C. Kittel, "Introduction to Solid State Physics," 4th ed. Wiley, New York, 1971.
5. E. A. Wood, "Crystal Orientation Manual." Columbia Univ. Press, New York, 1963;

"Crystals and Light." Van Nostrand-Reinhold, Princeton, New Jersey, 1964.
6. "International Tables for X-Ray Crystallography," Vol. I, "Symmetry Groups." International Union of Crystallography, Kynoch Press, Birmingham, England, 1952.
7. W. L. Bond, Private communication.
8. J. A. Stratton, "Electromagnetic Theory," pp. 330–340. McGraw-Hill, New York, 1941.
9. W. G. Cady, "Piezoelectricity," Vol. 2. Dover, New York, 1964.
10. E. E. Wahlstrom, "Optical Crystallography." Wiley, New York, 1969.

CHAPTER II

NONLINEAR DIELECTRIC EFFECTS

1. Introduction

In the preceding chapter, the dielectric medium was characterized by one of several alternative tensor constants: the dielectric constant K_{ij}, the impermeability B_{ij}, and the susceptibility χ_{ij}. We noted that these parameters vary with frequency in the neighborhood of lattice and electron resonances and may have considerably different values at low frequencies below the lattice resonances and at high frequencies above these resonances. However, these parameters were assumed to be independent of the strength of the fields in the dielectric medium; that is, the response of the medium was taken to be a linear function of the applied field.

In fact, however, no medium is truly linear, and these parameters are functions of the fields present in the medium. The nonlinear dielectric response leads to a number of interesting applications because it permits the control of the dielectric properties of the medium by auxiliary applied fields, or, from a different viewpoint, it permits the mixing of fields. We will be concerned mainly with the change in the optical dielectric properties by radio frequency electric fields—the electrooptic effect; but we will also discuss briefly other nonlinear interactions involving combinations of optical and rf electric fields, and acoustic and optic phonon fields.

Since deviations from linearity are usually quite small, the nonlinear effects can be represented by expanding the dielectric parameters in a power series in field quantities, such as the electric field E_i, polarization P_i, or strain S_{ij}. Normally, only the first nonvanishing term need be retained.

In this chapter, we define the nonlinear coefficients that describe the Pockels (linear) and Kerr (quadratic) electrooptic effects, the elastooptic effect, the piezoelectric effect, and various nonlinear optical and rf dielectric effects. We show how the third- and the fourth-rank tensors describing these effects can be reduced by symmetry considerations; correlate the various coefficients that appear in the literature; and discuss the dispersion of the nonlinear coefficients. Finally, we discuss Raman and Brillouin scattering effects and show their connection with the previously discussed nonlinear coefficients.

2. Electrooptic Effects

2.1 *Tensor Definition*

When we speak of the electrooptic effect here, we refer to the change in optical dielectric properties induced by an electric field whose frequency is well below the lattice resonances of the medium.

Traditionally, the electrooptic coefficients are defined in terms of B_{ij}, which describe the optical indicatrix, as

$$\begin{aligned} B_{ij}(\mathbf{E}) - B_{ij}(0) \equiv \Delta B_{ij} &= r_{ij,k} E_k + s_{ij,kl} E_k E_l + \cdots \\ &= f_{ij,k} P_k + g_{ij,kl} P_k P_l + \cdots . \end{aligned} \tag{1}$$

The coefficients $r_{ij,k}$ and $f_{ij,k}$ are the *linear or Pockels coefficients* and $s_{ij,kl}$ and $g_{ij,kl}$ are the *quadratic or Kerr coefficients*. The quadratic effect was first observed by Kerr in liquids and glasses in 1873, and about 20 years later the linear effect was observed by Röntgen and Kundt in quartz and studied by Pockels in quartz, tourmaline, potassium chlorate, and Rochelle salt.[1] Pockels proved the existence of an intrinsic electrooptic effect independent of piezoelectrically induced strain (see Section 3.3). Higher-order terms than quadratic have not been observed.

It will be shown later that the indices i and j can be permuted and that the indices k and l can also be permuted, provided the medium is lossless and the frequencies of the rf fields represented by the indices k and l are much less than the optical frequencies of the fields represented by i and j. We emphasize the permutation symmetry by separating (ij) and (kl) with a comma. Further, we will have occasion to abbreviate the notation by using the *contracted indices*: $1 \rightarrow (11)$, $2 \rightarrow (22)$, $3 \rightarrow (33)$, $4 \rightarrow (23, 32)$,

$5 \rightarrow (13,31)$, and $6 \rightarrow (12,21)$. It should be noted, however, that matrix elements do not have their usual tensor transformation or multiplication properties in the contracted notation. We use Greek letters for the contracted indices as a reminder. The *permutation symmetry* reduces the number of independent elements of $r_{ij,k}$ and $f_{ij,k}$ from 27 to 18, and the number of elements of $s_{ij,kl}$ and $g_{ij,kl}$ from 81 to 36.

A further reduction is demanded by crystal symmetry according to relations (2.4.7) and (2.4.8) of Chapter I. Consider first the effect of an inversion center I on a third-rank tensor. The inversion operation takes T_{ijk} into

$$T_{ijk}(I) = T'_{ijk} = -T_{ijk}. \tag{2}$$

But if the crystal is invariant under inversion, then

$$T_{ijk}(I) = T_{ijk}(E) = T_{ijk} \tag{3}$$

Equations (2) and (3) can be satisfied simultaneously only if $T_{ijk} \equiv 0$. Hence, *all third-rank tensors vanish identically in the* 11 *crystal classes that possess a center of inversion*. Conversely, only crystals that lack a center of inversion can exhibit a linear Pockels electrooptic effect.

Further reduction results from applications of other elements of a particular point group. Consider, for example, the group $\bar{4}2m$ that describes KH_2PO_4 (KDP) and the chalcopyrites (e.g., $ZnSiP_2$). In Chapter I, the symmetry elements are listed in Table 1.2 and illustrated in the stereogram of Fig. 1.4. The full third-rank tensor array is

$$\begin{matrix} T_{111} & T_{112} & T_{113} \\ T_{221} & T_{222} & T_{223} \\ T_{331} & T_{332} & T_{333} \\ T_{231} & T_{232} & T_{233} \\ T_{321} & T_{322} & T_{323} \\ T_{131} & T_{132} & T_{133} \\ T_{311} & T_{312} & T_{313} \\ T_{121} & T_{122} & T_{123} \\ T_{211} & T_{212} & T_{213} \end{matrix} \tag{4}$$

The twofold axis about x_1, $C_2(x_1)$, transforms the coordinates to

$$x'_1 = x_1, \qquad x'_2 = -x_2, \qquad x'_3 = -x_3. \tag{5}$$

Therefore, $C_2(x_1)$ requires that all elements of (4) containing the indices "2" and/or "3" an odd number of times vanish; e.g.,

$$T_{112}(C_2) = -T_{112} = T_{112}(E) = 0. \tag{6}$$

The twofold axes $C_2(x_2)$ and $C_2(x_3)$ have a similar effect and together leave only those elements containing each index number once (e.g., T_{123}). The mirror plane $\sigma(\bar{x}_1)$ normal to $\bar{x}_1$, at 45° to x_1 and x_2, transforms

$$x_1' = -x_2, \qquad x_2' = -x_1, \qquad x_3 = x_3 \tag{7}$$

so that the indices "1" and "2" can be permuted; e.g.,

$$T_{123}(\sigma) = T_{213} = T_{123}(E). \tag{8}$$

Thus, (4) becomes

$$\begin{matrix} 0 & 0 & 0 \\ 0 & 0 & 0 \\ 0 & 0 & 0 \\ T_{231} & 0 & 0 \\ T_{321} & 0 & 0 \\ 0 & T_{231} & 0 \\ 0 & T_{321} & 0 \\ 0 & 0 & T_{123} \\ 0 & 0 & T_{123} \end{matrix} \tag{9}$$

and in the contracted notation that takes account of the (ij) permutation symmetry, the electrooptic tensor for $\bar{4}2m$ is

$$\begin{matrix} 0 & 0 & 0 \\ 0 & 0 & 0 \\ 0 & 0 & 0 \\ r_{41} & 0 & 0 \\ 0 & r_{41} & 0 \\ 0 & 0 & r_{63} \end{matrix} \tag{10}$$

The cubic $\bar{4}3m$ class, which describes GaAs, has a threefold axis C_3 about $\langle 111 \rangle$, in addition to the C_2 and σ elements of $\bar{4}2m$. Since C_3 transforms

$$x_1' = x_2, \qquad x_2' = x_3, \qquad x_3' = x_1, \tag{11}$$

all three indices may be permuted in sequence (e.g., $T_{231} = T_{123}$) and the only nonvanishing elements of the electrooptic tensor are $r_{41} = r_{52} = r_{63}$.

The contracted electrooptic tensors $r_{\mu k}$ and $f_{\mu k}$ for the 21 acentric classes are given in Table 2.1.[2] The elements of the acentric group 432 require that all the tensor components vanish identically. No crystals are known to belong to this class, however.

The fourth-rank tensors $s_{ij,kl}$ and $g_{ij,kl}$ can be simplified in similar fashion as shown in Table 2.1 for the contracted elements $S_{\mu\nu}$ and $g_{\mu\nu}$. All 32 classes contain nonvanishing fourth-rank tensor elements. The uncontracted third- and fourth-rank tensors T_{ijk} and T_{ijkl} for the 32 points groups are given by Butcher.[3]

The electrooptic coefficients defined in terms of polarization and electric field are simply related in a principal axis system,

$$r_{ij,k} = \varepsilon_0(K_k - 1)f_{ij,k} \tag{12}$$

$$s_{ij,kl} = \varepsilon_0(K_k - 1)(K_l - 1)g_{ij,kl}. \tag{13}$$

Since $f_{ij,k}$ and $g_{ij,kl}$ are defined in terms of the polarization of the medium rather than of an external electric field, these coefficients give an intrinsic description of the medium that is preferred for a discussion of the physics of the process.

TABLE 2.1

Tabulation, in Contracted Notation, of Allowed Third-Rank ($T_{\mu k}$) and Fourth-Rank ($T_{\mu\nu}$) Tensor Elements for the 32 Point Groups[ab]

TRICLINIC SYSTEM

1

$i \backslash j$	$T_{ij,kl} = T_{\mu\nu}$						$T_{ij,k} = T_{\mu k}$		
	1	2	3	4	5	6	1	2	3
1	●	●	●	●	●	●	●	●	●
2	●	●	●	●	●	●	●	●	●
3	●	●	●	●	●	●	●	●	●
4	●	●	●	●	●	●	●	●	●
5	●	●	●	●	●	●	●	●	●
6	●	●	●	●	●	●	●	●	●

$\bar{1}$

$i \backslash j$	$T_{ij,kl} = T_{\mu\nu}$						$T_{ij,k} = T_{\mu k}$		
	1	2	3	4	5	6	1	2	3
1	●	●	●	●	●	●			
2	●	●	●	●	●	●			
3	●	●	●	●	●	●			
4	●	●	●	●	●	●			
5	●	●	●	●	●	●			
6	●	●	●	●	●	●			

MONOCLINIC SYSTEM

2

$i \backslash j$	$T_{ij,kl} = T_{\mu\nu}$						$T_{ij,k} = T_{\mu k}$		
	1	2	3	4	5	6	1	2	3
1	●	●	●		●			●	
2	●	●	●		●			●	
3	●	●	●		●			●	
4				●		●	●		●
5	●	●	●		●			●	
6				●		●	●		●

m

$i \backslash j$	$T_{ij,kl} = T_{\mu\nu}$						$T_{ij,k} = T_{\mu k}$		
	1	2	3	4	5	6	1	2	3
1	●	●	●		●		●		●
2	●	●	●		●		●		●
3	●	●	●		●		●		●
4				●		●		●	
5	●	●	●		●		●		●
6				●		●		●	

2/m

$i \backslash j$	$T_{ij,kl} = T_{\mu\nu}$						$T_{ij,k} = T_{\mu k}$		
	1	2	3	4	5	6	1	2	3
1	●	●	●		●				
2	●	●	●		●				
3	●	●	●		●				
4				●		●			
5	●	●	●		●				
6				●		●			

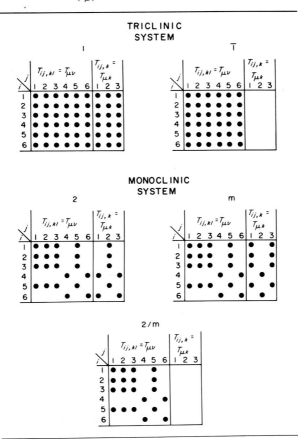

The expansion in (1) does not contain the strain, and it has been tacitly assumed that the coefficients are defined at *constant strain* $S_{ij} \equiv 0$. The piezoelectric and electrostrictive contributions to the *constant stress* electrooptic coefficients will be discussed later. Unless otherwise noted, in future we will be talking about constant strain coefficients. Constant strain conditions can be approximated by *clamping* the crystal between lead blocks or, more effectively, by applying the rf electric fields at frequencies well above the fundamental acoustic resonances of the sample.

2.2 *Deformation of the Optical Indicatrix*

The electrooptically induced ΔB_{ij} will in general change the dimensions of the index ellipsoid and rotate it in the coordinate frame. We wish to determine the changes in orientation and length of the principal axes of the

TABLE 2.1 (*continued*)

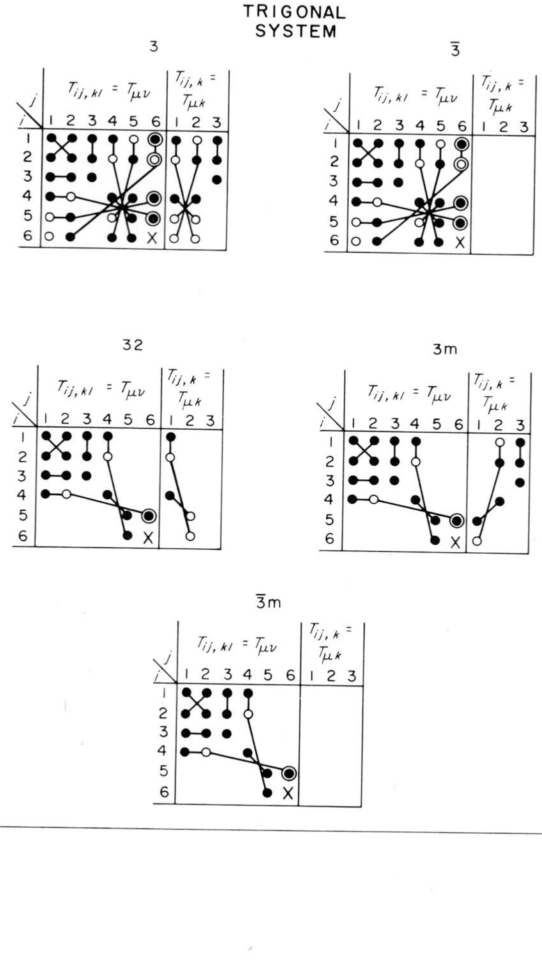

ellipsoid in order to find the induced refractive indices appropriate to various polarization and propagation directions of the optical beam. Symmetry considerations can often provide a clue to the orientation of the ellipsoid. The applied electric field **E** transforms like a vector, and the ellipsoid may only have symmetry elements common to both **E** and to the crystal with $\mathbf{E} \equiv 0$. We will illustrate electrooptically induced changes in the indicatrix for a few crystal classes of practical interest, taking **E** and **k** along symmetry axes for simplicity. In some classes, the optimum general orientations of these vectors depend on the sizes of electrooptic coefficients. These optimum configurations have been calculated for some crystals.[4,5]

For a cubic crystal in class 23 or $\bar{4}3m$, the ellipsoid is a sphere for $\mathbf{E} \equiv 0$, and there is only one nonvanishing coefficient r_{41}. For a field along x_1, the

TABLE 2.1 (*continued*)

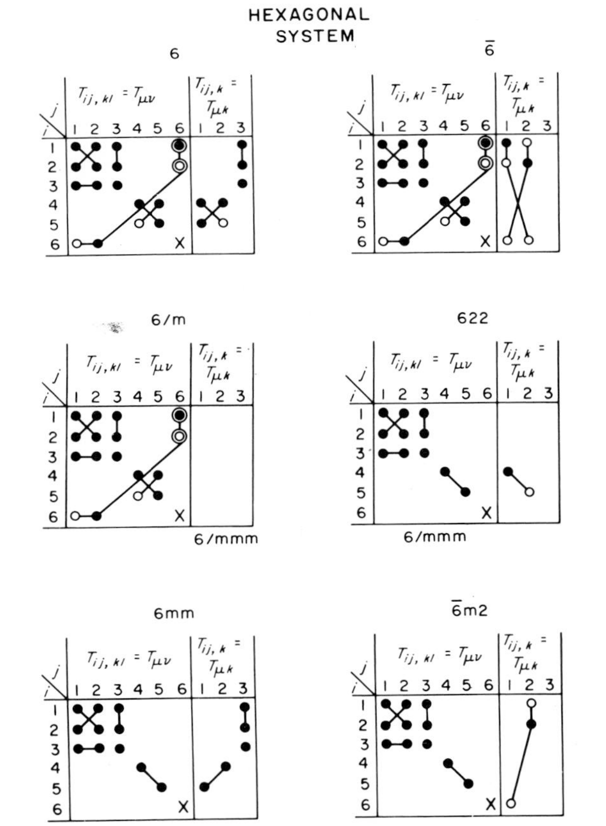

(*continued*)

ellipsoid is, from (2.1.1),

$$(1/n^2)(x_1^2 + x_2^2 + x_3^2) + 2r_{41}E_1x_2x_3 = 1. \quad (1)$$

The factor 2 enters because the cross product x_2x_3 can be formed in two ways. The problem is to find a principal axis coordinate transformation which eliminates all cross products. A 45° rotation about x_1 gives $x_1 = x_1'$, $x_2 = 2^{-1/2}(x_2' + x_3')$, $x_3 = 2^{-1/2}(x_2' - x_3')$ and the ellipsoid becomes

$$(x_1'^2/n^2) + [(1/n^2) + r_{41}E_1]x_2'^2 + [(1/n^2) - r_{41}E_1]x_3'^2 = 1. \quad (2)$$

Reference to the stereograms in Fig. 1.4 of Chapter I shows that the only elements common to E_1 and the crystal point group are $C_2(x_1')$, $\sigma(x_2')$, and $\sigma(x_1')$; they also describe the deformed ellipsoid (2).

The index changes experienced by light polarized along the principal axes

TABLE 2.1 (*continued*)

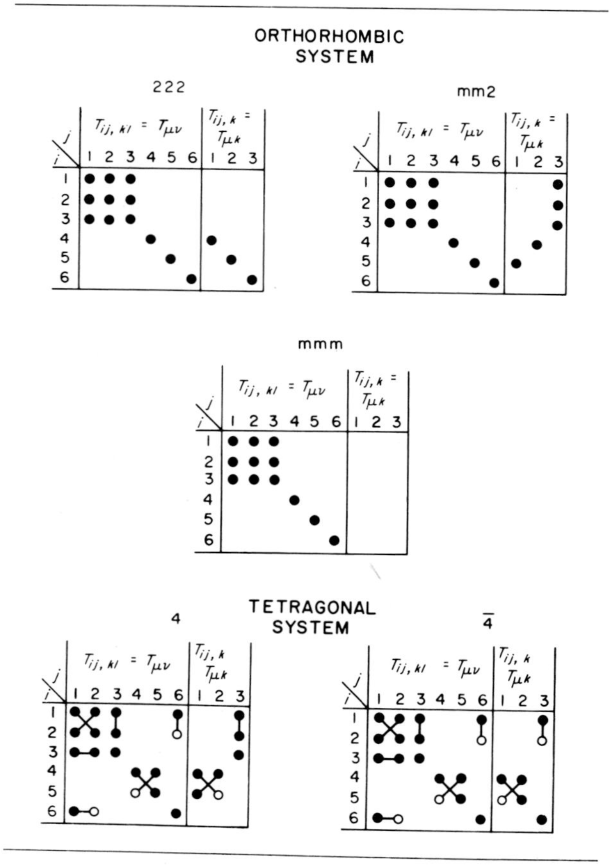

are

$$\Delta n'_{11} = 0, \qquad \Delta n'_{22} = -\Delta n'_{33} = -\tfrac{1}{2}n^3 r_{41} E_1 \tag{3}$$

with $\Delta(1/n^2) \approx -2\ \Delta n/n^3$ for $\Delta n \ll n$. The electrooptically induced phase shift for a wave traveling through a crystal of length L in the x_2' direction (transverse to E_1) is

$$\eta = (2\pi L/\lambda)\ \Delta n'_{33} = \pi n^3 r_{41} E_1 L/\lambda \tag{4}$$

for x'_3 polarization, and $\eta = 0$ for x'_1 polarization.

The induced retardation is

$$\Gamma = (2\pi L/\lambda)(\Delta n'_{33} - \Delta n'_{11}) = \pi n^3 r_{41} E_1 L/\lambda. \tag{5}$$

TABLE 2.1 (*continued*)

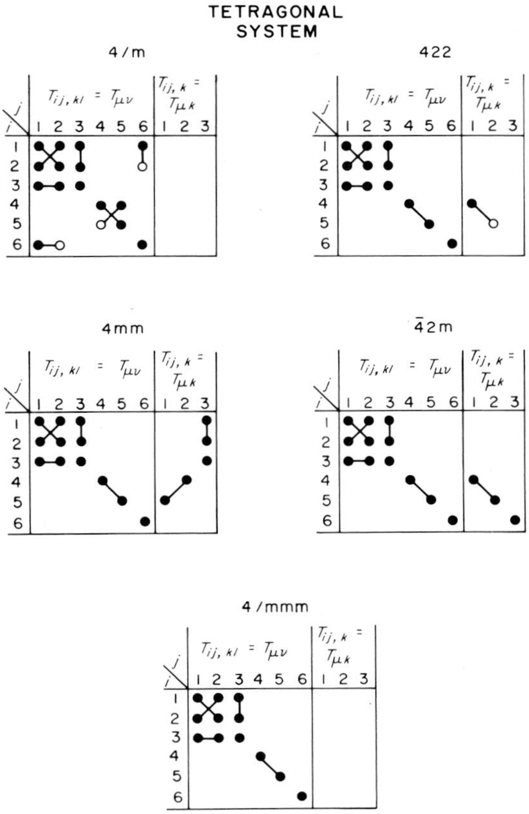

(*continued*)

For propagation along E_1 (longitudinal configuration), the retardation is doubled

$$\Gamma = (2\pi L/\lambda)(\Delta n'_{33} - \Delta n'_{22}) = 2\pi n^3 r_{41} E_1 L/\lambda. \tag{6}$$

TABLE 2.1 (*continued*)

CUBIC SYSTEM

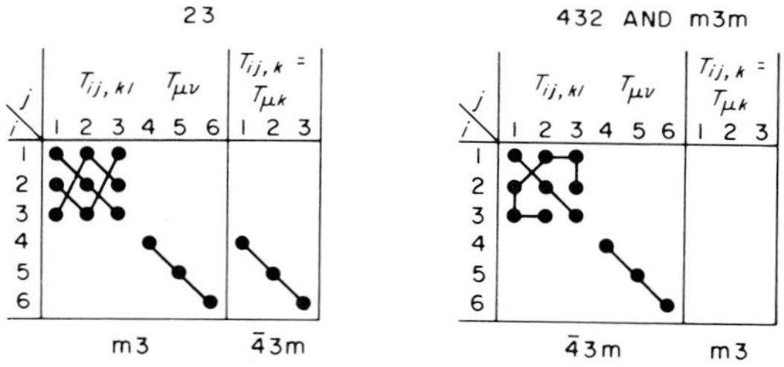

[a] From S. H. Wemple and M. DiDomenico, Jr., Appl. Solid State Sci. **3**, 263–383 (1972).
[b] The symbols denote the following for the electrooptic tensors:

- ●—● equal components.
- ●—○ equal magnitude and opposite sign.
- ◉ equal to twice the heavy dot component to which it is joined.
- ◎ equal to minus 2 times the heavy dot component to which it is joined:
- × equal to (11–12).

In trigonal and hexagonal systems certain tensor elements describing physical properties other than the electrooptic effect differ from those given above by trivial factors of two. Thus for the fourth-rank elatooptic p-tensor, we have

- ◉ equal to the heavy dot component to which it is joined.
- ◎ equal to minus the heavy dot component to which it is joined.
- × equal to $\frac{1}{2}$ (11–12).

For the fourth-rank electrostriction Q-tensor the tensor elements are the same as the quadratic electrooptic tensor elements except for the following:

Trigonal Classes

$$Q_{64} = 2Q_{25}, \qquad Q_{65} = -2Q_{24}, \qquad Q_{66} = 2(Q_{11} - Q_{12}).$$

Hexagonal Classes

$$Q_{16} = -Q_{26} = Q_{62} = -Q_{61}, \qquad Q_{66} = 2(Q_{11} - Q_{12}).$$

The third-rank piezoelectric tensors (d, b, or e) are the transpose of the $T_{\mu k}$ tensors in Table 2.1 in all crystal systems except trigonal and hexagonal. In these systems the following additional factors of 2 must be included;

$$d_{16} = -2d_{22}, \qquad d_{26} = -2d_{11}.$$

If the field is applied in the [111] direction ($E_1 = E_2 = E_3 = E/\sqrt{3}$), then the ellipsoid becomes

$$(1/n^2)(x_1^2 + x_2^2 + x_3^2) + (2r_{41}E/\sqrt{3})(x_2x_3 + x_1x_3 + x_1x_2) = 1. \quad (7)$$

Since [111] remains a threefold axis in the presence of **E**, [111] must be the axis of revolution of the ellipsoid. If x''_1 is taken as the [111] axis and x''_2 and x''_3 are any orthogonal axes, say, $[1\bar{1}0]$ and $[11\bar{2}]$, respectively, then, making use of the fact that the inverse rotation matrix is just the transpose of the direct matrix (Chapter I), we have

$$\begin{aligned} x''_1 &= (1/\sqrt{3})(x_1 + x_2 + x_3) & x_1 &= (1/\sqrt{6})(\sqrt{2}x''_1 + \sqrt{3}x''_2 + x''_3) \\ x''_2 &= (1/\sqrt{2})(x_1 - x_2) & x_2 &= (1/\sqrt{6})(\sqrt{2}x''_1 - \sqrt{3}x''_2 + x''_3) \quad (8) \\ x''_3 &= (1/\sqrt{6})(x_1 + x_2 - 2x_3) & x_3 &= (1/\sqrt{6})(\sqrt{2}x''_1 - 2x'_3) \end{aligned}$$

and the ellipsoid becomes

$$[(1/n^2) + (2r_{41}E/\sqrt{3})]x''^2_1 + [(1/n^2) - (r_{41}E/\sqrt{\ })](x''^2_2 + x''^2_3) = 1. \quad (9)$$

This orientation provides the *maximum phase shift* available with $\bar{4}3m$,

$$\eta = (2\pi L/\lambda)\ \Delta n''_{11} = 2\pi n^3 r_{41} EL/\sqrt{3}\lambda, \quad (10)$$

for polarization along x''_1.

If the applied field lies in the (001) plane normal to x_3 and makes an angle θ with x_1, then it can be shown[4] that the principal axes of the ellipsoid will be oriented along (x, y, z) defined in Fig. 2.1. Equal and opposite changes

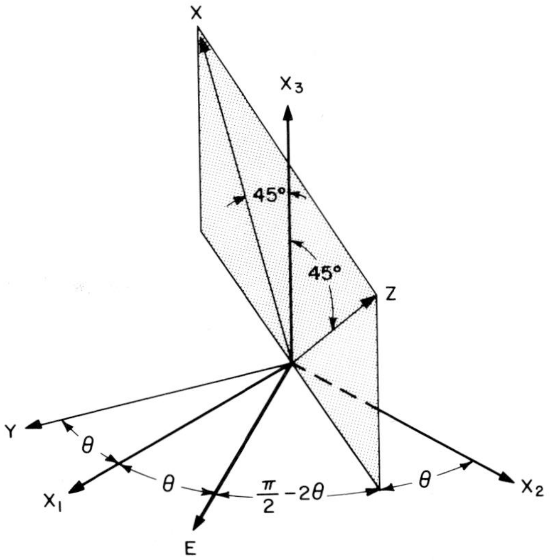

Fig. 2.1 Principal axes of the indicatrix of a cubic crystal for an applied field in the (001) plane. [After I. P. Kaminow and E. H Turner, *Appl. Optics* **5**, 1612 (1966).]

in index occur along x and z, respectively, with no change along y. The index change is independent of θ and

$$\Delta n_x = -\Delta n_z = n^3 r_{41} E/2. \qquad (11)$$

Propagation along y gives the *maximum retardation* available in $\bar{4}3m$; the configuration is transverse for $\theta = \pi/4$ and longitudinal for $\theta = 0$.

Finally, if light propagates along a [111] axis and the field is applied normal to that axis, the retardation is $\sqrt{\frac{2}{3}}n^3 r_{41} E$ independent of the orientation of **E** in the (111) plane. However, the axes of the elliptical section of the elipsoid rotate at half the rate at which the applied field rotates in the (111) plane. Hence, one can produce a rotating birefringent plate which can be employed as phase shifter or single-side band modulator.[4]

For the tetragonal $\bar{4}2m$ class with the field E_3 along the optic axis, the ellipsoid is

$$(1/n_{11}^2)(x_1^2 + x_2^2) + (1/n_{33}^2)x_3^2 + 2r_{63} E_3 x_1 x_2 = 1 \qquad (12)$$

and, with principal axes given by $x_1 = (1/\sqrt{2})(x_1' + x_2')$, $x_2 = (1/\sqrt{2})(x_1' - x_2')$, and $x_3' = x_3$, the ellipsoid becomes

$$[(1/n_{11}^2) + r_{63} E_3]x_1'^2 + [(1/n_{11}) - r_{63} E_3]x_2'^2 + (1/n_{33})x_3'^2 = 1. \qquad (13)$$

For the field applied normal to the optic axis along x_1, the ellipsoid is

$$(1/n_{11}^2)(x_1^2 + x_2^2) + (1/n_{33}^2)x_3^2 + 2r_{41} E_1 x_2 x_3 = 1. \qquad (14)$$

It can be shown[4,6] that the ellipsoid is rotated through an angle α given by

$$\tan 2\alpha = 2r_{41} E_1/[(1/n_{11})^2 - (1/n_{33})^2], \qquad (15)$$

which is usually very small. The length of the semiaxis along x_1 remains unchanged and the other axes experience changes of order $(r_{41} E_1)^2$. A first-order change is obtained for light propagating with **k** in the $x_2 x_3$ plane at 45° to x_2 (i.e., not along a principal axis of the indicatrix). The index change for the ordinary wave polarized along E_1 is $\Delta n_0 \simeq 0$ and the index change for the extraordinary wave polarized in the $x_2 x_3$ plane at 45° to x_3 is[6]

$$\Delta n_e \simeq \sqrt{2} r_{41} E_1[(1/n_{11}^2) + (1/n_{33}^2)]^{-3/2}. \qquad (16)$$

The indicatrix deformation is especially simple for the uniaxial 4, 4*mm*, 6, 6*mm*, 3, and 3*m* crystals with the field E_3 applied along the optic axis because no cross terms are introduced. Only the coefficients r_{33} and $r_{13} = r_{23}$ are involved, and the ellipsoid becomes

$$[(1/n_{11}^2) + r_{13} E_3](x_1^2 + x_2^2) + [(1/n_{33}^2) + r_{33} E_3]x_3^2 = 1. \qquad (17)$$

For **k** along x_2,

$$\Delta n_{11} = -n_{11}^3 r_{13} E_3/2, \quad \Delta n_{33} = -n_{33}^3 r_{33} E_3/2, \tag{18}$$

and

$$\Gamma = (2\pi L/\lambda)(\Delta n_{33} - \Delta n_{11}) = -\pi n_{33}^3 r_c E_3 L/\lambda \tag{19}$$

where

$$r_c = r_{33} - (n_{11}/n_{33})^3 r_{13}. \tag{20}$$

Lastly, consider the Kerr effect in a cubic crystal with **E** along [111], $E_1 = E_2 = E_3 = E/\sqrt{3}$. From (2.1.1), the ellipsoid is

$$(1/n^2)(x_1^2 + x_2^2 + x_3^2) + \tfrac{2}{3}s_{44} E^2(x_2 x_3 + x_1 x_3 + x_1 x_2) = 1. \tag{21}$$

With the coordinate transformation (8), the ellipsoid becomes

$$[(1/n^2) + \tfrac{2}{3}s_{44} E^2]x''_1 + [(1/n^2) - \tfrac{1}{3}s_{44} E^2](x''^2_2 + x''^2_3) = 1, \tag{22}$$

from which one can find η and Γ as in the previous examples.

2.3 *Electrooptic Modulation and Deflection*

In this section we demonstrate the principles of operation of electrooptic light modulators and deflectors.

Figure 2.2a shows an electrooptic crystal through which a beam propagates in the z direction over a path length L. If the applied (modulating) field is sinusoidal $E_m \sin \omega_m t$ and the light is polarized along x, which is a principal axis of the indicatrix, the transmitted beam will be *phase modulated* (PM) with phase shift

$$\eta_x(t) = \eta_0 \sin \omega_m t \tag{1}$$

with *modulation index*

$$\eta_0 = 2\pi L \ \Delta n_x(\max)/\lambda \sim \pi n^3 r E_m L/\lambda \tag{2}$$

where the tensor indices have been dropped for simplicity. Phase and frequency modulation (FM) are closely related: the frequency deviation is

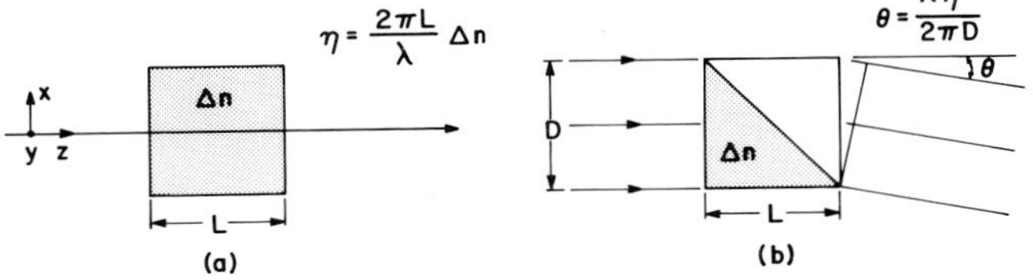

Fig. 2.2 (a) Electrooptic phase modulation; (b) beam deflection.

the time derivative of the phase deviation and the peak frequency deviation is

$$\omega_d = \eta_0 \omega_m. \tag{3}$$

Thus, the electrooptic effect naturally provides phase or frequency modulation. It is well known that a phase modulated wave can be represented by[7]

$$e(t) = A \sin(\omega t + \eta_0 \sin \omega_m t) = A \sum_{-\infty}^{\infty} J_n(\eta_0) \sin(\omega + n\omega_m)t. \tag{4}$$

Thus, the output spectrum consists of side bands with amplitudes equal to the nth-order Bessel functions $J_n(\eta_0)$. For $\eta_0 \ll 1$, $J_0(\eta_0) \approx 1$, $J_1(\eta_0) \approx \eta_0/2$ and $J_n(\eta_0) \approx 0$ for $n \geq 2$.

It is often desirable to modulate the intensity of a light beam to provide amplitude modulation (AM) or pulse code modulation (PCM). This effect can be accomplished by interfering the two phase modulated normal modes polarized along x and y, respectively. Polarizers are placed before and after the crystal with their axes at $\pm 45°$ to x and y. In Chapter I, we showed that the transmission through such a combination is (3.5.9)

$$I/I_0 = \sin^2[\Gamma(t)/2]. \tag{5}$$

Thus, varying Γ electrooptically by a half-wave $(0 \leq \Gamma \leq \pi)$ fully opens and closes the shutter, but it does so in a nonlinear fashion. A linear modulation can be approximated by introducing a fixed retardation bias $\Gamma_B = \pi/2$ (quarter-wave plate) in series with the time-dependent $\Gamma(t)$. If $\Gamma(t) \ll \Gamma_B$, (5) becomes

$$I/I_0 = \sin^2[(\Gamma_B + \Gamma(t))/2] \approx \tfrac{1}{2}[1 + \Gamma(t)] = \tfrac{1}{2}[1 + \Gamma_0 \sin \omega_m t] \tag{6}$$

with

$$\Gamma(t) = \Gamma_0 \sin \omega_m t. \tag{7}$$

An amplitude modulated signal is usually written

$$\begin{aligned} e(t) &= B(1 + m \sin \omega_m t) \sin \omega t \\ &= B[\sin \omega t + (m/2)\cos(\omega - \omega_m)t - (m/2)\cos(\omega + \omega_m)t] \end{aligned} \tag{8}$$

where m is the *degree of modulation*. For $m \ll 1$, the intensity is

$$I = \langle e(t)^2 \rangle = (B^2/2)(1 + 2m \sin \omega_m t) \tag{9}$$

and

$$\Gamma_0 = 2m. \tag{10}$$

Thus, comparing (8) and (4), the ratio of first side band to the carrier amplitude for AM is $m/2 = \Gamma_0/4$ and for PM it is $J_1(\eta_0) \approx \eta_0/2$.

For a number of applications, it is necessary to scan a beam (i.e., modulate its direction). A simple method is to construct a time-varying prism[8] as in Fig. 2.2b by electroding only a triangular shaped portion of a square crystal face. If the beam diameter D equals the length L of the crystal, the deviation angle θ, for small θ, is

$$\theta = \lambda\eta/2\pi D \tag{11}$$

where η is the phase difference between paths along the upper and lower edges of the crystal. The minimum deviation that can be detected is equal to the diffraction half-width ϕ of the beam, $\phi \approx \lambda/D$, and the peak phase difference η_0 required to obtain N resolvable spots is

$$\eta_0 \approx 2\pi N. \tag{12}$$

For AM, PM, or PCM, one requires $\eta_0 \approx \pi$; the average phase shift for the N-spot deflector is $\frac{1}{2}\eta_0$. Thus, an N-spot deflector of this type requires $\sim N$ times the phase shift required for a modulator.

3. Elastooptic Effects

3.1 *Tensor Definition*

The elastic deformation of a medium may be described by a deformation gradient tensor

$$\varepsilon_{ij} = \partial u_i/\partial x_j \tag{1}$$

in which u_i is the displacement of a point that initially had the coordinate x_j. The gradient tensor is not necessarily symmetric in ij. It is customary to construct a symmetric *strain tensor* S_{ij}

$$S_{ij} = \tfrac{1}{2}(\varepsilon_{ij} + \varepsilon_{ji}) \tag{2}$$

and an antisymmetric *rotation* tensor

$$R_{ij} = \tfrac{1}{2}(\varepsilon_{ij} - \varepsilon_{ji}). \tag{3}$$

In 1889, Pockels defined a photoelastic coefficient $p_{ij,kl}$ in terms of S_{kl} assuming that R_{kl} was negligible for typical experimental conditions. Nelson and Lax[9] have recently pointed out that it is not always valid to overlook R_{kl}, particularly for propagating acoustic waves, and that $\varepsilon_{kl} = S_{kl} + R_{kl}$ is the natural variable. The point is that a rigid rotation of an anisotropic dielectric will induce changes in the impermeability tensor. Hence, the photoelastic or elastooptic effect is defined by

$$\Delta B_{ij} = p_{ij,kl} S_{kl} + p'_{ij,kl} R_{kl} = \bar{p}_{ijkl} \varepsilon_{kl}. \tag{4}$$

All three coefficients are symmetrical in ij, but only $p_{ij,kl}$ is symmetrical in kl. Thus, $p_{\mu\nu}$ has the same form as the quadratic electrooptic tensor, except for the factors of 2 noted in Table 2.1.

For most materials, only $p_{ij,kl} \equiv p_{\mu\nu}$ has been tabulated.[11] However, p'_{ijkl} can be calculated directly from the B_{ij} tensor[9]; it is antisymmetric in kl and is nonvanishing only for shear waves $k \neq l$; it vanishes for isotropic media and cubic crystals; and it vanishes in uniaxial crystals except for p'_{2323}, p'_{2332}, p'_{1313}, p'_{1331}. Thus, for many applications, the rotational effect can be ignored. However, Nelson and Lazay[10] have shown in a Brillouin scattering experiment that $\bar{p}_{2332} = 30\bar{p}_{2323}$ and that $p_{2323} = -0.12$ while $p'_{2323} = +0.13$.

3.2 *Acoustooptical Devices*

A piezoelectric transducer may be bonded to an optically transparent medium in order to generate an acoustic traveling wave or standing wave in the medium, as illustrated in Fig. 3.1. The elastooptic interaction then sets up a periodic variation in refractive index characterized by acoustic angular frequency Ω and wave vector $\mathbf{K}$ of magnitude $2\pi/\Lambda$ where sound velocity $V = \Omega/K$. Assuming the interaction of infinite plane waves, an incident optical wave $(\mathbf{k}_i, \omega_i)$ will be diffracted by (K, Ω) into a wave $(\mathbf{k}_d, \omega_d)$ where

$$\mathbf{k}_d = \mathbf{k}_i \pm \mathbf{K}, \qquad \omega_d = \omega_i \pm \Omega. \tag{1}$$

It is usually a good approximation to neglect Ω with respect to $\omega_i \approx \omega_d$

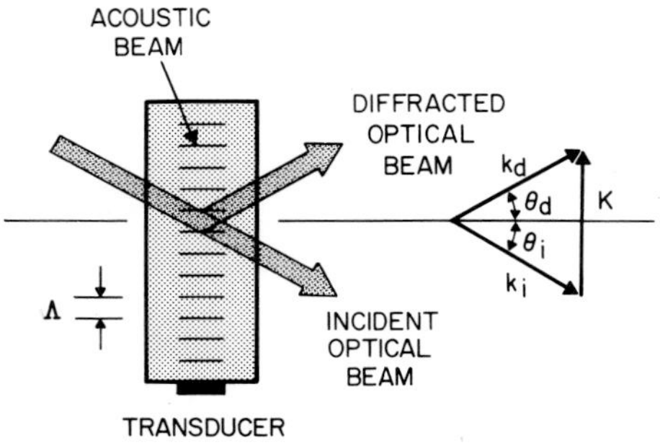

Fig. 3.1 Bragg diffraction of an optical beam by an acoustic beam.

$= \omega$. Then, for an isotropic medium, $k_i \approx k_d = k$ and we have the *Bragg condition*

$$\sin \theta_B = K/2k = \Omega c/2n\omega V \tag{2}$$

where $2\theta_B$ is the angle between $\mathbf{k}_i$ and $\mathbf{k}_d$ that gives maximum diffraction. If a sufficiently wide range of optical wave vector $\Delta\mathbf{k}$ or acoustic wave vector $\Delta\mathbf{K}$ is present, for example, as a result of focusing the incident optical or acoustic beam, then the diffracted optical beam can be *acoustically scanned* by tuning Ω. However, only a fraction of the incident optical or acoustic beam will be effective in the process.

The diffraction efficiency of the process is a function of the product of the acoustic power and figure of merit $M = n^6 p^2/\rho V^3$ where p is the appropriate photoelastic coefficient and ρ the density of the material. In principle, all the incident energy can be coupled into the diffracted wave. Thus, an *acoustooptic light modulator*[11,12] can be produced by keeping Ω fixed and modulating the acoustic power. Since the diffraction angle for an optical beam of diameter D is $\sim\lambda/D$, the acoustic frequency Ω must be greater than $4\pi nV/D$ in order to obtain angular separation between the incident and diffracted beams. A typical frequency band for an acoustooptic modulator is 60–100 MHz.

3.3 *Piezoelectric and Electrostrictive Contributions to the Electrooptic Effect*

It was assumed in Section 2.1 that the electrooptic effects were defined at zero strain (clamped). However, an applied electric field will induce strains via the piezoelectric and electrostrictive effects in a material that is free to respond (unclamped). This freedom is present when the acoustic modes of the sample excited by the applied field are not clamped by the surroundings. The acoustic resonance frequency of a mode is $\sim qV/2L$ where L is the appropriate sample dimension and q the integral order of the mode. The energy excited in the qth mode by a uniform electric field is proportional to $1/q^2$, and one can usually assume the crystal to be effectively clamped by its mounting for $q > 10$; i.e., at frequencies greater than $5V/L \sim 10$ MHz for $V = 2 \times 10^5$ cm/sec and $L = 0.1$ cm. If the crystal is purposely clamped by an acoustically lossy and well-matched substance (such as lead), then all acoustic modes can be suppressed.

The electrically induced strain is given by[2]

$$S_{mn} = E_k d_{k,mn} + E_k E_l \gamma_{kl,mn} = P_k b_{k,mn} + P_k P_l Q_{kl,mn} \tag{1}$$

where the linear and quadratic terms are the piezoelectric and electrostrictive effects, respectively. The coefficients are symmetrical in (kl) and (mn), so that the third- and fourth-rank tensors have the same forms as those given in Table 2.1 for the electrooptic effects. However, factors of 1/2 are introduced because of the symmetrization of the S_{ij} tensor (3.1.2).

If we insert (1) into (3.1.4), neglecting the rotational contribution, and combine the result with (2.1.1), we find

$$\begin{aligned} \Delta B_{ij} &= (r_{ij,k}^{\mathrm{S}} + p_{ij,mn}^{\mathrm{E}} d_{k,mn}^{\mathrm{T}}) E_k + (s_{ij,kl}^{\mathrm{S}} + p_{ij,mn}^{\mathrm{E}} \gamma_{kl,mn}^{\mathrm{T}}) E_k E_l \\ &= (f_{ij,k}^{\mathrm{S}} + p_{ij,mn}^{\mathrm{P}} b_{k,mn}^{\mathrm{T}}) P_k + (g_{ij,kl}^{\mathrm{S}} + p_{ij,mn}^{\mathrm{P}} Q_{kl,mn}^{\mathrm{T}}) P_k P_l \\ &= r_{ij,k}^{\mathrm{T}} E_k + s_{ij,kl}^{\mathrm{T}} E_k E_l \\ &= f_{ij,k}^{\mathrm{T}} P_k + g_{ij,kl}^{\mathrm{T}} P_k P_l . \end{aligned} \tag{2}$$

We have introduced the superscripts S and T, and E and P to indicate coefficients measured at constant strain and stress, and at constant field and polarization, respectively. Unless explicitly indicated by a superscript, we will mean constant strain electrooptic coefficients.

4. Nonlinear Optical Effects

4.1 *Definitions of Nonlinear Optical Coefficients*

The electrooptic and elastooptic effects were defined in terms of the impermeability tensor B_{ij} by Pockels at the turn of the century. This formulation was convenient because the effects were then observed as induced changes in birefringence. With the advent of the laser it became possible to observe other nonlinear optical effects by mixing of electromagnetic waves to produce combination frequencies (side bands) and harmonics. The analysis of these effects is more convenient in terms of the nonlinear polarization wave induced at the combination frequency. In this section we demonstrate the connection between the two formulations. The various types of interaction possible in acentric crystals are cataloged according to the frequency ranges in which the three interacting waves occur.

In a principal axis system, the induced change in linear susceptibility is

$$\Delta\chi_{ij} \equiv \Delta K_{ij} = -K_{ii}\ \Delta B_{ij}\ K_{jj} \tag{1}$$

for $\Delta K_{ij} \ll K_{ii}$ and K_{jj}. Then with (2.1.1) the induced polarization is

$$P_i(t) = \varepsilon_0\ \Delta\chi_{ij}\ E_j = -\varepsilon_0 K_{ii} K_{jj} r_{ijk} E_j(t) E_k(t). \tag{2}$$

If $E_j(t)$ and $E_k(t)$ are sinusoidal,

$$\begin{aligned} E_j(t) &= E_j \cos(\omega_\alpha t + \phi_\alpha) \\ &= \tfrac{1}{2}\{e_j(\omega_\alpha)\exp(-i\omega_\alpha t) + e_j^*(-\omega_\alpha)\exp[-i(-\omega_\alpha)t]\}, \end{aligned} \tag{3}$$

and similarly for $E_k(t)$ with α replaced by β. We use lower case letters for the complex amplitudes,

$$e_j = E_j \exp(-i\phi_\alpha). \tag{4}$$

Note that the complex conjugated term $e_j^*(-\omega_\alpha)$ in (3) corresponds to a negative frequency. Then

$$\begin{aligned} P_i(t) &= \tfrac{1}{2}\{ p_i(\omega_\alpha + \omega_\beta)\exp[-i(\omega_\alpha + \omega_\beta)t] + p_i(\omega_\alpha - \omega_\beta)\exp[-i(\omega_\alpha - \omega_\beta)t] \\ &\quad + \text{c.c.}\} \\ &= -\tfrac{1}{4}\varepsilon_0 K_{ii} K_{jj} r_{ijk}\{e_j(\omega_\alpha)e_k(\omega_\beta)\exp[-i(\omega_\alpha + \omega_\beta)t] \\ &\qquad + e_j(\omega_\alpha)e_k^*(-\omega_\beta)\exp[-i(\omega_\alpha - \omega_\beta)t] + \text{c.c.}\} \end{aligned} \tag{5}$$

where the asterisk and c.c. denote the complex conjugate. It is now convenient to equate the amplitudes of components at the same frequency,

$$p_i(\omega_\alpha + \omega_\beta) = -\tfrac{1}{2}\varepsilon_0 K_{ii}(\omega_\alpha) K_{jj}(\omega_\beta) r_{ijk}\, e_j(\omega_\alpha) e_k(\omega_\beta) \tag{6}$$

and

$$p_i(\omega_\alpha - \omega_\beta) = -\tfrac{1}{2}\varepsilon_0 K_{ii}(\omega_\alpha) K_{jj}(\omega_\beta) r_{ijk}\, e_j(\omega_\alpha) e_k^*(-\omega_\beta). \tag{7}$$

In the event that $E_k(t) = e_k(0)$ is a dc field, (6) and (7) contract to give

$$p_i(\omega_\alpha) = p_i(\omega_\alpha + 0) + p_i(\omega_\alpha - 0) = -\varepsilon_0 K_{ii}(\omega_\alpha) K_{jj}(\omega_\alpha) r_{ij,k}\, e_j(\omega_\alpha) e_k(0), \tag{8}$$

which is consistent with (2).

In order to simplify the notation, a *second-order nonlinear susceptibility* χ_{ijk} has been defined such that[13]

$$P_i(t) = \varepsilon_0 \chi_{ijk} E'_j(t) E'_k(t) \tag{9}$$

where $E'_j(t)$ and $E'_k(t)$ represent the *total* fields polarized along x_j and x_k. Thus, if waves of two frequencies are present, we permit each to have a component along both x_j and x_k, e.g.,

$$E'_j(t) = \tfrac{1}{2}\Big[e_j(\omega_\alpha)\exp(-i\omega_\alpha t) + e_j(\omega_\beta)\exp(-i\omega_\beta t) + \text{c.c.}\Big], \tag{10}$$

and similarly for $E'_k(t)$. Then

$$P_i(t) = \tfrac{1}{2}\Big[p_i(2\omega_\alpha)\exp[-i2\omega_\alpha t] + p_i(2\omega_\beta)\exp[-i2\omega_\beta t]$$
$$+ p_i(\omega_\alpha + \omega_\beta)\exp[-i(\omega_\alpha + \omega_\beta)t] + p_i(\omega_\alpha - \omega_\beta)\exp[-i(\omega_\alpha - \omega_\beta)t]$$
$$+ 2p_i(0) + \text{c.c.}\Big]$$
$$= \tfrac{1}{4}\varepsilon_0 \chi_{ijk}\Big[e_j(\omega_\alpha)e_k(\omega_\alpha)\exp[-i2\omega_\alpha t] + e_j(\omega_\beta)e_k(\omega_\beta)\exp[-i2\omega_\beta]t \qquad (11)$$
$$+ \{e_j(\omega_\alpha)e_k(\omega_\beta) + e_j(\omega_\beta)e_k(\omega_\alpha)\}\exp[-i(\omega_\alpha + \omega_\beta)t]$$
$$+ \{e_j(\omega_\alpha)e_k^*(-\omega_\beta) + e_j^*(-\omega_\beta)e_k(\omega_\alpha)\}\exp[-i(\omega_\alpha - \omega_\beta)t]$$
$$+ e_j(\omega_\alpha)e_k^*(-\omega_\alpha) + e_j(\omega_\beta)e_k^*(-\omega_\beta) + \text{c.c.}\Big].$$

For up- and down-conversion, respectively, (11) gives

$$\begin{aligned} p_i(\omega_\alpha + \omega_\beta) &= \tfrac{1}{2}\varepsilon_0 \chi_{ijk}[e_j(\omega_\alpha)e_k(\omega_\beta) + e_j(\omega_\beta)e_k(\omega_\alpha)] \\ &\equiv \varepsilon_0 \chi_{ijk}\, e_j(\omega_\alpha)e_k(\omega_\beta) \end{aligned} \qquad (12)$$

and

$$p_i(\omega_\alpha - \omega_\beta) = \varepsilon_0 \chi_{ijk}\, e_j(\omega_\alpha)e_k^*(-\omega_\beta). \qquad (13)$$

Note that

$$\sum_{jk} e_j(\omega_\alpha)e_k(\omega_\beta) = \sum_{jk} e_j(\omega_\beta)e_k(\omega_\alpha)$$

and

$$\sum_{jk} e_j(\omega_\alpha)e_k^*(-\omega_\beta) = \sum_{jk} e_j^*(-\omega_\beta)e_k(\omega_\alpha).$$

Equation (11) assumes no dispersion in χ_{ijk}. However, as we will show subsequently, the nonlinear coefficients r_{ijk} and χ_{ijk} are functions of the frequencies of the three fields involved in each term. If ω_γ is the frequency of the polarization component, then

$$-\omega_\gamma + \omega_\alpha + \omega_\beta = 0 \qquad (14)$$

where we allow the frequencies to take on positive and negative values to represent sum and difference interactions. We show the frequencies involved in r_{ijk} and χ_{ijk} explicitly by including the argument $(-\omega_\gamma;\, \omega_\alpha,\, \omega_\beta)$, in which the three frequencies must sum to zero in order to satisfy (14). In (6) and (7), we write $r_{ijk}(-\omega_\gamma;\omega_\alpha,\omega_\beta)$ with $\omega_\gamma = \omega_\alpha + \omega_\beta$ and $r_{ijk}(-\omega_\gamma;\omega_\alpha,-\omega_\beta)$

with $\omega_\gamma = \omega_\alpha - \omega_\beta$, respectively. In (12) and (13), we write $\chi_{ijk}(-\omega_\gamma; \omega_\alpha, \omega_\beta)$ with $\omega_\gamma = \omega_\alpha + \omega_\beta$, and $\chi_{ijk}(-\omega_\gamma; \omega_\alpha, -\omega_\beta)$ with $\omega_\gamma = \omega_\alpha - \omega_\beta$, respectively.

For *second harmonic generation* (SHG) and *optical rectification* (OR), taking $e_j(\omega_\beta) = e_k(\omega_\beta) = 0$, we have, respectively,

$$\begin{aligned} p_i(2\omega_\alpha) &= \tfrac{1}{2}\varepsilon_0 \chi_{ijk}(-2\omega_\alpha; \omega_\alpha, \omega_\alpha)e_j(\omega_\alpha)e_k(\omega_\alpha) \\ &= \varepsilon_0 d_{ijk}(-2\omega_\alpha; \omega_\alpha, \omega_\alpha)e_j(\omega_\alpha)e_k(\omega_\alpha) \end{aligned} \tag{15}$$

and

$$\begin{aligned} p_i(0) &= \tfrac{1}{2}\varepsilon_0 \chi_{ijk}(0; \omega_\alpha, -\omega_\alpha)e_j(\omega_\alpha)e_k^*(-\omega_\alpha) \\ &= \varepsilon_0 d_{ijk}(0; \omega_\alpha, -\omega_\alpha)e_j(\omega_\alpha)e_k^*(-\omega_\alpha). \end{aligned} \tag{16}$$

Note that only one term in (11) contributes to the polarization at $2\omega_\alpha$ or at dc, which accounts for the factors of 1/2 in (15) and (16). The SHG and OR coefficients $d_{i,jk}$ have been introduced to avoid these factors of 1/2.

It can also be seen from (11) that, in the absence of dispersion, the coefficients χ_{ijk} are the same for all interactions in (12), (13), (15), and (16). In particular,

$$\chi_{ijk}(-2\omega_\alpha; \omega_\alpha, \omega_\alpha) = \chi_{ijk}(-\omega_\alpha - \omega_\beta; \omega_\alpha, \omega_\beta).$$

We can now show the formal relationships among the electrooptic and nonlinear optic formulations of the coefficients. Comparing (6), (7), and (8) with (12), (13), (15), and (16), we see that

$$\begin{aligned} 2\chi_{ijk}(-\omega_\gamma; \omega_\alpha, \omega_\beta) &= 4d_{ijk}(-\omega_\gamma; \omega_\alpha, \omega_\beta) \\ &= -K_{ii}(\omega_\alpha)K_{jj}(\omega_\beta)r_{ijk}(-\omega_\gamma; \omega_\alpha, \omega_\beta) \end{aligned} \tag{17}$$

where ω_α is the carrier frequency, ω_β the modulating frequency (usually $\omega_\beta \ll \omega_\alpha$), and ω_γ is the side band frequency.

If the dielectric susceptibility $\chi(E)$ is a well-behaved function of the field, it can be expanded in a polynomial series, in which higher-order terms are generally successively smaller (except for terms that vanish by symmetry or near-symmetry). Thus, one expects that in some sense materials with large linear susceptibility will also have a large nonlinear susceptibility; and to examine the intrinsic nonlinear behavior it is useful to define a normalized coefficient in which the linear susceptibility is taken into account. One formulation is indicated in (2.1.1) where the electrooptic coefficients f_{ijk} and g_{ijk} are defined in terms of the polarization induced by the applied field. Another empirical normalization, which takes account of polarizability at all three frequencies, has been proposed by Miller.[14] Experimentally, these normalized coefficients exhibit much less variation with temperature, frequency, and substance than do r_{ijk} and s_{ijk}. In a principal axis system, the

Miller delta coefficient is given by†

$$\delta_{ijk}(-\omega_\gamma;\omega_\alpha,\omega_\beta) = \frac{d_{ijk}(-\omega_\gamma;\omega_\alpha,\omega_\beta)}{\chi_{ii}(\omega_\gamma)\chi_{jj}(\omega_\alpha)\chi_{kk}(\omega_\beta)} = \frac{-K_{ii}(\omega_\gamma)K_{jj}(\omega_\alpha)r_{ijk}(-\omega_\gamma;\omega_\alpha,\omega_\beta)}{4\chi_{ii}(\omega_\gamma)\chi_{jj}(\omega_\alpha)\chi_{kk}(\omega_\beta)}. \tag{18}$$

It is found[14] experimentally that $\delta_{ijk}(-2\omega;\omega,\omega)$ varies over a much narrower range for a variety of materials than $d_{ijk}(-2\omega;\omega,\omega)$. It is easy to see how this formulation can be applied to higher-order nonlinear coefficients by dividing out the appropriate linear susceptibilities. It can also be seen that $\varepsilon_0 f_{ijk}$ and $-4\delta_{ijk}$ are very nearly the same for materials with large $\chi_{ii}(\omega_\gamma)$ and $\chi_{jj}(\omega_\alpha)$:

$$\varepsilon_0 f_{ijk}(-\omega_\gamma;\omega_\alpha,\omega_\beta) = \frac{r_{ijk}(-\omega_\gamma;\omega_\alpha,\omega_\beta)}{\chi_{kk}(\omega_\beta)}. \tag{19}$$

4.2 *Dispersion and Classification of Nonlinear Coefficients*

As noted in Chapter I, Section 3.7, the linear dielectric constant is a strong function of frequency near the lattice and electron resonances. This dispersion is illustrated in Fig. 4.1. The resonances at infrared ($\sim 10^{13}$ Hz) and ultraviolet ($\sim 10^{15}$ Hz) frequencies divide the spectrum into three regions in which $K(\omega)$ is nearly constant. In the radio frequency range $K(\omega) \approx K(0)$, in the optical range $K(\omega) \approx K(\infty) = n^2$, and in the far ultraviolet $K(\omega) = 1$.

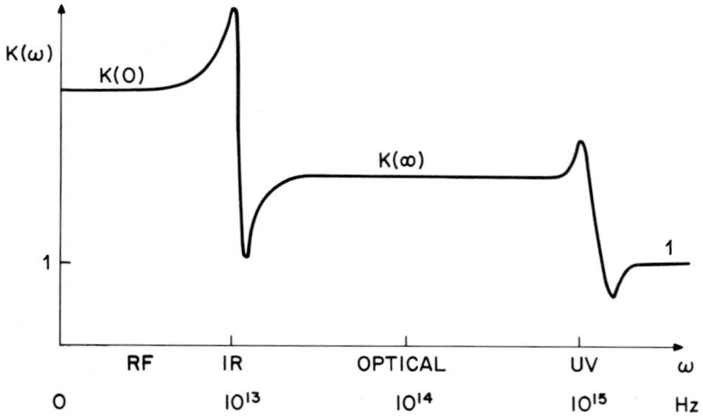

Fig. 4.1 Dispersion of the dielectric constant $K(\omega)$.

† An alternative definition[2] places a factor ε_0^{-1} on the right-hand side of (18), since δ_{ijk} like f_{ijk} is more naturally defined in terms of polarization $p(\omega_\beta)$ than electric field.

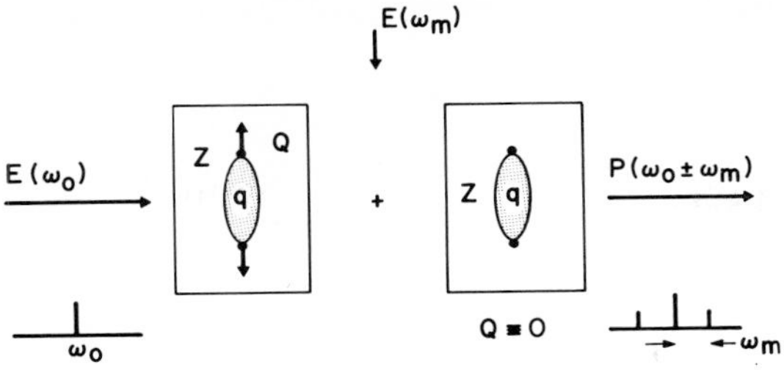

Fig. 4.2 Lattice (Q) and electron (q) contributions to the electrooptic coefficient.

The nonlinear coefficients also exhibit dispersion near the lattice and electron resonances and are relatively insensitive to frequency far from the resonances. However, in the case of a second-order nonlinearity, three frequencies $\omega_\gamma = \omega_\alpha \pm \omega_\beta$ must be stated in order to specify dispersion. The ranges in which the component frequencies fall serve to identify the nonlinear process. If ω_α, ω_β, and ω_γ are all in the optical range, the process is called *optical mixing*, and if ω_β is a radio frequency while ω_α and ω_γ are optical frequencies, the process is called *electrooptic modulation* or the *Pockels effect*. A transition occurs as the modulating frequency is increased from the rf range through the lattice resonance to the optical range.

The physical situation is illustrated schematically in Fig. 4.2. An optical carrier $E(\omega_0)$ at frequency ω_0 is incident on a nonlinear dielectric consisting of two independent systems: a polarizable electronic charge q with displacement z situated in a rigid lattice ($Q \equiv 0$), and a polar lattice with charge Z and displacement Q. A modulating field $E(\omega_m)$ induces two independent changes in the optical susceptibility

$$\frac{d\chi(\omega_0)}{dE(\omega_\mathrm{m})} = \left(\frac{\partial\chi(\omega_0)}{\partial Q}\right)_{E(\omega_\mathrm{m})=0} \frac{\partial Q}{\partial E(\omega_\mathrm{m})} + \left(\frac{\partial\chi(\omega_0)}{\partial E(\omega_\mathrm{m})}\right)_{Q=0}. \tag{1}$$

The second term is purely electronic in origin and is due to the change in electronic polarizability caused by the direct interaction between $E(\omega_\mathrm{m})$ and z when $Q \equiv 0$. The first term accounts for the change in optical polarizability caused by the lattice displacement, which in turn is caused by $E(\omega_\mathrm{m})$. The partial derivative $\partial\chi(\omega_0)/\partial E(\omega_\mathrm{m}) \equiv \xi$ represents a deformation of the electron potential function by the direct action of the electric field; while $\partial\chi(\omega_0)/\partial Q \equiv \alpha$ represents a deformation of the potential due to a change in lattice spacing. Since we are concerned with the *electronic* susceptibility $\chi(\omega_0)$, neither ξ nor α are dispersive at modulating frequencies well below the electronic resonance.

If the lattice is represented by a damped harmonic oscillator, the quantity

$$\frac{\partial Q}{\partial E(\omega_\mathrm{m})} \equiv \beta(\omega_\mathrm{m}) = \frac{\beta(0)\omega_\mathrm{T}^2}{(\omega_\mathrm{T}^2 - \omega_\mathrm{m}^2) + i2\omega_\mathrm{m}\Gamma} \tag{2}$$

is resonant at the lattice frequency ω_T with line width 2Γ. At $\omega_m = 0$

$$\beta(0) = \varepsilon_0 \Delta K\, v/Z = Z/k = [\varepsilon_0 \Delta K\, v/k]^{1/2} \tag{3}$$

where Q is the change in lattice spacing from equilibrium, $\Delta K \equiv K(0) - K(\infty)$, Z is the ionic charge on the lattice, k is the spring constant, and v is the volume per bond.

It is helpful to relate the coefficients in (1) to previously defined nonlinear coefficients and to introduce other coefficients employed in the literature. Thus, from (4.1.17)

$$d\chi(\omega_0)/dE(\omega_m) \equiv -n^4 r = 2\chi = 4d \tag{4}$$

and, introducing tensor indices and corresponding frequencies, (1) becomes

$$\begin{aligned} 4d_{ijk}(-\omega_0 \mp \omega_m; \omega_0, \pm\omega_m) &= -K_{ii}(\omega_0 \pm \omega_m) K_{jj}(\omega_0) r_{ijk}(-\omega_0 \mp \omega_m; \omega_0, \pm\omega_m) \\ &= \alpha_{ijk} \beta_{kk}(\omega_m) + \xi_{ijk} \\ &= 4\overset{\circ}{d}_{ijk}(C(\omega_m) + 1). \end{aligned} \tag{5}$$

Here $4\overset{\circ}{d}_{ijk} \equiv \xi_{ijk}$ is the electronic contribution to the nonlinearity and

$$C(\omega_m) = \alpha_{ijk} \beta_{kk}(\omega_m)/\xi_{ijk} \tag{6}$$

is the ratio of the lattice to the electronic contributions.

Returning to Fig. 4.2, we see that $E(\omega_m)$ phase modulates $E(\omega_0)$ via the nonlinear susceptibility to produce polarization components that radiate at the side band frequencies $\omega_0 \pm \omega_m$. As shown in Section 2.3, the side band strength is a function of the nonlinear coefficient, and conversely the strength of the side bands can be used to measure the coefficient.

A striking demonstration of the dispersion in the nonlinear coefficient near the lattice resonance is provided by experiments on GaP by Faust et al.[15] In their work $E(\omega_0)$ is provided by a 633-nm He–Ne laser and $E(\omega_m)$ by several lines of an infrared laser that lie near the lattice resonance at 365 cm^{-1}. The observed dispersion in the only nonvanishing component $d_{123}(-\omega_0 - \omega_m; \omega_0, \omega_m)$ for the various ω_m is plotted in Fig. 4.3. The *form* of $C(\omega_m)$ is known from infrared measurements of ω_T and Γ in GaP. Then by fitting the data to (5), one can calculate $C(0) = -0.5$. Thus in GaP, the lattice and electron contributions to the electrooptic effect have opposite signs. The optical mixing coefficient d°_{123} is insensitive to frequency when $\omega_\gamma = \omega_0 \pm \omega_m$, $\omega_\alpha = \omega_0$, and $\omega_\beta = \omega_m$ are all in the optical range; the electrooptic coefficient $r_{123} = 4d_{123}(\omega_0; \omega_0, 0)/n^4 \equiv 4d^{\text{eo}}_{123}/n^4$ is insensitive to frequency when $\omega_m \ll \omega_T$; and for GaP, $d^{\text{eo}} \approx d^{\circ}/2$. (See (5).)

Other distributions of ω_α, ω_β, and ω_γ throughout the rf and optical ranges have also been studied. If ω_α and ω_β are both optical frequencies and $\omega_\gamma = \omega_\alpha - \omega_\beta$ is dc or rf, the process is called *optical rectification*. If all three

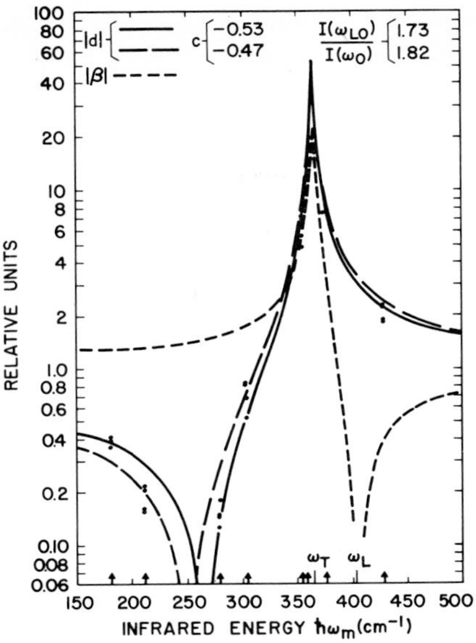

Fig. 4.3 Dispersion of the electrooptic coefficient d and the infrared strength β versus modulating frequency ω_m in GaP. [After W. L. Faust, C. H. Henry, and R. H. Eick, *Phys. Rev.* **173**, 781 (1968).]

frequencies are in the rf range, the process is called the *microwave nonlinear effect*, because it has been observed using microwave frequencies.[16]

4.3 *Relationship between Electrooptic and Raman Scattering Coefficients*

The thermal energy of a crystal resides in excitations of its lattice vibrational modes. If an excited optic mode has suitable symmetry, it will produce fluctuations in the optical dielectric constant at the vibrational frequency. In the notation of Section 4.2, such coupling implies that α_{ijk} is nonvanishing. These fluctuations will scatter (or modulate) an optical beam with frequency ω_0 passing through the crystal. Side bands will appear at $\omega_0 \pm \omega_v$, where ω_v is the vibrational frequency. The lower and upper side bands are called the Stokes and anti-Stokes frequencies, respectively. A crystal containing many atoms in the unit cell may have many such *Raman active modes*. If a crystal is centric, then one can show that Raman active modes are infrared inactive, and vice versa. However, if the crystal is acentric, a given mode may be both Raman and *infrared* active; i.e. α_{ijk} and β_{kk} nonvanishing. A thorough discussion of the Raman effect in crystals is given by Loudon.[17]

The cubic zinc blende lattice is particularly simple. It has only one optic mode, and it is both Raman and infrared active. The threefold degeneracy of the mode frequencies is raised by the macroscopic electric field associated with the longitudinal mode. Thus, one observes both a transverse and a longitudinal mode, at frequencies ω_T and ω_L, respectively. The strengths of the Raman side bands for transverse and longitudinal modes also differ because of the macroscopic electric field associated with the longitudinal mode. This field introduces a modulation of the optical dielectric constant independent of that produced directly by the lattice displacement. *The physical processes responsible for Raman scattering from an infrared active mode are identical with those responsible for the electrooptic effect.*[18]

We can illustrate the connection between these two effects most simply for GaAs.[19] Raman scattering is produced by fluctuations in $\chi_{ij}(\omega_0)$ induced by thermally excited displacements Q_k in the polar optic mode. The power scattered into a side band is proportional to the squared total derivative $|d\chi_{ij}(\omega_0)/dQ_k|^2$. For the transverse optic mode

$$d\chi_{ij}(\omega_0)/dQ_k = \partial\chi_{ij}(\omega_0)/\partial Q_k = \alpha_{ij,k}, \tag{1}$$

and for the longitudinal optic mode

$$\frac{d\chi_{ij}(\omega_0)}{dQ_k} = \left(\frac{\partial\chi(\omega_0)}{\partial Q_k}\right)_{E=0} + \left(\frac{\partial\chi(\omega_0)}{\partial E(\omega_L)}\right)_{Q=0}\frac{1}{\partial Q_k/\partial E(\omega_L)} = \alpha_{ij,k} + \frac{\xi_{ijk}}{\beta_{kk}(\omega_L)}. \tag{2}$$

The Stokes scattering efficiency $S_{ij,k}$ is defined as the power scattered into the lower side band for unity incident power,[17,20]

$$S_{ij,k}^{\mathrm{T}} = D_{\mathrm{T}}|\alpha_{ij,k}|^2 \tag{3}$$

$$S_{ij,k}^{\mathrm{L}} = D_{\mathrm{L}}|\alpha_{ij,k} + \xi_{ijk}/\beta_{kk}(\omega_L)|^2 \tag{4}$$

$$D_{\mathrm{L,T}} = \frac{v}{\bar{m}}\sigma_{\mathrm{L,T}} = \frac{v\hbar\omega_s^4(\bar{n}_{\mathrm{L,T}} + 1)L\,d\Omega}{32\pi^2 c^4\bar{m}\omega_{\mathrm{L,T}}} \tag{5}$$

where ω_s is the Stokes frequency, v is the primitive cell volume, $\bar{n} = [\exp(\hbar\omega/kT) - 1]^{-1}$ is the Bose factor, L is the scattering length in the crystal, $d\Omega$ is the solid angle (inside the crystal) within which the radiation is collected, and $\bar{m}$ is the reduced mass of the oscillator in v. The preceding treatment assumes that no local field correction is needed in a semiconductor[17] such as GaAs. However, local field corrections do not alter the following discussion if $\alpha_{ij,k}$, β_{kk}, and ξ_{ijk} are suitably interpreted.[20,21]

For zinc blende crystals, the only nonvanishing second-rank tensor element has indices $(ijk) = 123$ or permutations thereof. Then for the Pockels electrooptic effect (4.2.5) becomes

$$-n^4 r_{12,3} = \alpha_{12,3}\beta_{33}(0) + \xi_{123} \equiv \alpha_{12,3}\beta_{33}(0)[1 + C^{-1}]; \tag{6}$$

here C is the lattice-electron ratio:

$$C = \alpha_{123}\beta_{33}(0)/\xi_{123} = d_{41}^{\mathrm{i}}/d_{41}^{\mathrm{o}}, \tag{7}$$

and $\beta_{33}(0)$ is given by (4.2.3). It is convenient to introduce the contracted coefficients: $r_{12,3} \equiv r_{41}$, $\xi_{123} \equiv 4d_{14}^{\mathrm{o}}$, and $\alpha_{12,3}\beta_3(0) \equiv 4d_{14}^{\mathrm{i}}$, where d_{14}^{i} is the ionic part of d_{14}^{eo}.

The nonlinear dielectric coefficients can be obtained from Raman measurements by means of the following fomulas[19] derived from (3)–(7):

$$C^{-1} = a[1 \pm (\sigma_{\mathrm{T}} S_{\mathrm{L}}/\sigma_{\mathrm{L}} S_{\mathrm{T}})^{1/2}] \tag{8}$$

$$r_{41}^2 = S_{\mathrm{T}} n_\infty^2 (1 + C^{-1})^2/\varepsilon_0 n^8 a\omega_{\mathrm{T}}^2 \sigma_{\mathrm{T}} \tag{9}$$

$$d_{14}^0 = -n^4 r_{41}/4(1 + C) \tag{10}$$

where

$$a = \omega_{\mathrm{T}}^2(\omega_{\mathrm{L}}^2 - \omega_{\mathrm{T}}^2)^{-1}, \tag{11}$$

$\sigma_{\mathrm{L,T}}$ is given by (5), n is the refractive index at the optical frequency, and n_∞ is the "high frequency" (dispersionless) refractive index. The square root leads to an ambiguity in the calculation of C in (8). As a rule, the values of r_{41} or d_{14}^{o} calculated from (9) or (10) with the two choices of C differ sufficiently so that the correct choice of C can be made by comparison with crude direct measurements of r_{41} or d_{14}^{o}. The absolute signs of r_{41} and d_{14}^{o} cannot be determined, but their relative sign is given by (10). Excellent agreement is found between directly measured values of r_{41} and d_{14}^{o} in GaAs and those obtained from Raman measurements.[19]

The foregoing analysis ignores two-phonon effects, which is a valid approximation in GaAs. However, two-phonon modes cannot be ignored in a zinc blende crystal like CuCl in which the fundamental and two-phonon modes have comparable strengths.[22]

The analysis is also complicated for crystals, such as $LiTaO_3$, that have more than one contributing mode.[21] In this case, if infrared strength ΔK_{kk}^m, which is the contribution of the m mode to the low frequency dielectric constant K_{kk}, is known for each mode, then[20]

$$-n_i^2 n_j^2 r_{ij,k} = \sum_m \pm (1/\omega_{\mathrm{T}}^m)\{\varepsilon_0 \Delta K_m S_{ij,k}^m/\sigma_{\mathrm{T}}^m\}^{1/2} + \xi_{ijk} \tag{12}$$

where $S_{ij,k}^m$, ω_{T}^m and σ_{T}^m refer to the appropriate transverse mode, and sign ambiguity for each term of the summation arises from the square root.

4.4 Permutation Relations

In Chapter I, Section 2.3 it was shown by a thermodynamic argument that $K_{ij} = K_{ji}$. The same approach is now employed to demonstrate important relationships among nonlinear coefficients with their indices permuted. A more rigorous treatment is given elsewhere.[23]

The differential Helmholtz free energy of a polarized dielectric can be written

$$dF = -S\,dT - P_i\,dE_i \tag{1}$$

where we have not included the vacuum energy $\varepsilon_0 E_i dE_i$ as we did in Chapter I. Then

$$\begin{aligned} p_i(\omega_\gamma) = \partial F/\partial e_i(\omega_\gamma) &= \varepsilon_0 \chi_{ij}(\omega_\gamma) e_j(\omega_\gamma) \\ &\quad + \varepsilon_0 \chi_{ijk}(-\omega_\gamma; \omega_\alpha, \omega_\beta) e_j(\omega_\alpha) e_k(\omega_\beta). \end{aligned} \tag{2}$$

The linear and nonlinear susceptibilities are given by

$$\varepsilon_0 \chi_{ij}(\omega_\gamma) = \partial^2 F/\partial e_i(\omega_\gamma)\,\partial e_j(\omega_\gamma) \tag{3}$$

and

$$\varepsilon_0 \chi_{ijk}(-\omega_\gamma; \omega_\alpha, \omega_\beta) = \partial^3 F/\partial e_i(\omega_\gamma)\,\partial e_j(\omega_\alpha)\,\partial e_k(\omega_\beta), \tag{4}$$

respectively. Since the partial derivatives can be taken in any sequence, the nonlinear coefficients have the permutation symmetry

$$\begin{aligned} \chi_{ijk}(-\omega_\gamma; \omega_\alpha, \omega_\beta) &= \chi_{jik}(\omega_\alpha; -\omega_\gamma, \omega_\beta) \\ &= \chi_{kji}(\omega_\beta; \omega_\alpha, -\omega_\gamma) = \chi_{ikj}(-\omega_\gamma; \omega_\beta, \omega_\alpha). \end{aligned} \tag{5}$$

The rule is that the indices may be permuted in any way so long as the associated frequencies are also carried along. Note that as a check the sums of frequencies in the arguments of (5) must vanish.

In order to ensure that $P_i(t)$ and $E_j(t)$, defined in Section 4.2, are real, it is necessary that

$$\chi_{ijk}(-\omega_\gamma; \omega_\alpha, \omega_\beta) = \chi_{ijk}^*(\omega_\gamma; -\omega_\alpha, -\omega_\beta), \tag{6}$$

and if χ_{ijk} is also real, as it will be if ω_α, ω_β, and ω_γ are far from resonances of the material, then

$$\chi_{ijk}(-\omega_\gamma; \omega_\alpha, \omega_\beta) = \chi_{ijk}^*(-\omega_\gamma; \omega_\alpha, \omega_\beta) \tag{7}$$

and, with (6)

$$\chi_{ijk}(-\omega_\gamma; \omega_\alpha, \omega_\beta) = \chi_{ijk}(\omega_\gamma; -\omega_\alpha, -\omega_\beta). \tag{8}$$

Two or three frequencies may be permuted without permuting the respective indices provided the frequencies are in the same nondispersive region of the spectrum of the crystal. Thus, if all three frequencies are in the optical region far from lattice or electronic resonances,

$$\begin{aligned}\chi_{ijk}(-\omega_\gamma;\omega_\alpha,\omega_\beta) &= \chi_{jik}(-\omega_\gamma;\omega_\alpha,\omega_\beta) = \chi_{kji}(-\omega_\gamma;\omega_\alpha,\omega_\beta)\\ &= \chi_{ikj}(-\omega_\gamma;\omega_\alpha,\omega_\beta) = 2d^{\mathrm{o}}_{ijk}(-\omega_\gamma;\omega_\alpha,\omega_\beta)\end{aligned} \tag{9}$$

using (4.1.17). These are the *Kleinman symmetry conditions*.[24]

For SHG, we have, with (4.1.17),

$$\begin{aligned}\chi_{ijk}(-2\omega;\omega,\omega) &= \chi_{ikj}(-2\omega;\omega,\omega)\\ &\equiv \chi_{i,jk}(-2\omega;\omega,\omega) = 2d^{\mathrm{o}}_{i\mu}(-2\omega;\omega,\omega)\end{aligned} \tag{10}$$

where the last pair of indices may be permuted even though there may be significant dispersion between ω and 2ω. If there is no dispersion, the Kleinman conditions further reduce the number of independent coefficients. In (10), μ is a contracted index running from 1 to 6: $1 \to (11)$, $2 \to (22)$, $3 \to (33)$, $4 \to (23, 32)$, $5 \to (13, 31)$, and $6 \to (12, 21)$.

Similarly, for optical rectification,

$$\chi_{ijk}(0;\omega,-\omega) = \chi_{ikj}(0;\omega,-\omega) = 2d^{\mathrm{OR}}_{i\mu}(0;\omega,-\omega); \tag{11}$$

and for the Pockels electrooptic effect, with (8) and (4.1.17),

$$\begin{aligned}\chi_{ijk}(-\omega;\omega,0) &= \chi_{ijk}(\omega;-\omega,0) = \chi_{jik}(-\omega;\omega,0) = \chi_{ij,k}(-\omega;\omega,0)\\ &= 2d^{\mathrm{eo}}_{\mu k}(-\omega;\omega,0) = -\tfrac{1}{2}K_{ii}(\omega)K_{jj}(\omega)r_{\mu k}(-\omega;\omega,0).\end{aligned} \tag{12}$$

If we apply (5) to the Pockels coefficient, we see that

$$\chi_{ijk}(-\omega;\omega,0) = \chi_{kji}(0;\omega,-\omega) \tag{13}$$

or, with (11) and (12),

$$d^{\mathrm{eo}}_{ij,k}(-\omega;\omega,0) = d^{\mathrm{OR}}_{k,ji}(0;\omega,-\omega). \tag{14}$$

Thus, *the Pockels and optical rectification coefficients are identical.*

For the microwave nonlinear effect all three frequencies are in the radio frequency range. If there is no dispersion between the frequencies, a low frequency equivalent of the Kleinman conditions (9) should hold with

$$\chi_{ijk}(-\omega_\gamma;\omega_\alpha,\omega_\beta) = 2d^{\mathrm{M}}_{ijk}(-\omega_\gamma;\omega_\alpha,\omega_\beta). \tag{15}$$

4.5 *Phenomenological Origin of Nonlinearity*

The linear dielectric behavior of a crystal arises from electronic and ionic displacements q and Q in response to an applied field E. The electrons and ions have charges z and Z, and effective masses $\overline{m}_q$ and $\overline{m}_Q$. They are bound to their equilibrium positions by springs that exert restoring forces $k_q q$ and $k_Q Q$. It is clear that if all the parameters $(z, \overline{m}_q, k_q)$ and $(Z, \overline{m}_Q, k_Q)$ are constant, then the response (q, Q) of the system will be proportional to the excitation E. It is equally clear that if any of the parameters is a function of q or Q, then the response will be nonlinear. For example, if E oscillates at frequency ω, then q and Q may have components at 2ω. Garrett[25] has examined anharmonic oscillator models in which k_q and k_Q are the nonlinear parameters and the lattice displacements correspond only to optic phonon modes—i.e., acoustic mode effects are not included. In the future, one might also wish to consider the effects of variations in charge or ionicity with displacement.

For the sake of illustration, consider an *electronic* oscillator with anharmonic potential energy

$$U_q = \tfrac{1}{2}\overline{m}_q \omega_q^2 q^2 + Dq^3 - Ezq \tag{1}$$

and restoring force

$$kq = (\partial U_q/\partial q)_{E=0} = (\overline{m}_q \omega_q^2 + 3Dq)q, \tag{2}$$

with ω_q the resonant frequency for $D = 0$. The equation of motion is

$$\ddot{q} + (\omega_q^2 + 3Dq/\overline{m})q = zE/\overline{m}_q. \tag{3}$$

For $3Dq \ll \overline{m}\omega_q^2$, an assembly of N such oscillators per unit volume yields[25] a linear susceptibility

$$\varepsilon_0 \chi(\omega) = Nz^2/\overline{m}_q(\omega_q^2 - \omega^2) \tag{4}$$

and an SHG nonlinear susceptibility

$$\varepsilon_0 \chi(-2\omega; \omega, \omega) = -\chi(\omega)\chi(\omega)\chi(2\omega)\{3\varepsilon_0^3 D/z^3 N^2\}. \tag{5}$$

It can be seen that the quantity $(3\varepsilon_0^3 D/z^3 N^2)$ is proportional to the Miller δ defined in (4.1.18). According to (5), all the dispersion in the optical nonlinearity is due to dispersion in the linear susceptibilities. (As shown by the Faust–Henry experiment, this statement is true only for a purely electronic oscillator.) Further, since experiment shows that the Miller δ for SHG in many substances varies over a much narrower range than $\chi(-2\omega; \omega, \omega)$, the nonlinear oscillator parameter $(D/z^3 N^2)$ must be understood to account for the nonlinear susceptibility. Garrett estimates D by equating the harmonic and anharmonic energy terms when q becomes equal to the interatomic spacing; this gives the right order magnitude for $(D/z^3 N^2)$ to account for observed SHG coefficients. However, since $\chi(-2\omega; \omega, \omega)$ vanishes identically for a centrosymmetric crystal, the effective value of D in a real case must depend on the symmetry of the potential function U. The acentricity depends not only on structural factors but also on ionicity of the bonding.[26]

Returning to the anharmonic oscillator, consider a molecule with both electronic and ionic displacements. Garrett writes the simplest potential function that will give a second-order susceptibility as a general third-order polynomial in (q, Q):

$$U = \tfrac{1}{2}\overline{m}_q \omega_q^2 q^2 + \tfrac{1}{2}\overline{m}_Q \omega_Q^2 Q^2 + AQ^3 + BQ^2 q + CQq^2 + Dq^3 - E(zq + ZQ). \tag{6}$$

At frequencies in the optical range $\omega_0 \gg \omega_Q$, ionic motion is effectively clamped: $Q = 0$. Thus, the D term accounts for the optical nonlinearity. When two optical fields and one rf field interact, as in the Pockels and optical rectification interactions, the C and D terms contribute. The C and D terms are responsible for the coefficients $\alpha\beta(0)$ and ξ, respectively, which were discussed in Section 4.2. [The C factor of Section 4.2 should not be confused with the C used here.]

When all three fields are in the rf range, as in the microwave nonlinear effect, then A, B, C, and D terms can all contribute.

In considering dielectric nonlinearities from several viewpoints in this section, we have introduced a variety of parameters to describe the same interaction. The various definitions often reflect the targets of the original investigators and can, therefore, each provide important insights. Various notations found in the literature are sorted out and summarized in Table 4.1 according to the frequency ranges occupied by the three interacting frequencies. Lattice resonances are typically in the neighborhood of 10^{13} Hz ($333\ \text{cm}^{-1}$) and electronic resonances are near 10^{15} Hz (3000 Å).

TABLE 4.1
Nonlinear Dielectric Effects

	Radio frequency	ω_Q	Optical	ω_q	Ultraviolet
$\omega/2\pi$	10^{12}	10^{13}	10^{14}	10^{15}	10^{16} Hz
Optical mixing; SHG coefficients D; d°, δ°; ξ			ω_m, ω_0, $\omega_0 \pm \omega_m$		
Pockels electrooptic; OR coefficients C, D; d^{eo}, δ^{eo}, d^{OR}, r; $\alpha\beta$, ξ	ω_m		ω_0, $\omega_0 \pm \omega_m$		
Microwave nonlinear coefficients A, B, C, D, ; d^M, δ^M	ω_m, ω_0, $\omega_0 \pm \omega_m$				

References†

1. F. Pockels, "Lehrbuch der Kristalloptic," Teubner, Leipzig, 1906.
2. S. H. Wemple and M. DiDomenico, Jr., *Appl. Solid State Sci.* **3**, 263–383 (1972).
3. P. N. Butcher, "Nonlinear Optical Phenomena," Bulletin 200. Engineering Experiment Station, Ohio State University, Columbus, Ohio, 1965.
4. I. P. Kaminow and E. H. Turner, *Appl. Opt.* **5**, 1612 (1966).
5. J. M. Ley, *Electr. Lett.* **2**., 139 (1966); C. H. Clayson, *ibid.* **2**, 139 (1966); K. F. Hulme, P. H. Davies, and V. M. Cound, *ibid.* **5** (1969); K. Hookabe and Y. Matsuo, *ibid.* **6**, 559 (1970); D. Kalymnios, J. M. Ley, and K. Rashidi, *ibid.* **6**, 771 (1970); K Kalymnios, *ibid.* **6**, 806 (1970); G. E. Francois, F. M. Librecht, and J. J. Engelen, *ibid.* **6**, 778 (1970); F. M. Librecht and G. E. Francois, *IEEE J. Quant. Electr.* **7**, 374 (1971).
6. B. H. Billings, *J. Opt. Soc. Amer.* **39**, 797 (1949).
7. F. E. Terman, "Electronic and Radio Engineering." McGraw-Hill, New York, 1955.
8. F. S. Chen, J. F. Geusic, S. K. Kurtz, J. G. Skinner, and S. H. Wemple, *J. Appl. Phys.* **37**, 388 (1966).
9. D. F. Nelson and M. Lax, *Phys. Rev. Lett.* **24**, 379 (1970).
10. D. F. Nelson and P. D. Lazay, *Phys. Rev. Lett.* **25**, 1187 (1970).
11. D. A. Pinnow, *IEEE J. Quant. Electr.* **6**, 223 (1970).
12. E. K. Sittig, "Progress in optics," Vol. 10 (E. Wolf, ed.). North Holland, Amsterdam, 1972.
13. G. D. Boyd and D. A. Kleinman, *J. Appl. Phys.* **39**, 3597 (1968).
14. R. C. Miller, *Appl. Phys. Lett.* **5**, 17 (1964)
15. W. L. Faust, C. H. Henry, and R. H. Eick, *Phys. Rev.* **173**, 781 (1968); W. L. Faust and C. H. Henry, *Phys. Rev. Lett.* **17**, 1265 (1966).
16. G. D. Boyd, T. J. Bridges, M. A. Pollack, and E. H. Turner, *Phys. Rev. Lett.* **26**, 387 (1971).
17. R. Loudon, *Adv. Phys.* **13**, 423 (1964), erratum **14**, 621 (1964).
18. I. P. Kaminow, in "Ferroelectricity" (E. F. Weller, ed.). Elsevier, Amsterdam, 1967.
19. W. D. Johnston, Jr., and I. P. Kaminow, *Phys. Rev.* **188**, 1209 (1969).
20. I. P. Kaminow and W. D. Johnston, Jr., *Phys. Rev.* **160**, 519 (1967); **178**, 1528 (E) (1969).
21. W. D. Johnston, Jr., *Phys. Rev.* **1B**, 3494 (1970).
22. I. P. Kaminow and E. H. Turner, *Phys. Rev.* **5B**, 1564 (1972).
23. J. A. Armstrong, N. Bloembergen, J. Ducuing, and P. S. Pershan, *Phys. Rev.* **127**, 1918 (1962).
24. D. A. Kleinman, *Phys. Rev.* **126**, 1977 (1962).
25. C. G. B. Garrett, *IEEE J. Quant. Electron.* **4**, 70 (1968).
26. B. F. Levine, *Phys. Rev. B* **7**, 2600 (1973).

† See Chapter III for reprints of References 1, 4, 6, 8, 15, 16, and 19.

CHAPTER III

REPRINTS

Reprinted from **APPLIED OPTICS**, Vol. 5, page 1612, October 1966

Simultaneously published *Proc. IEEE* **54**, 1374–1390 (1966).

Electrooptic Light Modulators

I. P. KAMINOW AND E. H. TURNER

***Abstract*—The field of electrooptic light modulation by means of the Pockels and Kerr effects in crystals is summarized with particular attention to communications applications using the optical maser. All available data on electrooptic materials are tabulated, and design considerations and operating principles for various modulator configurations are outlined.**

I. Introduction

APPLICATIONS of the optical maser often require a means for modulating the amplitude, phase, frequency, or direction of a light beam at high speed. Mechanical shutters and moving mirrors have too much inertia to permit modulation at the required frequencies, which range from megahertz to gigahertz. Hence, it is necessary to rely upon optical interactions with electrical, magnetic, and acoustic fields at the modulating frequency via the nonlinearities of matter. Some of these interactions are intrinsically lossy at the optical frequency: e.g., free carrier absorption, and Franz-Keldysh effect (band edge shift by an electric field); others are intrinsically reactive (or parametric in the electrical engineering sense): e.g., magnetooptic Faraday effect, acoustooptic effect, and electrooptic Kerr and Pockels effects. This paper is concerned only with reactive electrooptic effects in solids; that is, the change in refractive index produced by an applied electric field.

Before the turn of the century Kerr observed a quadratic electrooptic effect in liquids such as carbon disulphide, and Röntgen and Kundt observed a linear effect in quartz. Pockels examined the linear effect in crystals of quartz, tourmaline, potassium chlorate, and Rochelle salt. He demonstrated the existence of a *direct* effect (independent of piezoelectrically induced strain) and characterized the linear electrooptic effect in crystals of various point symmetry using either the applied electric field or dielectric polarization as bases [1].

In 1944 Zwicker and Scherrer reported the dc electrooptic properties of KH_2PO_4 and KD_2PO_4 and related these properties to the ferroelectric behavior of these crystals. They observed that the electrooptic coefficient, based on electric fields, was proportional to the dielectric constant, exhibiting a Curie-Weiss behavior as a function of temperature. The electrooptic coefficient based on dielectric polarization is the same temperature-independent constant for both crystals [2], [3]. In 1949 Billings,

Manuscript received June 30, 1966.
The authors are with the Crawford Hill Laboratory, Bell Telephone Laboratories, Inc., Holmdel, N. J.

and later Carpenter, built and studied the properties of high-speed (about 1 MHz) light shutters using KH_2PO_4 and $NH_4H_2PO_4$ for use in recording sound on film and other engineering applications [4], [5]. In 1961, Holshouser, von Foerster, and Clark reported on a microwave liquid Kerr cell for use in studying high-speed photomixing [6]; and Froome and Bradsell described a microwave modulator employing the Pockels effect in $NH_4H_2PO_4$ for use in a distance measuring device [7].

Since the advent of the optical maser with its potential application to communication and switching, the electrooptic properties of a number of different materials have been studied. These measurements are summarized below, and the general properties of the materials commented on briefly. Several new modulator configurations have been proposed recently and the principles and characteristics of their operation are outlined in a later section, along with some general design considerations. Before getting into the details of modulator materials and designs, however, a description of the electrooptic effect and its application to various types of optical modulation is given.

II. Electrooptic Behavior of Crystals[1]

It is convenient to consider the change in $1/n^2$ with application of a field, where n is the refractive index, rather than a change in n directly. The quantity $1/n^2$ can be written

$$\frac{1}{n^2} = \frac{1}{n_0^2} + rE + RE^2 + \cdots, \tag{1}$$

where r and R are the linear and quadratic electrooptic coefficients, respectively. The coefficients in (1) are those for a direct (primary) effect which is independent of crystal strain. In addition, if the crystal develops macroscopic strain under the influence of the field, there will be a change in index through the elastooptic effect. All solids exhibit an elastooptic effect and all solids are strained by an electric field, either through the converse piezoelectric effect (strain$=dE$) or through electrostriction (strain $=\gamma E^2$). The resultant secondary effect can be shown to depend on crystal symmetry in the same way as the direct effect. It is not, however, necessary that the direct and secondary effects have the same algebraic sign: the overall electrooptic effect in a crystal strained by the field can be larger or smaller than the direct effect alone [9]. If the driving fields are at a frequency corresponding to an acoustic resonance of the material, the secondary effect may be as large as, or larger than, the direct one because of large strain amplitudes. At sufficiently high frequencies the material cannot strain macroscopically and only the direct effect is important.

If the material has a center of symmetry, reversing the sense of the applied field E does not change the physical situation and, in particular, $1/n^2$ will be independent of the sign of E. Terms of odd power in E in (1) will change sign, however, so the coefficients of these terms must vanish in centrosymmetric materials. Only noncentrosymmetric (piezoelectric) crystals can produce a linear effect. There is, of course, no restriction on the terms of even powers of E.

In order to carry the discussion further, it must be recognized that the index of refraction of a crystal depends on optical polarization relative to crystal axes, that the electric field is a vector quantity, and that the r and R coefficients must reflect the crystal symmetry. The optical properties of a crystal are frequently described in terms of the *index ellipsoid* (or *indicatrix*). The equation of this surface is

$$\frac{x_1^2}{n_1^2} + \frac{x_2^2}{n_2^2} + \frac{x_3^2}{n_3^2} = 1, \tag{2}$$

where the coordinates x_i are parallel to the axes of the ellipsoid and n_i are the principal refractive indices. The properties of the indicatrix can be seen from a simple example. If a wavefront has its normal in the x_3 direction, then we consider the ellipse formed by the indicatrix and the $x_3=0$ plane. The wave has components polarized along x_1 and x_2 and indices given by the semi-axes of the ellipse (n_1 and n_2). In a more general case, the wave normal direction can be chosen arbitrarily and the two indices obtained as the semi-axes of the elliptical section perpendicular to the arbitrary direction.

If an electric field is applied to a crystal, the general equation of the indicatrix can be written as

$$\sum_{i,j,k,l} \left(\frac{1}{n_{ij}^2} + z_{ijk}E_k + R_{ijkl}E_kE_l\right) x_ix_j = 1 \tag{3}$$

where the indices run from 1 to 3. The z_{ijk} and R_{ijkl} are linear and quadratic electrooptic tensor components, respectively. The indices i, j can be interchanged, as can k and l, so the usual contraction can be made: $r_{mk} \leftrightarrow z_{(ij)k}$ and $R_{mn} \leftrightarrow R_{(ij)(kl)}$, where m and n run from 1 to 6 and m is related to (ij) and n to (kl) as follows: $1\leftrightarrow 11$, $2\leftrightarrow 22$, $3\leftrightarrow 33$, $4\leftrightarrow 23$, $5\leftrightarrow 13$, $6\leftrightarrow 12$. The linear electrooptic matrix for a specific crystal class has the same form as the inverse of the piezoelectric coefficient matrix, but no factors of 2 appear in the electrooptic case [8], [10].

The entire formalism outlined above could have been written using dielectric polarization rather than electric field as a basis. In fact, such a description would be more appropriate since polarization is a property of the physical medium in which the effect occurs. In the case of the linear effect, however, the electric field dependence (i.e., r as defined above) is usually given, since it is most nearly the measured quantity, and this practice is followed here. In the quadratic case there is not as much precedent in the literature and, instead of terms such as $R_{mn}E_kE_l$ in (3), the polarization terms $g_{mn}P_kP_l$ are used. Since $P_k = \epsilon_0(\epsilon_{ki} - 1)E_i$, where ϵ_{ki} is the permittivity, the descriptions can be interchanged. In the situations considered here only diagonal elements, $\epsilon_{ii} \equiv \epsilon_i$, are required. For

[1] A clear, concise description of the properties of crystals alluded to here is given in [8].

simplicity, we denote RF and optical dielectric constants by ϵ and n^2, respectively.

It may be useful to consider an example of the use of the indicatrix in describing the electrooptic effect. In a crystal in which only the linear effect is appreciable, if a wave normal along χ_3 is chosen and the applied field is along χ_1, then the equation for the $\chi_3=0$ section of the indicatrix is

$$\left(\frac{1}{n_1^2} + r_{11}E_1\right)x_1^2 + \left(\frac{1}{n_2^2} + r_{21}E_1\right)x_2^2 + 2r_{61}E_1x_1x_2 = 1. \quad (4)$$

Depending on symmetry, n_1 and n_2 may be equal and one or more r_{mi} may be equal or may vanish. If the term in r_{61} is disregarded for the moment, it is seen that the effect of $r_{11}E_1$ is to change the index of refraction for a wave polarized along x_1, so that the new index $(n_1+\Delta n_1)$ is given by

$$\frac{1}{(n_1 + \Delta n_1)^2} = \left(\frac{1}{n_1^2} + r_{11}E_1\right).$$

Now, Δn_1 is a small quantity compared to n_1, so to good accuracy we have

$$\Delta n_1 = -\frac{n_1^3 r_{11}E_1}{2}.$$

Similarly, for the wave polarized along x_2,

$$\Delta n_2 = \frac{-n_2^3 r_{21}E_1}{2}.$$

The x_3-directed wave at frequency ω polarized along x_2 can be described by

$$A_2 \exp i\left(\omega t - \frac{2\pi n_2 x_3}{\lambda_0}\right),$$

where λ_0 is the free space wavelength. An x_1 polarized wave can be described similarly. Clearly the phase of the wave depends upon the value of n_2. After traversing a length $x_3=L$, the change in phase due to the electrooptic effect is

$$-\frac{2\pi L}{\lambda_0}[n_2 - (n_2 + \Delta n_2)] = -\frac{\pi n_2^3 r_{21}E_1 L}{\lambda_0} \equiv \eta. \quad (5)$$

If E_1 varies sinusoidally with time, then the phase delay of the wave varies sinusoidally with peak value η, the modulation index. In this sense, the electrooptic effect leads most naturally to phase modulation.

In order to obtain amplitude modulation it is necessary to consider interference of phase modulated components. For example, in the same crystal, if the incident beam is plane polarized at 45° to x_1 and x_2 so that $A_1=A_2=A/\sqrt{2}$, the emergent beams are, respectively,

$$\frac{A}{\sqrt{2}} \exp i\left(\omega t - \frac{2\pi n_1 L}{\lambda_0}\right)$$

and

$$\frac{A}{\sqrt{2}} \exp i\left(\omega t - \frac{2\pi n_2 L}{\lambda_0}\right).$$

Since free space is isotropic we can choose any pair of orthogonal polarizations to describe the resultant combination. In particular, components parallel and normal to the incident polarization have amplitudes

$$A \cos \frac{\pi L}{\lambda_0}(n_1 - n_2 + \Delta n_1 - \Delta n_2) = A \cos(\Gamma/2)$$

and

$$A \sin \frac{\pi L}{\lambda_0}(n_1 - n_2 + \Delta n_1 - \Delta n_2) = A \sin(\Gamma/2) \quad (6)$$

where Γ is the *retardation.*

If $\pi L(n_1-n_2)/\lambda_0$ is an even multiple of $\pi/2$, the parallel amplitude is zero except for the part contributed by the electrooptic effect. Its value is

$$\pm \cos\left[\frac{\pi L}{2\lambda_0}(n_2^3 r_{21} - n_1^3 r_{11})E_1\right] \approx 1 - \frac{1}{2}\left[\frac{\pi L}{2\lambda_0}(n_2^3 r_{21} - n_1^3 r_{11})E_1\right]^2,$$

where the approximation is for small values of the argument. The modulation contains only even powers of E and is relatively small. If $\pi L(n_1-n_2)/\lambda_0$ is an odd multiple of $\pi/2$, the roles of the polarizations are interchanged and the above is true for the perpendicular component. If $\pi L(n_1-n_2)/\lambda_0$ is an odd multiple of $\pi/4$, the amplitude of either parallel or perpendicular polarization is

$$\pm \frac{1}{\sqrt{2}}\left(1 \pm \sin \frac{\pi L}{2\lambda_0}(n_2^3 r_{21} - n_1^3 r_{11})E_1\right) \approx \pm \frac{1}{\sqrt{2}}\left(1 \pm \frac{\pi L}{2\lambda_0}(n_2^3 r_{21} - n_1^3 r_{11})E_1\right)$$

and the amplitude modulation is approximately linear in E_1 and larger than in the previous case. The condition that $\pi L(n_1-n_2)/\lambda_0$ be an odd multiple of $\pi/4$ is sometimes referred to as *optical bias.* A fixed external compensator with axes of birefringence along x_1 and x_2 can be used to obtain this quarter wave bias if $n_1=n_2$. If $n_1 \neq n_2$, the temperature dependence of birefringence in the crystal itself allows one to meet the condition, but at the same time it can impose stringent requirements on temperature control of the crystal in order to keep the optical bias in the proper range. Alternatively, the temperature may be fixed and a variable external compensator employed.

Referring back to (4), the third pertinent coefficient for x_3 directed waves with E_1 applied is a skew coefficient r_{61}. One effect of this coefficient is to rotate the axes of the elliptical cross section by an angle α, where

$$\tan 2\alpha = \frac{2r_{61}E_1}{\frac{1}{n_1^2} - \frac{1}{n_2^2} + (r_{11} - r_{21})E_1}. \quad (7)$$

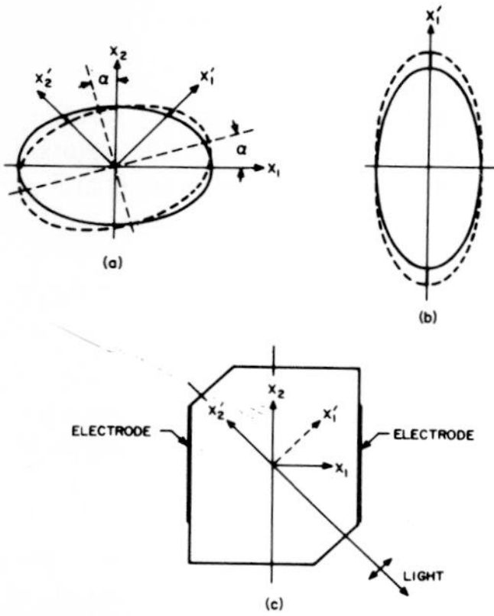

Fig. 1. (a) $x_3=0$ cross section of the indicatrix with x_1 directed field (dashed) and no field (solid). The effects of $r_{11}E_1$ and $r_{21}E_1$ have been omitted. The change in $1/x_1'^2$, where x_1' is the radius vector, is a maximum when x_1' is at 45° to x_1. The change in x_1' (and hence in index of refraction) is a maximum at angles near 45° unless the natural birefringence is very large as in the sketch. (b) $x_2'=0$ cross section of the indicatrix with x_1 directed field (dashed) and no field (solid). The change in x_1' axis is due to $r_{61}E_1$. The effect of $r_{31}E_1$ on the x_3-axis has been neglected. (c) Crystal cut for measurement or use of r_{61} coefficient. Propagation direction and polarization of the light are indicated.

If the natural birefringence (n_1-n_2) is appreciable, this angle is very small. The lengths of the axes (and hence the indices) are changed by an amount of second order in $r_{61}E_1$ that is usually negligible. However, the radius vector of the ellipse at 45° to x_1 and x_2 is changed linearly in E_1 by an amount $n'^3r_{61}E_1/2$, where n' is an effective index intermediate between the principal indices. The situation is indicated in Fig. 1(a). Since this radius is not an axis of the elliptical section normal to x_3, it does not correspond to the polarization of a principal wave propagating along x_3. The first-order effect does occur for a wave propagating in some other direction for which the radius vector at 45° to x_1 and x_2 is a principal axis. For example, if the wave normal is at 45° to $-x_1$ and x_2 [along x_2' in Fig. 1(a)], the perpendicular section is

$$\left\{\frac{1}{2}\left(\frac{1}{n_1^2}+\frac{1}{n_2^2}\right)+r_{61}E_1+\frac{(r_{11}+r_{21})}{2}E_1\right\}x_1'^2 + \left\{\frac{1}{n_3^2}+r_{31}E_1\right\}x_3^2+\sqrt{2}\,r_{51}E_1x_1'x_3 + \sqrt{2}\,r_{41}E_1x_1'x_3 = 1 \qquad (8)$$

where x_1' is at 45° to x_1 and x_2. The axes of this ellipse are determined in large part by the birefringence of the crystal. The effect of r_{41} and r_{51} is a small rotation of axes, as in (7). The alteration of the $x_2'=0$ section described in (8) is indicated in Fig. 1(b). A crystal cut which allows observation of the linear change $r_{61}E_1$ is shown in Fig. 1(c). From (8) we see that r_{11} and r_{21} also cause first-order effects. If we had chosen the x_2' polarization of the x_1' directed wave the signs of r_{11} and r_{21} terms would remain unchanged, but the r_{61} term would be reversed. Thus, for one case the effects of the coefficients add and in the other they subtract.

The fact that specific elements of the electrooptic coefficient matrix (including skew components) can be used in producing phase modulation has been shown above, and the fact that the interference of two such waves produces amplitude modulation has also been indicated. In doing this, the restrictions imposed on the matrix elements by symmetry have not been used. At this point, one effect of crystal symmetry will be mentioned specifically. In crystals with a threefold axis it is possible to rotate a birefringent section of constant retardation by rotation of the applied field, which in turn allows construction of single sideband modulators and frequency shifters [11]. If a wave normal is directed along x_3, in this case a threefold axis, then the perpendicular section is circular in the absence of an applied field; i.e., $n_1=n_2$. Moreover, symmetry requires that

$$r_{12} = r_{61} = -r_{22}$$
$$r_{21} = r_{62} = -r_{11}. \qquad (9)$$

If fields E_1 and E_2 are applied, the equation of the $x_3=0$ section is

$$\left[\frac{1}{n_1^2}+(r_{11}E_1-r_{22}E_2)\right]x_1^2 + \left[\frac{1}{n_1^2}+(r_{22}E_2-r_{11}E_1)\right]x_2^2 + 2[-r_{22}E_1-r_{11}E_2]x_1x_2 = 1. \qquad (10)$$

If we choose new axes x_1', x_2' along the axes of the ellipse in the $x_3=0$ plane, (10) can be written

$$\left[\frac{1}{n_1^2}+(r_{11}^2+r_{22}^2)^{1/2}E\right]x_1'^2 + \left[\frac{1}{n_1^2}-(r_{11}^2+r_{22}^2)^{1/2}E\right]x_2'^2 = 1. \qquad (11)$$

where E is the applied field with components $E_1=E\cos\Phi$, $E_2=E\sin\Phi$. As shown in [11] the primed axes are rotated relative to the crystal axes through an angle

$$\theta = -\frac{1}{2}\left[\Phi + \arcsin\frac{r_{22}}{\sqrt{r_{11}^2+r_{22}^2}}\right]. \qquad (12)$$

From (11) we note that a field of fixed magnitude causes a specific amount of birefringence (and hence a fixed magnitude of retardation Γ) in the $x_3=0$ plane, regardless of field orientation in this plane. From (12) we see that the axes of the birefringence rotate through an angle $\theta=-\frac{1}{2}\Phi$ when the field rotates through an angle Φ.

The effect of a rotating birefringent plate on an incident circularly polarized wave is merely summarized here in order to indicate how single sideband modulation can be effected [12]. The emergent wave has a component in the

TABLE I

KDP-ADP TYPE: POINT GROUP ($\bar{4}2m$) ABOVE T_c

	T_c	r_{63}	r_{41}	n_3	n_1	ϵ_3	ϵ_1	tan δ_3	tan δ_1
KH_2PO_4(KDP)	123 [2]	(T) −10.5 [5]	+8.6 [5]	1.47 [27]	1.51 [27]	(T) 21 [28]	42 [28]	(T) see [76], [32]	
		(S) 9.7 [26]				(S) 21 [29]	44 [29]	(S) 7.5×10^{-3} [29]	4.5×10^{-3} [29]
KD_2PO_4(DKDP)	222 [16]	(T) 26.4 [16]	8.8 [24]	1.47 [27a]	1.51 [27a]	(T) 50 [16]		(T) see [33]	
						(S) 48 [14]	58 [14]	(S) 1.0×10^{-1} [14]	2.5×10^{-2} [14]
KH_2AsO_4(KDA)	97 [2]	(T) 10.9 [24]	12.5 [24]	1.52 [24]	1.57 [24]	(T) 21 [28]	54 [28]		
						(S) 19 [14]	53 [14]	(S) 8.0×10^{-3} [14]	7.5×10^{-3} [14]
RbH_2AsO_4(RDA)	110 [2]	(T) 13.0 [24]		1.52 [24]	1.56 [24]	(T) 27 [31]	41 [31]	(T) see [31]	
						(S) 24 [31]	39 [31]	(S) 5×10^{-2} [31]	3×10^{-2} [31]
$NH_4H_2PO_4$(ADP)	148* [2]	(T) −8.5 [5]	+24.5 [24]	1.48 [27]	1.53 [27]	(T) 15 [28]	56 [28]	(T) see [76]	
		(S) 5.5 [5]				(S) 14 [14]	58 [14]	(S) 6.0×10^{-3} [14]	7.0×10^{-3} [14]

* Antiferroelectric transition temperature; T_c in °K; r_{mi} in 10^{-12}m/V. (T) = constant stress, (S) = constant strain; refractive index at 0.546 μ; tan $\delta(S)$ at $\sim10^{10}$ c/s

original sense of circular polarization of amplitude cos $\Gamma/2$ and phase independent of θ. In addition, there is a component of opposite sense whose amplitude is sin $\Gamma/2$ and whose phase is proportional to 2θ (or $-\Phi$). Thus, if the field rotates at a rate ω_m, the phase of the wave with altered sense of circular polarization varies as $-\omega_m t$ and the instantaneous frequency of this wave is changed by ω_m. The direction of change depends on the relative direction of field rotation and incident circular polarization. The amplitude of the frequency shifted component is constant in time.

III. MATERIALS

The electrooptic materials are grouped according to their general crystallographic and physical properties as follows: 1) KDP, ADP, and their isomorphs, 2) ABO_3 crystals similar to perovskites, 3) AB-type semiconducfors with cubic or hexagonal ZnS structure, and 4) various miscellaneous crystals. The tabulations of electrooptic coefficients may give two or more conflicting values for the same crystal. Oftentimes, poor materials are the cause. The reader should consult the original works to decide which result is more reliable.

KDP-ADP Type

Potassium dihydrogen phosphate (KDP) and ammonium dihydrogen phosphate (ADP) are the most widely known electrooptic crystals. Their general properties are reviewed elsewhere [2], [3]. They are grown at room temperature from a water solution and are free of the strains often found in crystals grown at high temperature. Excellent crystals as large as 5 cm in any dimension can be obtained commercially at nominal cost. Although the crystals are water soluble and fragile, they can be handled, cut, and polished without difficulty. The resistivity of these crystals is typically 10^{10} ohm-cm [13].

Both KDP and ADP belong to the piezoelectric point group $\bar{4}2m$ at room temperature where they are normally used. Below the Curie temperature T_c, KDP type crystals become ferroelectric and, below the transition temperature, ADP type crystals become antiferroelectric. No electrooptic measurements have been made below T_c because of the experimental complexity involved.

The atoms K, H, P in KH_2PO_4 can be replaced by some of the atoms from corresponding columns in the periodic table without changing the crystal structure. A dramatic change in dielectric properties occurs when H is replaced by deuterium. For partially deuterated KDP, $KD_{2x}H_{2(1-x)}PO_4$, the Curie temperature is given [14] approximately by

$$T_c \approx (123 + 106x)°\text{K}. \qquad (13)$$

The KDP-ADP isomorphs for which electrooptic coefficients have been measured are listed in Table I along with pertinent electrical and optical properties. Additional data will often be found in the references given. Measurements at constant stress are noted by (T) and those at constant strain (high frequency) by (S). The only nonvanishing r_{mi} coefficients are $r_{41}=r_{52}$ and r_{63}. At 0.633 μ, optical loss [15] in KDP is $\frac{1}{2}$ dB/m, which is about as good as that found in the best fused quartz. The refractive indices and ultraviolet absorption, which are associated with electronic transitions in the oxygen ions, are about the same for all isomorphs. The crystals are transparent for wavelengths as short as 0.2 μ [16]–[18]. The infrared absorption is the result of hydrogen vibrations, the frequencies of which are approximately inversely proportional to the square root of the proton mass. Thus, the low-frequency absorption edge for the deuterated salt occurs at roughly $\sqrt{2}$ times the wavelength for undeuterated salts: KDP, 1.55μ [16]; ADP, 1.4 μ [19]; DKDP, 2.15 μ [19].

The quantity $r_{63}/(\epsilon_3-1)$ is roughly the same for all isomorphs and, despite the rapid increase in ϵ_3 near T_c, is independent of temperature [2], [3]. It is possible to obtain larger r_{63} and, hence, lower modulating voltage by, operating near the Curie temperature or by choosing an isomorph with T_c closer to room temperature so as to increase ϵ_3. However, the loss tangent also increases and in such a way as to make this expedient unattractive in some applications [14], [20]. The electrooptic coefficient r_{63} is practically independent of wavelength in the transparent region for KDP and ADP [5], [21], [22].

In the absence of an applied electric field, KDP-type crystals are uniaxial: light polarized parallel to or normal to the z-axis travels as a principal wave with refractive index n_3 or n_1, respectively. When a field E_3 is applied along the x_3-axis, the principal axes become x_3 and x_1' and x_2', at 45° to the x_1 and x_2 axes. The refractive index for x_3-polarization remains n_3 while,

$$n_{x_1'} \approx n_1 - \tfrac{1}{2}n_1^3 r_{63}E_3, \quad n_{x_2'} \approx n_1 + \tfrac{1}{2}n_1^3 r_{63}E_3.$$

Light polarized along x_1' or x_2' traveling through a crystal of length L experiences a phase modulation with index

$$\eta = \pi n_1^3 r_{63} E_3 L/\lambda. \tag{14}$$

Light traveling along x_3 and initially polarized along x_1 or x_2 experiences a phase retardation

$$\Gamma = 2\eta. \tag{15}$$

The voltage E_3L required to produce a retardation of π radians is called the *half-wave voltage*

$$V_{1/2} = \lambda/2n_1^3 r_{63}. \tag{16}$$

For a wide area light shutter [4] or amplitude modulator both applied field and light path are along x_3. Because of natural birefringence in directions off the x_3-axis, the angular aperture is severely restricted for thick samples. Methods for increasing the aperture are described by Billings [4]. Natural birefringence is not normally a problem with a well-collimated optical maser beam. Phase or amplitude modulation with field normal to the optical path may be accomplished with electric field along x_3, optical polarization along x_1', and optical path along x_2'.

Small strains in the crystal can partially destroy the relative phase relationships required to produce amplitude modulation [119]. Normally, KDP-type crystals as grown are quite strain-free. However, despite the relatively low loss tangent, the crystal is heated throughout its volume by the modulating field but cooled only on its surface. The resultant thermal gradient produces strains that are sufficiently great when the power dissipated in the crystal is greater than a watt, independent of crystal dimensions, to make amplitude modulation ineffective [23].

A field applied along x_1 rotates the indicatrix through a small angle about x_1. The semi-axis along x_1 remains unchanged and the other axes experience changes of order $(r_{41}E_1)^2$. The situation is similar to that discussed in Section II, where the effect of the skew coefficient r_{61} was mentioned. To obtain first-order changes in refractive index [5], [24], light should be polarized in the x_2x_3 plane along x_2'' or x_3'', at 45° to x_2 and x_3, and propagated in the x_3'' or x_2'' direction, respectively. The $x_2''=0$ section of the indicatrix is

$$\frac{x_1^2}{n_1^2} + \left[\frac{1}{2}\left(\frac{1}{n_1^2} + \frac{1}{n_3^2}\right) + r_{41}E_1\right] x_3''^2 = 1$$

and the modulation index for x_3'' polarization

$$\eta = 2\pi\sqrt{2}\left(\frac{1}{n_1^2} + \frac{1}{n_3^2}\right)^{-3/2} r_{41}E_1L/\lambda$$
$$\approx \pi n_1^3 r_{41} E_1 L/\lambda. \tag{17}$$

Since r_{41} at constant stress is large in ADP, it has been suggested that a modulator with E along x_1 might be advantageous [10]. However, inasmuch as r_{41} at constant strain is not known, it is not clear that this configuration will be useful at high frequency. For intensity modulation using this configuration, there is the added complication that the ordinary and extraordinary ray paths are not parallel. A two crystal method for overcoming this difficulty is described by Ley [25], [30].

Perovskite Family

The large group of crystals with structure resembling that of the mineral perovskite, $CaTiO_3$, form the perovskite family [34]. Of particular interest are the oxides $A^{2+}B^{4+}O_3$ and $A^{1+}B^{5+}O_3$, which often exhibit ferroelectric behavior. Their properties are discussed in detail elsewhere [2], [3]. In general, they are insoluble in water and are more rugged and have larger refractive index and dielectric constant than KDP. As a rule, the oxides are transparent between 0.4 and 6 μ [35]–[37]. The infrared absorption is caused largely by vibrations of the BO_6 octahedra and the ultraviolet absorption by electronic transitions in the oxygen ions.

Perovskites may exist in several forms, with different point symmetries, that are derived from the ideal cubic perovskite structure by continuous lattice distortions. The cubic form, which is often the high temperature phase, belongs to the nonpiezoelectric, nonferroelectric point group m3m. In the ferroelectric phase, the crystals of interest here are tetragonal 4mm, with the c-axis along one of the original cube edges, or rhombohedral 3m, with the c-axis along one of the cube body diagonals. Both phases are piezoelectric. The cubic (paraelectric) and ferroelectric phases of various perovskites are discussed separately below.

Cubic: $BaTiO_3$, $SrTiO_3$, $KTaO_3$, $K(Ta, Nb)O_3$: Since the cubic phase is centrosymmetric the change in refractive index is a quadratic function of applied field or dielectric polarization. It is convenient to use the polarization P as a basis because the corresponding electrooptic coefficients g_{mn} are then insensitive to temperature and optical wavelength far from the band edges [35]. As discussed in Section II,

$$\Delta\left(\frac{1}{n_m^2}\right) = \sum g_{mn}P_jP_k \tag{18}$$

where m, n run from 1 to 6 and j, k from 1 to 3. For m3m the only nonvanishing components are $g_{11}=g_{22}=g_{33}$, $g_{12}=g_{13}=g_{23}=g_{32}=g_{31}=g_{21}$, and $g_{44}=g_{55}=g_{66}$. To obtain a linear effect, which is both larger in magnitude and more suitable for most applications, it is customary to induce a large dc bias polarization P_{dc} along with the much smaller RF modulation polarization $(\epsilon-1)\epsilon_0E_i$. In effect, P_{dc} a vector quantity removes the center of symmetry. If P_{dc} is along a cube diagonal the symmetry is lowered to 3m; if P_{dc} is along a cube edge the symmetry becomes 4mm.

If P_{dc} has only an x_3-component,

$$\begin{aligned}
&\Delta(1/n_1^2) = \Delta(1/n_2^2) = g_{12}P_{dc}(P_{dc} + 2\epsilon\epsilon_0E_3)\\
&\Delta(1/n_3^2) = g_{11}P_{dc}(P_{dc} + 2\epsilon\epsilon_0E_3)\\
&\Delta(1/n_4^2) = g_{44}P_{dc}\epsilon\epsilon_0E_2, \quad \Delta(1/n_5^2) = g_{44}P_{dc}\epsilon\epsilon_0E_1\\
&\Delta(1/n_6^2) = 0,
\end{aligned} \tag{19}$$

where quantitites quadratic in RF polarization are neglected and it is assumed that $\epsilon \gg 1$. As the temperature is reduced toward the Curie point T_c, ϵ becomes large and large values of P_{dc} can be induced with modest fields.

Values of g_{mn} for several cubic perovskites are given in Table II. The quantity $(g_{11}-g_{12})$ appears when intensity modulation rather than phase modulation measuring techniques are employed. Only constant stress (low frequency) values have been reported. Clamping on g_{mn} (as well as ϵ) may reduce the effect by as much as 50 percent [40], [41].

Although g_{mn} is about the same for all the perovskites in Table II, $SrTiO_3$ and $KTaO_3$ are not particularly interesting because their Curie points are well below room temperature. On the other hand, $BaTiO_3$ must be heated in order to operate above T_c where the effect is large. A material with T_c near room temperature can be synthesized by forming a solid solution of two materials, one with T_c above and the other with T_c below room temperature. Such a material is $KTa_{.65}Nb_{.35}O_3$(KTN). However, despite considerable effort, it has not been possible to grow these mixed crystals consistently with sufficient uniformity, optical quality, and electrical resistivity. Nevertheless, KTN remains interesting because of the large electrooptic effects that have been observed experimentally [43].

Several difficulties are inherent in the use of biased perovskites slightly above T_c. The properties of the material, particularly ϵ, which varies as $(T-T_c)^{-1}$, are very temperature sensitive so that T must be carefully controlled [40]. Further, even with relatively high resistivity and low photoconductivity, the dc bias field leads to space charge effects that eventually reduce the internal biasing field. A two-crystal, ac biasing scheme to overcome the latter difficulty has been proposed but not tested [42]. In connection with the former difficulty, note that if the temperature is reduced below T_c and the crystal poled into a single ferroelectric domain, then the spontaneous polarization P_s can take the part of P_{dc}. Although P_s is several times greater than the induced P_{dc}, ϵ_3 in the ferroelectric state will be much smaller than it is just above T_c. As compensation, however, ϵ_3 and the corresponding electrooptic coefficients are insensitive to T well below T_c [2]. Related single domain ferroelectrics are considered below.

Ferroelectric: $BaTiO_3$, $LiNbO_3$, $LiTaO_3$: Barium titanate is the most widely studied perovskite ferroelectric [2]. It is available in crystals with good optical and electrical properties in the form of thin platelets (typically $\frac{1}{2}$mm $\times$10mm$\times$10mm) grown by the Remeika method [47] and faceted boules (10mm$\times$10mm$\times$10mm) as grown by Linz [38]. The crystals are in a tetragonal phase (4mm) between 0° and 120°C,[2] and can be poled into a single domain with the polar axis along one of the cube edges existing above 120°C.

[2] T_c appears to be different for Remeika (120°C) and Linz (131°C) crystals.

The only nonvanishing coefficients are $r_{13}=r_{23}$, r_{33}, and $r_{42}=r_{51}$. These coefficients are listed in Table III with

$$r_c = r_{33} - \left(\frac{n_1}{n_3}\right)^3 r_{13}, \qquad (20)$$

the quantity observed in intensity modulation measurements. Both r_{13} and r_{33} are temperature insensitive, but r_{42} increases rapidly as T approaches 0°C, the tetragonal-to-orthorhombic transition temperature [41], [48]. At room temperature, r_{42} at constant strain is about 8×10^{-10} m/V which is about 30 times r_{33}. The temperature dependence of r_{42}, and r_{13} and r_{33} is similar to that of ϵ_1 and ϵ_3, respectively. To take advantage of the large r_{42}, it is necessary to employ a special crystal cut [49] similar to that in Fig. 1(c).

The wide disparity in clamped and free values of r_{mi} and ϵ_j indicated in Table III is due in part to the large piezoelectric coupling coefficient [28]. The large coupling coefficient and low acoustic loss mean that high-order acoustic resonances can be very troublesome in modulator design [50]. Further, large natural birefringence (n_1-n_2) implies that intensity modulators must have closely parallel end faces.

The structures of $LiNbO_3$ [51] and presumably $LiTaO_3$ [34], [51] are rhombohedral, with point group 3m below 1200°C and 620°C, respectively. The structure is not strictly perovskite but it is very nearly so [34]. The electrooptic tensor has the nonvanishing components: $r_{13}=r_{23}$, r_{33}, $r_{22}=-r_{12}=-r_{61}$, and $r_{42}=r_{51}$. Crystals were first grown from a flux [52] and more recently were pulled from the melt [52a]. Techniques have now been developed that permit large crystals (typically $1\times1\times3$ cm) of good optical and electrical quality to be pulled from the melt and poled into a single domain while near T_c [51], [53]. Because of the large T_c, considerable mechanical energy would be required to depole these materials at room temperature. Hence, unlike $BaTiO_3$ with $T_c=120$°C, these crystals may be cut, polished, and roughly handled without creating additional domains.

The properties of $LiNbO_3$, $LiTaO_3$, and $BaTiO_3$ are compared in Table II. The measurements [49], [50] indicate that $r_{13}/r_{33}>0$ for all three materials.

Where the electrooptic properties are comparable, $LiNbO_3$ and $LiTaO_3$ are preferable to $BaTiO_3$ because of the relative ease in handling and availability of crystals. Further, it has been observed that piezoelectric resonance effects for c-axis fields are smaller in $LiNbO_3$ and $LiTaO_3$ [49], [54]. In addition the dielectric Q of $BaTiO_3$ is lower.

Recently [55] it has been observed that when exposed to intense laser beams $LiNbO_3$, $LiTaO_3$, and $BaTiO_3$ develop refractive index inhomogeneities which scatter the beam.

AB-Type Semiconductors

The group of binary compounds which crystallize in either the cubic ($\bar{4}3$m) zincblende structure or the hexagonal (6mm) wurtzite structure are similar in many re-

TABLE II

Cubic Perovskites: m3m

	T_C	g_{11}	g_{12}	$g_{11}-g_{12}$	g_{44}	n	ϵ, tan δ
$BaTiO_3$	401	+0.12[60]	$-\|<0.01\|$[60]	+0.13 [40]		2.4	see [2], [38], [41]
				0.10 [38]			
				(T)0.088[41]			
				(S)0.031[41]			
$SrTiO_3$	low			+0.14		2.38	see [39], [44]
$KTaO_3$	4			+0.16	+0.12	2.24	see [45], [46]
$KTa_{.65}Nb_{.35}O_3$	~283	+0.136	−0.038	0.174	+0.147	2.29	see [40]

T_c, g_{mn}, n from [40] except where noted; T_c in degrees K; g_{mn} in m^4/C^2; all measurements at constant stress except where noted; (T) = constant stress, (S) = constant strain.

TABLE III

Ferroelectric Perovskites

	Sym	T_c	r_{13}	r_{33}	$r_{51}=r_{42}$	r_{22}	r_c	$n_1=n_2$	n_3	$\epsilon_1=\epsilon_2$	ϵ_3	tan δ
$BaTiO_3$	4mm	393			(T) 1640 [48]		(T) 108 [48]	(a) 2.44 [36]	(a) 2.37 [36]	(T) 3000 [28]	170 [28]	see [2]
					(S) 820 [41]		(S) 23 [41]			(S) 2000 [41]	100 [41]	
			(c) (S) 8 [50]	(c) (S) 28 [50]			(S) 19 [50]	(b) 2.39 [50]	(b) 2.33 [36]			
$LiNbO_3$	3m	1470	(c) (S) 8.6 [49]	(c) (S) 30.8 [49]	(S) 28 [49]	(S) 3.4 [49]	(S) 21 [49]	(b) 2.286 [56]	(c) 2.200 [56]	(S) 43 [59]	(S) 28 [49, 59]	see [59]
						(T) 7 [58]	(T) 19 [58]			(T) 78 [51]	(T) 32 [51]	
$LiTaO_3$	3m	890	(c) (S) 7 [9]	(c) (S) 30.3 [9]			(S) 24 [9]				(T) 47 [9]	
			(S) 7.9 [49]	(S) 35.8 [49]	(S) 20 [49]	(S) ≈1 [49]	(S) 28 [49]	(b) 2.176 [57]	(b) 2.180 [57]		(S) 43 [9]	
							(T) 22 [9]					

(a) at 546 μ, (b) at 633 μ, (c) $r_{13}/r_{33}>0$; T in °K, r_{mi} in 10^{-12} m/V, (T) = constant stress, (S) = constant strain.

TABLE IV

AB-Type Semiconductors

	Sym	r_{mi}	λ	n_i	λ	ϵ_i
ZnO	6mm	(S) $r_{33}=2.6$	.63 [61]	$n_3=2.123$	.45 [57]	$\epsilon\approx 8.15$ [62]
		(S) $r_{13}=1.4$	.63 [61]	$n_2=n_1=2.106$	.45	
		$r_{33}/r_{13}<0$	[61]	$n_3=2.015$	.60 [57]	
				$n_3=n_1=1.999$	.60	
ZnS	$\bar{4}3m$	(T) $r_{41}=1.2$	.40 [63]	$n_0=2.471$	.45 [57]	(T) 16 [64]
		2.0	.546	2.364	.60	(S) 12.5 [64]
		2.1	.65	2.315	.8	8.3 [65]
	6mm	(S) $r_{33}=1.85$	.63 [66]	$n_3=2.709$	.36 [67]	
	[see 66]	(S) $r_{13}=.92$	.63 [66]	$n_2=n_1=2.705$	.36	
		$r_{33}/r_{13}<0$	[66]	$n_3=2.368$	.60 [67]	
				$n_2=n_1=2.363$	.60	
ZnSe	$\bar{4}3m$	(T) $r_{41}=2.0$	.546 [68]	$n_0=2.66$	.546 [69]	9.1 [65]
						8.1 [70]
ZnTe	$\bar{4}3m$	(T) $r_{41}=4.55$	.59 [71]	$n_0=3.1$	.57 [71]	10.1 [65]
		3.95	.69 [71]	2.91	.70 [71]	
		(S) $r_{41}=4.3$	.63 [72]			
CuCl	$\bar{4}3m$	(T) $r_{41}=6.1$	[73]	$n_0=1.996$	.535 [75]	(T) 10 [76]
		(T) $r_{41}=1.6$	[74]	1.933	.671	(S) 8.3 [76]
						(S) 7.7 [77]
CuBr	$\bar{4}3m$	(T) $r_{41}=.85$	[74]	$n_0=2.16$	.535 [75]	
				2.09	.656	
GaP	$\bar{4}3m$	(S) $r_{41}=.5$	[78]	$n_0=3.4595$	.54 [57]	10 [83]
		(S) $r_{41}=1.06$	.63 [78]	3.315	.60 [57]	12 [78]
GaAs	$\bar{4}3m$	(T) $r_{41}=.27$ to 1.2	1 to 1.8 [79]	$n_0=3.60$	.90 [82]	(T) 12.5 [84]
				3.50	1.02 [82]	(S) 10.9 [84]
		(S–T) $r_{41}=1.3$ to 1.5	1 to 1.8 [79]	3.42	1.25 [82]	(S) 11.7 [85]
		(S) $r_{41}=1.2$	.9 to 1.08 [80]	3.30	5.0 [84]	
		(T) $r_{41}=1.6$	3.39 & 10.6 [81]			
CdS	6mm	(T) $r_{51}=3.7$	.589 [86]	$n_3=2.726$	.515 [67]	(T) $\epsilon_1=10.6$ [87]
		(T) $r_c=4$	.589 [86]	$n_2=n_1=2.743$	.515 [67]	(T) $\epsilon_3=7.8$ [87]
		(S) $r_{33}=2.4$	.63 [72]	$n_2=n_1=2.493$	.60 [67]	(S) $\epsilon_1=8.0$ [87]
		(S) $r_{13}=1.1$	.63 [72]			(S) $\epsilon_3=7.7$ [87]
		$r_{33}/r_{13}<0$	[72]			

r_{mi} in 10^{-12} m/V; λ in microns; (T) = constant stress, (S) = constant strain.

spects and are, therefore, treated together. For example, in both structures the four nearest neighbors of an $A(B)$ ion are $B(A)$ ions situated on the corners of a tetrahedron. One must look to the next nearest neighbors before the differences in the two structures become evident. Several of these compounds, including ZnS, CuCl, and CdS, can crystallize in either form. In fact, it is difficult to obtain single phase crystals of ZnS and CuCl, because the wurtzite structure is stable at high temperatures at which the crystals may be grown, and the cubic form is stable at room temperature. Some of the crystals in this group are of technical importance as semiconductors, phosphors, photodectectors, and, more recently injection laser materials. There is an extensive literature on the preparation, band structure, and electrical properties of many of these crystals, but as yet a relatively small amount of electrooptic information. All available electrooptic information is included in Table IV. With the single exception of gallium arsenide, the crystals whose electrooptic effect has been measured are transparent in at least part of the visible spectrum, and can be obtained in an insulating or semi-insulating form. Of the crystals listed in Table IV, only gallium arsenide, cadmium sulfide, and zinc telluride are readily available with dimensions of the order of a centimeter. Zinc sulphide, zinc oxide, and cuprous chloride are found in nature but are generally not of suitable quality. There is a wide variation in mechanical properties in the zincblende group even among those listed in the table. For example, the hardness (Mohs' scale) of cuprous chloride and bromide is 2 to 2.5, whereas gallium phosphide is about 7. All the cubic crystals listed have (110) cleavage, which fact is often used in preparing crystals for use although they can be cut and polished. The hexagonal crystals cleave less readily but are easily cut and polished. Cuprous chloride and bromide are attacked by moist air but the other materials can be used without protection in usual laboratory surroundings.

All the materials listed have large indices of refraction: from 2 for CuCl to 3.5 for GaAs near the band edge. As a result, the important n^3r product may be relatively large even though the coefficient r is not in itself large. The hexagonal crystals are, of course, birefringent. The maximum range of transparency for all the crystals listed in Table IV is fixed on the short wavelength end by the band edge and on the long wavelength end by reststrahl absorption. The transparency is limited, however, also by impurities and dislocations and in the long wavelength region free carriers cause appreciable absorption.

The 6mm crystals have the same r_{mi} matrix as the 4mm point group crystals: the coefficients are $r_{13}=r_{23}$, r_{33}, and $r_{42}=r_{51}$. Thus, the useful modulator configurations are the same (regarding symmetry) as those of room temperature $BaTiO_3$ described earlier.

The fact that the $\bar{4}3m$ crystals are cubic and hence optically isotropic makes them particularly attractive for modulation applications in which large acceptance angles are necessary. However, this also means that small amounts of residual birefringence, due to strain or nonuniformity, can cause an appreciable depolarizing of an optical beam. (In an anisotropic crystal, these perturbations have a relatively minor effect on the already large natural birefringence.) There is only one electrooptic coefficient ($r_{41}=r_{52}=r_{63}$) for cubic crystals, and the discussion of symmetry behavior which follows is applicable, therefore, to all cubics with a linear electrooptic effect. The zincblende crystals listed in Table IV are those for which values of r_{41} either at constant stress (T) or constant strain (S) have been reported.

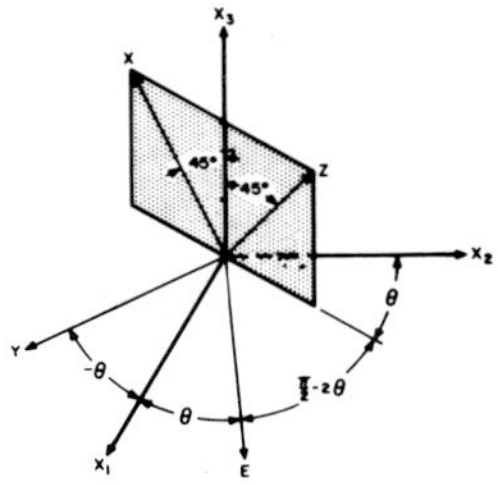

Fig. 2. Change in orientation of indicatrix axes of a cubic crystal when applied field E lies in (001) plane. x_1, x_2, x_3 are the cubic crystal axes. The unchanged semi-axis of the indicatrix lies along y—also in (001) plane. The other semi-axes are along x and z. Maximum birefringence is obtained when light propagates along y.

Application of an electric field in a general direction relative to the crystal axes causes the initially isotropic crystals to become biaxial. There are three conditions which are of most practical importance. The first of these is a requirement of maximum induced birefringence, since this is desirable for an amplitude modulator. It can be shown that a field applied normal to one of the cube axes always produces the same (maximum) birefringence. In Fig. 2 an electric field is shown applied normal to the [001] direction (x_3) and at an angle θ to the [100] direction (x_1); i.e., the coordinate system (x_1, x_2, x_3) is parallel to the cubic crystal axes. The coordinate system (x, y, z) is used to locate the axes of the indicatrix, whose properties are altered by the electric field as follows: equal and opposite changes occur along x and z, respectively, with no change along y. In order to achieve the maximum birefringence, light is propagated in the y direction, which is in the (001) plane at an angle ($-\theta$) to the [100] axis. The change in index of refraction for light polarized along x, which is at an angle $\pi/4$ to the x_3 axis, is $+(n^3r_{41}E)/2$ and for polarization along z, the change is $-(n^3r_{41}E)/2$. The applied field is at right angles to the direction of propagation for $\theta=\pi/4$.

A second important crystal orientation is one which gives maximum change in index of refraction for a specific linear polarization and hence is most suitable for phase modulation. This configuration is one in which the electric field and the optical polarization are parallel and directed along a [111] crystal axis. A maximum change in index of refraction of $-n^3r_{41}E/\sqrt{3}$ is then found. The advantage over using a field in a (100) plane is $2/\sqrt{3}$ and a given phase modulation can be obtained with $\frac{3}{4}$ of the power.

TABLE V

Miscellaneous Crystals

	Sym	r_{mi}	λ	n_i	λ
$Bi_4(GeO_4)_3$	$\bar{4}3m$	(T) $r_{41}=1.03$	.45 to .62 [91]	$n_0=2.07$	[91]
$C_6H_{12}N_4$—(HMT)	$\bar{4}3m$	(T) $r_{41}=4.18$	.365 to .60 [88]	$n_0=1.591$	.589 [88]
		(T) $r_{41}=.8$	.546 [90]		
		(T) $r_{41}=7.3$	.547 [92]		
Hauynite (mineral)	$\bar{4}3m$	(T) $r_{41}<.04$	[93]	$n_0=1.496$	
Langbeinites:					
$K_2Mg_2(SO_4)$	23	$r_{41}<.04$	[93]	$n_0=1.535$	[94]
$(NH_4)_2Cd_2(SO_4)_3$	23	(T) $r_{41}=.8$	.546 [102]	$n_0=1.57$	
$(NH_4)_2Mn_2(SO_4)_3$	23	(T) $r_{41}=.6$	.546 [102]	$n_0=1.57$	[94]
$NaClO_3$	23	(T) $r_{41}=.4$	.589 [75]	$n_0=1.515$	[96]
$Na_3SbS_4\cdot 9H_2O$	23	(T) $r_{41}=5.66/n_0^3$	.42 [89]		
		(T) $r_{41}=5.62/n_0^3$	1.08 [89]		
Sodium Uranyl Acetate	23	(T) $r_{41}=.87$	.546 [97]	$n_0=1.507$	.546 [97]
$LiKSO_4$	6	(T) $r_c=1.6$	.546 [90]	$n_3\approx n_1=n_2=1.474$	.546 [90]
$LiNaSO_4$	3m	(T) $r_{22}<.02$	.546 [90]	$n_3=1.495$	[96]
				$n_1=n_2=1.490$	
Tourmaline	3m	(T) $r_{22}=0.3$	.589 [75]	$n_3=1.65$	[96]
				$n_1=n_2=1.63$	
$K_2S_2O_6$	32	(T) $r_{11}=0.26$	.546 [90]	$n_3=1.1518$	[96]
				$n_1=n_2=1.456$	[90]
$Cs_2C_4H_4O_6$	32	(T) $r_{11}=1.0$	.546 [90]	$n_3=1.546$	
				$n_1=n_2=1.564$	[90]
$SrS_2O_6\cdot 4H_2O$	32	(T) $r_{11}=0.1$	.546 [90]	$n_3=1.528$	[96]
				$n_1=n_2=1.532$	[96]
SiO_2—(Quartz)	32	(T) $r_{11}=-0.47$	.409 to .605 [75]	$n_3=1.555$	.546 [75]
		(T) $r_{41}=0.20$	[75]	$n_1=n_2=1.546$	.546 [75]
		(S) $r_{11}=0.23$ (calculated)	[98]		
		(S) $r_{11}=0.1$	[99]		
$(C_6H_{12}O_6)_2NaBr\cdot H_2O$	32	(T) $r_{11}=0.1$	.546 [90]	$n_3=1.560$	.546 [90]
				$n_1=n_2=1.528$	
Rochelle Salt	222	(T) $r_{41}=-2.0$	.589 [75]	$n_1=1.491$	.589 [75]
		(T) $r_{52}=-1.7$	.589 [75]	$n_2=1.493$	.589 [75]
		(T) $r_{63}=0.3$	.589 [75]	$n_3=1.497$	.589 [75]
$C(CH_2OH)_4$	2	(T) $r_{52}=1.45$	.46 to .70 [100]	$n_1=1.528$	
		(T) $\lvert r_{12}-r_{32}\rvert=0.7$	.46 to .70 [100]	$n_2\approx n_3=1.56$	[75]
$Ca_2Nb_2O_7$	2	(T) $\left\lvert r_{22}-\frac{n_3^3}{n_2^3}r_{32}\right\rvert=14$	.63 [101]	$n_1=1.97$	[101]
		(T) $\left\lvert r_{22}-\frac{n_1^3}{n_2^3}r_{12}\right\rvert=12$	.63 [101]	$n_2=2.16$	[101]
		(S) $\left\lvert r_{22}-\frac{n_3^3}{n_2^3}r_{32}\right\rvert=13$	.63 [101]	$n_3=2.17$	[101]

r_{mi} is 10^{-12} m/v; λ in microns; (T) = constant stress; (S) = constant strain.

The only requirement on the direction of propagation is that it be normal to the applied field, since for this configuration the crystal is uniaxial under the application of the field.

A third useful configuration is one in which light propagates along a threefold [111] axis and the electric field is applied normal to this axis. The axes of the elliptical section of the indicatrix rotate at half the rate of a rotating electric field, as was mentioned in Section II. The retardation Γ for this case is $\sqrt{\frac{2}{3}}\, n^3 r_{41} E$.

Miscellaneous Crystals

This group includes many crystals which were measured simply because they were known to be piezoelectric and were also transparent. Crystals of various symmetry are included. In many instances the other electrical and optical properties of the materials are incompletely known. The results are arranged in order of decreasing symmetry in Table V.

Among the cubic crystals, the first listed (bismuth germanate) may prove to be of technical interest since it can be obtained in crystals of good optical quality with dimensions of a few centimeters. A second $\bar{4}3m$ crystal, (HMT) hexamethylenetetramine, is of both scientific (because it is a molecular crystal) and technical interest because of the size of the electrooptic coefficient. The dielectric constant at radio frequency is close to the optical value, 2.6, and the loss tangent is small [88], [124]. The material is inexpensive and crystals can be grown with ease. However, it appears that large crystals and in particular crystals grown from solution do not exhibit a large electrooptic effect, presumably because of dislocations [88]. Additionally, practical use of the material requires protection from water vapor and elevated temperatures, and the material is soft. In the case of the mineral Hauynite only an upper limit on r_{41} has been established. The remaining cubic crystals are in point group 23, and are, in general, optically active. This fact complicates the measurement and may limit the usefulness of the materials [89].

The only representative of symmetry 6 is $LiKSO_4$. There are four coefficients and only the difference between two of them has been measured to date.

In class 3m, which has four coefficients, the value of r_{22} only has been measured in $LiNaSO_4$ and tourmaline. Since the latter is a mineral of varying composition, the measured values might be expected to vary also.

Many of the measurements of 32 crystals were made as part of a survey of existing piezoelectric crystals [90]. There are only two coefficients for this point group. Both coefficients have been measured for quartz. The interest in quartz derives, of course, from its availability and excellent optical properties rather than a large electrooptic effect. Crystals in the 32 point group are optically active and this activity, which is manifested principally when light is propagated along the optic axis complicates the measurement of the r_{11} coefficient.

The lowest symmetry group for which coefficients have been measured is point group 2. Here there are eight independent coefficients. The coefficients or combinations of coefficients that have been measured are ones for which a field is applied along the x_2 axis. This is the axis of 2-fold symmetry and the crystal symmetry remains unchanged. The measurements on pentaerythritol yielded the coefficients that could be found with light propagating along the x_2 direction (parallel to the applied field). The calcium pyroniobate measurements were made with light propagating normal to the x_2 direction.

IV. Modulator Design

This section contains some general design considerations as well as capsule descriptions of a few modulator configurations. Space limitations do not permit a discussion of electrooptic beam scanners such as prisms [40], electrooptic gratings [109], and digital light deflectors [110]. Some of these devices are discussed elsewhere in this issue.

Geometrical Considerations

As a rule, the light beam to be modulated passes along a straight line through the electrooptical crystal, which for efficient operation should be just large enough to contain the beam. The colinear case is considered below. Later on, we mention briefly a modulator in which the beam follows a zig-zag path through the crystal and another modulator in which the light travels as a trapped wave along a dielectric discontinuity (*p-n* junction).

Consider a Gaussian optical maser beam propagating in the lowest order transverse mode and focused, by means of a lens, so as to just pass through a cylinder of length L with refractive index n. It can be shown by differentiating the Gaussian beam formulas [103] that the diameter of the cylinder will be a minimum when the lens is chosen to make L equal the confocal parameter b of the beam. Then, the beam diameter is $2w_0$ at the waist and $\sqrt{8}\, w_0$ at the ends of the cylinder, where

$$w_0^2 = \lambda L/2\pi n, \tag{21}$$

and beam diameters are measured to points where the field is $1/e$ its value on the beam axis.

For a cylinder of diameter

$$d = S\cdot\sqrt{8}\, w_0, \tag{22}$$

where S is a safety factor ($S\geq 1$), the minimum value of d^2/L is

$$d^2/L = S^2\cdot 4\lambda/n\pi \tag{23}$$

The situation is illustrated in Fig. 3.

In practice [50], [125], beams have been passed through a rod, with some difficulty in alignment but little added loss, with $S\approx 3$ and, with easy alignment, with $S\approx 6$.

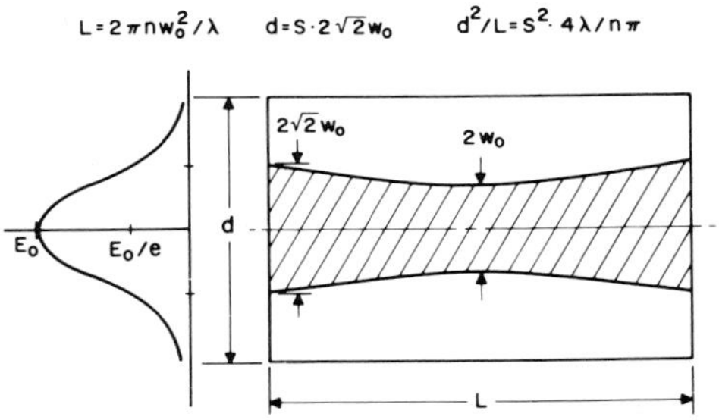

Fig. 3. A beam of Gaussian cross section passing through a rod of diameter d and length L.

Lumped Modulator

In Section II it was tacitly assumed that the field in the sample is uniform over the length L and constant during the time nL/c for the light to pass through the modulator, i.e.,

$$L \ll 2\pi c/2\omega_m \sqrt{\epsilon} \quad \text{and} \quad L \ll 2\pi c/2\omega_m n \tag{24}$$

where ω_m is the highest modulating frequency and ϵ the appropriate dielectric constant at ω_m. Since $\sqrt{\epsilon}\geq n$, normally, the first restriction is dominant and when it is satisfied the modulator may be regarded as a lumped circuit element. For a rod of square cross section d^2, the lumped capacitance is

$$C = \epsilon_0\epsilon L \tag{25}$$

and the parallel conductance

$$G = \omega_m C \tan \delta. \tag{26}$$

In practice, additional parallel circuit capacitance C_a and conductance G_a may be unavoidable or may be required to achieve a certain bandwidth. If the peak voltage V across the crystal is to be provided by a particular voltage generator V_g with impedance R_g, $|V/V_g|$ will be a maximum when R_g is matched to the specified load resistance by an ideal transformer.[3] The ratio $|V/V_g|^2$ will be reduced to $\frac{1}{2}$ its matched dc value at frequency

$$\Delta\omega = 2(G + G_a)/(C + C_a). \tag{27}$$

If parallel inductance is provided to produce resonance at ω_0, the bandwidth over which $|V/V_g|^2$ is at least half its matched value at ω_0 is also $\Delta\omega$ as in (27). The resonant circuit, including an impedance matching transformer, is shown in Fig. 4.

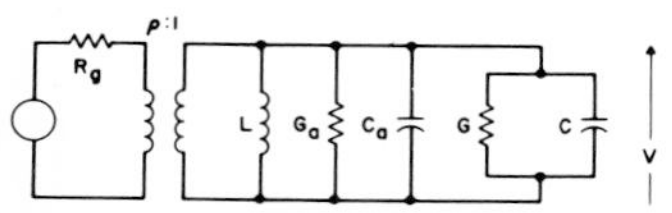

Fig. 4. Equivalent driving circuit for a lumped modulator.

The peak voltage V is determined by the desired index η. The power dissipated is

$$P = \frac{V^2}{2}(G + G_a) = \frac{1}{2}\left(\frac{\lambda \eta d}{\pi n^3 r L}\right)^2 (G + G_a) \tag{28}$$

or in terms of $\Delta\omega$

$$P = \frac{V^2}{4}(C + C_a)\Delta\omega = \frac{1}{4}\left(\frac{\lambda \eta d}{\pi n^3 r L}\right)^2 (C + C_a)\Delta\omega, \tag{29}$$

where n and r are appropriate values of refractive index and electrooptic coefficient. If $C \gg C_a$, a situation which may be difficult to achieve in practice,

$$P = \left(\frac{\epsilon_0}{4\pi^2}\right)(\lambda^2)\left(\frac{\epsilon}{n^6 r^2}\right)\left(\frac{d^2}{L}\right)\cdot \eta^2 \Delta\omega. \tag{30}$$

The maximum L is set by (24) and the minimum d^2/L by (23). For $C \gg C_a$, P is a minimum when d^2/L is a minimum. But for $C_a \gg C$, P is minimum when L is maximum *and* d^2/L is minimum.[4] Thus, for the optimum design, P is proportional to the material parameter $\epsilon/n^6 r^2$ for $C \gg C_a$ and $\epsilon^{1/2}/n^6 r^2$ for $C_a \gg C$.

When bandwidth is not important, $(G+G_a)$ should be minimized. For $G \gg G_a$, P is proportional to d^2/L and, for $G_a \gg G$, to d^2/L^2. Hence, when the added conductance G_a is dominant, as when C_a is dominant, it is advantageous to use large L.[4]

In practice, at frequencies below about 200 MHz, a capacitor may be formed by the crystal using silver paint or evaporated metal electrodes and placed into a circuit with lumped R, L, C elements or coaxial tuners [50]. At higher frequencies, the crystal must be placed in a resonant cavity [7], [104] to obtain the small parallel inductance required and to avoid series inductance in the lead wires.

Traveling Wave

As noted above, P varies as $1/L$ when C_a and/or G_a are dominant and the minimum d^2/L is employed. The transit time restriction on L given in (24) can be lifted if the modulating field is a traveling wave with phase velocity equal to the optical group velocity [105]. Then an optical disturbance will experience a constant modulating field as it passes through the crystal. The velocity match should be such that the optical disturbance does not slip more than a quarter wavelength along the modulation wave during the transit [106], i.e.,

$$\frac{\omega L}{c}(N - n) \leq \frac{\pi}{2}, \tag{31}$$

where N is the ratio of light velocity c to the phase velocity of the modulating wave. The matching condition (31) must be satisfied over the modulating bandwidth. For finite bandwidth, then, the group velocities at optical and modulating frequencies should be equal. The matching of N and n becomes more critical for large ωL and in this sense (31) limits L.

If the modulating field travels as a plane wave completely within the crystal, then $N = \sqrt{\epsilon}$ at all modulating frequencies. In materials for which electronic, rather than lattice, polarization is dominant at the modulating frequency, $\sqrt{\epsilon} \approx n$ and, in principle, a broadband velocity match can be readily achieved. However, crystals with this property are not available in suitable size and quality at present.

When $\sqrt{\epsilon} > n$, a match can be effected over a limited band by filling a TEM line partially with the crystal and the remainder with a lower dielectric constant material, such as air [106]–[108]. In the case of an air filled, parallel plate transmission line containing a crystal of square cross section as shown in Fig. 5, the characteristic admittance at sufficiently low frequencies is

$$G_0 = \frac{N}{z_0}\left(\frac{\epsilon - 1}{N^2 - 1}\right), \tag{32}$$

in which z_0 is 377 ohms, the impedance of free space. For

[3] The ratio is given by

$$\left|\frac{V}{V_g}\right| = \frac{\rho}{\rho^2 + R_g(G + G_a)},$$

where the transformer ratio ρ is supposed to be the only design parameter. Of course, $R_g(G+G_a)$ should be reduced if possible. In certain pulse applications dc coupling is required and in other cases broadband transformers are not available, then matching is not possible.

[4] This discussion assumes C_a and G_a independent of d and L.

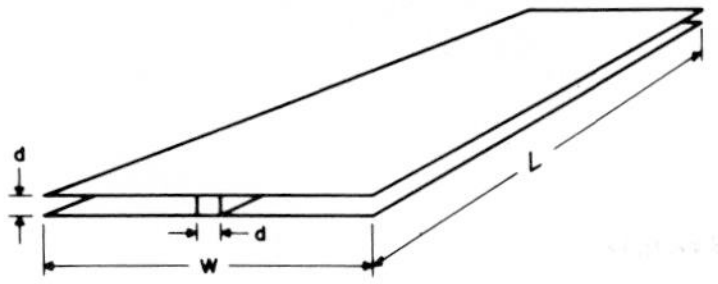

Fig. 5. Partially filled parallel plate transmission line.

a velocity match the dimensions of the line are adjusted so that $N=n$, i.e.,

$$\frac{W}{d} = \frac{\epsilon - 1}{n^2 - 1}, \tag{33}$$

where W is the width of the plates and d a transverse dimension of the crystal. When the line is terminated in G_0, the power required is given by (28) with G_0 substituted for $(G+G_a)$. When $\epsilon=n^2=N^2$, G_0 and P have their minimum values. A wide disparity in ϵ and n^2 makes for inefficient operation because much of the input power travels outside the crystal to the load.

The line will approximate a constant phase velocity TEM line up to frequencies at which d becomes comparable with a half wavelength in the medium [106], i.e.,

$$\Delta\omega \ll \frac{2c}{d\sqrt{\epsilon}} \tag{34}$$

or, roughly,

$$\Delta\omega_{max} = \frac{c}{5d\sqrt{\epsilon}}. \tag{35}$$

Thus, d is limited by $\Delta\omega$, and L, in turn, is limited by (23) and (31). The length is further restricted by considerations of transmission line loss, optical loss, and the availability of large crystals of good quality. When transmission line loss is appreciable, it is more efficient to feed the line by a tapered coupling along its length rather than from one end [111]. For materials with $n<1.6$, optical matching liquids or cements can be found which permit a number of crystals to be joined to provide a large L.

Parallel plate modulators have been constructed by Peters [107], [108] and others [112] with $L\approx 100$ cm using 20 to 25 crystals of ADP or KDP. Even with the refractive indices of crystal and cement matched within 0.001 (using a mixture of silicone oils) and the rods polished with care, the scattering at the 40 to 50 interfaces accounts for most of the observed 6 dB optical loss [112].

The broadband RF matching section, required at the input and termination to take advantage of the potential 0–2 GHz band, have not yet been designed. In addition to the impedance matching problem, operation at the low-frequency end of the band is limited by piezoelectric resonances at frequencies for which d is a small integral number of acoustic half wavelengths. However, resonances have been suppressed by clamping the crystals mechanically [113].

Standing-Wave Modulator

If broadband operation is not an important consideration, it is possible to realize the low power (large L) advantage of the traveling-wave device without the problem of impedance matching by forming a resonant cavity from a velocity matched transmission line. A resonator must be an integral number of half waves long. The resultant standing wave may be regarded as the sum of two oppositely traveling waves. The component traveling in synchronism with the optical wave produces the required modulation. The incident optical disturbance approaches the backward wave component at twice the phase velocity and, therefore, interacts with an integral number of modulating waves within the resonator. Because of the linearity of the electrooptic effect, therefore, the backward wave produces no net modulation. Standing-wave modulators have been built using a KDP rod on the axis of a TM_{01n} resonator [114].

Fabry-Perot Modulator

The effective length of time spent by an optical disturbance bouncing back and forth within a Fabry-Perot resonator is determined by the optical Q. When the optical losses are set by mirror reflectivity R, the effective distance traveled by the light before decaying to $1/e$ of its initial value is

$$L_{eff} = FL/\pi = L\sqrt{R}/(1 - R), \tag{36}$$

in which F is the *finesse* and L the length of the resonator. If the velocity matching requirements are satisfied over L_{eff}, using the standing-wave technique if necessary, it is possible to obtain a modulation corresponding to L_{eff} while dissipating power corresponding to L [115]. Only those optical carrier and sideband frequencies that fall under the Fabry-Perot transmission function will retain the proper phases on successive bounces, however. Thus, the optical carrier must fall on one mode and the sideband energy must appear within the band of that mode or any other of the modes which occur at intervals of $c/2nL$. An increase in bandwidth requires a decrease in Q and corresponding reduction L_{eff}.

A Fabry-Perot modulator has been built at 70 MHz under conditions not requiring velocity match [116]. Experiments at high frequency and/or high finesse, requiring velocity matching, appear to be difficult and have not been reported.

Zig-Zag and Phase Reversal Modulators

Up to this point, it has been assumed, unnecessarily, that the optical and modulating waves travel along the same path through a uniform medium. Electrooptic modulation is a parametric process in which the perturbed parameter is the refractive index and the interacting waves are the optical carrier (ω_0, k_0), an optical sideband (ω_s, k_s), the modulating wave (ω_m, k_m), and possibly a time-invariant periodicity in the medium $(0, k_p)$, where ω_α is an angular frequency and k_α a wave vector. The phase or velocity matching requirement is equivalent to conservation of ω and k,

$$\sum \omega_\alpha = 0, \qquad \sum \boldsymbol{k}_\alpha = 0. \tag{37}$$

When all the beams are parallel, k_p can always be designed to satisfy (37) by reversing the phase of the modulating wave at intervals [117], [118]

$$\lambda_p/2 = \pi c/\omega_m(N - n), \tag{38}$$

or by eliminating the modulation altogether at alternate intervals. The match is effective only in the neighborhood of the specified ω_m so that the technique is narrow band.

In a uniform medium ($k_p=0$), $\boldsymbol{k}$ conservation may be accomplished by permitting an angle γ between $\boldsymbol{k}_0$ and $\boldsymbol{k}_m$ such that

$$\cos \gamma = n/\sqrt{\epsilon}, \tag{39}$$

where dispersion is neglected and use is made of the fact that $\epsilon\omega_m \ll n^2\omega_0$. In general, the component of phase velocity along the light path should equal the optical group velocity. This type of match can be achieved by having the light follow a zig-zag path at angle γ along the transmission line carrying the modulating wave [105]. Then power into the line can be used most efficiently [$N^2=\epsilon$ in (32)]. Only relatively short lengths of crystal are required so that it may not be necessary to optically match several separate sections of crystals. Technical complexity has so far discouraged such efforts [119].

p-n Junction Modulator

A technique for confining optical and modulating fields to the same small volume, other than that using a crystal with diffraction limited dimensions, makes use of *p-n* junctions in GaP and GaAs. The discontinuity at the junction provides an optical guide of a few microns thickness [120], and back biasing of the junction can yield modulating field strengths approaching 10^6 volts/cm [121]. Modulating junctions have usually been made with the junction plane normal to a [111] direction in the crystal. The junction itself is 0.2 to 0.8 micron thick and the total crystal thickness a few mils. The other crystal dimensions are each typically 25 mils (0.025 inch).

The guided modes can be classified as either TE or TM, depending on whether the optical electric field or magnetic field is parallel to the plane of the junction. The guiding action is believed to depend primarily on a higher optical dielectric constant inside the depletion layer than outside, rather than on the conductivity of the p and n regions. The fractional difference in dielectric constant responsible for the guiding is found to be about 10^{-3} [121], [122]. In GaP this is larger than one can account for on the basis of a reduction in dielectric constant due to charge carriers in the n or p region. The guiding in GaAs is also not completely accounted for. Thus, this modulator is in the happy position of working better than one would predict.

The *p-n* junction modulator has usually been operated as an amplitude modulator. In order to do this, equal amounts of the TE and TM modes are excited by using polarization at 45° to the junction. The two modes have different phase lengths in the material and on leaving the modulator the waves are recombined to give the initial polarization plus a polarization at right angles—the amounts depending on phase difference. This difference is [121]:

$$\Delta\phi = \frac{(2\pi)^3\sqrt{3}\, n^5 t^2 L r_{41} \bar{E}}{\lambda^3}\left(\Delta - \frac{r_{41} n^2 \bar{E}}{2\sqrt{3}}\right) \tag{40}$$

where $2t$ is the junction width, L the length, and Δ the fractional change in optical dielectric constant. The average field $\bar{E}$ in the junction can be of order 10^5 volts/cm for applied voltages of 20 volts. The junction width and hence the waveguide width changes with applied field, so both $\bar{E}$ and t are functions of voltage. The experimental results [121], [122] confirm the functional form [40] which indicates that the *linear* electrooptic effect is the predominant cause of modulation *even* with the large field strengths used. The anomalously large value of dielectric discontinuity remains unexplained.

The high-frequency limit of *p-n* junction modulating diodes is fixed by the time constant of the series resistance and the capacitance. In order to reduce the latter, the use of a mesa structure which reduces the width of the diode has been proposed [123]. The resistance can be reduced by using more heavily doped material and by reducing the diode height as much as possible. Estimates based on properties of existing diodes indicate a phase modulation index of $\pi/4$ up to 1 GHz with 200 mW of power is within the realm of possibility [123].

Conclusions

The electrooptic properties of a large number of materials have been examined in the search for suitable modulator materials. Unfortunately, the fundamental nature of the electrooptic effect is not well understood, and the search has been guided mainly by incidental practical considerations: the availability of crystals of good optical quality transparent in the spectral region of interest, point group symmetry—piezoelectric groups for linear electrooptic effect, cubic or axial groups for simplicity of interpretation and applicability in certain devices, low dielectric loss to avoid thermal strain and reduce modulating power, high resistivity to reduce space charge effects, and heating. The particular application determines which material parameters are of greater importance, often in contradicting fashion. In all applications, the modulation produced by a given field is proportional to n^3r so that both large refractive index and electrooptic coefficient are desirable. It is often found that r is proportional to ϵ, so that large ϵ is desirable. On the other hand, it is difficult to provide optical matching from air into the material or to provide a matching cement for joining two crystals (for a long traveling-wave modulator) when n is large. When ϵ is large, the reactive power required to drive a lumped modulator is large. Further, it is difficult to provide an RF match and to make the sample small enough to avoid dielectric resonances at high frequency. Additionally, large values of ϵ generally imply a large disparity in n and $\sqrt{\epsilon}$ so that broadband velocity matching becomes inefficient for the colinear, but not necessarily the zig-zag, traveling-wave modulator.

Lumped modulators using materials like $LiTaO_3$, however, appear to be suitable for certain engineering applications [125]. The *p-n* junction modulator is also promising. For certain laboratory applications, where smaller modulation or high power are permissible, KDP and DKDP have proven useful. Nevertheless, materials with higher electrooptic coefficient, possibly also with $n \approx \sqrt{\epsilon}$ and $n \approx 1.5$, are needed for many applications.

The discovery of powerful infrared masers has created an interest in modulators that operate efficiently at wavelengths as long as 10 μ. Although many of the crystals already studied are transparent to 5 μ and some (e.g. GaAs, ZnSe, CdS) to $>10\ \mu$, the electrooptic coefficient in the infrared would have to be proportionately larger than in the visible region to make up for the λ^{-1} dependence of modulation index. However, the electrooptic coefficient for GaAs, and probably for other known materials as well, is found to remain constant between 1 μ and 10 μ [81].

Perhaps the development of a theoretical understanding of the electrooptic effect will lead to the discovery or synthesis of the ideal substances for each application in a logical way.

A number of modulator configurations that make the most efficient use of a particular material in a given application have been described. Most of these have not been developed fully because the demand of a particular application has not warranted the effort, or because a material with the ideal properties was not available. However, as the characteristics of electrooptic modulators and modulators of other types become clearer, so that applications can be seriously considered, some of these devices may receive the full treatment. The simplest configuration is the lumped modulator. However, in order to approach the optimum efficiency, the effective path length for the electrooptic perturbation must be made very large by means of traveling-wave techniques. Where large bandwidth is important, a nonresonant structure with broadband velocity and impedance matching is required. Where narrow bandwidths are permissible, structures resonant at optical (e.g., Fabry-Perot modulator), and/or modulating (e.g., standing-wave modulator) frequencies may be employed.

References

[1] F. Pockels, Lehrbuch der Kristalloptik. Leipzig: Teubner, 1906.

[2] F. Jona and G. Shirane, *Ferroelectric Crystals.* New York: Macmillan, 1962.

[3] W. Kanzig, *Solid State Physics*, vol. 4, F. Seitz and D. Turnbull, Eds. New York: Academic, 1957, pp. 1–197.

[4] B. H. Billings, "The electrooptic effect in uniaxial crystals of the dihydrogen phosphate (XH_2PO_4) type, Parts I, II, IV," *J. Opt. Soc. Am.*, vol. 39, pp. 797–801, and pp. 802–808, October 1949, vol. 42, pp. 12–20, January 1952.

[5] R. O'B. Carpenter, "The electrooptic effect in crystals of the dihydrogen phosphate type, Part III," Measurement of coefficients," *J. Opt. Soc. Am.*, vol. 40, pp. 225–229, April 1950.

—— "Electrooptic sound-on-film modulator," *J. Opt. Soc. Am.*, vol. 25, pp. 1145–1148, November 1953.

[6] D. F. Holshouser, H. Von Foerster, and G. L. Clark, "Microwave modulation of light using the Kerr effect," *J. Opt. Soc. Am.*, vol. 51, pp. 1360–1365, December 1961.

[7] K. D. Froome and R. H. Bradsell, "Distance measurement by means of a light ray modulated at a microwave frequency," *J. Sci. Instr.*, vol. 38, pp. 458–462, December 1961.

[8] J. F. Nye, *Physical Properties of Crystals.* Oxford, England: Oxford University Press, 1960.

[9] P. V. Lenzo, E. H. Turner, E. G. Spencer, and A. A. Ballman, "Electrooptic coefficients and elastic wave propagation in single-domain ferroelectric lithium tantalate," *Appl. Phys. Letters*, vol. 8, pp. 81–82, February 1966.

[10] Incorrect results, however, have been presented in quite recent publications such as G. N. Ramachandran and S. Ramaseshan, "Crystal Optics," in *Handbuch der Physik*, vol. 25/1. Berlin: Springer-Verlag, 1961, pp. 1–217.

[11] C. F. Buhrer, D. Baird, and E. M. Conwell, "Optical frequency shifting by electrooptic effect," *Appl. Phys. Letters*, vol. 1, pp. 46–49, October 1962.

[12] C. F. Buhrer, L. R. Bloom, and D. H. Baird, "Electrooptic light modulation with cubic crystals," *Appl. Opt.*, vol. 2, pp. 839–846, August 1963.

[13] W. P. Mason, "The elastic, piezoelectric, and dielectric constants of KDP and ADP," *Phys. Rev.*, vol. 69, pp. 173–194, March 1946.

[14] I. P. Kaminow, "Microwave dielectric properties of $NH_4H_2PO_4$, KH_2ASO_4, and partially deuterated KH_2PO_4," *Phys. Rev.*, vol. 138, pp. A1539–A1543, May 1965.

[15] F. R. Nash, "Measurements made by substitution inside laser resonator," unpublished.

[16] T. R. Sliker and S. R. Burlage, "Some dielectric and optical properties of KD_2PO_4," *J. Appl. Phys.*, vol. 34, pp. 1837–1840, July 1963.

[17] W. J. Deshotels, "Ultraviolet transmission of dihydrogen arsenate and phosphate crystals," *J. Opt. Soc. Am.*, vol. 50, p. 865, September 1960.

[18] S. F. Pellicor, "Transmittances of some optical materials for use between 0.19 and 0.34 μ," *Appl. Opt.*, vol. 3, pp. 361–366, March 1964.

[19] E. F. Kingsbury, unpublished memorandum, 1950.

[20] I. P. Kaminow, "Temperature dependence at the complex dielectric constant in KH_2PO_4-Type crystals and the design of microwave light modulators," in *Quantum Electronics III*, P. Grivet and N. Bloembergen, Eds., New York: Columbia University Press, 1964, pp. 1659–1665.

[21] O. G. Blokh, "Dispersion of r_{63} for crystals of ADP and KDP," *Sov. Phys.-Cryst.*, vol. 7, pp. 509–511, January-February 1963.

[22] J. F. Ward and P. A. Franken, "Structure of nonlinear optical phenomena in KDP," *Phys. Rev.*, vol. 133, pp. A183–A190, January 1964.

[23] I. P. Kaminow, "Strain effects in electrooptic light modulators," *Appl. Opt.*, vol. 3, pp. 511–515, April 1964.

[24] J. H. Ott and T. R. Sliker, "Linear electrooptic effects in KH_2PO_4 and its isomorphs," *J. Opt. Soc. Am.*, vol. 54, pp. 1442–1444, December 1964.

[25] C. H. Clayson, "Low-voltage light-amplitude modulation," *Electronic Letters*, vol. 2, p. 138, April 1966; reply by J. M. Ley, *ibid.*, p. 139.

[26] B. H. Billings, "The electrooptic effect in crystals and its possible application to distance measure," in *Optics in Metrology*, P. Mollet, Ed. New York: Pergamon, 1960, pp. 119–135.

[27] F. Zernike, Jr., "Refractive indices of ADP and KDP between 0.2 and 1.5 μ," *J. Opt. Soc. Am.*, vol. 54, pp. 1215–1220, October 1964; V. N. Vishnevskii and I. V. Stefanski, "Temperature dependence of the dispersion of the refractivity of ADP and KDP single crystals," *Opt. and Spectr.*, vol. 20, pp. 195–196, February 1966.

[27a] R. A. Phillips, "Temperature variation of the index of refraction of ADP, KDP and deuterated KDP," *J. Opt. Soc. Am.*, vol. 56, pp. 629–632, May 1966.

[28] D. A. Berlincourt, D. R. Curran, and H. Jaffe, *Physical Acoustics*, vol. I, pt. A, W. P. Mason, Ed. New York: Academic, 1964, pp. 169–260.

[29] I. P. Kaminow and G. O. Harding, "Complex dielectric con-

stant of KH_2PO_4 at 9.2 Gc/sec," *Phys. Rev.*, vol. 129, pp. 1562–1566, February 1963.
[30] J. M. Ley, "Low voltage light-amplitude modulation," *Electronics Letters*, vol. 2, pp. 12–13, January 1966.
[31] I. S. Zheludev and T-Z Ludupov, "Complex dielectric constant of RbH_2PO_4 in the range 8×10^{2}–3.86×10^{10} cps," *Kristallografiia*, vol. 10, pp. 764–766, September–October 1965.
[32] A. von Hippel, *Dielectric Materials and Applications*. New York: Wiley, 1954.
[33] R. M. Hill and S. K. Ichiki, "Paraelectric response of KD_2PO_4," *Phys. Rev.*, vol. 130, pp. 150–151, April 1961.
[34] Helen D. Megaw, *Ferroelectricity in Crystals*. London: Methuen, 1957.
[35] J. E. Geusic, S. K. Kurtz, L. G. van Uitert, and S. H. Wemple, "Electrooptic properties of some ABO_3 perovskites in the paraelectric phase," *Appl. Phys. Letters*, vol. 4, pp. 141–143, April 1964.
[36] M. S. Schumate, "Interferometric determination of the principal refractive indices of barium titanate single crystals," *Appl. Phys. Letters*, vol. 5, pp. 178–179, November 1964.
[37] J. A. Noland, "Optical absorption of single crystal strontium titanate," *Phys. Rev.*, vol. 94, p. 724, May 1, 1954.
R. C. Casella and S. P. Keller, "Polarized light transmission of $BaTiO_3$ single crystals," *Phys. Rev.*, vol. 116, pp. 1469–1473, December 1959.
C. Hilsum, "Infrared transmission of barium titanate," *J. Opt. Soc. Am.*, vol. 45, pp. 771–772, September 1955.
J. T. Last, "Infrared-absorption studies of barium titanate and related materials," *Phys. Rev.*, vol. 105, pp. 1740–1750, March 1957.
[38] C. J. Johnson, "Some dielectric and electrooptic properties of $BaTiO_3$ single crystals," *Appl. Phys. Letters*, vol. 7, pp. 221–223, October 1965.
[39] G. Rupprecht and R. O. Bell, "Microwave losses in strontium titanate above the phase transition," *Phys. Rev.*, vol. 125, pp. 1915–1920, March 1962.
[40] F. S. Chen, J. E. Guesic, S. K. Kurtz, J. G. Skinner, and S. H. Wemple, "Light modulation and beam deflection with potassium tantalate-niobate crystals," *J. Appl. Phys.*, vol. 37, pp. 388–398, January 1966.
[41] A. R. Johnston, "The strain-free electrooptic effect in single-crystal barium titanate," *Appl. Phys. Letters*, vol. 7, pp. 195–198, October 1965.
[42] S. K. Kurtz, "Design of an electrooptic polarization switch for a high capacity high-speed digital light deflection system," *Bell Sys. Tech. J.*, to be published.
[43] F. S. Chen, J. E. Guesic, S. K. Kurtz, J. G. Skinner, and S. H. Wemple, "The use of perovskite paraelectrics in beam deflectors and light modulators," *Proc. IEEE* (*Correspondence*), vol. 52, pp. 1258–1259, October 1964.
[44] A. Linz, Jr. "Some electrical properties of strontium titanate," *Phys. Rev.*, vol. 91, pp. 753–754, August 1953.
[45] J. K. Hulm, B. T. Matthias, and E. A. Long, "A ferromagnetic Curie point in $KTaO_3$ at very low temperatures," *Phys. Rev.*, vol. 79, pp. 885–886, September 1950.
[46] J. E. Guesic, S. K. Kurtz, T. J. Nelson, and S. H. Wemple, "Nonlinear dielectric properties of $KTaO_3$ near its Curie point," *Appl. Phys. Letters*, vol. 2, pp. 185–187, May 1963.
[47] J. P. Remeika, "A method for growing barium titanate single crystals," *J. Am. Chem. Soc.*, vol. 76, pp. 940–941, February 1954.
[48] A. R. Johnston and J. M. Weingart, "Determination of the low-frequency linear electrooptic effect in tetragonal $BaTiO_3$," *J. Opt. Soc. Am.*, vol. 55, pp. 828–834, July 1965.
[49] E. H. Turner, Paper 6B-2, presented at the 1966 Intnat'l Quantum Electronics Conf., Phoenix, Ariz., and "High frequency electrooptic coefficients of lithium niobate," *Appl. Phys. Letters*, vol. 8, pp. 303–304, June 1966.
[50] I. P. Kaminow, "Barium titanate light phase modulator," *Appl. Phys. Letters*, vol. 7, pp. 123–125, September 1965, "Erratum," vol. 8, p. 54, January 1966.
——, "Barium titanate light modulator II," *Appl. Phys. Letters*, vol. 8, pp. 305–306, June 1966.
[51] The structure and growth of $LiNbO_3$ are described and earlier work reviewed in a series of five papers: K. Nassau, H. J. Levinstein, and G. M. Loiacono (I and II); S. C. Abrahams, J. M. Reddy, and J. L. Bernstein (III); S. C. Abrahams, W. C. Hamilton, and J. M. Reddy (IV); S. C. Abrahams, H. J. Levinstein, and J. M. Reddy (V); "Ferroelectric lithium niobate," *J. Phys. Chem. Solids*. vol. 27, 1966.
[52] B. T. Matthias and J. P. Remeika, "Ferroelectricity in the ilmenite structure," *Phys. Rev.*, vol. 76, pp. 1886–1887, December 1949.
[52a] A. A. Ballman, "The growth of piezoelectric and ferroelectric materials by the Czochralski technique," *J. Am. Ceram. Soc.*, vol. 48, pp. 112–113, February 1965.
[53] H. J. Levinstein, A. A. Ballman, and C. D. Capio, "The domain structure and Curie temperature of single crystal lithium tantalate," *J. Appl. Phys.*, to be published.
[54] R. T. Denton, Paper 6B-4, presented at the 1966 Internat'l Quantum Electronics Conf., Phoenix, Ariz.
[55] A. Ashkin, G. D. Boyd, J. M. Diedzic, R. G. Smith, A. A. Ballman, H. J. Levinstein, and K. Nassau, "Optically induced refractive index inhomogeneities in $LiNbO_3$ and $LiTaO_3$," *Appl. Phys. Letters*, to be published.
[56] G. D. Boyd, R. C. Miller, K. Nassau, W. L. Bond, and A. Savage, "$LiNbO_3$: An efficient phase matchable nonlinear optical material," *Appl. Phys. Letters*, vol. 5, pp. 234–236, December 1964.
[57] W. L. Bond, "Measurement of the refractive indices of several crystals," *J. Appl. Phys.*, vol. 36, pp. 1674–1677, May 1965.
[58] P. V. Lenzo, E. G. Spencer, and K. Nassau, "Electrooptic coefficients in lithium niobate," *J. Opt. Soc. Am.*, vol. 56, pp. 633–636, May 1966.
[59] F. A. Dunn, unpublished. Measurements at 9.3 GHz show that made from −180 degrees C to +100 degrees C ϵ_3 decreases by 15 percent and $\epsilon_1=\epsilon_2$ by 7 percent from +100 to −180 degrees C. At room temperature $\epsilon_1=45$ and $\epsilon_3=27$. The dielectric loss was too low to be measured, i.e., $\tan\delta<0.01$.
[60] E. P. Ippen, "Electrooptic deflection with $BaTiO_3$ prisms," *Proc. IEEE*, to be published.
[61] E. H. Turner, to be published. These are results of heterodyne measurements on vapor grown and hydrothermally grown crystals.
[62] R. J. Collins and D. A. Kleinman, "Infrared reflectivity of zinc oxide," *J. Phys. Chem. Solids*, vol. II, nos. 3–4, pp. 190–194, 1959.
[63] S. Namba, "Electrooptical effect of zincblende," *J. Opt. Soc. Am.*, vol. 51, pp. 76–79, January 1961.
[64] S. J. Czyzak, D. C. Reynolds et al., "On the properties of single cubic zinc sulfide crystals, *J. Opt. Soc. Am.*, vol. 44, pp. 864–867, November 1954.
[65] D. Berlincourt, H. Jaffe, and L. R. Shiozawa, "Electroelastic properties of the sulfides, selenides, and tellurides of zinc and cadmium," *Phys. Rev.*, vol. 129, pp. 1009–1017, February 1, 1963.
[66] E. H. Turner, to be published. These are results of heterodyne measurements on crystals termed "primarily hexagonal."
[67] T. M. Bieniewski and S. J. Czyzak, "Refractive indexes of single hexagonal ZnS and CdS crystals," *J. Opt. Soc. Am.*, vol. 53, pp. 496–497, April 1963.
[68] R. W. McQuaid, "Electrooptic properties of zinc selenide," *Proc. IRE* (*Correspondence*), vol. 50, pp. 2484–2485, December 1962; and "Correction to 'Electrooptic properties of zinc selenide,' " *Proc. IEEE*, vol. 51, p. 470, March 1963.
[69] D. T. F. Marple, "Refractive index of ZnSe, ZnTe, and CdTe," *J. Appl. Phys.*, vol. 35, pp. 539–542, March 1964.
[70] M. Aven, D. T. F. Marple, and B. Segall, "Some electrical and optical properties of ZnSe," *J. Appl. Phys.*, supplemental to vol. 32, pp. 2261–2265, October 1961.
[71] T. R. Sliker and J. M. Jost, "Linear electrooptic effect and refractive indices of cubic ZnTe," *J. Opt. Soc. Am.*, vol. 56, pp. 130–131, January 1966.
[72] E. H. Turner, unpublished. Heterodyne measurement.
[73] C. D. West, "Electrooptic and related properties of crystals with the zinc blend structure," *J. Opt. Soc. Am.*, vol. 43, p. 335, April 1953.
[74] L. M. Belyaev, G. F. Dobrzhanskii, Yu. U. Shaldin, "Electrooptical properties of copper chloride and bromide crystals," *Soviet Phys.—Solid State*, vol. 6, p. 2988, June 1965.
[75] Landolt-Börnstein, Zahlenwerte und Funktionen, II Band, 8 Teil, Optische Konstanten.
[76] L. M. Belyaev, G. S. Belikova, G. F. Dobrzhanskii, G. B. Netesov, and Yu. U. Shaldin, "Dielectric constant of crystals

having an electrooptical effect," *Soviet Phys.—Solid State*, vol. 6, pp. 2007–2008, February 1965.

[77] I. P. Kaminow, unpublished. This value measured at 9.3 GHz. It was also found that tan $\delta = 0.002$.

[78] K. K. Thornber, A. J. Kurtzig, and E. H. Turner, unpublished. The value $r_{41} = 0.5$ was obtained using pulse methods on relatively low resistivity samples. The 1.06 value was from a heterodyne measurement on a sample having $>10^5$ ohm cm resistivity at 75 MHz, where ϵ was measured. More weight should be given the larger value.

[79] L. Ho and C. F. Buhrer, "Electrooptic effect of gallium arsenide," *Appl. Opt.*, vol. 2, pp. 647–648, June 1963.

[80] E. H. Turner and I. P. Kaminow, "Electrooptic effect in gallium arsenide," *J. Opt. Soc. Am.*, vol. 53, p. 523, April 1963.

[81] A. Yariv and C. A. Mead, "Semiconductors as electrooptic modulators for intrared radiation," Paper 5C-3, presented at the 1966 Internat'l Quantum Electronics Conf. Phoenix, Ariz.; also, T. E. Walsh, "Gallium-arsenide electrooptic modulators," *RCA Rev.*, to be published.

[82] D. T. F. Marple, "Refractive index of GaAs," *J. Appl. Phys.*, vol. 35, pp. 1241–1242, April 1964.

[83] C. Hilsum and A. C. Rose-Innes, *Semiconducting III–V Compounds*. New York: Pergamon, 1961.

[84] K. G. Hambleton, C. Hilsum, and B. R. Holeman, "Determination of the effective ionic change of gallium arsenide from direct measurements of the dielectric constant," *Proc. of the Physical Soc.*, vol. 77, pp. 1147–1148, June 1961.

[85] F. A. Dunn, unpublished. Measurement on semi-insulating material at 9.3 GHz, where tan $\delta < 0.01$ also was determined.

[86] D. J. A. Gainon, "Linear electrooptic effect in CdS," *J. Opt. Soc. Am.*, vol. 54, pp. 270–271, February 1964.

[87] S. J. Czyzak, H. Payne, W. M. Baker, J. E. Manthuruthil, and T. M. Bieniewski, "The study of properties of single ZnS and CdS crystals," Tech. Rept. 6, ONR Contract Nonr 1511(01)NR015218, 1960.

[88] G. H. Heilmeier, "The dielectric and electrooptical properties of a molecular crystal-hexamine," *Appl. Opt.*, vol. 3, pp. 1281–1287, November 1964.

[89] C. F. Buhrer, L. Ho, and J. Zucker, "Electrooptic effect in optically active crystals," *Appl. Opt.*, vol. 3, pp. 517–521, April 1964.

[90] T. R. Sliker, "Linear electrooptic effects in class 32, 6, 3m, and $\bar{4}3$m crystals," *J. Opt. Soc. Am.*, vol. 54, pp. 1348–1351, November 1964.

[91] R. Nitsche, "Crystal growth and electrooptic effect of bismuth germanate, $Bi_4(GeO_4)_3$," *J. Appl. Phys.*, vol. 36, pp. 2358–2360, August 1965.

[92] R. W. McQuaid, "The Pockels effect of hexamethylenetetramine," *Appl. Opt.*, vol. 2, pp. 320–321, March 1963.

[93] K. K. Thornber and E. H. Turner, "A determination of the electrooptic coefficients of haüynite, langbeinite and gallium phosphide," unpublished.

[94] W. E. Ford, *Dana's Textbook of Mineralogy*, fourth ed. New York: Wiley, 1932. This reference gives the value $n = 1.535$ for the mineral compound $K_2Mg_2(SO_4)_3$ and is assumed approximately correct for the other two. Also $n \approx 1.572$ for $K_2Mn_2(SO_4)_3$.

[95] R. W. McQuaid, "Cubic piezoelectric crystals for electrooptic modulation," *1963 Proc. Nat'l Aerospace Electronics Conf.*, pp. 282–286.

[96] A. N. Winchell and H. Winchell, *The Microscopical Characters of Artificial Inorganic Substances*. New York: Academic, 1964.

[97] J. Warner, D. S. Robertson, and H. T. Parfit, "The electrooptic effect of sodium uranyl acetate," *Phys. Letters*, vol. 19-pp. 479–480, December 1965.

[98] W. G. Cady, *Piezoelectricity*. New York: McGraw-Hill, 1946, p. 721.

[99] D. D. Eden and G. H. Thiess, "Measurement of the direct electrooptic effect in quartz at UHF," *Appl. Opt.*, vol. 2, pp. 868–869, August 1963.

[100] O. G. Blokh, I. S. Zheludev, and U. A. Shamburov, "The electrooptic effect in crystals of pentaerythritol $C(CH_2OH)_4$," *Soviet Phys.—Cryst.*, vol. 8, pp. 37–40, July–August 1963.

[101] C. H. Holmes, E. G. Spencer, A. A. Ballman, and P. V. Lenzo, "The electrooptic effect in calcium pyroniobate," *Appl. Opt.*, vol. 4, pp. 551–553, May 1965.

[102] C. F. Buhrer and L. Ho, "Electrooptic effect in $(NH_4)_2Cd_2(SO_4)_3$ and $(NH_4)_2Mn_2(SO_4)_3$," *Appl. Opt.*, vol. 3, p. 314, February 1964.

[103] G. D. Boyd and J. P. Gordon, "Confocal multimode resonator for millimeter through optical wavelength masers," *Bell Sys. Tech. J.*, vol. 40, pp. 489–508, March 1961;
H. Kogelnik and T. Li, "Laser beams and resonators," this issue.

[104] R. H. Blumenthal, "Design of a microwave-frequency light modulator," *Proc. IEEE*, vol. 50, pp. 452–456, April 1962.

[105] W. W. Rigrod and I. P. Kaminow, "Wide-band microwave light modulation," *Proc. IEEE*, vol. 51, pp. 137–140, January 1963.

[106] I. P. Kaminow and J. Liu, "Propagation characteristics of partially loaded two-conductor transmission line for broadband light modulators," *Proc. IEEE*, vol. 51, pp. 132–136, January 1963.

[107] C. J. Peters, "Gigacycle bandwidth coherent light traveling-wave phase modulator," *Proc. IEEE*, vol. 51, pp. 147–153, January 1963.

[108] ——, "Gigacycle-bandwidth coherent-light traveling-wave amplitude modulator," *Proc. IEEE*, vol. 53, pp. 455–460, May 1965.

[109] E. I. Gordon and M. G. Cohen, "Electro-Optic diffraction grating for light beam modulation and diffraction," *IEEE J. of Quantum Electronics*, vol. QE-1, pp. 191–198, August 1965.

[110] W. J. Tabor, "A high capacity digital light deflector using Wollaston prisms," *Bell Sys. Tech. J.*, to be published.
R. A. Soref and D. H. McMahon, "Optical design of Wollaston-prism digital light deflectors," *Appl. Opt.*, vol. 5, pp. 425–434, March 1966.

[111] I. P. Kaminow, R. Kompfner, and W. H. Louisell, "Improvements in light modulators of the traveling-wave type," *IRE Trans. on Microwave Theory and Techniques*, vol. MTT-10, pp. 311–313, September 1962.

[112] J. A. Ernest and I. P. Kaminow, 1963, unpublished.

[113] E. A. Ohm, private communication.

[114] I. P. Kaminow, "Microwave modulation of the electrooptic effect in KH_2PO_4," *Phys. Rev. Letters*, vol. 6, pp. 528–530, May 1961.
I. P. Kaminow, "Splitting of Fabry-Perot rings by microwave modulation of light," *Appl. Phys. Letters*, vol. 2, pp. 41–42, January 1963.

[115] E. I. Gordon and J. D. Rigden, "The Fabry-Perot electrooptic modulator," *Bell Sys. Tech. J.*, vol. 42, pp. 155–179, January 1963.

[116] J. T. Ruscio, "A coherent light modulator," *IEEE J. of Quantum Electronics* (*Correspondence*), vol. QE-1, pp. 182–183, July 1965.

[117] S. M. Stone, "A microwave electro-optic modulator which overcomes transit time limitation," *Proc. IEEE* (*Correspondence*), vol. 52, pp. 409–410, April 1964.

[118] R. A. Myers and P. S. Pershan, "Light modulation experiments at 16 Gc/sec," *J. Appl. Phys.*, vol. 36, pp. 22–28, January 1965.

[119] M. DiDomenico, Jr., and L. K. Anderson, "Broadband electrooptic traveling-wave light modulators," *Bell Sys. Tech. J.*, vol. 42, pp. 2621–2678, November 1963.

[120] A. Ashkin and M. Gershenzon, "Reflection and guiding of light at *p-n* junction," *J. Appl. Phys.*, vol. 34, pp. 2116–2119, July 1963.

[121] D. F. Nelson and F. K. Reinhart, "Light modulation by the electrooptic effect in reverse-biased GaP *p-n* junctions," *Appl. Phys. Letters*, vol. 5, pp. 148–150, October 1964.

[122] W. L. Walters, "Electrooptic effect in reverse-biased GaAs *p-n* junctions," *J. Appl. Phys.*, vol. 37, p. 916, February 1966.

[123] F. K. Reinhart, private communication.

[124] I. P. Kaminow, unpublished. Measurements at 9.2 GHz indicate $\epsilon = 2.6 \pm 0.2$, with no observable trend between -200 and $+100$°C, and tan $\delta < 0.005$.

[125] R. T. Denton, T. S. Kinsel, and F. S. Chen, "224 Mc/s Optical Pulse Code Modulator," *Proc. IEEE*, to be published; I. P. Kaminow, "Lithium niobate light modulator at 4 GHz (abstract)," *J. Opt. Soc. Am.*, vol. 55, November 1966, to be published.

Modulators for Optical Communications

FANG-SHANG CHEN, MEMBER, IEEE

Abstract—This paper reviews the field of high-speed small-aperture modulators for applications in optical communications, with emphasis on electrooptic modulation. The capabilities and limitations of electrooptic modulators are discussed based on a review of the physical origin of the electrooptic effect. Thermal and photoconduction phenomena, which may severely limit the operation of practical devices, are emphasized. The modulation power and bandwidth limitations using various schemes of electrooptic interaction are derived and compared. It is shown that lumped modulators are capable of efficient modulation for bandwidths up to about 1 GHz for visible wavelengths and are also attractive for their simplicity. For broader bandwidth capability the traveling wave or zigzag types of interaction become more efficient but with added complexity. Finally, acousto-optic and magnetooptic modulators are briefly discussed and compared with electrooptic modulators.

Introduction

ONE of the key links in the realization of transmitting large amounts of information over laser beams is a means of impressing the information onto the laser beam. This can be accomplished by modulation of variable reactive or absorptive elements outside the laser cavity, or by direct modulation of the laser. The reactive-type modulation includes electrooptic, acoustooptic, and magnetooptic interactions. Informative reviews of electrooptic modulators have been given by Anderson [1] and by Kaminow and Turner [2]; the latter also includes a tabulation of electrooptic crystals. Further discussions and extensive data on electrooptic crystals have been given by Rez [3]. A review of acoustooptic modulation has been given by Gordon [4].

In this paper a review of optical modulators for communications applications is given. Such modulators do not require a large aperture, which helps to reduce the modulation power. Only reactive-type modulators are discussed with emphasis placed on the electrooptic interaction. The direct modulation of lasers is included here while that of semiconductor lasers is reviewed by Paoli and Ripper [5].

Although different approaches to explaining the physical origin of electrooptic effects in solids have been proposed, their common feature is that the electrooptic effect is the result of field-induced shifts of optical transitions above the band gap. The approach convenient in describing the electrooptic effect in ferroelectrics is followed here. This analysis brings out naturally the capabilities and limitations of these crystals for device applications. Thermal and photoconduction phenomena, which may present serious problems that must be overcome in practical devices, are also discussed.

The modulation power required for various schemes of electrooptic interaction is derived and expressed as a product of parameters dependent on the material and the scheme of interaction. Comparison of modulation power and bandwidth limitations for various schemes of interaction is then made. Finally, acoustooptic and magnetooptic modulations are briefly discussed and compared with the electrooptic modulation.

Manuscript received in final form August 21, 1970.

The author is with Bell Telephone Laboratories, Inc., Murray Hill, N. J. 07974.

The Electrooptic Effect and Electrooptic Materials

Wave Propagation Inside Electrooptic Crystals

Electromagnetic wave propagation inside an anisotropic dielectric medium has two distinct properties: 1) the phase velocity depends on the propagation and light polarization directions relative to the crystal axes, and 2) the phase velocity direction may be different from the direction of energy flow. The phase velocity can be obtained by constructing an index ellipsoid [6] (or indicatrix) if the crystal does not show optical activity. The orientation of the indicatrix is related to the crystal axes (the principal axes of indicatrix are along the crystal axes except for monoclinic and triclinic systems) and the half-lengths of the principal axes are equal to the principal indices of refraction. The indicatrix has the following properties. Draw a straight line from the origin parallel to the phase velocity direction of a plane wave propagating in the crystal. A plane perpendicular to this line and passing through the origin forms an ellipse at its intersection with the ellipsoid. The semiaxes of this ellipse define two directions of light polarization which may be considered to be the directions of polarization of the normal modes. The indices of refraction of these modes are equal to the length of the semiaxes. Only an incident plane wave with its displacement vector linearly polarized along one of these two directions remains linearly polarized on emerging from the crystal. Since displacement vectors are related to electric fields by a permittivity tensor, they are not generally in the same direction. Waves of other polarizations will be decomposed into the normal modes and, on emerging from the crystal, they recombine in general with nonzero phase difference and thus the wave will be elliptically polarized.

The indicatrix can be expressed as

$$\frac{x_1^2}{n_1^2} + \frac{x_2^2}{n_2^2} + \frac{x_3^2}{n_3^2} = 1 \tag{1}$$

where $x_{1,2,3}$ are coordinate axes and $n_{1,2,3}$ are the principal refractive indices. A small change of refractive indices by application of an electric field induces a small change in the shape, size, and orientation of the indicatrix. This

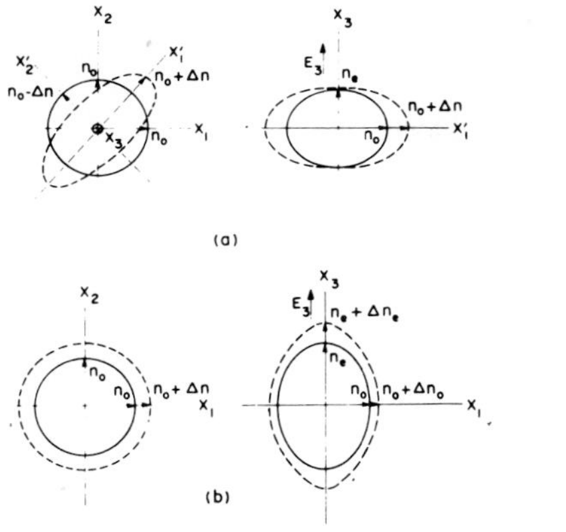

Fig. 1. Indicatrix before (solid line) and after (dashed line) a field is applied. (a) Indicatrix of KDP when a field is applied along the x_3 axis. (b) Indicatrix of $LiTaO_3$ when a field is applied along the x_3 axis.

change can be specified by giving the change in the coefficients of the indicatrix. Linear field-induced changes of the coefficients can be expressed as

$$\Delta\left(\frac{1}{n^2}\right)_{ij} = \sum_k r_{ijk}E_k \tag{2}$$

where E_k is the applied field, r_{ijk} are components of the linear electrooptic tensor, and the subscripts i and j run from 1 to 3. The tensor is expressed in contracted matrix notation, and it has been listed for all crystal classes [6], [7].

The use of the indicatrix to describe the electrooptic effect can be illustrated by considering an example of KDP (tetragonal system, $\bar{4}2m$ symmetry at room temperature) which has two nonvanishing coefficients, r_{41} and r_{63}. When an electric field E_3 is applied along the crystallographic c axis, the indicatrix becomes

$$\frac{x_1^2 + x_2^2}{n_o^2} + \frac{x_3^2}{n_e^2} + 2r_{63}E_3x_1x_2 = 1, \tag{3}$$

where n_o and n_e are the ordinary and the extraordinary indices of refraction, respectively, and $x_{1,2,3}$ are along the crystallographic a, b, and c axes. By rotating the coordinates 45° around the x_3 axis, (3) can be diagonalized, and it becomes

$$\frac{x_1'^2}{(n_o + \Delta n)^2} + \frac{x_2'^2}{(n_o - \Delta n)^2} + \frac{x_3^2}{n_e^2} = 1 \tag{4}$$

$$\Delta n = \frac{n_o^3}{2} r_{63}E_3 \tag{5}$$

where $x'_{1,2}$ are the new coordinate axes, and an approximation $n_o \gg \Delta n$ is used. The indicatrices with and without E_3 are shown in Fig. 1(a).

For a plane wave with phase velocity along the x_3 axis, the ellipse defining the normal modes is obtained from (4) by setting $x_3 = 0$. The directions of polarization of these modes are along the x'_1 and x'_2 axes, and their indices of refraction are $n_o \pm \Delta n$. A plane wave polarized linearly along one of these directions emerges from the crystal as a linearly polarized wave with E_3-dependent phase $(2\pi l/\lambda)\Delta n$, where l is the optical path length and λ is the vacuum wavelength.

An intensity modulation can be obtained by interference of these phase-modulated normal modes. For example, let a wave of unit intensity linearly polarized along the x_1 or x_2 axis propagate along the x_3 axis. Then the component of emergent light intensity polarized parallel to the incident polarization can be expressed as

$$I_{\|} = \frac{1}{2}\left[1 - \cos\left(\frac{4\pi l \Delta n}{\lambda}\right)\right] \tag{6}$$

and this can be spatially separated from the perpendicular component by a polarization-selective prism. The intensity of either component is not linear with E_3, however. For a small depth of modulation, this difficulty can be removed by adding a static phase difference of $\pi/2$ radians between the x'_1 and x'_2 axis. Then the intensity of one of the components becomes

$$I_{\|} = \frac{1}{2}\left[1 - \sin\left(\frac{4\pi l \Delta n}{\lambda}\right)\right], \tag{7}$$

which is linear with small E_3. The addition of static phase difference between the two normal modes is called optical biasing. The voltage required to change $I_{\|}$ from zero to one is usually called the half-wave voltage v_π. It is one of the parameters often used to compare materials and can be derived from (5) and (7). Since the applied voltage $v = E_3 l$ in this case,

$$v_\pi = \frac{\lambda}{2n_o^3 r_{63}}. \tag{8}$$

The electrooptic effect is called a longitudinal effect if the electric field is applied along the optical path. In this case v_π is independent of the size of the crystal as can be seen from (8).

A transverse electrooptic effect, where the applied field is normal to the light path, can be realized with KDP by choosing a light path along the x'_2 axis and a field E_3 along the x_3 axis. In order to obtain an intensity modulation, the incident wave is polarized 45° to the x'_1 and x_3 axes. The half-wave voltage can be shown to be

$$v_\pi = \frac{\lambda}{n_o^3 r_{63}}\left(\frac{d}{l}\right) \tag{9}$$

where d is the electrode spacing. Equation (9) shows that v_π can be reduced by choosing a small geometrical factor d/l. This is why the transverse electrooptic effect is preferred when a large index of modulation is desired.

Another well-known electrooptic material is $LiTaO_3$ which is a trigonal crystal with 3m symmetry. The indicatrix with a field E_3 along the c axis becomes

$$\frac{x_1^2}{(n_o + \Delta n_o)^2} + \frac{x_2^2}{(n_o + \Delta n_o)^2} + \frac{x_3^2}{(n_e + \Delta n_e)^2} = 1 \quad (10)$$

$$\Delta n_o = -\frac{n_o^3}{2} r_{13} E_3$$

$$\Delta n_e = -\frac{n_e^3}{2} r_{33} E_3$$

where $x_{1,2,3}$ axes are along the crystallographic a, b, and c axes, respectively. The indicatrix is shown in Fig. 1(b). Intensity modulation can be obtained by interference of the x_1 and x_3 polarized light components. The half-wave voltage becomes

$$v_\pi = \frac{\lambda}{n_e^3 r_{33} - n_o^3 r_{13}} \cdot \frac{d}{l}. \quad (11)$$

Since r_{33} and r_{13} have the same sign and $\Delta n_e > \Delta n_o$ for $LiTaO_3$ [8], the voltage required to change the phase of the x_3 polarized wave by π is less than that necessary to change the phase difference of x_3 and x_1 polarized waves by π. Thus phase modulation is more efficient than intensity modulation in $LiTaO_3$.

The indicatrix provides information about the phase velocities inside an anisotropic crystal. The direction in which a bounded part of the wavefront travels is the direction of energy flow. The directions of phase velocities and energy flow will be different unless the directions of polarization of the normal modes are parallel to the principal axes of the indicatrix [6], [9]. Thus it is possible that the two normal modes for a given wave normal propagate along different paths inside the crystal and are spatially separated on emergence. This adds inconvenience to intensity modulation, which depends on interference of the two normal modes. This inconvenience can be removed, however, by use of two pieces of crystal oriented so that the path difference is compensated [10]–[12].

Physical Origin of Electrooptic Effect

It has been shown [13], [14] that the linear electrooptic effect in piezoelectric crystals far above their acoustic resonance frequencies (i.e., clamped electrooptic effect) can be separated into two types of microscopic interaction: an applied electric field modifies the electronic polarizability directly in the absence of lattice displacements and an applied field produces a lattice displacement, which in turn modifies the electronic polarizability. The first type, which may be called a purely electronic contribution to the electrooptic effect (nonlattice contribution), is also the physical origin of optical mixing or second-harmonic generation and its magnitude can be obtained from second-harmonic measurements. The second type, the lattice contribution to the electrooptic effect, can be determined from a combination of Raman scattering and infrared absorption measurements. The electrooptic coefficients thus determined are in good agreement with the coefficients measured directly for $LiNbO_3$ and $LiTaO_3$ [13]. For $LiNbO_3$ the nonlattice contribution was found to be less than 10 percent.

There is a third contribution to the electrooptic coefficients when the frequency of the applied electric field falls below or near the acoustic resonant frequencies of the sample. The applied field strains the crystal via piezoelectric and/or electrostrictive coupling, and the indices of refraction change due to the strain-optic effect. This component of electrooptic coefficients can be neglected if the frequency of the applied field is far above the acoustic resonant frequencies, in which case the crystal is effectively clamped. The field-induced change of electronic polarizability has been shown to originate in field-dependent shifts of the frequency and strength of individual dipole oscillators representing interband optical transitions [15]–[18]. These shifts can be observed experimentally by measuring the electroreflectance above the band gap [19]–[21].

DiDomenico and Wemple described a model of electrooptic effects [18] of oxygen octahedra ferroelectrics that may be thought of as being composed of a network of oxygen octahedra (BO_6) with a transition metal ion (B) at its center. This class of ferroelectrics includes many of the well-known electrooptic and nonlinear crystals such as $LiTaO_3$, $LiNbO_3$, $BaTiO_3$, and $Ba_2NaNb_5O_{15}$. The change in B–O spacing as the temperature is lowered through the transition not only produces a spontaneous polarization but also shifts the energy band. Thus the energy shift ΔE, measured with respect to the energy bands in the centrosymmetric phase, can be expressed as proportional to P^2, where P is the total polarization, spontaneous plus any field-induced component. Through the Sellmeier equation, the change in index of refraction, Δn, can be linearly related to ΔE; hence $\Delta n \propto P^2$. This relation was observed earlier by Merz in $BaTiO_3$ [22]. The linear electrooptic coefficients of these ferroelectric oxides can be calculated using this relation in the following way. The change of refractive index of the perovskites (cubic system, point group m3m) can be expressed as

$$\Delta n = -\frac{n_o^3}{2} g P^2 \quad (12)$$

where n_o is the index of refraction and g is the temperature-independent quadratic-electrooptic coefficient. The linear electrooptic effect in ferroelectrics can be regarded as fundamentally a quadratic effect biased by the spontaneous polarization. Let an electric field E be applied parallel to the spontaneous polarization P_s. By substituting $P = P_s + \varepsilon_0(\kappa - 1)E$, where ε_0 is the free-space permittivity and κ is the dielectric constant of the crystal along the P_s direction, into (12), one obtains

$$\Delta n = -\frac{n_o^3}{2} g P_s^2 - n_o^3 g \varepsilon_0 (\kappa - 1) P_s E \quad (13)$$

where the term containing E^2 is neglected since $\kappa\varepsilon_0 E \ll P_s$. The first term in (13) is the spontaneous-polarization-induced index change and the second term is the linear electrooptic effect. Comparing (13) with the definition of linear electrooptic r coefficients defined by (2) and (10), and neglecting the subscripts, we find that

$$r = 2g\varepsilon_0(\kappa - 1)P_s. \tag{14}$$

Since κ follows the Curie–Weiss law, r is therefore anomalous at the transition temperature. In order to compare the g coefficients of different ferroelectrics, the volume density of BO_6 octahedra in a nonperovskite ferroelectric compared to that of a perovskite must be taken into account. This can be done [18] by defining a packing density ζ as the ratio of the BO_6 density of the nonperovskite to that of a reference perovskite with a 4-Å lattice constant. The g coefficients of nonperovskites referred to in (13) and (14) should be replaced approximately by $g\zeta^3$ where g now refers to the reference perovskite. ($\zeta = 1 \sim 1.06$ for perovskite and tungsten bronze and $\zeta = 1.2$ for $LiNbO_3$.) Using the measured values of r, κ, and P_s for various oxygen octahedra ferroelectrics and (14), the values of g are found to be essentially the same among these crystals and also the same as those observed in the paraelectric perovskites [18], [23], [24]. The existence of such universal constants in these crystals simplifies the analysis of practical modulator performances using oxygen octahedra ferroelectrics.

Temperature Dependence of Electrooptical Parameters in Oxygen Octahedra Ferroelectrics

Since the oxygen octahedra ferroelectrics include many important electrooptic materials, and since their g coefficients are not only the same both above and below their transition temperatures but also very similar among crystals having different transition temperatures, it is of interest to determine whether there is an optimum operating temperature from the device point of view.

The subscripts of the r and g coefficients neglected in (14) can be restored if the direction of polar axis of the ferroelectric with respect to the symmetry axes of the oxygen octahedron is known. It has been shown [18] that

$$r_{33} - r_{13} \approx 2\varepsilon_0(\kappa - 1)P_s G/\zeta^3 \tag{15}$$

where $G/\zeta^3 \equiv g_{11} - g_{12} \approx g_{44} \approx 0.13/\zeta^3\ m^4/C^2$ and $g_{11,12,44}$ are the nonzero elements of the g tensor. Using (11) and (15), and defining a reduced half-wave voltage by setting $d = l$ in (11), i.e.,

$$V_\pi = v_\pi \frac{l}{d} \tag{16}$$

one obtains

$$V_\pi = \left(\frac{\lambda\zeta^3}{2n_o^3\varepsilon_0 G}\right)\cdot\left(\frac{1}{\kappa P_s}\right) \tag{17}$$

where it is assumed that $\kappa \gg 1$ and $n_o \approx n_e$. Equation (17) also applies to the paraelectric phase of the crystal if P_s is replaced by a field-induced bias polarization [24]. A parameter that often appears in the analysis of modulators is the stored-energy parameter $U_\pi = \kappa V_\pi^2$. Its value from (17) is

$$U_\pi = \left(\frac{\lambda\zeta^3}{2n_o^3\varepsilon_0 G}\right)^2\cdot\left(\frac{1}{\kappa P_s^2}\right). \tag{18}$$

It is remarkable that (17) and (18) relate V_π and U_π of all oxygen octahedra ferroelectrics, at all temperature ranges, to only two material parameters: κ and P_s. Except for ζ, the other factors in the equations are approximately independent of materials and temperature. For a given κ and P_s, the $LiNbO_3$-type crystals have V_π higher by 1.7 due to their large $\zeta(\approx 1.2)$. Equation (17) also points out the limitation of ferroelectrics for applications in modulators, i.e., a small V_π is accompanied by a large κ. Nevertheless, V_π and U_π are still small compared to nonferroelectrics and they are still important electrooptic materials. The inverse relationship of κ and V has been verified experimentally [25] using Ba, Sr, Na niobate composite crystals that have tungsten-bronze-like structures. P_s of these crystals remains relatively constant while the Curie temperature varies between 560°C and 200°C. It has been observed that the product κV_π remains constant.

It has been shown [26] that both $V_\pi(\propto 1/\kappa P_s)$ and $U_\pi(\propto 1/\kappa P_s^2)$ decrease monotonically as the Curie temperature T_C is approached from either higher or lower temperatures. However, there are a few factors that mitigate against operating modulators very near T_C. The static birefringence $\Delta(n_e - n_o)_s$ arising from the first term in (13) is temperature sensitive via its dependence on P_s^2 and dP_s^2/dT increases as $|T - T_C|$ approaches zero.

A scheme will be discussed later that minimizes the degrading effect of fluctuations of $\Delta(n_e - n_o)_s$ on the modulator performance if $d\Delta(n_e - n_o)_s/dT$ is spatially uniform. The spatially inhomogeneous static birefringence due to internal heating of the crystal by an applied electric field is difficult to compensate, hence the temperature sensitivity of the static birefringence remains an important consideration in selecting $(T - T_C)$.

The half-wave voltage V_π is also temperature dependent. Fortunately, for the practically important case of $T < T_C$, the temperature dependence of V_π is not large enough to impose a difficulty.

The electrical Q of ferroelectrics is known to decrease as T_C is approached. Together with finite thermal conductivity and $d\Delta(n_e - n_o)_s/dT$, lower Q implies a large spatial inhomogeneity of indices of refraction which degrade the modulator performance [26]. The ferroelectrics also tend to depole near T_C unless an electric field is applied to prevent it. It can be easily seen from (13) that the completely depoled ferroelectrics show no linear electrooptic effect. Thus the choice of $(T - T_C)$ will have to be decided by balancing these opposing factors.

Other Material Properties Pertinent to Electrooptic Modulators

Practical electrooptic materials should preferably have the following properties: small V_π and U_π, small dielectric dissipation, good thermal conductivity, good optical quality in proper size, and easy polishing. In addition to these, good ohmic contacts to the crystals may be necessary in some applications, and in the case of ferroelectrics they should remain poled and free of optically induced refractive index changes (optical damage). Problems associated with electrodes and optical damage will be discussed here, since these are often critical factors in selecting the material.

When a dc electric field is applied to a solid having a finite electrical conductivity via blocking contacts (which permit transfer of charge carriers to but not from the electrode), the field distribution inside the material may no longer be uniform. In order to simplify the problem, assume that a cloud of free and trapped electrons compensated by an immobile matrix of positive charges is distributed throughout the crystal [27], [28]. When a dc field is applied, these electrons drift toward the positive electrode, in the meantime getting trapped and thermally reexcited out of the traps until eventually leaving the anode; however, they cannot reenter at the cathode due to the blocking contact. A region adjacent to the cathode will be swept clear of electrons leaving behind an immobile positive space-charge layer. This process continues until the applied voltage is completely absorbed by the space-charge layer. If the initial concentration of electrons is sufficiently small and the applied voltage sufficiently large, the electrons will be completely swept out through the anode, leaving behind only positive immobile charges in the crystal. On the other hand, for a high electron concentration or a low voltage, the final state will consist of two regions, one with positive charges near the cathode where the total voltage drops and the other a field-free neutral region. (Ferroelectric oxides are often p-type. The space-charge layer then appears at the anode.) Let V_0 be the applied voltage, ρ the electron charge density, and x_d the thickness of the space-charge layer. Then by integrating Poisson's equation, the space-charge field E becomes

$$E = \frac{\rho}{\varepsilon}(x - x_d) \tag{19}$$

where ε is the permittivity of the crystal and $x=0$ is at the cathode. Integrating E along x and setting it equal to V_0, one obtains

$$x_d = \sqrt{\frac{2\varepsilon V_0}{\rho}}. \tag{20}$$

The motion of the layer is regulated by a relaxation time

$$\tau = \frac{x_d D}{2\mu V_0}, \tag{21}$$

where D is the electrode spacing, and μ is the drift mobility of the electrons (including the effect of trapping). By substituting (20) into (21), τ can be shown to be proportional to the classical dielectric relaxation time. As the solid is repeatedly charged and discharged, space-charge layers build up on both electrodes.

By applying a dc field to $BaTiO_3$ above its Curie temperature [29] and to KTN [28], [30], the building up in time of space-charge layers near the electrodes has been observed with samples viewed between crossed polarizers.[1] From a practical device point of view, the formation of space-charge layers increases V_π because most of the applied field is not seen by the light beam, causes a poor extinction due to the nonuniform field distribution, and causes the optical bias to drift due to the finite relaxation times τ. The best way to avoid difficulties associated with blocking contacts is obviously to use ohmic contacts [30], although the practice of providing such contacts to most of the electrooptic crystals is not well known. If use of blocking contacts is inevitable, then (20) suggests that the resistivity of the crystal must be sufficiently large so as to extend x_d (the region of nonzero field) to a large cross section of the crystal. If the electron clouds are completely swept out of the crystal, the electric field inside the crystal will consist of a linear term expressed in (19) and a constant term. If the latter is much larger than the former, the difficulties associated with blocking contact can be expected to be minimal. Also, if the period of the applied field is much shorter than τ, there is no time for the space-charge layers to build up and the applied field distributes uniformly inside the crystal [31]–[33].

There is another anomalous behavior of electrooptic crystals often observed when a dc field is applied transverse to the illuminating light. The photoexcited carriers drifting out of the illuminated region get trapped near the periphery and remain there [34]–[36]. The local space-charge field thus created causes an inhomogeneity of the index of refraction via the electrooptic effect of the crystal. A similar mechanism is also thought to be responsible for the optical damage observed in poled ferroelectric crystals [37]–[41]. In the latter case, a spatial inhomogeneity of the refractive index near the laser beam is present without a dc applied field. The resistance to optical damage in $LiTaO_3$ has been increased from the laser intensity the order of 1 W/cm^2 at $\lambda=0.488\ \mu$ to 500 W/cm^2 by annealing the crystal at 700°C with an electric field along the c axis [42]. It was later shown that hydrogen was diffused into the crystal during the field annealing [43]. The mechanism by which the resistance to optical damage is enhanced by the presence of hydrogen is not understood, although it is speculated that trapping sites are modified by the presence of hydrogen in such a way that photoconduction is minimized. In addition to improving the resistance to optical damage, the presence of hydrogen in ferroelectric oxides is found to speed up the process of poling [44]. The degree to which problems associated with thermal and/or photoconduction can be overcome often dictates the choice of crystals for practical device applications.

Electrooptic Materials

Since Kaminow and Turner [2] have given an extensive list of electrooptic crystals, Table I here lists only those crystals which are in common use (DKDP, $LiTaO_3$), which represent fairly recent growth effort on oxygen octahedran ferroelectrics ($Ba_2NaNb_5O_{15}$, SBN), which are improved early ferroelectrics ($BaTiO_3$), or which are useful at 10.6 μ (GaAs, CdTe).

The Curie temperature T_C of ferroelectric oxides can be

[1] Depletion layer of 200-μ thickness has been observed in KTN of $10^8\ \Omega\cdot$cm resistivity [28].

TABLE I

ELECTROOPTIC MATERIALS PARAMETERS

Material	Sym.[(a)]	T_C	$\kappa^{(c)}$	n_c	n_a	$K^{(d)}$	$\frac{d(n_c - n_a)}{dT}$	$V_\pi^{(b)}$	$U_\pi^{(b)}$
			(K)			(W/m C)	(C^{-1})	(kV)	(10^8 volt^2)
KD_2PO_4(DKDP)	$\bar{4}2m$	222 [45]	(T) 50 [45] (S) 48 [46]	1.47 [47]	1.51 [47]		7×10^{-6} [47]	7.5	30
$LiTaO_3$	3m	890	(T) 47 [48] (S) 43 [48]	2.180 [49]	2.176 [49]	4.4 [50]	5×10^{-5} [51]	2.8 [48]	3.7
$Ba_2NaNb_5O_{15}$	mm2	833	(T) 51 [52] (S) 33 [51]	2.22 [52]	2.32 [52] ($\approx n_b$)	3.4 [50]	4×10^{-5} [51]	1.57 [52]	1.26
$Sr_{0.25}Ba_{0.75}Nb_2O_6$ [53]	4mm	470	(T) 250 [51] (S) 160 [51]	2.26	2.32	1.98 [50]	1.3×10^{-4} [51]	0.48 [51]	0.58
$BaTiO_3$ [54]	4mm	405	(T) 135 [55] (S) 60 [55]	2.36	2.42		1.1×10^{-4} [54]	0.48 [56]	0.35
GaAs [57]	$\bar{4}3m$		(T) 11.5	3.34 (cubic)				91	
CdTe [58]	$\bar{4}3m$			2.3 (cubic)				44	

(a) All data listed are measured at room temperature and at $\lambda = 0.63\ \mu$, except GaAs and CdTe which are for $\lambda = 10.6\ \mu$.
(b) For intensity modulation; unclamped. Use r_{63} in DKDP, r_{41} in GaAs, and CdTe, r_{13}, and r_{33} for the other materials.
(c) Dielectric constant along the c axis. (T) = constant stress (unclamped). (S) = constant strain (clamped).
(d) Thermal conductivity.

varied over a wide range by mixed compounds substituting the cations, while the basic BO_6 oxygen octahedra remain unmodified. The values of κP_s at room temperature (especially κ) change with T_C, which in turn change V_π. It is emphasized that lower V_π alone, if accompanied by a large increase in κ, does not necessarily make the material superior. Many other composite niobates other than those listed in Table I have lower V_π by having T_C near the room temperature [25], [59], [60]. The smaller V_π is accompanied by a large dielectric constant and other difficulties associated with operating a modulator near T_C as mentioned earlier.

ELECTROOPTIC MODULATORS

In this section, various schemes of electrooptic interaction using the transverse linear electrooptic effect will be discussed. Emphasis will be placed on broad-band intensity modulation using interference of the extraordinary and ordinary rays. Before discussing different schemes of interaction, considerations common to all of them will be discussed first.

General Considerations

Geometrical Factor: The half-wave voltage in materials showing a transverse electrooptic effect is proportional to a geometrical factor d/l as shown in (9) and (11). Thus the optimum geometry is to have the aperture of the crystal just large enough so that the beam passes through the sample. A Gaussian beam with the smallest cross section over the crystal length l is one that is focused so as to have a near-field length equal to l (i.e., confocal mode in the crystal [2]). In this case the geometry of the crystal is given by

$$\frac{d^2}{l} = S^2 \frac{4\lambda}{n\pi}, \tag{22}$$

where n is the refractive index and S is a safety factor (≥ 1) for the beam to pass through the crystal. For $S = 1$, the light intensity at the end faces of the crystal decreases by a factor e^{-2} at the crystal edges from its peak value (if the beam is perfectly aligned). In practice, a beam has been passed through a rod with little difficulty for $S \approx 3$ [31].

Effect of Velocity Matching and Finite Transit Time: In order to have a cumulative interaction between the modulating wave and the light wave, the component of the modulating wave group velocity in the direction of the light propagation must be equal to the group velocity of the light beam [61]. The group velocity of light is approximately the same as the phase velocity if the dispersion is small, and for broad-band modulation, the group velocity of the modulating wave must be equal to its phase velocity over the desired bandwidth. Thus the condition for matching the group velocities will be met if the phase velocities are matched.

For imperfect velocity matching, the optical phase retardation is reduced by a factor $\sin u/u$, where

$$u = \frac{\omega l}{2}\left(\frac{1}{v_0} - \frac{1}{v_m}\right), \tag{23}$$

in which v_0 and v_m are the parallel components of the phase velocities of the light and modulating wave, respectively, and ω is the angular frequency of the modulating wave.

It will be assumed in the following that the light velocities for the extraordinary and ordinary rays are the same. If they differ, and u for both rays becomes significantly different, broad-band intensity modulation can be accomplished by phase modulating one light polarization followed by an optical discriminator [62], [63]. The entire discussion in this paper remains essentially unaltered.

For narrow-band modulation, a scheme has been proposed to overcome the problem associated with the velocity mismatch [64]. The modulating and the optical waves are allowed to propagate without velocity synchronism until a phase difference of π radians (relative to ω) is accumulated. This corresponds to $u = \pi/2$ in (23). Further interaction would reduce the accumulated modulation unless the following section of the modulator is arranged so that the induced refractive indices have opposite signs. For light propagating along the x_2 axis and the voltage along the x_3 axis of either KDP or $LiTaO_3$ this can be accomplished by inverting the x_3 axis of the second section of the modulator.

Velocity matching over a broad-band will be considered in detail later.

Compensation of Temperature Dependence of Birefringence: Temperature dependence of the static birefringence can cause fluctuation of the depth of intensity modulation and/or a poor extinction. However, this can be compensated by the schemes [65] shown in Fig. 2. In the first scheme, a half-wave plate is inserted between the two sections so that the extraordinary ray of the first section becomes the ordinary ray of the second section and vice versa.

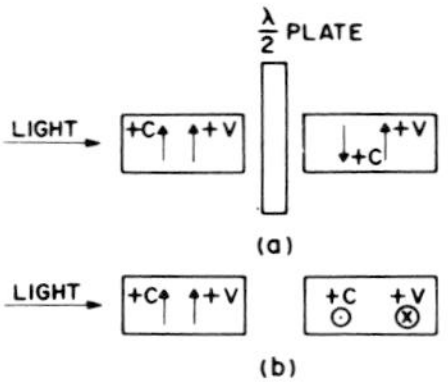

Fig. 2. Schemes of compensating temperature dependence of the static birefringence.

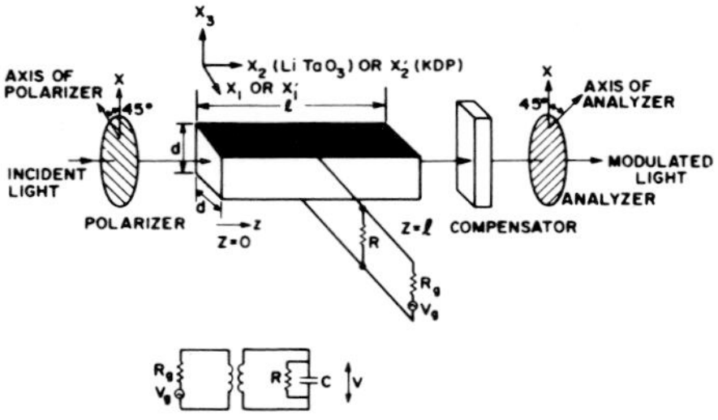

Fig. 3. Lumped modulator and its equivalent electrical circuit.

In the second scheme, the second section is rotated by 90° to achieve the same effect without a half-wave plate. In order to cancel the static birefringence and yet add the induced birefringence of the two sections, the relative sense of the $+c$ axis (or the $+x_3$ axis) and the modulating voltage must be opposite for the two sections and their optical path length must be equal.

Fluctuation of the static birefringence due to the ambient temperature can be easily stabilized with these schemes. A spatially inhomogeneous temperature distribution inside the modulator can be compensated only if the beam is essentially uncollimated by the refractive index gradient and if the temperature distribution in both sections of the modulator is the same.

Compensation of the temperature dependence of the static birefringence can also be achieved by using an interferometer with phase modulators in each arm [66]. Only the temperature difference between the two arms has to be stabilized. Decollimation of the optical beam due to the index gradient, which is caused by finite thermal conductivity, finite electrical Q, and finite temperature dependence of the refractive index, sets the maximum modulating power density that can be applied to the modulator, and this, in turn, eventually becomes a limiting factor on the bandwidth. In this paper it will be assumed that the bandwidth limitation from the temperature dependence of static birefringence can be ignored.

Various Schemes of Electrooptic Interactions

Lumped Modulators: If the optical path length of the modulator l is much shorter than one half of the modulating wavelength inside the crystal, i.e., $l \ll \pi c/\omega\sqrt{\kappa}$ where κ is the dielectric constant of the crystal, then the modulator may be regarded as a lumped capacitance C terminating the RF generator as shown in Fig. 3 and the modulating field is

TABLE II

COMPARISON OF LUMPED MODULATORS AT $\lambda = 0.63\ \mu$

Material	$LiTaO_3$ [31][(b)]	DKDP [68]	$LiTaO_3$ [69]	$LiNbO_3$ [70][(e)]
f_0 (GHz)	baseband	baseband	4.2	1.5
Δf (GHz)[(a)] (limited by capacitance)	1.3	0.22	0.04	1.5
Δf (GHz) (limited by transit time)	3	0.53	—	—
d (mm)	0.25	0.75	0.23	0.5
l (mm)	10	57	4.2	5
S	2.9	4.3	6.7	11.6
$P/\Delta f$[(c)] (mW/MHz)	1.1	60[(d)]	24	37

(a) Assume the load resistance $R = 50$ ohms.
(b) Based on round-trip mode.
(c) For 100 percent intensity modulation.
(d) A capacitance equalization network effective for $\Delta f = 100$ MHz is used.
(e) For $LiNbO_3$ [53], $\kappa V_\pi^2 \approx 2.9 \times 10^7$ volt^2.

uniform inside the crystal. The lossy component of the crystal can be generally ignored, and the modulator is terminated with a load resistance R that is matched to the generator impedance R_g through an ideal transformer with a bandwidth assumed to be as broad as necessary. The voltage across the modulator v decreases by a factor of $1/\sqrt{2}$ from the peak value at dc at the angular frequency

$$\Delta\omega = 2/CR, \tag{24}$$

where $\Delta\omega$ will be defined as the bandwidth of the modulator. In (24), C includes the capacitance of the crystal and the parasitic capacitance of the crystal mount; the latter, however, will be neglected in the following analysis. The depth of modulation also decreases as the transit time of light across l becomes a significant fraction of the period of the modulating voltage. It decreases by a factor of $1/\sqrt{2}$ at the frequency which makes $u = 1.4$ in (23). For the lumped modulator, one can approximate $1/v_m$ as zero and thus the modulation bandwidth from the finite transit time effect alone is

$$\Delta\omega = \frac{2.8c}{nl}. \tag{25}$$

The bandwidth of a lumped modulator is given either by (24) or (25) depending on which effect is dominant.

As the modulating frequency increases such that one half of its wavelength inside the medium is a significant fraction of l, the modulating field will no longer be uniformly distributed inside the crystal (i.e., $1/v_m \neq 0$). The modulating field can then be regarded as composed of two traveling waves propagating in opposite directions, each interacting independently with the light beam. The bandwidth limitation from the velocity mismatch for such modulators, which may be called standing-wave modulators, has been derived by Bicknell [67]. It will be assumed in this paper, however, that (24) determines the bandwidth of the lumped modulator. The percent modulation can be defined as [31]

$$\frac{\text{percent modulation}}{100} = 2J_1\left(\frac{\pi v}{v_\pi}\right)$$

where J_1 is the Bessel function of first order, and v is the peak modulating voltage across the crystal. A 100 percent modulation is obtained when $v = 0.383\, v_\pi \equiv v_0$. The reactive power stored in the crystal in order to obtain 100 percent modulation at low frequencies can be expressed as

$$P = \frac{\Delta\omega C}{2}\left(\frac{v_0}{\sqrt{2}}\right)^2. \tag{26}$$

Note that P of (26) provides only 70.7 percent modulation at the band edge. P can also be regarded as a measure of efficiency of the particular type of modulation interaction. For the crystal with a square cross section as shown in Fig. 3 and using (22), (26) becomes

$$P = \frac{0.587\varepsilon_0\lambda S^2}{4n\pi}\cdot \kappa V_\pi^2 \cdot \Delta\omega. \tag{27}$$

The necessary drive power increases linearly with bandwidth because the terminating resistance R has to be decreased in order to maintain an approximately constant voltage (and a constant depth of modulation) over the increased bandwidth. If a parallel inductance is provided to resonate the capacitance at ω_0, (27) gives the power necessary to produce at least 70.7 percent modulation over the bandwidth $\Delta\omega$ centered at ω_0, provided the finite transit time of light through the crystal is not a limiting factor.

It can be easily shown that the power expressed in (27) can be reduced by one half if the light beam makes a round trip [31] inside the modulator and if the cross section of the crystal d^2 is enlarged so that S for the single-trip and the round-trip modes remains the same. There is no change in the bandwidth as long as it is not limited by transit time.

Characteristics of some lumped modulators are listed in Table II. The small $P/\Delta f$ achieved by Denton *et al.* [31] is mainly due to the small S and the round-trip mode used.

For all the modulators listed, the measured values of $P/\Delta f$ agree within a factor of two with the calculated values using (27) and Table I.

Other lumped or standing-wave modulators have been reported in [71]–[77].

Traveling-Wave Modulators: The bandwidth limitation resulting from the mismatch of velocities of light and modulating waves can be extended by using a substantially dispersionless structure in which both waves can propagate with equal phase velocities. One such structure is the two-parallel-plate guide shown in Fig. 4. The modulating wave propagates as a TEM wave with its phase velocity increased so as to approach the light velocity inside the crystal. This is achieved by propagating part of the energy of the modulating wave outside of the crystal. Since this part does not contribute to the interaction of light and modulating waves, the velocity synchronization is achieved at the expense of the increased modulating power in this broad-banding scheme.

The phase velocity of a modulating wave in such structures can be expressed in terms of an effective dielectric constant κ_e which is the square of the ratio of the velocity in free space to that in the structure. At the low-frequency limit, κ_e becomes [78]

$$\kappa_e \approx \frac{\kappa d}{w} \tag{28}$$

where w is the width of the plates as shown in Fig. 4. For $(n/\sqrt{\kappa}) \lesssim 0.3$, the structure is essentially dispersionless only in the frequency band where $d \lesssim 0.1\,\lambda_m$ ($\lambda_m = 2\pi c/\omega\sqrt{\kappa}$ is the modulating wavelength in the medium) is satisfied [78], which sets the maximum bandwidth achievable by a traveling-wave modulator using such structures. Within the frequency band where the phase velocity is independent of frequency, the modulator bandwidth $\Delta\omega$ depends on the mismatch between the light and modulating wave velocities and can be expressed as

$$\frac{\Delta\omega l}{2c}(\sqrt{\kappa_e} - n) = 1.4, \tag{29}$$

where $\Delta\omega$ is defined as the angular frequency at which the depth of modulation decreases to 70.7 percent.

The impedance of the transmission line is

$$Z = \frac{377}{\sqrt{\kappa_e}} \cdot \left(\frac{d}{w}\right) \text{ ohms.} \tag{30}$$

In order to provide 100 percent modulation, the power applied to the transmission line (assumed lossless) is

$$P = \frac{1}{2Z}\left(0.383\, V_\pi \frac{d}{l}\right)^2. \tag{31}$$

Substituting (22), (28), and (30) into (31), one obtains

$$P = \frac{0.587\lambda S^2 \varepsilon_0}{4n\pi} \cdot (\kappa V_\pi^2) \cdot \frac{2c}{l\sqrt{\kappa_e}}. \tag{32}$$

Note that P of the traveling-wave modulators is inversely

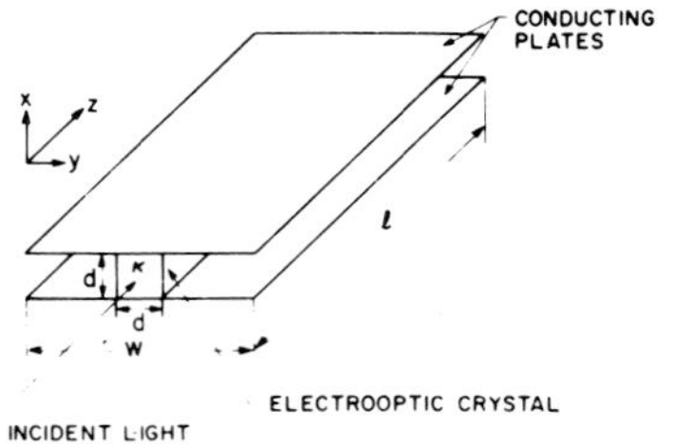

Fig. 4. Traveling-wave modulator using the two-plate guide structure.

proportional to l in contrast to the lumped modulators where P is independent of l.

By reflecting both the light beam and the modulating wave at the end of the traveling-wave structure and also by matching the velocity of the forward light wave to the forward modulating wave, the reflected light and modulating waves can also interact cumulatively [79]. This scheme is equivalent to doubling the length of the crystal. The modulation power is reduced by one half as in the round-trip lumped modulator, provided S and κ_e remain unchanged. The bandwidth for the round-trip traveling-wave modulator will be smaller by one half due to the increased light path as can be seen from (29).

Traveling-wave modulators using parallel-plate guides have been constructed [80]–[82] with $l \approx 100$ cm using many pieces of ADP or KDP. The potential modulation bandwidth of a few gigahertz can be realized if impedance matching over this bandwidth can be accomplished. Bicknell *et al.* [83] have constructed a traveling-wave modulator with $l = 16$ cm using a chain of potassium-dihydrogen-arsenate (KDA) crystals loading a coaxial transmission line. Broadband impedance matching at the input and termination of the coaxial line has been achieved over 0 ~ 3 GHz, which is also the bandwidth as limited by the velocity matching. A traveling-wave modulator using a rod of $LiTaO_3$ of dimensions 0.25 by 0.25 by 10 mm^3 (the same as the lumped modulator of [31]) mounted in microstrip has been described by White and Chin [84]. The bandwidth is limited to 2.9 GHz by the velocity matching, in contrast to 1.3 GHz limited by the load capacitance in the case of the lumped modulator [31].

A traveling-wave modulator at 6 GHz and 10 percent bandwidth has also been constructed using KDP in the ring-plane traveling-wave circuit [85]. The phase velocity of such a structure is relatively constant only within a small percent bandwidth ($\Delta f/f_0 \approx 20$ percent), although Δf (≈ 1.2 GHz for $f_0 = 6$ GHz) is still comparable to that in baseband traveling-wave modulators using a parallel-plate guide or a coaxial line. In contrast to lumped modulators where the modulation power is proportional only to the bandwidth Δf and not to the percent bandwidth $\Delta f/f_0$, the traveling-wave modulators are not bound by such a rule.

Zigzag Modulator: The velocity matching condition of (23) states only that the parallel components of the phase velocities of optical and modulating waves be matched. In

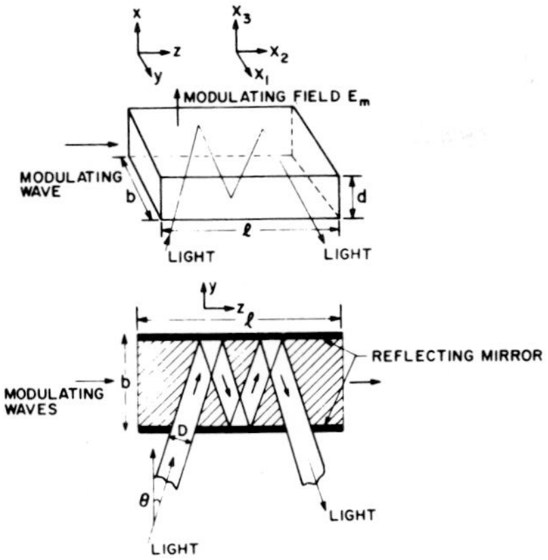

Fig. 5. Zigzag modulator.

addition to matching the velocities by increasing the modulating wave, it can also be achieved by having the light travel a zigzag path at an angle

$$\theta = \sin^{-1} \frac{n}{\sqrt{\kappa}} \tag{33}$$

along the transmission line carrying the modulating wave [86]–[88] (see Fig. 5).

Let us assume that the light is propagating in the y–z plane of Fig. 5 and the modulating electric field is along the x axis, which is also the crystallographic x_3 axis of the crystal (assume either $LiTaO_3$ or KDP). The peak voltage required for 100 percent intensity modulation is

$$v_0 = 0.385\, V_\pi \left(\frac{d \sin \theta}{l}\right), \tag{34}$$

and the power for 100 percent intensity modulation is

$$P = \frac{1}{2} \cdot \frac{\sqrt{\kappa}}{377}\, bd \left(\frac{v_0}{d}\right)^2 \tag{35}$$

where b and d are the width and the electrode spacing, respectively, of the crystal as shown in Fig. 5. To avoid beam divergence, we impose a restriction that the light path inside the crystal ($=l/\sin\theta$) be the same as the near-field length, and modify (22) as

$$\frac{d^2 \sin \theta}{l} = S^2 \frac{4\lambda}{n\pi}. \tag{36}$$

In order to bounce a parallel light beam of diameter D ($\approx d/S$) more than once inside the crystal, it is necessary that $b \geq D/(2 \sin \theta)$ from a geometrical consideration. The crystal will be swept twice by the light beam (once by zig and once by zag) when $b = D/(2 \sin \theta)$ and this choice of b will result in the minimum modulation power. However, from a practical consideration of focusing the beam into the crystal with some ease, it will be assumed that

$$b = d/(2 \sin \theta). \tag{37}$$

Using (33)–(37), one obtains

$$P = \frac{0.587 \lambda S^2 \varepsilon_0}{4 n \pi} \cdot (\kappa V_\pi^2) \cdot \frac{c}{l}. \tag{38}$$

The bandwidth of a zigzag modulator is limited by two factors. Both the phase velocity of the modulating wave and the impedance of the circuit become frequency dependent as the width b of the modulator approaches a significant fraction of the wavelength of the modulating wave in the medium, and the projection of the beam diameter D along the direction of propagation of the modulating wave must be smaller than a half-wave of the modulating signal in the medium. Generally the latter is less restrictive than the former. For the same crystal size, the zigzag structure is less dispersive compared to the two-plate guide where the modulating crystal occupies only a small volume of the guide. Since the dispersion of these structures is known only approximately, the bandwidth of zigzag modulators will be somewhat arbitrarily defined as

$$b \approx 0.2\, \lambda_m. \tag{39}$$

Upon substitution of (33) and (37) into (39), the bandwidth becomes

$$\Delta f = \frac{0.4c}{d} \cdot \frac{n}{\kappa}. \tag{40}$$

In spite of a potentially efficient interaction between the optical and modulating waves over a large bandwidth, technical complexities involved in constructing zigzag modulators have made this approach rather unattractive in practice. Only recently Auth [89] reported construction of such a modulator using DKDP in X-band waveguide. Modulation was observed from 7.8 GHz to 12.4 GHz but the depth of modulation versus the modulating power was not shown. The scheme of noncollinear velocity matching has also been used to modulate a 0.63-μ laser beam with a HCN laser beam at 964 GHz using $LiNbO_3$ [90].

Optical Waveguide Modulators: If an optical waveguide can be built using an electrooptic material, the diffraction spread of the light beam can be eliminated and the cross section of the modulator can be reduced to the order of a wavelength, independently of the optical path length. This can reduce the required modulation power [91], [92].

One-dimensional waveguide modulators where the light is confined in only one dimension have been realized with GaP diodes [93], [94]. The reverse-biased p-n junctions of these diodes form dielectric discontinuities in the direction normal to the plane of the junction, but there are no dielectric discontinuities in the direction parallel to the junction to confine the light. Thus, guiding of the light beam is achieved only in one dimension in these diodes instead of the more desirable two-dimensional guiding. The power required for 100 percent intensity modulation in such a one-dimensional waveguide modulator can be calculated as follows. Let d be the thickness of the junction over which the modulating voltage is applied, l the optical path length (junction length), and b the junction width. It will be assumed that a light beam is focused to a diameter d to il-

TABLE III

DRIVE POWER AND BANDWIDTH FOR VARIOUS SCHEMES OF ELECTROOPTIC INTERACTION

	Lumped	Traveling Wave	Zigzag
$\left(\frac{2n}{0.587\varepsilon_0\lambda S_u^2}\right)\cdot P$	Δf	$\frac{c}{\pi l\sqrt{\kappa_e}}$	$\frac{c}{2\pi l}$
Δf	$1/\pi CR^*$ $1.4c/\pi nl$	$\frac{1.4c}{\pi l(\sqrt{\kappa_e}-n)}$	$\frac{0.4c}{d}\cdot\frac{n}{k}$

* Limited by load capacitance. The rest are limited by transit time or velocity mismatch.

luminate the junction, and, on emerging from the junction, the beam size remains d in the direction of modulating field but becomes larger along the junction width due to diffraction spread. The dimension b must be larger than the maximum beamwidth by a safety factor S as defined in (22). Let us also assume that the diffraction spread derived for Gaussian beams [95] also applies to the one-dimensional case; then

$$b = Sd\sqrt{1 + (4l\lambda/n\pi d^2)^2} \approx 4Sl\lambda/n\pi d \tag{41}$$

where the approximation is valid for typical parameters [93], $d \approx 5\ \mu$, and $l = 1$ mm. Substituting the junction capacitance $C = \kappa\varepsilon_0 bl/d$, $v_0 = 0.383\ V_\pi d/l$, and (41) into (26), the power for 100 percent modulation in the case of the diode modulator becomes

$$P_{\text{diode}} = \frac{0.587\varepsilon_0\lambda S^2}{4n\pi}\cdot(\kappa V_\pi^2)\cdot\frac{\Delta\omega}{S}. \tag{42}$$

Comparing the lumped modulator power P_{lm} given by (27) with (42),

$$\frac{P_{\text{diode}}}{P_{lm}} = \frac{1}{S} \tag{43}$$

Thus, due to its ability to confine light beams in one dimension, the diode modulator requires only 1/3 of the power required of a lumped modulator composed of the same electrooptic crystal for a typical value of $S = 3$. Since κV_π^2 of bulk GaP is approximately 1/3 of $LiTaO_3$, the modulation powers of GaP diode modulators and $LiTaO_3$ lumped modulators are approximately equal.

Comparison of the Lumped, Traveling-Wave, and Zigzag Modulators: Baseband intensity modulators using these three types of interaction will now be compared. Generally, a lumped modulator is suitable in terms of small power required for modulation bandwidths less than 1 GHz and crystal lengths of about 1 cm. As the required bandwidth or available crystal length increases, a traveling-wave or zigzag interaction becomes more efficient. As the available modulation bandwidth increases from the lumped to the traveling-wave or zig-zag modulators, technical complexities involved in building them also increase. The relationships between the modulation power, which is a measure of the efficiency of interaction, bandwidth, and crystal length, will be derived here so that the type of modulator that meets the requirements with the fewest technical complexities can be chosen. The modulation power and bandwidth are summarized in Table III. The subscripts lm, tw, and zz will be used to indicate the lumped, traveling-wave, and zigzag modulation, respectively.

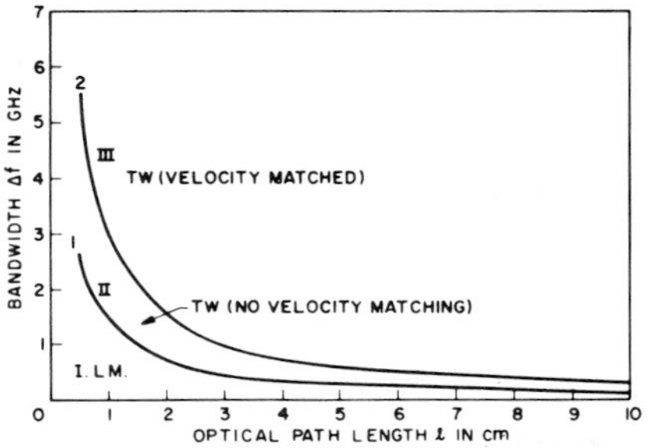

Fig. 6. Bandwidth of modulation versus optical path length for various schemes of electrooptic interaction using $LiTaO_3$. Curve 1 gives the bandwidth at which lumped modulators and traveling-wave modulators without velocity matching require equal power. Curve 2 gives the bandwidth above which traveling-wave modulators require velocity matching. In region I, the lumped modulator requires less power; in regions II and III, the traveling-wave modulator requires less power. In region II, no velocity matching is necessary; in region III, a partial velocity matching is necessary.

From Table III, one obtains

$$\frac{P_{lm}}{P_{tw}} = \frac{\pi l\Delta f\sqrt{\kappa_e}}{c}. \tag{44}$$

Let us assume for the moment that the effect of finite transit time for lumped modulators and velocity matching for traveling-wave modulators can be ignored; then one can set $\kappa_e = \kappa$ in (44) and P_{lm} equals P_{tw} at Δf_1, where

$$\Delta f_1 = \frac{c}{\pi\sqrt{\kappa}l}. \tag{45}$$

Substituting (45) into (24), the terminating resistance for the lumped modulator becomes $R = 377/\sqrt{\kappa}$ ohms, which is equal to that of a traveling-wave modulator as shown in (30). Thus, at the bandwidth Δf_1 for which both types of modulator require the same power, the terminating resistances are identical. As the required bandwidth Δf becomes smaller than that given by (45), R_{lm} can be increased from $R = 377/\sqrt{\kappa}$ by a factor $\Delta f_1/\Delta f$, while R_{tw} remains unchanged. Since v_π is independent of the terminating resistance, P_{lm} becomes smaller than P_{tw} by a factor $\Delta f/\Delta f_1$. For $LiTaO_3$ (45) becomes

$$\Delta f_1 = \frac{1.4}{l(\text{cm})}\ \text{GHz} \tag{46}$$

and it is shown as curve 1 in Fig. 6. The region below curve 1 is designated region I in Fig. 6; in this region, lumped modulators require less power than traveling-wave modulators. Modulation power for lumped modulators in region I can be further reduced by one half if a round-trip mode is used. It can be shown from (25) that the effect of finite transit time in region I is negligible and this justifies the assumption made earlier.

As the required modulation bandwidth becomes larger than Δf_1, the traveling-wave interaction becomes more efficient than lumped modulation. The bandwidth of a traveling-wave modulator without velocity matching (i.e., $\kappa_e = \kappa$) can be found from (29), and for $LiTaO_3$ it becomes

$$\Delta f_2 = \frac{3}{l(\text{cm})}\,\text{GHz}. \tag{47}$$

Equation (47) is shown as curve 2 in Fig. 6. The region between curves 1 and 2 is designated region II. In region II and for a given l, the modulation power P_{tw} remains unchanged as Δf increases from Δf_1 to Δf_2, since κ_e is unchanged. Thus, a lumped modulator is not only much simpler to build but is also more efficient than a traveling-wave modulator if the required bandwidth is smaller than Δf_1 given by (46). On the other hand, for a given crystal length l and a modulation power just sufficient to drive a lumped modulator over Δf_1, a traveling-wave modulator, even without velocity matching, has a bandwidth $\Delta f_2/\Delta f_1$ ($=2.14$ for $LiTaO_3$) times larger than a lumped modulator. Thus, whether the lumped or the traveling-wave modulation is more suitable depends on the required bandwidth, power, and available crystal length. It is emphasized that the bandwidth of a lumped modulator can be increased further than that given by (46) simply by terminating the crystal with a lower resistance until the transit time effect becomes important. It is less efficient, however, than a traveling-wave modulator of the same length but has the advantage of a simpler construction.

As the bandwidth increases beyond Δf_2, a partial velocity matching ($d \neq w$ in Fig. 4) becomes necessary and P_{tw} increases correspondingly. The maximum bandwidth Δf_3 using a two-plate guide traveling-wave structure will be reached as the structure becomes dispersive, and this has been set previously to occur for $d \leq 0.1\,\lambda_m$. Using this condition and (22), one obtains

$$\Delta f_3 = \frac{0.05c}{S\sqrt{\kappa}}\sqrt{\frac{n\pi}{l\lambda}}. \tag{48}$$

For $LiTaO_3$ and using $S=3$ and $\lambda = 0.63\ \mu$, (48) becomes

$$\Delta f_3 = \frac{24}{\sqrt{l(\text{cm})}}\,\text{GHz}. \tag{49}$$

In the case of zigzag modulation, the structure becomes dispersive at Δf_4. Using (39) and (43),

$$\Delta f_4 = \frac{0.2\,cn^2}{S\kappa\sqrt{\kappa}}\cdot\sqrt{\frac{n\pi}{l\lambda}}. \tag{50}$$

Using the same conditions as for (49), (50) becomes

$$\Delta f_4 = \frac{9.6}{\sqrt{l(\text{cm})}}\,\text{GHz}. \tag{51}$$

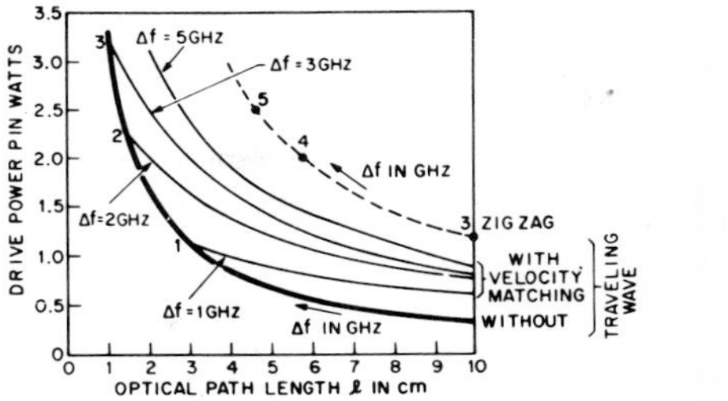

Fig. 7. Power required for 100 percent intensity modulation using $LiTaO_3$ for various interaction schemes. Bandwidths vary along the broken curves for zigzag modulators and along the heavy solid curve for traveling-wave modulators without velocity matching. With velocity matching, longer crystals permit reduction of drive power while maintaining bandwidth as shown by light solid curves. Approximately one half of the bandwidth marked on the heavy solid curve can be obtained using lumped modulators.

For a given l and S, a zigzag modulator becomes dispersive at a lower frequency than a two-plate guide traveling-wave modulator due to the large crystal width b in the zigzag case.

It is of interest to calculate the required modulation power versus the crystal length l for a given bandwidth Δf. The power required on curve 2 of Fig. 6 can be found from (32) by setting $\kappa_e = \kappa$ and, for $LiTaO_3$, $S=3$, and $\lambda = 0.63\ \mu$, it becomes $P = 3.5\ W/l(\text{cm})$. This is plotted as a heavy line in Fig. 7 with Δf_2 from (47) marked on it. For the same power and l, the bandwidth will be reduced by a factor 2.14 from those marked if a lumped modulator is used instead of a traveling-wave modulator. The power required for bandwidth marked on the heavy line of Fig. 7 becomes smaller as l increases even with the expense of the necessary partial velocity matching (in region III of Fig. 6). From (29) and (32), this power can be expressed as

$$P = \frac{0.587\lambda S^2\varepsilon_0}{2n}\cdot(\kappa V_\pi^2)\cdot\Delta f c/(nl\pi\Delta f + 1.4c). \tag{52}$$

Upon substitution of numerical values for $LiTaO_3$ and using $S=3$ and $\lambda = 0.63\ \mu$, (52) becomes

$$P = 0.22/\{2.2\times10^{-2}\times l(\text{cm}) + 0.134/\Delta f(\text{GHz})\}\ \text{watts}. \tag{53}$$

Equation (53) is shown as light solid curves in Fig. 7 for various values of Δf as labeled. With velocity matching, longer crystals permit reduction of drive power while maintaining bandwidth as shown by light solid curves.

Let us now compare the modulation power of zigzag and traveling-wave modulators. From Table III, one obtains

$$\frac{P_{zz}}{P_{tw}} = \frac{\sqrt{\kappa_e}}{2}. \tag{54}$$

The bandwidth of a traveling-wave modulator without velocity matching (i.e., $\kappa_e = \kappa$) is marked on the heavy line of Fig. 7. For this bandwidth and using $LiTaO_3$, $P_{zz}/P_{tw} \approx 3.4$ from (54). On the other hand, the bandwidth of a zigzag modulator is larger than that of a traveling-wave modulator without velocity matching. Also one should note that

$P_{zz}/P_{tw} > 1$ is the result of using the electrode spacing d in (37) instead of the beam diameter D, which causes the light beam to fill only a small volume of the crystal and thus causes a poor interaction efficiency. If $D(=d/S)$ instead of d is used in (37), then the crystal is completely filled with the light beam, and (38) and (54) must be divided by S. Then for $S \approx 3$ and using $LiTaO_3$, $P_{zz}/P_{tw} \approx 1$, and the zigzag modulator still retains the advantage of a larger bandwidth. The price to be paid for such an advantage with zigzag modulators is its practical complexity in construction. The power required for 100 percent intensity modulation using the zigzag modulation [see (38)] and the limiting bandwidth [from (51)] is also shown in Fig. 7.

Optically Resonant Modulators and Coupling Modulators: Let us assume that the two end faces of a lumped modulator are mirror-coated with power reflectivity R to form an optically resonant cavity. If optical losses are set only by the mirror reflectivity, a packet of light decays to e^{-1} of its initial intensity after bouncing N times inside the cavity where

$$N \approx \frac{1}{1-R} \tag{55}$$

for $R \lesssim 1$. It can be recognized that the right side of (55) is equal to the ratio of light intensity inside the cavity to that outside the cavity. If the transit time effect can be neglected, then it is easily seen that the depth of modulation increases by approximately a factor of N in such a modulator compared to the same modulator placed outside the optical cavity; for the same depth of modulation, the saving in modulation power is proportional to N^2. This result has been confirmed by a more sophisticated analysis [96]. Such an optical cavity has a series of passbands equally spaced in frequency by $c/2nL$, where L is the mirror spacing, and each passband has a bandwidth $c/2nNL$. The optical carrier, as well as the sidebands produced by the modulation, must fall within these passbands. Thus the factor N by which the depth of modulation is improved also limits the bandwidth available in such modulators. Another disadvantage of such modulators is that a small change in the refractive index of the crystal due to temperature has a large effect on light transmission through the modulator. Optically resonant modulators have been constructed using a cavity external to the laser cavity [97] and also within the laser cavity itself [98], [99] at the baseband with bandwidth less than 100 MHz.

The efficiency-bandwidth limitation of optically resonant modulators can be overcome by the coupling modulation scheme, in which the modulator couples out of the laser cavity an amplitude-modulated optical signal and leaves the total internal laser power essentially unperturbed [100]. The reduction in modulation power compared to the same modulator placed outside the cavity is given by the ratio of the internal to the external intensities [101], instead of the square of the ratio as for the optically resonant modulators, but the bandwidth is no longer limited by this factor. If the laser is permitted to oscillate in only one mode, if only a small fraction of the internal intensity is coupled out, and if large attenuation can be introduced for modes outside the gain profile of the laser medium (i.e., at the cold modes), there is no bandwidth limitation except from the modulator itself [102] (i.e., from the transit time and the capacitive loading of the modulator). The experiment has been performed using a short He–Ne laser at $\lambda = 0.63\ \mu$ and modulation frequency of 2 GHz [103]. In order to obtain a single-mode oscillation, the length of the laser cavity must be short enough so that only a single-cavity mode falls within the gain profile of the laser medium, which forces the output power from such lasers to be small. This difficulty has been overcome by use of a three-mirror resonator of the Fox–Smith type [101]. Efficient baseband modulation over 700 MHz has been achieved with 3 mW output optical power. The distortion due to the cold modes was suppressed to a negligible level by proper choice of reflectivity of the beam splitter in the resonator system.

Although the scheme of coupled modulation is quite promising, a practical difficulty is presented by additional optical components that must be placed inside the laser cavity. These introduce losses that reduce the available laser power, and also impose a fairly stiff requirement on the quality of crystals that can be used in such modulators due to low gain per transit of the laser medium. At present, the modulation power per megahertz of coupling modulators using DKDP, which is the most commonly used crystal for intracavity modulation because of its good optical quality, is still larger than for the $LiTaO_3$ lumped modulator external to the optical cavity [101].

Acoustooptic and Magnetooptic Modulators

There are optical interactions other than electrooptic effects which have received only limited interest for applications in broad-band optical modulators, but which may be more appealing than electrooptic modulators under some specific requirements. Only two of them, acoustooptic and magnetooptic modulators, will be discussed here.

Acoustooptic Modulators

The light beam to be modulated traverses across an acoustic beam that is amplitude-modulated by the signal to be impressed on the light with the Bragg angle θ as shown in Fig. 8. Part of the incident light will be diffracted by the periodic index variation produced by the acoustic wave via the photoelastic effect, and both the diffracted and the undiffracted light intensities follow the envelope of the acoustic wave, their variations being in-phase and out-of-phase, respectively, with the modulation of the acoustic signal. The device is essentially a baseband intensity modulator with its cutoff frequency determined by the transit time of the acoustic wave across the light beam [104], [105].

A few other factors must be considered in order to achieve successful operation of this device. The acoustic beam must be allowed to spread, either from diffraction or by focusing,

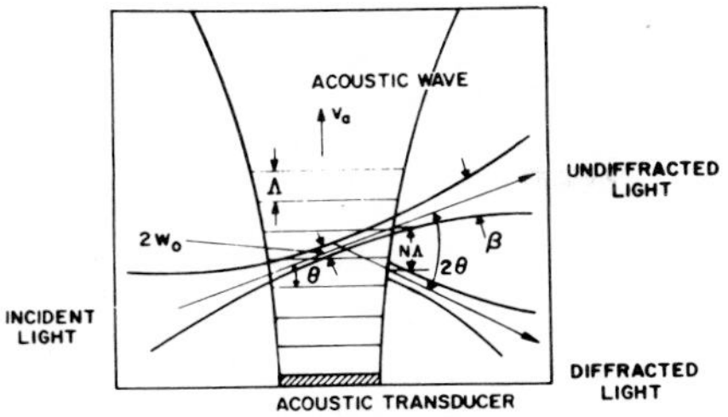

Fig. 8. Acoustooptic modulation, where Λ is the wavelength of the acoustic wave.

so that the Bragg scattering interaction takes place over the bandwidth of the modulator. The light beam must also have a diffraction spread of the same order of magnitude as that of the acoustic beam in order that the light diffracted by the acoustic carrier and its sidebands will overlap to produce an efficient intensity modulation [4]. To diffract nearly 100 percent of the incident light [104], the number of lines of the grating intercepted by the light beam N (see Fig. 8) must be $\gtrsim 1$. This will be satisfied when the diffraction spread of the light beam is made slightly large than that of the acoustic beam [106].

The bandwidth of the modulator due to the finite transit time of the acoustic wave across the light beam can be determined as follows. The rise time of the diffracted light intensity due to Bragg scattering by a step-function acoustic wave is shown [106] as $t_r \approx 1.3\,(w_0/v_a)$, where v_a is the velocity of the acoustic wave and $2w_0$ is the diameter of the light amplitude (assumed to be Gaussian) at its waist. Using the familiar relationship between the rise time and bandwidth of a low-pass filter $\Delta f = 0.35/t_r$, the modulation bandwidth becomes

$$\Delta f \approx 0.27 \frac{v_a}{w_0}. \quad (56)$$

Thus the acoustic wave must traverse the light beam in approximately one half of the period of the highest modulation frequency in the band.

The diffracted light beam has the same diffraction angle β as the incident light when the diffraction spread of light and acoustic waves are about equal. In order to insure a good separation of the diffracted and undiffracted light beam, let

$$\theta = \beta. \quad (57)$$

The Bragg angle is

$$\theta = \sin^{-1} \frac{\lambda f_a}{2nv_a} \approx \frac{\lambda f_a}{2nv_a}$$

where n is the refractive index and f_a is the acoustic frequency, and $\beta \approx 2\lambda/n\pi w_0$ for a Gaussian light beam. Upon substitution into (57), one obtains

$$f_a = \frac{4v_a}{\pi w_0}. \quad (58)$$

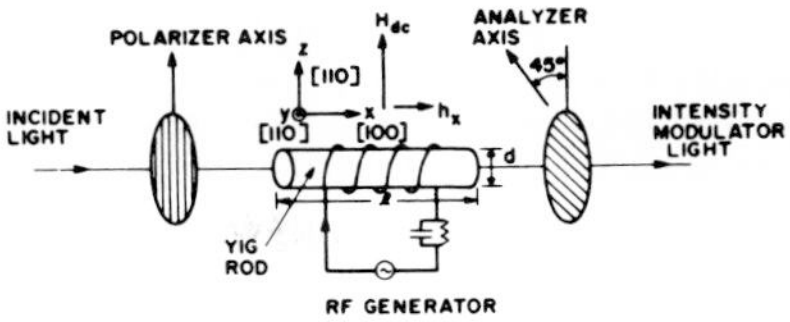

Fig. 9. Magnetooptic modulation.

From (56) and (58), the relation between the bandwidth Δf and the acoustic carrier frequency f_a can be found as

$$f_a \approx 5\Delta f. \quad (59)$$

Thus the bandwidth of the acoustic modulators is limited to about 20 percent of the acoustic frequency, which in turn is limited to the order of 1 GHz at present from practical considerations in making transducers [107].

Maydan [106] has built an acoustooptic pulse modulator using As_2S_3 glass. The pulse rise time was 6 ns, $f_a = 350$ MHz, and over 70 percent of the incident light at $\lambda = 0.63\ \mu$ was diffracted with an electrical power of 0.6 watt applied to the ZnO transducer. The bandwidth of this modulator is $\Delta f = 59$ MHz from (59), and the calculated pulse rise time t_r is $t_r = 0.35/\Delta f = 6$ ns, in agreement with the measurement. Using rutile and $f_a = 750$ MHz, the rise time has been decreased to 3 ns but with less efficiency (5 percent of incident light diffracted with 1 watt of electrical power at $\lambda = 0.63\ \mu$) [108].

Although the bandwidth of acoustooptic modulators is not large compared to electrooptic modulators, good acoustooptic materials with high optical quality can be found, which makes this type of modulator suitable for use inside laser cavities [109].

Magnetooptic Modulators

High-quality single crystals of yttrium iron garnet (YIG) have absorptions of less than 0.3 dB/cm at room temperature in the wavelength range of 1.15 μ to 4.5 μ [110]. Together with high-saturation optical rotation (172°/cm at $\lambda = 1.52\ \mu$) and low RF losses, this material offers an interesting possibility for efficient modulation in the near infrared [111].

Intensity modulation using the magnetic rotation can be accomplished with the arrangement shown in Fig. 9. A dc magnetic field H_{dc} (z axis) is applied to saturate the YIG rod in the direction normal to the rod axis, and a small RF magnetic field is applied along the rod axis (x axis) to wobble the magnetization within a small angle, producing a small component of RF magnetization m_x along the x axis. Since the magnetic rotation is proportional to the component of magnetization along the direction of light propagation [112], which is assumed to be along the rod axis, the emergent light beam will have its plane of polarization rotated by an amount proportional to $m_x l$ where l is the length of the rod. A linear intensity modulation is obtained after the light passes through an analyzer set to 45° with respect to the input polarizer.

The modulation power required for this type of device can be estimated as follows [113]. For a frequency much smaller than the magnetic resonance frequency, the time-varying component of magnetization along the x axis is

$$m_x \approx \frac{h_x}{H_i} M \tag{60}$$

where h_x is the applied RF magnetic field, M is the saturation magnetization of the sample, and H_i is the dc effective internal field. For the configuration shown in Fig. 9 and if there is no magnetic anisotropy, $(H_i = (H_{dc} - 2\pi M)^{\frac{1}{2}} \cdot H_{dc}^{\frac{1}{2}}.)$ The H_i has to be such that the magnetic resonance frequency of the rod, f_{mr}(MHz) = 2.8 H_i (Oe), is outside the modulation bandwidth in order to avoid RF losses. For baseband modulation, f_{mr} must be larger than the highest frequency in the modulation band. The RF magnetic rotation due to m_x can be expressed as

$$\phi = \phi_S l \frac{m_x}{M} \tag{61}$$

where ϕ_S is the saturated magnetic rotation per unit length. For small intensity modulation, a modulation index $\eta(\eta = 1$ for 100 percent modulation) can be expressed as

$$\eta \approx 2\phi_{rad} \tag{62}$$

where ϕ_{rad} is the peak value of the angle of rotation ϕ expressed in radians. Using CGS units, the time-averaged RF stored energy in the rod is

$$W = \frac{1}{8\pi} \cdot \frac{\pi d^2 l}{4} \cdot m_x h_x \text{ erg} \tag{63}$$

where d is the diameter of the rod, and m_x and h_x are expressed in peak values. The reactive power (assuming no losses in the circuit) required for modulation bandwidth Δf is

$$P = 2\pi \Delta f \cdot W \cdot 10^{-7} \text{ watt.} \tag{64}$$

Substituting (60)–(63) into (64) and denoting $\phi_{S\,rad}$ as ϕ_S expressed in radians, one obtains

$$P = \frac{\pi}{64} \cdot \Delta f \cdot M H_i \cdot \left(\frac{\eta}{\phi_{S\,rad}}\right)^2 \cdot \left(\frac{d^2}{l}\right) \cdot 10^{-7} \text{ watt.} \tag{65}$$

Equation (65) shows that in order to reduce P, the saturation magnetization M must be small, the saturation optical rotation must be large, and the effective internal field H_i must be small. The dependence of P on the bandwidth and size of the crystal is the same as the lumped electrooptic modulators.

The magnetooptic modulator at $\lambda = 1.52\ \mu$ built by LeCraw [111] used gallium-doped YIG, which has a much smaller saturation magnetization than YIG and a comparable optical rotation. The choice of crystal orientation as shown in Fig. 9, where [100] and [110] are the hard and the intermediate anisotropic axes, respectively, helps to increase the efficiency of an applied RF field in tilting the magnetization along the rod axis, and thereby increases the efficiency of modulation. It is of interest to see how the calculation compares with LeCraw's experimental result. The following data are pertinent to the modulator: $\phi_{S\,rad} = 1.95$ rad/cm, $4\pi M = 270$ gauss, $H_i = 100$ Oe ($H_{dc} = 232$ Oe), $d = 5 \times 10^{-2}$ cm, $l = 1$ cm, $\eta = 0.2$, and $\Delta f = 200$ MHz. Substituting these into (65), one obtains $P = 53$ mW compared to the measured 86 mW—satisfactory agreement in view of the crudeness of the analysis.

The magnetooptic modulators can also be used in the round-trip mode to reduce the modulation power in the same manner as the electrooptic modulator. The power will be decreased by a factor of two if diameter of the rod d is enlarged so that the safety factor S defined in (22) remains unchanged. Using gallium-doped YIG, the round-trip mode, and $\Delta f < 200$ MHz ($H_i = 100$ Oe), the power required for 100 percent modulation per megahertz can be calculated using (65), and it becomes

$$\frac{P(\eta = 1)}{\Delta f} = 1.1 \text{ mW/MHz}$$

at $\lambda = 1.52\ \mu$, $n = 2.2$, and $S = 3$. This is the same as the lumped $LiTaO_3$ electrooptic modulators at $\lambda = 0.63\ \mu$. Note that $P/\Delta f$ for magnetooptic modulators increases as Δf exceeds 200 MHz due to the necessary increase in H_i. For $\lambda = 1.52\ \mu$, $LiTaO_3$ modulators require approximately $(1.52/0.63)^3 = 14$ times larger power, keeping S unchanged. Thus, gallium-doped YIG modulators have their advantage in the near-infrared spectral range where $LiTaO_3$ modulators are less efficient. Also, the modulation power of magnetooptic modulators is supplied in the form of current rather than voltage, which makes it convenient to drive with transistors.

Conclusions

The electrooptic effects, especially these observed in ferroelectric crystals, have received much attention in recent years; their origin has been better understood and more varieties of crystals have been grown. From a device point of view, it is desirable to have materials not only with large electrooptic effects (i.e., small half-wave voltages) but also with small dielectric constants. Unfortunately, these two requirements contradict each other in the case of ferroelectrics, which is the only known class of materials with large electrooptic effects. The electric energy needed for modulation using ferroelectrics is smaller than with nonferroelectrics, and the effort in growing ferroelectrics of good optical quality in large size, with high dark resistivity and photoresistivity, and small RF dissipation should be highly rewarding. Large nonlinear optical effects observed in these crystals should also add a strong incentive to such an effort. As large crystals of good quality become available, the diameter of the incident light beam can be enlarged, which helps to increase the optical power that the modulator can handle without undue heating and optical damage. Also, fewer pieces of crystals are needed to build a long traveling-wave modulator if a very broad bandwidth is required.

It has been shown that lumped modulators are adequate

for bandwidths of about 1 GHz in the visible spectrum. Impedance matching of the crystal, which usually has a large dielectric constant, to the RF generator can be accomplished simply by a resistive termination at the crystal in such a configuration. As the required bandwidth increases further, either the traveling-wave or zigzag interaction becomes more efficient. The price to be paid for efficient modulation over a broad bandwidth is the increasing complexity in building one. Even with an efficient interaction, the required power is fairly high if the optical path is short. A long optical path can be obtained by segmenting many short crystals, which require good antireflection coatings and alignment of individual crystals. Also, each crystal must be of better optical quality so that imperfections accumulated over many pieces can still be held within a tolerable level. Impedance matching to such modulators over several gigahertz bandwidth also requires an intensive effort. When small modulation power is the dominant consideration, coupling modulators seem to be the most attractive, provided crystals become available with smaller κV_π^2 than DKDP and with much better quality than is needed for external modulation, and provided single-frequency lasers with the necessary output power are available. The bandwidth of such modulators is the same as lumped modulators.

Materials suitable for acoustooptic interactions are often of better optical quality than electrooptic crystals, which makes the acoustooptic modulation attractive if a good extinction (but of limited bandwidth) is the prime concern.

Magnetooptic modulation using gallium-doped YIG is attractive for a bandwidth of a few hundred megahertz and wavelengths in the near infrared. The optical absorption is 0.25 dB per cm at $\lambda = 1.52\ \mu$.

Acknowledgment

The author wishes to thank S. H. Wemple for valuable discussions on the electrooptic effect and for critically reading the manuscript, and L. K. Anderson, I. P. Kaminow, R. C. LeCraw, D. Maydan, F. R. Nash, and F. K. Reinhart for helpful discussions and comments. The constant encouragement of J. E. Geusic is deeply appreciated.

References

[1] L. K. Anderson, "Microwave modulation of light," *Microwave J.*, vol. 4, pp. 42–53, January 1965.
[2] I. P. Kaminow and E. H. Turner, "Electrooptic light modulators," *Proc. IEEE*, vol. 54, pp. 1374–1390, October 1966.
[3] I. S. Rez, "Crystals with nonlinear polarizability," *Sov. Phys.—Usp.*, vol. 10, pp. 759–782, May–June 1968.
[4] E. I. Gordon, "A review of acoustooptical deflection and modulation devices," *Proc. IEEE*, vol. 54, pp. 1391–1401, October 1966.
[5] T. L. Paoli and J. E. Ripper, "Direct modulation of semiconductor lasers," this issue, pp. 1457–1465.
[6] J. F. Nye, *Physical Properties of Crystals*. Oxford: Oxford University Press, 1960.
[7] W. P. Mason, "Electrooptic and photoelastic effects in crystals," *Bell Syst. Tech. J.*, vol. 29, pp. 161–188, April 1950.
[8] P. V. Lenzo, E. H. Turner, E. G. Spencer, and A. A. Ballman, "Electrooptic coefficients and elastic-wave propagation in single-domain ferroelectric lithium tantalate," *Appl. Phys. Lett.*, vol. 8, pp. 81–82, February 1966.
[9] M. Born and E. Wolf, *Principles of Optics*. New York: Macmillan, 1964.
[10] J. M. Ley, "Low voltage light-amplitude modulation," *Electron. Lett.*, vol. 2, pp. 12–13, January 1966.
[11] C. H. Clayson, "Low voltage light-amplitude modulation," *Electron. Lett.*, vol. 2, p. 138, April 1966.
[12] M. Dore, "A low drive power light modulator using a readily available material ADP," *IEEE J. Quantum Electron.*, vol. QE-3, pp. 555–560, November 1967.
[13] I. P. Kaminow and W. D. Johnston, Jr., "Quantitative determination of sources of the electrooptic effect in $LiNbO_3$ and $LiTaO_3$," *Phys. Rev.*, vol. 160, pp. 519–522, August 1967.
[14] ——, "Contributions to optical nonlinearity in GaAs as determined from Raman scattering efficiencies," *Phys. Rev.*, vol. 188, pp. 1209–1211, December 1969.
[15] S. K. Kurtz and F. N. H. Robinson, "A physical model of the electrooptic effect," *Appl. Phys. Lett.*, vol. 10, pp. 62–65, January 1967.
[16] C. G. B. Garrett, "Nonlinear optics, anharmonic oscillators, and pyroelectricity," *IEEE J. Quantum Electron.*, vol. QE-4, pp. 70–84, March 1968.
[17] J. D. Zook and T. N. Casselman, "Electrooptic effects in paraelectric perovskites," *Appl. Phys. Lett.*, vol. 17, pp. 960–962, 1966.
[18] M. DiDomenico, Jr., and S. H. Wemple, "Oxygen-octahedra ferroelectrics. I. Theory of electrooptical and nonlinear optical effects," *J. Appl. Phys.*, vol. 40, pp. 720–724, February 1969.
[19] S. K. Kurtz, "Visible and ultraviolet optical properties of some ABO_3 ferroelectrics," *Proc. Int. Conf. on Ferroelectricity* (Prague, Czechoslovakia), 1966.
[20] A. Frova and P. J. Boddy, "Optical field effects and band structure of some perovskite-type ferroelectrics," *Phys. Rev.*, vol. 153, pp. 606–616, 1967.
[21] J. D. Zook, "Oscillatory electroreflectance of $SrTiO_3$," *Phys. Rev. Lett.*, vol. 20, pp. 848–852, 1968.
[22] W. J. Merz, "Electric and optical behavior of $BaTiO_3$ single-domain crystals," *Phys. Rev.*, vol. 76, pp. 1221–1225, 1949.
[23] J. D. Zook, D. Chen, and G. N. Otto, "Temperature dependence and model of the electrooptic effect in $LiNbO_3$," *Appl. Phys. Lett.*, vol. 11, pp. 159–161, September 1967.
[24] F. S. Chen, J. E. Geusic, S. K. Kurtz, J. G. Skinner, and S. H. Wemple, "Light modulation and beam deflection with potassium tantalate-niobate crystals," *J. Appl. Phys.*, vol. 37, pp. 388–398, January 1966.
[25] L. G. Van Uitert, J. J. Rubin, W. H. Grodkiewicz, and W. A. Bonner, "Some characteristics of Ba, Sr, Na niobates," *Mater. Res. Bull.*, vol. 4, pp. 63–74, 1969.
[26] S. H. Wemple and M. DiDomenico, Jr., "Oxygen octahedra ferroelectrics. II. Electrooptical and nonlinear-optical device applications," *J. Appl. Phys.*, vol. 40, pp. 735–752, February 1969.
[27] A. von Hippel, E. P. Gross, J. G. Jelatis, and H. Geller, "Photocurrent, space-charge buildup, and field emission in alkali halide crystals," *Phys. Rev.*, vol. 91, pp. 568–579, August 1953.
[28] S. K. Kurtz and P. J. Warter, Jr., "Space charge effects in p-type semiconducting $KTa_{.65}Nb_{.35}O_3$ (KTN)," *Bull. Amer. Phys. Soc.*, vol. 11, p. 34, 1966.
[29] S. Triebwasser, "Space charge fields in $BaTiO_3$," *Phys. Rev.*, vol. 118, pp. 100–105, April 1960.
[30] S. H. Wemple, "Electrical contact to n- and p-type ferroelectric oxides," in *Ohmic Contacts to Semi-Conductors*, B. Schwartz, Ed. New York: The Electrochemical Society, 1969, pp. 128–137.
[31] R. T. Denton, F. S. Chen, and A. A. Ballman, "Lithium tantalate light modulators," *J. Appl. Phys.*, vol. 38, pp. 1511–1617, March 1967.
[32] I. P. Kaminow, "Measurements of the electrooptic effect in CdS, ZnTe, and GaAs at 10.6 microns," *IEEE J. Quantum Electron.*, vol. QE-4, pp. 23–26, January 1968.
[33] T. Kimura and T. Yamada, "Intensity-dependent electrooptic effect of ZnTe," *IEEE J. Quantum Electron.* (Correspondence), vol. QE-6, pp. 158–159, March 1970.
[34] F. S. Chen, "A laser-induced inhomogeneity of refractive indices in KTN," *J. Appl. Phys.*, vol. 38, pp. 3418–3420, July 1967.
[35] J. P. Thaxter, "Electrical control of holographic storage in strontium-barium niobate," *Appl. Phys. Lett.*, vol. 15, pp. 210–212, October 1969.
[36] S. I. Waxman, M. Chodrow, and H. E. Panthoff, "Optical damage in KDP," *Appl. Phys. Lett.*, vol. 16, pp. 157–159, February 1970.
[37] A. Ashkin, G. D. Boyd, J. M. Dziedzic, R. G. Smith, A. A. Ballman,

H. J. Levinstein, and K. Nassau, "Optically induced refractive index inhomogeneities in $LiNbO_3$ and $LiTaO_3$," *Appl. Phys. Lett.*, vol. 9, pp. 72–74, July 1966.

[38] F. S. Chen, J. T. LaMacchia, and D. B. Fraser, "Holographic storage in $LiNbO_3$," *Appl. Phys. Lett.*, vol. 13, pp. 223–225, October 1968.

[39] F. S. Chen, "Optically induced change of refractive indices in $LiNbO_3$ and $LiTaO_3$," *J. Appl. Phys.*, vol. 40, pp. 3389–3396, July 1969.

[40] E. P. Harris and M. L. Dakss, "Optical damage to $LiNbO_3$ from GaAs laser radiation," *IBM J. Res. Develop.*, vol. 13, pp. 722–723, November 1969.

[41] W. D. Johnston, Jr., "Optical index damage in $LiNbO_3$ and other pyroelectric insulators," *J. Appl. Phys.*, vol. 41, pp. 3279–3285, July 1970.

[42] H. J. Levinstein, A. A. Ballman, R. T. Denton, A. Ashkin, and J. M. Dziedzic, "Reduction of the susceptibility to optically induced index inhomogeneities in $LiTaO_3$ and $LiNbO_3$," *J. Appl. Phys.*, vol. 38, pp. 3101–3102, July 1967.

[43] R. G. Smith, D. B. Fraser, R. T. Denton, and T. C. Rich, "Correlation of reduction in optically induced refractive-index inhomogeneity with OH content in $LiTaO_3$ and $LiNbO_3$," *J. Appl. Phys.*, vol. 39, pp. 4600–4602, September 1968.

[44] S. Singh, H. J. Levinstein, and L. G. Van Uitert, "Role of hydrogen in polarization reversal of ferroelectric $Ba_2NaNb_5O_{15}$," *Appl. Phys. Lett.*, vol. 16, pp. 176–178, February 1970.

[45] T. R. Slicker and S. R. Burlage, "Some dielectric and optical properties of KD_2PO_4," *J. Appl. Phys.*, vol. 34, pp. 1837–1840, July 1963.

[46] I. P. Kaminow, "Microwave dielectric properties of $NH_4H_2PO_4$, KH_2AsO_4, and partially deuterated KH_2PO_4," *Phys. Rev.*, vol. 138, pp. A1539–A1543, May 1965.

[47] R. A. Phillips, "Temperature variation of the index of refraction of ADP, KDP and deuterated KDP," *J. Opt. Soc. Am.*, vol. 56, pp. 629–632, May 1966.

[48] P. V. Lenzo, E. H. Turner, E. G. Spencer, and A. A. Ballman, "Electrooptic coefficients and elastic wave propagation in single-domain ferroelectric lithium tantalate," *Appl. Phys. Lett.*, vol. 8, pp. 81–82, February 1966.

[49] W. L. Bond, "Measurements of the refractive indices of several crystals," *J. Appl. Phys.*, vol. 36, pp. 1674–1677, May 1965.

[50] Measured by R. C. Bearisto of Bell Telephone Labs. and can be found in [51].

[51] F. S. Chen, "Demultipliers for a high-speed optical PCM" (to be published).

[52] J. E. Geusic, H. J. Levinstein, J. J. Rubin, S. Singh, and L. G. Van Uitert, "The nonlinear optical properties of $Ba_2NaNb_5O_{15}$," *Appl. Phys. Lett.*, vol. 11, pp. 269–271, November 1967.

[53] E. G. Spencer, P. V. Lenzo, and A. A. Ballman, "Dielectric materials for electrooptic, elastooptic, and ultrasonic device applications," *Proc. IEEE*, vol. 55, pp. 2074–2108, December 1967.

[54] S. H. Wemple, M. DiDomenico, Jr., and I. Camlibel, "Dielectric and optical properties of melt-grown $BaTiO_3$," *J. Phys. Chem. Solids*, vol. 29, pp. 1797–1803, 1968.

[55] ——, "Dielectric properties of single-domain melt-grown $BaTiO_3$," *J. Phys. Chem. Solids* (to be published).

[56] A. R. Johnston, "The strain-free electrooptic effect in single-crystal barium titanate," *Appl. Phys. Lett.*, vol. 7, pp. 195–198, October 1965.

[57] A. Yariv, C. A. Mead, and J. V. Parker, "GaAs as an electrooptic modulator at 10.6 μ," *IEEE J. Quantum Electron.*, vol. QE-2, pp. 243–245, August 1966.

[58] J. E. Kiefer and A. Yariv, "Electrooptic characteristics of CdTe at 3.39 and 10.6 μ," *Appl. Phys. Lett.*, vol. 15, pp. 26–27, July 1969.

[59] E. A. Giess, G. Burns, D. F. O'Kane, and A. W. Smith, "Ferroelectric and optical properties of $KSr_2Nb_5O_{15}$," *Appl. Phys. Lett.*, vol. 11, pp. 233–234, 1967.

[60] G. Burns, E. A. Giess, D. F. O'Kane, B. A. Scott, and A. W. Smith, "Crystal growth and ferroelectric and optical properties of $K_xNa_{1-x}Ba_2Nb_5O_{15}$," *J. Appl. Phys.*, vol. 40, pp. 901–902, 1969.

[61] W. W. Rigrod and I. P. Kaminow, "Wide-band microwave light modulation," *Proc. IEEE*, vol. 51, pp. 137–140, January 1963.

[62] S. E. Harris, "Conversion of FM light to AM light using birefringent crystals," *Appl. Phys. Lett.*, vol. 2, pp. 47–49, February 1963.

[63] I. P. Kaminow, "Balanced optical discriminator," *Appl. Opt.*, vol. 3, p. 507, April 1964.

[64] S. M. Stone, "A microwave electro-optic modulation which overcomes transit time limitation," *Proc. IEEE* (Correspondence), vol. 2, pp. 409–410, April 1964.

[65] C. J. Peters, "Gigacycle-bandwidth coherent-light traveling-wave modulator," *Proc. IEEE*, vol. 53, pp. 455–460, May 1965.

[66] W. H. Steier, "A push-pull optical amplitude modulator," *IEEE J. Quantum Electron.*, vol. QE-3, pp. 664–667, December 1967.

[67] W. E. Bicknell, "Synchronization bandwidth of capacitive transverse-field electrooptic modulators," *IEEE J. Quantum Electron.* (Correspondence), vol. QE-4, pp. 35–37, January 1968.

[68] W. J. Rattman, W. E. Bicknell, B. K. Yap, and C. J. Peters, "Broadband, low drive power electrooptic modulator," *IEEE J. Quantum Electron.*, vol. QE-3, pp. 550–554, November 1967.

[69] I. P. Kaminow and W. M. Sharpless, "Performance of $LiTaO_3$ and $LiNbO_3$ light modulators at 4 GHz," *Appl. Opt.*, vol. 6, pp. 351–352, February 1967.

[70] K. K. Chow, R. L. Comstock, and W. B. Lonard, "1.5-GHz bandwidth light modulator," *IEEE J. Quantum Electron.* (Correspondence), vol. QE-5, pp. 618–620, December 1969.

[71] I. P. Kaminow, "Microwave modulation of the electrooptic effect in KH_2PO_4," *Phys. Rev. Lett.*, vol. 6, p. 528, May 1961.

[72] R. H. Blumenthal, "Design of a microwave-frequency light modulator," *Proc. IRE*, vol. 50, pp. 452–456, April 1962.

[73] K. M. Johnson, "Solid-state modulation and direct demodulation of gas laser light at a microwave frequency," *Proc. IRE* (Correspondence), vol. 51, pp. 1368–1369, October 1963.

[74] H. Brand, B. Hill, E. Holtz, and G. Wencker, "External light modulation with low microwave power," *Electron. Lett.*, vol. 2, pp. 317–318, August 1966.

[75] T. E. Walsh, "Gallium-arsenide electrooptical modulators," *RCA Rev.*, vol. 27, pp. 323–335, September 1966.

[76] M. Dore, "A low drive-power light modulator using a readily available material ADP," *IEEE J. Quantum Electron.*, vol. QE-3, pp. 555–560, November 1967.

[77] R. P. Riesz and M. R. Biazzo, "Gigahertz optical modulation," *Appl. Opt.*, vol. 8, pp. 1393–1395, July 1969.

[78] I. P. Kaminow and J. Liu, "Propagation characteristics of partially loaded two-conductor transmission line for broadband light modulators," *Proc. IRE*, vol. 51, pp. 132–136, January 1963.

[79] T. Sueta, K. Goto, and T. Makimoto, "A reflection-type traveling-wave light modulator," *IEEE J. Quantum Electron.*, vol. QE-5, p. 330, June 1969.

[80] C. J. Peters, "Gigacycle bandwidth coherent light traveling-wave phase modulator," *Proc. IRE*, vol. 51, pp. 147–153, January 1963.

[81] ——, "Gigacycle-bandwidth coherent-light traveling-wave modulator," *Proc. IEEE*, vol. 53, pp. 455–460, May 1965.

[82] J. A. Ernest and I. P. Kaminow (unpublished). See also [2].

[83] W. E. Bicknell, B. K. Yap, and C. J. Peters, "0 to 3 GHz traveling-wave electrooptic modulator," *Proc. IEEE* (Letters), vol. 55, pp. 225–226, February 1967.

[84] G. White and G. M. Chin, "A 1 Gbit-sec^{-1} optical PCM communications system," presented at IEEE Int. Conf. on Communications, San Francisco, Calif., June 1970.

[85] J. L. Putz, "A wide-band microwave modulator," *IEEE Trans. Electron Devices*, vol. ED-15, pp. 695–698, October 1968.

[86] W. W. Rigrod and I. P. Kaminow, "Wide-band microwave light modulation," *Proc. IEEE*, vol. 51, pp. 137–140, January 1963.

[87] M. DiDomenico, Jr., and L. K. Anderson, "Broadband electrooptic traveling-wave light modulators," *Bell Syst. Tech. J.*, vol. 42, pp. 2621–2728, November 1963.

[88] W. A. Scanga, "Traveling-wave light modulator," *Appl. Opt.*, vol. 4, pp. 1103–1106, September 1965.

[89] D. C. Auth, "Half-octave bandwidth traveling-wave *X*-band optical phase modulator," *IEEE J. Quantum Electron.* (Correspondence), vol. QE-5, pp. 622–623, December 1969.

[90] I. P. Kaminow, T. J. Bridges, and M. A. Pollack, "A 964 GHz traveling-wave electrooptic light modulator," *Appl. Phys. Lett.* (to be published).

[91] E. R. Schineller, "Single-mode-guide laser components," *Microwave J.*, vol. 7, pp. 77–85, January 1968.

[92] S. E. Miller, "Integrated optics: An introduction," *Bell Syst. Tech. J.*, vol. 48, pp. 2059–2069, September 1969.

[93] F. K. Reinhart, "Reverse-biased gallium phosphide diodes as high-frequency light modulators," *J. Appl. Phys.*, vol. 39, pp. 3426–3434, June 1968.

[94] F. K. Reinhart, D. F. Nelson, and J. McKenna, "Electrooptic and waveguide properties of reverse-biased gallium phosphide p-n

junctions," *Phys. Rev.*, vol. 177, pp. 1208–1221, January 1969.
[95] H. Kogelnik and T. Li, "Laser beams and resonators," *Proc. IEEE*, vol. 54, pp. 1312–1329, October 1966.
[96] E. I. Gordon and J. D. Rigden, "The Fabry–Perot electrooptic modulator," *Bell Syst. Tech. J.*, vol. 42, pp. 155–179, January 1963.
[97] J. T. Ruscio, "A coherent light modulator," *IEEE J. Quantum Electron.*, vol. QE-1, pp. 182–183, July 1965.
[98] E. A. Ohm, "A linear optical modulator with high FM sensitivity," *Appl. Opt.*, vol. 6, pp. 1233–1235, July 1967.
[99] T. Uchida, "Direct modulation of gas lasers," *IEEE J. Quantum Electron.*, vol. QE-1, pp. 336–343, November 1965.
[100] K. Gürs and R. Muller, "Internal modulation of optical masers," in *Proc. Symp. on Optical Masers*. Brooklyn, N. Y.: Polytechnic Press, 1963, pp. 243–252.
[101] F. R. Nash and P. W. Smith, "Broadband optical coupling modulation," *IEEE J. Quantum Electron.*, vol. QE-4, pp. 26–34, January 1968.
[102] I. P. Kaminow, "Internal modulation of optical masers (bandwidth limitations)," *Appl. Opt.*, vol. 4, pp. 123–127, January 1965.
[103] G. Grau and D. Rosenberger, "Low-power microwave modulation of a 0.63 μ He–Ne laser," *Phys. Lett.*, vol. 6, pp. 129–131, September 1963.
[104] H. V. Hance and J. K. Parks, "Wide-band modulation of a laser beam, using Bragg-angle diffraction by amplitude-modulated ultrasonic wave," *J. Acoust. Soc. Am.*, vol. 38, pp. 14–23, July 1965.
[105] E. I. Gordon and M. G. Cohen, "Electrooptic diffraction grating for light beam modulation and diffraction," *IEEE J. Quantum Electron.*, vol. QE-1, pp. 191–198, August 1965.
[106] D. Maydan, "Acoustooptical pulse modulators," *IEEE J. Quantum Electron.*, vol. QE-6, pp. 15–24, January 1970.
[107] E. K. Sittig, private communication.
[108] D. Maydan, private communication.
[109] —, "A fast modulator for extraction of internal laser power," *J. Appl. Phys.*, vol. 41, pp. 1552–1559, March 1970.
[110] R. C. LeCraw, D. L. Wood, J. F. Dillon, Jr., and J. P. Remeika, "The optical transparency of yttrium iron garnet in the near infrared," *Appl. Phys. Lett.*, vol. 7, pp. 27–28, July 1965.
[111] R. C. LeCraw, "Wideband infrared magneto-optic modulation," presented at the 1966 INTERMAG Conf., Stuttgart, Germany. *IEEE Trans. Magn.*, vol. MAG-2, p. 394, September 1966 (Abstract only).
[112] N. Bloembergen, P. S. Pershan, and L. R. Wilcox, "Microwave modulation of light in paramagnetic crystals," *Phys. Rev.*, vol. 120, pp. 2014–2023, December 1960.
[113] L. K. Anderson, private communication. Also, L. K. Anderson and R. C. LeCraw, "Practical magnetooptical modulations," presented at the 1968 New England Radio Eng. Meeting (NEREM), Boston, Mass.

Reprinted from "Handbook of Lasers" (R. J. Pressley, ed.), pp. 447–459. Chemical Rubber Co., Cleveland, Ohio, 1971.

Linear Electrooptical Materials

Ivan P. Kaminow and Edward H. Turner

Bell Telephone Laboratories, Incorporated
Holmdel, New Jersey 07733

DEFINITIONS[1]

(1) The *linear electrooptic (or Pockels) effect* refers to a change in relative optical dielectric impermeability B_{ij} proportional to an applied electric field E_k, whose highest frequencies are below the lattice resonances of a crystal.

(2) The *refractive index* of a crystal is described by an ellipsoid (indicatrix)

$$B_{ij}X_iX_j = 1 \equiv B_{11}X_1^2 + B_{22}X_2^2 + B_{33}X_3^2 + 2B_{23}X_2X_3 + 2B_{13}X_1X_3 + 2B_{12}X_1X_2,$$

in which summation over repeated indices is understood and $B_{ij} = B_{ji}$. By definition

$$B_{ij} = \varepsilon_0 \, \partial E_i/\partial D_j = \left(\frac{1}{\varepsilon}\right)_{ij}$$

with ε_0 the vacuum permittivity and ε the relative dielectric constant.

(3) The *electrooptic coefficient* $r_{ij,k} \equiv r_{lk}$ is defined by

$$\Delta B_{ij} = r_{ij,k} E_k$$

$$\Delta B_l = r_{lk} E_k$$

in which the indices i, j, k each cover the rectangular coordinate axes 1, 2, 3 and $l = (ij)$ refers to the six reduced combinations $1 = (11)$, $2 = (22)$, $3 = (33)$, $4 = (23)$, $5 = (13)$, $6 = (12)$.

(4) If $r_{ij,k}$ is determined at constant strain—for example, by making a measurement at high frequencies well above acoustic resonances of the sample—the crystal is *clamped*, as indicated by the letter (S) or $r_{ij,k}^S$. If $r_{ij,k}$ is determined at constant stress—for example, at low frequencies well below the acoustic resonances of the sample—the crystal is *free*, as indicated by the letter (T) or $r_{ij,k}^T$. Thus,

$$r_{ij,k}^T = r_{ij,k}^S + p_{ij,rs} d_{k,rs}$$

in which $p_{ij,rs}$ and $d_{k,rs}$ are elastooptic and piezoelectric coefficients, respectively.

(5) The linear electrooptic effect occurs only in acentric crystals. The form of the electrooptic tensor is determined by the point group symmetry of the crystal. Only the 21 acentric groups (those lacking a center of inversion) may have non-vanishing coefficients. Their reduced matrix forms are summarized in Table 15-1.

(6) A *nonlinear susceptibility* χ_{ijk} can be defined[2] by

$$P_i = \varepsilon_0 \chi_{ijk} E_j E_k .$$

In a principal axis system where $B_{ij} = 0$ for $i \neq j$, and $B_{ii} \equiv B_i \equiv 1/\varepsilon_i$

$$\Delta B_{ij} = -\Delta\varepsilon_{ij}/\varepsilon_i \varepsilon_j ,$$

for $\Delta\varepsilon_{ij} \ll \varepsilon_i, \varepsilon_j$. Then

$$r_{ij,k} = -2B_i B_j \chi_{ij,k}(-\omega; \omega, 0)$$

and

$$r_{ij,k} = -4B_i B_j d_{k,ji}(0;\, \omega,\, -\omega)$$

or

$$r_{lk} = -4B_i B_j d_{kl}(0;\, \omega,\, -\omega)$$

in which $d_{kl}(0;\omega, -\omega)$ is the *optical rectification* coefficient for optical frequency ω, and the arguments in parenthesis represent the frequencies of the (i, j, k) fields, respectively.

(7) If an electrooptic coefficient is defined in terms of polarization as suggested by Pockels,[3] rather than electric field, the resulting coefficient

$$f_{ij,k} = \frac{r_{ij,k}}{\varepsilon_0(\varepsilon_k - 1)}$$

varies over a much narrower range, for a variety of crystals, than $r_{ij,k}$. The *Miller delta*[4] is a similar coefficient

$$\delta_{ij,k} = \frac{\chi_{ij,k}}{2(\varepsilon_i - 1)(\varepsilon_j - 1)(\varepsilon_k - 1)}$$

$$= \frac{-\varepsilon_i \varepsilon_j r_{ij,k}}{4(\varepsilon_i - 1)(\varepsilon_j - 1)(\varepsilon_k - 1)}$$

with ε_i and ε_j optical dielectric constants and ε_k the dielectric constant at the modulating frequency.

(8) If the principal refractive indices are $n_\alpha^2 = \varepsilon_\alpha$, in the presence of an applied electric field E_β, then

$$\Delta B_\alpha = r_{\alpha\beta} E_\beta = \Delta\left(\frac{1}{\varepsilon_\alpha}\right) = -\left(\frac{\Delta\varepsilon_\alpha}{\varepsilon_\alpha^2}\right) = -\frac{2\Delta n_\alpha}{n_\alpha^3}$$

for $\Delta\varepsilon_\alpha \ll \varepsilon_\alpha$. For applications of the electrooptic effect to modulation of light, a *figure of merit F* may be defined for a particular substance by[5]

$$F = \frac{n_\alpha^7 r_{\alpha\beta}^2}{\varepsilon_\beta} = \left(\frac{2\varepsilon_0}{\pi^2}\right)\left(\frac{\lambda^3 \eta_\alpha^2 \Delta f}{P}\right)$$

where ε_β is the dielectric constant at the modulating frequency, λ is the optical wavelength, Δf is the modulating bandwidth, P is the modulating power, and η_α is the phase modulation index.

(9) The half-wave voltage of an electrooptic crystal, $[E_k \cdot l]_{\lambda/2}$, is the product of applied electric field strength, E_k, and propagation distance, l, required to produce a phase difference of π between orthogonal polarizations, i.e., a half-wave retardation. In the case of uniaxial crystals in which the optic axis is the z (or 3) axis, and the propagation direction is normal to this axis,

$$[E_3\, l]_{\lambda/2} = \frac{\lambda}{n_3^3 r_{33} - n_1^3 r_{13}} = \frac{\lambda}{n_3^3 r_c}$$

Here, $r_c \equiv r_{33} - (n_1^3/n_3^3) r_{13}$.

TABLES OF COEFFICIENTS

The tables are divided according to the general structure of the electrooptic materials. Table 15-2 contains isomorphs of ferroelectric KH_2PO_4 and antiferroelectric $NH_4H_4PO_4$. Table 15-3 contains ABO_3-type crystals, which are ferroelectric or pyroelectric. Table 15-4 contains tetrahedrally coordinated binary AB compounds, which are semiconductors. Table 15-5 contains the remaining miscellaneous materials that do not fit the previous categories.

We have attempted to select the most recent and reliable data; however, the reader should consult the original work to determine its reliability. Typical accuracies for r_{lk} are $\pm 15\%$. References containing more extensive wavelength and temperature dependence are indicated by λ and t, respectively. Electrooptic coefficients are stated in MKS units (m/volt); to convert to CGS units (cm/stat volt), multiply by 3×10^4. Unless stated explicitly, the signs of r_{lk} have not been determined.

As a rule, r_{lk} has little optical wavelength dependence in the transparent region of a crystal, and little modulating frequency dependence below infrared lattice mode resonances and above dimensional acoustic mode resonances. In ferroelectrics and other materials exhibiting a phase transition, the electrooptic coefficients may depend strongly on temperature and generally increase approximately in proportion to $(\varepsilon - 1)$ as the transition temperature, T_c, is neared. For the most part, electrooptic coefficients are quoted for room temperature.

TABLE 15-1. ELECTROOPTIC MATRICES

TRICLINIC — $1 - C_1$

$$\begin{pmatrix} \Delta B_{11} \\ \Delta B_{22} \\ \Delta B_{33} \\ \Delta B_{23} \\ \Delta B_{13} \\ \Delta B_{12} \end{pmatrix} = \begin{pmatrix} r_{11} & r_{12} & r_{13} \\ r_{21} & r_{22} & r_{23} \\ r_{31} & r_{32} & r_{33} \\ r_{41} & r_{42} & r_{43} \\ r_{51} & r_{52} & r_{53} \\ r_{61} & r_{62} & r_{63} \end{pmatrix} \begin{pmatrix} E_1 \\ E_2 \\ E_3 \end{pmatrix} \quad \text{(18) elements}$$

MONOCLINIC

$2 - C_2$ $(2 \| X_2)$

$$\begin{pmatrix} 0 & r_{21} & 0 \\ 0 & r_{22} & 0 \\ 0 & r_{23} & 0 \\ r_{41} & 0 & r_{43} \\ 0 & r_{52} & 0 \\ r_{51} & 0 & r_{63} \end{pmatrix} \quad (8)$$

$m - C_s$ $(m \perp X_2)$

$$\begin{pmatrix} r_{11} & 0 & r_{13} \\ r_{21} & 0 & r_{23} \\ r_{31} & 0 & r_{33} \\ 0 & r_{42} & 0 \\ r_{51} & 0 & r_{53} \\ 0 & r_{62} & 0 \end{pmatrix} \quad (10)$$

ORTHORHOMBIC

$222 - D_2$

$$\begin{pmatrix} 0 & 0 & 0 \\ 0 & 0 & 0 \\ 0 & 0 & 0 \\ r_{41} & 0 & 0 \\ 0 & r_{52} & 0 \\ 0 & 0 & r_{63} \end{pmatrix} \quad (3)$$

$mm2 - C_{2v}$

$$\begin{pmatrix} 0 & 0 & r_{13} \\ 0 & 0 & r_{23} \\ 0 & 0 & r_{33} \\ 0 & r_{42} & 0 \\ r_{51} & 0 & 0 \\ 0 & 0 & 0 \end{pmatrix} \quad (5)$$

TETRAGONAL

$4 - C_4$

$$\begin{pmatrix} 0 & 0 & r_{13} \\ 0 & 0 & r_{13} \\ 0 & 0 & r_{33} \\ r_{41} & r_{51} & 0 \\ r_{51} & -r_{41} & 0 \\ 0 & 0 & 0 \end{pmatrix} \quad (4)$$

$\bar{4} - S_4$

$$\begin{pmatrix} 0 & 0 & r_{13} \\ 0 & 0 & -r_{13} \\ 0 & 0 & 0 \\ r_{41} & -r_{51} & 0 \\ r_{51} & r_{41} & 0 \\ 0 & 0 & r_{63} \end{pmatrix} \quad (4)$$

$422 - D_4$

$$\begin{pmatrix} 0 & 0 & 0 \\ 0 & 0 & 0 \\ 0 & 0 & 0 \\ r_{41} & 0 & 0 \\ 0 & -r_{41} & 0 \\ 0 & 0 & 0 \end{pmatrix} \quad (1)$$

$4mm - C_{4v}$

$$\begin{pmatrix} 0 & 0 & r_{13} \\ 0 & 0 & r_{13} \\ 0 & 0 & r_{33} \\ 0 & r_{51} & 0 \\ r_{51} & 0 & 0 \\ 0 & 0 & 0 \end{pmatrix} \quad (3)$$

$\bar{4}2m - D_{2d}$ $(2 \| X_1)$

$$\begin{pmatrix} 0 & 0 & 0 \\ 0 & 0 & 0 \\ 0 & 0 & 0 \\ r_{41} & 0 & 0 \\ 0 & r_{41} & 0 \\ 0 & 0 & r_{63} \end{pmatrix} \quad (2)$$

TABLE 15-1. ELECTROOPTIC MATRICES (*Continued*)

TRIGONAL

$3 - C_3$

$$\begin{pmatrix} r_{11} & -r_{22} & r_{13} \\ -r_{11} & r_{22} & r_{13} \\ 0 & 0 & r_{33} \\ r_{41} & r_{51} & 0 \\ r_{51} & -r_{41} & 0 \\ -r_{22} & -r_{11} & 0 \end{pmatrix} \quad (6)$$

$32 - D_3$

$$\begin{pmatrix} r_{11} & 0 & 0 \\ -r_{11} & 0 & 0 \\ 0 & 0 & 0 \\ r_{41} & 0 & 0 \\ 0 & -r_{41} & 0 \\ 0 & -r_{11} & 0 \end{pmatrix} \quad (2)$$

$3m - C_{3v}$

$$\begin{pmatrix} 0 & -r_{22} & r_{13} \\ 0 & r_{22} & r_{13} \\ 0 & 0 & r_{33} \\ 0 & r_{51} & 0 \\ r_{51} & 0 & 0 \\ -r_{22} & 0 & 0 \end{pmatrix} \quad (4)$$

HEXAGONAL

$6 - C_6$

$$\begin{pmatrix} 0 & 0 & r_{13} \\ 0 & 0 & r_{13} \\ 0 & 0 & r_{33} \\ r_{41} & r_{51} & 0 \\ r_{51} & -r_{41} & 0 \\ 0 & 0 & 0 \end{pmatrix} \quad (4)$$

$\bar{6} - C_{3h}$

$$\begin{pmatrix} r_{11} & -r_{22} & 0 \\ -r_{11} & r_{22} & 0 \\ 0 & 0 & 0 \\ 0 & 0 & 0 \\ 0 & 0 & 0 \\ -r_{22} & -r_{11} & 0 \end{pmatrix} \quad (2)$$

$622 - D_6$

$$\begin{pmatrix} 0 & 0 & 0 \\ 0 & 0 & 0 \\ 0 & 0 & 0 \\ r_{41} & 0 & 0 \\ 0 & -r_{41} & 0 \\ 0 & 0 & 0 \end{pmatrix} \quad (1)$$

$6mm - C_{6v}$

$$\begin{pmatrix} 0 & 0 & r_{13} \\ 0 & 0 & r_{13} \\ 0 & 0 & r_{33} \\ 0 & r_{51} & 0 \\ r_{51} & 0 & 0 \\ 0 & 0 & 0 \end{pmatrix} \quad (3)$$

$\bar{6}m2 - D_{3h}$ $(m \perp X_1)$

$$\begin{pmatrix} 0 & -r_{22} & 0 \\ 0 & r_{22} & 0 \\ 0 & 0 & 0 \\ 0 & 0 & 0 \\ 0 & 0 & 0 \\ -r_{22} & 0 & 0 \end{pmatrix} \quad (1)$$

CUBIC

$432 - 0$

$$\begin{pmatrix} 0 & 0 & 0 \\ 0 & 0 & 0 \\ 0 & 0 & 0 \\ 0 & 0 & 0 \\ 0 & 0 & 0 \\ 0 & 0 & 0 \end{pmatrix} \quad (0)$$

23 and $\bar{4}3m - T$ *and* T_d

$$\begin{pmatrix} 0 & 0 & 0 \\ 0 & 0 & 0 \\ 0 & 0 & 0 \\ r_{41} & 0 & 0 \\ 0 & r_{41} & 0 \\ 0 & 0 & r_{41} \end{pmatrix} \quad (1)$$

TABLE 15-2. KDP- AND ADP-TYPE CRYSTALS

$\bar{4}2m$ ABOVE T_c

	T_c (°K) [6]	*Electrooptic coefficients*		*Refractive index*		*Dielectric const.*	
		$r_{63}(10^{-12} m/V)$	$r_{41}(10^{-12} m/V)$	n_3	n_1	ε_3	ε_1
KH_2PO_4 (KDP)	123	(*T*)−10.5[7]; [8,λ]; [9,*t*]					
		(*T*)9.37[10]	+8.6[7]	1.47	1.51[13,14;λ,*t*]	(*T*)21	42[15]
		(*S*)8.8[16]; [8,λ]					
		(*S*)8.15[17]; $r_{63} < 0$[11]	$r_{41} < 0$[12]			(*S*)21	44[18]
KD_2PO_4 (DKDP)	222	(*T*)26.4[19][8,λ][9,*t*]	8.8[21]	1.47	1.51[14,λ,*t*]	(*T*)50[19]	
		(*S*)24.0[20]; $.93 r_{63}^T$ [8,λ]				(*S*)48	58[22]
KH_2AsO_4 (KDA)	97	(*T*)10.9	12.5[21]	1.52	1.57[21]	(*T*)21	54[15]
						(*S*)19	53[22]
KD_2AsO_4 (DKDA)	162	(*T*)18.2[23,λ]			1.56[23]		
RbH_2PO_4 (RDP)	147	(*T*)15.5[23,λ]			1.51[23]		
		(*S*).91 r_{63}^T [8,λ]					
RbH_2AsO_4 (RDA)	110	(*T*)13.0[21]		1.52	1.56[21]	(*T*)27	41[24]
						(*S*)24	39[24]
RbD_2AsO_4 (DRDA)	178	(*T*)21.4[23,λ]			1.56[23]		
CsH_2AsO_4 (CDA)	143	(*T*)18.6[23,λ]			1.57[23]		
CsD_2AsO_4 (DCDA)		(*T*)36.6[23,λ]			1.57[23]		
$NH_4H_2PO_4$ (ADP)	148*	(*T*) −8.5[7], [25], [8,λ]	24.5[21], 23.1[26]	1.48	1.53[13,14;λ,*t*]	(*T*)15	56[15]
		(*S*)5.5[7], 4.1[27], [8,λ]	$r_{41} < 0$[12]			(*S*)14	58[22]
$ND_4D_2PO_4$ (DADP)	242*	(*T*)11.9[23,λ], [28,*t*]			1.52[23]		
$NH_4H_2AsO_4$ (ADA)		(*T*)9.2[23,λ]			1.58[23]		

* Antiferroelectric transition.

TABLE 15-3. ABO$_3$-TYPE COMPOUNDS

Material and Symmetry (critical temp., °K)	*Electrooptic coefficients* $r_{13}(10^{-12}m/V)$	$r_{ik}(10^{-12}m/V)$	$\lambda(\mu m)$	*Refractive index* n_i	$\lambda(\mu m)$	*Dielectric const.* ε_1
$LiNbO_3$, *3m*	$(T)r_c = 19$	$(T)r_{22} = 7$	.633[29]	$n_1 = n_2 = 2.3780$	.45[38,λ]	$(T)\varepsilon_1 = \varepsilon_2 = 78[37,t$
(1470)	$(T)r_c = 17.4$	$(T)r_{22} = 3.2$	.633[30]	2.2716	.70[39,t,λ]	$(T)\varepsilon_3 = 32$
		$(T)r_{51} = 32$		2.2370	1.00[41,t,λ]	$(S)\varepsilon_1 = \varepsilon_2 = 43[61]$
	$(T)r_{33} = +32.2$	$(T)r_{22} = 6.8$	.633[31,t]	2.1974	2.00	$(S)\varepsilon_3 = 28$
	$(T)r_{13} = +10$			2.1155	4.00	
	$(T)r_c = 18$	$(T)r_{22} = 6.7$	.633[34]	$n_3 = 2.2772$	.45	
	$(T)r_c = 17$	$(T)r_{22} = 5.7$	1.15[34]	2.1874	.70	
	$(T)r_c = 16$	$(T)r_{22} = 3.1$	3.39[34]	2.1567	1.00	
	All $(T)r_{ij} > 0$		.633[32]	2.1250	2.00	
	$(S)r_{33} = +30.8$	$(S)r_{22} = 3.4$	.633[35]	2.0553	4.00	
	$(S)r_{13} = +8.6$	$(S)r_{51} = +28$				
	$(S)r_{33} = 28$	$(S)r_{22} = 3.1$	3.39[36]			
	$(S)r_{13} = 6.5$	$(S)r_{51} = 23$				
$LiTaO_3$, *3m*	$(T)r_c = 22$		.633[40]	$n_1 = n_2 = 2.1834$	.60[42,λ]	$(T)\varepsilon_2 = \varepsilon_1 = 51[43]$
(890)	$(S)r_{33} = 30.3$	$(S)r_{51} = 20$	.633[40]	2.1305	1.20	$(T)\varepsilon_3 = 45$
	$(S)r_{13} = 7$	$(S)r_{22} \approx 1$		2.0335	4.00	$(S)\varepsilon_2 = \varepsilon_1 = 41$
	$(S)r_{33} = 27$	$(S)r_{51} = 15$	3.39[36]	$n_3 = 2.1878$	.60	$(S)\varepsilon_3 = 43$
	$(S)r_{13} = 4.5$	$(S)r_{22} \approx .3$		2.1341	1.20	
	All $(T)r_{ij} > 0$		.633[33]	. 2.0377	4.00	
$BaTiO_3$, *4mm*	$(T)r_c = 108$	$(T)r_{51} = 1640$	.546[44,t]	$n_1 = n_2 = 2.46$	.546[47λ]	$(T)\varepsilon_1 = \varepsilon_2 = 3600$ [47t]
(395)	$(S)r_c = 23$	$(S)r_{51} = 820$	.546[45,t]	$n_3 = 2.40$		$(T)\varepsilon_3 = 135[48;47t]$
	$(S)r_c = 19$		.633[46]	$n_1 = n_2 = 2.41$	.633[47λ]	$(S)\varepsilon_1 = \varepsilon_2 = 2300$ [47t]
	$(S)r_{33} = 28$			$n_3 = 2.36$		$(S)\varepsilon_2 = 60[48; 47t]$
	$(S)r_{13} = 8$					
$K_3Li_2Nb_5O_{15}$, *4mm*	$(T)r_{33} = 78$		.633[49]	$n_1 = n_2 = 2.277$	.633[49]	$(T)\varepsilon_1 = \varepsilon_2 = 309[49]$
(693)	$(T)r_{13} = 8.9$			$n_3 = 2.163$		$(T)\varepsilon_3 = 100[49]$
$Sr_{.75}Ba_{.25}Nb_2O_6$, *4mm*	$(T)r_c = 1410$		.633[50]	$n_1 = n_2 = 2.3117$	.633[50]	$\varepsilon_3 = 3400[50]$
($\sim$330)	$(T)r_{33} = 1340$	$(T)r_{51} = 42$		$n_3 = 2.2987$		(15MHz)
	$(T)r_{13} = 67$					
	$(S)r_c = 1090$					
$Sr_{.5}Ba_{.5}Nb_2O_6$, *4mm*	$(T)r_c = 218$		.633[50]	$n_1 = n_2 = 2.3123$	.633[50]	$\varepsilon_3 = 450[50]$
	(15MHz)r_c = 96			$n_3 = 2.2734$		(15MHz)
$Sr_{.25}Ba_{.75}Nb_2O_6$, *4mm*			.633[50]	$n_1 = n_2 = 2.3144$	.633[50]	$\varepsilon_3 = 118[50]$
($\sim$520)	(15MHz)r_c = 45					(15MHz)
$KTa_xNb_{1-x}O_3$, *4mm*	$(T)r_c = 450$	$(T)r_{51} = +50$	.633[51,t]	$n_1 = n_2 = 2.318$	.633[51,t]	
($\sim$330)				$n_3 = 2.277$		
$PbTiO_3$, *4mm*	$(S)r_{33} = 5.9$		.633[52]	$n_1 = n_2 = 2.668$	.633[52]	$(S)\varepsilon_3 = 31[52]$
(765)	$(S)r_{13} = 13.8$			$n_3 = 2.659$		
$KSr_2Nb_5O_{15}$, *4mm*	$(T)r_c = 130$		.633[53,t]	$n \sim 2.25$	.633[53]	$(T)\varepsilon_3 = 1000[53,t]$
(433) or *4*						$(T)\varepsilon_1 = 1200$
$LiIO_3$, *6*	$(S)r_{33} = +6.4$	$(S)r_{41} = 1.4$	.633[54]	$n_1 = n_2 = 1.881$	.633[55,λ]	$(T)\varepsilon_3 = 554[54,t]$
(Pyroel.)	$(S)r_{13} = +4.1$	$(S)r_{51} = +3.3$		$n_3 = 1.736$		$(T)\varepsilon_1 = 65$
						$(S)\varepsilon_3 = 6.5[56]$
						$(S)\varepsilon_1 = 8[57]$
$Ba_2NaNb_5O_{15}$, *mm2*	$(T)r_c = 34$		.633[59,t]	$n_1 = 2.322$	.633[58,λ]	$(T)\varepsilon_1 = 235[60]$
(833)	$(T)r_{33} = 48$	$(T)r_{42} = 92$	.633[58]	$n_2 = 2.321$		$(T)\varepsilon_2 = 247$
	$(T)r_{13} = 15$	$(T)r_{51} = 90$		$n_3 = 2.218$		$(T)\varepsilon_3 = 51$
	$(T)r_{23} = 13$					$(S)\varepsilon_1 = 222$
	$(S)r_{33} = +29$	$(S)r_{42} = 75$	.633[52]			$(S)\varepsilon_2 = 227$
	$(S)r_{23} = 8$	$(S)r_{51} = 88$				$(S)\varepsilon_3 = 32$
	$(S)r_{13} = 7$					

TABLE 15-4. AB-TYPE COMPOUNDS

		Electrooptic coefficients		*Refractive index*		*Dielectric const.*
Material	*Sym*	$r_{lk}(10^{-12} m/v)$	$\lambda(\mu m)$	n_i	$\lambda(\mu m)$	ε_i
GaAs	$\bar{4}3m$	$(S)r_{41} = 1.2$	.9 to 1.08[63]	$n_o = 3.60$	.9[70]	$(S)\varepsilon = 13.2$[72]
		$(S)r_{41} = -1.5$	3.39[64]	$n_o = 3.50$	1.02[70]	$(S)\varepsilon = 12.3$[73]
		$(S+T)r_{41} = 1.2$ to 1.6	1.0 to 3.0[65]	$n_o = 3.42$	1.25[70]	$(T)\varepsilon = 12.5$[71]
		$(T)r_{41} = 1.0$ to 1.2	4.0 to 12.0[65]	$n_o = 3.30$	>5.0[71]	
		$(T)r_{41} = 1.6$	10.6[66,67]			
		$(S)r_{41} = 1.5$	Raman Scat. 68,69			
GaP	$\bar{4}3m$	$(S)r_{41} = -1.07$ to $-.97$	.56 to 3.39[74]	$n_o = 3.4522$ to 3.2462	.545[74] to .7	$(S)\varepsilon = 12$[76]
				$n_o = 3.2422$ to 3.0137	.7[74] to 4.0	$(S)\varepsilon = 10$[77]
ZnTe	$\bar{4}3m$	$(T)r_{41} = 4.45$	.59[78,λ]	$n_o = 3.1$	.57[78,λ]	$(T)\varepsilon = 10.1$[82]
		to 3.95	.69[78,λ]	2.91	.7[78,λ]	$(S)\varepsilon = 10.1$[82]
		$(T)r_{41} = 1.4$	10.6[67]	2.76	1.24[79]	
		$(S)r_{41}$ (rel.)	5.8 to 6.9[81,λ]	2.71	2.06[79]	
		$(S)r_{41} = 4.3$	.633[84]	2.70	10.6[80]	
		$(S)r_{41} = 3.2$	3.39[84]			
ZnSe	$\bar{4}3m$	$(T)r_{41} = 2.0$	.546[85]	$n_o = 2.66$	.546[79]	$(T)\varepsilon = 9.1$[82]
		$(S)r_{41} = 2.0$	.633[84]			$(S)\varepsilon = 9.1$[82]
		$(T)r_{41} = 2.2$	10.6[88]	$n_o = 2.3$	10.6[88]	
ZnS	$\bar{4}3m$	$(T)r_{41} = 1.2$	.4[86,λ]	$n_o = 2.471$	.45[75]	$(T)\varepsilon = 16$[87]
		$(T)r_{41} = 2.1$	.65[86,λ]	2.364	.6[75]	$(S)\varepsilon = 12.5$[87]
		$(S)r_{41} = 1.6$	.633[84]	2.315	.8[75]	$(T,S)\varepsilon = 8.3$[82]
		$(S)r_{41} = 1.4$	3.39[84]	2.260	2.4[75]	
ZnS	$6mm$	$(S)r_{33} = 1.8$	.633[84]	$n_3 = 2.709$	.36[89]	$(T)\varepsilon_1 = \varepsilon_3 = 8.7$[96]
		$(S)r_{33} = 1.7$	3.39[84]	$n_1 = n_2 = 2.705$	.36[89]	$(S)\varepsilon_1 = 8.7$
		$(S)r_{13} = .9$	.633[84]	$n_3 = 2.368$	.6[89]	
				$n_1 = n_2 = 2.363$	.6[89]	
ZnO	$6mm$	$(S)r_{33} = +2.6$	.633[84]	$n_3 = 2.123$	.45[75]	$(S)\varepsilon_1 = \varepsilon_2 = 8.15$[90] $\approx \varepsilon_3$
		$(S)r_{13} = -1.4$	.633[84]	$n_1 = n_2 = 2.106$	.45[75]	
		$(S)r_{33} = +1.9$	3.39[84]	$n_3 = 2.015$	.6[75]	
		$(S)r_{13} = +.96$	3.39[84]	$n_1 = n_2 = 1.999$	.6[75]	
				$n_3 = 1.9068$	4.0[75]	
				$n_1 = n_2 = 1.8891$	4.0[75]	
CdTe	$\bar{4}3m$	$(T)r_{41} = 6.8$	3.39[91]	$n_o = 2.82$	1.3[79]	
		$(T)r_{41} = 6.8$	10.6[91]	$n_o = 2.60$	10.6[93]	$(S)\varepsilon = 9.4$[73]
		$(T)r_{41} = 5.5$	23.35[92]	$n_o = 2.58$	23.34[93]	
		$(T)r_{41} = 5.0$	27.95[92]	$n_o = 2.53$	27.95[93]	
CdSe	$6mm$	$(S)r_{33} = 4.3$	3.39[84]	$n_3 = 2.542$	1.15[75]	$(T)\varepsilon_3 = 10.65$[82]
		$(S)r_{13} = 1.8$	3.39[84]	$n_1 = n_2 = 2.522$	1.15[75]	$(T)\varepsilon_1 = 9.70$[82]
				$n_3 = 2.471$	3.39[75]	$(S)\varepsilon_1 = 9.33$[82]
				$n_1 = n_2 = 2.452$	3.39[75]	$(S)\varepsilon_3 = 10.20$[82]
CdS	$6mm$	$(T)r_c = 4$	.589[94]	$n_3 = 2.48$	.63[80]	$(T)\varepsilon_3 = 10.33$[82]
		$(T)r_{51} = 3.7$	.589[94]	$n_1 = n_2 = 2.46$	.63[80]	$(T)\varepsilon_1 = 9.35$[82]
		$(T)r_c = 5.5$	10.6[67]	$n_3 = 2.3$	10.0[80]	$(S)\varepsilon_1 = 9.02$[82], 8.7[83]
		$(S)r_{33} = 2.4$	.633[84]			$(S)\varepsilon_3 = 9.53$[82], 9.25[83]
		$(S)r_{13} = 1.1$	.633[84]			

TABLE 15-4. AB-TYPE COMPOUNDS (*Continued*)

		Electrooptic coefficients		Refractive index		Dielectric const.
Material	*Sym*	$r_{lk}(10^{-12}m/V)$	$\lambda(\mu m)$	n_l	$\lambda(\mu m)$	ε_l
CuBr	$\bar{4}3m$	$(T)r_{41} = .85$	.525[95]	$n_0 = 2.16$ $n_0 = 2.09$	.535[96] .656[96]	
CuCl	$\bar{4}3m$	$(T)r_{41} = 3.6$ $(T)r_{41} = 3.2$ $(S)r_{41} = +2.35$ $(S)r_{41} = +2.20$	.633[97] 10.6[97] .633[84] 3.39[84]	$n_0 = 2.02$ $n_0 = 1.958$ $n_0 = 1.91$ $n_0 = 1.90$	.5[98] .633[98] 3.39[98] 10.0[98]	$(S)\varepsilon = 7.5$[99]
HgS	32	$(S)r_{11} = 3.1$ $(S)r_{41} = 1.4$ $(S)r_{11} = 4.2$ $(S)r_{41} = 2.4$	.633[100] .633[100] 3.39[100] 3.39[100]	$n_3 = 3.232$ $n_1 = n_2 = 2.885$ $n_3 = 2.900$ $n_1 = n_3 = 2.637$	.633[101] .633[101] 3.39[101] 3.39[101]	

TABLE 15-5. MISCELLANEOUS CRYSTALS

		Electrooptic constants		Refractive index	
Material	*Sym*	$r_{lk}(10^{-12}m/V)$	$\lambda(\mu m)$	n_l	$\lambda(\mu m)$
$Bi_4(GeO_4)_3$	$\bar{4}3m$	$(T)r_{41} = 1.03$	.45 to .62[102]	$n_0 = 2.07$	[102]
$(CH_2)_6N_4$: (HMT-hexamethylenetetramine)	$\bar{4}3m$	$(T)r_{41} = 0.71 - 0.8$ $(T)r_{41} = 0.78$ $(S)r_{41} < 0.14$	.546[103] .633[105] .633[105]	$n_0 = 1.591$ $n_0 = 1.594$	.589[104] .633[105]
Hauynite (mineral)	$\bar{4}3m$	$(T)r_{41} < .04$	[106]	$n_0 = 1.496$	
Langbeinites:					
$K_2Mg_2(SO_4)_3$	23	$(T)r_{41} = 0.40$	.546[107]	$n_0 = 1.535$	.589[107]
$(NH_4)_2Cd_2(SO_4)_3$	23	$(T)r_{41} = 0.70$	.546[107]	$n_0 = 1.606$	.589[107]
$(NH_4)_2Mn_2(SO_4)_3$	23	$(T)r_{41} = 0.53$	.546[107]	$n_0 = 1.57$	.589[107]
$Tl_2Cd_2(SO_4)_3$	23	$(T)r_{41} = 0.37$	.546[107]	$n_0 = 1.730$	.589[107]
$K_2Mn_2(SO_4)_3$	23	$(T)r_{41} = 2.0$	.453 to .642[108]	1.62	.45 to .65 [108]
$Rb_2Mn_2(SO_4)_3$	23	$(T)r_{41} = 1.9$	.453 to .642[108]	1.60	.45 to .65 [108]
$Tl_2Mn_2(SO_4)_3$	23	$(T)r_{41} = 2.1$	.453 to .642[108]	1.80	.45 to .65 [108]
$K_2Ni_2(SO_4)_3$	23	$(T)r_{41} = 1.0$	.453 to .642[108]	1.70	.45 to .65 [108]
$NaClO_3$	23	$(T)r_{41} = .4$	.589[109]	$n_0 = 1.515$	[110]
$Na_3SbS_4 \cdot 9H_2O$	23	$(T)n_1^3r_{41} = 5.66$ $(T)n_1^3r_{41} = 5.62$	.42[111] 1.08[111]		
Sodium uranyl acetate	23	$(T)r_{41} = .87$	.546[112]	$n_0 = 1.507$	.546[112]
$LiKSO_4$	6	$(T)r_c = 1.6$	.546[113]	$n_3 \approx n_1 = n_2 = 1.474$	.546[113]
$LiNaSO_4$	3m	$(T)r_{22} < .02$	.546[113]	$n_3 = 1.495$ $n_1 = n_2 = 1.490$	[110]

TABLE 15-5. MISCELLANEOUS CRYSTALS (*Continued*)

Material	Sym	*Electrooptic constants* $r_{ik}(10^{-12} m/V)$	$\lambda(\mu m)$	*Refractive index* n_i	$\lambda(\mu m)$
Tourmaline	3m	$(T)r_{22} = 0.3$	.589[109]	$n_3 = 1.65$	[110]
		$(S)r_{33} = r_{13} = 1.7$	.633[129]	$n_1 = n_2 = 1.63$	
$Na_3Li(CrO_4)_2 \cdot 6H_2O$	3m	$(T)r_{22} = 0.92$	.50[134]	$n_1 = n_2 = 1.643$	.50[134]
		$(T)r_{22} = 0.82$	.52[134]	$n_1 = n_2 = 1.635$	.52[134]
		$(T)r_{22} = 0.77$	.60[134]	$n_1 = n_2 = 1.612$	.60[134]
Ag_3AsS_3 (Proustite)	3m	$(S)(n_1^3 r_{13} - n_3^3 r_{33}) = 70$	.633[114]	$n_1 = 3.02$	.633[114]
		$(S)n_1^3 r_{22} = 29$	.633[114]	$n_3 = 2.74$	.633[114]
	NOTE:	Transparent 0.6 to 13 μm; $\varepsilon_1 \approx \varepsilon_3 = 20$; $\rho = 10^5$ Ωcm [114].			
$K_2S_2O_6$	32	$(T)r_{11} = 0.26$	.546[113]	$n_3 = 1.1518$	[110]
				$n_1 = n_2 = 1.456$	[113]
$Cs_2C_4H_4O_6$	32	$(T)r_{11} = 1.0$	.546[113]	$n_3 = 1.546$	
				$n_1 = n_2 = 1.564$	[113]
$SrS_2O_6 \cdot 4H_2O$	32	$(T)r_{11} = 0.1$	.546[113]	$n_3 = 1.528$	[110]
				$n_1 = n_2 = 1.532$	[110]
Se	32	$(S)n_1^3 r_{11} = 89$	1.15[115]	$n_1 = 2.737$, $n_3 = 3.573$	1.15[116,λ]
		$(S)r_{11} \sim 2.5$	10.6[117]	$n_1 = 2.64$, $n_3 = 3.41$	10.6[116,λ]
		NOTE: Absorption-edge $\sim$ 8 μm [118,λ], $\varepsilon_1 = 8$ [119].			
SiO_2 (Quartz)	32	$(T)r_{11} = -0.47$	.409 to .605[109], [120λ]	$n_3 = 1.555$	.546[109]
		$(T)r_{41} = 0.20$	[109]	$n_1 = n_2 = 1.546$	.546[109]
		$(S)r_{11} = 0.23$ (calculated)	[121]		
		$(S)r_{11} = 0.29$	.633[122]		
		$(S)r_{11} = 0.174$	.633[123]		
		NOTE: $r_{11} < 0$ and $r_{41} > 0$ in left-handed quartz [123].			
$(C_6H_{12}O_6)_2NaBr \cdot H_2O$	32	$(T)r_{11} = 0.1$	.546[113]	$n_3 = 1.560$	.546[113]
$AgGaS_2$	$\bar{4}2m$	$(T)r_{63} = 3.0$	.633[130]	$n_1 = n_2 = 2.55$	.633[131,λ]
		$(T)r_{41} = 4.0$		$n_3 = 2.50$	
		NOTE: $(S)\varepsilon_3 = 14$, $(S)\varepsilon_1 = 10$[130].			
$Gd_2(MoO_4)_3$	$\bar{4}2m$ (450°K)	$(T)n_1^3 r_{63} = 17$ (450°K)	.633[125t]	$n_1 = n_2 = 1.528$	
				$n_1 \approx n_2 = 1.848$	.633[125]
	mm2 (300°K)	$(T)n_1^3 r_{13} - n_3^3 r_{33} = 17.5$ (300°K)	.633[125t]	$n_3 = 1.901$	.633[125]
		NOTE: $T_c = 432$°K, $\varepsilon_3 = 8$ [125t].			
$CdGa_2S_4$	$\bar{4}$	$(T)r_{13} = 0.37$	.50[135]	$n_1 = n_2 = 2.3$	.50[135]
		$r_{63} = 3.5$	.50[135]		
$(NH_4)_2C_2O_4 \cdot H_2O$	222	$(T)r_{41} = 230$	.633[136]	$n_1 = 1.437$	.65[138]
		$(T)r_{52} = 330$		$n_2 = 1.547$	

TABLE 15-5. MISCELLANEOUS CRYSTALS (*Continued*)

		Electrooptics coefficients		*Refractive index*	
Material	*Sym*	$r_{ik}(10^{-12} m/V)$	$\lambda(\mu m)$	n_i	$\lambda(\mu m)$
		$(T)r_{63}=250$		$n_3=1.590$	
		$(T)r \ll 250$	.633[137]		
		$(S)r_{63}\approx 2$	.633[129]		
Rochelle Salt	222	See Ref. [120]			
$NaNO_2$	mm2	$(T)r_{22}-\left(\frac{n_3}{n_2}\right)^3 r_{32}=4.1$	.546[126t]	$n_1=1.347$	.546[126]
		$(T)r_{32}-\left(\frac{n_1}{n_3}\right)^3 r_{12}=4.2$		$n_2=1.415$	
		$(T)r_{22}-\left(\frac{n_1}{n_2}\right)^3 r_{12}=0.6$		$n_3=1.661$	
		$(T)r_{43}=-1.9$			
		$(T)r_{61}=-3.0$			
NOTE: Author takes X_2 as polar axis. Transition to *mmm* at 423°K, [126]; $(S)\varepsilon_1=5$, $\varepsilon_2=4$, $\varepsilon_3=8$ [132t].					
Triglycine sulfate (TGS) and deuterated triglycine sulfate (DTGS)	2	see Ref. [120] NOTE: (S) ε, see [132,t].			
$C(CH_2OH)_4$	2	$(T)r_{52}=1.45$	.46 to .70[127]	$n_1=1.528$	
		$(T)\lvert r_{12}-r_{32}\rvert=0.7$	.46 to .70[127]	$n_2\approx n_3=1.56$	[109]
$Ca_2Nb_2O_7$	2	$(T)\left\lvert r_{22}-\frac{n_1^3}{n_2^3}r_{12}\right\rvert=12$	.63[128]	$n_1=1.97$	[128]
		$(T)\left\lvert r_{22}-\frac{n_3^3}{n_2^3}r_{32}\right\rvert=14$	.63[128]	$n_2=2.16$	[128]
		$(S)\left\lvert r_{22}-\frac{n_3^3}{n_2^3}r_{32}\right\rvert=13$	.63[128]	$n_3=2.17$	[128]
		$(S)r_{12}=6.7$	.63[133]		
		$(S)r_{22}=25.5$			
		$(S)r_{32}=6.4$			
		$(S)r_{41}=2.7$			
		$(S)r_{52}<0.6$			
		$(S)r_{63}=0.9$			

REFERENCES

1. J. F. Nye, "Physical properties of crystals," Oxford Univ. Press, London, 1964.
2. G. D. Boyd and D. A. Kleinman, "Parametric Interaction of Focused Gaussian Light Beams," *J. Appl. Phys. 39*, 3597–3639, 1968.
3. F. Pockels, "Lehrbuch der Kristalloptik," Tübner, Leipzig, 1906.
4. R. C. Miller, "Optical second harmonic generation in piezoelectric crystals," *Appl. Phys. Lett.*, *5*, 17–19, 1964.
5. I. P. Kaminow, "Measurements of the electrooptic effect in CdS, ZnTe and GaAs at 10.6 microns," *IEEE J. Quant. Electronics*, *4*, 23–26, 1968.
6. F. Jona and G. Shirane, "Ferroelectric crystals." New York: Macmillan, 1962.
7. R. O'B. Carpenter, "The electrooptic effect in crystals of the dihydrogen phosphate type, Part III, Measurement of coefficients," *J. Opt. Soc. Am.*, *40*, 225–229, 1950.
   — "Electrooptic sound-on-film modulator," *J. Opt. Soc. Am.*, *25*, 1145–1148, 1953.
8. A. S. Vasilevskaya, "The electrooptic properties of crystals of KDP type," *Sov. Phys.-Cryst. 11*, 644–647, 1967; J. F. Ward and P. A. Frankcen, "Structure of nonlinear optical phenomena in potassium dihydrogen phosphate,"*Phys. Rev.133*, A183–190, 1964.

9. A. S. Sonin, A. S. Vasilevskaya and B. A. Strukov, "Electrooptic properties of potassium dihydrogen phosphate and deuterated potassium dihydrogen phosphate in the region of their phase transitions," *Sov. Phys.-Solid State*, *8*, 2758–60, 1967.
10. O. G. Blokh, "Dispersion of r_{63} for crystals of ADP and KDP," *Sov. Phys.-Cryst.* *7*, 509–511, 1962.
11. E. H. Turner, unpublished.
12. J. F. Ward and G. H. C. New, "Optical rectification in ammonium dihydrogen phosphate, potassium dihydrogen phosphate and quartz," *Proc. Roy Soc.* *A299*, 238–263, 1967.
13. F. Zernike, Jr., "Refractive indices of ADP and KDP between 0.2 and 1.5μ," *J. Opt. Soc. Am.*, *54*, 1215–1220, 1964, correction *ibid.*, *55*, 210E, 1965; V. N. Vishnevskii and I. V. Stefanski, "Temperature dependence on the dispersion of the refractivity of ADP and KDP single crystals," *Opt. and Spectr.*, *20*, 195–196, February 1966.
14. M. Yamazaki and T. Ogawa, "Temperature dependences of the refractive indices of $NH_4H_2PO_4$, KH_2PO_4, and partially deuterated KH_2PO_4," *J. Opt. Soc. Am.*, *56*, 1407–1408, 1966; R. A. Phillips, "Temperature variation of the index of refraction of ADP, KDP and deuterated KDP*," *J. Opt. Soc. Am.*, *56*, 629–632, 1966.
15. D. A. Berlincourt, D. R. Curran, and H. Jaffe, "Physical acoustics," vol. I, pt. A, W. P. Mason, Ed. New York: Academic, 1964, pp. 169–260.
16. R. D. Rosner, E. H. Turner and I. P. Kaminow, "Clamped electrooptic coefficients of KDP and quartz," *Appl. Optics*, *6*, 778, 1967.
17. E. A. Ohm, "A linear optical modulator with high FM sensitivity," *Appl. Optics*, *6*, 1233–1235, 1967.
18. I. P. Kaminow and G. O. Harding, "Complex dielectric constant of KH_2PO_4 at 9.2 Gc/sec," *Phys. Rev.* *129*, 1562–1566, 1963.
19. T. R. Sliker and S. R. Burlage, "Some dielectric and optical properties of KD_2PO_4," *J. Appl. Phys.* *34*, 1837–1840, 1963.
20. T. M. Christmas and C. G. Wildey, "Pulse measurement of r'_{63} in KD*P," *Electr. Lett.* *6*, 152–153, March 1970.
21. J. H. Ott and T. R. Sliker, "Linear electrooptic effects in KH_2PO_4 and its isomorphs," *J. Opt. Soc. Am.*, *54*, 1442–1444, 1964.
22. I. P. Kaminow, "Microwave dielectric properties of $NH_4H_2PO_4$, KH_2AsO_4, and partially deuterated KH_2PO_4," *Phys. Rev.* *138*, A1539–A1543, 1965.
23. R. S. Adhav, "Linear electro-optic effects in tetragonal phosphates and arsenates," *J. Opt. Soc. Am.*, *59*, 414–418, 1969.
24. I. S. Zheludev and T-Z Ludupov, "Complex dielectric constant of RbH_2PO_4 in the range 8×10^2–3.86×10^{10} cps," *Sov. Phys.-Cryst.*, *10*, 645–646, 1966.
25. H. Koetser, "Measurement of r_{63} for ADP up to electric breakdown," *Electronics Lett.*, *3*, 52–54, 1967.
26. J. M. Ley, "Low-voltage light-amplitude-modulation," *Electronics Lett.*, *2*, 12–13, 1966.
27. L. Silverstein and M. Sucher, "Determination of the Pockels electro-optic coefficient in ADP at 5.5 GHz," *Electronics Lett.*, *2*, 437–438, 1966.
28. A. S. Vasilevskaya, "Electrooptic and elastooptical properties of deuterated ammonium dihydrogen phosphate crystals," *Sov. Phys.-Solid State*, *8*, 2756–57, 1967.
29. P. V. Lenzo, E. G. Spencer and K. Nassau, "Electrooptic coefficients in lithium niobate," *J. Opt. Soc. Am.*, *56*, 633, 1966.
30. E. Bernal, G. D. Chen and T. C. Lee, "Low frequency electrooptic and dielectric constants of lithium niobate," *Phys. Lett.*, *21*, (3), 259, 1966.
31. J. D. Zook, D. Chen and G. N. Otto, "Temperature dependence and model of the electrooptic effect in $LiNbO_3$," *Appl. Phys. Lett.*, *11*, (5), 159, 1967.
32. K. F. Hulme, P. H. Davies and V. M. Cound, "The signs of the electrooptic coefficients for lithium niobate," *J. Phys. C* (*Solid State Phys.*), *2*, 855, 1969.
33. B. Luther-Davies, P. H. Davies, V. M. Cound and K. F. Hulme, "The signs of the electrooptic coefficients for lithium tantalate," *J. Phys. C.* (*Solid State Phys.*), *3*, L106–L107, 1970.
34. P. H. Smakula and P. C. Claspy, "The electrooptic effect in $LiNbO_3$ and KTN," *Trans. AIME.* *239*, 421, 1967.
35. E. H. Turner, "High frequency electrooptic coefficients of lithium niobate," *Appl. Phys. Lett.*, *8*, (11), 303, 1066. Signs of coefficients were determined later; determination to be published.
36. E. H. Turner, "Electrooptic coefficients of some crystals at 3.39 microns," Paper Th A13, Opt. Soc. Am., San Francisco, October 20, 1966.
37. K. Nassau, H. J. Levinstein and G. M. Loiacono, "Ferroelectric lithium niobate, 2. Preparation of single domain crystals," *J. Phys. Chem. Solids*, *27*, 989,1966.
38. G. D. Boyd, Robert C. Miller, K. Nassau, W. L. Bond and A. Savage, "$LiNbO_3$: an efficient phase matchable nonlinear optical material," *Appl. Phys. Lett.*, *15*, (11), 234, 1964.
39. H. Iwasaki, T. Yamada, N. Niizeki and H. Toyoda, "Piezoelectric and optical properties of $LiNbO_3$ single crystals," *Rev. Elec. Comm. Lab.*, *16*, (5–6), 385, 1968.
40. P. V. Lenzo, E. H. Turner, E. G. Spencer and A. A. Ballman, "Electrooptic coefficients and elastic wave propagation in single domain ferroelectric lithium tantalate," *Appl. Phys. Lett.*, *8*, (4), 81, 1966.
41. G. D. Boyd, W. L. Bond and H. L. Carter, "Refractive index as a function of temperature in $LiNbO_3$," *J. Appl. Phys.*, *38*, (4), 1941, 1967.
42. W. L. Bond, "Measurement of the refractive indices of several crystals," *J. Appl. Phys.*, *36*, 1674, 1965.
43. A. W. Warner, M. Onoe and G. A. Coquin, "Determination of elastic and piezoelectric constants for crystals in class (3m)," *J. Acoust. Soc. Am.*, *42*, 1223, 1967.
44. A. R. Johnston and J. M. Weingart, "Determination of the low frequency linear electrooptic effect in tetragonal $BaTiO_3$," *J. Opt. Soc. Am.*, *55*, 828, 1965.
45. A. R. Johnston, "The strain free electrooptic effect in single crystal barium titanate." *Appl. Phys. Lett.*, *7*, 195, 1965.
46. I. P. Kaminow, "Barium titanate light phase modulator," *Appl. Phys. Lett.*, *7*, 123, 1965. "Erratum," *8*, 54, 1966. "Barium titanate light modulator II," *Appl. Phys. Lett.*, *8*, 305, 1966.
47. S. H. Wemple, M. DiDomenico, Jr., and I. Camlibel, "Dielectric and optical properties of melt-grown $BaTiO_3$," *J. Phys. Chem. Solids*, *29*, 1797, 1968.
48. I. Camlibel, M. DiDomenico, Jr., and S. H. Wemple, "Dielectric properties of single-domain melt-grown $BaTiO_3$," *J. Phys. Chem. Solids*, *31*, 1417–1419, 1970.
49. W. A. Bonner, J. E. Geusic, H. J. Levinstein, S. Singh and L. G. Van Uitert, "A new and stable nonlinear optical material," *Appl. Phys. Lett.*, *11*, (5), 161, 1967.
50. P. V. Lenzo, E. G. Spencer and A. A. Ballman, "Electro-optic coefficients of ferroelectric strontium barium niobate," *Appl. Phys. Lett.*, *11*, (1), 23, 1967.
51. John A. vanRaalte, "Linear electrooptic effect in ferroelectric KTN," *J. Opt. Soc. Am.*, *57*, (5), 671, 1967.
52. E. H. Turner, unpublished.
53. E. A. Giess, Gerald Burns, D. F. O'Kane and A. W. Smith, "Ferroelectric and optical properties of $KSr_2Nb_5O_{15}$," *Appl. Phys. Lett.*, *11*, (7), 233, 1967.
54. F. R. Nash, J. G. Bergman, G. D. Boyd and E. H. Turner, "Optical nonlinearities in $LiIO_3$," *J. Appl. Phys.*, *40*, 5201, 1969. The quoted signs are relative to IRE piezoelectric standards and were determined after the above publication. E. H. Turner, to be published.
55. G. Nath and S. Haussühl, "Large nonlinear optical coefficient and phase matched second harmonic generation in $LiIO_3$," *Appl. Phys. Lett.*, *14*, 154, 1969.

56. S. Haussühl, "Piezoelectric and electrical properties of $LiIO_3$," *Phys. Stat. Solidi, 29*, K159, 1968.
57. A. W. Warner, D. A. Pinnow, J. G. Bergman and G. R. Crane, "Piezoelectric and photoelastic properties of lithium iodate," *J. Acoust. Soc. Am., 47*, 791, 1970.
58. S. Singh, D. A. Draegert and J. E. Geusic, "Optical and ferroelectric properties of barium sodium niobate," *Phys. Rev. B*, pp. 2709, October, 1970.
59. R. L. Byer, S. E. Harris, D. J. Kuizenga, J. F. Young and R. S. Feigelson, "Nonlinear optical properties of $Ba_2NaNb_5O_{15}$ in the tetragonal phrase," *J. Appl. Phys., 40*, (1), 444, 1969.
60. A. W. Warner, G. A. Coquin and J. L. Fink, "Elastic and piezoelectric constants of $Ba_2NaNb_5O_{15}$," *J. Appl. Phys., 40*, 4353, 1969.
61. I. P. Kaminow and E. H. Turner, "Electrooptic light modulators," *Proc. IEEE, 54*, 1374, 1966.
62. S. Singh, private communication.
63. E. H. Turner and I. P. Kaminow, "Electrooptical effect in gallium arsenide," *J. Opt. Soc. Am., 53*, 523, 1963.
64. E. H. Turner, to be published.
65. T. E. Walsh, "Gallium arsenide electrooptic modulators," *RCA Review, XXVII*, 323, 1966.
66. A. Yariv, C. A. Mead and J. V. Parker, "GaAs as an electrooptic modulator at 10.6 microns," *IEEE J. Quant. Electronics, QE-2*, 243, 1966.
67. I. P. Kaminow, "Measurements of the electrooptic effect in CdS, ZnTe and GaAs at 10.6 microns," *IEEE J. Quant. Electronics, QE-4*, 23, 1968.
68. A. Mooradian and A. L. McWhorter, "Light scattering from plasmons and phonons in GaAs," p. 297 in "Light scattering spectra of solids," G. B. Wright, ed. Springer, New York, 1969.
69. W. D. Johnston, Jr., and I. P. Kaminow, "Contributions to optical nonlinearity in GaAs as determined from Raman scattering efficiencies," *Phys. Rev., 188*, 1209, 1969.
70. D. T. F. Marple, "Refractive index of GaAs," *J. Appl. Phys., 35*, 1241, 1964.
71. K. G. Hambleton, C. Hilsum and B. R. Holeman, "Determination of the effective ionic charge of gallium arsenide from direct measurements of the dielectric constant," *Proc. Phys. Soc., 77*, 1147, 1961.
72. S. Jones and Shing Mao, "Further investigation of the dielectric constant of gallium arsenide," *J. Appl. Phys., 39*, 4038, 1968.
73. C. J. Johnson, G. H. Sherman and R. Weil, "Far infrared measurement of the dielectric properties of GaAs and CdTe at 300K and 8K," *Appl. Optics, 8*, 1667, 1969.
74. D. F. Nelson and E. H. Turner, "Electrooptic and piezoelectric coefficients and refractive index of gallium phosphide," *J. Appl. Phys., 39*, 3337, 1968.
75. W. L. Bond, "Measurement of the refractive indices of several crystals," *J. Appl. Phys., 36*, 1674, 1965.
76. I. P. Kaminow and E. H. Turner, "Electrooptic light modulators," *Proc. IEEE, 54*, 1374, 1966.
77. C. Hilsum and A. C. Rose-Innes, "Semiconducting III-V Compounds," New York, Pergamon, 1961.
78. T. R. Sliker and J. M. Jost, "Linear electrooptic effect and refractive indices of cubic ZnTe," *J. Opt. Soc. Am., 56*, 130, 1966.
79. D. T. F. Marple, "Refractive index of ZnSe, ZnTe, and CdTe," *J. Appl. Phys., 35*, No. 3 (Part 1), 1964.
80. L. R. Shiozawa and J. M. Jost, "Research on II-VI compound semiconductors," Clevite Corporation, Palo Alto, California, *Report AD 620297*, May 1965.
81. H. Pursey, P. A. Page and M. J. P. Musgrave, "On the dispersion of optical and electrooptical coefficients in zinc telluride," *J. Phys. C. (Solid State Physics) 2*, 1085, 1969.
82. Don Berlincourt, Hans Jaffe and L. R. Shiozawa, "Electroelastic properties of the sulfides, selenides and tellurides of zinc and cadmium," *Phys. Rev., 129*, 1009, 1963.
83. A. S. Barker, Jr., and C. J. Summers, "Infrared dielectric function of CdS," *J. Appl. Phys. 41*, 3552–3554, 1970.
84. E. H. Turner, to be published.
85. R. W. McQuaid, "Electrooptic properties of zinc selenide," *Proc. IRE (correspondence), 50*, 2484, 1962; and "Correction to 'Electrooptic properties of zinc selenide,'" *Proc. IEEE, 51*, 470, 1963.
86. S. Namba, "Electrooptical effect of zincblende," *J. Opt. Soc. Am., 51*, 76, 1961.
87. S. J. Czyzak, D. C. Reynolds et al, "On the properties of single cubic zinc sulfide crystals," *J. Opt. Soc. Am., 44*, 864, 1954.
88. C. Kojima, T. Shikama, S. Kuninobu, A. Kawabata and T. Tanaka, "The electrooptic effect in cubic ZnSe at 10.6μ," *Jap. J. Appl. Phys., 8*, 1361, 1969.
89. T. M. Bieniewski and S. J. Czyzak, "Refractive indexes of single hexagonal ZnS and CdS crystals," *J. Opt. Soc. Am., 53*, 496, 1963.
90. R. J. Collins and D. A. Kleinman, "Infrared reflectivity of zinc oxide," *J. Phys. Chem. Solids, II*, 190, 1959.
91. James E. Kiefer and Amnon Yariv, "Electrooptic characteristics of CdTe at 3.39 and 10.6μ," *Appl. Phys. Lett., 15*, (1), 26, 1969.
92. C. J. Johnson, "Electrooptic effect in CdTe at 23.35 and 27.95 microns," *Proc. IEEE, 56*, 1719, 1968.
93. O. G. Lorimer and W. G. Spitzer, "Infrared refractive index and absorption of InAs and absorption of InAs and CdTe," *J. Appl. Phys., 36*, 1841, 1965.
94. D. J. A Gainon, "Linear electrooptic effect in CdS," *J. Opt. Soc. Am., 54*, 270, 1964.
95. L. M. Belyaev, G. F. Dobrzhanskii, Yu. U. Shaldin, "Electrooptical properties of copper chloride and bromide crystals," *Sov. Phys.-Solid State, 6*, 2988, 1965.
96. Landolt-Bornstein, "Zahlenwerte and Funktionen," II Band, 8 Teil, Optische Konstanten.
97. T. Sueta, T. Matsushima, T. Nishimoto and T. Makimoto, "Modulation of 10.6 micron laser radiation by CuCl," *Proc. IEEE, 58*, 1378, Sept. 1970.
98. Albert Feldman and Deane Horowitz, "Refractive index of cuprous chloride," *J. Opt. Soc. Am., 59*, 1406, 1969.
99. P. Alonas, G. Sherman, C. Wittig and P. D. Coleman, "Dielectric properties of CuCl at 300K in the 3–30μ region," *Appl. Optics, 8*, 2557, 1968.
100. E. H. Turner, "Linear electrooptic effect in HgS (cinnabar) at .63 and 3.39 microns," *IEEE, J. Quant. Electronics, QE-3*, 695, 1967.
101. W. L. Bond, G. D. Boyd and H. L. Carter, Jr., "Refractive indices of HgS (cinnabar) between .62 and 11μ," *J. Appl. Phys., 38*, 4090, 1967.
102. R. Nitsche, "Crystal growth and electrooptic effect of bismuth germanate, $Bi_4(GeO_4)_3$," *J. Appl. Phys., 36*, 2358–2360, 1965.
103. R. W. Lee, "Linear electro-optic (Pockels) effect in hexamethylenetetramine: Influence of crystal strain," *J. Opt. Soc. Am., 59*, 1574–1580, 1969.
104. G. H. Heilmeier, "The dielectric and electrooptic properties of a molecular crystal-hexamine," *Appl. Opt., 3*, 1281–1287, 1964.
105. K. F. Rodgers, "The Pockels effect in hexamine," *Appl. Optics, 8*, 2369–2370, 1969.
106. K. K. Thornber and E. H. Turner, "A determination of the electrooptic coefficients of haüynite, langbeinite and gallium phosphide," unpublished.
107. A. S. Vasilevskaya, I. G. Ganeev, I. S. Rez and A. S. Sonin, "Electrooptic properties of thallium-cadmium langbeinite," *Sov. Phys.-Cryst. 14*, 421–422, 1969.

108. F. P. Emmenegger, R. Nitsche and A. Miller "Crystal growth and electro-optic effect of some double sulfates with the langbeinite structure," *J. Appl. Phys. 39*, 3039, 1968.
109. R. Bechmann, "Piezooptische and elektrooptische konstanten von piezoelectrische kristallen," Landolt-Börnstein, "Zahlenwerte and Funktionen," II Band, 8 Teil, "Optische Konstanten;" K-H and A. M. Hellwege, eds., Springer-Verlag, Berlin, 1962, pp. 2–453–464.
110. A. N. Winchell and H. Winchell, "The microscopical characters of artificial inorganic substances," New York: Academic, 1964.
111. C. F. Buhrer, L. Ho and J. Zucker, "Electrooptic effect in optically active crystals," *Appl. Opt.*, *3*, 517–521, 1964.
112. J. Warner, D. S. Robertson and H. T. Parfit, "The electrooptic effect of sodium uranyl acetate," *Phys. Lett.*, *19*, 479–480, 1965.
113. T. R. Sliker, "Linear electrooptic effects in class 32, 6, 3m, and $\bar{4}$3m crystals," *J. Opt. Soc. Am.*, *54*, 1348–1351, 1964.
114. J. Warner, "The electrooptic effect in proustite (Ag_3AsA_3)," *Brit. J. Appl. Phys.* (*J. Phys. D.*), *1*, 66–67, 1968.
115. E. H. Turner, I. P. Kaminow and E. D. Kolb, "Electrooptic effect in trigonal selenium at 1.15 microns," *IEEE J. Quant. Electronics 7*, 234, 1968.
116. L. Gampel and F. M. Johnson, "Index of refraction of single-crystal selenium," *J. Opt. Soc. Am.*, *59*, 72–73, 1969.
117. M. C. Tiech and T. Kaplan, "Electrooptic effect in trigonal selenium at 10.6μm," *IEEE J. Quant. Electronics*, *2*, 702–703, 1966.
118. G. G. Roberts, S. Tutihasi and R. C. Keezer, "Optical absorption-edge of trigonal selenium," *Phys. Rev.*, *1*, 637–643, 1968.
119. V. Prosser, M. Sicha and E. Klier, "Dielectric constant of hexagonal selenium single crystals," in "Recent Advances in Selenium Physics," European Selenium-Tellurium Committee, London: Pergamon, 1965, p. 105.
120. R. Bechmann, "First and second order piezooptic and electrooptic constants of crystals," Landolt-Börnstein, Group III, vol. 2, K. H. Hellwege, ed. Springer-Verlag, New York, 1969, pp. 126–166.
121. W. G. Cady, "Piezoelectricity." New York: McGraw-Hill, 1964, p. 721.
122. R. D. Rosner, E. H. Turner, I. P. Kaminow, "Clamped electrooptic coefficients of KDP and quartz," *Appl. Optics*, *6*, 779, 1967.
123. H. Pursey and R. J. Newman, "Measurements of the Pockels effect in quartz at 9 GHz," *Brit. J. Appl. Phys.*, (*J. Phys. D*), *1*, 707–710, 1968.
124. J. F. Ward and G. H. C. New, "Optical rectification in ammonium dihydrogen phosphate, potassium dihydrogen phosphate and quartz," *Proc. Roy. Soc. A299*, 238–263, 1967.
125. A. W. Smith and G. Burns, "Optical properties and switching in $Gd_2(MoO_4)_3$," *Phys. Letters*, *28A*, 501–502, 1969.
126. A. R. Johnston and T. Nakamura, "Determination of the low-frequency electro-optic coefficients of $NaNO_2$," *J. Appl. Phys.*, *40*, 3656–3658, 1969.
127. O. G. Blokh, I. S. Zheludev and U. A. Shamburov, "The electrooptic effect in crystals of pentaerythritol $C(CH_2OH)_4$," *Soviet Phys.-Cryst.*, *8*, 37–40, 1963.
128. C. H. Holmes, E. G. Spencer, A. A. Ballman and P. V. Lenzo, "The electrooptic effect in calcium pyroniobate," *Appl. Opt.*, *4*, 551–553, 1965.
129. E. H. Turner, unpublished.
130. V. M. Cound, P. H. Davies, K. F. Hulme and D. Robertson, "The electrooptic coefficients of silver thiogallate ($AgGaS_2$)," *J. Phys. C*, *3*, L83–L84, 1970.
131. M. V. Hobden, "Optical activity in a non-enantiomorphous crystal: $AgGaS_2$," *Acta Crystallogr.*, *24A*, 676–680, 1968.
132. E. Nakamura, "Measurement of microwave dielectric constants of ferroelectrics Part II. Dielectric constants and dielectric losses of $NaNO_2$ and $(Glycine)_3 \cdot H_2SO_4$," *J. Phys. Soc. Jap.*, *17*, 961–966, 1962.
133. R. D. Rosner and E. H. Turner, "Electrooptic coefficients in calcium pyroniobate," *Appl. Optics*, *7*, 171–173, 1968.
134. A. Miller, A. G. Karipides and T. M. Peltz, "Enhancement of electro-optic effects at wavelengths in the proximity of electronic resonances," to be published.
135. A. V. Cafiero, A. G. Karipides and A. Miller (unpublished).
136. A. S. Vasilevskaya, L. I. Kuznetsova, I. S. Rez and A. S. Sonin, "A new crystal with a large electro-optic effect," *Sov. Phys. Solid State*, *10*, (5), 733–734, 1968.
137. Private communication, K. S. Hulme and independently, D. A. Draegert.
138. A. N. Winchell, "Optical properties of organic compounds," Academic Press, New York, 1954.

2. Characterization and Measurement of the Electrooptic Effect

Effects of the Electrical and Magnetic Fields†

F. POCKELS

1. EFFECTS WHICH ARE NOT REVERSED WITH THE FIELD DIRECTION.

Kerr [1] was the first to observe that certain nonconducting liquids, for example carbon disulfide, become doubly refracting when placed in a strong electrical field (between two condenser plates) in such a way that the direction of the electrical lines of force is an isotropy axis. The sign of this "electrical double refraction" is positive in some liquids and negative in others and its intensity is proportional to the square of the electrical field intensity for the same liquid. Kerr, and later Brongserma [2], also observed double refraction in glass between two conductors of opposite charge located close to each other. It is not certain whether or not this is a secondary effect since electrical double refraction in glass was not observed in a different experimental arrangement where it should have been much more distinct [3].

In crystals an optical effect, not reversible with the field direction, analogous to Kerr's phenomenon has been observed only for Rochelle salt [4] for a certain field direction (parallel to the crystallographic *a*-axis) and under such circumstances that it could be a secondary effect. However, since Rochelle salt also exhibits polar (reversible) electrooptical effects, characteristic of piezoelectric crystals, this questionable phenomenon will be discussed later (Sec. 6).

An effect of the magnetic field analogous to Kerr's electrooptical phenomenon was recently discovered by Kerr and Majorana for certain colloidal iron and iron oxide solutions [5]; the latter, are doubly refracting and pleochroic when observed in a direction perpendicular to the magnetic field lines. Since these liquids are not homogeneous solutions but rather suspensions, it is quite possible that this phenomenon is caused by the orientation of suspended particles in the magnetic field [6] as is actually the case in crystal powder suspensions according to Meslin [see p. 491 of original text, footnote 4].

2. REVERSIBLE ELECTROOPTICAL EFFECTS (FIRST OBSERVATIONS OF QUARTZ CRYSTALS)

In acentric crystals an electrical field may have optical effects which are reversible with the direction of the lines of force, since in this case the

† Excerpt from: F. Pockels, "Lehrbuch der Kristalloptik." Part IV, Chapter III, pp. 492–510. Teubner, Leipzig, 1906. Translated by A. Werner.

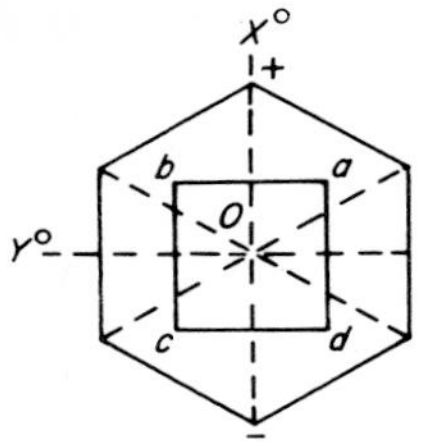

Fig. 163

opposite directions in the crystal are not equivalent. Such an electrooptical effect, i.e., variation of the double refraction due to a field perpendicular to the major axis, was discovered almost simultaneously by Röntgen and Kundt in quartz crystals [7]. The experimental apparatus used by Kundt which renders this phenomenon visible is as follows. A rectangular parallelepiped, cut from a quartz crystal in such a way that its end faces are perpendicular to its major axis and the two side faces (*ab*, *cd*, Fig. 163) are perpendicular to one of the three twofold axes (X^0) of the crystal. Metal coatings are applied to a pair of side faces (AB and CD or AD and BC, Fig. 164). It is then placed in a polarization apparatus for convergent light so that the circles of equal path difference around the major axis can be observed in the end face. If the two metal coatings are connected with the poles of an electrical source and charged to a high potential difference, then the circles of the same path difference exhibit a deformation analogous to the case of unilateral pressure perpendicular to the major axis. The direction in which the rings exhibit the largest elongation (which corresponds to the pressure direction) is parallel or perpendicular to the electrical lines of force when surfaces *ab* and *cd* are charged in the one or the other sense, and are inclined ±45° with respect to the lines of force when side faces *bc* and *ad* are charged (see Fig. 164 which shows the deformation of a curve having the same path difference). At the same time, a certain relationship exists between this variation of the ring system and the piezoelectric properties of quartz crystals. It is already known that quartz crystals are polarized electrically in a direction perpendicular to the major axis such that the ends of a twofold axis (X^0) become electrically

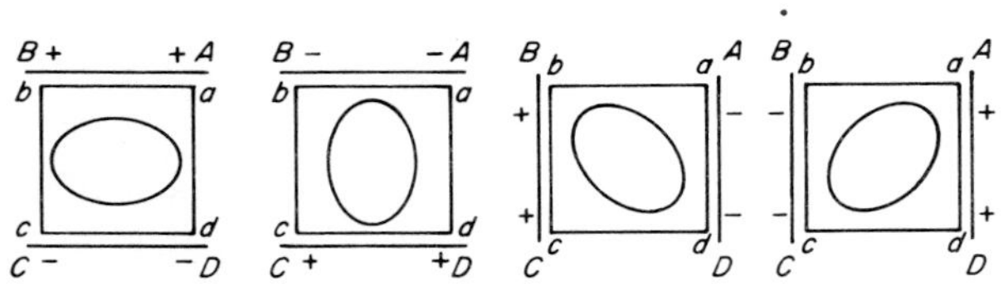

Fig. 164

charged in one sense (Fig. 163) as a result of pressure parallel to this axis and in the opposite sense when the pressure is applied perpendicular to this axis. Pressure at a 45° angle with respect to X^0 generates charges on surfaces *ad* and *bc* parallel to X^0 [8]. The ring system is deformed as a result of charging of the surface pair in the same sense as the pressure which would give rise to the opposite charge of this surface pair. Lipmann [9] has shown that, on the basis of thermodynamic principles, the quartz parallelopiped under consideration must actually undergo deformation as a result of the charges imparted to its side faces from the outside. These deformations would be qualitatively capable of producing the observed optical changes, i.e., the crystal must expand precisely in the direction in which the rings contract and it must contract in the direction of the major axis of the deformed rings. Accordingly, it was assumed that the optical effect of an electrical field in quartz is only an indirect effect, i.e., that it originates from the deformations generated by the field due to the piezoelectric properties. Quantitative experiments were necessary in order to confirm the validity of the assumption made by Kundt and Röntgen. However, before going into a detailed discussion of these observations (see Secs. 4–6) we shall demonstrate how these laws of the reversible electrooptical effects can be developed without the aid of any assumption as to their formation.

3. GENERAL THEORY OF ELECTROOPTICAL EFFECTS REVERSIBLE WITH THE FIELD DIRECTION[1]

The electrooptical phenomenon can be described mathematically (in analogy with the elasto- and piezo-optical effects in Chap. II) by expressing the polarization constants of a crystal in an electrical field as linear functions of the field components or also as functions of specific electrical moments induced by the field. If the components of the electrical moment[2] per unit volume are denoted by A, B, C and if the initial major axes of polarization X^0, Y^0, Z^0 are chosen as coordinate axes, then we have[3]

[1] Pockels, F., *N Jahrb. Mineral Suppl.* **7.** 201 (1890). W. Voigt (*Wied. Ann.* **69.** 297 (1899)) later postulated an approach to electrooptical effects, yielding the same results on the basis of the equations of the theory of light, expanded by the assumption of electron oscillations.

[2] These may vary from point to point in a crystal of arbitrary shape in an electrical field. We shall assume that they are constant, i.e., the field in the crystal is homogeneous. This is always valid if only a small portion of the crystal is studied at a time; this was approximately realized for all the crystals investigated in a suitable experimental apparatus.

[3] Since the specific electrical moments are linear functions of the electrical field components in the crystal—if the coordinate axes are also the symmetry axes of the dielectric properties, A, B, C differ from the corresponding field components only by the factors $(D_h - 1)/4\pi$, $(h = 1, 2, 3)$, where D_1, D_2, D_3 are the main dielectric constants—an analogous statement can be set up where the field components are substituted for the moments.

[Note: $a_{hk} = (1/n^2)_{hk}$, $a^0 = 1/n_{11}$, $b^0 = 1/n_{22}$, $c^0 = 1/n_{33}$.]

$$\begin{aligned} a_{11} &= a^{02} + e_{11}A + e_{12}B + e_{13}C, & a_{23} &= e_{41}A + e_{42}B + e_{43}C, \\ a_{22} &= b^{02} + e_{21}A + e_{22}B + e_{23}C, & a_{31} &= e_{51}A + e_{52}B + e_{53}C, \\ a_{33} &= a^{02} + e_{31}A + e_{32}B + e_{33}C, & a_{12} &= e_{61}A + e_{62}B + e_{63}C, \end{aligned} \tag{1}$$

where e_{hk} are the characteristic constants for the respective crystal which are called "electrooptical constants". The most general form of these equations with 18 constants must be retained for the hemihedral group of the triclinic system, which does not possess a symmetry element. Simplifications can be introduced for all other groups through the conditions which must be satisified by e_{hk} in order that the equations for a_{hk} do not change their form for transformations from the initial coordinate system to an equivalent crystallographic (also dielectric and optical) system. Since the signs of all electrical moments change when all coordinate directions are reversed, but the signs of a_{hk} do not, then in all crystals with a center of symmetry, where all opposing directions are equivalent, all e_{hk} must vanish so that the electrooptical phenomenon under consideration cannot occur at all. However, all e_{hk} also vanish in one acentric group, i.e., enanthiomorphic hemihedry of the regular system, so that only 20 groups remain. These are the groups which also exhibit piezoelectricity. The special forms of Eq. (1) are compiled below for these groups which also include the symbols of the characteristic symmetry elements [see p. 316 of original text]. [Note: $e = 1/n_e = 1/n_{33}$, $o = 1/n_0 = 1/n_{11}$.]

I. Triclinic System. Hemihedral: General Eq. (1) with 18 constants.

II. Monoclinic System. Hemihedral: E_x (10 constants)

$$\begin{aligned} a_{11} - a^{02} &= e_{12}B + e_{13}C, \qquad a_{22} - b^{02} = e_{22}B + e_{23}C, \\ a_{33} - c^{02} &= e_{32}B + e_{33}C, \\ a_{23} &= e_{42}B + e_{43}C, \qquad a_{31} = e_{51}A, \qquad a_{12} = e_{61}A, \end{aligned} \tag{2}$$

Hemimorphic; $A_x^{(2)}$ (eight constants).

$$\begin{aligned} a_{11} - a^{02} &= e_{11}A, \qquad a_{22} - b^{02} = e_{21}A, \qquad a_{33} - c^{02} = e_{31}A, \\ a_{23} &= e_{41}A, \qquad a_{31} = e_{52}B + e_{53}C, \qquad a_{12} = e_{62}B + e_{63}C. \end{aligned} \tag{3}$$

III. Rhombic System. Hemihedral: $A_z^{(2)}$, $A_x^{(2)}$ (three constants).

$$\begin{aligned} a_{11} &= a^{02}, \qquad a_{22} = b^{02}, \qquad a_{33} = c^{02}, \\ a_{23} &= e_{41}A, \qquad a_{31} = e_{52}B, \qquad a_{12} = e_{63}C. \end{aligned} \tag{4}$$

Hemimorphic; $A_z^{(2)}$, E_x (five constants).

$$\begin{aligned} a_{11} - a^{0^2} &= e_{13} C, & a_{22} - b^{0^2} &= e_{23} C, & a_{33} - c^{0^2} &= e_{33} C, \\ a_{23} &= e_{42} B, & a_{31} &= e_{51} A, & a_{12} &= 0. \end{aligned} \tag{5}$$

IV. Tetragonal System. $a^0 = b^0 = o$, $c^0 = e$. Tetartohedral with mirror axis: $S_x^{(2)}$ (four constants).

$$\begin{aligned} a_{11} - o^2 &= e_{13} C, & a_{22} - o^2 &= -e_{13} C, & a_{33} - e^2 &= 0, \\ a_{23} &= e_{41} A + e_{42} B, & a_{31} &= -e_{42} A + e_{41} B, & a_{12} &= e_{63} C. \end{aligned} \tag{6}$$

Hemihedral with mirror axis: $S_z^{(2)}$, $A_x^{(2)} = A_y^{(2)}$ (two constants).

$$\begin{aligned} a_{11} &= a_{22} = o^2, & & & a_{33} &= e^2, \\ a_{23} &= e_{41} A, & a_{31} &= e_{41} B, & a_{12} &= e_{63} C. \end{aligned} \tag{7}$$

Hemimorphic tetartohedral: $A_z^{(4)}$ (four constants).

$$\begin{aligned} a_{11} - o^2 &= e_{13} C, & a_{22} - o^2 &= e_{13} C, & a_{33} - e^2 &= e_{33} C, \\ a_{23} &= e_{41} A + e_{42} B, & a_{31} &= e_{42} A - e_{41} B, & a_{12} &= 0. \end{aligned} \tag{8}$$

Hemimorphic hemihedral: $A_3^{(4)}$, E_x (three constants).

$$(9) \text{ as } (8) \text{ but } \quad e_{41} = 0. \tag{9}$$

Enantiomorphic hemihedral: $A_z^{(4)}$, $A_x^{(2)}$ (one constant).

$$\begin{aligned} a_{11} &= a_{22} = o^2, & & & a_{33} &= e^2, \\ a_{23} &= e_{41} A, & a_{31} &= -e_{41} B, & a_{12} &= 0. \end{aligned} \tag{10}$$

V. Rhombohedral System. $a^0 = b^0 = o$, $c^0 = e$. Tetartohedral: $A_z^{(3)}$ (six constants).

$$\begin{aligned} a_{11} - o^2 &= e_{11} A - e_{22} B + e_{13} C, & a_{22} - o^2 &= -e_{11} A + e_{22} B + e_{13} C, \\ a_{33} - e^2 &= e_{33} C, & a_{23} &= e_{41} A + e_{42} B, \\ a_{31} &= e_{42} A - e_{41} B, & a_{12} &= -e_{22} A - e_{11} B. \end{aligned} \tag{11}$$

Hemimorphic hemihedral: $A_z^{(3)}$, E_x (four constants).

$$\begin{aligned} a_{11} - o^2 &= -e_{22} B + e_{13} C, & a_{22} - o^2 &= e_{22} B + e_{13} C, & a_{33} - e^2 &= e_{33} C, \\ a_{23} &= e_{42} B, & a_{31} &= e_{42} A, & a_{12} &= -e_{22} A. \end{aligned} \tag{12}$$

Enantiomorphic hemihedral: $A_z^{(3)}$, $A_x^{(2)}$. (two constants.)

$$\begin{aligned} a_{11} - o^2 &= e_{11} A, & a_{22} - o^2 &= -e_{11} A, & a_{33} - e^2 &= 0, \\ a_{23} &= e_{41} A, & a_{31} &= -e_{41} B, & a_{12} &= -e_{11} B. \end{aligned} \tag{13}$$

VI. Hexagonal System. $a^0 = b^0 = o$, $c^0 = e$. Tetartohedral with three-fold axis: $A_z^{(3)}$, E_z (two constants).

$$\begin{aligned} a_{11} - o^2 &= e_{11} A - e_{22} B, \qquad a_{22} - o^2 = -e_{11} A + e_{22} B, \\ a_{33} &= e^2, \quad a_{23} = 0, \quad a_{31} = 0, \quad a_{12} = -e_{22} A - e_{22} B. \end{aligned} \tag{14}$$

Hemihedral with three-fold axis: $A_z^{(3)}$, $A_x^{(2)}$, E_z (one constant).

$$\text{as previous group with } e_{22} = 0. \tag{15}$$

Hemimorphic tetartohedral: $A_z^{(6)}$ (four constants).

$$\begin{aligned} a_{11} - o^2 &= e_{13} C, & a_{22} - o^2 &= e_{13} C, & a_{33} - e^2 &= e_{33} C, \\ a_{23} &= e_{41} A + e_{42} B, & a_{31} &= e_{42} A - e_{41} B, & a_{12} &= 0. \end{aligned} \tag{16}$$

Hemimorphic hemihedral: $A_z^{(6)}$, E_x (three constants).

$$\text{as (16) but with } e_{41} = 0 \tag{17}$$

Enantiomorphic hemihedral: $A_z^{(6)}$, $A_x^{(2)}$ (one constant).

$$\text{as (10)} \tag{18}$$

VII. Regular System. $a^0 = b^0 = c^0$. Tetartohedral: $A_z^{(2)} = A_x^{(2)} = A_y^{(2)}$; and Hemimorphic hemihedral: $S_z^{(2)} = S_x^{(2)} = S_y^{(2)}$ (one constant).

$$\begin{aligned} a_{11} &= a_{22} = a_{33} = a^{0^2}, \\ a_{23} &= e_{41} A, \quad a_{31} = e_{41} B, \quad a_{12} = e_{41} C. \end{aligned} \tag{19}$$

The above compilation implies that the multiplicity of electrooptical effects is a large one. However, the investigation will be limited to those types which have been observed, i.e., the following groups: (13)—represented by quartz, (12)—tourmaline, (19)—sodium chlorate, and (4)—Rochelle salt.

4. ELECTROOPTICAL PROPERTIES OF QUARTZ AND TOURMALINE

According to Eqs. (13) the field component parallel to the major axis in quartz has no optical effects at all as already corroborated by Röntgen's observations. Consequently, it is negligible and it can be assumed that the electrical lines of force lie in the $X^0 Y^0$ plane. Since the properties of all directions perpendicular to the major axis are the same with respect to dielectric induction, then the induced electrical moment M coincides with the direction of the lines of force and if the latter form the angle ϕ with the positive X^0 axis the following holds

$$A = M \cos \phi, \qquad B = M \sin \phi. \tag{20}$$

If V is the electrical potential and D_1 is the dielectric constant for the directions perpendicular to the major axis, then the following holds

$$M = -\frac{D_1 - 1}{4\pi}\left\{\frac{\partial V}{\partial x}\cos\phi + \frac{\partial V}{\partial y}\sin\phi\right\}. \tag{20'}$$

The above values of A and B are inserted into eq. (13) in order to determine the polarization constants characterizing the optical properties of quartz in an electrical field *in the absence of circular polarization* [optical activity]. On the basis of observations we shall assume that rotation remains unchanged so that the resulting optical behavior is calculated according to the formulas in Pt. II, Chap. II, Sec. 2.

The theory can be compared with the observations on the basis of the technique in Sec. 2, using the binormal plane of quartz rendered biaxial by the electrical field. This plane is parallel to the major axis of the deformed curves of equal path difference. Its position is calculated with the aid of Eqs. (7) of Chap. II which imply that the deviation of the axial line (Z) from the major axis is very small. Angle Φ formed by the two other principal axes of polarization with respect to the X^0 or Y^0 axis is determined as follows

$$\text{tg } 2\phi = -\frac{B}{A} = -\text{tg } \Phi, \qquad \text{i.e.,} \qquad \Phi = -\tfrac{1}{2}\Phi \tag{21}$$

(see Fig. 165).

Accordingly, Eq. (32) [p. 67 of original text] gives

$$\begin{aligned} a^2 &= \tfrac{1}{2}(a_{11} + a_{22}) + \tfrac{1}{2}(a_{11} - a_{22})\cos 2\Phi + a_{12}\sin 2\Phi = o^2 + e_{11}M, \\ b^2 &= \tfrac{1}{2}(a_{11} + a_{22}) - \tfrac{1}{2}(a_{11} - a_{22})\cos 2\Phi - a_{12}\sin 2\Phi = o^2 - e_{11}M. \end{aligned} \tag{22}$$

The intensity of the double refraction in the direction of the major axis and also the binormal angle and the variation of the ring diameters, for an equal

Fig. 165

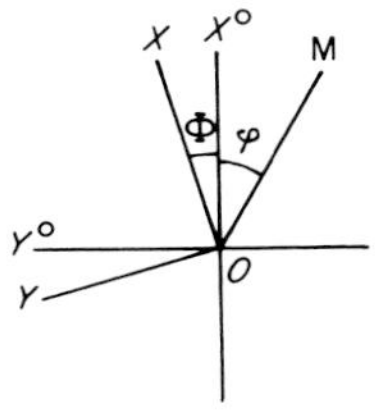

induced moment, are independent of its direction and are determined by the constant e_{11}. If the direction of $+X^0$ axis is chosen in such a way that it coincides with a prism edge rendered electrically positive by pressure (this is the case for a levorotational quartz crystal when the $+Y^0$ axis emerges from a plane of the positive rhombohedron for the standard mutual position of coordinates), then the observation made in connection with Fig. 164 implies that for a negatively charged plane perpendicular to $+X^0$, i.e., positive moment $A = M$, b is the mean principal velocity of light and since $o > e$ in quartz, the constant e_{11} is positive.

Now, if the lines of force, starting from the position where they are parallel to the $+X^0$ axis, rotate in the positive sense, then, on the basis of Eq. (21), the minor axis of the interference rings, which coincides with the field in this initial position, rotates in the opposite direction at half the velocity. This means that if $\phi = 30°$ (if the direction of the lines of force is equivalent to the $-Y^0$ axis), it must form a 45° angle with the lines of force; if $\phi = 60°$ (if the direction of the lines of force is equivalent to the $-X^0$ axis), it must be perpendicular to it as determined experimentally by Kundt and Röntgen (see Sec. 2). This rule was corroborated for the rotation of the X and Y axes by the observations of Czermak [10] who interpreted these observations in a different way; the values obtained in this case were $\phi \approx -15°$, $\phi = 6°12'$, whereas Eq. (21) gives 7°30′. At the same time, this observation confirmed that the difference in the Z^0 direction, determined from Eq. (22) was independent of the direction of the lines of force.

Pockels [11] measured this path difference and the one parallel to the Y^0 axis for certain field intensities which make it possible to make absolute measurements of constant e_{11}. The following mean value is derived from numerous measurements (assuming an absolute electrostatic standard)

$$e_{11}(D_1 - 1)/4\pi = +1.40 \times 10^{-8}.$$

Constant e_{41} was determined by measuring the path difference formed in the directions which form ±45° angles with the major axis in the Y^0Z^0 plane [12] due to dielectric polarization parallel to X^0. This path difference is also dependent on the value of a_{23} which, according to (13) is proportional to $e_{41}A$. The following is derived

$$e_{41}(D_1 - 1)/4\pi = +0.59 \times 10^{-8}.$$

If the value of 4.6 is assumed for the dielectric constant D_1 in the direction perpendicular to the major axis, then [CGS electrostatic units]

$$e_{11} = 0.49 \times 10^{-8}, \qquad e_{41} = 0.20 \times 10^{-8}.$$

The problem discussed at the end of Sec. 2 could be solved for quartz on the basis of these results. The variations of the optical polarization constants resulting from the deformation of quartz in the electrical field can be represented through formulas of the type (13), where e'_{11} and e'_{41} are substituted for e_{11} and e_{41} calculated from the piezoelectric constants δ_{11}, δ_{41}[1] and the elastooptical contains p_{hk} as follows

$$e'_{11}\frac{D_1 - 1}{4\pi} = \delta_{11}(p_{11} - p_{12}) + \delta_{14}p_{14},$$
$$e'_{41}\frac{D_1 - 1}{4\pi} = 2\delta_{11}p_{41} + \delta_{14}p_{44}. \tag{23}$$

Using the values of δ_{11}, δ_{41} determined for the same crystal (loc. cit. p. 131), we have

$$e'_{11} = 0.235 \times 10^{-8}, \qquad e'_{41} = 0.157 \times 10^{-8}.$$

These values are considerably smaller than the observed $e_{11}\,e_{41}$. Consequently, the optical properties of quartz are affected *directly* by the dielectric induction in addition to the indirect influence due to deformation.

For crystals of the hemimorphic group of the rhombohedral system (which includes tourmaline) the optical effect of an electrical field perpendicular to the major axis (neglecting the very small rotation of the Z axis) differs from the above only in that the Y^0 axis, lying in one of the three symmetry planes passing through the major axis, plays the same role as the X^0 axis defined above for quartz. Therefore, the rule based on eq. (21) for the location of the main polarization axes, X, Y, with respect to the field direction must be valid here also. Since tourmaline does not exhibit rotation, then the oscillation directions of the waves propagated parallel to the major axis, i.e., the extinction directions induced by an electrical field, are observed in a plate between crossed Nicols arranged perpendicularly to the main axis (as long as birefringence occurs in the direction of the main axis, which is the case for most tourmalines). This effect was observed for a blue tourmaline and the validity of (21) was corroborated [13]. In contrast to quartz, the birefringence in tourmaline may be varied (on the basis of Eq. (12)) by an electrical field parallel to the main axis (in which case it remains uniaxial). This effect also could be detected in the same blue tourmaline; such a variation with electrical field results in a hyperbolic path difference visible in converging light on observation perpendicularly to the main axis, and indicates that birefringence is increased through a dielectric

[1] They also determine the specific electrical moments, generated through elastic pressures, according to $A = \delta_{11}(X_x - Y_y) - \delta_{14}Y_z$, $B = \delta_{14}Z_x + 2\delta_{11}X_y$, and the deformations related to dielectric induction as a result of:

$$x_x = -y_y = \delta_{11}\frac{4\pi A}{D_1 - 1}, \qquad z_z = 0,$$
$$y_z = \delta_{14}\frac{4\pi A}{D_1 - 1}, \qquad z_x = -\delta_{14}\frac{4\pi B}{D_1 - 1}, \qquad x_y = -2\delta_{11}\frac{4\pi B}{D_1 - 1}$$

movement of a direction opposite to the one generated by a pressure parallel to the main axis [14].

5. SODIUM CHLORATE.

Sodium chlorate belonging to the tetrahedral group was investigated as a representative of piezoelectric regular [cubic] crystals ([11], l.c. p. 29 ff.). Since then the optical variations expected in the electric field must again be calculated according to the equations (developed in Pt. II, Chap. I) of Sec. 2, assuming superposition of the rotation and the birefringence determined through eq. (19). For the electric field induced birefringence in the absence of rotation we derive the following equations from the general eqs. (31) (Pt. I, Chap. II, Sec. 19) by substituting the terms (19) for the direction cosines $\alpha_1 \cdots \gamma_3$ of the polarization main axes for the cube normals X^0, Y^0, Z^0:

$$\begin{aligned} A(\beta_2\gamma_3 + \beta_3\gamma_2) + B(\beta_3\gamma_1 + \beta_1\gamma_3) + C(\beta_1\gamma_2 + \beta_2\gamma_1) &= 0, \\ A(\gamma_2\alpha_3 + \gamma_3\alpha_2) + B(\gamma_3\alpha_1 + \gamma_1\alpha_3) + C(\gamma_1\alpha_2 + \gamma_2\alpha_1) &= 0, \\ A(\alpha_2\beta_3 + \alpha_3\beta_2) + B(\alpha_3\beta_1 + \alpha_1\beta_3) + C(\alpha_1\beta_2 + \alpha_2\beta_1) &= 0, \end{aligned} \tag{24}$$

and the following for the principal velocities of light:

$$\begin{aligned} a^2 &= a^{02} + 2e_{41}(A\alpha_2\alpha_3 + B\alpha_3\alpha_1 + C\alpha_1\alpha_2), \\ b^2 &= a^{02} + 2e_{41}(A\beta_2\beta_3 + B\beta_3\beta_1 + C\beta_1\beta_2), \\ c^2 &= a^{02} + 2e_{41}(A\gamma_2\gamma_3 + B\gamma_3\gamma_1 + C\gamma_1\gamma_2). \end{aligned} \tag{25}$$

These equations imply that the orientation of the principal polarization axis and of the binormals of a regular [cubic] crystal rendered birefringent by an electrical field are dependent only on the direction of the electrical field (or the lines of force, with which the direction of the moment of regular crystals always coincides). Chap. II, Sec. 6 indicates that this is also the case for the binormal in regular crystals under the influence of unilateral pressure. We shall limit our discussion of this dependence to cases where the electrical lines of force are parallel to either a cube face (X^0Y^0 plane) or to a rhombododecahedron face (dividing plane of the positive quadrant between the Z^0X^0 and Z^0Y^0 planes).

(a) *Lines of force in the X^0Y^0 plane*, forming angle ϕ with X^0. Let $A = M\cos\phi$, $B = M\sin\phi$, $C = 0$, and we have from (24):

$$\alpha_1 = \cos\phi, \qquad \alpha_2 = -\sin\phi, \qquad \alpha_3 = 0,$$

$$\beta_1 = \gamma_1 = \sqrt{\tfrac{1}{2}}\sin\phi\mu \qquad \beta_2 = \gamma_2 = \sqrt{\tfrac{1}{2}}\cos\phi, \qquad -\beta_3 = \gamma_3 = \sqrt{\tfrac{1}{2}},$$

which implies that the X axis also lies in the X^0Y^0 plane forming angle $\Phi = -\phi$ with X^0 (so that it lies symmetrically opposite M with respect to

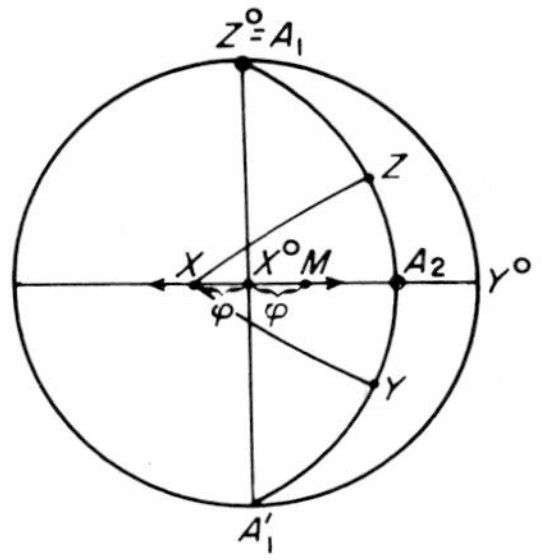

Fig. 166

X^0), whereas the Y and X axes lie symmetrically on both sides of the X^0Y^0 plane (i.e., at a 45° angle to it). (See Fig. 166.) Equations (25) also imply that

$$a = a^0, \qquad b^2 = a^{02} - e_{41} M, \qquad c^2 = a^{02} + e_{41} M.$$

Accordingly, if the moment is directed in the X^0Y^0 plane the crystal is always optically biaxial with its binormal plane perpendicular to the X^0Y^0 plane and with a 90° binormal angle; whereas one of the binormals coincides with the invariant direction of the Z^0 axis, the other coincides with the intercept of the X^0Y^0 and YZ planes. (See Fig. 166 where A_1 (or A_1') and A_2 denote the binormals.) The magnitude of the birefringence is also independent of ϕ.

If the lines of force are parallel to a cube normal, then the binormals are parallel to the two other cube normals and the largest path difference lies in the direction of the lines of force.

If the lines of force are parallel to a rhombododecahedron normal (i.e., $\phi = 45°$), then a binormal is parallel to them and the largest path difference corresponds to the direction of the dodecahedron normal perpendicular to them.

(b) *Lines of force parallel to a rhombododecahedron face* forming angle ϑ with Z^0.

Equations (24), where $A = B = M\sqrt{\frac{1}{2}} \sin \vartheta$, $C = M \cos \vartheta$ must be inserted, imply that two principal polarization axes (Y and/or Z) lie in the same dodecahedron plane as M and that the angle $\chi = (Z, Z^0)$ is determined through $\tan 2\chi = -2 \tan \vartheta$. Now, if $\vartheta = 0$ (for $M \parallel Z^0$) and $\chi = 90°$ correspond to each other, then the mutual position of M and Z is as follows: (also see Fig. 167 where the arrows indicate the directions of moments of M and Z):

$$0 < \vartheta < 54°44' < \vartheta < 90°$$

$$90° > \chi > 54°44' > \chi > 45°.$$

For the principal velocities of light Eq. (25) gives:

$$a^2 = a^{02} - e_{41} M \cos \vartheta,$$

$$b^2 = a^{02} + e_{41} M(\cos \vartheta \cos^2\chi - \sin \vartheta \sin 2\chi),$$

$$c^2 = a^{02} + e_{41} M(\cos \vartheta \sin^2\chi + \sin \vartheta \sin 2\chi).$$

Consequently, the crystal is also optically biaxial but its binormal angle is now dependent on M; for $\vartheta < 54°44'$ the binormal plane is perpendicular to the Z^0M plane, for $\vartheta > 54°44'$ it is parallel to it. The crystal is uniaxial only when the lines of force are exactly parallel to the octahedron normal given by $\vartheta = 54°44'$; in such a case we have

$$\chi = \theta, \qquad a^2 = b^2 = a^{02} - Me_{41}/\sqrt{3}, \qquad c^2 = a^{02} + 2Me_{41}/\sqrt{3}.$$

As a result, $NaClO_3$ crystals are transformed into optically biaxial crystals with rotation, in an electrical field the orientation of the binormal and its angle being quite different depending on the direction of the lines of force. The theory of light propagation, developed in Pt. II, Chapter II, Sec. 2, must be applied to these crystals in order to interpret the observed phenomena on the basis of the specified laws of pure birefringence.

Since the birefringence generated by the electric field is weak, the path differences in regular [cubic] crystals cannot be determined on the basis of interference curve observations in converging light, although compensator observations are suited for these purposes. However, in the presence of rotation the latter do not directly yield the field generated path differences so that a rather complex equation must be used.

The directions of the principal axes of the oscillation ellipses of the waves propagated in different directions were also investigated according to Pt. II, Chapter Il, p. 311; these would represent the oscillation directions in the absence of rotation and are theoretically derived from the ovaloid determined by $a_{11} \cdots a_{12}$ as the major axes of its diametric segments. Experimentally these directions are determined by inserting the crystal plate under investigation between two rotatable Nicols, establishing those positions for

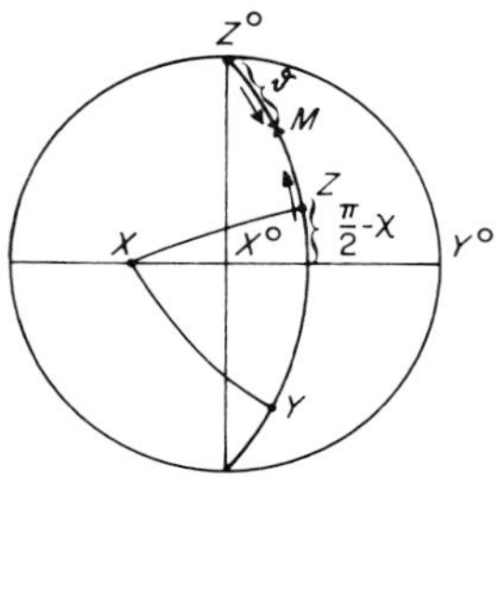

Fig. 167

which the plate is dark in homogeneous light and exhibits the least illumination when the electrical field is applied;[1] in such a case the axes of the oscillation ellipses in the crystal cut the angles between the oscillation direction of the polarizer and the normal to the analyzer in half. The directions of the binormals are also determined for this material as the observation directions for which intensity or color variation does not occur with application of the electrical field for any orientation of the Nicols.

The observations were made for such orientations of the crystal plates in the electrical field that the lines of force were parallel to a cube, dodecahedron, or octahedron normal[2] and completely corroborated the above predictions of the theory. Compensator measurements yielded the following for the electrooptical constant (for Na light)

$$e_{41} = 1.19 \times 10^{-8}[4\pi/(D - 1)];$$

where the sign is positive if the coordinate system, formed by the cube normals, is chosen in such a way that one of the tetrahedral faces formed on the crystals lies in the first octant. The dielectric constant of sodium chlorate is not known exactly so that e_{41} cannot be calculated; however, an exact determination of the dependence of the electrooptic effect on the electrical field deformation requires only the product $e_{41}(D - 1)/4\pi$. As a result, it was necessary to investigate the piezoelectric behavior and the piezooptical properties (as far as it is dependent on p_{44}). In acentric regular [cubic] crystals the former is characterized by a constant δ_{41} and the electrical moments are given by

$$A = -\delta_{14} Y_z, \qquad B = -\delta_{14} Z_x, \qquad C = -\delta_{14} X_y;$$

and for the deformation in the electric field [15] we have:

$$y_z = \frac{4\pi}{D - 1}\delta_{14} A, \qquad z_x = \frac{4\pi}{D - 1}\delta_{14} B, \qquad x_y = \frac{4\pi}{D - 1}\delta_{14} C,$$

and for the constant e'_{41} which determines the "indirect" electrooptical effect resulting from deformation:

$$e'_{41} = [4\pi/(D - 1)]\delta_{14} p_{44}. \tag{26}$$

The experimentally determined values $\delta_{14} = -4.84 \times 10^{-8}$ and $p_{44} = -0.0197$ give

$$e'_{41} = 0.096 \times 10^{-8}[4\pi/(D - 1)]$$

i.e., a value which is much lower than the above value of e_{41} which represents the actual electrooptic properties. Consequently, the electric field has a direct effect on the propagation of light also in sodium chlorate.

---

[1] The sensitive coloring and its least variation in white light can be used instead.

[2] The electrical field was applied between transparent liquid layers so that observations could also be made in the direction of the lines of force.

6. ROCHELLE SALT (PURE POTASSIUM-SODIUM TARTRATE).

According to Eq. (14) for the hemihedral group of the rhombic system three constants play an important role in the electrooptical effect in such a way that each of these constants determines the optical effect with respect to a field component parallel to one of the three symmetry axes, independent of the two others. These three constants are determined separately by observation on three plates, ground perpendicularly to the symmetry axes X^0, Y^0, Z^0 and metal coated on their top and bottom surfaces. Since only one of the quantities a_{23}, a_{31}, a_{12} differs from zero, then only one rotation (Φ_x, or Φ_y, Φ_z) of the principal polarization axes about the direction of the lines of force takes place. This rotation is given to within a satisfactory accuracy through the approximate Eqs. (7′) in the previous Chapter for the strong birefringence of Rochelle salt. Since a_{11}, a_{22}, a_{33} do not vary, the general Eqs. (32) (Pt. I, Chap. II, Sec. 19) imply that (to within small second order quantities) the principal light velocities also remain unchanged so that these rotations represent the only variation of the optical properties in the electric field. They can be measured by observing the variations of the path difference parallel to the bisectrices of the angles between the two symmetry axes (perpendicular to the lines of force) in the plane of which the rotation takes place.

The results determined in this way (using the values of the dielectric constants determined by Borel [Dissertation, Geneva 1893]), assuming a coordinate system where the X^0, Y^0, Z^0 axes coincide with the crystallographic *a*, *b*, *c* axis, are as follows

$$e_{52} = -10.8 \times 10^{-8}, \qquad e_{63} = +2.1 \times 10^{-8}.$$

Constant e_{41} could not be determined with certainty because an intense electrical residue was observed in the crystal plates for dielectric polarization parallel to the *a* axis (first center line). It was determined, however, that e_{41} was negative and of the same order of magnitude as e_{52}, probably even considerably larger. Compared with the constants for quartz and $NaClO_3$, the above values indicate that the reversible electrooptic effect for Rochelle salt is considerably stronger than for quartz and sodium chlorate. It could not be determined how much of this effect is generated by the deformation since the constants of elasticity, required for calculating the electrooptical constants p_{44}, p_{55}, p_{66}, were not known. In the case of dielectric polarization parallel to the Z^0 axis it could be determined that e_{63} and the corresponding constant e'_{63} which determines the optical effect of deformation, have opposite signs so that a direct electrooptic effect, at least, must exist. It is remarkable also that a field parallel to the X^0 axis possesses an optical variation which is not reversible with the field direction (namely, an increased birefringence in the directions Y^0 and Z^0) which is analogous to the Kerr effect discussed in Sec. 1 and which, as far as the present observations permit one to draw any conclusions, also cannot be interpreted as an indirect effect (generated by deformation or temperature variation). It is possible that in view of the residual phenomena in this field direction, it is related to a relatively high internal electrical conductivity of Rochelle salt in this particular direction.

7. ROTATION IN THE MAGNETIC FIELD.

Faraday was the first to observe that the polarization plane of certain simple refracting bodies, for example lead glass, rotates in the direction of the lines of force in a strong magnetic field. The rotation direction is reversed with the direction of the field and its amount per unit length increases with the field intensity—in weakly magnetic substances proportional to the field intensity and in strongly magnetic metals (where the rotation can be observed only in extremely thin layers), according to Kundt, proportional to the specific magnetic moment. This "magnetic rotation" differs from the natural one essentially in that on reversal of the propagation direction, the rotation direction is also reversed with respect to the latter so that, in absolute terms, it remains unchanged. As a result, in naturally rotating quartz the total rotation is zero for a beam propagated along the direction of the major axis if it returns the same way due to perpendicular reflection; however, in an analogous experimental arrangement with a magnetically rotating body the rotation would be doubled. The axial nature of a vector characterizing a magnetic field (see footnote 2, p. 334) implies that this type of behavior must be exhibited by the rotation resulting from the magnetic field.

The laws of propagation of plane waves in an isotropic medium, optically rotating due to a magnetic field, are derived (at least to a rough approximation) assuming that the constant difference of the propagation velocities $q_1 - q_2$, observed for naturally rotating isotropic media, is replaced with a difference which is proportional to the projection of the specific magnetic moment m on the propagation direction. Since this difference is very small with respect to q_1 or q_2, the normal surface (and also the ray surface) consists approximately of two spheres, the centers 0, 0′, of which are slightly displaced[1] with respect to each other in the direction of the magnetic axis (MM^1, Fig. 168).

Fig. 168

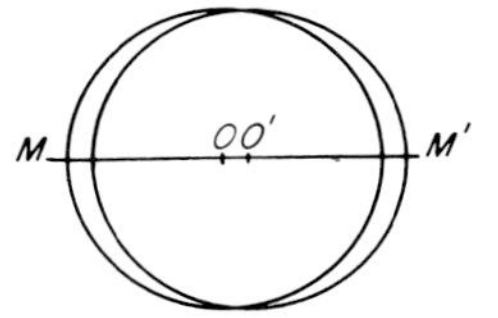

[1] See B. W. Voigt, "Compendium of Theoretical Physics," Pt. V, Chap. II, Sec. 18, for derivation of the properties of magnetically rotating media from the appropriate auxiliary terms of the differential equations.

The laws of the propagation velocities and mode of vibration for crystals with magnetic field induced rotation are derived from the laws (Pt. II, Chap. II; Secs. 2 and 3) for crystals with natural rotation simply by substituting the linear function

$$\rho' = \mu m \cos(m, q) = \mu(\nu_1 \beta_1 + \nu_2 \beta_2 + \nu_3 \beta_3) m \tag{27}$$

for the rotation ρ which has been considered a quadratic function of the direction cosine, (ν_1, ν_2, ν_3) of the wave normal where μ is a (positive or negative) constant characteristic of the crystal and β_1, β_2, β_3 represent the direction cosines of moment m (the direction of which does not coincide with that of the lines of force in crystals). The same result is derived from the theory based on differential equations, however, it includes a certain dependence of μ on the oscillation period [16].

The magnetic rotation was first observed in crystals by E. Becquerel [17] for quartz, beryllium, and tourmaline in the direction of the optical axis. Chauvin [18] studied calcite to determine the optical effect of a magnetic field parallel to the major axis. His experiment consisted in transmitting homogeneous light, polarized in its main section, at different angles with respect to the optical axis (which is also the plate normal) through a calcite plate; he then analyzed the emitted, weakly elliptical oscillation by a method similar to that one used by Jamin and Beaulard for quartz. Assuming that Gouy's formulas (Eqs. (1) amd (2), p. 311) are valid, the behavior observed in a certain magnetic field can be completely explained by a constant rotation superposed on the regular birefringence. This result is expected on the basis of the above theoretical considerations since the largest angle between the observation direction and the optical axis amounted to only $1 - \frac{1}{2}°$ and $\cos(m, q)$ in Eq. (27) is appreciably constant and equals unity. For larger angles the ellipticity of the oscillations in calcite is no longer measurable since its magnetic rotation is very weak (0.019′ for a path length of 1 cm parallel to the major axis for a magnetic field intensity of one cgs) and its natural birefringence is very strong.

The dispersion of the magnetic rotation was investigated by Joubin [19] for rock salt and by Borel [20] for quartz parallel to the major axis. The magnetic rotation, as the natural rotation, was found to be approximately inversely proportional to the square of the wavelength.

It is pointed out once more (see footnote 3, p. 313) that it is possible that an optical behavior analogous to the one artificially induced by a magnetic field may naturally exist in those crystal groups the symmetry elements of which are compatible with the existence of a distinct direction, having the nature of an axial vector [21]. Such a symmetry is found in the paramorphous (or pyramidal) hemihedral groups of the tetragonal, rhombohedral, and hexagonal systems and also in those tetrahedral groups which become identical with the former by adding a symmetry center. In such a case the optical behavior obviously has the nature of an axial vector. This behavior could also be found in all monoclinic and triclinic crystals.[1] In these crystals ρ would be a linear function of ν_1, ν_2, ν_3, the coefficients of which could be interpreted as the components of a vector fixed in the crystal, oriented according to its symmetry properties. A natural rotation of this type analogous to the magnetic rotation, has not been observed yet in any case.

BIBLIOGRAPHY

1. Kerr, J., *Phil. Mag.* **50**(4). 337, 446 (1875); **8**(5). 185, 229 (1879); **9**. 114 (1880) Recent studies of this phenomenon have been made by Quincke, Röntgen, and also by W. Schmidt (Dissertation, Gottingen 1901).
2. Brongserma, *Wied. Ann* **16.** 422 (1882).
3. Gordon, J. E., *Phil. Mag.* **2**(5). 203 (1876) Mackenzie, J. J., *Wied. Ann.* **2.** 356 (1877) Quincke, G., *Wied. Ann.* **10.** 553 (1880)
4. Pockels, F., *Abh. Gottinger Ges. d Wiss.* **39.** 169 (1894),
5. Kerr, J., *Brit. Assoc. Rep.* 1901: 568; Majorana, Q. *Accad Lincei Rend.* **11.** 374 (1902) Vergl dazu Voigt, W., *Drudes Ann.* **8.** 880 (1902).
6. This view is defended by Kerr (1.c.), also see Schmauss, B. A., *Drudes Ann.* **12.** 186 (1903).
7. Röntgen, W. C., *Wied. Ann.* **18.** 213, 534 (1883); **19.** 319 (1883) Kundt, A., *Wied. Ann.* **18.** 228 (1883).
8. Voigt. W., *Kristallphysik*, p. 100, or *Winkelmanns Handb d Physik 2. Aufl.* (1905), Bd. IV^2, p. 780.
9. Lippman, *Ann. Chim. Phys.* **24**(5). 145 (1881) General calculations of the derivations in the electrical field were first made by F. Pockels (N. Jahrb. f. Miner. Beil.-Bd. **7.** 224 (1890))
10. Czermak, P., *Wiener Sitzungsber* **97**(2). 301 (1888) Also see Pockels, F., *N. Jahrb. f. Miner. Beil*-Bd. **7.** 218 (1890).
11. Pockels, F., Einflub d elektrostat Feldes auf d opt Verhalten piezoelektr Kristalle Abh Gottinger Ges d Wiss **39.** 99, 117 (1894).
12. 1. c. p. 127.
13. Pockels, F. 1.c. p. 152.
14. 1.c. p. 159
15. Pockels, F., 1.c. p. 7, 32.
16. Voigt W., Compendium, Pt. V, Chap. 1I, Sec. 18.
17. Becquerel, E., *Ann. Chim. Phys.* **17.** 445 (1846).
18. Chaubin, *Phys.* **9**(2). 5 (1890).
19. Joubin, *Phys.* **8.** 53 (1889).
20. Borel, *Arch. de Geneve* **16.** 24 and 157 (1903).
21. Voigt, W, Compendium, II, p. 571.

[1] This includes all groups specified in Chap. II, Sec. 4, under I, 1I, IVb, Vb, VIb.

Reprinted from *J. Opt. Soc. Amer.* **39**, 797–801 (1949).

The Electro-Optic Effect in Uniaxial Crystals of the Type X H_2PO_4. I. Theoretical

BRUCE H. BILLINGS
Research Laboratory, Baird Associates, Inc., Cambridge 38, Massachusetts
(Received June 22, 1949)

When voltage is put across a crystal of the type X H_2PO_4, the index ellipsoid in the crystal is rotated and the length of the axes changes. Two electro-optic coefficients are necessary to describe the effect in the most general plate of the crystal. The necessity for two coefficients is shown from consideration of the crystal symmetry. The behavior of Z-cut and X-cut plates are treated in detail. For Z-cut plates with the voltage in the *Z* direction the crystal becomes biaxial with the plane of the optic axes at 45° to the *X* and *Y* crystallographic axis. The retardation along the normal to the plate is directly proportional to the voltage and independent of the thickness. The characteristics of the polarization interference pattern for excited X and Z plates are discussed.

INTRODUCTION

THERE are many places where an electric light valve or shutter has useful applications. One of the most obvious forms of light valve is the Kerr cell. This cell contains a liquid between a pair of parallel plate electrodes. When an electric field is applied, the liquid becomes birefringent. If the cell is placed between crossed polarizers, light will not pass through the combination until voltage is applied. There are many difficulties associated with the ordinary liquid Kerr cell. This liquid cell uses nitrobenzene which has a high Kerr constant only when it is extremely pure. The operation of the cell tends to decompose the material and the most successful cells have been those in which the nitrobenzene is continuously redistilled as the cell is used. In addition, the liquid has a disagreeable odor and is intensely poisonous.

A solid electro-optic shutter avoids many of these difficulties. As a result, such a device becomes a practical solution for many different problems and should be a useful scientific tool.

The Kerr effect in most solids is extremely small. In certain crystals, however, there is a large electro-optic effect which requires voltage no higher than those required in the liquid cell. This effect varies with first power of the electric field rather than with the square of the field as does the normal Kerr effect.

During the last few years several papers[1,2,3,4] have appeared discussing the electro-optic effect in tetragonal scalenohedral crystals of the type X H_2PO_4. Now that some of these crystals such as $NH_4H_2PO_4$ or ADP[5] are available as light valves, it seems appropriate to give a more complete treatment of the useful effect than is available in any of these papers.

THEORETICAL

The birefringence of a crystal can be described in terms of its index ellipsoid. The index ellipsoid has axes which are equal to the three crystal indices. If a plane is passed through the center of this ellipsoid at right angles to the direction in which a ray of light is going, it will cut the ellipsoid in an ellipse whose major and minor axes are the two indices associated with that particular direction in the crystal. In the case of a biaxial crystal the equation for this ellipsoid can be written

$$a^2x^2+b^2y^2+c^2z^2=1 \qquad (1)$$

where *a*, *b* and *c* are the three reciprocal indices of

[1] G. D. Gottschall, J. Soc. Mot. Pict. Eng. **51**, 13 (1948).
[2] Hans Jaffe, Phys. Rev. **73**, 95 (1948).
[3] B. Zwicker and P. Scherrer, Helv. Phys. Acta **16**, 214 (1943).
[4] B. Zwicker and P. Scherrer, Helv. Phys. Acta **17**, 346 (1944).
[5] This crystal is grown under the trademark "PN" by the Brush Development Company, 3405 Perkins Avenue, Cleveland, Ohio.

refraction. In a uniaxial crystal two of the coefficients become equal and the equation reduces to

$$o^2(x^2+y^2)+e^2z^2=1 \tag{2}$$

where o is the ordinary reciprocal index and e the extraordinary reciprocal index. The electro-optic effect in crystals is a change in crystalline birefringence which occurs when a crystal is placed in an electric field. The first general treatment of the effect was given by Pockels.[6,7] He showed the number of constants to be expected in the different crystal classes and made experimental measurements in the case of quartz, $NaClO_3$ and rochelle salts. This change can be described in terms of a change of the orientation and the dimensions of the index ellipsoid. The numerical constants involved in this change can be considered as small corrections to be applied to the index ellipsoid constants. In order to write them it is necessary to put the equation of the index ellipsoid in its most general form. Crystallographers commonly refer the faces of a crystal to a cartesian coordinate system. The directions of these crystallographic axes are prescribed for each crystal class. Instead of referring the ellipsoid to its own principal axes it is referred instead to these crystallographic symmetry axes. The equation of the ellipsoid then becomes

$$1=a_{11}x^2+a_{22}y^2+a_{33}z^2+2a_{23}yz+2a_{31}zx+2a_{12}xy. \tag{3}$$

The new constants, a_{11}, a_{12}, etc., are called the polarization constants. If the a's are all known, it is possible

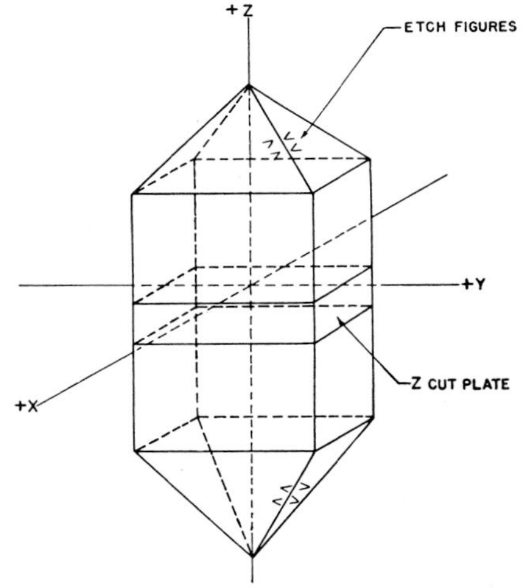

FIG. 1. Sketch of an $NH_4H_2PO_4$ crystal with its crystallographic axes labelled.

[6] F. Pockels, Abhandlungen der Gesellschaft der Wissenschaften zu Gottingen, **39**, 1 (1893).
[7] F. Pockels, *Lehrbuch der Kristalloptik* (Leipzig, 1906).

to find the orientation of the axes of the ellipsoid with respect to the crystallographic axes.

The direction cosines connecting the two sets of axes may be described in the matrix

$$\begin{array}{c|ccc} & X' & Y' & Z' \\ \hline X & \alpha_1 & \alpha_2 & \alpha_3 \\ Y & \beta_1 & \beta_2 & \beta_3 \\ Z & \gamma_1 & \gamma_2 & \gamma_3 \end{array} \tag{4}$$

where the primed axes are the crystallographic axes, the unprimed axes are the axes of the index ellipsoid, and α_1 is the cosine of the angle between x and x', etc. When an electric field is applied, the polarization constants can be written

$$\begin{aligned} a_{11}-a_0^2&=r_{11}E_x+r_{12}E_y+r_{13}E_z\\ a_{22}-b_0^2&=r_{21}E_x+r_{22}E_y+r_{23}E_z\\ a_{33}-c_0^2&=r_{31}E_x+r_{32}E_y+r_{33}E_z\\ a_{23}&=r_{41}E_x+r_{42}E_y+r_{43}E_z\\ a_{31}&=r_{51}E_x+r_{52}E_y+r_{53}E_z\\ a_{12}&=r_{61}E_x+r_{62}E_y+r_{63}E_z \end{aligned} \tag{5}$$

where the r_{ij} are the electro-optic coefficients and E_x, E_y, E_z are the components of the field along the three crystallographic axes. These equations have been written for a crystal in which the crystallographic axes coincide with the polarization axes. They differ from the equations of Pockels by referring to the field instead of the electrical polarization. The constants r_{ij} are thus related to Pockels' constants e_{ij} by the equation

$$r_{ij}=\frac{K_j-1}{4\pi}e_{ij}$$

where K_j is the dielectric constant in the direction in which the field is applied. The symbol r_{ij} is used in accordance with Cady's[8] suggestion that the Mueller[9] convention be used. If no field were applied the constants would reduce to the three coefficients given in Eq. (1).

The most striking characteristic of a crystal is its symmetry. This symmetry is described by a set of operations sometimes called "covering operations" which can be performed on the crystal without altering its appearance or physical behavior. For example, if a cube is rotated 90° about an axis normal to any face the cube will not appear to have been moved. If the cube is isotropic with respect to all its other physical properties, the operations which leave its external appearance unchanged will be the characteristic symmetry operations. If the cube is made of wood which has a grain perpendicular to one face, the tensile strength would not be the same in the case of the 90° rotation about an axis parallel to this face. In general the physical characteristics of a crystal possess the same or higher symmetry as the symmetry of its form. This is,

[8] W. G. Cady, *Piezoelectricity* (McGraw-Hill Book Company, Inc., New York, 1946).
[9] H. Mueller, Phys. Rev. **58**, 805–811 (1940).

of course, true only for an ideal crystal of any material.

Since many readers are perhaps rusty in their crystallography, it seems apropos to carry through the actual reduction of the constants in Eq. (4). In Fig. 1 is a sketch of an $NH_4H_2PO_4$ crystal with its crystallographic axes labeled. At first glance the crystal appears to possess a center of symmetry, i.e., it looks as though every point in the crystal could be reflected through the center to an equal distance on the other side and the resulting crystal would be identical. This turns out not to be the case. It is most simply demonstrated by etch figures. If one of the end faces is slightly moistened and dried, a series of little pits appear. These pits are triangular in shape and are oppositely oriented on opposite faces. There are two main symmetry operations which can be performed on the crystal. The first is a rotation through $\pi/2$ about the z axis followed by an inversion through the center. This, of course, does not mean that the crystal has a center of symmetry because the inversion must always be preceded by the $\pi/2$ rotation about z. The second operation is a rotation of π about either the x or y axis. Crystals whose characteristics are unchanged after these operations are said to belong in the class V_d or $42m$. If these operations are now performed on Eq. (5) the constants must remain unchanged. The operation of rotating through an angle π about the x axis leaves x unchanged and changes y to $-y$ and z to $-z$. The field E_x is unchanged whereas E_y becomes $-E_y$ and E_z becomes $-E_z$. When these substitutions are made in Eq. (5) and Eq. (3) the coefficients a_{11} through a_{12} must change sign in such a way that Eq. (3) is unchanged. The effect on the electrooptic coefficients may be simply shown by writing Eq. (5) in matrix form. For further aid the multiplier of the a_{ij}'s in Eq. (3) is placed in the a_{ij} vector.

$$\begin{vmatrix} a_{11}(x^2) \\ a_{22}(y^2) \\ a_{33}(z^2) \\ a_{23}(yz) \\ a_{31}(xz) \\ a_{12}(xy) \end{vmatrix} = \begin{vmatrix} r_{11} & r_{12} & r_{13} \\ r_{21} & r_{22} & r_{23} \\ r_{31} & r_{32} & r_{33} \\ r_{41} & r_{42} & r_{43} \\ r_{51} & r_{52} & r_{53} \\ r_{61} & r_{62} & r_{63} \end{vmatrix} \cdot \begin{vmatrix} E_x(x) \\ E_y(y) \\ E_z(z) \end{vmatrix}.$$

If the substitutions $x \rightarrow x$, $y \rightarrow -y$; $z \rightarrow -z$ are made in this matrix equation, it is apparent that a_{11}, a_{22} and a_{33} will not change signs. Since E_y and E_z do change sign, this means that all the r_{ij}'s in the first three rows are zero with the exception of r_{11}, r_{21}, and r_{31}. The operation of rotating the crystal through an angle π about the y axis changes the sign of x and z but leaves y unchanged. This operation makes these the remaining three coefficients in the first three rows vanish. The final array of elements in the matrix becomes

$$\begin{vmatrix} 0 & 0 & 0 \\ 0 & 0 & 0 \\ 0 & 0 & 0 \\ r_{41} & 0 & 0 \\ 0 & r_{41} & 0 \\ 0 & 0 & r_{63} \end{vmatrix} \tag{7}$$

The constants a_{ij} thus reduce to

$$\begin{aligned} a_{11}=a_{22}=o^2 \quad & a_{23}=r_{41}E_x \\ a_{33}=e^2 \quad & a_{31}=r_{41}E_y \\ & a_{12}=r_{63}E_z. \end{aligned} \tag{8}$$

FIELD IN Z DIRECTION

The crystal section which is most useful as a shutter is the Z-cut or basal plate with field applied in the Z direction and the light traveling in the same direction. For light thus parallel to the optic axis the plate has no retardation and appears isotropic. The analysis below shows that in this direction the electrically induced retardation is also highest for a given voltage.

For this case the fields E_x and E_y become zero and the only non-zero coefficients are thus a_{11}, a_{22}, a_{33} and a_{12}. These values can be inserted into Eq. (3) to give

$$e^2z^2+o^2(x^2+y^2)+2r_{63}E_zxy=1. \tag{9}$$

From this equation it is apparent that the Z and Z' axes coincide. This shows that $\gamma_1=\gamma_2=\alpha_3=\beta_3=0$ and $\gamma_3=1$.

To find the remaining cosines and hence the angle by which the ellipsoid is rotated, Eq. (9) is transformed to the coordinate system which has its axes along the ellipsoid axes. This equation connecting the two sets can be written down directly from the matrix (4) which represents the direction cosines between them.

$$\begin{aligned} x' &= \alpha_1x+\beta_1y \\ y' &= \alpha_2x+\beta_2y. \end{aligned}$$

Since the rotation is in a plane

$$-\alpha_2=\beta_1; \quad \alpha_1=\beta_2.$$

These equations can now be put in Eq. (9) and the cross terms set equal to zero so that the axes will coincide with the ellipsoid axes.

$$2r_{63}C(\alpha_1^2-\alpha_2^2)xy=0. \tag{10}$$

The expression for the angle then becomes

$$\cos 2\alpha=0 \quad \alpha=\pm 45°. \tag{11}$$

Since this rotation is independent of the field it is possible at this stage of the analysis to say what will be the appearance between polarizers of a z-cut slab of PN when a field is applied in the z direction. The crystal becomes biaxial and the characteristic uniaxial fringe pattern of circles is replaced by a series of ovals. The long axis of the oval lies at 45° to the crystallographic axis. The length of the long axes of the ovals in the pattern will change as the field is changed. The direction, however, remains constant. To find how the axis length changes with the field it is necessary to compute the actual value of the crystal indices.

It is necessary now to find the new reciprocal indices, a, b and c. These are related to the polarization constants by formulas which can be written directly from Eq. (3) and the matrix (4)

$$a^2=a_{11}\alpha_1^2+a_{22}\alpha_2^2+a_{33}\alpha_3^2+2a_{23}\alpha_2\alpha_3+2a_{31}\alpha_3\alpha_1+2a_{12}\alpha_1\alpha_2$$
$$b^2=a_{11}\beta_1^2+a_{22}\beta_2^2+a_{33}\beta_3^2+2a_{23}\beta_2\beta_3+2a_{31}\beta_3\beta_1+2a_{12}\beta_1\beta_2 \quad (12)$$
$$c^2=a_{11}\gamma_1^2+a_{22}\gamma_2^2+a_{33}\gamma_3^2+2a_{23}\gamma_2\gamma_3+2a_{31}\gamma_3\gamma_1+2a_{12}\gamma_1\gamma_2.$$

Since the only rotation is ϕ_z in the xy plane,

$$a^2=a_{11}\cos^2\phi+a_{22}\sin^2\phi+2a_{12}\sin\phi\cos\phi =o^2\cos^2\phi+o^2\sin^2\phi+2r_{63}E_z\sin\phi\cos\phi$$
$$b^2=a_{11}\sin^2\phi+a_{22}\cos^2\phi-2a_{12}\sin\phi\cos\phi =o^2\sin^2\phi+o^2\cos^2\phi-2r_{63}E_z\sin\phi\cos\phi \quad (13)$$
$$c^2=a_{33}=e^2$$

since $\phi_z=-45°$

$$a^2=o^2-2r_{63}E_z\frac{1}{\sqrt{2}}\cdot\frac{1}{\sqrt{2}}=o^2-r_{63}E_z$$

$$b^2=o^2+2r_{63}E_z\frac{1}{\sqrt{2}}\cdot\frac{1}{\sqrt{2}}=o^2+r_{63}E_z. \quad (14)$$

One can write

$$c^2=e^2=\frac{1}{\epsilon^2}=\frac{1}{\alpha^2}$$
$$a^2=\frac{1}{\gamma^2}\quad b^2=\frac{1}{\beta^2}. \quad (15)$$

Since the only field is in the Z direction, E_z can be replaced by V/d when V is the applied voltage and d is the plate thickness. The value of r_{63} then includes the dielectric constant.

The retardation which will appear along the normal to the basal section after the voltage is applied can be written:

$$\Gamma=\frac{d}{\lambda}\left(\frac{1}{a}-\frac{1}{b}\right). \quad (16)$$

This can be rewritten:

$$\Gamma=\frac{d}{\lambda}\frac{a^2-b^2}{(a+b)ab}$$
$$=\frac{d}{2\lambda}(a^2-b^2)\omega^3. \quad (17)$$

If Eq. (13) is inserted in this final equation, one gets the equation:

$$\Gamma=\frac{r_{63}V\omega^3}{\lambda}=pV. \quad (18)$$

This shows that in this particular cut of crystal the retardation along the normal is a function of the voltage rather than the field strength. In other words, the retardation for a given voltage is independent of the thickness of the plate.

The value for r_{63} becomes:

$$r_{63}=\lambda\Gamma/\omega^3V \quad (19)$$

The value of this constant has been determined for $NH_4H_2PO_4$ or "PN" under a variety of conditions by Dr. Hans Jaffe of The Brush Development Company.

The value of the new indices can now be calculated from Eq. (13):

$$\gamma=\frac{1}{a}=\frac{1}{\left(o^2-\frac{\lambda\Gamma}{\omega^3 d}\right)^{\frac{1}{2}}} \quad (20)$$

or

$$\gamma=\omega+\frac{\lambda\Gamma}{2d}. \quad (21)$$

Similarly,

$$\beta=\omega-\frac{\lambda\Gamma}{2d}. \quad (22)$$

One of the striking things about these two index values is the small change which occurs with the application of voltage. A half-wave retardation requires nearly 10,000 volts for PN and this retardation is the result of index changes of only a few parts in a million for plate thicknesses of the order of a centimeter.

Although this value seems small, it is larger in ADP than in other crystals which have been previously studied. The coefficient r_{63} in ADP is 8.2×10^{-7} whereas the largest coefficients for quartz and rochelle salts are $r_{11(\text{quartz})}=4.67\times10^{-8}$ cm/kv and $r_{52(\text{Rochelle})}=-36.0\times10^{-8}$ cm/kv.

When voltage is applied to the crystal it becomes biaxial with an axial angle Ω. The retardation along the normal which was expressed in Eq. (14) can be written in terms of this axial angle. The expression for the retardation as a function of angle of incidence in a Z-cut slab of biaxial crystal can be written:

$$\frac{\Gamma}{kd}=\sin\theta_1\sin\theta_2/\cos r \quad (23)$$

where θ_1 and θ_2 are the angles made by the ray with the two axes; r is the angle of incidence of the ray; d is the thickness of the slab, k is a constant. When $r=0$, this equation becomes:

$$\Gamma=kd\sin^2\Omega \quad (24)$$

where Ω is the angle between the optic axes and the Z axis. In combination with Eq. (14) this becomes:

$$kd\sin^2\Omega=pV \quad (25)$$

where p is a constant and V is the voltage across the crystal plate.

It is apparent from these equations that the value of the axial angle is inversely proportional to the square root of the thickness and directly proportional to the square root of the voltage.

FIELD IN X OR Y DIRECTIONS

Since the equations are symmetrical, the effect produced by a field in the X direction is the same as a field in the Y direction. Accordingly, this section will be limited to a discussion of the effect of a field along X. In this case the only non-zero coefficients are a_{11}, a_{22}, a_{32} and a_{23}. These values can be inserted into Eq. (3) to give

$$o^2(x^2+y^2)+e^2z^2+2r_{41}E_xyz=1. \qquad (26)$$

From this equation it is apparent that the X and X' axes coincide and the only rotation is in the yz plane. From an analysis similar to that used in the case of the basal section it can be shown that the axes are rotated through an angle

$$\tan 2\xi=-\frac{2r_{41}E_x}{e^2-o^2}. \qquad (27)$$

This differs from the previous case in that the angle is dependent on the field and that it is quite small. Its size can, of course, only be stated with a knowledge of r_{41}. This coefficient will be discussed in a later paper. For $NH_4H_2PO_4$ it is of such a size that the rotation is only a few minutes.

The reciprocal indices can be found from Eq. (11) which can be rewritten

$$\begin{aligned} b^2&=o^2\\ a^2&=o^2\cos^2\xi+e^2\sin^2\xi+2r_{41}E_x\cos\xi\sin\xi \qquad (28)\\ c^2&=o^2\sin^2\xi+e^2\cos\xi-2r_{41}E_x\cos\xi\sin\xi. \end{aligned}$$

As in the first case this represents a biaxial crystal. To go from Eq. (12) to Eq. (28) it is necessary to interchange a and b. This is because b is by definition intermediate between a and c. If the field had been applied in the Y direction, no such interchange would have been necessary. Since the axial plane is always at right angles to b and since the direction of b is independent of the field, the plane of the axis is again independent of the field as in the Z case. By inspection of Eq. (26) it is apparent that the section of the ellipsoid perpendicular to Z is a circle, and the position of this circular section is independent of the field. This indicates that one of the optic axes of the crystal coincides with the original optic axis and is independent of the field. The other axis moves from this first axis as the field is applied. The axial angle which is the angle between the ellipsoid axis and the optic axis is exactly ξ. This can also be checked by using the equation

$$\sin^2\Omega=b^2-c^2/a^2-c^2. \qquad (29)$$

Observation in the Z direction thus does not give a useful effect when field is applied in the X direction. Furthermore, the axial angle of the new biaxial crystal is only a few minutes as opposed to several degrees which is obtained when the field is applied in the Z direction.

In the Z-cut case the retardation was zero in the Z direction until the field was applied in this direction. In the X-cut case the retardation in the X direction is already large. For practical use the change in retardation for a reasonable voltage must be large. The retardation without field is:

$$\Gamma=(\epsilon-\omega)d/\lambda. \qquad (30)$$

The change in retardation may be calculated to be

$$\Delta\Gamma=\tfrac{1}{2}r_{41}{}^2\frac{V^2}{d}\,\frac{\omega^2\epsilon^2(\omega^3+\epsilon^3)}{\omega^2-\epsilon^2}. \qquad (31)$$

This turns out to be of the order of 10^{-3} for a PN crystal 1-cm thick with 25 kv applied in the x direction. Even in an isotropic medium such low induced birefringence would not be particularly useful.

CONCLUSIONS

The conclusions of these analyses can be summarized as follows:

For the field in the Z direction:

1. Uniaxial crystals of the form X H_2PO_4 become biaxial.
2. The plane of the optic axes is independent of the magnitude of the voltage and is inclined at 45° to the crystallographic axis.
3. For rays parallel to the field and at a given wavelength the retardation through the plate depends only on the voltage and is independent of the plate thickness.

For a field in the X direction:

4. The crystal again becomes biaxial.
5. The plane of the axes is independent of the magnitude of the voltage and is perpendicular to the X axis.
6. The retardation change through the plate for rays parallel to the field depends on the square of the applied voltage and the inverse first power of the plate thickness.
7. If the r_{41} and r_{63} coefficients are of the same order of magnitude a 1-cm plate of ADP gives a retardation change of the order of 10^{-3} for 25 kv applied voltage.

The problem of measuring the coefficients and of determining experimentally the properties of the specific crystal ADP will be discussed in the next paper.

In conclusion the author wishes to express appreciation to Miss Elizabeth Weichel of this laboratory for her help during the preparation of this paper.

JOURNAL OF THE OPTICAL SOCIETY OF AMERICA VOLUME 40, NUMBER 4 APRIL, 1950

The Electro-Optic Effect in Uniaxial Crystals of the Dihydrogen Phosphate Type.*,† III. Measurement of Coefficients

ROBERT O'B. CARPENTER

Physics Department, Harvard University, Cambridge, Massachusetts and Research Laboratory, Baird Associates, Inc., Cambridge, Massachusetts

(Received February 2, 1950)

The electro-optic coefficients of two crystals have been measured by both static and dynamic methods. For $NH_4H_2PO_4$, $r_{63}=2.54$, $r_{41}=6.25$; for KH_2PO_4, $r_{63}=3.15$, $r_{41}=2.58$ (units 10^{-7} c.g.s., 20°C λ5560). The variation of the electro-optic response with the frequency of the applied field is given and related to the piezoelectric vibrations of the crystal. A theoretical relation for the difference in the electro-optic constants measured at constant stress and at constant strain is derived, which provides a check on the consistency of the presently available electro-optic, photo-elastic, piezoelectric, and elastic coefficients for these crystals. The use of a.c. methods to obtain high precision in polarization measurements is discussed.

INTRODUCTION

In two previous papers[1] of this series, hereinafter referred to as (I) and (II), Billings has discussed the theory and some applications of the electro-optic effect in crystals of tetragonal scalenohedral symmetry. In addition to the applications to high frequency light modulation, the electro-optic properties of $NH_4H_2PO_4$ and KH_2PO_4 are of considerable interest because of their relation to the anomalous piezoelectric and ferroelectric properties of these crystals.[2] Zwicker and Scherrer[3] investigated the optical behavior of KH_2PO_4 under fields parallel to the Z or optic axis to temperatures below the ferroelectric transition, utilizing the optical effects for a very graphic means of observing the spontaneous polarization, hysteresis, Barkhausen jumps, etc.

In this paper are presented methods and results of measurements of the electro-optic coefficients r_{63} and r_{41} of $NH_4H_2PO_4$ and KH_2PO_4 at room temperature. Some of these values have also been measured by H. Jaffe and W. L. Bond but not published. The method for the measurement of r_{41} is new. Under an electric field parallel to the x axis in these crystals the principal axes of the index ellipsoid are rotated. The method consists of a direct measurement of this rotation. Sensitivity and precision are obtained by the use of a.c. fields on the crystal and detection by means of a multiplier photo-cell and sharply tuned amplifier.

Since most of the previous measurements of electro-optic coefficients have utilized visual compensator methods, the chief contribution which this paper seeks to make is the discussion of the advantages of the a.c. method for precision in measuring very small changes in the polarization properties of a light beam. In addition, by measuring the variation of the electro-optic coefficient with frequency, the effect of the piezoelectric vibrations is observed and a new method is obtained for distinguishing the electro-optic coefficient at constant strain and at constant stress.

THEORY OF MEASUREMENTS

In (I) it was shown that the equation of the Fresnel index ellipsoid for crystals of tetragonal scalenohedral symmetry under arbitrary electric fields can be written

$$o^2(x^2+y^2)+e^2z^2+2r_{41}(E_xyz+E_yzx)+2r_{63}E_zxy=1, \quad (1)$$

where the coordinate axes xyz are taken as the standard crystallographic axes, o and e are the reciprocals of the ordinary and extraordinary refractive indices ω and ϵ of the crystal in the absence of an electric field and r_{41} and r_{63} are the two independent electro-optic coefficients describing the changes in the index ellipsoid when a field is applied. Thus, r_{63} describes the effect of a field parallel to the optic axis and r_{41} the effect of a field perpendicular to this axis. Under an electric field the crystal becomes biaxial and the three axes of the index ellipsoid no longer coincide with the standard crystallographic axes xyz. The determination of the new principal axes and indices is a purely algebraic problem of rotating the coordinate axes to coincide with the principal axes of the ellipsoid defined by Eq. (1). This was discussed at some length in (I), so that the results only will be repeated here.

For a field in the z direction ($E_x=E_y=0$), the axes of the ellipsoid will be called $x'y'z'$. z' coincides with z, while x' and y' are rotated by $-45°$ from x and y. The values of the three indices of refraction are

$$\begin{aligned} n_{x'}&=\omega+\tfrac{1}{2}\omega^3r_{63}E_z\\ n_{y'}&=\omega-\tfrac{1}{2}\omega^3r_{63}E_z,\\ n_{z'}&=\epsilon \end{aligned} \quad (2)$$

and the birefringence of plane waves of light propagated along these axes is given by

$$\begin{aligned} B_{x'}&=n_{y'}-n_{z'}=\omega-\epsilon-\tfrac{1}{2}\omega^3r_{63}E_z\\ B_{y'}&=n_{z'}-n_{x'}=\omega-\epsilon+\tfrac{1}{2}\omega^3r_{63}E_z\\ B_{z'}&=n_{x'}-n_{y'}=\omega^3r_{63}E_z. \end{aligned} \quad (3)$$

* This work was done as part of a thesis to be submitted in partial fulfillment of the requirements for the Ph.D. degree at Harvard University.

† This work was supported in part by the Air Force Cambridge Research Laboratories under Contract W19-122 ac-32.

[1] B. H. Billings, J. Opt. Soc. Am. **39**, 797 (1949); **39**, 802 (1949).
[2] W. P. Mason, Phys. Rev. **69**, 173 (1946).
[3] B. Zwicker and P. Scherrer, Helv. Phys. Acta **17**, 346 (1944).

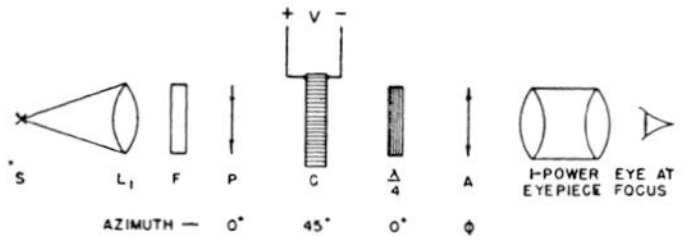

FIG. 1. Senarmont compensator method for static measurement of r_{63}; F—filter, P—polarizer, C—z cut crystal of retardation, $\Gamma = \omega^3 r_{63} V/\lambda$, A—2° split field analyzer. When analyzer is rotated to match intensities, $\phi = \pi\Gamma$.

The maximum induced birefringence is for light along the z axis and further, observation along this direction is not complicated by any natural birefringence.

For a field in the x direction ($E_y = E_z = 0$) the principal axes of refraction will be denoted by $x''y''z''$. In this case x'' coincides with x, but $y''z''$ are rotated from yz by an angle α which depends on the field.

$$2\alpha \approx \tan 2\alpha = \frac{2r_{41}E_x}{e^2 - o^2}. \tag{4}$$

As shown in the measurements given below, α is only a few minutes of arc for the largest practical fields, so that $\tan\alpha \approx \alpha$. To the order of terms in the square of the field the principal indices become

$$\begin{aligned} n_{x''} &= \omega \\ n_{y''} &= \omega + \tfrac{1}{2}\frac{\omega^5\epsilon^2}{\omega^2 - \epsilon^2}(r_{41}E_x)^2 \\ n_{z''} &= \epsilon - \tfrac{1}{2}\frac{\epsilon^5\omega^2}{\omega^2 - \epsilon^2}(r_{41}E_x)^2. \end{aligned} \tag{5}$$

This situation is somewhat more complicated than the case of E_z. If light is propagated along $x(\equiv x'')$ the crystal forms a retardation plate with directions of vibration rotated by the field (angle α) while the change in indices is a very small quantity proportional to the square of the field. Observation along the direction y or z introduce no induced birefringence as is seen by inspection of Eq. (1) (for $E_y = E_z = 0$). However, a first-order induced birefringence is obtained by propagating the light along the bisector of the direction y and z, i.e., normal to the plane

$$y - z = 0. \tag{6}$$

The birefringence in this direction denoted B_{yz}, will be given by the major and minor axes of the elliptical intersection of the plane (6) and the ellipsoid (1). After making use of the approximations $r_{41}E_x \ll 1$ and $\omega \approx \epsilon$, the result can be written

$$B_{yz} = \tfrac{1}{2}(\omega - \epsilon) - (\omega^3/2)r_{41}E_x. \tag{7}$$

MEASUREMENT OF r_{63}

For the static measurement of r_{63} there are a number of simple optical compensator methods[4] for the determination of the retardation through a basal section of crystal which is given by

$$\Gamma = \frac{B_{z'}d}{\lambda} = \frac{\omega^3 r_{63} V}{\lambda}, \tag{8}$$

where V is the voltage applied across the crystal. If the crystal is placed between parallel polarizers, the light is extinguished when the voltage is increased to give one-half wave retardation. This can be determined by a photo-cell or by visual observation. The precision is considerably increased by using split field half-shadow analyzer. By insertion of a Babinet compensator between crystal and analyzer a series of interference fringes are produced whose displacement on applying a field can be observed. A third method involves the observation of the angle between the two optic axes on a suitable goniometer. In air this angle is given by

$$\Omega = 2\omega\left(\frac{2r_{63}E_z}{e^2 - o^2}\right)^{\frac{1}{2}}.$$

The method which was finally selected as being most convenient and accurate was the use of the Senarmont compensator shown in Fig. 1. The electro-optic retardation plate and a fixed $\lambda/4$ plate are oriented at 45° and 0° to the initial polarizer and the split field analyzer is mounted on a calibrated circle with a vernier reading to 0.1°. The intensity transmitted by this system is

$$\frac{I}{I_0} = \cos^2(\pi\Gamma - \phi), \tag{9}$$

where Γ is the retardation of the unknown plate and ϕ is the aximuth angle of the analyzer. Therefore, the retardation for any voltage is read directly from the extinction angle.

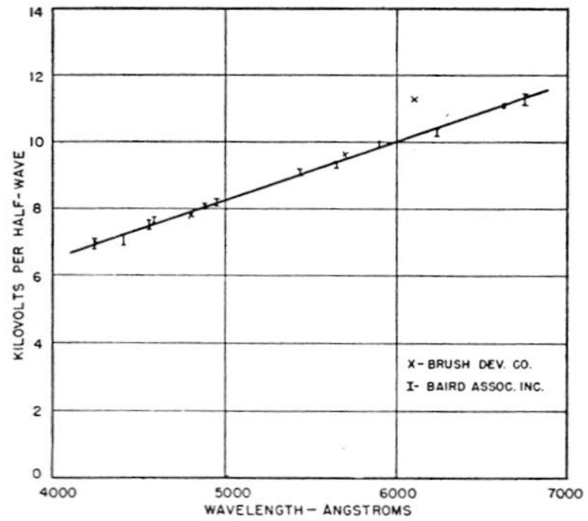

FIG. 2. Voltage required to produce $\frac{1}{2}$-wave retardation in basal section of $NH_4H_2PO_4$ as function of wave-length.

Figure 2 shows the voltage required to produce one-

[4] H. G. Jerrard, J. Opt. Soc. Am. 38, 35 (1948).

half wave retardation as a function of wave-length for $NH_4H_2PO_4$. The wave-lengths were chosen by a series of Baird Associates, Inc. interference filters. Linearity of retardation with voltage as indicated by Eq. (8) was verified. Since the results show a linear relation between voltage and wave-length, no dispersion of the value of r_{63} was found in the range 4000–7000A within the precision of the measurements (about 2 percent). The crosses on the figure are data supplied by H. Jaffe of the Brush Development Company in which the wave-lengths were chosen by means of rather broad Corning glass filters, which perhaps explains the small discrepancy at λ6100. Reduced to c.g.s. units, the value of r_{63} obtained is $2.54\pm0.05\times10^{-7}$ cm/statvolt. A similar measurement of the coefficient for KH_2PO_4 resulted in the value $r_{63}=3.15\pm0.05\times10^{-7}$.

The value of r_{63} for $NH_4H_2PO_4$ was checked on a total of five crystals in which different methods of mounting and attaching electrodes were utilized. The technique of laminating the crystal between Nesa glass electrode plates was discussed in paper (II). An error in the measurement of r_{63} might conceivably be introduced by the mounting in two ways, by a loss of voltage across the laminating layer or by a mechanical stress introduced by the mount.

All crystals were approximately 2 in.×2 in.×$\frac{1}{8}$ in. One crystal was prepared with directly adherent evaporated chromium electrodes, two were laminated between 2-in. squares of Nesa glass and two were laminated between $1\frac{1}{2}$-in. circles of Nesa. Identical results were observed on all crystals, indicating that the laminating techniques used do not introduce any loss in efficiency at low frequencies.

Many of the most interesting applications of the electro-optic plate involve the use of a.c. fields. Therefore, the variation of r_{63} with frequency was determined. This is done by placing the crystal in series with a fixed quarter-wave plate between crossed polarizers and applying alternating voltage $V_s \sin\omega t$ (Fig. 3). The transmitted intensity is given by

$$I/I_0=\sin^2\pi\Gamma=\tfrac{1}{2}(1-\cos2\pi\Gamma). \quad (10)$$

By Eq. (8), the combined retardation of crystal and λ/4 plate is

$$\Gamma=\tfrac{1}{4}+\frac{\omega^3 r_{63}V_s \sin\omega t}{\lambda}.$$

On using the trigonometric identity $\cos(\pi/2-\theta)=-\sin\theta$ and restricting the voltage V_s to small amplitudes where $\sin\theta\approx\theta$, the intensity can be written

$$\frac{I}{I_0}=\tfrac{1}{2}-\frac{\pi\omega^3 r_{63}V_s}{\lambda}\sin\omega t. \quad (11)$$

A voltage of approximately 500 volts and variable frequency was applied to the crystal and the horizontal plates of an oscilloscope. The amplified output of an

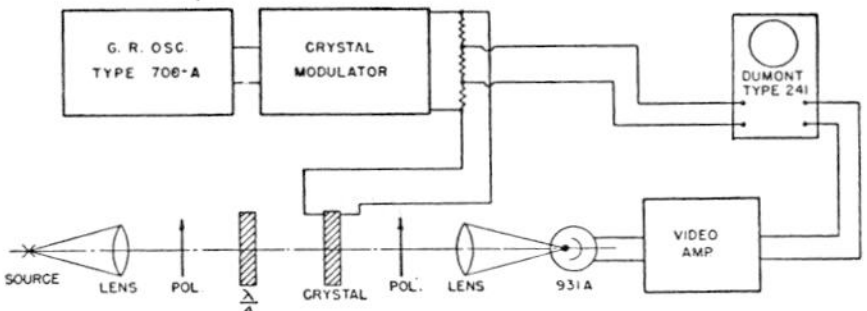

FIG. 3. Arrangement for measuring relative frequency response of electro-optic effect.

RCA 931 multiplier photo-cell was applied to the vertical deflection plates. The ratio of the light modulation to the crystal voltage then gives the relative variation of r_{63} or the electro-optic response with frequency. The results for a crystal of $NH_4H_2PO_4$ are shown in Fig. 4.

For an explanation of the frequency response one must consider the photo-elastic and piezoelectric behavior of the crystal. For a crystal of general symmetry the index ellipsoid is written

$$a_1x^2+a_2y^2+a_3z^2+2a_4yz+2a_5zx+2a_6xy=1. \quad (12)$$

The changes Δa_i in the coefficients of the index ellipsoid, due to both electro-optic and photo-elastic effects, can be expressed in terms of the electric field and either the stress or the strain in the crystal.

$$\Delta a_i=\sum_{j=1}^{3} r_{ij}E_j+\sum_{j=1}^{6} \pi_{ij}X_j \quad (13)$$

$$\Delta a_i=\sum_{j=1}^{3} r_{ij}'E_j+\sum_{k=1}^{6} p_{ik}x_k, \quad (14)$$

where X_j and x_j are the components of stress and strain, π_{ij} and p_{ik} the stress-optic and strain-optic coefficients. These relations are not independent because of the piezoelectric relations

$$x_k=-\sum_{j=1}^{6} s_{kj}X_j+\sum_{j=1}^{3} d_{jk}E_j, \quad (15)$$

where s_{kj} and d_{kj} are the elastic and piezoelectric constants. Substituting Eq. (15) in Eq. (14) we obtain

$$\Delta a_i=\sum_{j=1}^{3}\{r_{ij}'+\sum_{k=1}^{6} p_{ik}d_{jk}\}E_j+\sum_{j=1}^{6}\{\sum_{k=1}^{6} p_{ik}s_{rj}\}X_j.$$

On comparing with Eq. (13) it is evident that

$$\pi_{ij}=\sum_{k=1}^{6} p_{ik}s_{kj} \quad (16)$$

$$r_{ij}=r_{ij}'+\sum_{k=1}^{6} p_{ik}d_{jk}. \quad (17)$$

Therefore, the electro-optic coefficient r_{ij}, measured at zero stress (free crystal), differs from r_{ij}' measured at zero strain (clamped).

The frequency response of Fig. 4 may now be interpreted as due to the variation in the amplitude of the piezoelectric vibrations with frequency. At low frequencies the crystal is free to move and the value of r_{63} at zero stress is obtained. At the highest frequencies the motion is inhibited by the inertia of the crystal so that the coefficient r_{63}' at zero strain is obtained. At the piezoelectric resonance frequencies large amplitudes of vibration are set up which can be directly observed by this optical method. Tawil[5] and others have used the polarized light method for the qualitative study of vibration patterns in quartz.

Similar curves were obtained for several other crystals of $NH_4H_2PO_4$ in different styles of mounting. The resonant amplitudes are quite sensitive to the size and shape of the crystals and electrodes and the mechanical load introduced by the mount, but the same values of r_{63} and r_{63}' were obtained at low and high frequencies.

This method of comparing the electro-optic coefficient at zero stress and at zero strain can be compared with values obtained by two other methods. H. Jaffe (unpublished) determined the clamped effect by applying the field to very small electrodes while the remainder of the crystal was shorted by an additional pair of electrodes which served to clamp the center section. His value for r_{63}' was 58 percent of r_{63} as compared to 65 percent found here. This discrepancy is probably not outside the uncertainties of the two measurements. The second method is the direct determination of the photo-elastic and piezoelectric constants and the use of Eq. (17), which for the case considered reduces to

$$r_{63}=r_{63}'+p_{66}d_{36}. \tag{18}$$

Using Mason's[2] value of $d_{36}=146\times10^{-8}$ c.g.s. and West's[6] value of $p_{66}=0.111$, r_{63}' calculates to be 37 percent of r_{63}. The source of this discrepancy has not been determined. Mason's value for d_{36} has been checked

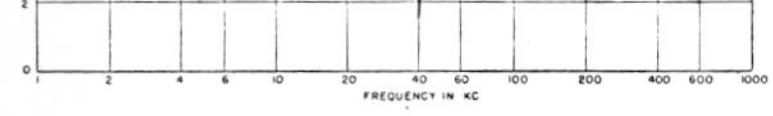

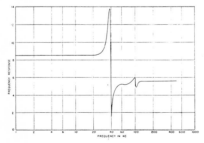

FIG. 4. High frequency response of electro-optic effect in $NH_4H_2PO_4$ crystal.

[5] E. P. Tawil, Comptes Rendus **183**, 1099 (1926); Rev. gén. de l'élec. **25**, 58 (1929); W. G. Cady, *Piezoelectricity* (McGraw-Hill Book Company, Inc., New York, 1946), p. 465.

[6] C. D. West and A. S. Makas, reported at April, 1949 meeting of Crystallographic Society of America.

in a number of laboratories. West's value for p_{66} was confirmed at the Crystal Section of the Naval Research Laboratory. However, G. W. Willard of the Bell Telephone Laboratories reports a measurement of $p_{66}=0.076$ which would make r_{63}' 57 percent of r_{63} in closer agreement with Eq. (18) and the other measurements.

MEASUREMENT OF r_{41}

With a 45° x cut crystal the induced birefringence indicated by Eq. (7) can be used to measure r_{41}. However, for a light path of $\frac{1}{4}$ inch at λ5500, the natural retardation will be about 275 waves and varying by one wave every 20A. With a monochromatic source, such as a mercury or sodium lamp, it is still possible to use a Babinet or Sernarmont compensator method. Dr. Jaffe made a rough determination of r_{41} in $NH_4H_2PO_4$ by the slightly different method of observing with a spectrograph the displacement of the chromatic interference fringes.

In order to obtain more precise values a new method was devised based on the direct measurement of the field induced rotation of the axes of the index ellipsoid. The optical arrangement is shown in Fig. 5. The crystal is an x cut plate prepared with transparent electrodes according to any of the methods described in paper (II). The light is propagated along the x direction in which case the crystal forms a plate of retardation Γ with the fast axis oriented at an angle α (Eq. (4)) to the initial polarizer. The intensity transmitted through the system is

$$I/I_0=\tfrac{1}{2}+\tfrac{1}{2}\sin^2\pi\Gamma\sin4\alpha,$$

since $\Gamma=(\omega-\epsilon)d/\lambda$ is a rapidly varying function of wave-length for a sufficiently thick crystal, by using a broad continuous source, $\sin^2\pi\Gamma$ may be integrated over wave-length and replaced by its mean value of $\frac{1}{2}$. Then substituting from Eq. (4) for $\alpha\approx\sin\alpha\approx\tan\alpha$ we obtain

$$\frac{I}{I_0}=\tfrac{1}{2}+\alpha=\tfrac{1}{2}-\frac{r_{41}E_x}{e^2-o^2}. \tag{19}$$

In order to detect this small modulation, 60 c.p.s. alternating voltage $V_s\sin\omega t$ was applied to the crystal and the resulting light intensity modulation $I_s\sin\omega t$ was detected by the multiplier photo-cell and a sharply tuned amplifier. Then r_{41} is given by

$$r_{41}=\frac{d(e^2-o^2)}{I_0}\frac{I_s}{V_s}. \tag{20}$$

I_0 is twice the observed d.c. current in the photo-cell.

The values obtained by this method for r_{41} in $NH_4H_2PO_4$ and KH_2PO_4 are tabulated in Table I. Three crystals of $NH_4H_2PO_4$ and two of KH_2PO_4 gave identical results within the reproducibility of the measurements.

TABLE I. Electro-optic coefficients of $NH_4H_2PO_4$ and KH_2PO_4 at 22°C, λ5560, in c.g.s. units $(\text{statvolts/cm})^{-1}$.

	ϵ	ω	$r_{63}\times10^7$	$r_{41}\times10^7$
$NH_4H_2PO_4$	1.5254	1.4798	2.54 ± 0.05	6.25 ± 0.1
KH_2PO_4	1.5100	1.4684	3.15 ± 0.07	2.58 ± 0.05

SENSITIVITY OF THE A.C. METHOD

The ultimate sensitivity of a.c. methods in light polarization measurements can be made considerably greater than can be obtained with the best visual compensator methods. When sufficient light intensity is available, the limiting noise becomes the electron shot effect in the multiplier photo-cell.

$$(I_N)_{\text{r.m.s.}}=\left(\frac{GIe}{\tau}\right)^{\frac{1}{2}},$$

where G=gain of multiplier, e=electronic charge, τ=time constant of amplifier-detector. The modulated photo-current is of the form

$$I(1+\beta\sin\omega t)$$

so that the signal-to-noise ratio is

$$\frac{I_s}{I_N}=\beta\left(\frac{I\tau}{2Ge}\right)^{\frac{1}{2}}$$

and the smallest detectable β is

$$\beta_{\min}=\left(\frac{2Ge}{I\tau}\right)^{\frac{1}{2}}.$$

Since I/G is just the photo-cell cathode current, the ultimate sensitivity depends only on the time constant, the available light energy and the absolute energy sensitivity of the photo-surface.

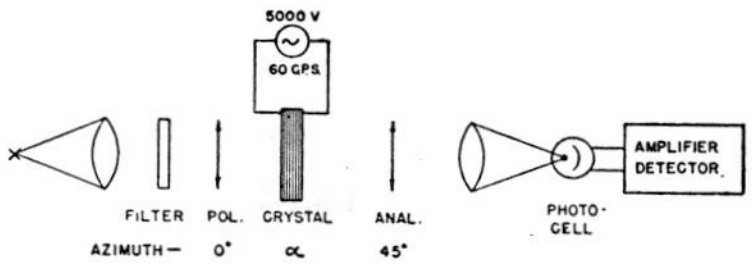

FIG. 5. Arrangement for measuring r_{41} by a.c. method; vibration direction of x cut crystal depends on the field: $(\alpha=r_{41}E_x/(e^2-o^2))$.

Under the conditions of the r_{41} measurement $G=10^3$, $I=10^{-4}$, $\tau=3$ seconds, $\beta_{\min}=10^{-6}$. In this experiment the modulation factor β is twice the angular rotation α of the principal index axes. Thus, $\alpha_{\min}=5\times10^{-7}$ radian, $(r_{41})_{\min}=10^{-9}$ for the field $E_x=21$ statvolts/cm which was used. In measuring r_{63}, β is the phase retardation $(2\pi\Gamma)$ of the retardation plate. According to Jerrard[4] the ultimate detection limit of the best optical compensators is not better than 10 sec. of arc or 5×10^{-5} radian.

ACKNOWLEDGMENT

The author wishes to express his appreciation to Dr. W. P. Mason for his discussions of and interest in the problem and to Dr. H. Jaffe for advice, suggestions, and the furnishing of crystals. To both are due thanks for the results of unpublished measurements at their respective laboratories. The interest and cooperation of Dr. B. H. Billings and the entire research staff at Baird Associates, Inc. have contributed much to this work. Acknowledgement should also be made to the Air Force Cambridge Research Laboratories whose support helped make this work possible.

Electro-Optical Effect of Zincblende

SUSUMU NAMBA
The Institute of Physical and Chemical Research, Komagome, Bunkyo-ku, Tokyo, Japan
(Received March 5, 1960)

The electro-optical coefficient of zincblende is measured by using the Senarmont compensator method for various wavelengths between 404 and 644 mμ and the application of the crystal to light modulator of wide optical aperture is discussed. The electro-optical coefficient is found to be 5.9×10^{-8} cm/statvolt at room temperature for wavelength of 546 mμ. The voltage for obtaining half-wave retardation is about 10 kv.

1. INTRODUCTION

THE crystals of class V_d, such as ammonium dihydrogen phosphate (ADP: $NH_4H_2PO_4$) and potassium dihydrogen phosphate (KDP: KH_2PO_4), are being used for light modulator or high-speed shutter because of the large electro-optical effect. The birefringence of the crystals limits, however, the optical aperture. Crystals of class T_d with large enough electro-optical effect permit the construction of a light modulator or shutter with wide optical aperture. ZnS and CuCl are such crystals,[1] but, it is difficult to obtain good-sized single crystals.

In this work, the electro-optical coefficient of zincblende found in Osarusawa mine in Japan was measured and the application to light modulator of wide optical aperture was discussed.

2. THEORY

The birefringence of crystal can be expressed in terms of its index ellipsoid as

$$\frac{x^2}{n_x^2}+\frac{y^2}{n_y^2}+\frac{z^2}{n_z^2}=1, \tag{1}$$

where n_x, n_y, and n_z are the three principal refractive indexes with the crystallographic axes as the optical axes. In a crystal of T_d class such as zincblende, Eq. (1) is reduced to

$$\left.\begin{aligned}\frac{x^2+y^2+z^2}{n_0^2}=1\\ n_x=n_y=n_z=n_0\end{aligned}\right\} \tag{2}$$

If an electric field is applied to the crystal, index ellipsoid is deformed as

$$\frac{x^2+y^2+z^2}{n_0^2}+2r_{41}(E_xyz+E_yzx+E_zxy)=1, \tag{3}$$

where E_x, E_y, and E_z are the components of the field in the directions of the three crystallographic axes, and r_{41} is the electro-optical coefficient of the crystal.

The directions of the new optical axes and the new principal refractive indexes are determined by rotating the original coordinate axes to coincide with those of the deformed index ellipsoid expressed by Eq. (3). By the new coordinate system $x'y'z'$, the index ellipsoid of Eq. (3) is rewritten as follows,

$$\frac{x'^2}{n_x'^2}+\frac{y'^2}{n_y'^2}+\frac{z'^2}{n_z'^2}=1, \tag{4}$$

$$\begin{vmatrix}x\\y\\z\end{vmatrix}=\begin{vmatrix}\alpha_1&\beta_1&\gamma_1\\\alpha_2&\beta_2&\gamma_2\\\alpha_3&\beta_3&\gamma_3\end{vmatrix}\begin{vmatrix}x'\\y'\\z'\end{vmatrix}, \tag{5}$$

where n_x', n_y', and n_z' are the three principal indexes when the electric field is applied to crystal, and α_1, β_1, γ_1 . . . are the direction cosines correlating the two sets of coordinates. n_x', n_y', and n_z' of Eq. (4) are given as the roots of η of the descrimination equation

$$\begin{vmatrix}\frac{1}{n_0^2}-\eta & r_{41}E_z & r_{41}E_y\\ r_{41}E_z & \frac{1}{n_0^2}-\eta & r_{41}E_x\\ r_{41}E_y & r_{41}E_x & \frac{1}{n_0^2}-\eta\end{vmatrix}=0. \tag{6}$$

Three cases are conceivable in applying the electric field to ZnS crystal which is of T_d class: the field perpendicular to (001), to (110), or to (111) planes. For these three cases, the results of calculation are summarized in Table I, where d and l are the thicknesses of the crystal in the directions of the field and the light beam, respectively, λ is the wavelength of light, P is the polarizer, and A the analyzer. Γ_z is the phase retardation of light traveling in the direction of the applied field as it is in the case of ADP crystal, and Γ_{xy}, Γ_{max}, and Γ are the phase retardations of light traveling perpendicular to the direction of the applied field.

[1] Bruce H. Billings, *American Institute of Physics Handbook*, edited by Dwight E. Gray (McGraw-Hill Book Company, Inc., 1957), pp. 6–97.

TABLE I. Electro-optical properties of ZnS crystal.

	$E \perp (001)$ plane $E_x = E_y = 0 \quad E_z = E$	$E \perp (110)$ plane $E_x = E_y = \frac{E}{\sqrt{2}} \quad E_z = 0$	$E \perp (111)$ plane $E_x = E_y = E_z = \frac{E}{\sqrt{3}}$
index ellipsoid	$\frac{x^2+y^2+z^2}{n_0^2} + 2r_{41}Exy = 1$	$\frac{x^2+y^2+z^2}{n_0^2} + \sqrt{2}r_{41}E(yz+zx) = 1$	$\frac{x^2+y^2+z^2}{n_0^2} + \frac{2}{\sqrt{3}}r_{41}E(yz+zx+xy) = 1$
n_x'	$n_0 + \frac{1}{2}n_0^3 r_{41} E$	$n_0 + \frac{1}{2}n_0^3 r_{41} E$	$n_0 + \frac{1}{2\sqrt{3}}n_0^3 r_{41} E$
n_y'	$n_0 - \frac{1}{2}n_0^3 r_{41} E$	$n_0 - \frac{1}{2}n_0^3 r_{41} E$	$n_0 + \frac{1}{2\sqrt{3}}n_0^3 r_{41} E$
n_z'	n_0	n_0	$n_0 - \frac{1}{\sqrt{3}}n_0^3 r_{41} E$
$x'y'z'$ coordinate	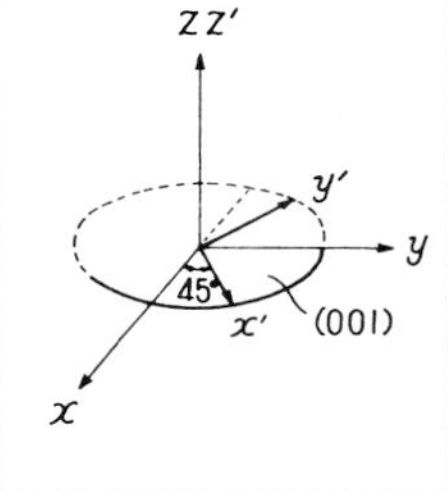	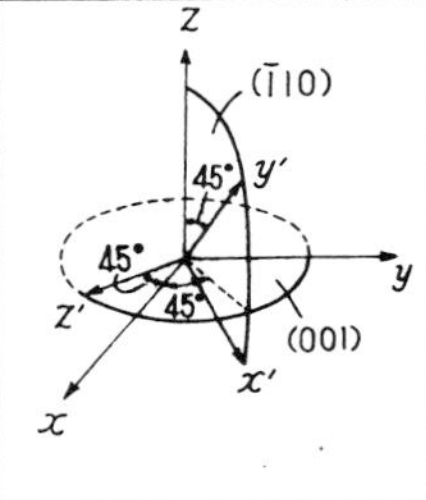	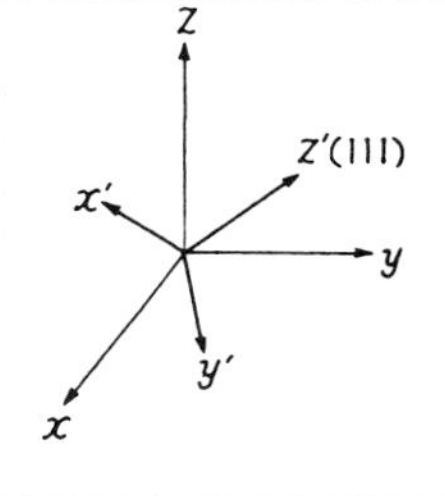
directions of optical path and axes of crossed polarizer	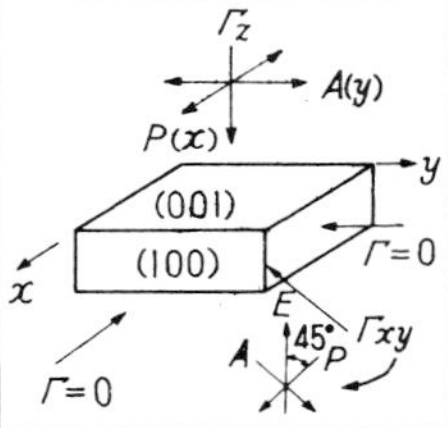	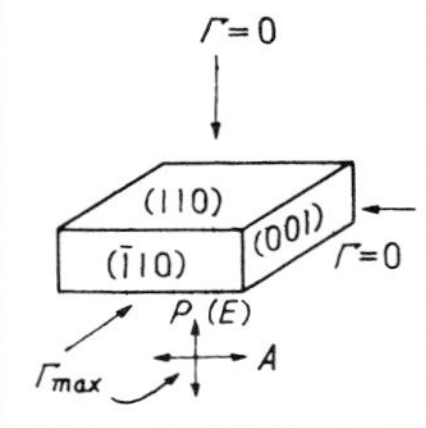	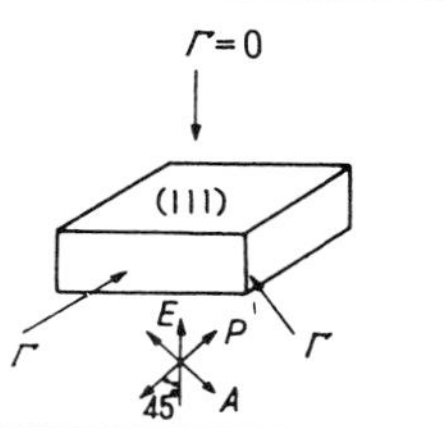
phase difference $\Gamma(V=Ed)$	$\Gamma_z = \frac{2\pi}{\lambda} n_0^3 r_{41} V$ $\Gamma_{xy} = \frac{\pi}{\lambda}\frac{l}{d} n_0^3 r_{41} V$	$\Gamma_{max} = \frac{2\pi}{\lambda}\frac{l}{d} n_0^3 r_{41} V$	$\Gamma = \frac{\sqrt{3}\pi}{\lambda}\frac{l}{d} n_0^3 r_{41} V$

3. MEASUREMENTS OF ELECTRO-OPTICAL COEFFICIENT IN ZINCBLENDE

The samples were single crystals of 2~3-mm cube with opposing cleaved (111) faces. They had resistivity of about $10^9 \sim 10^{10}$ Ω-cm, but were not photoconductive.

As crystals with strain can not be used for measuring electro-optical effect because of resulting birefringence, samples with small strain were chosen out from many, and annealed at about 800°C to remove the strain.

As shown in Fig. 1, the optical arrangement for the static measurement of r_{41} was of Senarmont compensator system with a monochromatic light source. The light intensity was measured photoelectrically.

Senarmont compensator method for measuring optical retardation was composed of the polarizer P, electro-optic retardation crystal, quarter wave plate Q, and analyzer A aligned in the above order with proper angular orientations as shown in the figure. The light

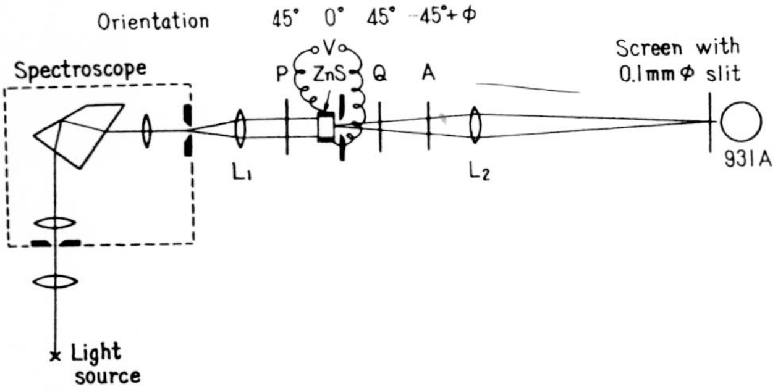

FIG. 1. The optical arrangement used to retardation measurement. P: polarizer, A: analyzer, Q: ¼λ plate.

intensity transmitted by the system is

$$\frac{I}{I_0}=\sin^2\left(\frac{\pi}{\lambda}\frac{C}{2}\frac{l}{d}n_0^3r_{41}V-\phi\right), \qquad (7)$$

where $\Gamma=C\pi l n_0^3 r_{41}V/\lambda d$ is the retardation in the crystal, ϕ is the orientation angle of the analyzer, and C is a constant for given directions of light beam and electric field. Thus, if ϕ_0 is the extinction angle of the analyzer,

$$r_{41}=\frac{\phi_0}{\pi}\cdot\frac{2}{C}\cdot\frac{d}{l}\cdot\frac{\lambda}{n_0^3}\cdot\frac{1}{V}. \qquad (8)$$

In this case, the direction of the electric field is perpendicular to (111) plane, and $C=\sqrt{3}$.

As the annealed crystals were not altogether free from birefringence, photoelastic pattern of crystal was first magnified about three times by the lens of 30-cm focal distance and projected on a screen with 0.1-mm ϕ slit, with which strainless points were found. Then, only the intensity of the light beam that passed the slit was measured by a photomultiplier placed behind the slit. The retardation at the strainless point for any applied voltage was measured from the extinction angle ϕ_0 of the analyzer. Figure 2 shows one example of $V-\phi_0$ relation given by Eq. (8) for various wavelengths. The effect of wavelength on the optical retardation was relatively small.

By using the measured $V-\phi_0$ relation (Fig. 2), the values of r_{41} for various wavelengths were calculated by Eq. (8).[2] They are given in Table II. In this calculation, measured values of n_0 by Czyzak[3] were used. The values of r_{41} obtained by Schramm[4] and Poulet[5] are also tabulated in Table II. The wavelength dependency of r_{41} is illustrated in Fig. 3. The dependency obtained by the author is similar to that obtained by Schramm, though the measured values of r_{41} by the author are somewhat different from those by Schramm and Poulet.

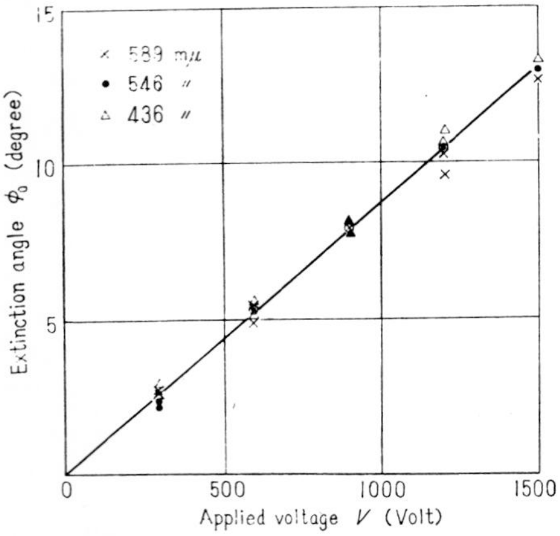

FIG. 2. Relation between applied voltage and extinction angle measured by Senarmont compensator method with monochromatic light.

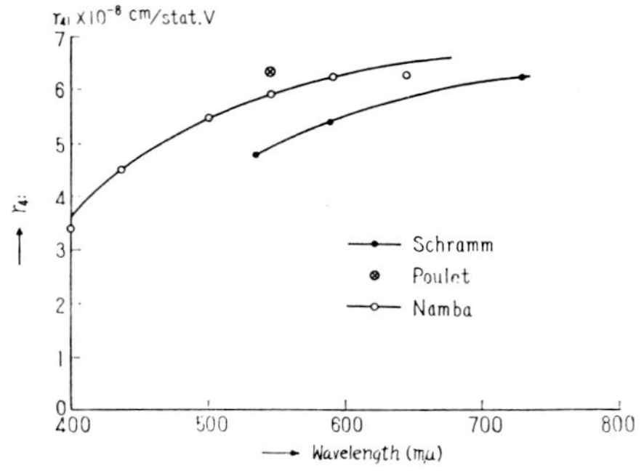

FIG. 3. Wavelength dependency of r_{41}.

[2] S. Namba, J. Appl. Phys. (Japan) **28**, 432 (1959).
[3] S. J. Czysak, W. M. Baker, R. C. Crane, and J. B. Howe, J. Opt. Soc. Am. **47**, 240 (1957).
[4] C. Schramm, Ann. Physik **25**, 309 (1936).
[5] H. Poulet, J. phys. radium **16**, 237 (1955).

TABLE II. Measured values of r_{41} for various wavelengths.

	$r_{41}\times 10^8$ cm/stat. V			n_0
λ (mμ)	C. Schramm	H. Poulet	S. Namba	S. J. Czyzak
404			3.4	2.546
436			4.5	2.496
504			5.45	2.411
535	4.8			
546		6.4	5.9	2.384
589	5.4		6.2	2.366
644			6.2	2.348
730	6.15			

This may be attributed to distributed minute strains still remained in the specimen and not to measurement errors, for the measuring technique of the optical retardation is of high accuracy. For better results the use of good-sized strainless single crystals is desirable.

4. ZnS CRYSTAL LIGHT MODULATOR

The optical arrangement of the ZnS cell light modulator is shown in Fig. 4. Crystals cleaved by (110) plane were used. In the case of ADP light modulator, the transmitting light has to be parallel. In using ZnS cell, however, light beam with aperture of about 20° can be modulated sufficiently as shown in oscilloscope pattern of Fig. 5. In this figure, the upper patterns show the waveforms of applied voltage of 1000 v, and the lower ones show those of photocurrent by the modulated light beam. Figure 5 (a) is without optical bias, and (b) is with optical bias of a quarter wave. In these cases,

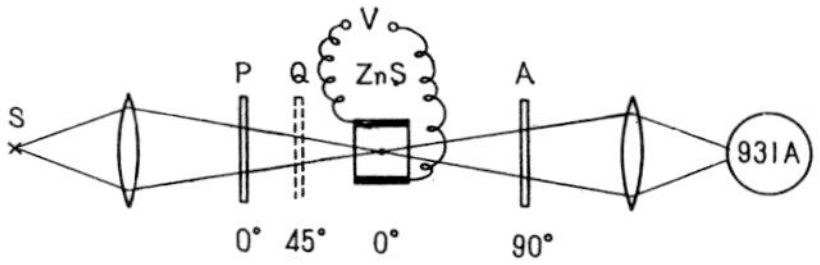

FIG. 4. The optical arrangement of light modulator using ZnS crystal cell. S: white light source, P: polarizer, A: analyzer, Q: $\frac{1}{4}\lambda$ plate.

(a) (b)

FIG. 5. Waveforms of applied voltage (upper) and modulated light intensity (lower). (a) no optical bias; (b) with optical bias of $\frac{1}{4}\lambda$.

the intensity of modulated parallel rays is expressed as

$$\left.\begin{aligned}&\text{(a)}\quad \frac{I}{I_0}=\sin^2\left(\frac{\pi}{\lambda}\frac{c}{2}\frac{l}{d}n_0^3 r_{41}V_0\cos wt\right)\\&\text{(b)}\quad \frac{I}{I_0}=\sin^2\left(\frac{\pi}{\lambda}\frac{c}{2}\frac{l}{d}n_0^3 r_{41}V_0\cos wt+\tfrac{1}{4}\pi\right)\end{aligned}\right\},\qquad (9)$$

where w is the angular frequency of the applied voltage.

By using the values of r_{41}, n_0, and $d=l$, $c=2$ in Eq. (9)-(a), a half-wave retardation voltage $V_0(=\lambda/2n_0^3r_{41})$ becomes about 10 kv, which is about the same as for ADP crystal. In the case of ZnS, however, V_0 can be lower if $l>d$.

MICROWAVE MODULATION OF THE ELECTRO-OPTIC EFFECT IN KH_2PO_4

I. P. Kaminow
Bell Telephone Laboratories, Holmdel, New Jersey
(Received April 17, 1961)

KH_2PO_4 (KDP) is a colorless transparent crystal that belongs to the tetragonal group $\bar{4}2m$ (V_d), which lacks a center of inversion, and exhibits a linear electro-optic effect. It undergoes a ferroelectric phase transition at 120°K.[1] According to a model of KDP and isomorphous compounds, the dielectric polarization depends upon the motion of the protons in a double minimum potential.[1,2] These protonic motions can alter the symmetry and magnitude of the electronic polarizability and, hence, the optical properties of the crystal.

In the paraelectric phase, KDP is optically uniaxial with the optic axis along the tetragonal Z axis. Light propagating along Z travels with the same velocity irrespective of the plane of polarization. The application of an electric field E along Z reduces the crystal symmetry to orthorhombic and the optical symmetry to biaxial.[3] Hence, the index of refraction for light propagating along Z is different for light polarized in the two principal planes. After passing through a length L, the phase retardation Γ between the principal waves is

$$\Gamma = \pi E L / V_0, \qquad (1)$$

where V_0 is the (zero-strain) value of EL for half-wave retardation.

Measurements of the dielectric constant at a frequency of 25 kMc/sec (at 25°C) agree with the low-frequency dielectric constant of a clamped crystal.[1,4] Since the electro-optic effect is proportional to the polarization,[1] one would not expect any appreciable reduction in V_0 below 25 kMc/sec.[5] Previous measurements have shown V_0 to be frequency independent to 500 Mc/sec.[6] We have observed the electro-optic effect in KDP at room temperature and 9.25 kMc/sec and find V_0 to be of the same order as the low-frequency value.

The apparatus [Fig. 1(a)] consists of a 25-watt zirconium concentrated arc lamp with a Corning 7-69 infrared filter peaked at 8000 A, a Glan-Thompson polarizer and crossed analyzer, an RCA 7102 (S-1) photomultiplier, and a pulsed X-band magnetron which feeds a cylindrical cavity containing the KDP rod. The cavity is filled with polystyrene and the dimensions are

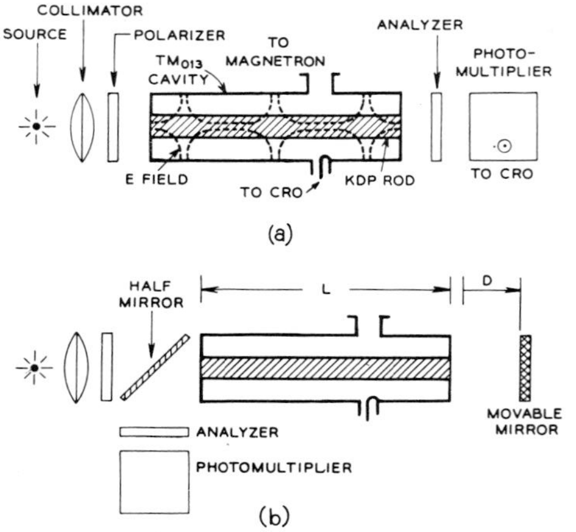

FIG. 1. (a) Transmission apparatus. (b) Reflection apparatus.

adjusted so that the microwave phase velocity approximates the light velocity when the cavity is excited in the "TM_{01s}-like" mode. If the cavity standing wave is decomposed into a forward and a backward travelling wave, it can be shown that, to good approximation, the backward wave produces no net retardation when the velocities are matched, while the forward wave provides a constant E at a given point in the light wave train as it passes through the crystal.[7] The light velocity in the crystal is $c/1.5$; the microwave velocity at 9.25 kMc/sec is $c/1.38$.

With the polarizer and analyzer crossed, pulses from the photomultiplier are observed coincident with the microwave pulses (3 μsec at 60 pulses/sec). In order to obtain direct evidence of microwave modulation, a movable mirror and half mirror are placed as shown in Fig. 1(b). When the transit time for light leaving the end of the crystal, reflecting from the movable mirror, and re-entering the crystal is equal to a multiple of the microwave period, light pulses are observed in the photomultiplier. When the mirror is moved a distance D equal to one-quarter the free-space microwave wavelength, no pulses are observed

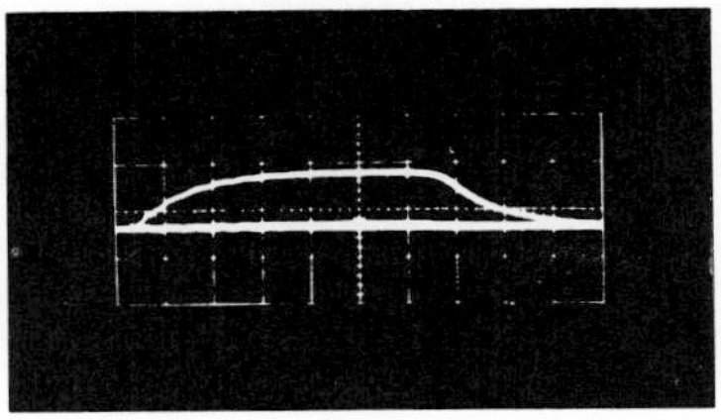

FIG. 2. Photomultiplier response with mirror set for maximum signal (top). With mirror displaced λ/4, the response is nearly coincident with that obtained by covering the source (bottom). ($\frac{1}{2}$ μsec/div. Circuit time constant ~ $\frac{1}{2}$ μsec.)

(Fig. 2). In the first case, the retardation is doubled, while in the latter the net retardation is zero.

The time-average relative intensity for modulated light with crossed polarizers, $\rho_{\perp}$, and with parallel polarizers, $\rho_{\parallel}$, is[8]

$$\rho_{\perp} = \tfrac{1}{2}[1 - J_0(\Gamma_p)], \quad \rho_{\parallel} = \tfrac{1}{2}[1 + J_0(\Gamma_p)], \tag{2}$$

where J_0 is the zero-order Bessel function and Γ_p is the peak retardation. With a peak power P of 760 watts absorbed in the cavity, $\rho_{\perp} = \rho_{\parallel}$ (Fig. 3) and $\Gamma_p = 2.40$.

The peak field intensity in the forward wave E may be estimated by assuming a uniform longitudinal E across the rod with sinusoidal variation along the rod and assuming all the power P to be dissipated in the rod. Then

$$E \sim (QP/\omega\epsilon\epsilon_0 v)^{1/2} \sim 70 \text{ volts/mm}, \tag{3}$$

in which ϵ and Q are the dielectric constant and dielectric Q for the rod at angular frequency ω

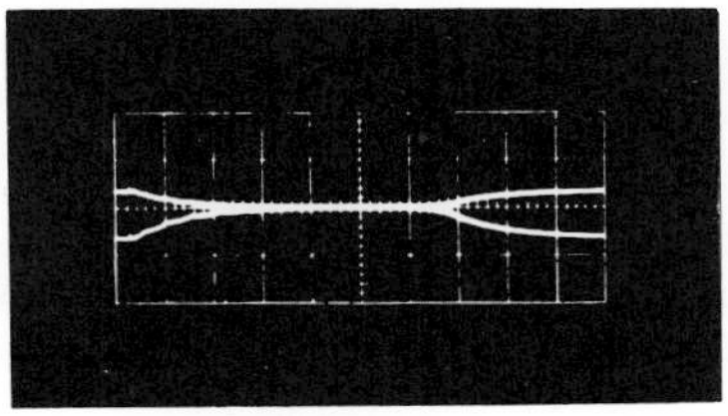

FIG. 3. Photomultiplier response with parallel polarizers (upper) and with crossed polarizers (lower) for $\rho_{\perp} = \rho_{\parallel}$.

and v is the rod volume ($L = 35.5$ mm, diameter 4 mm). In the absence of 9-kMc/sec data, we have used the 25-kMc/sec values[4] $\epsilon \sim 20$, $Q \sim 30$. For $\Gamma_p = 2.40$,

$$V_0 = \pi E 2L/\Gamma_p \sim 7 \text{ kv}. \tag{4}$$

This estimate may be compared with the low-frequency clamped value of 11 kv obtained by extrapolating measurements of W. L. Bond to 8000 A.

KDP is transparent between 4000 A and 13 000 A. Since V_0 decreases with decreasing wavelength,[6] the effect may be enhanced by operating at shorter wavelengths. Further enhancement, with increased loss, may be obtained by increasing L and by operating nearer to the Curie temperature, either by reducing the temperature, or by choosing an isomorphous compound with a higher Curie temperature.[2]

The tunnelling frequency[2] for protons in the double minimum potential occurs at ~200 cm^{-1} (6000 kMc/sec). Therefore, it may be possible to extend the modulating frequency to much higher frequencies than the 9.25 kMc/sec used here.

It may also be possible to construct a broad-band low-power microwave light modulator, using more sophisticated structures or other materials, for use in a practical optical communication system.[9] The bandwidth for the present structure is limited by the cavity Q: $\Delta f \sim f/150 \sim 60$ Mc/sec. In a pure travelling wave structure, a limitation would be the band over which the microwave and light velocities can be matched.

A microwave light modulator might also be used as an instrument for studying short relaxation times and other effects in optically pumped systems or for refined measurements of the velocity of light.

It is a pleasure to acknowledge instructive discussions with R. Kompfner, A. G. Fox, E. H. Turner, and R. F. Trambarulo, and the assistance of F. A. Dunn.

---

[1]W. Känzig, in Solid State Physics, edited by F. Seitz and D. Turnbull (Academic Press, Inc., New York, 1957), Vol. 4.

[2]R. Blinc, J. Phys. Chem. Solids 13, 204 (1960).

[3]B. H. Billings, J. Opt. Soc. Am. 39, 797 (1949).

[4]W. A. Yager, quoted in Piezoelectric Crystals and Their Application to Ultrasonics, edited by W. P. Mason (D. Van Nostrand and Company, New York, 1950), p. 258.

[5]N. Bloembergen, P. S. Pershan, and L. R. Wilcox, Phys. Rev. 120, 2014 (1960).

[6]R. O'B. Carpenter, J. Opt. Soc. Am. 40, 225 (1950).

[7]The use of a travelling wave structure has been suggested by N. Bloembergen [talk, NEREM, Boston, No. 1960] and the possibility of using the standing wave structure by R. Kompfner.

[8]Clark, Holshouser, and von Foerster, Technical Note 1-2, Engineering Experimental Station, University of Illinois, 1957 (unpublished).

[9]E. H. Turner attempted to observe microwave light modulation (1952) using $NH_4H_2PO_4$ (ADP) in a rectangular TE_{101} cavity but was unsuccessful because of the short length of ADP permitted by the structure. Bloembergen, Pershan, and Wilcox[5] have suggested, independently, the use of dihydrogen phosphates for microwave modulation of light.

Reprinted from
Volume 7, Number 7 APPLIED PHYSICS LETTERS **1 October 1965**

THE STRAIN-FREE ELECTRO-OPTIC EFFECT IN SINGLE-CRYSTAL BARIUM TITANATE[1]

(5 to 150°C; ferroelectric materials; nonlinear dielectrics; E)

Alan R. Johnston
Jet Propulsion Laboratory, California Institute of Technology
Pasadena, California
(Received 2 July 1965; in final form 23 August 1965)

Most measurements of the linear electro-optic effect in crystals have been made with dc applied fields, even though one of the applications of current interest is that of light modulation at microwave frequencies. It is well known that the electro-optical effect measured at low frequency must contain a strain-optical contribution which is not present at very high frequencies. Careful measurement of this contribution has been reported for only a few materials, including ADP by Carpenter,[2] and KDP by Billings.[3]

The purpose of this Letter is to describe an experimental determination of the linear electro-optic effect under the strain-free condition, in single-crystal $BaTiO_3$ as a function of temperature between 10°C and 120°C, and, also, to report a surprisingly large strain contribution to the quadratic electro-optic response above the Curie transition. These results are compared to a previously reported[4] measurement of the low-frequency, or stress-free, response of $BaTiO_3$ in the tetragonal state.

Flux-grown barium titanate[5] 0.07 to 0.19 mm thick, which had been cleaved into wavers 2–3 mm square, was used, after being poled such that [001] was along one of the 3-mm dimensions, and the light was passed through the thickness of the waver, along [100]. All measurements were at 5461 Å. Electrodes of colloidal graphite[6] were applied to opposite edges of the wafer.

The transient optical response of the crystal to an applied voltage step obtained from a mercury relay pulser was observed. The optical configuration of the polarimeter was similar to that previously employed,[4,7,8] but, in this measurement, the output of the photomultiplier following the analyzing prism of the polarimeter was fed directly into a sampling oscilloscope triggered by the voltage applied to the crystal. This experimental technique will be described in a future paper.

The typical optical response in terms of retardation, δ, is shown in Fig. 1 as a function of time. Two recorder tracings are shown, one on a time scale which shows the initial transient, and the other covering a much longer time, showing the effect of the mechanical resonance of the crystal on the induced optical retardation. The period of this resonance, 1.7 μsec, agrees well with that of the fundamental mode of the crystal wafer for extensional strain in the [001] direction. Both tracings were taken at room temperature with the field applied along [001]. The shape of the initial 10 nsec of the transient was due to the photomultiplier used, an RCA type 6199, and was not related to the response of the crystal. Comparison to the separately measured response time of the photomultiplier indicates that, as expected, there is no transient in the optical response of the crystal lasting longer than approximately 2 nsec. The rise time of the photomultiplier, 6 nsec, is to a step function in light intensity, which is somewhat longer than the more typically quoted response to a light pulse such as that generated by a scintillator.

The assumption is made that the initial retardation, as shown by δ_i in Fig. 1, represents the response under a true strain-free condition. This is a good assumption in the case of the fundamental stretching resonance seen in Fig. 1. However, the corresponding thickness mode, having a period of 50 nsec for a thickness of 0.1 mm, could be excited, and higher harmonics could also be present. These resonances represent angular frequencies of the same order as the reciprocal of the rise time of the photomultiplier. Significant change in the electro-optical response in the first few nanoseconds caused by these higher frequency mechanical resonances is not likely, because the optical transient shown in Fig. 1 did not depend on crystal thickness, nor could any resonance be observed optically. Any resonance of measurable amplitude would have been easily detected, even if damped out within 2 or 3 cycles.

Both $r_c' = r_{33}' - (n_a/n_c)^3 r_{13}'$ and r_{42}' were measured. Primes are used to designate quantities measured under strain-free conditions. r_{ij} designates one of the conventional[9] electro-optic coefficients which relate index changes to electric field.

$$\Delta(1/n_i)^2 = \sum_j r_{ij}E_j; \quad i = 1-6, j = 1-3.$$

The experimental results for r_c' in three crystals are shown in Fig. 2, and similarly for r_{42}' in three crystals in Fig. 3, both as a function of temperature.

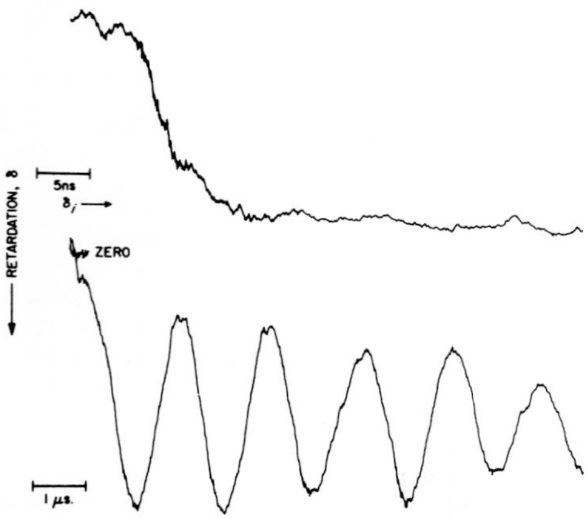

Fig. 1. Recorder tracings of the electro-optical response of a $BaTiO_3$ crystal to an applied field in the form of a step function. Induced optical retardation, δ, is plotted downward on both tracings vs time. The time scale is indicated for each tracing. The vertical scale is not the same for both tracings. The initial retardation, δ_i, used as a measure of the strain-free electro-optic coefficients is indicated.

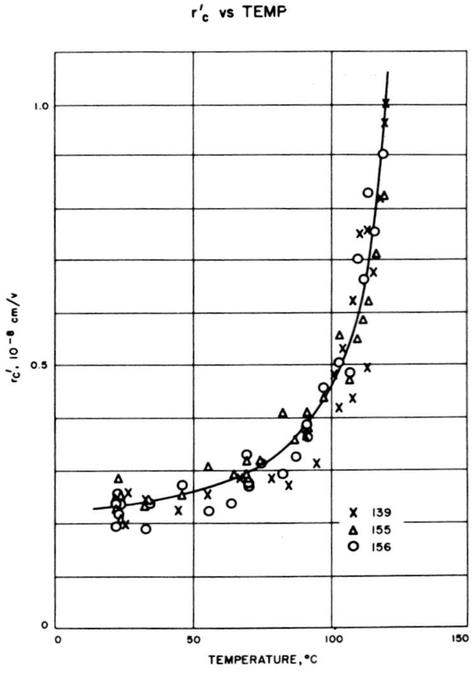

Fig. 2. r_c' for three crystal samples, plotted as a function of temperature. Data points from different crystals are indicated by different symbols.

At a temperature of 25°C, $r_c' = (0.23 \pm 0.02) \times 10^{-8}$ cm/V; $r_{42}' = (8.2 \pm 1.0) \times 10^{-8}$ cm/V.

A comparison with earlier measurements made at low frequency[4] shows that at room temperature $r_c'/r_c = 0.22$; $r_{42}'/r_{42} = 0.50$. At constant field, almost four-fifths of the effect observed at low frequency for an [001] field is due to the strain contribution, and one-half for a [100] field.

The dielectric constants K_a' and K_c' were also measured as a function of temperature, in order to compare r_{42}' to K_a' and r_c' to K_c'. To do this a single-domain crystal sample, appropriately poled and electroded, was series mounted in a 50-Ω coaxial transmission line. A pulse from the mercury switch pulser was coupled through the crystal into the 50-Ω input of the sampling scope. If the dimensions of the crystal were properly chosen, a semilog plot of the resulting RC type decay could be obtained that was linear out to approximately 3 nsec, but then curved in the direction of a longer time constant. This type of behavior can be explained by the presence of the mechanical thickness resonance at approximately 50 Mc. The initial time constant, determined from the first 3 nsec of the semilog plot, was converted into a dielectric constant, again assumed to be under the strain-free condition. Figure 4 shows K_c' vs temperature. K_a' determined by this method agreed closely with Benedict and Durand's 24 kMc values,[10] and K_c' at 25°C agrees with Berlincourt and Jaffe.[11]

Using these dielectric constants, $r_{42}'/\epsilon_0(K_a' - 1) = 0.046\ m^2/C$; and $r_c'/\epsilon_0(K_c' - 1) = 0.025\ m^2/C$, independent of temperature from 10°C to 110°C, within the experimental accuracy. The corresponding low-frequency values are $r_{42}/\epsilon_0(K_a - 1) = 0.045\ m^2/C$, independent of temperature from 10°C to 110°C, and $r_c/\epsilon_0(K_c - 1) = 0.075\ m^2/C$ at 25°C, decreasing toward higher temperature. If the electro-optic response is expressed in terms of induced polarization, there is no clamping effect for a [100] field, but for an [001] field a 68% clamping effect remains.

Similar measurements were made of the quadratic or Kerr response in the cubic region above 120°C. The geometry was appropriate to measurement of $g_{11} - g_{12}$, using the notation of Geusic;[12] that is, the field was applied along [001]. At low frequency (1 kc) the value of $g_{11} - g_{12} = 0.088 \pm 0.015\ m^4/C^2$ independent of temperature from 125° to 195°C was obtained for five samples, somewhat smaller than $g_{11} - g_{12} = 0.13 \pm 0.02\ m^4/C^2$ obtained by Geusic. The error assignments were determined by the sample-to-sample variation. Under strain-free conditions, $g_{11}' - g_{12}' = 0.031 \pm 0.005\ m^4/C^2$. Thus, the

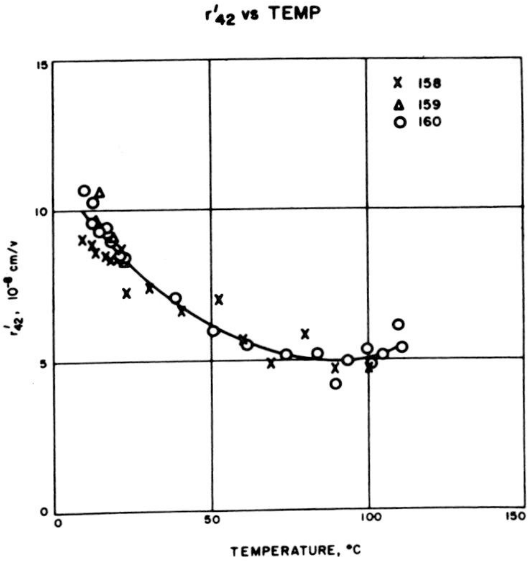

Fig. 3. r_{42}' **for three crystal samples, plotted as a function of temperature. Data points from different crystals are indicated by different symbols.**

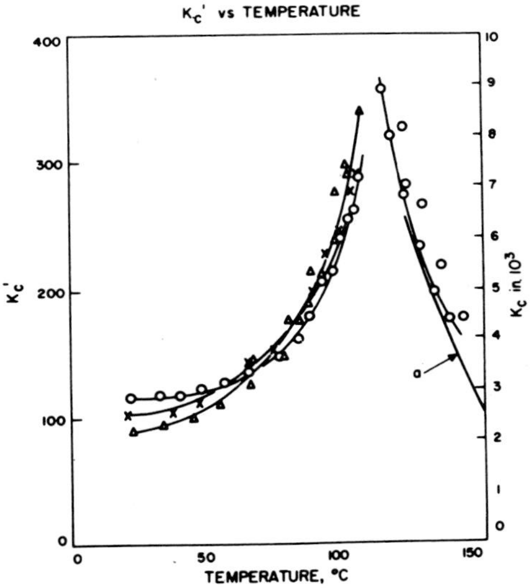

Fig. 4. The dielectric constant K_c' measured under the strain-free condition by the transient method discussed in the text. The curve labeled "a" in the cubic region is taken from ref. 9.

ratio of the strain-free to the stress-free quadratic response was 0.35 ± 0.05, remaining constant with temperature up to 195°C within the experimental error. The present conclusion is that there is a large contribution due to electrostrictive strain[13] in the quadratic electro-optic response in $BaTiO_3$. No comparable clamping effect was found in the dielectric constant.

If Δn is taken proportional to P^2 where P is the total polarization, r_c can be related to $g_{11} - g_{12}$ as follows:

$$r_c = 2(g_{11} - g_{12})P_s\epsilon_0 K_c .$$

This assumes the quadratic response extends without saturation to the level of the spontaneous polarization.

Taking $r_c = 1.06 \times 10^{-8}$ cm/V, from an earlier paper,[4] the calculated $g_{11} - g_{12}$ is 0.14 m^4/C^2, compared to the measured 0.088 m^4/C^2. The calculated $g_{11}' - g_{12}' = 0.048$ m^4/C^2, compared to the measured 0.031 m^4/C^2. The 65% strain contribution in the quadratic response in the cubic state is thus consistent with the strain contribution in the tetragonal state, although Geusic's higher value for $g_{11} - g_{12}$ is in better agreement with the calculated $g_{11} - g_{12}$. It should be noted, however, that his data were obtained at 6328 Å on $BaTiO_3$ specimens grown by a different method.

The spontaneous birefringence may also be calculated from $g_{11} - g_{12}$;

$$\Delta n_s = -n^3/2(g_{11} - g_{12})P_s^2 .$$

Using $g_{11} - g_{12} = 0.088$ m^4/C^2, at 5461 Å, $\Delta n_s = 0.042$ is calculated, whereas $g_{11} - g_{12} = 0.13$ m^4/C^2 at 6328 Å yields $\Delta n_s = 0.059$. The measured Δn_s are 0.072 at 5461 Å and 0.047 at 6328 Å.[14]

[1] This paper presents the results of one phase of research sponsored by the National Aeronautics and Space Administration.

[2] R. O'B. Carpenter, Dissertation, Harvard, 1951.

[3] B. H. Billings, in *Optics in Metrology*, International Commission for Optics Conference, Brussels, 1958 (Pergamon Press, New York, 1960), p. 119.

[4] A. R. Johnston and J. M. Weingart, *J. Opt. Soc. Am.* **55**, 828 (1965).

[5] Obtained from Harshaw Chemical Corp., Cleveland, Ohio.

[6] Obtained from Acheson Colloids Corp., Port Huron, Michigan.

[7] S. J. Williamson, J. M. Weingart, and R. D. Andrews, *J. Opt. Soc. Am.* **57**, 337 (1964).

[8] J. M. Weingart and A. R. Johnston, Proceedings of 1963 Symposium on Ellipsometry, National Bureau of Standards, Sept. 1963.

[9] J. F. Nye, *Physical Properties of Crystals* (Clarendon Press, Oxford, England, 1960).

[10] T. S. Benedict and J. L. Durand, *Phys. Rev.* **109**, 1091 (1958).

[11] D. Berlincourt and H. Jaffe, *Phys. Rev.* **111**, 143 (1958).

[12] J. E. Geusic, S. K. Kurtz, L. G. van Uitert, and S. H. Wemple, *Appl. Phys. Letters* **4**, 141 (1964).

[13] F. S. Chen, J. E. Geusic, S. K. Kurtz, J. G. Skinner, and S. H. Wemple, *J. Appl. Phys.*, to be published.

[14] M. S. Shumate, *Appl. Phys. Letters* **5**, 178 (1964).

Reprinted from
Volume 7, Number 5 APPLIED PHYSICS LETTERS **1 September 1965**

BARIUM TITANATE LIGHT PHASE MODULATOR

I. P. Kaminow
Bell Telephone Laboratories, Incorporated
Crawford Hill Laboratory
Holmdel, New Jersey

(optical heterodyning; electrooptical properties; E)
(Received 8 July 1965)

An optical *phase* modulator using a ferroelectric barium titanate crystal plate has been built and tested at 70 Mc. The magnitudes of the clamped electro-optic coefficients r_{33} and r_{13} have been measured separately using an optical heterodyne technique.

The use of ferroelectric $BaTiO_3$ for light *intensity* modulation was considered by W. J. Merz.[1] He estimated[2,3] the pertinent unclamped electro-optic coefficient $r_c = r_{33} - (n_a/n_c)^3 r_{13}$ to be about 10^{-8} cm/V at room temperature by considering the variation in natural birefringence $(n_a - n_c)$ with spontaneous polarization along the ferroelectric c axis as the temperature passes through the Curie point (120°C). Johnston and Weingart[4] have measured the unclamped r_c directly and find a value of 11×10^{-9} cm/V, which is insensitive to temperature variations in the neighborhood of 25°C. Their method does not permit a determination of r_{33} and r_{13} separately. The electro-optic properties of $BaTiO_3$ and the mixed perovskite KTN and their application to light modulation have been studied in the para-electric phase above the Curie temperature.[5] A dc biasing field is required to produce a large and linear effect in the para-electric case whereas the spontaneous polarization acts as the bias in the ferroelectric phase.

Crystals grown by the Remeika method[6] occur in very thin platelets, a form well suited to modulation of an optical maser beam. Selected crystals can be poled[7] into single *c* domains. Such crystals, chosen to be 0.004 in. thick, were cut into 0.110-in.-wide wafers and the narrow edges polished. With care a wafer could be repoled into a *c* domain after the processing, which included heating above 120°C. Ideally a focused fundamental gaussian mode can pass through the edges of a plate of these dimensions easily. Experimentally both a higher order "donut" mode of a 0.633-μ He-Ne maser and the fundamental mode maintained their identities on passing through the wafer. Some extraneous scattered light was observed in the transmitted patterns for both modes however. The measured insertion loss due to reflection, scattering, and absorption was 2 dB. It may be noted in passing that barium titanate is

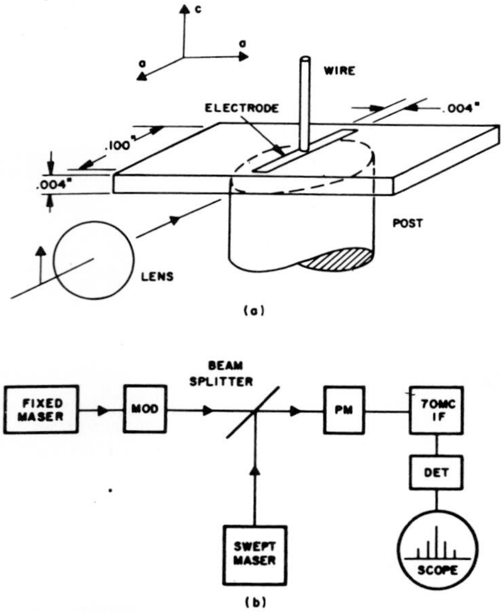

Fig. 1. (*a*) Barium titanate modulator employing a *c*-domain wafer. (*b*) 70-Mc heterodyne measuring set showing oscilloscope presentation for phase modulated signal without image frequencies present. The optical maser resonators are 20 cm long and are driven piezoelectrically. Mixing takes place in RCA 7326 photomultiplier (PM).

sufficiently transparent[8] to be useful between 0.45 and 7 μ.

A 0.100-in.-diam silver electrode was evaporated on the bottom surface of the wafer and a 0.004 × 0.100-in. strip on top as shown in Fig. 1*a*. Care was taken not to heat the crystal above 120°C. A 0.003-in. gold wire was attached to the strip and the crystal was bonded to a brass post with conducting silver epoxy in each case.

The crystal was placed in a circuit with a bandwidth of about 30 Mc tuned to 70 Mc. Two piezoelectric resonances within the band caused scattering of the beam, detuning of the circuit, and heating and fracture of the crystals when driven near 72 or 55 Mc. These resonances are probably third-harmonic extensional vibrations in the wafer thickness and electrode width (extended by fringing) dimensions, respectively.[9]

The phase modulation index η (peak optical phase shift) was measured using the 70-Mc optical heterodyne set shown in Fig. 1*b*. With the modulating frequency close to the intermediate frequency, both direct and image frequencies appear on the oscilloscope as in Fig. 2. The relative amplitudes of the carrier and first sidebands [proportional to the Bessel functions $J_0(\eta)$ and $J_1(\eta)$, respectively] were measured using either optical or i.f. calibrated attenuators with similar results. The voltage across the crystal was measured with a high-

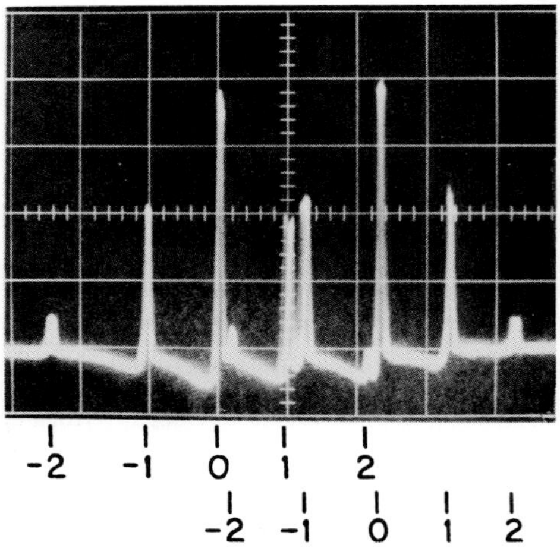

Fig. 2. Carrier, first and second sidebands for 65-Mc modulation with overlapping image frequencies. Intensity and frequency scales not linear.

124

frequency electronic voltmeter. The electro-optic coefficient was determined from

$$r_{33} = \eta \lambda t / \pi n_e^3 l V \qquad (1)$$

in which λ is the optical wavelength (0.633-μ), t the wafer thickness, l the strip length, V the voltage amplitude, n_e the extraordinary index[10] (2.33), and η is obtained from the observed $J_1(\eta)/J_0(\eta)$. Measurements on two crystals at frequencies away from the acoustic resonances fell within the range $(8 \pm 1.5) \times 10^{-9}$ cm/V. The magnitude of r_{13} was determined in a similar way and the magnitude ratio found to be $r_{13}/r_{33} = 0.3 \pm 0.1$. The signs of the coefficients are not determined. In the measurements V was always less than 10 V.

Impedance measurements on the condenser element, regarded as a parallel RC circuit, indicate that the crystal is essentially clamped at frequencies above the fundamental acoustic resonances (25 and 17 Mc) although small excursions in R and C are still evident near the harmonics. At low frequencies C is about 20 pF. Above the fundamental frequencies to at least 150 Mc, the mean value of C is 10 pF. The ratio of unclamped to clamped C agrees with the ratio of corresponding dielectric constants.[2,11] However, the absolute values of C are about five times as large as one would calculate using the $0.004 \times 0.004 \times 0.100$-in. geometry and known[11] dielectric constant ϵ_c. The discrepancy is attributed to fringing fields which are encouraged by the fact that ϵ_a is about ten times (ref. 2) ϵ_c. The electrical Q of the condenser element at frequencies removed from the acoustic resonances appears to be about 3. The reason for the poor Q is not yet understood although it may be noted that higher-Q condensers have been reported earlier.[11]

The power required to drive the crystal in a parallel resonant circuit is

$$P = V^2/2R_p = CV^2\Delta\omega/4\,, \qquad (2)$$

where it has been assumed that the generator impedance matches the parallel resistance R_p of the crystal and any added loading resistor so that $\Delta\omega = 2/CR_p$. The peak voltage V across C is determined by Eq. (1) and the desired modulation index η, with the limitation that V/t not exceed the coercive field (ref. 2) ($\sim 10^3$ V/cm) at the modulating frequency.

In the absence of fringing, P is proportional to aperture area (t^2), the minimum value of which is set by the ability to prepare the sample and pass a gaussian beam through it. It is clearly important to reduce the fringing capacitance in order to minimize P and techniques for doing so are being explored. The minimum bandwidth is limited by the Q of the crystal element (provided no additional capacitor is added in parallel). In order to reduce heating and allow design flexibility it is preferable that the crystal element have a high Q and that $\Delta\omega$ be increased by means of an external resistor as required. The bandwidth and frequency restrictions imposed by piezoelectric resonances can be reduced by operating at frequencies high enough that all dimensions are much greater than an acoustic wavelength so that these resonances are only weakly excited. Alternatively, one may operate at base band with a bandwidth less than the fundamental resonance frequencies.

I am indebted to O. E. DeLange and A. F. Dietrich for the use of their heterodyne measuring set. I am also grateful to J. P. Remeika for providing the crystals.

[1] W. J. Merz, unpublished memorandum (1954).
[2] F. Jona and G. Shirane, *Ferroelectric Crystals*, The Macmillan Co., New York, 1962, pp. 108–215.
[3] W. J. Merz, *Phys. Rev.* **76**, 1221 (1949).
[4] A. R. Johnston and J. M. Weingart, *J. Opt. Soc. Am.* **55**, 828 (1965).
[5] A. W. Hornig, Dissertation, Stanford University, Stanford, California (1955); A. C. Koelsch, IRE National Convention Record, Part 3, 169 (1957); F. S. Chen, J. E. Geusic, S. K. Kurtz, J. G. Skinner, and S. H. Wemple, *J. Appl. Phys.* (to be published).
[6] J. P. Remeika, *J. Am. Chem. Soc.* **76**, 940 (1954).
[7] R. C. Miller, *Phys. Rev.* **134**, A1313 (1964).
[8] R. C. Casella and S. P. Keller, *Phys. Rev.* **116**, 1469 (1959); C. Hilsum, *J. Opt. Soc. Am.* **45**, 771 (1955).
[9] W. L. Bond, W. P. Mason, and H. J. McSkimin, *Phys. Rev.* **82**, 442 (1951).
[10] M. S. Shumate, *Appl. Phys. Letters* **5**, 178 (1964).
[11] A. H. Meitzler and H. L. Stadler, *Bell System Tech. J.* **37**, 719 (1958).

Erratum: In I. P. Kaminow, Barium titanate light phase modulator, *Appl. Phys. Lett.* **7**, 123 (1965) the measured value for r_{33} does not correspond to a clamped value as stated, probably because of the unexpectedly strong effect of nearby piezoelectric resonances. Recent high frequency measurements (to 250 Mc) on small bar-shaped samples give the values: $r_{33} = (2.8 \pm 0.5) \times 10^{-9}$ cm/v and $r_{13}/r_{33} = +0.3 \pm 0.1$. Then $r_c = r_{33} - (n_a/n_c)^3 r_{13} = 1.9 \times 10^{-9}$ cm/v, in reasonable agreement with the value found by Johnston using an entirely different method. [A. R. Johnston, *Appl. Phys. Lett.* **7**, 195 (1965).]

Reprinted from
Volume 8, Number 11 **APPLIED PHYSICS LETTERS** **1 June 1966**

BARIUM TITANATE LIGHT MODULATOR. II

(high-frequency electro-optic coefficients; rm temp; 632 Å; E)

I. P. Kaminow
Bell Telephone Laboratories, Incorporated
Crawford Hill Laboratory
Holmdel, New Jersey
(Received 4 April 1966)

A light modulator, operating between 5 and 200 MHz, has been constructed from a single-domain $BaTiO_3$ rod cut from a crystal grown by the Remeika method. The electro-optic coefficients and their relative sign were measured using a heterodyne technique.[1] The high frequency values are: $r_{33} = (2.8 \pm 0.5) \times 10^{-9}$ cm/V and $r_{13}/r_{33} = +0.3 \pm 0.1$. The calculated value for $r_c = r_{33} - (n_a/n_c)^3 r_{13}$ is 1.9×10^{-9} cm/V which agrees within experimental error with the strain-free value measured by Johnston using an entirely different technique.[2]

Rods were gang-cut with thin silicon carbide saws, polished on the ends with alumina powder, etched in phosphoric acid at 150°C for 30 min and then poled under de-ionized water at room temperature using a 45-V battery.

A rod was secured to the brass pedestal at the end of the center conductor of a coaxial mount and a .003 in. gold wire attached, using slow drying silver paint baked at 100°C, as shown in Fig. 1. The rod has the following thichness, t, width, w, and length, L: .0105 × .0135 × .150 in. The c axis is along the .0105 dimension.

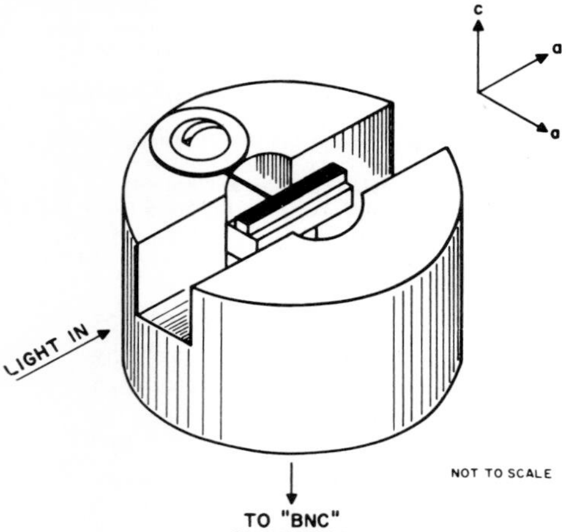

Fig. 1. Coaxial modulator mount and crystal.

The equivalent parallel RC circuit parameters are given in Fig. 2. The capacity of the crystal, C_x, found by subtracting 2 pF for the mount from the total C, is close to the value calculated using the high-frequency dielectric constant.[2] Thus, the large fringing capacity present in the modulator reported earlier,[1] which was formed by evaporating a narrow electrode on a broad crystal platelet, is absent in the rod geometry.

Acoustic resonances excited by the strong piezoelectric coupling in $BaTiO_3$ produce the minima in R which persist beyond the 15th harmonic for the width and thickness dimensions. Since the energy coupled into the p-th harmonic by a uniform field is proportional to $1/p^2$, the resonance effects ultimately disappear and ωRC_x, the crystal Q, approaches a constant value of about 15.

The modulator was driven directly as an RC element or as a resonant element, using a coaxial stub stretcher, up to about 250 MHz where series-inductive reactance becomes appreciable. The peak phase modulation index η at a wavelength λ of .633 μ and

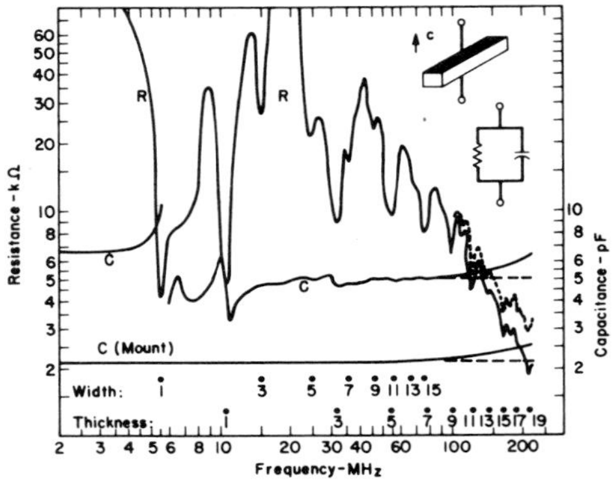

Fig. 2. Equivalent circuit resistance and capacitance parameters for .0105 × .0135 × .150 in. rod. Only odd acoustic harmonics, as indicated for width and thickness dimensions, are excited by uniform field. The bulge in the first resonance is produced by a taper in the width dimension. Corrections for series inductance in modulator and RX-meter are shown dashed.

the peak voltage V across the crystal were measured as described earlier.[1] The electro-optic coefficient for light polarized along the c axis is

$$r_{33} = (\lambda t / \pi n_c^3 L)\,(\eta / V),$$

where n_c is the refractive index, with a similar expression for r_{13}. The apparent coefficients, as determined from the observed η/V shown in Figs. 3 and 4, take on large values at the low acoustic resonance frequencies and then approach a constant high frequency value. The device is clearly unsuitable for communications application in the resonance region. Acoustic resonances and the associated narrow band circuit employed employed probably led to the erroneous value for r_{33} reported earlier.[1]

In order to find the sign of r_{13}/r_{33} using the heterodyne measuring set, the incident light is polarized at 45° to the c axis and a variable (Ehringhaus) compensator placed in front of the crystal with axes parallel to the a and c axes. The relative optical phase of the a- and c-axis signals can then be adjusted before they enter the photomultiplier along with the swept local oscillator signal, which is also polarized at 45° to the c axis. The photocurrents produced by the a- and c-axis components are added at the 70-Mc intermediate frequency, detected, and displayed on an oscilloscope.[1] Observing the combined side-band spectrum as the compensator is adjusted, it is found that when the carrier is a maximum (optical carriers in-phase) the first side bands, due to r_{33} and r_{13}, are maximum and when the carrier cancels (optical carriers anti-phase) the side bands are minimum. Therefore, since the first side-band level is linear in r_{33} and r_{13}, these coefficients must have the same sign. The combined relative side-band levels can also be checked quantitatively using the measured r_{33} and r_{13}.

The power dissipated P is $V^2/2R$. From Figs. 2 and 3, P is found to be less than 215 mW for a unity index phase modulator for all frequencies below 200 MHz. If the added capacities associated with the mount and coaxial tuning elements were eliminated, and if the resultant resonant circuit were critically coupled to the oscillator, the loaded Q would be $\omega RC_x/2$ and the bandwidth Δf at 200 MHz would be 27 Mc. Then, approximately 6 mW/MHz would be required. Experimentally, added circuit capacity, chiefly from the coaxial tuning element, raised this figure by as much as five times. A proper lumped tuning inductance would eliminate much of the capacitance.

In the limiting cases, where all the loss or all the capacity is provided by the crystal itself, it can be shown[3] that the driving power is proportional to the ratio of cross-sectional area to length, wt/L. The dimensions used here were chosen so as to separate the width and thickness acoustic modes and to simplify the experiment. The area/length ratio is 2.5×10^{-3} cm, which is larger than the minimum value dictated by diffraction limitations. One can readily show by differentiation of the gaussian beam formulas[4] that the minimum value for the ratio occurs for a fundamental gaussian beam focused so that L is the confocal length. Then, for a square cross section, the minimum area/length ratio is

$$t^2/L = S^2 \cdot 4\lambda/n\pi = S^2 \cdot (3.5 \times 10^{-5}\ \text{cm})\ ,$$

where S, the ratio of t to the gaussian spot diameter at the rod input, is a safety factor. In practice, it is possible to use S as small as 3 without appreciable optical loss.[1] Hence, the efficiency of the present device could be improved by as much as 8 times.

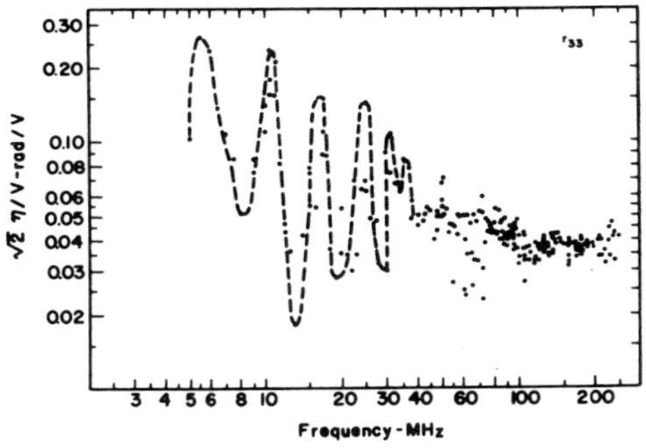

Fig. 3. Phase modulation index η per peak volt V for optical polarization along c axis. $r_{33} = 7.9 \times 10^{-8}\ (\sqrt{2}\ \eta/V)$ cm/V.

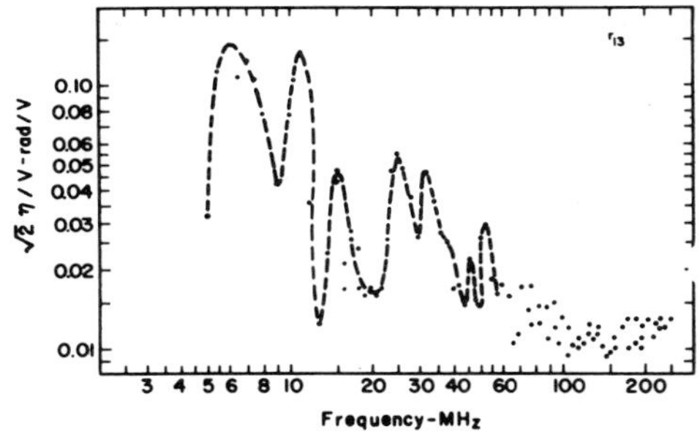

Fig. 4. Phase modulation index η per peak volt V for optical polarization along a axis. $r_{13} = 7.3 \times 10^{-8}\ (\sqrt{2}\ \eta/V)$ cm/V.

306

[1] I. P. Kaminow, *Appl. Phys. Letters* **7**, 123 (1965); Erratum, **8**, 54 (1966).

[2] A. R. Johnston, *Appl. Phys. Letters* **7**, 195 (1965).

[3] E. H. Turner and I. P. Kaminow, *Proc. IEEE*, to be published.

[4] G. D. Boyd and H. Kogelnik, *Bell System Tech. J.* **41**, 1347 (1962).

Reprinted from
Volume 8, Number 11 **APPLIED PHYSICS LETTERS** **1 June 1966**

HIGH-FREQUENCY ELECTRO-OPTIC COEFFICIENTS OF LITHIUM NIOBATE

(laser beam modulation; 0.633 μ; E)

E. H. Turner
Bell Telephone Laboratories, Incorporated
Crawford Hill, Holmdel, New Jersey
(Received 8 April 1966)

Observation of a high-frequency electro-optic effect in multidomain lithium niobate has been reported perviously.[1] More recently, quantitative low-frequency measurements of one electro-optic coefficient and of a quantity involving two other coefficients have been made[2] on single-domain[3] crystals. Since lithium niobate is in point group $3m$, four coefficients are required to describe the electro-optic behavior of the crystal. In this Letter the magnitudes of these fou coefficients are reported for 0.633-μ light wavelength and modulating electric field frequencies of 50 to 86 Mc/sec.

The measurements were made using a heterodyne technique[4] in which the sideband amplitudes of a phase-modulated optical signal are measured relative to the carrier. The modulation is produced by the variation in phase length which occurs when an electric field is applied to the crystal being tested. This change in phase length can be related to any one of the four electro-optic coefficients by suitable choices of the directions of modulating field and optical polarization relative to the crystallographic axes.[5]

The crystal remains uniaxial under the application of an electric field, E_3, along the threefold x_3 axis. However, the index of refraction for light polarized parallel to the x_3 axis changes by an amount $\Delta n_{33} = (-n_e^3 r_{33} E_3/2)$ and the index for light polarized perpendicular to the x_3 axis changes by an amount $\Delta n_{13} = (-n_0^3 r_{13} E_3/2)$, where n_e and n_0 are the principal indices and r_{33}, r_{13} are electro-optic coefficients. Thus by using the appropriate light polarization the same samples could be used to determine $|r_{33}|$ and $|r_{13}|$. Four samples from two different boules were used. One of these had been used in the dc measurements.[2] The values of the coefficients, which are listed in Table I, were independent of modulating frequency. Moreover, the c axis dielectric constant at room temperature was the same ($\epsilon_r = 28$) from 20 Mc/sec (which was well above the fundamental acoustic resonant frequencies for the samples used) to 250 Mc/sec. The lack of frequency dependence indicates that the quoted values of r_{33} and r_{13} are for constant strain conditions. Modulating field strengths were varied from an rms value of 35 V/cm to over 1000 V/cm; the modulation was linear in this range.

In addition to the magnitude of the coefficients r_{33} and r_{13}, it is important to know their relative signs, since the difference $(\Delta n_{33} - \Delta n_{13})$ is the change in birefringence that is useful for amplitude modulation. The relative sign was found in two ways. The more direct method required the light to pass through two separate crystals which were oriented

Table I. Electro-optic Behavior of $LiNbO_3$.

	r_{33}	r_{13}	r_{22}	r_{42}	$\left(\frac{n_e^3 r_{33} - n_0^3 r_{13}}{2}\right)$	$n_0^3 r_{22}$
This work:	30.8	8.6	3.4	28	112	37
Low frequency values (ref. 2)	[a]	[a]	6.7	[a]	95	74

[a] Not measured.
Units: 10^{-10} cm/V.

so that Δn_{33} of the first crystal was added to Δn_{13} of the second. The modulating fields in the two crystals had the same sense relative to the polar axes. The second method effectively measured sidebands produced by a single crystal used as an amplitude modulator.[6] The signs of r_{33} and r_{13} were found to be the same as was true in $LiTaO_3$.[7]

An electric field applied normal to x_3 causes the crystal to become biaxial. The index change for light propagating along the former optic axis is $(\pm n_0^3 r_{22}E/2)$, with a birefringence $n_0^3 r_{22}E$. The orientation of the axes of birefringence depends on the direction in which the field is applied: Electric fields parallel to x_2 lie in a mirror plane, so the axes of birefringence develop along x_1 and x_2, and fields in the x_1 direction remove all mirror symmetry so the axes lie at $\pi/4$ to x_1 and x_2.[2,8] Two samples were used in the r_{22} determination and both x_1 and x_2 fields were used on each sample. Fields ranging up to 1000 V/cm were used and the modulating frequency was again varied. There was some indication of frequency dependence, but at field strengths of over 50 V/cm this dependence caused variations of less than 5% in r_{22}. High field values are quoted in Table I. However, when the crystal was not driven so hard, large variations of r_{22} with frequency were found. As frequency was varied between 50 Mc/sec and 100 Mc/sec, with the drive too low to give measurable sideband amplitude, sharp resonances occurred in which the modualtion increased at points spaced irregularly about 2 Mc/sec apart. While modulating at these resonant frequencies, if the laser beam was moved across the lithium niobate crystal, spatial variations could also be found. The resonances were more pronounced when the modulating field was in the x_2 direction. The capacitance and resistance of the crystals were also checked as a function of frequency and rather large variations were plotted out. Presumably the resonances were high-order harmonics of the fundamental acoustic resonances. The situation, then, was markedly different from that in which the driving field was along x_3 where frequency dependence was not found.

An electric field applied normal to the x_3 axis also causes a change in birefringence through the r_{42} coefficient. This change is of first order in the electric field and depends solely on r_{42} if the modulating field lies along x_1 and the optical polarization is at $\pi/4$ to x_3 and in the plane determined by the electric field and x_3. The index of refraction for such a ray is

$$\left(n'_e - \frac{n'^3_e r_{42}E}{2}\right),$$

where

$$n'_e = \frac{\sqrt{2}n_e n_0}{\sqrt{n_0^2 + n_e^2}}.$$

The value given for r_{42} in Table I is the least accurate of the electro-optic coefficient values for several reasons. First, the geometry used made the optical path short. Second, there may have been appreciable electric field components not along x_1. Finally, there was some variation with modulating frequency.

The values given in Table I, together with the availability of crystals with good optical and electrical properties, show lithium niobate to be a very attractive electro-optic modulating medium. The change in birefringence produced by a c-axis field is nearly the same at dc and high frequency as indicated in the table. This, together with the lack of frequency dependence of the c-axis dielectric constant, indicates that r_{33} and r_{13} are sensibly independent of frequency and the material should make a good modulator over a very large span of modulating frequencies.

I thank K. Nassau who furnished the crystals used in these measurements. In addition I am indebted to I. P. Kaminow for the use of his measuring set.

[1] G. E. Peterson, A. A. Ballman, P. V. Lenzo, and P. M. Bridenbaugh, *Appl. Phys. Letters* **5**, 62 (1964).
[2] P. V. Lenzo, E. G. Spencer and K. Nassau, *J. Opt. Soc. Am.* (in press) **56**, (1966).
[3] K. Nassau and H. J. Levinstein, *Appl. Phys. Letters* **7**, 69 (1965).
[4] I. P. Kaminow, *Appl. Phys. Letters* **7**, 123 (1965); *Appl. Phys. Letters* **8**, 54 (1966).
[5] A choice of field direction and polarization direction which allows any coefficient to be determined by one measurement can be made for all point groups except 1, 2, 3, m. Here two measurements are necessary for some of the coefficients.
[6] A more detailed discussion of this method of relative sign determination is given by I. P. Kaminow, *Appl. Phys. Letters* **8**, 305 (1966).
[7] P. V. Lenzo, E. H. Turner, E. G. Spencer, and A. A. Ballman, *Appl. Phys. Letters* **8**, 81 (1966).
[8] C. F. Buhrer, D. Baird, and E. M. Conwell, *Appl. Phys. Letters* **1**, 46 (1962).

304

Reprinted from **APPLIED OPTICS**, Vol. 7, page 171, January 1968

Electrooptic Coefficients in Calcium Pyroniobate

R. D. Rosner and E. H. Turner

Six of the eight linear electrooptic coefficients have been measured in a crystal of class C_2 (calcium pyroniobate). This is the first time so many coefficients of a low symmetry crystal such as this have been measured. Some of the coefficients are large enough to make this material interesting for optical modulators. However, other properties of the crystal make it less desirable than other known modulator crystals. The geometry used in measuring some of the skew coefficients is discussed in some detail as are methods for determining relative signs of the coefficients.

Introduction

Holmes *et al.*[1] showed that calcium pyroniobate has a large electrooptic effect at dc and at 3 GHz. The amplitude modulation measurements made in that work yielded values for differences between some of the electrooptic coefficients but not the individual coefficients. The differences, however, were large and suggested that individual coefficients might be large enough to make the material of technical importance as a phase modulator. Our measurements have been made using an optical heterodyne technique[2,3] at 0.63 μ, which allows the values of separate coefficients to be found and makes it possible to measure some of the coefficients which were not accessible to the amplitude modulation technique. These measurements are the first in which so many coefficients of a low symmetry crystal have been determined.

Calcium pyroniobate ($Ca_2Nb_2O_7$) is in class C_2 and has a single twofold axis which is taken as the x_2 direction. There is a pronounced cleavage plane which is normal to the x_1 direction. The x_3 direction is at right angles to x_1 and x_2. Using the coordinate system defined in this way, there are eight allowed linear electrooptic coefficients,[1,4] including three principal axis coefficients (r_{12}, r_{22}, r_{32}) and five skew coefficients (r_{52}, r_{41}, r_{61}, r_{43}, r_{63}). In the following sections we discuss first the measurement of the three principal axis coefficients and then the measurement of three of the skew coefficients using a less than optimum geometry.

Principal Axis Coefficients

The coefficients r_{12}, r_{22}, and r_{32} (abbreviated r_{k2}) were measured by applying an electric field parallel to the x_2 axis, and propagating light from a He–Ne laser at $\lambda = 0.633\ \mu$ through the crystal with optical polarization parallel to the x_1, x_2, or x_3 axes, respectively. The emergent beam is thus phase modulated and consists of a carrier of amplitude proportional to $J_0(\eta_{k2})$ and sidebands of amplitude $J_n(\eta_{k2})$ at frequencies $\omega_0 \pm n\omega_m$. The modulation index η_{k2} is ordinarily so small that only the first order Bessel's function $J_1(\eta_{k2})$ is significant relative to $J_0(\eta_{k2})$. The modulation index is related to the r_{k2} coefficients by the relation

$$\eta_{k2} = -\pi L n_k^3 r_{k2} E_2/\lambda_0, \tag{1}$$

where E_2 is the applied electric field amplitude, L is the path length in the crystal, n_k is the appropriate index of refraction, and λ_0 is the light wavelength (0.63 μ). The electric field was applied using silver paint electrodes. Field strengths of up to 1.5×10^5 V/m were used at frequencies near 60 MHz. Some measurements were made at nearby frequencies to detect piezoelectric resonances that might affect the measurement, but no evidence of such resonances was found, indicating we are measuring the direct electrooptic effect. Three samples* were used. Each sample was about 3.5 mm measured along the x_3 axis and 2 mm along the x_2 axis. The x_1 dimension varied from 0.5 mm to 1.2 mm. The measurement of r_{22} was made with x_2 polarized light propagating in the x_1 or the x_3 direction, so two determinations were made for each sample. The r_{12} and r_{32} coefficients are based on one determination per sample.

Results are presented in Table I. The actual spread of measured values is indicated by the $\pm$ numbers. In Table I, two quantities $[r_{22} - (n_3/n_2)^3 r_{32}]$ and $[r_{22} - (n_1/n_2)^3 r_{12}]$ involving the differences between coefficients are also tabulated. These are the pertinent quantities for amplitude modulation and allow our results to be compared with the earlier values.[1] Our

The authors are with the Bell Telephone Laboratories, Inc., Crawford Hill Laboratory, Holmdel, New Jersey 07733.

* Two of these crystals were used in Ref. 1. The third was also from the same source.

Table I. Electrooptic Coefficients of $Ca_2Nb_2O_7$

Principal axis coefficients[a]			Combination coefficients		Skew coefficients		
r_{12}	r_{22}	r_{32}	r_{c1}	r_{c3}	r_{41}	r_{52}	r_{63}
6.7 ± 0.4	25.5 ± 1.5	6.4 ± 0.4	20.4 ± 1.8 (12.3)(dc)[a]	19.0 ± 1.9 (13.7)(dc)[b] (13.0)(3 GHz)[b]	2.7 ± 1	<0.6	0.9

[a] Units: 10^{-12} m/V.
$r_{c1} = r_{22} - (n_1/n_2)^3 r_{12}$.
$r_{c3} = r_{22} - (n_3/n_2)^3 r_{32}$.

[b] Ref. 1.

values are approximately 50% higher. Since the dc values include contributions owing to the secondary electrooptic effect, one should not expect the two sets of measurements to agree. Microwave measurements are difficult and probably good agreement is not to be expected.

In order to compute the difference quantities from our measurements of individual coefficients, it is necessary to know the relative signs of the coefficients. The method used has been alluded to previously,[3] but has not been described in any detail, so it is included here. We examine the phase modulation produced when light is propagated through the crystal with its polarization vector at some arbitrary angle θ with respect to one of the crystal axes. For definiteness assume the relative sign between r_{22} and r_{32} is desired. The beam is propagated through the crystal along the x_1 direction, with polarization at angle θ with respect to x_2 and angle $\pi/2 - \theta$ with respect to x_3. An external compensator is placed with axes parallel to x_2, x_3 and adjusted to compensate for crystal birefringence. The unmodulated beam then remains linearly polarized at an angle θ. The beam is then modulated with a field in the x_2 direction, so that modulation on the output contains components owing to r_{22} and r_{32}. In general, the polarizaton of the modulated beam is different from the input beam polarization. The modulated beam has frequency components at ω_0, $\omega_0 \pm \omega_m$, $\omega_0 \pm 2\omega_m, \ldots,$ where ω_0 is the unmodulated optical frequency and ω_m is the modulating frequency. Each of these components has a different polarization. For small modulation index only the carrier (ω_0) and the first sidebands ($\omega_0 \pm \omega_m$) need be considered.

For the carrier, the polarization angle measured from x_2 is

$$\varphi_0 = \tan^{-1}\{[J_0(\eta_3)/J_0(\eta_2)] \tan\theta\}, \quad (2)$$

while for the sidebands

$$\varphi_m = \tan^{-1}\{[J_1(\eta_3)/J_1(\eta_2)] \tan\theta\}, \quad (3)$$

where η_k = index of modulation owing to r_{k2}, and J_0, J_1 are the zero and first order Bessel functions which arise from the phase modulation.

An analyzer at the output of the modulating crystal can be used to find φ_0 and φ_m as indicated by a maximum of the carrier or sidebands, respectively. Note, however, that $J_0(\eta)$ is an even function, while $J_1(\eta)$ is an odd function. If η_3 and η_2 are different in sign (indicating that r_{32} and r_{22} have different signs), then $[J_1(\eta_3)/J_1(\eta_2)]$ will be negative and φ_0 and φ_m will be in different quadrants. If η_3 and η_2 have the same sign, then φ_0 and φ_m will be in the same quadrant. Using this procedure, it was found that the algebraic signs of r_{12}, r_{22}, and r_{32} are the same.

Skew Coefficients

Application of an electric field produces a maximum change in (index of refraction)$^{-2}$ for light polarized at 45° to the principal axes and no change in index for light polarized along the principal axes. The manner in which the samples we used were cut precluded use of a 45° polarization. However, it was possible to achieve angles of a few degrees between polarization and axis as indicated in Fig. 1. Using this less than optimum geometry, a measurement was made of the size of some of the coefficients.

In general, the refractive index is altered through the action of more than one coefficient.

For clarity, the following discussion describes only the r_{52} measurement. A similar treatment can be given for the other skew coefficients. In the measurement of r_{52} the electric field E is applied parallel to the x_2 axis, and the light is propagated through the crystal perpendicular to the field direction, and at an angle φ with respect to the x_3 axis, see Fig. 1. The polarization vector then lies in the x_1x_3 plane and is at an angle φ with respect to the x_1 axis.

Under these conditions, the cross section of the indicatrix in the x_1x_3 plane can be written[5]

$$(1/n_1^2 + r_{12}E)x_1^2 + (1/n_3^2 + r_{32}E)x_3^2 + 2r_{52}Ex_1x_3 = 1. \quad (4)$$

In polar coordinates, with $x_3 = \rho \sin\varphi$ and $x_1 = \rho \cos\varphi$, Eq. (4) becomes:

$$(1/n_1^2 + r_{12}E)\rho^2 \cos^2\varphi + (1/n_3^2 + r_{32}E)\rho^2 \sin^2\varphi + 2r_{52}E\rho^2 \cos\varphi \sin\varphi = 1. \quad (4a)$$

From Eq. (4a) we find that the change in refractive index due to the applied field is

$$\Delta\rho = -(\rho_0^3/2)E(r_{12}\cos^2\varphi + r_{32}\sin^2\varphi + r_{52}\sin 2\varphi), \quad (5)$$

where ρ_0 is the index with $E = 0$:

$$\rho_0 = (\cos^2\varphi/n_1^2 + \sin^2\varphi/n_3^2)^{-1/2}. \quad (6)$$

The modulation index for a ray with polarization at an angle φ to the x_1 axis has the form given in Eq. (1), where the effective electrooptic coefficient is the quan-

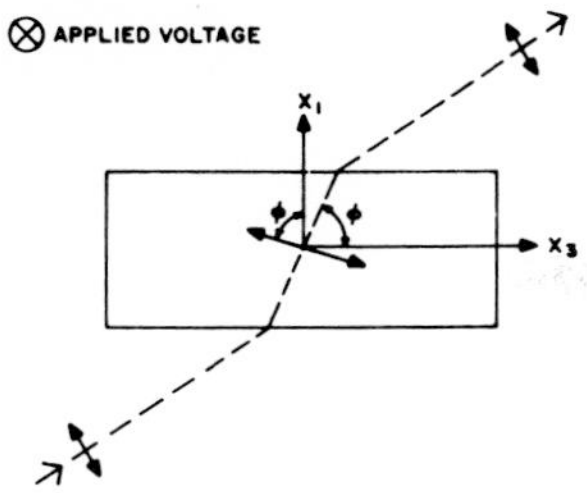

Fig. 1. $x_2 = 0$ section of crystal showing polarization and path of beam for measuring r_{52}.

tity in parentheses in Eq. (5) and the refractive index is ρ_0. Since r_{12} and r_{32} are known from the principal axis measurements and the angle of incidence of the beam is known, the values of r_{52} can be determined from a measured value of η. Also, the contributions of r_{12} and r_{32} to the modulation are independent of the sign of the angle φ, whereas the contribution of r_{52} will either add or subtract, depending on the sign of φ. Thus if measurements are made for equal but opposite angles of incidence on the same crystal, the difference between the observed indices of modulation measures the effect of r_{52}.

The values found for three of the skew coefficients are included in Table I. The measurements of r_{41} and r_{63} were complicated by the fact that the crystal faces thought to be normal to x_2 and x_3 were almost 5° off. Back reflection Laue photographs confirmed this later. The error in orientation made it appear that coefficients forbidden by symmetry were present. In the case of r_{41}, the modulating field is along x_1 and a beam propagating and polarized normal to x_1 was used. The propagation direction was varied by an angle $\pm \varphi$ relative to what was believed to be the x_3 direction. The modulation was zero when φ was about 5° and increased as φ was changed to zero and then 5° beyond zero. The effective coefficient then was [as in Eq. (5)]: $r_{41} \sin 2(\varphi - 5°)$. The measurement of r_{63} also showed anomalies since the supposed x_3 directed electric field had an x_2 component of $E \sin 5°$. Thus a beam polarized along x_2 had a modulation proportional to $r_{22} \sin 5°$ and one polarized along x_3 a modulation proportional to $r_{32} \sin 5°$. Since r_{22} and r_{32} are much larger than r_{63}, the resultant probable error in the measurement is large.

Discussion

Other things being equal, the size of the electrooptic coefficients (r_{22} in particular) would make $Ca_2Nb_2O_7$ a competitor of such materials as $LiNbO_3$ for electrooptic modulators. The crystal has some disadvantages, however. First, it is difficult to grow. Second, optical quality is not good. There was considerable scattering of the light which, along with absorption, caused a loss of about 10 dB in 3.5 mm. Third, the crystal has a micaceous cleavage which makes it difficult to polish well. Fourth, optically induced index inhomogeneities[6] are generated even by low power density 0.63-μ beams. These inhomogeneities are most pronounced for polarizations along x_2, which is the polarization that is needed to use the largest coefficient. Since performance as a wideband modulator depends also on the dielectric constant, we measured ϵ_2 and ϵ_3, the elements for fields along x_2 and x_3. At 50 MHz, the relative dielectric constants ϵ_2 and ϵ_3 are both approximately 45. This is comparable with $LiTaO_3$ (Ref. 7) and somewhat larger than ϵ_3 of $LiNbO_3$ numbers, so again the material has no technical advantage.

The general method used in measuring the skew coefficients should be of particular use in cases where one has only one sample to work with or where the cutting and polishing of several crystals is undesirable. Since the individual coefficients appear in combination, the method can be used to determine relative signs of skew and principal axis coefficients. In Eq. (5), for example, if the directions of $+x_2$ and $+x_3$ had been determined, the relative signs of the coefficients could have been found by relating the angle φ to these axes.

References

1. C. H. Holmes, E. G. Spencer, A. A. Ballman, and P. V. Lenzo, Appl. Opt. **4**, 551 (1965).
2. I. P. Kaminow, Appl. Phys. Letters **7**, 123 (1965). Erratum Appl. Phys. Letters **8**, 54 (1966).
3. E. H. Turner, Appl. Phys. Letters **8**, 303 (1966).
4. J. F. Nye, *Physical Properties of Crystals*, Oxford University Press, Oxford, 1960).
5. I. P. Kaminow and E. H. Turner, Appl. Opt. **5**, 1612 (1966); Proc. IEEE **54**, 1374 (1966).
6. A. Ashkin, *et al.*, Appl. Phys. Letters **9**, 72 (1966).
7. P. V. Lenzo, E. H. Turner, E. G. Spencer, and A. A. Ballman, Appl. Phys. Letters **8**, 81 (1966).

Reprinted from JOURNAL OF APPLIED PHYSICS, Vol. 39, No. 7, 3337–3343, June 1968

Electro-optic and Piezoelectric Coefficients and Refractive Index of Gallium Phosphide

D. F. NELSON*

Bell Telephone Laboratories, Incorporated, Murray Hill, New Jersey

AND

E. H. TURNER

Bell Telephone Laboratories, Incorporated, Holmdel, New Jersey

(Received 16 October 1967)

Measurements of the constant-strain electro-optic coefficient of GaP between 0.56 and 3.39 μ wavelength were made using both pulsed electric field and optical heterodyne techniques. At 0.6328 μ wavelength its value is -0.97×10^{-12} m/V. A dispersion of only 10% is present between 0.56 and 3.39 μ. Approximate values of the piezoelectric coefficient and the constant-stress electro-optic coefficient are also obtained from the analysis of the experiments. For GaP the magnitude of the constant-stress coefficient is less than the constant-strain coefficient. The analysis also points out an often ignored effect: electro-optic measurements made with electric field frequencies in the range of resonant acoustic frequencies may not exhibit the expected symmetry of the crystal plus field but may also evidence effects from the crystal shape. Accurate refractive index measurements made on many GaP crystals between 0.545 and 0.70 μ wavelength are also reported.

I. INTRODUCTION

Recent studies[1,2] of the linear electro-optic effect caused by the electric field within a *p–n* junction in GaP have required accurate values of the electro-optic coefficient as a function of wavelength.[3] For this reason the present work was undertaken. Two methods of measuring the constant-strain electro-optic coefficient were used: measurement of the retardation immediately following the application of a pulsed electric field and measurement of the phase modulation from a high-frequency electric field by an optical heterodyne technique. The mathematical analysis of the first method, in addition to accounting for the observations, gives a method for an optical measurement of the piezoelectric coefficient and indicates conditions under which the indirect electro-optic effect will not possess the symmetry of the crystal plus field, an effect not generally recognized.

During the study of the electro-optic effect in the GaP diodes a suspicion arose that the refractive index of GaP varied with donor or acceptor doping more strongly than the classical Drude formula would predict. For this reason measurements of the refractive index of bulk crystals of GaP with various doping levels were made. Though no such effect was found, the measurements led to more accurate refractive index values than known before[4] and to a determination of how much the index typically varies with uncontrolled and unidentified growth parameters under normal growth conditions. A summary of these index measurements is given in the last section of this paper.

* Present address: Physics Department, University of Southern California, Los Angles, Cal.

[1] D. F. Nelson and F. K. Reinhart, Appl. Phys. Letters **5**, 148 (1964).

[2] D. F. Nelson and J. McKenna, J. Appl. Phys. **38**, 4057 (1967).

[3] Preliminary values at $\lambda=0.6328\ \mu$, where quoted in the review paper by I. P. Kaminow and E. H. Turner, Appl. Opt. **5**, 1612 (1966).

[4] W. L. Bond, J. Appl. Phys. **36**, 1674 (1965).

II. ELECTRO-OPTIC COEFFICIENT MEASUREMENTS

The major difficulty in electro-optic coefficient measurements in a semiconductor like GaP is the presence of electrical conductivity. Low-resistivity crystals cannot be used since excessive heating results from the current flow at the high electric fields needed for the measurements. New problems show up for crystals of high resistivity (such as 10^7 Ω·cm crystals used in these experiments). In these crystals the dc current–voltage characteristic indicated the presence of space-charge-limited currents. Such a current regime requires an electric field which varies with position. Electro-optic measurements are thus made considerably more difficult. This problem can be avoided if measurements are made in a time short compared to the dielectric relaxation time of the crystal after application of the field. For GaP with a resistivity of $\rho=10^7$ Ω·cm the dielectric relaxation time $\tau_d=\rho K\epsilon_0\approx10$ μsec ($K=11.1$ is the relative dielectric constant of GaP and ϵ_0 is the permitivity of free space). For measurements on this time scale (at least for available size crystals of GaP) the problem of acoustic resonances excited by the abrupt application of the electric field then arises. The acoustic resonances appear through a combination of the converse piezoelectric effect and the elasto-optic effect. The electro-optic coefficient measured at the instant of application of an abrupt electric field pulse will be the true or constant-strain value. That measured after the acoustic resonances have died away will be the constant-stress value. The constant-strain and constant-stress values differ by what is called the indirect electro-optic effect. Generally the direct and indirect electro-optic effects have the same algebraic sign; in GaP, we will see, this is not the case.

An alternate method of measurement is to apply the electric field as an oscillating field at a frequency large compared both to the inverse dielectric relaxation time and to the highest acoustic resonance frequency which can be appreciably excited. The modulation on the light beam is then determined by an optical heterodyne technique.[5] For all practical purposes such a technique is limited to use at certain laser wavelengths.

Both of the above methods were used in this study on GaP. The pulsed electric field technique was used at wavelengths of 0.56, 0.585, 0.6328, 0.66, and 1.153 μ and the high-frequency oscillating electric field technique was used at 0.6328 and 3.39 μ wavelengths.

GaP crystallizes as a cubic crystal of point group $\bar{4}3m$. As such it possesses only a single electro-optic coefficient, r_{41}.[6] Two crystals were used in this study; one had the electric field E applied in the [111] direction (crystal A) with the light propagating in a direction perpendicular to this; the other had the electric field applied in the [001] direction with the light propagating in the [1$\bar{1}$0] direction (crystal B). For the former case the two refractive indices are

$$n_{\|}=n(1-n^2Er_{41}/\sqrt{3}), \tag{1}$$

$$n_{\perp}=n(1+n^2Er_{41}/2\sqrt{3}), \tag{2}$$

while for the latter case

$$n_{\|}=n, \tag{3}$$

$$n_{\perp}=n(1-n^2Er_{41}/2), \tag{4}$$

where n is the normal refractive index and $\|$ and $\perp$ denote the orientation of the optical electric field with respect to the electric field applied to the crystal. The quantity measured in the pulsed electric field measurements is the retardation Γ defined by

$$\Gamma=\omega l(n_{\perp}-n_{\|})/c, \tag{5}$$

where ω is the angular frequency of the light, l the crystal length, and c the speed of light. In the high frequency oscillating field method the time derivative of a particular component of the refractive index is measured by an optical heterodyne technique.

Crystal A had dimensions of 0.256 cm in the direction of light travel, 0.0229 cm in the direction of the applied electric field, and 0.0685 cm in the third direction. Crystal B had dimensions of 0.484 cm in the direction of light travel, 0.055 cm in the direction of the applied electric field, and 0.106 cm in the third direction. In each case the contacts were applied with silver paste and the crystal suspended by attaching a wire to one of the contacts. A 1-mil diameter wire was attached to the other contact. In this manner of mounting no significant mechanical forces are applied to the crystal. The large dielectric constant of GaP prevents any significant fringing of the field within the crystal. Silicon monoxide single layer antireflective coatings were placed on the ends of crystal B to avoid optical resonance between its cleaved surfaces.

For the retardation measurements the crystal was placed between crossed polarizers, whose axes were at 45° to the induced optic axes of the crystal, in a Zeiss polarizing microscope equipped with a quartz Ehringhaus compensator, which was also between the polarizers. The voltage was applied to the crystal with a SKL model 503A fast rise pulse generator. Light from either a He–Ne laser or a xenon flash tube as filtered by a small Bausch and Lomb grating monochromator was directed through a small portion of the crystal. The exit surface of the crystal was focused on a mask in front of a photomultiplier tube. Its signal was fed into a Hewlett–Packard model 185B sampling oscilloscope whose output fed an X–Y recorder. Figure 1 shows a recording of the time dependence of the optical signal when the compensator is set to pass the light. The figure was obtained with crystal B and with the 0.6328 μ laser source. The indirect electro-optic effect from a piezoelectric resonance at 2.81 MHz is readily observed. The initial half cycle of the oscillation is distorted because of transients on the initial edge of the voltage pulse. This prevents a reliable direct measurement of the constant-strain electro-optic coefficient at the instant of voltage application. Thus, knowledge of the expected form of the optical signal in the presence of piezoelectric resonance is needed to justify an extrapolation procedure to the beginning of the pulse.

It is shown in the Appendix that the retardation Γ between the components of light of the two polarizations after traversing a distance l in a crystal oriented such as crystal B is given by

$$\Gamma=\frac{\pi n^3lE}{\lambda}\left\{r_{41}+\frac{(2p_{44}+p_{11}-p_{12})e_{14}}{2\gamma_{44}+\gamma_{11}+\gamma_{12}}\right.$$
$$\left.\times\left[1-\frac{4}{\pi}\sum_{k=0}^{\infty}(2k+1)^{-1}\sin\frac{(2k+1)\pi s}{a}\cos\frac{(2k+1)\pi vt}{a}\right]\right\}, \tag{6}$$

where λ is the free space wavelength of the light, r_{41} the constant-strain electro-optic coefficient, γ_{ij} the reduced stiffness constants of a plate (see the Appendix), p_{ij} the elasto-optic coefficients, e_{14} the piezoelectric coefficient, a the distance between the surfaces, s the coordinate measured between the two surfaces from

[5] I. P. Kaminow, Appl. Phys. Letters 7, 123 (1965).
[6] J. F. Nye, *Physical Properties of Crystals* (Oxford, Clarendon Press, 1964), p. 243–251.

one of them, t the time, and v the speed of a longitudinal acoustic wave traveling in the [110] direction given by Eq. (A20) of the Appendix.

The usefulness of solutions of this general type is attested to by their successful use by Stephany to account for the spatial patterns in piezo-optic resonance.[7] Five observations support the use of the above one-dimensional solution here: (1) the oscillation in Fig. 1 extrapolates to the beginning of the electrical pulse with a phase consistent with a cosine as in Eq. (6) (this agrees with the results of Johnston[8] on $BaTiO_3$); (2) the frequency of oscillation, 2.81 MHz, agrees adequately with the prediction of the fundamental resonant frequency by Eqs. (6) and (A20) which yields $v/2d=2.85$ MHz using reduced stiffness constants for the plate of $\gamma_{11}=11.40\times10^{10}$ N/m², $\gamma_{12}=3.475\times10^{10}$ N/m² and $\gamma_{44}=7.043\times10^{10}$ N/m² calculated from the recently measured stiffness constants of GaP[9]; (3) at the two positions where $\sin\pi s/a=\frac{1}{2}$ the oscillation amplitude was indeed found to drop to $\frac{1}{2}$ of its value found midway between the sides where measurements were normally made; (4) the oscillation amplitude was constant if the point of measurement was moved in a direction parallel to the applied electric field; (5) there is no evidence in Fig. 1 of acoustic waves traveling in the [1$\bar{1}$0] direction where the fundamental resonance period would be 4.5 times that observed for the resonance in the [110] direction.

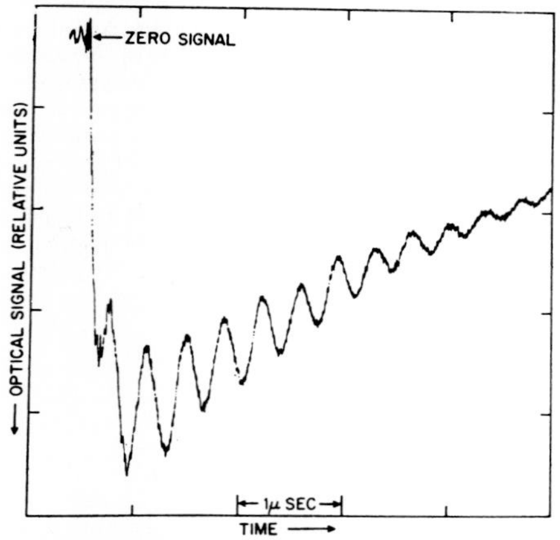

FIG. 1. The electro-optic signal from a GaP crystal following application of the voltage pulse. The effects of piezoelectrically excited acoustic vibrations and of dielectric relaxation falloff are seen.

[7] J. F. Stephany, J. Opt. Soc. Amer. **55**, 136 (1965).
[8] A. R. Johnston, Appl. Phys. Letters **7**, 195 (1965).
[9] R. Weil and W. O. Groves, Bull. Amer. Phys. Soc., Ser. II, Vol. 11, 764 (1966).

TABLE I. Constant-strain values of the electro-optic coefficient of GaP versus wavelength. Column 1, pulsed electric field and laser beams used; column 2, pulsed electric field and flash lamp used; column 3, high-frequency electric field, optical heterodyne detection, and laser beams used.

	r_{41} (units of 10^{-12} m/V)		
λ	1	2	3
0.56μ		−1.07±0.06	
0.585		−1.07±0.06	
0.6328	−0.97±0.02	−0.97±0.06	−0.98±0.04
0.66		−0.98±0.06	
1.153	−1.10±0.15		
3.39			−0.97±0.10

Equation (6) is also reasonable because it includes only the odd harmonics and because these are excited inversely to their order number. This is expected since each resonance should have a coupling coefficient which is an integral over the strain pattern between the surfaces. It should be remarked concerning Eq. (6) that the coefficient of the square brackets is not the usual indirect electro-optic effect contribution, which is $p_{44}e_{14}s_{44}$ where s_{44} is a compliance component. It is, instead, the indirect electro-optic effect for a crystal whose end surfaces are prevented from moving in the direction of their normals while its side surfaces are free. This can be easily verified by considering the static two-dimensional problem. This form of end-clamping results from the large length in the direction of the plate along which the light travels compared to the width which allows ignoring the coordinate dependence in the length direction. Equation (6) should thus represent at least the physical situation during the time that the long dimension of the crystal is effectively clamped. It is during this initial time interval that the measurements were made.

From the above considerations it is apparent that the electro-optic coefficient should be measured at each point in time corresponding to an oscillation maximum and the values used to obtain an extrapolated value for $t=0$. Such an extrapolation will remove from the final result the effects of the finite damping constant of the piezoelectric resonance, the finite dielectric relaxation time, and the distortion from initial electrical transients. Measurements at signal maxima are used for the extrapolation since the oscillation phase is such as to produce a maximum signal at $t=0$ if a perfectly abrupt electrical pulse had been used. The presence of a maximum signal at $t=0$ shows that the indirect electro-optic effect has the opposite sign to the direct electro-optic effect, that is, the constant-strain electro-optic coefficient is larger in magnitude than the constant-stress one.[10] Measurements at a particular point in time were made by fixing the sampling oscilloscope at this time and feeding its output to a recorder. A minimum in this signal as the compensator was varied determined the phase difference introduced by the electro-optic effect on the light beam for a given voltage. Voltages up to 500 V were used; Γ vs V was always found to be linear.

The results of this method are shown in column 1 of Table I. Results for the two crystals of different orientations agreed within the errors quoted. The refractive indices used for the calculation of r_{41} in the visible are given in Sec. III; those used in the infrared are given in Ref. 4. The sign of the coefficient was found by determining the sign of the phase difference, the direction of the electric field, and the sense of the crystal orientation.[11] The values given in Table I are for the direct or constant-strain electro-optic effect.

A measurement of the piezoelectric coefficient of GaP can be obtained by measuring the coefficient of the square brackets in Eq. (6) since the elasto-optic coefficients are known.[12] This is done by extrapolating the phase difference measurements made at the oscillation minima to zero and equating the difference of this value and r_{41} to twice the coefficient of the square brackets. This yields $e_{14}=-0.10$ C/m^2. This leads to a calculated indirect electro-optic effect of $p_{44}s_{44}e_{14}\approx +0.11\times 10^{-12}$ m/V. The constant-stress electro-optic coefficient is thus smaller in magnitude by this amount from the constant-strain values given in Table I. Because of the indirect nature of this measurement of e_{14} and the use of an involved mathematical model, it is difficult to assess its accuracy. It is probably best to regard it as only an approximate value.

A slight variation of the above method was used when a xenon flash lamp was employed as a source. Because the electrical pulse to the GaP had to be delayed 2 μsec with respect to the flash lamp trigger pulse, the risetime of the electrical pulse was lengthened somewhat. This leads to a considerable reduction in the amplitude of the piezoelectric resonance. Also, extrapolation to $t=0$ did not lead to any significant increase in the value of the coefficient in this case. This may be due to a longer dielectric relaxation time in the presence of a weaker light source since even at wavelengths longer than the bandgap wavelength there is some photoconductivity. The values obtained with flash lamp excitation are given in column 2 of Table I.

The constant-strain electro-optic coefficient at 0.6328 and 3.39 μ was measured in the two crystals by a heterodyne method,[5] which we describe only briefly here. In this technique a beam from a single frequency (ω) laser passes through a crystal to which a modulating electric field of frequency ω_m is applied. Assuming that the beam polarization and the direction of the modulating field are chosen properly relative to the crystal axes, the emergent beam is phase modulated at ω_m because of the change in refractive index brought about by the electro-optic effect. The phase modulated beam has components at frequencies ω, $\omega\pm\omega_m$, $\cdots$, $\omega\pm N\omega_m$. The amplitudes of these components are given by Bessel functions $J_0(\eta)$, $J_1(\eta)$, $\cdots$, $J_N(\eta)$, where η, the modulation index, is the magnitude of the periodic change in phase length of the crystal. The beam then impinges on a beam splitter where it is combined with the output of a swept single frequency laser so as to give good spatial and angular overlap of the two beams. The resultant beam strikes a photodiode (Si at 0.6328 μ and InAs at 3.39 μ) which is followed by a narrow band intermediate frequency amplifier (70 MHz). A signal is produced and amplified every time the swept laser frequency is 70 MHz from one of the components of the phase modulated beam. The signal is proportional to the product of the swept laser amplitude and the amplitude of the pertinent component of the modulated beam. The optical attenuation required to reduce the $J_0(\eta)$ signal component to the unattenuated $J_1(\eta)$ level is then measured and leads to the ratio $J_1(\eta)/J_0(\eta)$, which then yields a value for η. The electro-optic coefficient can then be calculated as is indicated below.

Measurements on crystal B were made with the field applied in the [001] direction and the electric vector of the light along the [110]. The resulting change in phase length is

$$\eta\cos\omega_m t=(F\pi n^3 r_{41}E_0 l\cos\omega_m t)/\lambda, \tag{7}$$

where we have set $E=E_0\cos\omega_m t$. F is a factor which depends on crystal orientation and is unity for the orientation of crystal B. This crystal was slightly birefringent with the axes of birefringence for a ray propagating along [1$\bar{1}$0] effectively coinciding with the [001] and [110] axes. Since the latter direction coincided with the polarization direction used, there were no complications due to depolarization of the beam.

Crystal A was measured with the applied electric field and the optical electric field parallel to a [111] direction. This is the condition for maximum change in index of refraction due to the electro-optic effect and here the factor F in Eq. (7) is $2/\sqrt{3}$.

The procedure in taking the measurements was as

[10] P. V. Lenzo, E. H. Turner, E. G. Spencer, and A. A. Ballman, Appl. Phys. Letters **8**, 81 (1966). This conclusion was based on finding that the electro-optic, piezoelectric, and stress-optic coefficients are all negative. In order to specifiy the algebraic signs of the electro-optic and piezoelectric coefficients, the sense of the crystal orientation had to be known. This was found both from etching experiments and from the assumption that the crystal retained the same sense as that of the GaAs substrate on which it was grown epitaxially.

[11] We use here the convention that the outward normal of a Ga-terminated crystal face is a [111] direction. See H. C. Gatos and M. C. Lavine, J. Electrochem. Soc. **107**, 427 (1960) and references contained therein.

[12] R. W. Dixon, J. Appl. Phys. **38**, 5149 (1967).

follows. Values of η were found for several different applied voltages at each modulating frequency and plots of η versus voltage were used to determine the best straight line fit to the data. Field strengths as high as 10^4 V/cm were used on crystal A. The modulating frequency voltage readings were made with a Hewlett–Packard 410C voltmeter whose accuracy is better than $\pm3\%$ of full scale. Values of r_{41} determined as above were then plotted against frequency in order to detect any apparent frequency dependence. No significant variation with frequency in the range 54 to 86 MHz was found. If appreciable strains had been caused by the converse piezoelectric effect, this frequency independence would not be expected.[13] This sort of check is necessary to justify the claim that the measurement is, in fact, of the true or constant-strain coefficient.

The end result at 0.6328 μ given in Table I was obtained both with crystal A and with crystal B after the cleaved faces of the latter had been antireflection coated. Measurements made before coating yielded values of r_{41} about 8% higher and showed less internal consistency. Probably the larger value obtained with the uncoated sample was caused by multiple passes of the light through the crystal, since the power reflection coefficient, R, for one dielectric–air interface is 0.29. To the extent that one of these multiple pass beams overlaps the swept laser beam at the detector, it can contribute to the measured signal and could have given results that indicated a larger r_{41}. In spite of the parallelism of the cleaved faces, Fabry–Perot resonances would be expected to produce only small effects because a beam diameter of about 25 μ was used which would require that the incident laser beam be perpendicular to the faces within about 20 min of arc. Multiple reflections in crystal A are unimportant because of the less perfect ends.

The result at 3.39 μ in Table I was obtained using crystal A. Strong evidence for Fabry–Perot resonances was found with crystal B when a beam diameter of approximately 250 μ was used at the 3.39 μ wavelength. These resonances could be tuned either by slight tilting of the crystal or by heating resulting from the modulating field itself. We estimate that a change of 1.5°C is sufficient to change the phase length of the crystal by $\lambda/2$. Such changes in length not only affect the power transmitted through the crystal but also change the apparent value of the modulation index, η. The apparent value of η is increased by a factor $(1+R)/(1-R)$ when the resonator is tuned for maximum transmission and decreased by $(1-R)/(1+R)$ at minimum. Our observations were consistent with this statement, but yielded a value of r_{41} 20% lower than for crystal B. Because of the approximate nature of the calculation and the extra complication, we prefer the value of r_{41} found in the nonresonating crystal A.

[13] I. P. Kaminow, Appl. Phys. Letters **8**, 305 (1966).

TABLE II. Index of refraction of GaP at 24.5°C vs wavelength.

λ	n
0.545 μ	3.4522
0.55	3.4411
0.56	3.4203
0.57	3.4012
0.58	3.3837
0.59	3.3675
0.60	3.3524
0.61	3.3384
0.62	3.3254
0.63	3.3132
0.64	3.3018
0.65	3.2912
0.66	3.2811
0.67	3.2716
0.68	3.2626
0.69	3.2541
0.70	3.2462

The experiment of Faust and Henry[14] on the mixing of visible and near resonance infrared light in GaP can be used to relate the constant-strain electro-optic coefficient r_{41} and the nonlinear optical coefficient $d_{123}^{2\omega}$ (experimental definition). The relation is

$$d_{123}^{2\omega}=-n^4r_{41}/16\pi G, \qquad (7)$$

where $G=0.47$ is the ratio of the nonlinear coefficients on the low frequency side of the lattice resonance to that on the high-frequency side.[14] At 0.56 μ we calculate $d_{123}^{2\omega}=+6.4\times10^{-12}$ m/V using $n=3.420$ and at 3.39 μ, which is further from the electronic resonance, we calculate $d_{123}^{2\omega}=+3.5\times10^{-12}$ m/V using $n=3.018$. This is to be compared with the measurements of Miller,[15] $(8.1\pm1.4)\times10^{-12}$ m/V, and of Soref and Moos,[16] 3.9×10^{-12} m/V, both of which used a 1.06 μ laser, as converted to absolute units by the results of Francois[17] and Bjorkholm and Siegman.[18] Note that Eq. (7) establishes the sign of $d_{123}^{2\omega}$.

III. REFRACTIVE INDEX MEASUREMENTS

The refractive index of GaP was measured between 0.545 and 0.70 μ wavelength at 24.5°C on ten prisms using the method of minimum deviation.[4] The apparatus used has been described previously.[4] One improvement on this apparatus was made prior to making the measurements reported here. It was found that the reference circle from which angle measurements were taken was in error in places by as much as 30 sec of arc. To rid the measurements of this error the circle was calibrated with respect to a Milichex indexing table, made by the Ex-Cello Corporation, which is accurate to $\frac{1}{4}$ sec of arc. The uncertainty in individual

[14] W. L. Faust and C. H. Henry, Phys. Rev. Letters **17**, 1265 (1966).
[15] R. C. Miller, Appl. Phys. Letters **5**, 17 (1964).
[16] R. A. Soref and H. W. Moos, J. Appl. Phys. **35**, 2152 (1964).
[17] G. E. Francois, Phys. Rev. **143**, 597 (1966).
[18] J. E. Bjorkholm and A. E. Siegman, Phys. Rev. **154**, 851 (1967).

values of the refractive index was ±0.0002. However, the values obtained for different prisms differed by substantially more than this. The differences are believed to be real and to reflect the variation in the index which can be expected from different samples of GaP. The refractive index versus wavelength for a crystal generally differed by an additive constant from that for another crystal. The values given in Table II are average values for the ten prisms studied. To include the values for all of the prisms an uncertainty of ±0.0012 would have to be assigned to the values in Table II. These variations did not correlate with the level of doping, which varied from no intentional doping to 10^{18} cm^{-3}, the type of dopant (Te, S, Zn), or the method of crystal growth (high pressure boat growth, floating zone, or solution growth). In fact, crystals grown ostensibly under the same conditions but in different batches in a solution growth apparatus differed by 0.0010 in refractive index.

ACKNOWLEDGMENTS

We would like to thank H. F. Tiersten for several very informative discussions on the vibration analysis and D. A. Kleinman, S. K. Kurtz, and F. K. Reinhart for helpful comments. We wish also to thank F. A. Trumbore and C. J. Frosch for growing most of the crystals used and K. F. Roegers and F. A. Dunn for technical assistance.

APPENDIX

Consider a rectangular plate of GaP oriented so that the electric field is in the [001] (height) direction, the light travels in the [1$\bar{1}$0] (length) direction, and the normal to one of the side surfaces is in the [110] (width) direction. The abrupt application of a voltage between the electrodes on the {001} faces causes a ringing of the acoustic resonances of the crystal. Since the piezoelectric coupling is small, the effect of these acoustic vibrations on the electric field is negligible. Hence, we may treat the electrical problem as simply applying a voltage across capacitor plates. The resultant electrical field may be taken as independent of position within the crystal and as having a component only in the [001] direction since the high dielectric constant of GaP makes fringing fields negligible. The piezoelectrically induced vibrations can then be characterized by

$$\rho(\partial^2 u_j/\partial t^2) = \partial T_{ij}/\partial x_i, \tag{A1}$$

$$T_{ij} = c_{ijkl}S_{kl} - e_{kij}E_k, \tag{A2}$$

$$S_{kl} = \tfrac{1}{2}[(\partial u_k/\partial x_l) + (\partial u_l/\partial x_k)], \tag{A3}$$

where ρ is the mass density, x_i is the particle position vector expressed in the crystallographic coordinate system, u_j the particle displacement vector, T_{ij} the stress tensor, c_{ijkl} the stiffness tensor, S_{kl} the strain tensor, e_{kij} a piezoelectric tensor, and E_k the electric field vector. Summation over repeated indices is implied.

Since no tractions are applied to any of the crystal surfaces, the boundary conditions for each surface are

$$n_i T_{ij} = 0, \tag{A4}$$

where n_i is a unit normal, different for each surface. The initial conditions are those of no particle displacement or velocity:

$$u_i = 0, \tag{A5}$$

$$\partial u_i/\partial t = 0. \tag{A6}$$

The mathematical problem, as formulated above, has never been solved exactly. We can, however, make the problem tractable by using two approximations. The first follows from the fact that the thickness of the crystal is small compared to its width or length. We may thus regard it as a thin plate in a state of plane stress[19] which is characterized by the approximations

$$T_{3j} = 0. \tag{A7}$$

Since Eq. (A7) holds on the top and bottom faces of the plate, we are assuming only that the plate is thin enough that Eq. (A7) holds approximately throughout the plate. This may be used to eliminate from consideration the $j=3$ component of Eq. (A1) and to alter the coefficients of Eq. (A2). The latter is done by solving Eq. (A2) for S_{ij} to yield

$$S_{ij} = s_{ijkl}T_{kl} + d_{kij}E_k, \tag{A8}$$

where s_{ijkl} is the compliance tensor and $d_{kij} = s_{ijrs}\, e_{krs}$ is another piezoelectric tensor. By substituting Eq. (A7) into Eq. (A8), solving for the nonzero T_{ij}, and putting $E_1 = E_2 = 0$, we get

$$T_1 = (s_{11}S_1 - s_{12}S_2)/(s_{11}^2 - s_{12}^2) = \gamma_{11}S_1 + \gamma_{12}S_2, \tag{A9}$$

$$T_2 = (s_{11}S_2 - s_{12}S_1)/(s_{11}^2 - s_{12}^2) = \gamma_{11}S_2 + \gamma_{12}S_1, \tag{A10}$$

$$T_6 = (S_6/s_{44}) - e_{14}E_3 = \gamma_{44}S_6 - e_{14}E_3, \tag{A11}$$

where the condensed matrix notation has been used. The right hand members of the latter three equations are used to define the reduced stiffness constants γ_{ij} of the plate, which are significantly different from the stiffness constants c_{ij}. Note that there is no modification of the piezoelectric coefficient e_{14}. This is expected when the piezoelectric coupling is small. These equations replace Eq. (A2) and in conjunction with Eq. (A7) can be seen to eliminate x_3 coordinate dependence from the $j=1$ and $j=2$ components of Eq. (A1).

The second approximation is to ignore all dependence on the coordinate measured along the length of the crystal since the length is so much larger than the width. This is best accomplished if we first rotate coordinates so as to have coordinates measured perpendicular to the crystal faces:

$$r = (x_1 - x_2)/\sqrt{2}, \tag{A12}$$

$$s = (x_1 + x_2)/\sqrt{2}, \tag{A13}$$

$$w_1 = (u_1 - u_2)/\sqrt{2}, \tag{A14}$$

$$w_2 = (u_1 + u_2)/\sqrt{2}. \tag{A15}$$

[19] A. E. H. Love, *A Treatise on the Mathematical Theory of Elasticity* (Dover Publications, New York, 1944), p. 82, 137.

If we substitute these equations into the $j=1$ and $j=2$ components of Eq. (A1), combine the resultant equations, and put all derivatives with respect to r equal to zero, we obtain

$$\rho(\partial^2 w_2/\partial t^2)=\tfrac{1}{2}(2\gamma_{44}+\gamma_{11}+\gamma_{12})(\partial^2 w_2/\partial s^2), \quad \text{(A16)}$$

$$\rho(\partial w_1/\partial t^2)=\tfrac{1}{2}(\gamma_{11}-\gamma_{12})(\partial^2 w_1/\partial s^2). \quad \text{(A17)}$$

The boundary conditions at $s=0$, a, given by Eq. (A4), yield

$$\partial w_2/\partial s=2e_{14}E_3/(2\gamma_{44}+\gamma_{11}+\gamma_{12}), \quad \text{(A18)}$$

$$\partial w_1/\partial s=0. \quad \text{(A19)}$$

The last equation in conjunction with Eqs. (A5) and (A6) requires $w_1=0$ everywhere at all times.

The lack of standing vibrations in the [1$\bar{1}$0] direction, which results from the large length-to-width ratio and the consequent neglect of dependence on the coordinate r, causes the strains involved in the vibrations to lack the symmetry expected of them from the symmetry of the crystal plus applied electric field. As we will show, this leads to a time and space varying indirect electro-optic effect which will not possess the expected symmetry.

Our problem is now reduced to solving Eq. (A16) subject to Eqs. (A5), (A6), and (A18). To simplify Eq. (A16), we define v as the velocity of a longitudinal acoustic wave traveling in the [110] direction:

$$v=[(2\gamma_{44}+\gamma_{11}+\gamma_{12})/2\rho]^{1/2}. \quad \text{(A20)}$$

The driving force of the vibrations appears in the boundary condition Eq. (A18). The time dependence of the electric field contained therein will be taken as a step function at $t=0$:

$$E_3=ES_0(t), \quad \text{(A21)}$$

where

$$S_0(t)=0 \quad (t\leq 0),$$
$$=1 \quad (t>0). \quad \text{(A22)}$$

Also define

$$\alpha=2e_{14}E/(2\gamma_{44}+\gamma_{11}+\gamma_{12}). \quad \text{(A23)}$$

Use of the Laplace transform is convenient for the solution of the reduced problem. Denote the transform of $w_2(s)$ by $f(p)$. The transform of Eq. (A16) with the use of Eqs. (A5) and (A6) is

$$p^2 f=v^2(\partial^2 f/\partial s^2) \quad \text{(A24)}$$

and that of Eq. (A18) is

$$\partial f/ds=\alpha/p \qquad (\text{at } s=0 \text{ or } a). \quad \text{(A25)}$$

Solution of these two equations yields

$$f=\frac{\alpha v}{p^2}\,\frac{\cosh ps/v-\cosh p(a-s)/v}{\sinh pa/v}. \quad \text{(A26)}$$

The inverse Laplace transform of this can be expressed as the sum of the residues of the poles of $f(p)e^{pt}$ in the complex plane.[20] The hyperbolic sine function gives simple poles to $f(p)$ along the imaginary axis at $p=ik\pi v/a$ where k is an integer. The pole of $f(p)$ at $p=0$ can also be shown to be a simple pole. The result of this summation is

$$w_2(s,t)=\alpha\left\{s-\tfrac{1}{2}a+\frac{4a}{\pi}\sum_{k=0}^{\infty}\frac{1}{(2k+1)^2}\times\cos\frac{(2k+1)\pi s}{a}\cos\frac{(2k+1)\pi vt}{a}\right\}. \quad \text{(A27)}$$

The nonzero strain components then are

$$S_1=S_2=\tfrac{1}{2}S_6=\tfrac{1}{2}(\partial w_2/\partial s). \quad \text{(A28)}$$

The nonzero components of the relative dielectric impermeability matrix[6] then are

$$B_1=B_2=(1/n^2)+\tfrac{1}{2}(p_{11}+p_{12})(\partial w_2/\partial s),$$
$$B_6=r_{41}E+p_{44}(\partial w_2/\partial s),$$
$$B_3=1/n^2+p_{12}(\partial w_2/\partial s). \quad \text{(A29)}$$

This matrix can be diagonalized in the coordinate system where the x_1', x_2', x_3' axes are, respectively, in the [1$\bar{1}$0], [110], and [001] directions. The diagonal elements are then

$$B_1'=(1/n_1^2)=(1/n^2)-r_{41}E+\tfrac{1}{2}(p_{11}+p_{12}-2p_{44})(\partial w_2/\partial s),$$
$$B_2'=(1/n_2^2)=(1/n^2)+r_{41}E+\tfrac{1}{2}(p_{11}+p_{12}+2p_{44})(\partial w_2/\partial s),$$
$$B_3'=(1/n_3^2)=(1/n^2)+p_{12}(\partial w_2/\partial s). \quad \text{(A30)}$$

It can be seen here that the time- and space-dependent indirect electro-optic effect does not have the same symmetry as the direct electro-optic effect since acoustic vibrations which do not preserve this symmetry are involved. In particular, an indirect electro-optic effect occurs for n_3 where no direct electro-optic effect is allowed. This effect is not special to the step function electric field but could equally well occur for a sinusoidally oscillating electric field provided its frequency is in the range of resonant acoustic vibrations.

The retardation Γ between the polarization components of the light wave is defined as

$$\Gamma=\omega l(n_3-n_2)/c. \quad \text{(A31)}$$

Substitution into this equation from Eqs. (A30), (A27), and (A23) yields Eq. (6) of Sec. II.

[20] R. V. Churchill, *Operational Mathematics* (McGraw-Hill Book Co., New York, 1958), p. 186.

Reprinted from IEEE JOURNAL OF *QUANTUM ELECTRONICS*
Vol. QE-4, Number 1, January 1968
Pp. 23-26

Measurements of the Electrooptic Effect in CdS, ZnTe, and GaAs at 10.6 Microns

IVAN P. KAMINOW, MEMBER, IEEE

***Abstract*—Low-frequency electrooptic coefficients have been measured for three semiconductors at 10.6 microns. The results are $r_c = (5.5 \pm 1) \times 10^{-12}$ m/V for CdS, $r_{41} = (1.4 \pm 0.2) \times 10^{-12}$ m/V for ZnTe, and $r_{41} = (1.6 \pm 0.1) \times 10^{-12}$ m/V for GaAs. A comparison is made of the efficiencies of these materials in different modulator configurations. The effect of photoelectrically induced space charge is discussed briefly.**

INTRODUCTION

THE DEVELOPMENT of the CO_2 laser operating at 10.6 microns has created an interest in electrooptic modulator materials for this wavelength. The electrooptic coefficients for CdS, ZnTe, and GaAs are reported in this paper.

Previous measurements[1] on GaAs have shown that the electrooptic coefficient r_{41} is only slightly larger at 10.6 microns than at 1 micron. Our results for GaAs confirm the earlier measurements. The lack of substantial variation in r_{41} with wavelength is to be expected because the lattice resonance (at ~40 microns) is far from 10.6 microns, where the crystal is still transparent. The present measurements on CdS indicate a similar invariance in electrooptic coefficient between the visible region[2],[3] (~0.6 micron) and 10.6 microns. The coefficient for ZnTe at 10.6 microns is found to be substantially less than the values previously found in the visible.[3],[5] The measurements on ZnTe in the vsiible[4] indicate that much of the reduction in electrooptic coefficient occurs near the bandedge.

Manuscript received September 13, 1967; revised October 4, 1967.
The author is with Bell Telephone Laboratories, Inc., Holmdel, N. J.

The phase retardation introduced by a light modulator of length L, thickness t, and width w, is[3]

$$\Gamma = \frac{\pi n^3 r V L}{\lambda t}, \tag{1}$$

where V is the voltage across the thickness, λ is the optical wavelength in vacuum, n is the appropriate refractive index, and r is an effective electrooptic coefficient. Clearly, V must increase as λ increases if all other parameters in

(1) remain fixed. If the modulator crystal, regarded as a lumped condenser, is placed in parallel with an inductance and resistance to form a resonant circuit with bandwidth Δf, then the power dissipated is[3]

$$P = \left(\frac{\epsilon_0}{2\pi}\right)\left(\frac{wt}{L}\right)\left(\frac{\epsilon}{n^6r^2}\right)(\lambda^2)(\Gamma^2\Delta f), \quad (2)$$

where ϵ_0 is the permittivity of vacuum and ϵ the appropriate low-frequency dielectric constant. The minimum value of (wt/L) is limited by diffraction[3] to $\sim(4\lambda/n\pi)$ and for the optimum (wt/L), P is then proportional to λ^3/F_1, where the figure of merit F_1 for the material is defined by

$$F_1 = n^7r^2/\epsilon. \quad (3)$$

Hence, for a fixed figure of merit, modulation at 10.6 microns will require considerably more power than in the visible region.

Equations (2) and (3) are based on the assumption that all circuit capacitance is lumped in the modulator crystal. If other parallel circuit capacitances are dominant, however, the figure of merit becomes[3]

$$F_2 = n^7r^2/\epsilon^{1/2}. \quad (4)$$

Finally, in the case of a traveling-wave modulator, the figure of merit is[3]

$$F_3 = n^6r^2(n^2 - 1)/(\epsilon - 1) \quad (5)$$

for the optimum (wt/L). In this case, materials with $n^2 \approx \epsilon$ have a clear advantage because of the near velocity match.

After presenting the experimental results, F_1, F_2, and F_3 are compared for CdS, GaAs, ZnTe, and also for selenium.

Experiment

In order to improve the sensitivity over conventional low-frequency methods, lock-in detection is employed and an optical bias is introduced so as to produce linear intensity modulation. The experimental arrangement for determining r_{41} in the cubic crystals (ZnTe and GaAs) is illustrated in Fig. 1. The samples are typically 2 by 2 by 4 mm. The voltage is applied in a [100] direction, and the width and length lie along [110] directions. The quarter-wave plate is made of CdS and the detector is nitrogen-cooled gold-doped germanium. The chopper produces a 300-Hz square wave. The analyzer consists of a gold grid evaporated on an AgCl substrate.

The analyzer is set normal to the incident polarization from the laser, and the [100] axis of the crystal and the principal axes of the quarter-wave plate are set at 45 degrees to the incident polarization. With this arrangement in the absence of modulation or chopping, the beam entering the analyzer is circularly polarized and half the available light intensity I_0 reaches the photodetector. With the chopper on, the lock-in amplifier measures the amplitude (kI_0/π) of the fundamental component of the 300-Hz square wave, where k is a constant of the system at fixed operating conditions. With the modulating voltage on and the chopper off, the light intensity has a sinusoidal component with amplitude ΔI at the modulating frequency and the lock-in amplifier measures $k\Delta I$. The peak retardation Γ corresponding to modulating voltage V is given by

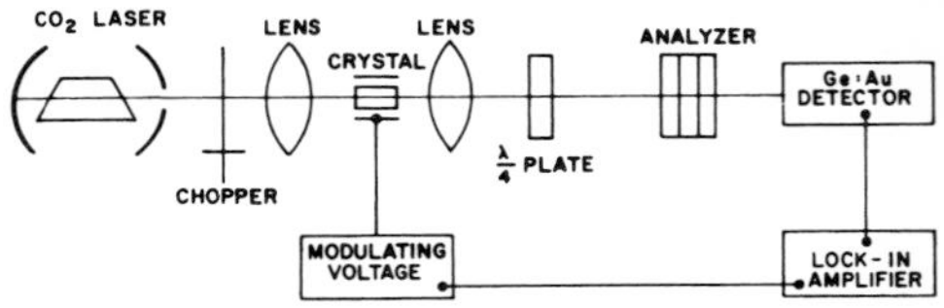

Fig. 1. Experimental arrangement.

$$\Gamma = 2\Delta I/I_0, \quad (6)$$

for small Γ and quarter-wave bias, and can be determined from the ratio of the two lock-in detector readings. The electrooptic coefficient r_{41} is obtained from the measured Γ and (1) with $r = r_{41}$.

For hexagonal CdS, it is necessary to compensate for the natural birefringence of the crystal so as to provide a net quarter-wave retardation bias. Adjustable compensators for this purpose are readily available for visible wavelengths but not for 10.6 microns. Two quarter-wave plates were used instead of the adjustable compensator. Alternatively, a single quarter-wave plate in a Senarmont compensator configuration biased at half power might have been used. The modulator crystal is cut with L and w along [100] and [010] and t along [001], the optic axis. The [001] axis is set at 45 degrees to the incident polarization. The measured retardation with the modulating field along [001] corresponds to substituting for n^3r in (1) the quantity

$$n_3^3r_c = n_3^3r_{33} - n_1^3r_{13}. \quad (7)$$

Results

CdS

The unclamped r_c at 10.6 microns is $(5.5 \pm 1) \times 10^{-12}$ m/V, from 50 Hz to $\sim$10 kHz, as indicated in Fig. 2.

The same coefficient was measured at 0.633 micron under similar conditions but with a variable compensator in place of the two quarter-wave plates. The result is $(5.0 \pm 1) \times 10^{-12}$ m/V, which is not inconsistent with previous measurements in the visible.[2],[3] In our 0.633 micron measurements, the observed r_c drops from 5×10^{-12} to $\sim 1 \times 10^{-12}$ m/V between 1 kHz and 20 Hz as shown in Fig. 3. This low-frequency relaxation, which is absent at 10.6 microns, is attributed to a reduction in the effective field in the neighborhood of the beam caused by the motion of light-generated carriers. The carriers are immobilized at frequencies above the dielectric relaxation frequency $f_d = (2\pi\rho\epsilon\epsilon_0)^{-1}$, where ρ is

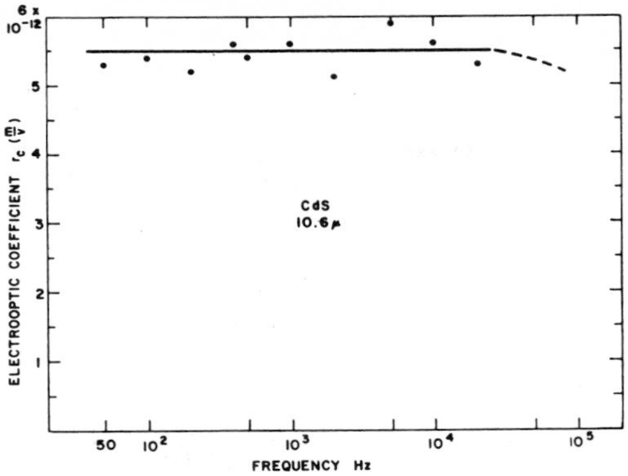

Fig. 2. Measured electrooptic coefficient $r_c = n_3^3(r_{33} - n_1^3 r_{13}/n_3^3)$ at 10.6 microns in CdS.

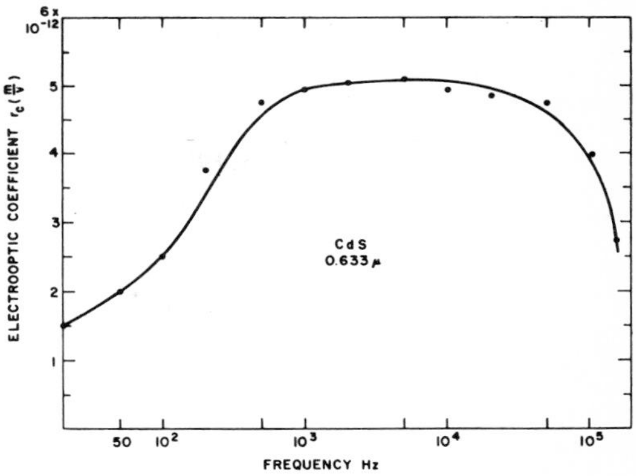

Fig. 3. Measure electrooptic coefficient r_c at 0.633 micron in CdS. Low-frequency cutoff is attributed to space-charge effects and high-frequency cutoff to detector time constant.

the conductivity. In CdS, $\epsilon = 8$, and, for our sample, $\rho \approx 5 \times 10^9\ \Omega\cdot$cm, so that $f_d \approx 50$ Hz, which agrees within the uncertainty in ρ with the curve in Fig. 3. At 10.6 microns, very far from the bandedge, no carriers are generated and space-charge effects are absent as in Fig. 2.

GaAs

At 10.6 microns, the observed r_{41} is $(1.6 \pm 0.1) \times 10^{-12}$ m/V from 50 Hz to the limit of the detector response (~5 kHz).

At 1.15 microns, relaxation at about 2 kHz is observed. The relaxation frequency calculated using $\epsilon = 12.5$ and $\rho = 7.5 \times 10^7\ \Omega\cdot$cm, as measured with a vacuum tube ohmmeter, is also 2 kHz.

ZnTe

At 10.6 microns, r_{41} is $(1.4 \pm 0.2) \times 10^{-12}$ m/V without any observable low-frequency relaxation.

At 0.633 micron and 1.15 micron free-carrier effects are especially troublesome because of the low resistivity of the sample, $\rho \approx 10^5\ \Omega\cdot$cm. With $\epsilon = 10$, $f_d \approx 2$ MHz, which is beyond the range of our apparatus. In addition to the dispersion with frequency, the observed r_{41} is found to depend upon the position of the light beam with respect to the electrodes.

CONCLUSIONS

The only substance other than the three discussed for which an electrooptic coefficient at 10.6 microns is known is trigonal selenium,[5] for which $r_{11} \approx 2.5 \times 10^{-12}$ m/V. A large uncertainty in r_{11} is attributed to the quality of the crystal measured.[1]

The four materials are compared in Table I. The values of r used to compute the figures of merit from (3), (4),

TABLE I
COMPARISON OF MODULATOR MATERIALS AT 10.6 MICRONS (UNCLAMPED)

	CdS	GaAs	ZnTe	Se
Symmetry	6 mm	$\bar{4}3$ m	$\bar{4}3$ m	32
ϵ	10(6)(ϵ_3)	12.5(9)	10(6)	8(7)(ϵ_1)
n	2.3(8)(n_3)	3.3(9)	2.7(8)	2.8(7)(n_1)
r(10^{-12}m/V)	5.5(r_c)	1.6(r_{41})	1.4(r_{41})	~2.5(r_{11})
F_1(10^{-21}m^2/V^2)	1.0	3.5	0.8	4.2(1.0)
F_2(10^{-21}m^2/V^2)	3.3	12.4	2.6	12.0(3.0)
F_3(10^{-21}m^2/V^2)	2.1	11.6	2.2	12.0(3.0)

and (5) are those appropriate to the optimum crystal orientation for amplitude modulation[3]; i.e., r_c (CdS), $2r_{41}$ (GaAs and ZnTe), and $2r_{11}$ (Se). It should be noted that the table consists of low-frequency (unclamped) values.

The figures of merit for GaAs are all superior to those for CdS or ZnTe. The figures of merit for selenium, using the somewhat uncertain value for r_{11}, are comparable to these for GaAs. However, in order to obtain an equivalent r of $2r_{11}$ for selenium, the beam must propagate along the c axis, as was done in the measurement[5] of r_{11}, where optical activity may be a problem. For propagation normal to the c axis, where optical activity vanishes, r becomes r_{11}; the appropriate figures of merit are indicated in parentheses in Table I. For phase modulation, the equivalent r for selenium is always r_{11}; for GaAs, it is[3] $2r_{41}/\sqrt{r_3}$; and for CdS, it is r_{33}, which is approximately[3] $2r_c/3$ because $r_{33}/r_{13} \approx -2$.

Space-charge effects limit the use of these materials at low modulation frequencies and at wavelengths near the bandedge. In the present measurements, the low-frequency limit appears to correspond to the dielectric relaxation frequency, which is the maximum frequency at which nonequilibrium charge distributions can relax. In general, more subtle factors may have to be considered.[10],[11]

[1] Recent measurements by Turner, Kaminow, and Kolb (to be published) yield a larger r_{11}. However, selenium is still not attractive for other reasons.

Acknowledgment

The measurements were made by J. V. Liptak. The laser setup was provided by A. A. Penzias and R. W. Wilson, and the detector by T. J. Bridges. The CdS and ZnTe were obtained from Clevite Corporation, and the GaAs from the Bell Telephone Laboratories, Inc., Allentown, Pa.

References

[1] A. Yariv, C. A. Mead, and J. V. Parker, "GaAs as an electooptic modulator at 10.6 microns," *IEEE J. Quantum Electronics*, vol. QE-2, pp. 243–245, August 1966; and also cited is T. E. Walsh, "Gallium-arsenide electrooptic modulators," *RCA Rev.*, vol. 27, p. 323, 1966.

[2] D. J. A. Gainon, "Linear electrooptic effect in CdS," *J. Opt. Soc. Am.*, vol. 54, p. 270, 1964.

[3] I. P. Kaminow and E. H. Turner, "Electrooptic light modulators," *Proc. IEEE*, vol. 54, pp. 1374–1390, October 1966.

[4] T. R. Sliker and J. M. Jost, "Linear electrooptic effect and refractive indices of cubic ZnTe," *J. Opt. Soc. Am.*, vol. 56, p. 130, 1966.

[5] M. C. Teich and T. Kaplan, "Electrooptic effect in trigonal selenium at 10.6 μm," *IEEE J. Quantum Electronics* (*Correspondence*), vol. QE-2, pp. 702–703, October 1966.

[6] D. Berlincourt, H. Jaffe, and L. R. Shiozawa, "Electroelastic properties of the sulfides, selenides, and tellurides of zinc and cadmium," *Phys. Rev.*, vol. 129, p. 1009, 1963.

[7] V. Prosser, M. Sicha, and E. Klier, "Dielectric constant of hexagonal selenium single crystals," in *Recent Advances in Selenium Physics*, European Selenium-Tellurium Committee, Ed. London: Pergamon, 1965, p. 105.

[8] L. R. Shiozawa and J. M. Jost, "Research a on II-VI compound semiconductors," Clevite Corp., Palo Alto, Calif., Rept. AD 620297, May 1965.

[9] K. G. Hambleton, C. H. Hilsum, and B. R. Holeman, "Determination of the effective ionic charge of gallium arsenide from direct measurements of the dielectric constant," *Proc. Phys. Soc.*, vol. 77, p. 1147, 1961.

[10] M. A. Lampert, "Volume-controlled current injection in insulators," *Repts. Progr. Phys.*, vol. 27, p. 329, 1964.

[11] S. K. Kurtz and P. J. Warter, Jr., "Space-charge effects in *p*-type semiconducting $KTa_{.65}NO_{.35}O_3$ (KTN)," *Bull. Am. Phys. Soc.*, vol. 11, p. 34, 1966.

3. Lumped Electrooptic Modulators

Reprinted from JOURNAL OF APPLIED PHYSICS, Vol. 38, No. 4, 1611–1617, 15 March 1967

Lithium Tantalate Light Modulators

R. T. DENTON, F. S. CHEN, AND A. A. BALLMAN
Bell Telephone Laboratories, Inc., Murray Hill, New Jersey
(Received 26 September 1966)

Light intensity modulators have been developed using single-domain lithium tantalate as the electro-optic material. A broadband transistor amplifier which can develop 0.2-W output power drives the modulator sample which presents a capacitive load of 5 pF. Approximately 80% modulation is achieved from dc to 220 Mc/sec, when the light is made to traverse the sample twice. The modulation bandwidth is limited by the transistor amplifier. Very little acoustic ringing is observed when the modulator is used as a fast light switch.

1. INTRODUCTION

An optical intensity modulator has been developed which provides 40% intensity modulation at an optical wavelength of 0.63 μ over a frequency band from dc to 220 Mc/sec. A transistor driver–amplifier is an integral part of the modulator. When the light is caused to make a round-trip inside the modulator crystal the modulator provides 80% intensity modulation over the same bandwidth.

Modulation is obtained by means of the linear electro-optic effect in single-domain, single-crystal lithium tantalate which is cut in the shape of a rod and is coupled into the driving circuitry as a lumped element. It can be shown that in modulators of this type modulation efficiency begins to fall off when the transit time for light through the modulating crystal approaches the period of the modulating signal. This sort of transit-time limitation on bandwidth could be avoided by providing for a traveling-wave interaction between the optical and electrical fields. In such a traveling-wave modulator the electrical circuit is designed so that the modulated and modulating waves travel through the structure together, and if the velocities are matched arbitrarily large modulation bandwidths are theoretically possible.[1–4] Such traveling-wave interactions are probably only useful for modulation frequencies higher than 1 Gc/sec. The crystal used in the modulator described here is short enough so that the time required for the light to traverse the crystal is less than one-tenth the period of the modulating signal at 1 Gc/sec and hence the transit time effect can be neglected. The theoretical highest modulation frequency is thus considerably higher than the actual high-frequency cutoff which is determined in our system by the transistor driver-amplifier.

Following a brief discussion of the physical properties of lithium tantalate in Sec. 2, a detailed description of the intensity modulator is covered in Sec. 3, a comparison of different modulator crystals in Sec. 4, and a summary in Sec. 5.

2. PHYSICAL PROPERTIES OF $LiTaO_3$

Lithium tantalate is in the $3m$ crystallographic point group and is ferroelectric.[5] The Curie temperature varies from 540°C to 660°C depending on the relative concentrations of lithium and tantalum.[6] The crystal from which the modulator was made has a Curie temperature of 595°C. The relative dielectric constant along the c axis at room temperature is 43 with a loss tangent at 100 Mc/sec of approximately 2×10^{-3}. The dielectric constant along the c axis has been found to be relatively independent of frequency.[7] The material is piezoelectric and the acoustic waves which are generated in the material can have undersirable effects on modulator performance unless care is taken in sample mounting. In particular, the sample surfaces should be mechanically loaded in order to reduce the effects of elastic resonances. Lithium tantalate is a uniaxial

[1] I. P. Kaminow and J. Liu, Proc. IEEE **51**, 132 (1963).
[2] W. W. Rigrod and I. P. Kaminow, Proc. IEEE **51**, 137 (1963).
[3] M. DiDomenico, Jr., and L. K. Anderson, Bell System Tech. J. **42**, 2621 (1963).
[4] C. J. Peters, Proc. IEEE **53**, 455 (1965).
[5] B. T. Matthias and J. P. Remeika, Phys. Rev. **76**, 1886 (1949).
[6] A. A. Ballman, H. J. Levinstein, C. D. Capio, and H. Brown, to be published in Mater. Res. Bull.
[7] P. V. Lenzo, E. H. Turner, E. G. Spencer, and A. A. Ballman, Appl. Phys. Letters **8**, 81 (1966).

TABLE I. Design parameters for $LiTaO_3$ modulators.

At $\lambda = 0.63\ \mu$	
	$r_{33} = 3.04 \times 10^{-9}$ cm/V [7]
	$r_{13} = 6.9 \times 10^{-10}$ cm/V [7]
	$[E \cdot l]_{\lambda/2} = 2700$ V
	$l^{-1}(\partial l \mid n_e - n_0 \mid / \partial T)_{T=40°C} = 4.7 \times 10^{-5}/°C$
Frequency constant of Z-plate compressional wave $= 3040$ kc·mm.[9]	

material with an ordinary index of refraction $n_0 = 2.175$ and an extraoridinary index of refraction $n_e = 2.180$ at a wavelength of $\lambda = 6328$ Å.[8] These indices are slightly temperature dependent. The electro-optic effect is the largest when voltage is applied along the c axis and light propagates perpendicular to the c axis. Hence this configuration is adopted in our modulators. The temperature-dependent static birefrigence which occurs for this orientation is stabilized by temperature control of the sample.

In Table I,[9] quantities pertinent to the design of amplitude modulators are summarized. The quantities r_{33} and r_{13} are elements of the electro-optic tensor, and $[E \cdot l]_{\lambda/2}$ is the voltage required across a pair of electrodes to produce π radians relative phase retardation between the extraordinary and the ordinary ray when the light path length is equal to the spacing of the electrodes. Materials, like $LiTaO_3$, with transverse electro-optic effects can be applied in modulators with geometries which provide a large ratio of light path length to electrode spacing and thus allow very much reduced drive voltages for large percentage modulation. The average measured $[E \cdot l]_{\lambda/2}$ which is listed in Table I is approximately 20% higher than would be calculated using the published values for r_{33} and r_{13}. This may be due to a difference in the degree of perfection of poling in the samples used.

3. CHARACTERISTICS OF THE $LiTaO_3$ INTENSITY MODULATOR

The crystal axes of the $LiTaO_3$ were located by x-ray orientation and the sample was ground and polished to a size typically $b = d = 0.01$ in. and $l = 0.4$ in., where b, d, and l are as shown in Fig. 1. The two surfaces normal to the c axis were vacuum deposited with Cr and Au, then electroplated with Cu and Au, and one of the surfaces soldered to a copper block. The temperature of the copper block was controlled to better than ± 0.05°C. The copper block serves as a heat sink as well as a damper to elastic waves excited in the sample due to piezoelectric coupling. The assembly was placed between a pair of crossed polarizers with the c axis of $LiTaO_3$ oriented 45° from the axes of the polarizers (see Fig. 1). The laser beam traveled along the a axis. A Babinet Soleil compensator or a quartz wedge was inserted between the polarizers to bias the light optically.

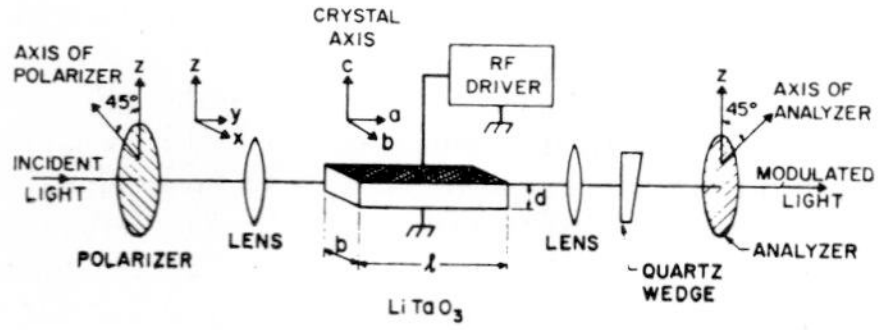

FIG. 1. Modulator configuration.

3.1. Temperature Dependence of the Static Birefringence

Since the static birefrigence of $LiTaO_3$ is temperature dependent, temperature stabilization is required. The required degree of stabilization can be estimated as follows: Let φ be the phase difference between the extraordinary ray and the ordinary ray going through the sample and the compensator. It can be expressed as

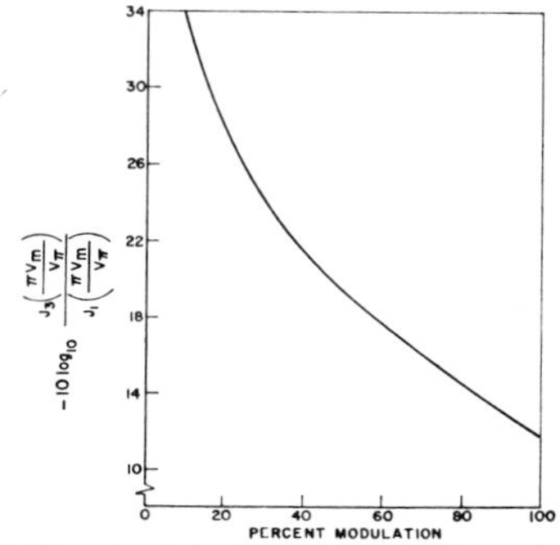

FIG. 2. The ratio of the third harmonic to the fundamental modulated light intensity in dB vs percent modulation.

$$\varphi = (2\pi l/\lambda)(n_e - n_0) + \Delta\varphi_1 + \Delta\varphi_2 + \Delta\varphi_3, \tag{1}$$

where λ is the vacuum wavelength of light. The first term on the right-hand side of Eq. (1) represents the phase difference due to the static birefrigence of $LiTaO_3$ at a fixed temperature T, $\Delta\varphi_1$ is due to the compensator, $\Delta\varphi_2$ is due to the deviation of the temperature from T by ΔT, and $\Delta\varphi_3$ is due to the voltage applied on the crystal (due to the electrically induced birefrigence). The output light intensity from the analyzer can be expressed as

$$I = (I_0/2)(1 - \cos\varphi), \tag{2}$$

where I_0 is the light intensity at the input to the modulator and optical loss is neglected.

If the compensator is adjusted for extinction in the absence of the applied voltage at the temperature T, i.e., $2\pi l/\lambda(n_e - n_0) + \Delta\varphi_1 = 2m\pi$, where m is an integer, then the amount of light leakage when the temperature deviates to $T + \Delta T$ is

$$I_{\Delta T}/I_0 = \tfrac{1}{2} + \tfrac{1}{2}(-1)^{2m+1}\cos\Delta\varphi_2. \tag{3}$$

[8] W. L. Bond, J. Appl. Phys. 36, 1675 (1965).
[9] A. W. Warner and M. Onoe, paper presented at 1966 Ultrasonic Symposium, Cleveland, Ohio.

In order to keep $I_{\Delta T}/I_0$ to better than, say 0.01 (20-db extinction), one can calculate from Eq. (3) and the quantity in Table I that the temperature must be controlled to better than $\pm 0.045°C$ for a 1-cm-long crystal at $\lambda = 0.63\mu$.

For linear intensity modulation, the compensator is adjusted for 50% light transmission in the absence of the modulating voltage, i.e.,

$$(2\pi l/\lambda)(n_e - n_0) + \Delta\varphi_1 = \tfrac{1}{2}(2m+1)\pi, \qquad m = 0,1,2,\cdots. \tag{4}$$

Then it can be shown on substituting from Eq. (1) into Eq. (2) that

$$2(I/I_0) = 1 + (-1)^{m+1}2\cos\Delta\varphi_2[J_1(\pi V_m/V\pi)\sin\omega_m t + J_3(\pi V_m/V_\pi)\sin 3\omega_m t + \cdots] + (-1)^{m+1}2\sin\Delta\varphi_2[\tfrac{1}{2}J_0(\pi V_m/V_\pi) + J_2(\pi V_m/V_\pi)\cos 2mt + \cdots], \tag{5}$$

where J's are the Bessel's functions of the first kind. In Eq. (5), $V_m \sin\omega_m t$ is the modulating voltage across the electrodes, and

$$V_\pi = (d/l)[E\cdot l]_{\lambda/2} = (d/l)[\lambda/(n_e^3 r_{33} - n_0^3 r_{13})], \tag{6}$$

where V_π is often called the half-wave voltage.

Equation (5) shows that harmonics are generated because of the effects of the temperature-dependent birefringence and fundamental nonlinearity of the modulation process. Let us define percentage modulation as the ratio of light intensity at the modulation frequency to $I_0/2$; then

$$\text{percentage modulation} = 2J_1(\pi V_m/V_\pi)\cos\Delta\varphi_2. \tag{7}$$

The ratios of second and third harmonic to the fundamental signal intensity are given by

$$\frac{I_{2\omega_m}}{I_{\omega_m}} = \frac{J_2(\pi V_m/V_\pi)}{J_1(\pi V_m/V_\pi)}\tan\Delta\varphi_2, \tag{8}$$

and

$$\frac{I_{3\omega_m}}{I_{\omega_m}} = \frac{J_3(\pi V_m/V_\pi)}{J_1(\pi V_m/V_\pi)}. \tag{9}$$

Note that the percentage of third harmonic distortion is independent of temperature drift and that, on the other hand, second harmonic distortion would be zero in the absence of temperature drift. The relationships given in Eqs. (8) and (9) are plotted in Figs. 2 and 3 as a function of percent modulation. These curves allow the distortion products to be determined in terms of percent modulation, maximum temperature variation, and material parameters. Equation (7) also shows the decrease of the modulated intensity at ω_m as the temperature deviates by ΔT. In order to maintain the fundamental modulation intensity to within, say one percent, one then has to maintain the temperature of the crystal to better than $\pm 0.032°C$ for $l = 1$ cm and $\lambda = 0.63\mu$ from Eq. (7) and Table I.

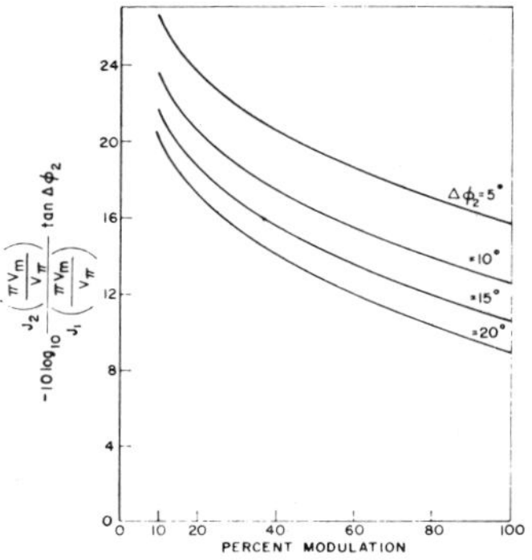

FIG. 3. The ratio of the second harmonic to the fundamental modulated light intensity in dB vs percent modulation.

Another problem which should be considered in connection with the temperature-dependent static birefrigence of $LiTaO_3$ is the possible degradation of extinction as the rf modulating voltage is increased. Since the electrical Q and the thermal conductivity of the crystal are finite, there will be a parabolic temperature distribution between the electrodes if only the electrodes are maintained at a constant temperature. This introduces a nonuniform index of refraction across the light beam and hence reduces the extinction, changes the optical bias from the optimum, and diffracts the light beam inside the crystal. This effect is obviously more pronounced at high modulating frequencies since the power dissipated in the crystal is larger at high frequencies for a given degree of intensity modulation. One can calculate the temperature distribution between the electrodes for a given degree of intensity modulation if Q and the thermal conductivity are known. Experimentally, however, one can estimate the average temperature change across the beam cross section due to rf heating from the necessary change in the compensator setting for the optimum optical biasing and making use of the known temperature dependence of birefringence. For a sample with dimensions $d = 0.015$ in., $1 = 0.384$ in. the change in temperature due to rf heating was less than 0.005°C at 50 Mc/sec to 0.05°C at 150 Mc/sec. The rms modulating voltage was 20 V (corresponding to approximately 85% intensity modulation) and the light propagates near the center of the crystal. In order to avoid the large distortion inherent in optical-amplitude modulators using the electro-optic effect, the depth of intensity modulation would perhaps be kept to less than 30% (the third harmonic is 24 dB down). Then the change in the temperature due to rf heating would be much smaller than the number just quoted. We did not, for example, observe any temperature change due to rf heating at 200 Mc/sec for 40% intensity modulation using a sample with a reduced cross-section.

3.2. Light Extinction

Extinction is defined as the ratio of the maximum to the minimum transmitted light intensity when the optical bias is correspondingly adjusted. It depends on the optical homogeneity of the sample and the optical path differences encountered by a ray over the beam cross section. For good extinction, the angle of the cone the beam makes inside the crystal should be small. Taking $n_0=2.175$, $n_e-n_0=0.005$, $l=1$ cm, and $\lambda=0.63\mu$, one arrives at the allowable half cone angle of 3.5° for an extinction of 20 dB. This angle is larger than one would encounter in a small angular aperture modulator such as the one being described here and hence this source of light leakage can be neglected.

The extinction was measured by four different methods. They are:

(1) adjusting the compensator but no voltage applied to the sample,
(2) applying a dc voltage,
(3) applying a 60 cps voltage of amplitude larger than $V_\pi/2$, and
(4) applying 50 Mc/sec voltage of amplitude larger than $V_\pi/2$.

The first method will show the uniformity of the static birefrigence, while the other three should show the uniformity of the induced birefringence. If the sample is conductive and the electrodes are nonohmic, the applied dc field would not be distributed uniformly between the electrodes which causes an error in the measurements of half-wave voltage and poor extinction. The distortion of the field distribution from this effect takes place within the dielectric relaxation time which is usually longer than a second. Thus, the use of 60 cps for the measurements of half-wave voltage and extinction avoids the buildup of possible field distortion because the polarity of the fields changes faster than the dielectric relaxation time. The fourth method is designed essentially to see the effect of rf heating and acoustic excitation on the induced birefringence. Most of the samples measured had an extinction from 15 dB to 19 dB by the first three methods. Better than 10-dB extinction was obtained by the fourth method.

3.3. Frequency Response

From the piezoelectric matrix appropriate for the point group symmetry of $LiTaO_3$, it is known that a compressional elastic wave can be excited along each crystal axis when a voltage is applied along the c axis.[10] As the modulating frequency approaches elastic resonant frequencies a pronounced electro-optic effect may be observed due to the strain-optic effect. The elastic wave resonance has the undesirable effects of causing peaks in the frequency response of the modulator and "ringing" of the output light intensity when a pulse voltage is applied across the electrodes. For the orientation of the sample as in our modulator, we observed only a weak effect of the elastic wave resonances because of limited excitation of elastic waves, damping of the elastic wave provided by soldering the sample to a copper block, and perhaps the small strain-optic coefficients involved. The resonance frequency of the Z-plate compressional wave, which appears to excite the largest strain-optic effect in our modulator, can be calculated from the constant listed in Table I.

The frequency response of the sample was measured by applying across the sample a constant modulating voltage, which was measured by an HP410B rf voltmeter. The modulated light output was detected in a Philco L4501 photodiode and its output voltage (to be called V_{out}) was measured by a Rhode and Schwarz type USWV selective voltmeter.

Figure 4 shows the output voltage of the photodiode vs frequency for a sample with dimension $d=b=0.01$ in. and $l=0.385$ in. The capacitance of the sample in its mount is 5 pF. A single mode He-Ne laser ($\lambda=0.63\mu$) generating 1.5 mW in a Gaussian beam was focused to approximately 0.002 in. diameter inside the sample. The rf voltage across the crystal was maintained at 0.5 V rms as the frequency was varied. The half-wave voltage of the sample was 76 V peak-to-peak. The accuracy of the measurements was approximately ±25%. One could observe the peak in V_{out} near 11 Mc/sec and its odd multiples. These were presumably due to the fundamental and the odd harmonic resonances of the compressional elastic waves along the c axis and the b axis. A weak peak of V_{out} was observed near 350 Kc/sec which was due to the resonance of the compressional elastic wave along the a axis.

The frequency response as shown was measured up to 400 Mc/sec which is the frequency range of the Rhode and Schwarz voltmeter. In addition, modulation was observed up to and over 900 Mc/sec using a Polarad spectrometer as a receiver. It should be noted, however, that as the modulation frequency gets higher the transit time of light across the sample would become significant compared to the period of the modulating voltage, and the efficiency of modulation would decrease accordingly. For lower frequencies, at least up to 1 Gc/sec where the light transit time is still less than one-tenth of the

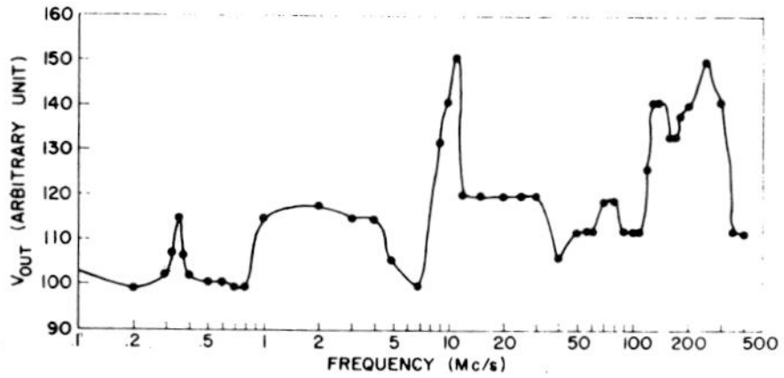

FIG. 4. The output voltage of photodiode vs frequency. The modulating voltage across the sample is kept constant.

[10] J. F. Nye, *Physical Properties of Crystals* (Oxford University Press, London, 1960), p. 299.

period of the modulating voltage, the transit time effect can be neglected. The sample length is also much shorter than the electrical wavelength at these frequencies so it can be regarded simply as a capacitor loading the modulating amplifier. The resistance shunting the sample capacitance to represent the dissipative part of the impedance can be neglected due to the high electrical Q of the sample. A sample with dimensions $b=d=0.01$ in. and $l=0.4$ in. would exhibit a capacitive reactance of 50 Ω at 800 Mc/sec. Therefore, the bandwidth of a modulator using this size sample would be from dc up to 800 Mc/sec if a driver of 50-Ω output impedance were available over this frequency bandwidth. Since the half-wave voltage of this sample is 76 V peak-to-peak, it can be shown that the required output voltage of the driver should be 5.15 V rms and the output power should be 0.53 W for 30% intensity modulation over 800 Mc/sec bandwidth.

A transistor amplifier was developed by R. C. Petersen of these Laboratories which is capable of driving the capacitance of 5 pF from dc up to over 200 Mc/sec. The output voltage of the amplifier is

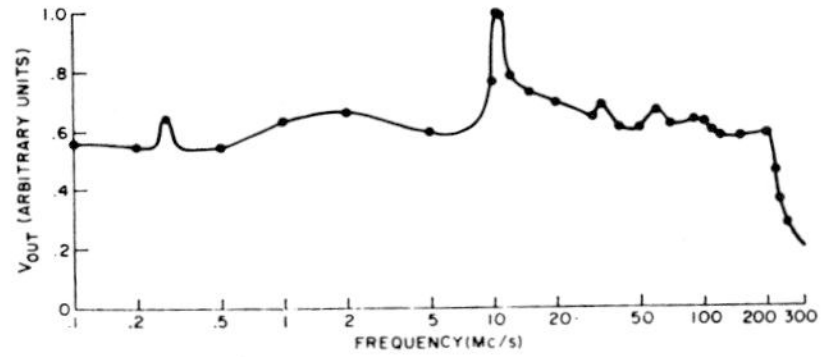

FIG. 5. The output voltage of photodiode vs frequency. The modulating voltage at the input to the broad-band transistor amplifier is kept constant.

6 V rms when it is terminated with 180-Ω resistive load, corresponding to over 40% intensity modulation with a sample of the same size as in Fig. 4. The voltage gain of the amplifier is about 30, and a resistor is connected in series with the sample to damp a series resonance near 200 Mc/sec due to the lead inductance and sample capacitance. The input to the amplifier was driven by a Jerrold constant output voltage uhf sweeper. The modulated light was detected in a Philco L4501 diode, the output of which was measured by the Rhode and Schwarz voltmeter in a frequency tracking mode of operation. Figure 5 shows the relative modulated output intensity vs frequency of the combined amplifier-crystal unit.

In order to evaluate harmonic distortions, the relative modulated light intensity at 35 Mc/sec and its harmonics were measured as a function of drive voltage on a second sample with results as plotted in Fig. 6. The light was made to pass through the sample twice ("round-trip" mode) resulting in a V_π of 31 V. The solid lines were calculated from Eqs. (7) to (9) with the light intensity at the modulating frequency arbitrarily set to 0 dB for 10% modulation. The second harmonic distortion was due almost entirely to distortion in the output of the transistor amplifier as determined from direct measurements on the amplifier. The third harmonic distortion is also a few dB higher than the calculated value with the difference also due to harmonic distortion in the transistor amplifier.

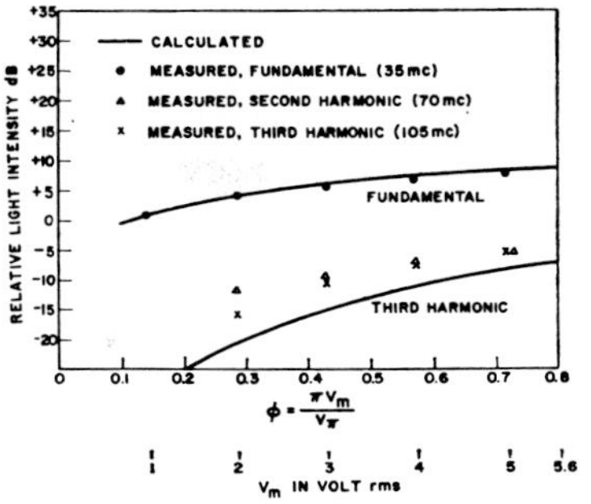

FIG. 6. Relative modulated light intensity at the fundamental, the second harmonic and the third harmonic vs the depth of modulation.

The effect of elastic wave excitation on the electro-optic interaction was observed by applying a fast rise voltage pulse directly on the sample. The lower trace of Fig. 7 shows the shape of the applied voltage pulse while the upper trace shows the laser intensity detected in a Philco L4501 diode and displayed on a sampling scope. The time scale is 100 nsec per scale division. Only a small amount of ringing can be observed.

3.4. Optical Loss

The optical loss of the sample with $b=d=0.01$ in. and $l=0.4$ in. was measured by first removing the sample and adjusting the compensator to get maximum transmission. Then the modulator was inserted between the crossed polarizers and the compensator was readjusted for maximum output intensity. The output intensity was detected by a photodiode in each case. The difference is the loss due to the sample. Its value

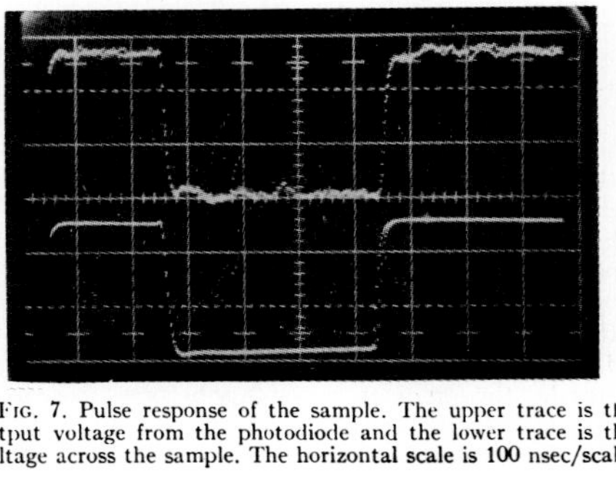

FIG. 7. Pulse response of the sample. The upper trace is the output voltage from the photodiode and the lower trace is the voltage across the sample. The horizontal scale is 100 nsec/scale.

TABLE II. Comparison of KDP, KTN, $LiTaO_3$, and $LiNbO_3$ for modulator applications.

	ϵ_r[a]	$(E\cdot l)_{\lambda/2}$ (V)	$\epsilon\cdot(E\cdot l)^2_{\lambda/2}$ (J/m)	$l^{-1}(\partial l\,\lvert n_e-n_0\rvert/\partial T)$ (°C^{-1})
KDP	21[b]	1.9×10^4 [b]	6.7×10^{-2}	1.1×10^{-5} [d]
KTN[c]	10^4	28.4	7.1×10^{-5}	
$LiTaO_3$	43	2.7×10^3	2.8×10^{-3}	4.7×10^{-5}
$LiNbO_3$	28[b]	2.8×10^3 [b]	1.9×10^{-3}	4.3×10^{-5}

[a] ϵ_r is the relative dielectric constant.
[b] Using the numbers quoted in Ref. 11.
[c] The sample is biased to 6×10^{-2} coulomb/m^2; see Ref. 12.
[d] Data taken from Ref. 4.

was approximately 1.5 dB with antireflection coatings on the ends of the sample. It was observed that the output beam shape appeared to be very little distorted from the input Gaussian beam.

3.5. "Round-Trip" Mode

It is evident that the modulating voltage can be reduced by one-half for a given depth of intensity modulation and a given sample length if the light beam is made to pass through the sample twice. In order to accomplish this, samples were antireflection coated on the front surface and mirror coated to reflect the beam on the back surface. The arrangement for intensity modulation with the "round-trip" mode is shown in Fig. 8. With the modulating voltage off, the Rochon prism and the compensator were adjusted so that 50% of the light intensity was reflected back to the laser and 50% was reflected toward the photodetector. This is equivalent to biasing the modulator optically to 50% transmission in the "single-transit" mode.

Compared to the "single-trip" mode, the "round-trip" mode reduces the required modulating voltage by one half for the same percent modulation and the same sample dimensions, while the driver amplifier "sees" the same sample capacitance. If the sample length were doubled for the "single-trip" mode, the voltage would also, of course, be reduced by one half but the sample capacitance would be doubled. Thus, the drive power required for a "single-trip" mode of operation is twice the drive power required for "round-trip" operation. The effect of the finite transit time of the light is still negligible at 500 Mc/sec for our typical sample size and the bandwidth of the modulator is still limited by the driver only. With a careful alignment of the sample 15-dB extinction was obtained. The optical loss between the input to the Rochon prism and the output to the photodetector was approximately 3 dB. Because of the doubled optical path, the requirement on the temperature stability becomes more severe compared to the "single-transit" mode. However, the temperature control used in the "single-transit" mode modulator appears to be satisfactory when used in the "round-trip" mode.

4. COMPARISON OF KDP, KTN, $LiNbO_3$, AND $LiTaO_3$ FOR MODULATOR APPLICATIONS

It is instructive at this point to make some comparisons among electro-optic materials in order to evaluate the characteristics of lithium tantalate for modulator applications. An important consideration for any modulator material is the drive power required for a given percentage modulation. The power required will be determined by the drive voltage needed and the impedance level presented by the electrooptic material. For the sake of comparison, we use the drive voltage $V_m=0.5V_\pi$, the voltage for 114% modulation. The modulating crystal is assumed to present only a capacitive load to the driver amplifier. This is appropriate for baseband modulators, since the dissipative part of the crystal can usually be neglected compared to the reactive part and very little power is actually dissipated in the sample. We make one other assumption in calculating the capacitance; namely, that the material presents a square aperture to the light beam. Then the area of the electrodes is ld and they are separated by a distance d. Using these assumptions the required drive power, P_d, is determined by

$$P_d\propto CV_\pi^2\propto(\epsilon l)\{(d/l)[E\cdot l]^2_{\lambda/2}\}$$

or

$$P_d\propto(d^2/l)\epsilon[E\cdot l]^2_{\lambda/2} \qquad (10)$$

where ϵ is the permittivity of the sample. Equation (10) shows that a figure of merit for electrooptic materials is $\epsilon[E\cdot l]^2_{\lambda/2}$ and also indicates the importance, as far as the geometry of the modulator is concerned, of having a large ratio l/d.

Rather than compile an exhaustive list of electro-optic materials we will only consider for comparison three other materials in order to illustrate some important considerations. One is the venerable linear electro-optic material potassium dihydrogen phosphate (KDP) which has been applied fairly widely. The second is a more recent material, potassium tantalate niboate (KTN), which has been proposed for electro-optic applications in a temperature range just above its Curie temperature and which exhibits a quadratic electro-optic effect. The third material is lithium ni-

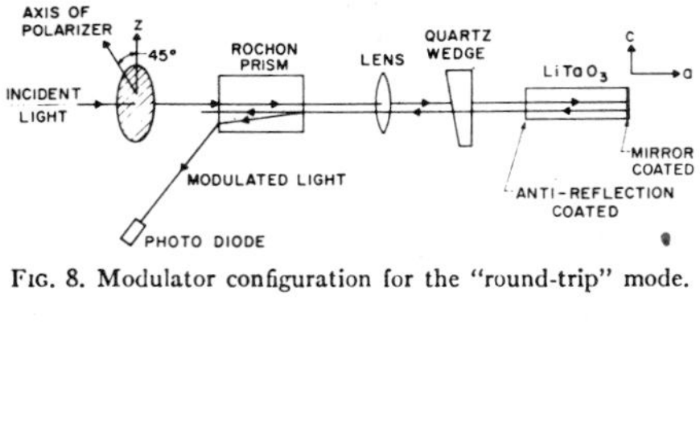

FIG. 8. Modulator configuration for the "round-trip" mode.

obate ($LiNbO_3$). This is a new material which is like lithium tantalate in many respects. Table II[11,12] summarizes the properties of these materials and shows that KDP requires roughly 20 times as much drive power as lithium tantalate. In addition, KDP is soft and very difficult to polish properly while lithium tantalate is relatively hard and can be readily polished. On the basis of lower drive requirements and superior mechanical properties, lithium tantalate is to be preferred. The table also shows that KTN would require an order of magnitude smaller drive power compared to lithium tantalate and on the basis of drive power only would indicate that KTN is the superior material. There are several practical problems, however, which limit the usefulness of KTN at this time. First, the optical homogeneity of the material is not sufficiently uniform, although this is not a serious problem for small aperture modulators like the one described in this paper. The second is the nonuniform distribution of the biasing dc electric field between the electrodes due to the space-charge effect associated with the finite resistivity of the crystal. The most serious problem for the modulator application with KTN is an induced optical inhomogeneity which occurs when the laser beam is focused in the sample and the *dc* field is applied simultaneously. This effect manifests itself in a poor optical extinction, an increased half-wave voltage and, often, a distortion of the beam shape, when the optical power density in the material exceeds a certain level (usually 0.1 W/cm^2 for $\lambda = 0.63\mu$). A similar and perhaps related phenomenon has also been observed in a number of other materials.[13] This distortion did not occur for the material used in the modulators under the experimental conditions that were encountered. The static and the induced birefringence of $LiTaO_3$ are quite homogeneous, at least over a small beam aperture, and the mechanical strain which may have been introduced during the polishing process has negligible effect on the homogeneity of the birefringence. Thus, from a practical point of view, $LiTaO_3$ seems superior to KTN even though higher driver power is required. In many respects $LiNbO_3$ as a modulator crystal is very similar to $LiTaO_3$. However, because of a much larger static birefringence, the requirements for both the cone angle the beam makes inside the sample and the parallelism of the sample surfaces are more severe compared to $LiTaO_3$. Also, at present $LiNbO_3$ is more susceptible to the laser induced distortion.

Table II also gives the temperature dependence of static birefringence in KDP and $LiTaO_3$. It can be seen that temperature variation in $LiTaO_3$ is four times as great as in KDP which means that more care must be taken in temperature control or compensation in this material. Since KTN is a cubic material, there is no static birefringence. However, induced birefringence caused by the dc biasing field is strongly temperature-dependent and the resulting requirements for temperature control are as severe as for $LiTaO_3$.

5. SUMMARY

Baseband optical intensity modulators were built using single-domain $LiTaO_3$ as the modulating material. The material has low optical loss in the visible region of the spectrum, and the static and the induced birefringence are sufficiently homogeneous, at least over a small beam cross section, that an optical extinction of 15 dB to 19 dB has been achieved.

A transistor amplifier which can provide 6 V rms across the 5 pF capacitive load was built to drive the crystal from dc to 220 Mc with approximately 80% modulation when the modulator was operated in the "round-trip" mode. The maximum output power of the driver amplifier was 200 mW, and the bandwidth of the modulator was limited by the transistor driver-amplifier.

A large aspect ratio (l/d) of the sample is necessary for small drive power. Our sample has an aspect ratio of 40, but the focusing of Gaussian beam through the sample is not very difficult even when operated in the "round-trip" mode. The ratio of d^2/l for the sample to the limiting d^2/l from Gaussian beam theory has been defined as a safety factor S_i by Kaminow and Turner.[11] In our modulator with the "round-trip" mode $S \approx 3$. Although a further increase of l/d to reduce the drive power is theoretically possible (until $S \approx 1$), the difficulties of focusing a light beam through the sample are expected to increase rapidly.

ACKNOWLEDGMENTS

The authors wish to thank D. Halvorsen for the mechanical design of the modulator, F. J. Sansalone for supervising preparation of the finished crystals, and R. C. Petersen for designing the transistor amplifier. R. P. Morris and H. Brown have provided very capable technical assistance during the course of this work.

[11] I. P. Kaminow and E. H. Turner, Proc. IEEE **54**, 1374 (1966).
[12] F. S. Chen, J. E. Geusic, S. K. Kurtz, J. G. Skinner, and S. H. Wemple, J. Appl. Phys. **37**, 388 (1966).
[13] A. Askin, G. D. Boyd, J. M. Dziedzic, R. G. Smith, A. A. Ballman, H. J. Levinstein, and K. Nassau, Appl. Phys. Letters **9**, 72 (1966).

Performance of $LiTaO_3$ and $LiNbO_3$ Light Modulators at 4 GHz

I. P. Kaminow and W. M. Sharpless

Bell Telephone Laboratories, Inc., Crawford Hill Laboratory, Holmdel, New Jersey 07733.
Received 31 October 1966.

Two light intensity modulators have been constructed using $LiTaO_3$ and $LiNbO_3$, respectively, in a reentrant microwave cavity tuned to 4.2 GHz. The loop-coupled cavity is shown schematically in Fig. 1. The crystal is attached to the chisel-shaped center post with silver paste and is oriented so that the (peak) voltage V is along the c axis. The cavity diameter D is 1.91 cm, the post diameter d is 0.38 cm and the resonant frequency is determined by the cavity height h.

Not all the electric field is concentrated in the gap containing the crystal. A rough estimate of the added capacity C_a in parallel with the crystal is $\epsilon_0 \pi D^2/4h$. The ratio of total capacity C_T to crystal capacity C is then

$$\alpha = C_T/C = 1 + (\pi D^2 t/4\epsilon_3 w d h), \tag{1}$$

where ϵ_3 is the relative dielectric constant along the c axis, w and t are the width and thickness of the crystal, and the crystal length L is slightly greater than d.

The peak phase change or phase modulation index η for light polarized along the c axis is[1]

$$\eta = \beta \cdot 2\pi d\, n_3^3 r_{33}\, V/\lambda t, \tag{2}$$

and, for light polarized at 45° to the c axis, the peak phase retardation Γ between the c and a axis components is[1]

$$\Gamma = \beta \cdot 2\pi d(n_3^3 r_{33} - n_1^3 r_{13}) V/\lambda t, \tag{3}$$

where λ is the optical wavelength, n_1 and n_3 are refractive indices, r_{13} and r_{33} electrooptic coefficients, and β is a fractional coefficient that takes account of the fact that the transit time for light passing through the crystal is comparable with the modulation period[2],

$$\beta = 1/2\{(\sin u^+/u^+) + (\sin u^-/u^-)\} \tag{4}$$

$$u^{\pm} = (\pi f d/c)(\epsilon_3^{1/2} \mp n), \tag{5}$$

with f the modulation frequency and c/n the velocity of light in the crystal.

A linear *intensity* modulation with index Γ is produced when a $\pi/2$ retardation bias is provided and when $\Gamma \ll 4$. The equivalent *amplitude* modulation index m is $\Gamma/2$. It may be noted in Eqs. (2) and (3) that, since r_{13} has the same sign[3] as r_{33}, η is larger than Γ.

The parameters for the two modulators, including the half-power bandwidth Δf measured with the cavities critically coupled, are given in Table I. The power dissipated in the matched cavity is[1]

$$P = 2\pi C_T V^2 \Delta f/4 = \alpha \cdot \pi C V^2 \Delta f/2. \tag{6}$$

For a given P, Γ is proportional to $\alpha^{-1/2}$.

The experimental arrangement is illustrated schematically in Fig. 2(a) and by a photograph in Fig. 2(b). The source is a 0.633 μ He–Ne laser operating in a doughnut or low order transverse mode with approximately 10 mW of light power available. A variable Babinet–Soleil compensator in combination with the natural birefringence of the crystal is adjusted to give the $\pi/2$ retardation bias required for linear intensity modulation. After thermal equilibrium is reached, only occasional adjustment of the compensator is required. The 4.2-GHz signal is detected by a high speed, epitaxial germanium point-contact photodiode having an

Table I. Material Parameters Taken from Summary in Reference 1.

	ϵ_3	n_1	n_3	r_{33}[a]	r_{13}[a]	h[b]
$LiTaO_3$	43	2.176	2.180	33	7.5	172
$LiNbO_3$	28	2.286	2.200	31	8.6	393

	w,t,L[b]	$\bar{S}$	$\alpha^{-1/2}$	β	Δf[c]
$LiTaO_3$	28,23,421	6.7	0.74	0.78	40
$LiNbO_3$	25,23,388	6.6	0.78	0.86	45

[a] In 10^{-12} m/V
[b] In 10^{-3} cm
[c] In MHz

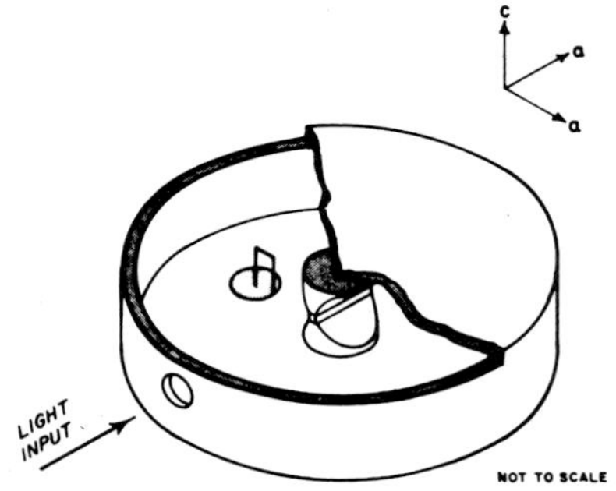

Fig. 1. Reentrant cavity cutaway to show crystal rod and coupling loop.

active region somewhat less than 10 μ in diam (Fig. 3). A microwave heterodyne receiver completes the measuring equipment. With this apparatus, the linearity of Γ with V, up to $\sim$30 V, was checked, and the $LiTaO_3$ and $LiNbO_3$ devices were compared quantitatively with one another and at various optical power levels.

The measured optical attenuation for the elements in Fig. 2 is about 7.5 dB, including the 3 dB introduced by the $\pi/2$ (circular polarization) bias, and the 4 dB loss due to Fresnel surface reflections from the various elements. The transverse crystal dimensions are larger than the diffraction limited value for given L by a factor[1] S, whose average over both dimensions is given in Table I.

The $LiNbO_3$ modulator operates satisfactorily for optical powers below 1 mW, but at 10 mW the transmitted beam becomes distorted[4] within a few minutes, and the apparent modulation is much reduced. This damage effect does not arise with the $LiTaO_3$ sample[4] and Γ is independent of optical power level, at least up to 10 mW. (We are grateful to A. A. Ballman and R. T. Denton for providing the $LiTaO_3$ crystal, and to K. Nassau for the $LiNbO_3$ crystal.)

In order to obtain an absolute measurement of Γ, a photomultiplier tube and oscilloscope is used as the detector, the microwave signal is square wave modulated, and the compensator is set to give a net retardation bias of either zero or π. The slow detector responds only to the intensity averaged over a microwave period. With the microwave signal off and π retardation bias, the transmitted intensity $I_\perp$ is a minimum; with the micro-

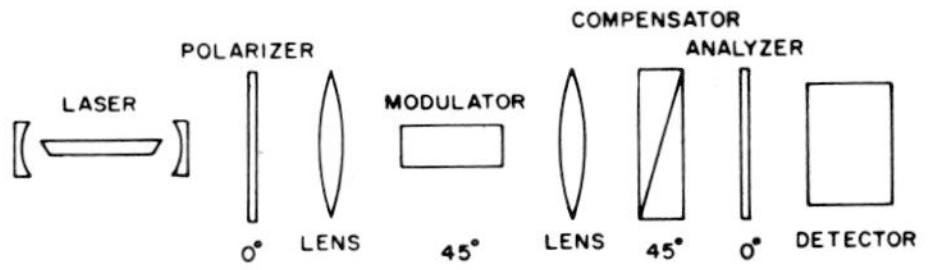

(a)

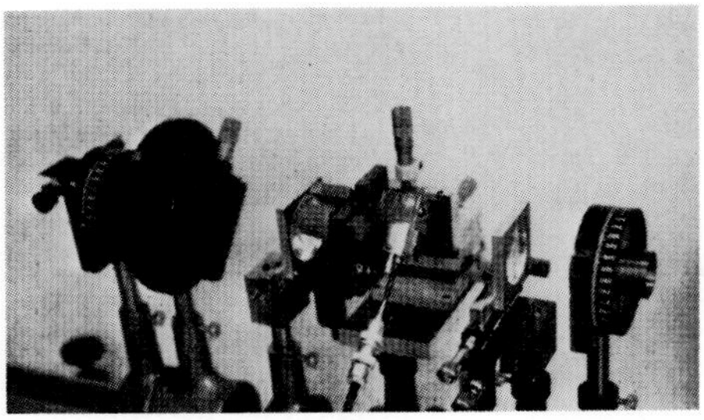

(b)

Fig. 2. (a)Experimental arrangement with orientations of principal axes noted. Lens focal length = 6.5 cm. (b)Photograph.

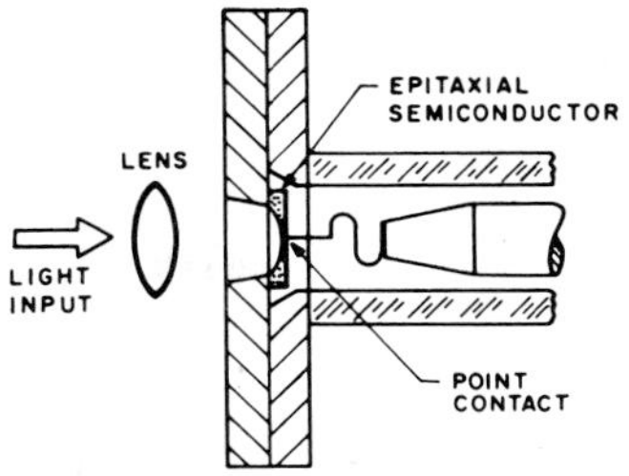

Fig. 3. Arrangement of point-contact photodetector.

wave signal on, the average intensity increases to ΔI; and, with the microwave signal off and with zero retardation bias, the intensity $I_{||}$ is a maximum. Then Γ is obtained[1,5] from the Bessel function:

$$J_0(\Gamma) = 1 - [2\Delta I/(I_{||} - I_\perp)]. \quad (7)$$

For the $LiTaO_3$ modulator, the measured Γ is 0.44 rad (or 44% intensity modulation) over a 40-MHz bandwidth with 180 mW of modulating power. The calculated Γ using the data in Table I, including the factors $\alpha^{-1/2}$ and β, is 0.52 rad. The 15% discrepancy is probably within the uncertainty of the experiment, although the observed reduction in Γ may be due in part to a series voltage drop across the silver paste junction between cavity and crystal. The phase modulation index η corresponding to a Γ of 0.44 rad is 0.57 rad.

The measurements on the $LiNbO_3$ modulator are perhaps less reliable than those for $LiTaO_3$ because of the necessarily lower intensity light beam (<1 mW) and the effects of optical damage that may have been present even at the reduced light level. The measured Γ and corresponding η are 0.43 rad and 0.62 rad, respectively, for 180-mW input and the 45-MHz band. The calculated Γ is 0.61 rad.

Thus, on the order of 10 mW/MHz of bandwidth will be required to produce a unity phase modulation index η or 75% intensity modulation Γ for either $LiNbO_3$ or $LiTaO_3$ at 4 GHz, with a slight advantage for $LiNbO_3$ due to its smaller ϵ_3. The comparable experimental result for a baseband, 200 MHz, $LiTaO_3$ modulator[6] is on the order of 1 mW/MHz, the difference arising largely from a smaller S ($S \sim 3$), much reduced α and β corrections, and round-trip configuration.

References

1. I. P. Kaminow and E. H. Turner, Appl. Opt. **5**, 1612 (1966).
2. I. P. Kaminow and J. Liu, Proc. IEEE **51**, 132 (1963).
3. E. H. Turner, Appl. Phys. Letter **8**, 303 (1966).
4. A. Ashkin, G. D. Boyd, J. M. Dziedzic, R. G. Smith, A. A. Ballman, J. J. Levinstein, and K. Nassau, Appl. Phys. Letters **9**, 72 (1966).
5. I. P. Kaminow, Appl. Optics, **3**, 511 (1964).
6. R. T. Denton, F. S. Chen, and A. A. Ballman, J. Appl. Phys. **38**, March (1967).

Reprinted from IEEE JOURNAL OF *QUANTUM ELECTRONICS*
Vol. QE-3, Number 12, December 1967
Pp. 664-667

A Push–Pull Optical Amplitude Modulator

WILLIAM H. STEIER, MEMBER, IEEE

***Abstract*—A push–pull optical amplitude modulator is described, and some experimental results are presented. The modulator is an interferometer with phase modulators in each arm. The design gives good temperature stability and allows a reduced modulating voltage by using a transverse modulating field. The use of a Köster's beamsplitting prism provided a compact practical design for the experimental KDP modulator. The modulator held a null in the output of 20 dB below the input for periods of one hour. The frequency response out to 30 MHz and the pulse response of the modulator were measured. Strong piezoelectric resonances were observed. The advantages of the push–pull modulator design for use with $LiNbO_3$ or $LiTaO_3$ are pointed out.**

THIS PAPER presents the results of an experimental investigation of an optical push–pull amplitude modulator. A schematic of the modulator is shown in Fig. 1. It is essentially an optical interferometer with each arm containing an optical phase modulator. If the phase modulation impressed on the light in one arm is 180° out of phase to that impressed on the other arm, the output light will be amplitude modulated.

Manuscript received May 22, 1967; revised September 5, 1967.
The author is with the Crawford Hill Laboratory, Bell Telephone Laboratories, Inc., Holmdel, N. J.

Kravtsov *et al.*,[1],[2] have published some limited experimental data on this type of interferometric modulator using ADP phase modulators, and Fried *et al.*,[3] have published an investigation of this modulator using piezoelectrically driven mirrors for the phase modulation.

When electrooptic crystals are used for the phase modulators, the modulating field can be transverse to the direction of light propagation and the required modulating voltage can be reduced by using long modulating crystals. Also for phase modulation the light is polarized so that it sees no natural birefringence in the electrooptic crystals. Hence, the extreme temperature sensitivity of natural birefringence is avoided and the stability of the push–pull modulator does not depend on its absolute temperature as in some previously reported amplitude modulators.[4],[5] To maintain a balance in the push–pull modulator requires the difference in optical path-length between the two arms to remain constant and therefore the temperature difference between the two arms must be kept to a minimum. This can be done by using a common high-heat conducting mounting block for the two arms.

I. Description of the Modulator

To maintain the two arms at the same temperature it is desirable to keep them as physically close together as possible. A Köster's beamsplitting prism[6] can do this and was the key element in the practical realization of the modulator. As shown in Fig. 1, the prism splits the incident beam into two equal intensity parallel output beams which can be conveniently close together.

An additional advantage of the Köster's prism is that the optical pathlength of each beam within the quartz prism is identical; this is not true in the conventional beamsplitter deposited on one side of a quartz flat. This makes the path difference independent of the absolute temperature and allows the light in each arm to reach the phase modulators at the same modulation phase. This second point is important in the case of high-frequency traveling-wave modulators where an optical delay in one arm of one half the modulating wavelength would result in no amplitude modulation at the output.

The prism input and output faces are cut at Brewster's angle. The dielectric beamsplitting surface was deposited on one half of the prism before cementing the two halves together.

Each arm contained 3 KDP crystals, 2mm by 2mm by 5 cm oiled together for a total crystal length in each arm of 15 cm. The KDP was oriented with the [001] direction perpendicular to the direction of light propagation with the light polarized along the [110] direction. The modulating voltage was applied along the [001] direction. This is the usual orientation for phase modulation.[7] The crystals in one arm had their [001] direction oriented 180° from those in the other arm. The two arms were driven in parallel and the phase modulation impressed on the light had the required 180° phase shift between the arms. Antireflection coated glass was oiled to the end crystal faces in each arm. Silver paint electrodes were used on the KDP.

For temperature stability the two arms were mounted on a large aluminum block. This thermally massive structure was capable of holding the temperature difference between the two paths to a very low value even when the room temperature varied. The two light paths were separated by 2.0 inches.

The light was reflected back down the KDP rods by mirrors on small adjustable mirror mounts. The mirrors were mounted on piezoelectric ceramic cylinders so that the optical length of each arm could be adjusted by a variable voltage. Fig. 2 shows the modulator.

For a modulator using KDP or ADP oriented as described the output intensity I is given by [3],[8]

$$I = \frac{I_0}{2}\left[1 - \cos\left(\frac{4\pi l}{\lambda d}\, n_0^3 r_{63} V_z - \varphi_0\right)\right]. \quad (1)$$

Where

I_0 = input light intensity
l = length of crystal in each arm
d = crystal height
λ = optical wavelength
V_z = modulating voltage applied along [001] direction
n_0 = ordinary index of refraction
r_{63} = electrooptic coefficient
φ_0 = biasing phase shift between the arms set by the difference in arm length.

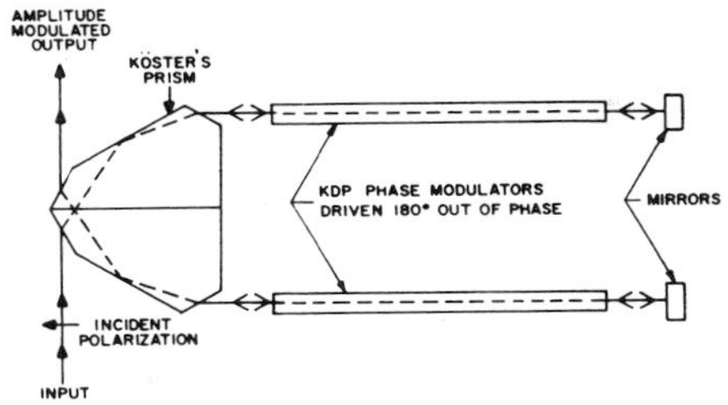

Fig. 1. Schematic of experimental KDP push-pull modulator.

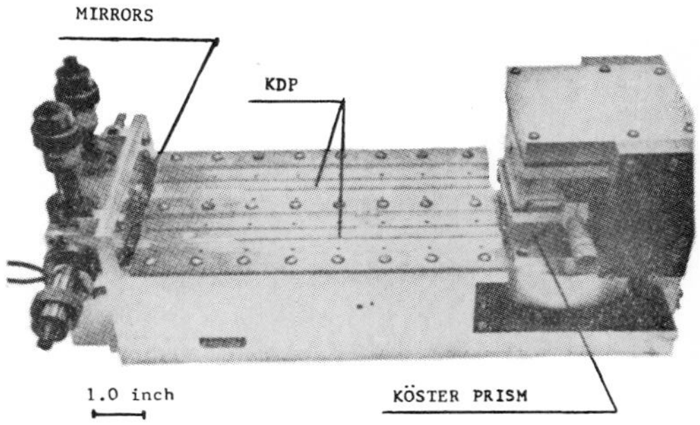

Fig. 2. Experimental KDP push–pull modulator.

From (1) it can be seen that increasing the ratio l/d reduces the required modulating voltage.

II. Modulator Performance

The modulator was evaluated at 6328 Å. The beams after passing up and down the KDP arms did not suffer any apparent deterioration. This was evidenced by an on–off ratio of 23 dB. The insertion loss when full on was 1.6 dB. The calculated dc half-wave voltage for the modulator was 75 volts, the measured voltage was 85 volts. Fig. 3 shows the output light intensity when a low-frequency sawtooth voltage was applied to the modulator. The curve has the expected cosine shape, as given by (1).

The stability of the modulator was checked by recording the output light intensity as a function of time. An output null of greater than 20 dB could be held for periods of about one hour without adjusting the modulator. During

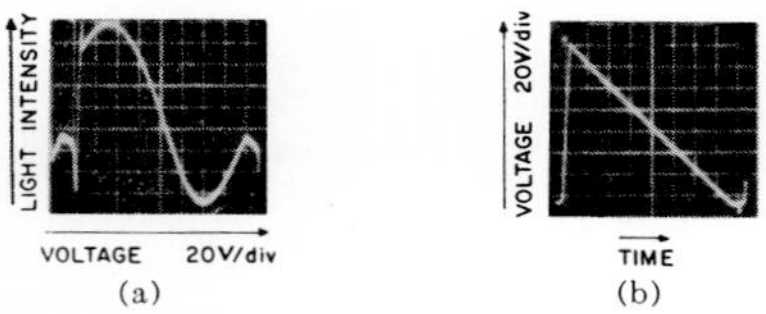

Fig. 3. Response of modulator to sawtooth voltage. (a) Light output of the modulator. (b) Applied sawtooth.

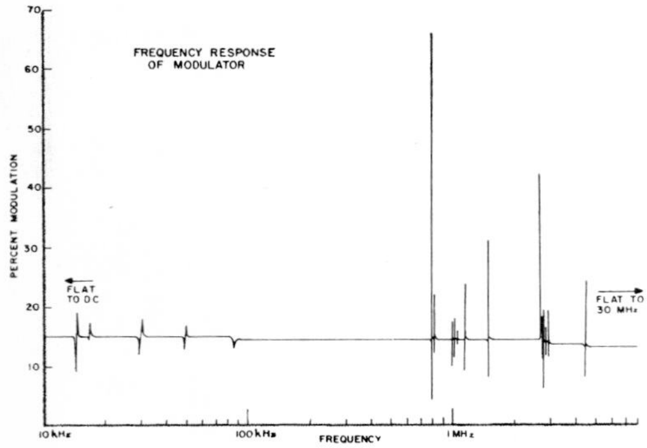

Fig. 4. Frequency response of the modulator.

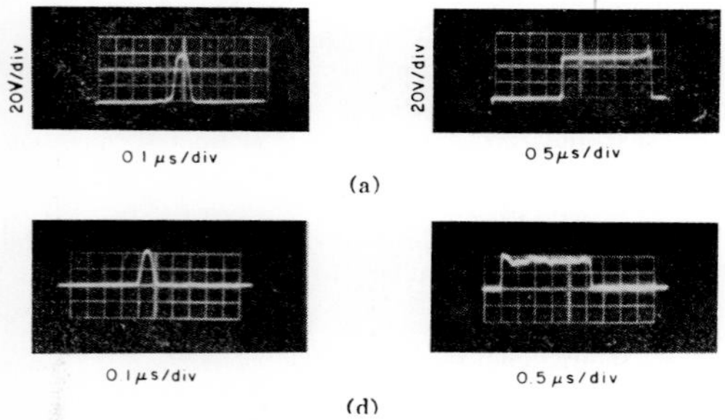

Fig. 5. Pulse response of the modulator. (a) Applied voltage pulse. (b) Light output from modulator.

these tests the modulator was covered with a plexiglass box to shield it from drafts and set in the open laboratory. No other temperature precautions were taken. It was uncertain how much of the observed drift was caused by movements of the incident light beam due to instabilities in the source laser.

The frequency response of the modulator is shown in Fig. 4. To obtain this data, the lengths of the modulator arms were adjusted for one-half maximum modulator output ($\Phi_0 = 90°$). A 9 volt peak-to-peak signal was applied directly to the two arms in parallel. The modulator was thus operated over the linear portion of the cosine curve. A 50 ohm resistor was connected in parallel to the two arms of the modulator and the 50 ohm signal generator connected to this combination. This baseband coupling should be effective up to about 50 MHz where the capacitance of the modulator (68 ρF) begins to cause a large mismatch.

The percent modulation in Fig. 4 is the ratio of the peak modulation voltage output to the dc voltage output measured by a square law detector. The acoustic resonances of the KDP are quite evident. The low-frequency resonances starting at about 12 kHz are probably due to acoustic waves traveling down the length of the crystals. The high-frequency resonances starting at about 800 kHz are probably due to waves traveling across the narrow crystal dimension perpendicular to the applied modulating field. The percent modulation at low frequencies is consistent with the dc half-wave voltage of the modulator. No transit-time effects are expected until about 75 MHz when the travel time of the light through the modulator becomes about 0.1 of the modulating frequency period.

The effect of the acoustic resonances can be seen in the pulse response of the modulator as shown in Fig. 5. When a 0.1 μs voltage pulse is applied, the output pulse is clean. When the longer 2.5 μs voltage pulse is applied, the top of the light pulse shows distortion. This distortion can be attributed to the high-frequency acoustic resonances.

It has been reported[9] that with suitable clamping the acoustic resonances in KDP can be effectively damped. No attempt was made in these experiments to clamp the KDP.

III. The Modulator Using $LiNbO_3$ or $LiTaO_3$

The push-pull modulator configuration is particularly suited for use with $LiTaO_3$ and $LiNbO_3$. This type of modulator using either of these materials would have a half-wave voltage proportional to $1/n_e^3 r_{33}$ as compared to $1/(n_e^3 r_{33} - n_o^3 r_{13})$ for an intensity modulator of the type described earlier by Denton *et al.*[4] In this case, n_0 and n_e are the ordinary and the extraordinary indices of refraction and r_{13} and r_{33} are electrooptic coefficients.

For example by using two crystals 0.25mm by 0.25mm by 1 cm, the half-wave voltage for either $LiNbO_3$ $LiTaO_3$ in the push-pull configuration would be about 13 volts. This compares to about 17 volts if these two crystals were combined into a two-pass amplitude modulator of the earlier type. The transit time of the light through the push-pull modulator would be one half that of type built by Denton *et al.*,[4] which would mean the push-pull modulator could be used up to twice the frequency before transit-time effects become important.

Acknowledgment

The advantages of the push-pull modulator were brought out in discussions with D. H. Ring, who also suggested the use of the Köster's prism. This work would not have been possible without his help. A. N. DeGano made some of the experimental measurements.

References

[1] N. V. Kravtsov and A. K. Shevchenko, "On the possibility of converting phase and frequency modulation of light into amplitude modulation," *Optics and Spectrosc.*, vol. 17, p. 74, July 1964.

[2] N. V. Kravtsov and L. Ye. Chirkov, "An optical modulator using Michelson's interferometer," *Radio Engrg. Electronic Phys.*, vol. 11, pp. 1319–1320, August 1966.

[3] D. L. Fried, W. S. Read, and D. B. Pollock, "An interferometric optical modulator," *Appl. Optics*, vol. 3, pp. 696–701, June 1964.

[4] R. T. Denton, T. S. Kinsel, and F. S. Chen, "224 Mc/s optical pulse code modulator," *Proc. IEEE (Letters)*, vol. 54, pp. 1472–1473, October 1966.

[5] C. J. Peters, "Gigacycle bandwidth coherent-light traveling-wave amplitude modulator," *Proc. IEEE*, vol. 53, pp. 455–460, May 1965.

[6] J. B. Saunders, "The Köster's double image prism," in *Concepts of Classical Optics*, J. Strong, Ed. San Francisco: W. H. Freeman, 1958, Appendix C; also, "The Köster's interferometer," *J. Research NBS*, vol. 58, p. 27, January 1957.

[7] C. J. Peters, "Gigacycle bandwidth coherent light traveling wave phase modulator," *Proc. IEEE*, vol. 51, pp. 147–153, January 1963.

[8] R. O'B. Carpenter, "The electro-optic effect in uniaxial crystals of the dihydrogen phosphate type-III measurement of coefficients," *J. Opt. Soc. Am.*, vol. 40, pp. 225–229, April 1950.

[9] E. A. Ohm, "An optical modulator with high FM sensitivity," *J. Opt. Soc. Am.*, vol. 56, p. 1443, October 1966.

Efficient Octave-Bandwidth Microwave Light Modulators

KUNGTA K. CHOW, MEMBER, IEEE, AND WILLIAM B. LEONARD

Abstract—The use of wide-bandwidth interdigital microwave circuits to provide electrooptic modulation of light is discussed. Two models employing lithium niobate crystals of different aspect ratios have been constructed and tested. Both have nominal bandwidth from 1.0 to 2.0 GHz but actually give somewhat greater modulation bandwidth. Single-pass modulation tests made using 6328-Å light at RF drive power level of 5 watts show that 30 percent modulation depth over a 1.5-GHz frequency band is obtained for one model while approximately 50 percent modulation depth over a 1.1-GHz band is obtained for the other. These results show excellent agreement with analytical predictions. Measurement techniques are also discussed.

I. Introduction

In recent years, broad-band light modulators [1]–[4] for use in optical communication systems have been receiving increasing attention. For air- and space-borne applications, a simple lightweight wide-band modulator is desired. In this paper, such modulators employing commercially available $LiNbO_3$ crystals are presented in detail. The use of these devices in a wide-bandwidth laboratory communication system is discussed elsewhere [5]. Two modulator models have been tested; preliminary performance data on the first model have been reported [6], [7]. Additional measurements on the first model and detailed measurements on the second model are reported here. About 50 percent intensity modulation over a 1.1-GHz (1.0–2.1) band has been obtained for the second model at 5-watt RF drive level. The 3-dB bandwidth extends over 1.2 GHz. These results agree well with our calculations.

The microwave circuit properties and theoretical modulation performance of this modulator are discussed briefly in Section II, followed by a presentation of measurement techniques in Section III and experimental results in Section IV. Conclusions are presented in Section V.

II. Modulator Circuit and Electrooptic Interaction

A particularly suitable microwave structure for wide-band modulation is the interdigital filter circuit, formed by interspersed resonant elements as shown in Fig. 1. The design of such circuits is well documented in published literature [8]. For this modulator, four foreshortened

Manuscript received May 18, 1970. This work was supported by the Lockheed Independent Research Fund.

The authors are with Lockheed Research Laboratory, Palo Alto, Calif.

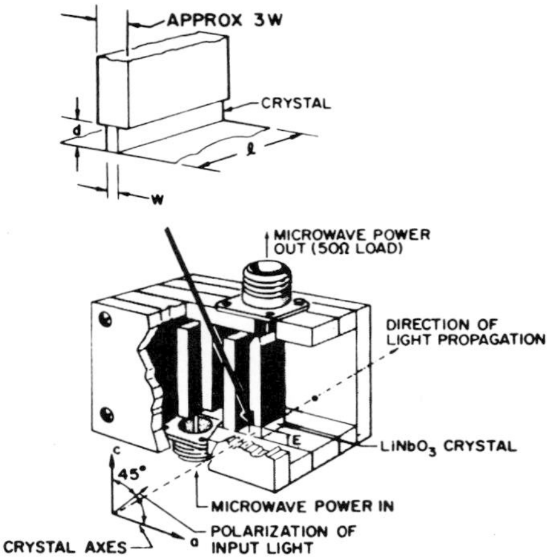

Fig. 1. Pictorial view of the modulator and the orientation of input light polarization with respect to the crystal axes.

digits are used to give a compact structure. Capacitive gaps between the digits and the end walls serve to resonate the inductive digits. In one of these gaps, a high-permittivity electrooptic crystal is accommodated. There is at present no exact method of calculating the frequency variation of the RF voltage in these gaps for this particular circuit, although from calculations on other types of coupled resonator filters [9], it is believed that the output gap will have the most uniform voltage over the entire passband at a given input power. The electrooptic crystal is placed at the output gap, with the crystal axes oriented as shown in Fig. 1 so that birefringence modulation can be effected. The detailed circuit dimensions are determined using a computer.

The light incident on the crystal is polarized at 45° to the crystal axes to give equal amplitude ordinary and extraordinary rays. An analyzer is crossed to the input polarization and quarter-wave optical bias is provided using an optical compensator. Under these conditions, the modulation index M is related to the peak phase retardation between the rays $\Delta\Gamma$ by

$$M = 2J_1(\Delta\Gamma) = 2J_1(kV_{RF}l/d) \approx kV_{RF}l/d \qquad \Delta\Gamma \leq 0.5, \qquad (1)$$

where

J_1 Bessel function of the first kind, first order,
k constant containing the appropriate optical coefficients, $(\pi/\lambda_o)(n_e^3 r_{33} - n_o^3 r_{13})$,
l/d crystal aspect ratio, shown in Fig. 1,
V_{RF} peak RF voltage across the crystal.

To determine the theoretical modulation index, an expression for the functional dependence of V_{RF} on the RF power P delivered to the modulator output circuit, the output circuit impedance Z_1, and the load impedance R_L must be obtained. An approximate equivalent circuit [10] for the output section of the modulator is shown in Fig. 2. At midband, the line length θ_1 is such that the impedance of the line (representing the last digit) resonates with the load capacitance C. Therefore, the input impedance of the line Z_{in} is zero and the RMS RF current i_o is related to P by

$$i_0 = (P/R_L)^{1/2}. \tag{2}$$

The peak RF voltage across the crystal is therefore given by

$$V_{RF} = \sqrt{2}\, i_0 Z_1 \sin\theta_1 = (2PZ_1^2/R_L)^{1/2} \sin\theta_1 \tag{3}$$

where $Z_1 \sin\theta_1$ is the line impedance at the crystal. Substituting (3) into (1),

$$M = 2J_1(\Delta\Gamma) = 2J_1[\sqrt{2}\, k(l/d)(Z_1^2/R_L)^{1/2}P^{1/2}\sin\theta_1]$$
$$\approx \sqrt{2}\, k(l/d)(Z_1^2/R_L)^{1/2}P^{1/2}\sin\theta_1. \tag{4}$$

Therefore, for efficient modulation, the product $(l/d) \cdot (Z^2/R_L)^{1/2} \sin\theta_1$ should be as high as possible.

Two models have been designed and fabricated. Model 1 uses a crystal of $l/d \approx 10$ (crystal size $0.5 \times 0.5 \times 5$ mm approximately) and operates at room temperature, whereas model 2 uses a crystal of $l/d \approx 23$ (crystal size $0.3 \times 0.3 \times 7$ mm approximately) and can be operated at temperatures up to 180°C. Practical considerations have so far limited the designed value for $(Z_1^2/R_L)^{1/2}$ to $\sqrt{50}$ and that for $\sin\theta_1$ to about 0.8. For operation at 6328 Å, the $\Delta\Gamma$ calculated for models 1 and 2, using the published electrooptic coefficients for lithium niobate [11] and the designed values for the circuit parameters are, respectively:

$$\Delta\Gamma_1 = 0.1\sqrt{P}$$
$$\Delta\Gamma_2 = 0.2\sqrt{P} \tag{5}$$

where P is in watts. The $\Delta\Gamma$ within the passband are assumed to be the same as given by (4) since V_{RF} is assumed to be uniform across the passband as discussed earlier.

Microwave performance of these models is as follows. The insertion loss for both is less than 0.5 dB; the input VSWR for model 1 is less than 1.25 for the entire 1–2 GHz passband, while for model 2 the same holds over most of the passband. Therefore, the input RF drive power is essentially equal to output circuit power P and is available to provide the modulating voltage V_{RF}.

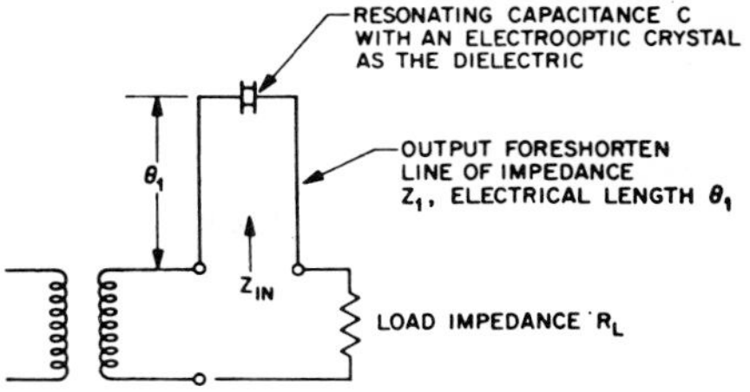

Fig. 2. An approximate equivalent circuit for the output section of the modulator.

III. Measurement Techniques

Three techniques were used to determine the modulation index.

Phase-Retardation Measurement: This was employed previously by other authors [12], [13]. In our particular arrangement [7], zero-degree optical bias was used so that for a given modulation power the reduction in light intensity gave a measure of the phase retardation between rays. The equivalent modulation index was calculated from this retardation angle.

Sideband Power Measurement: Because of modulation, optical sidebands are created; the amount of power in the sidebands gives a measure of the degree of modulation. Using an optical scanning interferometer, carrier and sideband powers can be independently measured to give another check of the modulation index as shown by the following calculation.

After modulation, the optical electric field E along the original direction of polarization is

$$E = \tfrac{1}{2} E_o \exp[j\omega_o t]\{\exp[-j(\Phi_o - x_o \sin\omega_M t)]$$
$$+ \exp[-j(\Phi_e - x_e \sin\omega_M t)]\} \tag{6}$$

where

E_o optical electric field at the input,
ω_o, ω_M optical and modulating angular frequencies, respectively,
Φ_o, Φ_e total dc phase delay for the ordinary and extraordinary rays, respectively,
x_o $(\pi/\lambda_o)(l/d)n_o^3 r_{13} V_{RF}$ = peak phase change of the ordinary ray due to modulation,
x_e $(\pi/\lambda_o)(l/d)n_e^3 r_{33} V_{RF}$ = peak phase change of the extraordinary ray due to modulation.

Carrying through the expansion for $\exp(jx \sin\omega_M t)$ and retaining first-order terms only, the normalized field is given by

$$2E/E_o = E_o + E_- + E_+, \tag{7}$$

where

$$E_o \text{ (carrier wave)} = [\exp(-j\Phi_o) + \exp(-j\Phi_e)] \cdot \exp(j\omega_o t)$$

$$E_- \text{ (lower sideband)} = -\tfrac{1}{2}[x_o \exp(-j\Phi_o) + x_e \exp(-j\Phi_e)] \cdot \exp[j(\omega_e - \omega_M)t]$$

$$E_+ \text{ (upper sideband)} = +\tfrac{1}{2}[x_o \exp(-j\Phi_o) + x_e \exp(-j\Phi_e)] \cdot \exp[j(\omega_e + \omega_M)t]. \quad (8)$$

Therefore, the ratio of the normalized upper (lower) sideband power P_+ to the optical carrier power P_c is

$$\frac{P_+}{P_c} = \frac{E_+E_+^*}{E_cE_c^*} = \frac{x_o^2 + x_e^2 + 2x_ox_e \cos(\Phi_o - \Phi_e)}{8[1 + \cos(\Phi_o - \Phi_e)]} \quad (9)$$

where x_o and x_e are related by

$$\frac{x_o}{x_e} = \left(\frac{n_o}{n_e}\right)^3 \frac{r_{13}}{r_{33}} = 0.314 \text{ for } LiNbO_3. \quad (10)$$

At quarter-wave bias, the light intensity after modulation is

$$I = EE^* = \tfrac{1}{2}E_c^2 + \tfrac{1}{2}E_c^2 \sin[(x_e - x_o)\sin\omega_M t]$$
$$\approx \tfrac{1}{2}E_c^2[1 + 2J_1(x_e - x_o)\sin\omega_M t]. \quad (11)$$

Therefore, the modulation index is

$$M = 2J_1(|x_e - x_o|) \approx |x_e - x_o|. \quad (12)$$

At zero bias, $\Phi_e - \Phi_o = 0$ and $x_o + x_e = 4(P_+/P_c)^{1/2}$, so that

$$M = 2J_1(2.08\sqrt{P_+/P_c}) \approx 2.08\sqrt{P_+/P_c}. \quad (13)$$

The approximation holds for $2.08\sqrt{P_+/P_c} \leqq 0.5$. At quarter-wave bias, $\Phi_o - \Phi_e = \pi/2$ and $x_o^2 + x_e^2 = 8(P_+/P_c)$, so that

$$M = 2J_1(1.852\sqrt{P_+/P_c}) \approx 1.852\sqrt{P_+/P_c}. \quad (14)$$

The approximation holds for $1.852\sqrt{P_+/P_c} \leqq 0.5$. Equations (13) and (14) show that for any RF drive level, by measuring the ratio of sideband to carrier power at various biases, the equivalent modulation index at this drive level may be computed. For this measurement to be accurate and meaningful, a stable single-mode laser was used in our experiments to ensure the correct reading of the sideband power.

Substitution Method: This method, in which a known signal was used to match the output of a photodiode, was also discussed previously [7]. Because of the falloff of the diode response with frequency, difficulties were encountered in determining the exact modulation index by this method [7]. An independent calibration procedure to determine the diode response has now been established as reported in the following.[1]

The interaction between an ultrasonic wave of frequency ω_s and an optical wave of frequency ω_e gives rise to two first-order Bragg-diffracted waves of equal amplitudes but of frequencies $(\omega_e + \omega_s)$ and $(\omega_e - \omega_s)$. When these two waves are mixed in a nonlinear device such as a photodiode, an output component having 100 percent modulation at $2\omega_s$ is obtained. Using the same substitution procedure, the apparent modulation index read by the photodiode for this 100 percent modulated light gives a calibration of the diode frequency response. For this calibration to be correct, care must be taken to ensure that 1) no unmodulated light appears at the diode to give higher dc readings, 2) the two wave amplitudes are equal so that 100 percent modulation is achieved, and 3) the two waves are approximately colinear so that there will be no spatial phase interference between the waves at the diode.

Carrying through these procedures, it was found that for a given silicon avalanche diode biased at low gains, the falloff characteristic was not critically dependent upon the bias voltage. However, the exact shape of the roll-off curve did vary from diode to diode.[2]

IV. Experimental Results

Model 1: All measurements on this model were made at room temperature using unfocused light (6328 Å). The amount of optical power passing through the crystal was between 50 and 100 μW.

Data obtained are presented in Fig. 3. Curve 1 was obtained by means of the retardation angle measurement on the first crystal that was also of the best optical quality. Over the band 0.8–2.3 GHz, about 30 percent modulation depth was obtainable at 5-watt RF drive power. Later crystals were strained as indicated by nonuniform extinction patterns. Typical performance at 5-watt drive was as shown in curve 2, which was obtained through sideband power measurements. For these measurements, both the 0 and $\pi/2$ bias were used [see (13) and (14)] and the equivalent modulation index M calculated from these data agreed remarkably well. Because of the free-spectral-range limitation of the scanning interferometer, no measurement at the band edges was made. Within the passband, M was uniform. Curve 3 was taken at 2-watt drive level in the same manner as curve 2, and was lower than curve 2 by approximately the square root of the power ratio. This ratio held true for power levels up to 10 watts as reported earlier. Theoretical modulation levels shown in this figure were calculated from (5).

Model 2: The thin crystals for this model showed more severe effects of strain than those for model 1. All measurements were made at temperatures of about 175°C to allow the use of a focused beam. Focusing was done by means of a 10-cm focal-length lens, giving a beam waist diameter approximately 4×10^{-3} cm at the center of the crystal. The optical power density at the waist was about 20 W/cm^2; no optical damage was observed.

Three crystals were used and a typical set of data for the best crystal is presented in Fig. 4. The data for curve 1 were obtained for 5-watt drive power using the substitution method, with the diode response corrected by

[1] We are indebted to Dr. H. V. Hance for originating this technique and designing the experimental apparatus.

[2] Between 6–9 dB/octave, falloff slopes have been measured in the 1–2 GHz band.

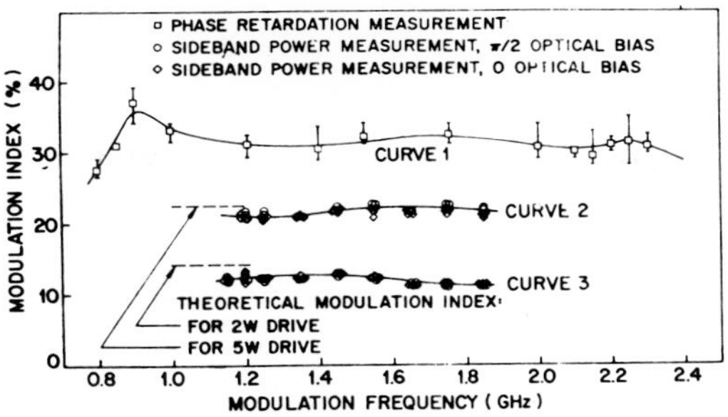

Fig. 3. Performance of modulator model 1 at various drive power levels. Curve 1—Good optical quality crystal, measured by the phase-retardation method at 5-watt RF drive. Curve 2—Poor optical quality crystal, measured by the sideband power method at 5-watt drive. Curve 3—Same as curve 2, except measured at 2-watt RF drive.

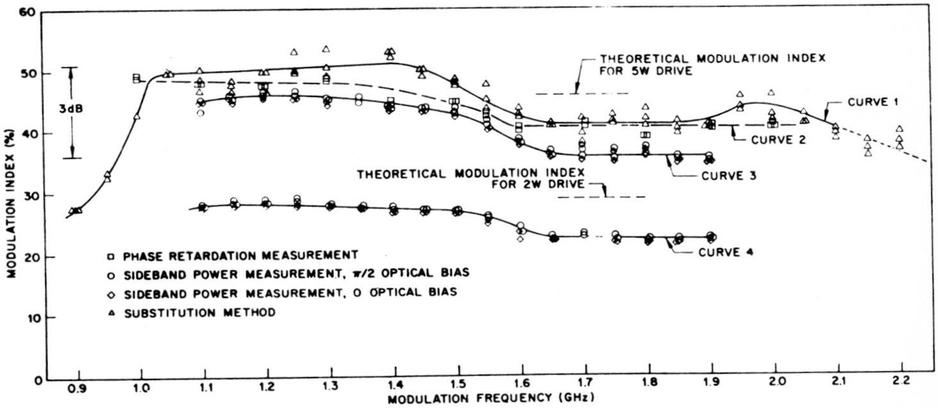

Fig. 4. Performance of modulator model 2 at various drive power levels. The optical quality of the crystal is inferior to that in model 1. Curve 1—Measured by the substitution method at 5-watt RF drive. Curve 2— Measured by the phase retardation method at 5-watt RF drive. Curve 3—Measured by the sideband power method at 5-watt RF drive. Curve 4—Measured by the sideband power method at 2-watt RF drive.

means of the calibration procedures described in Section III. Band-edge measurements were made to define the modulation bandwidth. The correction factors for 2.15 and 2.2 GHz, however, were estimated from the calibration curve. The slight scatter is due primarily to impedance mismatches and calibration errors. The data for curve 2 were derived from the retardation-angle measurements at 5-watt drive level. Those for curve 3 were from the sideband power measurements at a power level of 5 watts, while those for curve 4 were similarly obtained at a drive level of 2 watts. Both $\pi/2$ and 0 optical biases were used for these two power levels. The ratio of the modulation indices between curves 3 and 4 is again equal to the square root of the power ratios.

The variations between crystals are within a few percent, showing the uniformity of our crystal quality. Crystal strain appears to degrade modulation, as can be seen by comparing the later results with curve 1, Fig. 3.

V. Conclusions

Two models of an interdigital line modulator working in the 1.0–2.0 GHz band were tested. For the first model, 30 percent modulation depth over 1.5 GHz band was obtainable with 5 watts of RF drive power. In an effort to increase the modulation index, crystals of larger aspect ratio were used in the second model. This increased the modulation index but unintentionally reduced the bandwidth. More strains were also found in these crystals. In spite of these problems, about 50 percent modulation index was measured at 5-watt drive level over a 1.1-GHz band. The 3-dB bandwidth extended over 1.2 GHz. Optical power density of 20 W/cm^2 CW was used with these crystals at 175°C; no adverse effects were observed.

The results obtained using the three measurement techniques gave good agreement with one another, showing the reliability of these techniques. Out of the three measurement methods, the substitution method required the most attention both in measurement and calibration. However, with proper care, accurate results were obtainable. The other methods, though indirect, were simpler and gave consistent results. While no comparison to an exact theoretical index could be made due to the approximate nature of the equivalent circuit representation, the measured results showed excellent agreement with the approximate analysis.

VI. Acknowledgment

The authors wish to thank Dr. R. C. Ohlmann for helpful discussions, Dr. H. V. Hance for suggesting the diode calibration technique, and F. Zobel of Vector Industries for helpful discussions and detail design of the modulator circuit. The lithium niobate crystals were grown and fabricated by Crystal Technology, Inc.

References

[1] W.E. Bicknell, B. K. Yap, and C. J. Peters, "0 to 3 GHz traveling-wave electrooptic modulator," *Proc. IEEE* (Letters) vol. 55, pp. 225–226, February 1967.
[2] R. T. Denton, F. S. Chen, and A. A. Ballman, "Lithium tantalate light modulators," *J. Appl. Phys.*, vol. 38, pp. 1611–1617, March 1967.
[3] F. R. Nash and P. W. Smith, "Broadband optical coupling modulation," *IEEE J. Quantum Electron.*, vol. QE-4, pp. 26–34, January 1968.
[4] J. L. Putz, "A wide-band microwave light modulator," *IEEE Trans. Electron Devices*, vol. ED-15, pp. 695–698, October 1968.
[5] H. V. Hance, R. C. Ohlmann, D. G. Peterson, R. B. Ward, and K. K. Chow, "Ultra-wide bandwidth laser communication, II. An operating laboratory system," *Proc. IEEE*, vol. 58, pp. 1714–1719, October 1970.
[6] K. K. Chow, R. L. Comstock, and W. B. Leonard, "A 0.8 to 2.3 GHz bandwidth light modulator," presented at the IEEE Conf. on Laser Engineering and Applications, Washington, D. C., May 26–28, 1969.
[7] K. K. Chow, R. L. Comstock, and W. B. Leonard, "1.5-GHz bandwidth light modulator," *IEEE J. Quantum Electron.*, vol. QE-5, pp. 618–620, December 1969.
[8] G. L. Matthaei, L. Young, and E. M. T. Jones, *Microwave Filters, Impedance Matching Networks and Coupling Structures*. New York: McGraw-Hill, 1964.
[9] L. Young, "Peak internal fields in direct-coupled-cavity filters," *IRE Trans. Microwave Theory Tech.*, vol. MTT-8, pp. 612–616, November 1960.
[10] G. L. Matthaei, B. M. Schiffman, E. G. Christal, and L. A. Robinson, "Microwave filters and coupling structures," Final Rept., Contract DA 36-039 SC-87398, Stanford Res. Inst., Menlo Park, Calif., February 1963.
[11] E. G. Spencer, P. V. Lenzo, and A. A. Ballman, "Dielectric materials for electrooptic, elastooptic and ultrasonic device applications," *Proc. IEEE*, vol. 55, pp. 2074–2108, December 1967.
[12] I. P. Kaminow and W. M. Sharpless, "Performance of $LiTaO_3$ and $LiNbO_3$ light modulator at 4 GHz," *Appl. Opt.*, vol. 6, pp. 351–352, February 1967.
[13] H. G. Heard, *Laser Parameter Measurements Handbook*. New York: Wiley, 1968.

Reprinted from **APPLIED OPTICS**, Vol. 10, page 1016, May 1971

Fabrication of a Lithium Tantalate Temperature-Stabilized Optical Modulator

M. R. Biazzo

$LiTaO_3$ optical modulators have been developed using the technique of self-compensation for therma stability. By using two crystals in cascade, with optic axes 180° apart, and a half-wave plate between them with axis at 45°, the birefringence of each crystal is equal but opposite and there is no net change in birefringence with temperature. Aside from thermal stability, the optical modulator described damps out mechanical resonances caused by the piezoelectric properties of the crystals, and its thin-film substrate mounting is applicable to wideband modulation. Experimental measurements show that 95% modulation depth can be attained over a 25°C temperature range with virtually no change in the amplitude or phase of the modulated signal.

Introduction

The problem of achieving thermal stability in electrooptic crystals such as $LiTaO_3$ and KDP is well known.[1,2] All these crystals exhibit a natural birefringence that is extremely temperature-dependent. This thermal instability renders the modulated output useless if temperature is not controlled. Control provided with an oven is limited to the response time of the temperature sensor and is inherently slower than the self-compensating temperature-stabilizing technique used in this experiment. This technique was first used to achieve thermal stability in light modulators whose electrooptic material was KDP.[3] The aperture of the KDP crystals used in those experiments was one hundred times larger than the aperture of the $LiTaO_3$ crystals described in this paper.

Figure 1 shows the top view of the complete assembly. The two lithium tantalate crystals are clearly visible in the center of the two solder electrodes. The solder shown bonds the crystal electrodes to the thin-film electrodes of the Al_2O_3 substrate. The reverse side of the substrate shown in Fig. 1 has a metallized ground plane of evaporated gold. One electrode of the modulator makes contact to this ground plane by means of four copper straps that are fed through four 10-mil-diam holes drilled through the substrate. The other electrode has two thin-film 50-Ω microstrip transmission lines etched as an integral part of the electrode. The modulation source was applied between this input and the ground plane of the substrate. The other 50-Ω microstrip was used to supply a trigger for the oscilloscope. The typical dimensions of the crystals are 0.25 mm square by 9.5 mm long. The over-all performance of the modulator was dependent on firmly soldering two of these crystals down on a suitable substrate and inserting a half-wave retardation plate between them without producing any optical distortion as the laser beam passed through both of these long, thin crystals. This difficult problem was accomplished by using the laser beam as an alignment tool. For test purposes, the modulating frequency used for all temperature stability experiments was 60 Hz. However, the theory is applicable to all frequencies.

Light intensity modulators using electrooptic crystals such as lithium tantalate are essentially electrooptic switches. The switching occurs by a change in the index of refraction of the crystal produced by the voltage applied to the electrodes of the crystal. When used in this manner, the crystals exhibit a natural birefringence which is extremely temperature-dependent. In addition, there may be temperature variations along the electrodes of the crystals due to power dissipation. Because of their intimate bonding to both electrodes of both crystals, the heat sinks described in this paper are very effective for eliminating temperature gradients within the crystals. Furthermore, the lead solder heat sinks have an absorbent quality that helps suppress the extraneous light modulation caused by the piezoelectric properties of the optical modulator crystals.[4] By firmly holding the crystals on two sides, the solder heat sinks effectively damp out the mechanical resonances produced by an electrical signal applied to the modulator crystals.

The author is with Bell Telephone Laboratories, Inc., Holmdel, New Jersey 07733.
Received 8 September 1970.

Fig. 1. Complete assembly of lithium tantalate thermal compensating optical modulator.

The thin-film pattern of the electrode areas on the substrate easily lends itself to wideband optical modulation, depending upon the type of driving circuits employed.[5,6]

Crystal Orientation

Self-compensating thermal stability with two $LiTaO_3$ crystals depends upon crystal orientation. For light intensity modulators the optic axis of one crystal is placed orthogonal to the other. By using two crystals in cascade whose axes are 90° apart as shown in Fig. 2(A), the dependence of their birefringence on temperature is eliminated. Observe the electrodes designated by the shaded areas in Fig. 2(A). With the orientation shown, the electrodes are disposed at 90° to one another, which makes it difficult to solder both crystals firmly onto the plane surface of a single substrate. All four electrodes of the crystals must be securely bonded to the substrate in order to provide a uniform pair of heat sinks with effective acoustical damping. In order to make this soldering possible, crystal 2 in Fig. 2(A) was rotated an additional 90° so that the optic axes of each crystal were 180° apart. As shown in Fig. 2(B), the electrodes of each crystal were then on the same plane, and this condition allows all four electrodes to be

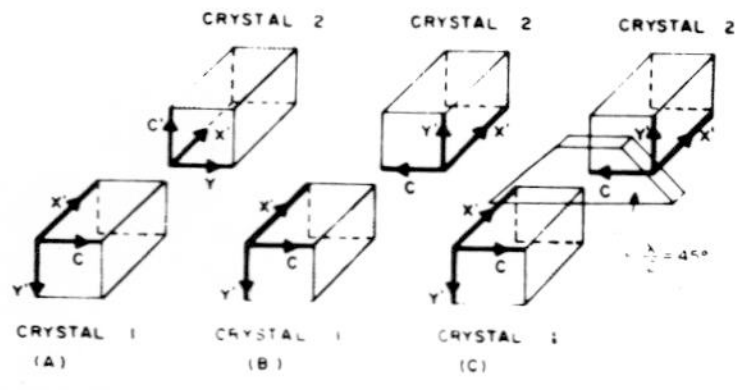

Fig. 2. Lithium tantalate modulator crystal orientation.

soldered to the electrode area of the substrate. With the optic axis of the crystals 180° apart, when modulated from a common source, the modulation of crystal 1 is canceled out by the equal but opposite modulation of crystal 2. In order to complete the modulator assembly so that the temperature effects canceled while the modulation of each crystal became additive, it was only necessary to include a half-wave retardation plate between the two crystal rods [Fig. 2(C)]. The axis of the half-wave plate was oriented at 45° to the C axis of crystal 1. The half-wave plate thus effectively rotates the beam by 90°, orienting the polarization of the beam so that it was 90° to the C axis of crystal 2. With this orientation, the temperature-dependent birefringence also cancels and the half-wave voltage of two crystals in cascade is reduced by a factor of 2 in comparison with the half-wave voltage of either single crystals.

Substrate

Both glass and ceramic (Al_2O_3) substrates were used in this experiment. Both materials are suitable for thin-film applications. Ceramic substrates are preferred because their thermal conductivity is much better. The substrate need only be large enough to accommodate the length necessary for the complete assembly and the associated electrode area. The electrode area of the substrate consisted of a single pair of electrodes, the length of which extended the length of the electrodes of both crystals as shown in Fig. 3. The space between the crystals was slightly more than 1 mm for insertion of the half-wave plate. The substrates available had a surface of gold over tantalum nitride. To facilitate soldering to the substrate, a layer of palladium was evaporated over the gold. The palladium-coated substrate was photoetched to provide electrodes 3 mm wide spaced 0.25 mm apart. The $LiTaO_3$ crystals were also 0.25 mm wide, so they spanned the electrode spacing perfectly.

Lithium Tantalate Fabrication

It is clear that if one $LiTaO_3$ crystal is to compensate the temperature characteristics of the other crystal, then the two crystals must exhibit similar characteristics. This similarity was arrived at by fabricating the crystal modulator rods simultaneously from a homogeneous single crystal. Two rods with similar characteristics were easily fabricated from this material.

For the experiments described here, the original crystal was 5 mm square by 9.5 mm long. The 5-mm-square faces were polished to a regularity of $\lambda/10$ or better. The parallelism of these faces was within 5 sec of arc. The best crystal was supplied by the Isomet Corporation, properly poled and annealed with the axis oriented as shown in Fig. 2. Because the parallelism of the two polished surfaces was so important to this experiment, it was measured with an autocollimator and verified to be within 5 sec of arc. When a batch of ten or twelve crystal rods with these specifications were processed at one time, all the rods exhibited the same characteristics. A durable antireflection coating may be applied to the entrance and exit faces of the original crystal before cutting begins. This coating was not readily available at the time of this experiment, so it was not applied.

A slab was cut from the original crystal and this slab was lapped to a thickness of 0.25 mm. Electrodes were evaporated on the two surfaces of the slab perpendicular to the optic axis. One electrode was chromium, gold, and copper, and the other was the same except that palladium was substituted for the copper. With different-color materials on opposite electrodes, the axis orientation of each complete rod was readily apparent. The finished rods are delicate, and this feature eliminated unnecessary handling. The slab was then cut into rods 0.25 mm wide with a wire saw 0.01 cm in diameter. With micrometer positioning, almost every rod can be cut uniformly without further lapping. Any two rods with equal dimensions were suitable for this modulator. If precise cutting of each rod cannot be assured, the group of rods may be lapped simultaneously as a batch to assure uniform rod-to-rod dimension.

Modulator Assembly Procedure

The problem of alignment of two long, thin $LiTaO_3$ crystals was solved by using a jig so designed that the two crystals were physically referenced along the 0.25-mm space between the two electrodes of the thin-film substrate. The jig consisted of a brass hot plate mounted on a gimbal mount with individual heaters under each rod. A dial thermometer was inserted into a hole in the hot plate to monitor temperature. A straight-edge reference surface was provided against which the two rods could be aligned. A pair of stainless steel springs were included to hold the two crystals in position against the reference surface [Fig. 4(A)]. A microscope was used to facilitate this alignment. When properly aligned, the uncoated length of each crystal spanned the space between the thin-film electrodes of the substrate. The axes of the two crystals were 180° apart. This was easily verified because the copper electrode of one crystal was adjacent to the palladium electrode of the second crystal and each electrode is distinctly different in color.

With the two crystals so aligned, a well-attenuated 6328-Å laser beam, focused with a 25-cm lens, was passed through the crystals and onto a suitable target area. The exit beam was easily observed for possible beam distortion. An undistorted beam shape exhibits a well-defined round spot with no distortion due to the light striking the walls of the modulator rods. If the crystal faces are parallel, the laser beam will pass through both lithium tantalate crystals undistorted. If the output beam showed spot shape distortion, the gimbal alignment with the beam was adjusted or the crystals were viewed through the microscope to be certain that their position had not shifted from the reference surface. Any shift was easily corrected by pushing the crystals firmly against the reference plate to produce an undistorted beam spot on the target [Fig. 4(B)].

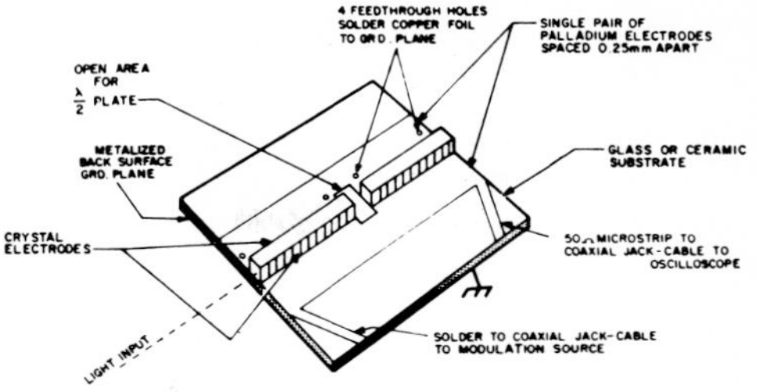

Fig. 3. Two lithium tantalate crystals positioned on substrate.

Soldering the $LiTaO_3$ Crystals

With the crystals properly aligned in the laser beam, the straight-edge reference plate was removed. The two rods were still firmly positioned by the springs, and the undistorted beam could be monitored on the target. The heaters were turned on and the temperature was allowed to rise to approximately 110°C, slightly higher than the 95° melting point of the solder. Solder was applied to the two electrodes of one crystal and then to the two electrodes of the other crystal. The flowing solder was observed through the microscope to be certain that all the electrodes were fully covered. This is an important feature. The solder-covered electrodes serve several purposes. Aside from their purpose as signal electrodes, these relatively large solder masses function as dampers for the mechanical resonances of the $LiTaO_3$ and as uniform heat sinks to prevent temperature gradients along the length of each crystal. When both crystals were completely soldered, the heaters were turned off and the assembly was allowed to cool to room temperature. The substrate was then cleaned in an ultrasonic bath with a detergent solution and rinsed with distilled water. The clean modulator assembly was reinserted in the beam to be certain that the laser beam still passed through both crystal rods undistorted. With the two rods securely soldered to the substrate, all that was needed to complete the ther-

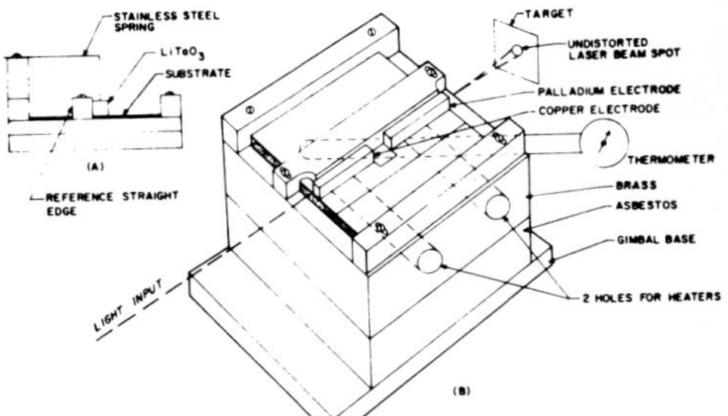

Fig. 4. Optical modulator assembly jig.

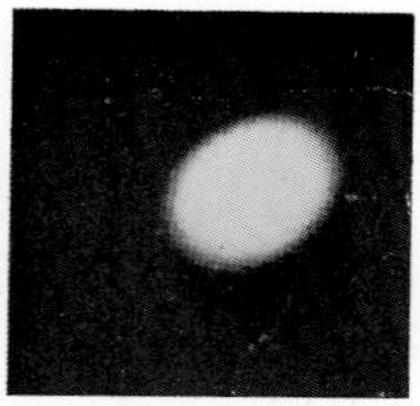

Fig. 5. The well-defined laser beam spot above shows the exit beam as it appears on the target after passing through two lithium tantalate rods 0.25 mm square by 9.5 mm long and a half-wave plate. The spot shows no trace of distortion due to the light striking the walls of the modulator rods. The spot shape is round. The apparent ellipticity was caused by the camera angle necessary to take the photograph.

mally stable modulator was a half-wave retardation plate cemented in the open space between the two rods.

Half-Wave Retardation Plate

Fabrication of a miniature half-wave retardation plate oriented at 45° was accomplished by cutting a larger square quartz retardation plate (supplied by Industrial Optics) at 45° to its axis. The extreme corners were initially cut away to avoid questionable surfaces. Then a trapezoidal-shaped half-wave retardation plate whose axis was oriented at 45° to its base was cut from each corner. The resulting plates were of good quality and properly oriented. The half-wave retardation plate was then antireflection-coated for 6328 Å and cemented in the space provided between the modulator crystals. A spot of lens cement was applied to each end of the base. With the modulator crystals aligned in the laser beam, the plate was maneuvered with a pair of tweezers until the laser beam on the target showed no distortion after passing through all three components of the modulator. The modulator assembly was left in the beam, allowing the lens cement to cure for approximately 15 min. The optical alignment was constantly monitored on the target to be certain that no beam distortion resulted due to component shift during the curing interval. Figure 5 shows a typical undistorted laser beam spot on the target after having passed through all three optical components of the optical modulator. With no distortion apparent in the optical beam, the thermally stabilized optical modulator was complete.

Thermal Testing of Individual Modulator Rods

A batch of ten modulator rods all cut from the same crystal was tested for thermal characteristics with respect to birefringence. Each rod was mounted on a substrate and placed in an oven. The oven was fitted directly to a gimbal mount with the modulator rod at its center so the modulator rod could be aligned with the laser beam while in the oven. The usual optical components for producing light intensity modulation were included as end plates for the oven. The laser beam entered the oven through a quarter-wave retardation plate oriented at 45° to the crystal axis, and the exit beam passed through the analyzer, also set at 45°, when leaving the oven. There were no laser beam entrance or exit holes in the oven, so air currents could not pass through the oven to influence the controlled temperature within it. The oven temperature was controlled with a proportional temperature controller. The temperature at the rod was measured with iron–constantan thermocouples soldered directly into each heat sink. The output of each thermocouple was monitored by a Model 150A Keithley Instruments microvoltmeter. The temperature at the crystal was allowed to stabilize at 37°C. Then the temperature in the oven was increased fractions of a degree until the modulated output of the crystal changed in phase by 180° as viewed on

(A)

(B)

(C)

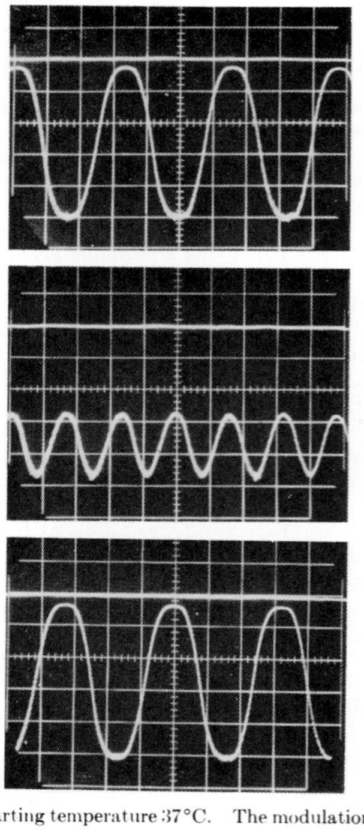

Fig. 6. (A) Starting temperature 37°C. The modulation output shows the vertical center line of the oscilloscope passing through the negative peak of the 60-Hz modulation. The straight sweep line in each photograph indicates zero dc bias. (B) Temperature increased to 37.5°C. The temperature increase of 0.5°C results in a phase shift of 90°. 60-Hz modulation has doubled in frequency to 120 Hz. (C) Temperature increased to 38°C. Another 0.5°C increase in temperature produces another 90° phase shift in the modulation. (A) and (C) are now 180° out of phase for a total temperature change of 1°C.

the oscilloscope. The same test was made at a starting temperature of 27°C. In all tests, temperatures at each thermocouple were equal. The 60-Hz modulated output from the crystals showed that for this size rod, the change in phase was 180° for a total change in temperature of 1°C. Figure 6 shows in three steps the output of this phase shift due to temperature. Figure 6(A) shows the stabilized phase of the modulated output at 37°C. Figure 6(B) shows a 90° phase change at 37.5°C. Figure 6(C) shows a total 180° phase shift at 38°C. All the rods tested showed the same results for a 1°C change in temperature. Increasing the temperature by an additional 1°C caused the phase to change another 180°, for a total phase shift of 360°. Reducing the temperature by 1°C reversed the phase shift by 180°, and a further reduction in temperature to 37°C returned the modulation phase to the original state shown in Fig. 6(A). The proportional temperature controller used for this test was the YSI Model 72 manufactured by the Yellow Springs Instrument Company. When used with a Model 421 temperature probe, this instrument is capable of maintaining temperature stability to 0.01°C for the long term and ±0.005°C for the short term. All the temperature tests were reproducible, and the results were always the same for each modulator rod fabricated from the crystal. Clearly, any two modulator rods whose birefringences are unequal cannot be used in the assembly of a thermally stabilized optical modulator, and the temperature tests described assure the selection of matched pairs of rods. In addition, the half-wave voltage of each rod was measured at this time and recorded at 80 V peak to peak for all rods.

Alignment Test

The completed three-component optical modulator assembly was placed in the previously described temperature-controlled oven and aligned in the laser beam with the ambient temperature at 25°C. The alignment for maximum modulation was easily adjusted because the oven was an integral part of the gimbal mount, with the optical modulator at the center. In addition to the horizontal and vertical tilt, the entire gimbal mount was attached to three mechanical stages that allow X, Y, Z positioning. The first necessary test is to measure the half-wave voltage. The half-wave voltage should be reduced by a factor of 2 to 40 V peak to peak. Figure 7(A) is a photograph of the half-wave voltage for a single rod. The voltage is shown along the horizontal scale as 16 V/div for five div totaling 80 V peak to peak. Figure 7(C) is a photograph of the half-wave voltage of the completed modulator with two rods in series. With the same voltage sensitivity on the horizontal scale, the half-wave voltage was reduced by a factor of 2 to 2.5 div or 40 V peak to peak. This test is positive proof that the optical modulator was properly aligned to allow the laser beam to pass through both modulator rods while both rods were modulated at 60 Hz. The laser beam was chopped for these tests so that the straight sweep line on the photographs indicates zero dc bias, or no light. Maximum modulation is in the negative direction in all photographs.

Results

With the completed optical modulator properly aligned with the laser beam and 60-Hz modulation maximized at 40 V peak to peak the temperature in the oven was increased by 2°C to 27°C and allowed to stabilize. During this rise in temperature there was no change in modulated output either in phase shift or amplitude. The temperature in the oven was continually increased in steps of 5°C with no change visible on the modulated output as viewed on the oscilloscope. The temperature limit of the oven was reached at 50°C.

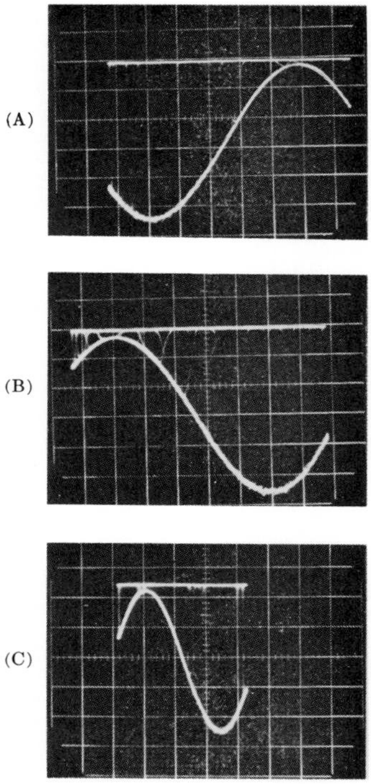

Fig. 7. (A) This photograph shows the half-wave voltage of a single lithium tantalate modulator rod. The voltage is along the horizontal scale, whose sensitivity is 16 V cm^{-1}. The total half-wave voltage is shown as 5 cm, or 80 V peak to peak. (B) Photograph of the modulated output after passing through the same rod and then the half-wave retardation plate oriented at 45°. The half-wave voltage is still 80 V peak to peak, but its phase has shifted 180° due to the half-wave plate. (C) In this photograph the light has passed through all three components of the modulator. After passing through the half-wave plate, the light passes through the second modulator rod, so the half-wave voltage has been reduced to 2.5 cm or 40 V peak to peak.

This constituted a 25° change in temperature with no visible change in the output. The temperature was subsequently reduced until the oven temperature was again the ambient temperature of 25°C. There was no evidence of any change in the modulated output as the temperature of the lithium tantalate was increased or decreased. Additional measurements made on this modulator showed that the optical loss through the modulator was 3 dB. This could be improved by antireflection coating the faces of the rods. The extinction ratio was better than 20 dB. The electrical capacity of this assembly measured 12 pF. This capacitance is not significanct for a traveling-wave-type optical modulator.[5]

Conclusion

It was shown in Fig. 6 that for the particular lithium tantalate optical modulator rods used in this experiment, the phase-angle shift of the modulated output was 180° for each 1°C change in modulator temperature. With the thermally stabilized optical modulator described in this paper there was no change in the modulated output for a total temperature change of 25°C. The optical modulator described here eliminates the need for a temperature-controlled oven by eliminating the effects of the change in birefringence with temperature. Additionally, optical modulation at gigahertz repetition rates with random patterns of pulses and spaces may induce instantaneous temperature changes within the optical modulator. For these reasons, a thermally stable optical modulator is very attractive.

The half-wave voltage for the two lithium tantalate rods described here is 40 V peak to peak. A few simple calculations indicate that by using two rods, each 0.25 mm square by 12.0 mm long, the half-wave voltage can be reduced to less than 30 V peak to peak, while the optical path length through the modulator is still maintained at less than 25 mm—a very reasonable length.

W. C. G. Ortel first suggested this thermally stable optical modulator and made significant contributions toward its completion. Fruitful discussions were held with B. G. King and P. Runge. The author wishes to thank H. T. Webber, who cut all the lithium tantalate rods used in this experiment.

References

1. R. T. Denton, F. S. Chen, and A. A. Ballman, J. Appl. Phys. **38**, 1611 (1967).
2. E. G. Spencer, P. V. Lenzo, and A. A. Ballman, Proc. IEEE **55**, 2074 (1967).
3. C. J. Peters, Proc. IEEE **53**, 455 (1965).
4. R. P. Reisz and M. R. Biazzo, Appl. Opt. **8**, 1393 (1969).
5. G. White, "Optical Modulation at Gigahertz Rates," presented at the IEEE International Conference on Communications, San Francisco, 8–10 June 1970 (Digest of Technical Papers, Session 22).
6. G. White, Proc. IEEE (Lett.) **58**, 1779 (1970).

A COMPARISON OF ACOUSTOOPTIC AND ELECTROOPTIC MODULATORS AT 10.6 MICRONS

D. M. HENDERSON and R. L. ABRAMS
Bell Telephone Laboratories, Incorporated, Whippany, New Jersey 07981, *USA*

Received 1 September 1970

Comparisons are made between acoustooptic and electrooptic modulators at 10.6 μ for AM and FM systems with emphasis on drive power requirements. The results show that the acoustooptic device is preferred for amplitude modulation and large index phase modulation while the electrooptic device is better for low index phase modulation.

1. INTRODUCTION

The lack of efficient modulation techniques for the CO_2 laser has limited its usefulness in communications and other applications. Until recently, the most efficient practical modulator for 10.6 μ was the GaAs electrooptic modulator [1]. Now the CdTe electrooptic modulator [2] and the Ge acoustooptic modulator [3] are known to be more efficient. In this correspondence comparisons are made between acoustooptic and electrooptic modulators for both amplitude and phase modulation systems with special emphasis on the drive power requirements as a function of modulation index and bandwidth. These results are expressed in terms of commonly used figures of merit for electrooptic and acoustooptic materials. The relative drive powers for both types of modulators using the above mentioned materials are discussed.

2. ACOUSTOOPTIC MODULATORS

We consider the scattering of a gaussian optical beam by a rectangular acoustic beam in the Bragg scattering limit. The diffraction angle of the optical beam is given by $\delta\phi = \lambda_0/\pi n w_0$ where λ_0 is the free space wave length, n is the refractive index of the modulator and w_0 is the $1/e$ amplitude radius at the beam waist. For the acoustic beam, the diffraction angle is given by $\delta\theta = \Lambda/2L$ where Λ is the acoustic wave length and L is the width of the acoustic beam. With $\delta\theta \gtrsim \delta\phi$, Gordon [4] has shown that the fraction of the incident light intensity scattered is $\sin^2\eta^{1/2}$ where

$$\eta = \frac{\pi^2}{2}\left(\frac{n^6 p^2}{\rho V^3}\right)\left(\lambda_0^2 H \cos^2\theta_0\right)^{-1} L P_a \,. \qquad (1)$$

In this expression, p is the relevant photoelastic component, ρ is the modulator material density, V is the acoustic velocity, H is the acoustic beam height, P_a is the acoustic power and θ_0 is the Bragg angle.

The scattered light is shifted up (or down) in frequency by the acoustic frequency. Thus the electric field of the scattered light E_{sc} is given in terms of the incident electric field E_0 by

$$E_{sc} = E_0 \sin\eta^{1/2} \exp i[(\omega_0 + \omega_a)t - \phi_a] \,. \qquad (2)$$

where $\omega_0/2\pi$ is the optical frequency and $\omega_a/2\pi = f_a$ is the acoustic frequency. We have included the acoustic phase ϕ_a for future reference.

For a pulse modulator, Maydan [5] has shown that the scattering efficiency bandwidth product is maximum for $\delta\phi/\delta\theta = 1.5$. For such a modulator, the rise time (10% to 90%) is $\tau = 1.7\, w_0/V$. The optimum efficiency results for the lowest value of f_a. The condition $f_a \geqslant 2/\tau$ is required to resolve the deflected beam from the undeflected beam [5]. If we take this value for f_a, and equate the modulation bandwidth Δf with $1/2\tau$, then $f_a \approx 4\Delta f$. By introducing a design safety factor S, such that $H = 2Sw_0$, and employing the above relations, eq. (1) can be written

$$\eta = \frac{3\pi^3}{64}\,\frac{M_3 P_a}{\lambda_0^3 \cos^2\theta_0 S\Delta f}, \qquad (3)$$

where $M_3 = (n^7 p^2/\rho V^2)$ is a figure of merit of the material [6].

The electrical drive power P_{AO} is determined by the coupling efficiency α_T of the transducer driving the acoustic waves. From eq. (3), we obtain

$$P_{AO} = \frac{P_a}{\alpha_T} = \frac{64}{3\pi^3} \frac{\lambda_0^3 \cos^2\theta_0 S\eta\Delta f}{\alpha_T M_3} . \qquad (4)$$

For future reference, we note that this result is for an acoustic wave of constant amplitude. When the acoustic wave is amplitude modulated, the time average power must be used.

The best material available for 10.6 μ acoustooptic modulation has recently been shown to be crystalline germanium [3] *. The numerical value of M_3 for germanium at 10.6 μ is $M_3 = 1.8 \times 10^{-8}$ (meter^3/joule) where the optical polarization and the acoustic $\boldsymbol{k}$ vector are directed along the [111] direction. With $LiNbO_3$ transducers, a 3 dB coupling loss over the required bandwidth is achievable at acoustic frequencies up to 500 MHz.

3. ELECTROOPTIC MODULATORS

At 10.6 μ the electrooptic crystals commonly used (GaAs and CdTe) possess $\bar{4}3$ m symmetry. Amplitude modulation is possible because of the induced birefringence in these normally isotropic crystals. For linearly polarized light incident on the crystal, the transmitted light is elliptically polarized. In amplitude modulation, the component of the light parallel to the initial polarization is suppressed with a polarizer. The perpendicular component $E_\perp$ which is transmitted by the polarizer is given by

$$E_\perp = E_0 \sin(\Gamma/2) \exp i(\omega_0 t - 2\pi n_0 L/\lambda_0 - \Gamma/2) , \quad (5)$$

where $\Gamma/2 = \pi L \Delta n/\lambda_0$. Here L is the length of the crystal, Δn is the change in the refractive index due to the applied electric field, and n_0 is the refractive index of the isotropic material. Maximum birefringence is obtained when the electric field is perpendicular to a cube axis of the $\bar{4}3$ m crystal. The resulting phase retardation is [7]

$$\frac{\Gamma}{2} = \pi \frac{n_0^3 r_{41}}{\lambda_0} \frac{L}{d} V . \qquad (6)$$

* Tellurium has not been considered because of its large absorption at 10.6 μ and difficulty in polishing.

Here r_{41} is the linear electrooptic coefficient of the crystal. We have taken the applied field to be V/d where V is the voltage applied across a crystal of thickness d.

When the crystal is oriented for phase modulation, the optical electric field is given by

$$E = E_0 \exp i(\omega_0 t - 2\pi n_0 L/\lambda_0 - \Delta\phi) , \qquad (7)$$

where $\Delta\phi = 2\pi L \Delta n/\lambda_0$. The most efficient phase modulation is obtained when the applied field is parallel to the optical polarization and directed along a [111] crystal axis. In this case [7]

$$\Delta\phi = \frac{2\pi}{\sqrt{3}} \frac{n_0^3 r_{41}}{\lambda_0} \frac{L}{d} V . \qquad (8)$$

Kaminow and Turner have computed the power required to drive the electrooptic modulator by treating the modulator as a lumped circuit element in a tuned RCL circuit. The drive power P_{EO} is given for amplitude modulation by

$$P_{EO} = \frac{\epsilon_0}{8\pi} \lambda_0^2 \frac{\epsilon}{n_0^6 r_{41}^2} \frac{d^2}{L} \Gamma_p^2 \Delta f , \qquad (9)$$

where Γ_p is the peak phase retardation obtained from eq. (6) for a sinusoidal applied voltage. The relative dielectric constant at the crystal is ϵ. For a gaussian focused beam, the minimum value of d^2/L is given by [7] $S^2 4\lambda_0/n_0\pi$ where $d = 2^{3/2} S w_0$. In practice, little loss is encountered but alignment is difficult with $S = 3$ and alignment is easy with $S = 6$. Combining eq. (9) with this expression yields

$$P_{EO} = \frac{1}{2} \frac{\epsilon_0}{F_1} \lambda_0^3 \left(\frac{\Gamma_p}{\pi}\right)^2 S^2 \Delta f . \qquad (10)$$

The drive power for phase modulation can be simply obtained from eq. (10) by replacing Γ_p^2 by $3(\Delta\phi_p)^2$ where $\Delta\phi_p$ is the peak phase change. The crystal parameters have been incorporated in the figure of merit $F_1 = n_0^7 r_{41}^2/\epsilon$. For GaAs, the numerical value at 10.6 μ is $F_1/\epsilon_0 = 1 \times 10^{-10}$ (meter^3/joule) **.

** Note that the definition of F_1 given here differs from that in ref. [1] by a factor of 4. The present definition is chosen so that a single figure of merit can be used in both amplitude and phase modulation.

4. COMPARISON OF MODULATORS

4.1. *Amplitude modulation*

The amplitude modulated optical electric field for both types can be written in the form

$$E(t) = E_0 \sin\theta \exp i\omega t \ . \tag{11}$$

For the electrooptic device, $\theta = \Gamma/2$ and $\omega = \omega_0$ while for the acoustooptic device, $\theta = \eta^{1/2}$ and $\omega = \omega_0 + \omega_a$. Eq. (11) describes suppressed carrier modulation when $\theta(t)$ is sinusoidally modulated.

As the electrooptic drive power has been computed for a sinusoidal applied electric field, we compute the acoustooptic drive power under the same condition. Thus, the time average power $\langle P_{AO}\rangle$ is used in the following comparison where $\langle P_{AO}\rangle = P_{AO}/2$. For $\eta^{1/2} = \Gamma_p/2$, the amplitude modulated electric field is seen to be the same for both modulators. From eqs. (4) and (10), the ratio of the drive powers for equal bandwidths is found to be ($\cos^2\theta_0 \approx 1$)

$$\frac{P_{EO}}{\langle P_{AO}\rangle} \equiv R_{AM} = \frac{3\pi}{16} S\alpha_T \frac{\epsilon_0}{F_1} M_3 \ . \tag{12}$$

As a numerical example, let $\alpha_T = \frac{1}{2}$ and $S = 5$. For these values a GaAs electrooptic device requires 265 times more power than a Ge acoustooptic device (CdTe is about 4 times better than GaAs [2]).

In work involving low level electrooptic modulation ($\Gamma_p \ll 1$), it is common practice to optically bias the detector by placing a quarter wave plate between the modulator and polarizer [2,7]. This biasing permits a constant amplitude signal at the carrier frequency to be transmitted with the amplitude modulated portion described by eq. (11). An improved detector response results from this homodyne detection system. With the acoustooptic device, in principle, a signal at the carrier frequency can be transmitted to provide the same biasing with no increase in the modulator drive power. When optical heterodyne detection is employed, as in a 10.6 μ communications link, optical biasing offers no improvement because the local oscillator signal will be much larger than the bias signal.

4.2. *Phase modulation*

For acoustooptic phase modulation, the amplitude of the transmitted signal is proportional to the drive power while the optical phase follows the acoustic phase and is independent of the drive power. In electrooptic modulation, the situation is reversed. As a result of this difference, the comparison of the drive powers must include the magnitude of the phase shift.

If we take the incident electric field E_0 to be the same for each modulator and take equal phase shifts ($\Delta\phi_p = \phi_a$), then comparing eqs. (2) and (7) reveals that η must equal $\pi^2/4$ for the modulated signals to be identical. Thus the power ratio for phase modulation becomes

$$\frac{P_{EO}}{P_{AO}} \equiv R_{PM} \left(\frac{\Delta\phi_p}{\pi}\right)^2 = \frac{9\pi}{32} S\alpha_T \frac{\epsilon_0}{F_1} M_3 \left(\frac{\Delta\phi_p}{\pi}\right)^2 . \tag{13}$$

For large index phase modulation, $\Delta\phi_p \gtrsim 1$, acoustooptic modulators again offers a significant reduction in drive power. If we take $\Delta\phi_p = \pi/2$ as an example, then the GaAs electrooptic device would require ≈ 100 times the power of the Ge acoustooptic device for the design parameters of the previous section. Phase shifts of this magnitude would be encountered in pulse code modulation with phase shift keying.

For low index phase modulation, $\Delta\phi_p < 1$, the electrooptic modulator can require less drive power. From eq. (13), it is seen that the two are equal for

$$\Delta\phi_p = \left(\frac{32\pi}{9} \frac{1}{S\alpha_T} \frac{F_1}{\epsilon_0 M_3}\right)^{1/2} . \tag{14}$$

Again using the above parameters, eq. (14) yields the value $\Delta\phi_p \approx 0.16$.

In this comparison, we have assumed 100% deflection for the acoustooptic device. Since the percent deflection is given by $\sin^2(\eta^{1/2})$, η must equal $\pi^2/4$ to achieve this value. For less than 25% deflection, the deflection is given by η so the drive power requirement per watt of transmitted power is less by a factor $\pi^2/4 \approx 2.5$. It is only in the acoustooptic device that one can make the trade off between electrical drive power and percent transmission. In electrooptic phase modulation, the transmitted beam is of constant amplitude and only the phase is controlled. Such a trade off can be beneficial in minimizing the total power requirements (laser and modulator power) at 10.6 μ because of the relatively high efficiency of the CO_2 laser.

5. CONCLUSIONS

The relative merits of the two modulation schemes for both amplitude and phase modulation have been given in terms of figures of merit for acoustooptic and electrooptic materials. For

10.6 μ applications, the Ge acoustooptic modulator is superior to both GaAs and CdTe electrooptic modulators when amplitude modulation or large index phase modulation is desired. For low index phase modulation, the electrooptic modulators become more efficient. However, only with the acoustooptic effect can the trade off between drive power and percent power transmission be made in phase modulation.

It is concluded that for most 10.6 μ applications, the Ge acoustooptic modulator is the best choice. However, for very large bandwidths * (above 100 MHz) the necessity for strong focusing to overcome acoustic transit time limitations will make the electrooptic devices more attractive.

* The highest acoustic frequency occurs when $\theta_0 = \pi/2$ (backscattering). This cutoff frequency possesses an additional bandwidth limitation but in practice transit time effects dominate. Electrooptic modulation is not subject to either of these limitations.

REFERENCES

[1] I. P. Kaminow, IEEE J. Quantum Electron. QE-4 (1968) 23.

[2] J. E. Kiefer and A. Yariv, Appl. Phys. Letters 15 (1969) 26.

[3] R. L. Abrams and D. A. Pinnow, J. Appl. Phys., to be published.

[4] E. I. Gordon, Proc. IEEE 54 (1966) 1391.

[5] D. Maydan, IEEE J. Quantum Electron. QE-6 (1970) 15.

[6] R. W. Dixon, J. Appl. Phys. 38 (1967) 5149.

[7] I. P. Kaminow and E. H. Turner, Appl. Opt. 5 (1966) 1612.

EVALUATION OF PLZT CERAMICS FOR APPLICATIONS IN OPTICAL COMMUNICATIONS

F.S. CHEN
Bell Laboratories, Murray Hill, New Jersey 07974, USA

Received 1 September 1972

An evaluation is made to determine the suitability of fine grained ferroelectric ceramic $Pb_{0.91}La_{0.09}Zr_{0.65}Ti_{0.35}O_3$ (PLZT) for applications in optical modulators. It was found that the electro-optic effect in the PLZT material substantially decreases at high frequencies. Comparisons of PLZT with other electro-optic materials and comparisons of the electrode geometries suitable for ceramics and for single crystals are made.

The lanthanum doped, hot pressed, lead zirconate lead titanate ferroelectric ceramic $Pb_{0.91}La_{0.09}Zr_{0.65}Ti_{0.35}O_3$ (to be referred to as PLZT [1–5] ceramic) has previously been evaluated for applications in light shutters [1]. It has some properties which are attractive for applications in optical communications as well. It is transparent between wavelengths of 0.4 and 6 μ, its scattering loss is small if the optical path length is kept to a few mils, and it has a large transverse, quadratic electro-optic effect which is relatively temperature independent due to its broad "Curie temperature". Processing of the PLZT modulators consists of polishing only two surfaces of the ceramic plate followed by evaporation of electrodes (fig. 1a). This is not only simpler than more elaborate processes required of the single crystal electro-optic modulators (fig. 1b) but also offers the possibility of constructing modulators for many channels on a single ceramic plate.

This paper reports evaluations made to determine the suitability of the PLZT ceramic for modulator applications. Thin plates (a few mils thick) of PLZT appear cubic between cross polarizers when no voltage is applied. The light leakage is 20 dB down from the incident light intensity (extinction ratio of −20 dB). The transmission loss of the sample is 1 dB, which can be accounted for by the surface reflection loss. As the voltage is applied transverse to the direction of observation, the material becomes birefringent and also domain-like regions of approximately 1 mil are

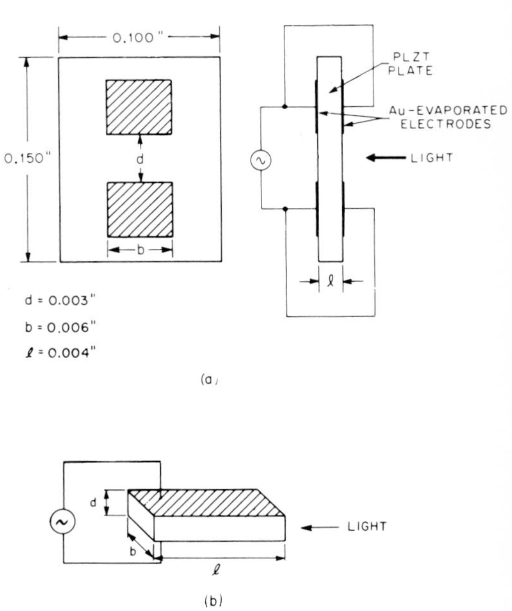

Fig. 1. (a) Electrodes configuration of light modulators using PLZT ceramics. (b) Typical electrodes configuration using single crystal ferroelectrics.

formed. This causes light scattering, and since the induced birefringence is slightly different at each region, the light beam emerging from the sample is no longer uniformly polarized, resulting in a transmission loss between cross polarizers. This loss is 0.5 dB at a wavelength of 0.63 μ. For this measurement the photodetector collected light rays falling within the solid angle of 0.087 steradian. The extinction ratio is -13 dB when a dc voltage ($\approx$ 50 V) is applied to the sample. The first half wave voltage of a sample with quadratic effect is [6]

$$v_\pi = (\lambda d^2/2Rl)^{1/2},$$

where λ is the wavelength, R is the quadratic electro-optic coefficient, d is the electrodes spacing and l is the optical path. The measured v_π at a wavelength of 0.63 μ for the geometry shown in fig. 1a varies from 60 to 100 V among the three samples tested and it is larger by a factor $(1.06/0.63)^{1/2}$ at 1.06 μ (negligible dispersion in this range of wavelengths).

The frequency dependence of the electro-optic effect was measured and is shown in figs. 2 and 3. The data shown in fig. 2 were obtained without a dc bias voltage. An applied voltage of 40 V peak (smaller than v_π) was used at all frequencies. The intensity modulated light was detected by a high speed photodiode and its output voltage was measured by a receiver tuned to twice the frequency of the modulating signal. The optical compensator was adjusted for the maximum photodetected voltage. The photodetected voltage has a fundamental frequency component about 15 dB down from the second harmonic, due to a small deviation from the quadratic dependence of the electro-optic effect on the applied voltage. No difference of v_π measured at dc and at 100 Hz were observed. One notices that the electro-optic effect begins to fall off at 1 kHz and also a few resonant peaks appear in the MHz range. Acoustic resonance might be the origin of these resonant peaks, although no resonance was observed in the dielectric constant. Although the electro-optic effect at a few MHz decreases to about 10% of the dc value, one can still construct a light shutter with relatively fast ($\approx$ 1 μsec) turn on/off performance [1] by overdriving the sample and by limiting the pulse width of the driving voltage so that the large but slow component of the electro-optic effect has no time to develop.

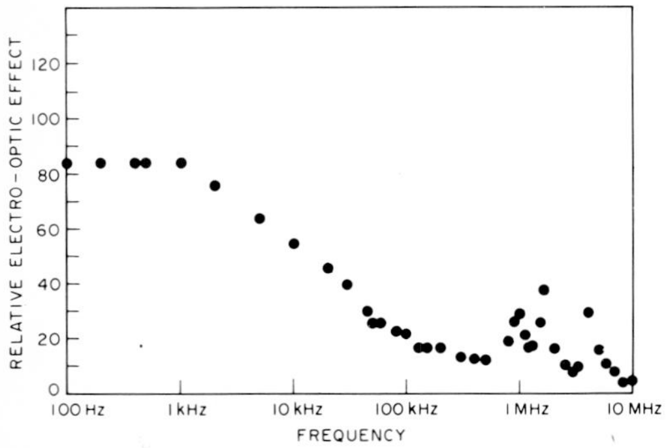

Fig. 2. Relative electro-optic response versus frequency of PLZT ceramics without dc bias.

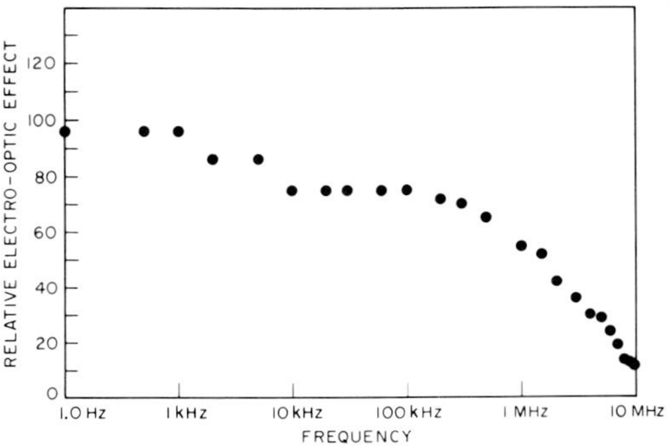

Fig. 3. Relative electro-optic response versus frequency of PLZT ceramics with dc bias field of 7 kV/cm.

The frequency dependence of the electro-optic effect with a dc biasing voltage is shown in fig. 3. The rf voltage applied to the sample was kept at 10 V peak and the dc biasing voltage and the optical compensator were adjusted to maximize the fundamental frequency component from the photodetector. The optimum dc bias was found to depend on the magnitude of the modulating voltage. For the modulating voltage of 10 V peak, the optimum bias is 50 V corresponding to an applied electric field of 7 kV/cm. Compared to the case without dc bias voltage, the electro-optic effect falls off more slowly as the frequency is increased. The dielectric constant at 100 kHZ is 8500 from the measured capacitance assuming that the electric field is uniformly distributed in the volume 0.003" × 0.006" × 0.004" shown in fig. 1a. It decreases by 30% from 100 kHz to 10 MHz. The dielectric constant at dc is 1.4×10^4, obtained by measuring the charge stored in the ceramic versus the applied voltage.

It is well known that the energy required to induce a phase retardation of π radians using materials with the quadratic electro-optic effect can be significantly reduced by dc biasing the sample to nearly saturate the polarization [6–8]. The PLZT sample measured has v_π equal to 100 V and $v_{2\pi}$ equal to 140 V at a wavelength of 0.63 μ and at dc where v_π and $v_{2\pi}$ are the first and the second half wave voltages, respectively. Hence one expects the difference, Δv_π ($\Delta v_\pi = v_{2\pi} - v_\pi$), to be 40 V by dc biasing to about 100 V (corresponding to 14 kV/cm). The measured Δv_π was 100 V peak to peak from 100 Hz to 1 kHz, much larger than the value expected from the measurements. The cause of the large increase in Δv_π between dc and 100 Hz when dc biased is not understood. As mentioned earlier, no difference between v_π measured at dc and at 100 Hz was observed when the sample was unbiased.

Some parameters essential to modulator applications are listed in table 1 and compared with $Sr_{0.5}Ba_{0.5}Nb_2O_6$ [9] and $LiNbO_3$ [10]. One notices that the energy required to induce π phase retardation (κv_π^2) does not vary widely. By dc biasing the PLZT shutter the frequency dependence of the electro-optic effect improves. However, the extinction ratio decreases and also the maximum light transmission through the analyzer decreases due to the increased inhomogeneity of the sample [11].

The configuration of ceramic modulators shown in fig. 1a, where electrodes are evaporated on a thin plate, has advantages of simpler processing, easier optical alignment and suitability for spatial multiplexing over the commonly used single crystal modulators shown in fig. 1b. It is also a proper choice for ceramics where the optical path length has to be short to reduce light scattering. There is however a disadvantage associated with this electrodes configuration. For materials processing linear transverse electro-optic effects (dc biased PLZT has this effect), the modulation power is proportional to S^2 where [10, 12]

$$S^2 = n\pi d^2/4\lambda l\,.$$

For the electrode geometry of fig. 1a, l has to be approximately equal to d to keep the field fairly uniform along the light path. Let us consider a typical example ($n = 2.5$, $\lambda = 1\mu$, $d = 75\ \mu$ and $d = l$). Then from the above equation S is equal to 12.3, compared to S of approximately 3 for typical single crystal electro-optic modulators shown in fig. 1b. A large S offers an advantage of easy optical alignment at the expense of modulation power.

Although PLZT ceramics have many potentially useful features, such as low absorption and scattering losses for a few mils thick samples over the wavelength region between 0.4 and 6 μ and availability of large apertures, their main forte of application is in devices [13] where large apertures are mandatory while the time of turn on/off can be in the microsecond range. They are suitable for applications in optical communications only when a few MHz modulations are required.

Table 1
Comparison of PLZT, SBN and $LiNbO_3$ at $\lambda = 0.63\ \mu$

	PLZT		$Sr_{0.5}Ba_{0.5}Nb_2O_6$	$LiNbO_3$
	unbiased	biased		
κ	14×10^3 a)	8.5×10^3 b)	450 c)	28 c)
v_π d) (volt)	100	100	580	3×10^3
κv_π^2 (volt^2)	1.4×10^8	2.4×10^8	1.5×10^8	2.5×10^8

a) Measured at dc.
b) Biased to the optimum value of 100 V (corresponding to 14 kV/cm) at 100 KHz.
c) Both κ and v_π are clamped values.
d) For unit aspect ratio ($d=l$) except the unbiased PLZT where the dimensions shown in fig. 1a are assumed.

The author wishes to thank G.A. Coquin for supplying the sample PLZT shutters and helpful discussions, D.A. Pinnow for suggesting this investigation and M. DiDomenico for this comments on the manuscript.

References

[1] G.A. Coquin, unpublished.
[2] C.E. Land and P.D. Thacher, Proc. IEEE 57 (1969) 751.
[3] P.D. Thacher and C.E. Land, IEEE Trans. Electron Devices ED-16 (1969) 515.
[4] C.E. Land and P.D. Thacher, Report SC-R-70-4353, Sandia Laboratories (1970).
[5] P.D. Thacher, J. Appl. Phys. 41 (1970) 4790.
[6] F.S. Chen, J.E. Geusic, S.K. Kurtz, J.G. Skinner and S.H. Wemple, J. Appl. Phys. 37 (1966) 388.
[7] M. DiDomenico Jr. and S.H. Wemple, J. Appl. Phys. 40 (1969) 720.
[8] S.H. Wemple and M. DiDomenico Jr., J. Appl. Phys. 40 (1969) 725.
[9] E.G. Spencer, P.V. Lenzo and A.A. Ballman, Proc. IEEE 55 (1967) 2074.
[10] I.P. Kaminow and E.H. Turner, Proc. IEEE 54 (1966) 1374.
[11] S.G. Varnado and W.D. Smith, IEEE J. Quantum Electron. QW-8 (1972) 88.
[12] F.S. Chen, Proc. IEEE 58 (1970) 1440.
[13] J.R. Maldonado and A.H. Meitzler, Proc. IEEE 59 (1971) 368.

4. Traveling Wave Electrooptic Modulators

Reprinted from *Appl. Phys. Lett.* **2**, 41–42 (1963).

SPLITTING OF FABRY-PEROT RINGS BY MICROWAVE MODULATION OF LIGHT

I. P. Kaminow
Bell Telephone Laboratories, Incorporated
Holmdel, New Jersey

(Received 16 November 1962)

When an electromagnetic wave at frequency Ω is phase-modulated at frequency ω with modulation index η, the signal may be described by

$$E(\eta) = E_0 \sin(\Omega t + \eta \sin \omega t)$$
$$= E_0 \sum_{-\infty}^{\infty} J_p(\eta) \sin(\Omega + p\omega)t \ , \quad (1)$$

where J_p is the pth order Bessel function and E_0 is the peak field strength. We report here an experiment in which the carrier frequency Ω, provided by a He-Ne maser[1] operating continuously at 6328 Å, is phase-modulated at 9.01 Gc by an electro-optic light modulator.[2] The first sidebands ($\Omega \pm \omega$) are observed photographically as a splitting of the rings produced by a Fabry-Perot interferometer. A related experiment, in which 10-Mc sidebands on an incoherent light source were observed photoelectrically with a very long scanning Fabry-Perot interferometer, has been reported earlier.[3]

Our apparatus is shown schematically in Fig. 1. Light from the visible maser passes through the modulator cavity to the Fabry-Perot etalon. The

INDEXING CATEGORIES

A. maser	modulator
A. phase modulation	C. interferometer
B. interference-pattern splitting	E
C. electro-optic	

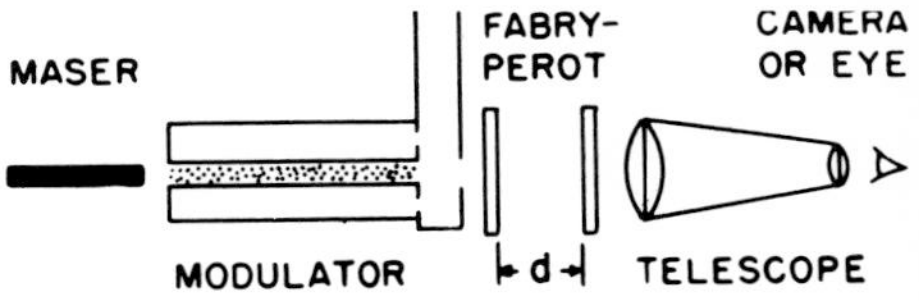

Fig. 1. Schematic of one pass apparatus.

41

resultant ring pattern is observed through a telescope either by eye (with suitable filter) or photographically.

The etalon consists of dielectric coated mirrors with about 2% transmission separated by a distance, d, of 5.65 mm. With this spacing, the change in optical frequency necessary to shift a ring of given order to the position occupied by an adjacent ring is $\Delta f = c/2d = 26.55$ Gc (ref 4).

The modulator contains a slender rod (0.035 × 0.035 × 3.75 in.) of KH_2PO_4 (KDP) and is an improved version of a device described earlier.[2] The ratio η^2/P, where P is the power absorbed in the cavity, is ideally

$$\eta^2/P = (\pi^2 L)/(4\omega\epsilon_0\epsilon'' V_0^2 a^2)\,, \qquad (2)$$

in which L and a are the length and width of the rod and ϵ_0 is the permittivity of free space. Taking 9.4×10^3 V for V_0, the clamped half-wave voltage[5] at 6328 Å, and 0.16 for ϵ'', the imaginary part of the dielectric constant[6] at 9.01 Gc, the calculated value of η^2/P is 4.2×10^{-2} rad^2/W for one pass and four times this value if the light is reflected back through the modulator. The values of η^2/P, measured on a pulsed basis with low-duty cycle to reduce heating effects, are approximately $(2.3 \pm 0.5) \times 10^{-2}$ rad^2/W and $(9 \pm 2) \times 10^{-2}$ rad^2/W for one and two passes, respectively. The chief source of the discrepancy is probably microwave loss in the cavity walls, which is neglected in Eq. (2). The loaded cavity Q is $\sim 10^3$.

Figure 2 is a photograph of the Fabry-Perot pattern observed with the apparatus of Fig. 1. The modulator is operated continuously with a power of 5 W. The modulation index, η, is then 0.34 rad and the relative intensities of the $p = 0, \pm 1$ components are $J_0^2 = 0.94$, $J_{\pm 1}^2 = 0.03$. The light, which is reasonably well collimated despite scattering, is directed off the axis of the etalon so that the sidebands appear as partial rings between the more intense $p = 0$ rings. Since the modulating frequency (9.01 Gc) is roughly one-third the ring spacing (26.55 Gc), the upper sideband from one ring and the lower sideband from an adjacent ring divide the interval between the rings into roughly equal parts.

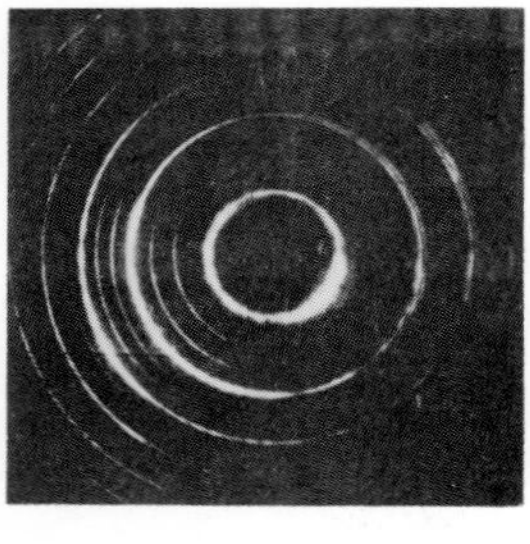

Fig. 2. Fabry-Perot pattern for light modulated at 9.01 Gc with etalon spacing 5.65 mm (Δf = 26.55 Gc).

Although polarized light is not important in observing the sidebands, it happens that the maser output is polarized by the Brewster angle windows.[1] The plane of polarization is about 45° from the optic axial plane of the KDP rod. The principal optical components are given by $E(\eta)$, as in Eq. (1), and by $E(-\eta)$. In the absence of an analyzer at the output of the modulator, these components contribute independently to the Fabry-Perot pattern.

Sidebands have also been observed with a reflection apparatus[2] in which the light passes through the modulator twice before entering the etalon. Operating on a pulsed basis, with a duty cycle of $\sim 1/20$, the depolarization and scattering caused by heating are reduced sufficiently to observe two interesting effects. With crossed polarizers at A and B set at 45° to the principal axes, the optical field incident on the etalon is proportional to $[E(\eta) - E(-\eta)]$, while with parallel polarizers the field is proportional to $[E(\eta) + E(-\eta)]$. In the first instance only components with p odd are present, while in the latter only even components are present. The $p = \pm 1$ components are observed to disappear when the polarizers are set parallel. The sidebands also vanish when the movable mirror is displaced a distance D equal to a quarter-of-a-microwave wavelength from the position of maximum sideband intensity.[2]

It is a pleasure to acknowledge the assistance of F. A. Dunn, particularly in the preparation of the KDP rods.

1. A. D. White and J. D. Rigden, *Proc. IRE* **50**, 1697 (1962).
2. I. P. Kaminow, *Phys. Rev. Letters* **6**, 528 (1961).
3. P. Connes, Duong Hong Tuan and J. Pinard, *J. Phys. Radium*, **23**, 173 (1962).
4. F. A. Jenkins and H. E. White, *Fundamentals of Optics*, (McGraw-Hill Book Company, Inc., New York, 1957) p 281.
5. B. H. Billings, *Optics in Metrology* (Pergamon Press, Inc., New York, 1960) p 119.
6. I. P. Kaminow and G. O. Harding, to be published.

Gigacycle-Bandwidth Coherent-Light Traveling-Wave Amplitude Modulator

CHARLES J. PETERS, SENIOR MEMBER, IEEE

Abstract—We have constructed an optical amplitude modulator having a bandwidth of approximately one Gc/s and requiring about a fifty volts drive to produce a 100 per cent amplitude modulation. The wide-bandwidth low drive power performance is obtained by using the traveling-wave approach previously used in the gigacycle bandwidth phase modulator. The electro-optic material is KDP cut in the same orientation used in the phase modulator and combined with other optical elements to produce retardation-amplitude modulation.

Temperature variations through the KDP produce a deflection and decollimation of the output beam. Experiments have been conducted to determine the magnitude of these effects. Corrective measures have been devised. Comparatively good agreement between the computed and the measured bandwidth has been obtained.

Introduction

A GIGACYCLE-bandwidth traveling-wave amplitude modulator for coherent light is described which uses the uniaxial crystal KDP cut in the same orientation previously used in the traveling-wave phase modulator.[1] With this orientation a simple traveling-wave microwave structure such as a coaxial line can be used to apply the modulating field to the crystals. In concept this amplitude modulator is similar to the usual retardation amplitude modulator.

The amplitude modulator described in this paper differs from the phase modulator in the polarization for the incident light and the inclusion of a temperature compensating scheme. In the orientation used here the crystals exhibit a natural birefringence. With coherent light for the carrier, the birefringence is not troublesome except that it is temperature dependent. A technique for canceling this temperature effect is described.

The index of refraction of KDP is a function of temperature. Power losses in the KDP crystal and the modulator conductors create a temperature gradient within the KDP. The resulting variation in index of refraction of the crystal produces both a deflection and decollimation of the optical output beam.

Both the deflection and decollimation of the beam can lead to serious optical system performance degradation. For example, if the modulator is used in a local oscillator chain in an optical superheterodyne receiver, the deflection of the beam can lead to a decollimation between the received signal and the local oscillator signal which could degrade the mixing efficiency of the receiver. Also if the modulator were used in the transmitted beam of a noncoherent CW radar in which modulation is imposed upon the CW light beam to measure range, deflection of the beam by the modulator could contribute serious errors to the measurement of azimuth and elevation.

Wide bandwidth at low modulation power is obtained in the traveling-wave modulator by matching the velocity of the modulation to the velocity of the light in the crystal. The microwave design for the coaxial configuration to achieve this objective is briefly described.

Several traveling-wave amplitude modulators have been constructed. These modulators have a bandwidth of about 1 Gc/s and require 50 volts to obtain 100 per cent amplitude modulation. The overall length of the active portion of the modulator is approximately 16 inches and the usable aperture is approximately 0.1 inch in diameter.

Modulator Description

The same orientation for the electro-optic crystals is used in this amplitude modulator as in the traveling-wave phase modulator. This orientation is shown in Fig. 1. The modulating electric field is applied along the [001] direction in the crystal. The electric vector of the incident light beam is oriented at a 45° angle with the [001] axis.

In the orientation described above the electro-optic effect is a variation in the index of refraction for light with its electric vector parallel to the [110] direction in response to an applied voltage along [001]. The index of refraction for light with its electric field along the [001] axis is substantially independent of the applied electric field.

A linearly polarized light beam is incident upon a KDP crystal oriented as described to which the modulation voltage is applied by means of a traveling-wave structure. The traveling-wave structure is designed so that the velocity of light in the crystal and the velocity of the modulation are equal. The light leaving the first half of the modulator has received a retardation or elliptic polarization proportional to the instantaneous value of the applied modulation field and also as a result of a natural birefringence of the KDP. The modu-

Manuscript received September 21, 1964; revised December 10, 1964. This work was partially supported by the Electronic Technology Div., Air Force Avionics Lab., Wright-Patterson AFB, Ohio, under Contract AF33(657)-11383.

The author is with the Applied Research Lab., Sylvania Electronic Systems, A Division of Sylvania Electric Products, Inc., Waltham, Mass.

[1] Peters, C. J., Gigacycle bandwidth coherent light traveling-wave phase modulator, *Proc. IEEE*, vol 51, Jan 1963, pp 147–153.

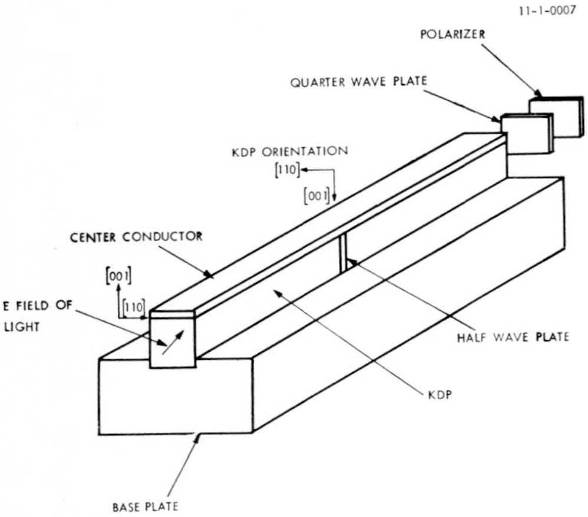

Fig. 1. Traveling-wave amplitude modulator configuration.

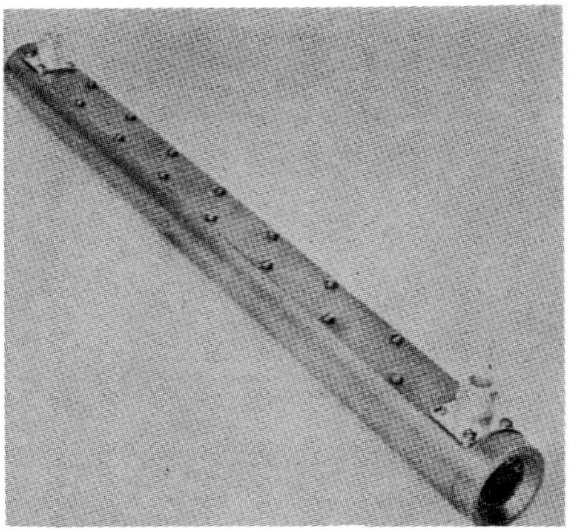

Fig. 2. The traveling-wave amplitude modulator.

lation retardation is imparted as a phase modulation of the component of the incident light polarized with the electric field parallel to the [110] direction.

The half-wave plate and the second half of the optical modulator are oriented to cancel out the natural birefringence, which is a function of temperature, and to impart a retardation to the component of light which was initially polarized with the electric field parallel to the [001] axis. The effect of the half-wave plate can be viewed as a superposition of two quarter-wave plates, the first of which imparts a circular polarization to the input light and the second which transforms this circular polarization into a linear polarization which is oriented 90° to the input. This operation is performed independently on the vertical and horizontal components of the input light. The result is a rotation of the polarization of the beam.[2] The amplitude modulation is extracted from the retardation-modulated wave by the usual sequence of quarter-wave plate and linear polarizer.

In order to simplify microwave drive arrangements and to prevent radiation of the modulation this modulator was constructed in a coaxial configuration. A major requirement for this design is to provide thermal uniformity throughout the length of the modulator. This has been provided by making the outside conductor thermally massive. A photograph of the completed modulator is shown in Fig. 2. In this particular modulator, a total of eight KDP crystals each 0.1 by 0.1 by 2 inches is used. The overall length of the active portion of the modulator is 16 inches and the usable aperture is approximately 0.1 inch.

[2] This particular configuration for the modulator was suggested by Carl Buhrer of the General Telephone and Electronics Labs., Bayside, L. I., N. Y. It evolved from a temperature compensating approach. See Peters, C. J., Traveling wave amplitude modulator, *1964 NEREM Record*, pp 70–71.

Modulator Design

Optical

The optical operation of this modulator can be described most concisely by the Jones Calculus.[3] This results in the following equation for the optical transfer function of the modulator:

$$\begin{bmatrix} e^{i(\delta/2)} & 0 \\ 0 & e^{-i(\delta/2-\phi/2)} \end{bmatrix} \begin{bmatrix} 0 & 1 \\ 1 & 0 \end{bmatrix} \begin{bmatrix} e^{i(\delta'/2)} & 0 \\ 0 & e^{-i(\delta'/2+\phi/2)} \end{bmatrix} \quad (1)$$

where

δ' is the natural retardation imposed on the incident light beam by the first half of the modulator

δ is the natural retardation imposed on the light by the second half of the modulator

$\phi/2$ is the phase shift imposed on the light wave by the modulation.

The expression in the brackets on the right in this equation describes the operation of the first half of the modulator. The center brackets describe the operation of the half-wave plate, the brackets on the left describe the last half of the modulator.

In this configuration the natural birefringence terms will cancel and the modulation terms will add. The two expressions for the active portion of the modulator are identical in so far as the natural birefringence is concerned. However, there is a difference in sign for the modulation terms since the crystals are oriented so that the optic axis of the crystals in one half the modulator are in the opposite direction to the optic axis of the crystal in the other half. (See Fig. 1.)

A simple calculation shows that the two sections of the modulator should be equal in length to within about a half wavelength of light to achieve a net natural bire-

[3] Shurcliff, W. A., *Polarized Light*, Cambridge, Mass.: Harvard University Press, 1962.

fringence of $\delta-\delta'<10°$. If the crystals are individually finished this dimensional tolerance is probably impossible to achieve. However, if the crystals are handled in batches, such tolerances are met almost automatically. The real significance of this tolerance lies not so much in the specification of the overall length, since a net birefringence can be accommodated by rotating the quarter-wave plate that precedes the output polarizer, but in the specification of the flatness and parallelism of the crystal faces.

Assuming that the electric field of the input light is oriented at 45° to the [001] axis and that a quarter-wave plate and polarizer are placed at the output of the modulator to develop amplitude modulation, the modulator output is described by

$$E = \frac{1}{2}\begin{bmatrix}1\\1\end{bmatrix}\left(\cos\frac{\phi}{2} + \sin\frac{\phi}{2}\right)\cos wt$$

or

$$|E| = \frac{\sqrt{2}}{2}\left(\cos\frac{\phi}{2} + \sin\frac{\phi}{2}\right)\cos wt \tag{2}$$

where

E is the electric field of the output light
ω is the angular frequency of the light,

and

$$\phi = \frac{\pi n^3 r_{63}}{\lambda}\frac{LV}{b} \tag{3}$$

where

ϕ is the retardation in radians imposed on the light beam by the traveling-wave amplitude modulator
n is the index of refraction
r_{63} is the electro-optic coefficient in meters per volt
λ is the wavelength of the light carrier in meters
L is the length of the modulator
V is the modulation voltage
b is the dimension of the electro-optic crystal across which modulation voltage is applied.

This expression for the retardation ϕ differs from the comparable expression given by Billings[4] for a Pockels cell in which the light travels parallel to the [001] axis by a factor of 2 and by the geometric factor L/b. The factor of 2 arises from the orientation of the crystals used in the modulator in which it is possible to phase modulate only one component of the light at a time. The factor L/b expresses the effect of the elongated geometry in reducing the total voltage required for the modulation. L/b for the modulator described here is approximately 160 implying that a reduction in modulator voltage by a factor of 80 is obtained by the traveling-wave approach.

Thermal

The advantage of the traveling-wave approach to optical modulation is that the modulation power loss in the conductors and in the electro-optic material is very small. However, the small power losses cause minute temperature gradients within the electro-optic crystal producing variations in the index of refraction throughout the crystal which are sufficiently large to deflect the beam noticeably.

An optical beam traveling through a medium with a nonuniform index of refraction follows a curved path with a radius of curvature of[5]

$$R = -\frac{n}{\nabla_\perp n}$$

where

n is the index of refraction of the material
$\nabla_\perp n$ represents the gradient of index of refraction in a direction perpendicular to the path of the beam.

For the traveling-wave modulator of length L this expression can be rewritten in terms of a deflection angle in the form

$$\alpha = -\frac{L}{n}\nabla_\perp n. \tag{4}$$

The index of refraction of the KDP over small temperature ranges is proportional to the temperature.

$$n = n_0 + N\theta \tag{5}$$

where

n_0 is the quiescent index of refraction of the material
N is the proportionality constant
θ is the temperature referenced to the quiescent temperature.

Substituting (5) into (4)

$$\alpha = -\frac{L}{n}N\frac{d\theta}{dz}. \tag{6}$$

Equation 6 shows that if a linear variation in temperature is established across the electro-optic crystal, the beam will be deflected uniformly in angle with no degradation in the collimation properties of the beam. On the other hand, if a nonlinear variation of temperature exists across a crystal, such as would arise from heat generated within the crystal, the beam would be decollimated as well as deflected, since each ray of a beam would suffer a different angular deflection. The following analysis will serve to define limits of the power which can be dissipated within the KDP crystal and in the center conductor.

Let us assume that no power is dissipated within the crystal and that the only source of heat is the I^2R loss

[4] Billings, B. H., The electro-optic effect in uniaxial crystals of the type XH_2PO_4, *J. Opt. Soc. Amer.*, vol 39, Oct 1949, p 800.

[5] Born, M., and E. Wolf, *Principles of Optics*. New York: Pergamon, 1959, pp 120–123.

in the center conductor. The thermal gradient within the KDP crystal is then

$$\frac{d\theta}{dz} = \frac{P_c}{\sigma A} \tag{7}$$

where

P_c is the power flowing through the crystal
σ is the thermal conductivity
A is the cross sectional area of the heat flow.

Substituting this expression into (6) we obtain

$$\alpha = -\frac{L}{n} N \frac{P_c}{\sigma A} \cdot \tag{8}$$

We measured an approximate value for N for KDP of $-1.5 \times 10^{-5}/°C$.

Equation (8) can be solved for P_c to yield a specification of themaximum permissible heat flow through the crystal for a tolerable beam deflection. The designer has some room for maneuver since it is possible to provide alternate heat paths for the power dissipated in the center conductor. In one experimental design we were able to reduce the heat flow through the KDP by a factor of five by backing the center conductor with thin sapphire rods in contact with the main body of the modulator. The heat flow from the conductors into KDP can in principle be reduced to zero by using a thermally symmetrical design.

Heat generated within the electro-optic material produces both a deflection and a decollimation of the beam. To analyze this situation let us assume that the two electrical conductors of the modulator are held at a temperature $\theta = 0°$ and that heat is generated uniformly throughout the modulator at a rate P_d watts/mm³ as shown in Fig. 3. These assumptions define a one-dimensional heat flow problem in which the resulting temperature distribution is given by

$$\theta = \frac{P_d}{2\sigma}\left(\frac{b^2}{4} - Z^2\right) \tag{9}$$

where

P_d is the power per unit volume dissipated in the material.

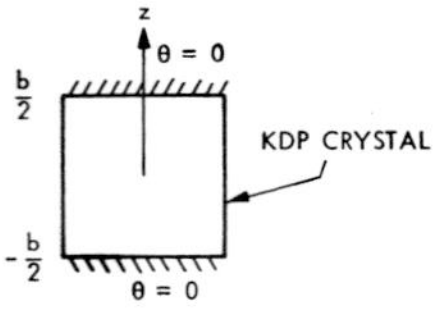

Fig. 3. Heat flow geometry for computing the temperature distribution within the crystal arising from dielectric loss within the crystal.

Differentiating (9) and substituting the result into (8) gives an equation for angular deflection of the beam

$$\alpha_d = \frac{LNP_d}{n\sigma} Z \cdot \tag{10}$$

Notice that the deflection suffered by any ray in the modulator beam is proportional to the distance of the ray from the center line of the modulator. Thus, the effect of this parabolic temperature distribution is to decollimate the beam.

In the modulator under consideration here, the power dissipated within the electro-optic material at one Gc/s is approximately 3 mW/mm³ when the modulator is driven to produce 100 per cent amplitude modulation. This power density will produce a deflection of approximately 5 milliradians for the ray at $Z = 0.5$ mm. Except for the frequency dependence of the loss tangent of the electro-optic material, the power loss in the modulator is directly proportional to frequency so that at 100 Mc/s the ray at $Z = 0.5$ mm would be deflected by 0.5 milliradian. In operation this modulator would probably be operated with a well-collimated beam of light having a diameter of approximately one millimeter at the entrance to the modulator. The diffraction limited divergence of this beam would be approximately one milliradian, thus the dispersion caused by the parabolic temperature distribution within the electro-optical material under certain circumstances could exceed the natural dispersion coming from diffraction.

Variation in temperature from one end of the modulator to the other will produce a shift in the net birefringence of the output so that $\delta - \delta' \neq 0$. The temperature dependence of the retardation can be described by

$$\Delta\Gamma = \frac{2\pi}{\lambda} Lk\theta \tag{11}$$

where

$\Delta\Gamma$ is the change in retardation, radians
θ is the temperature in °C
k is the thermal retardation coefficient, radians per °C.

Our rough measurements give a value for k of $1.1 \times 10^{-5}/°C$ for KDP and $4.7 \times 10^{-5}/°C$ for ADP. An estimate for the required temperature uniformity can be obtained from (11). Assuming that each eight-inch half of the KDP modulator is at a uniform temperature, we find that a temperature difference of 0.01°C between the two halves will produce a residual retardation of 10°. The main body of the experimental modulator was milled from a $1\frac{1}{2}$-inch OD aluminum rod. This thermally-massive structure is capable of maintaining the necessary temperature uniformity even when the ambient temperature is changing rapidly.

This discussion of the thermal behavior in the traveling-wave optical modulator suggests that the ultimate choice of the most appropriate material for electro-optic modulation may be determined not only by the primary material parameters such as the electro-optic coefficient and the dielectric constant but also by detailed consideration of the thermal conductivity, the thermal refractive index coefficient, and the loss tangent. These quantities are not known for many attractive candidates for this application such as KH_2AsO_4, $NH_4H_2AsO_4$, etc.

Microwave

Most efficient utilization of the electro-optic material is obtained by using a square cross section. However, if a square cross section for the electro-optic material is used, it is no longer possible to design the modulator to have both a particular characteristic impedance and phase velocity. Since the bandwidth of the modulator is determined by the phase velocity this design is predicated on meeting the phase velocity requirement and accepting whatever characteristic impedance results.

The characteristic impedance and the phase velocity of the modulator at low frequencies can be expressed in terms of the distributed inductance L and distributed capacity C of the modulator. Electro-optic materials of the KDP class have a very high dielectric constant on the order of 15 to 20. Because of this, it is reasonable as a first approximation to neglect the stray capacity from other portions of the modulator and to attribute all the capacity to the electric field which exists in the electro-optic material. Under this assumption the capacity per unit length for the square cross section modulator is given by $C=\epsilon\epsilon_0$ where C is the capacity per unit length, farads per meter, ϵ is the dielectric constant of the electro-optic material, ϵ_0 is the permittivity of free space, 8.854×10^{-12} farads per meter. This constraint on the distributed capacity can be inserted into the expressions for the phase velocity and characteristic impedance for a transmission line to yield expressions for the distributed inductance and characteristic impedance. The KDP modulator has a characteristic impedance of 27 ohms.

The modulation efficiency M of the modulator in terms of the velocities of the modulation and light is given by

$$M = \frac{\sin \frac{\omega L}{c}(n' - n)}{\frac{\omega L}{c}(n' - n)} \qquad (12)$$

where

L is the length of the modulator
c is the speed of light
n' is the microwave index of refraction of the modulator $=c/v_p$.

The frequency dependence of n' can be computed for the simple two-conductor configuration used in the traveling-wave phase modulator under certain simplifying assumptions.[6,7] Solution of this field theory problem leads to a transcendental equation for the phase velocity which for convenient solution on a computer can be put in the form

$$\tan x = \beta \tanh \beta g x$$

where

$$\beta = \left[\frac{(n')^2 - 1}{\epsilon_1 - (n')^2}\right]^{1/2}$$

$$g = \frac{\epsilon_1 - n^2}{n^2 - 1}. \qquad (14)$$

The expression for g comes from the matching of the microwave phase velocity to the light velocity at zero frequency. From values of x obtained from (13) and programmed increments of n' the frequency dependence of n' can be computed from

$$\omega = \frac{xc}{a\left[\epsilon_1 - (n')^2\right]^{1/2}}. \qquad (15)$$

It is to be noted that the frequency scale is inversely proportional to the width a of the electro-optic crystal. The above equations were evaluated for several electro-optical materials. The predicted and the experimentally measured frequency response obtained is shown in Fig. 4.

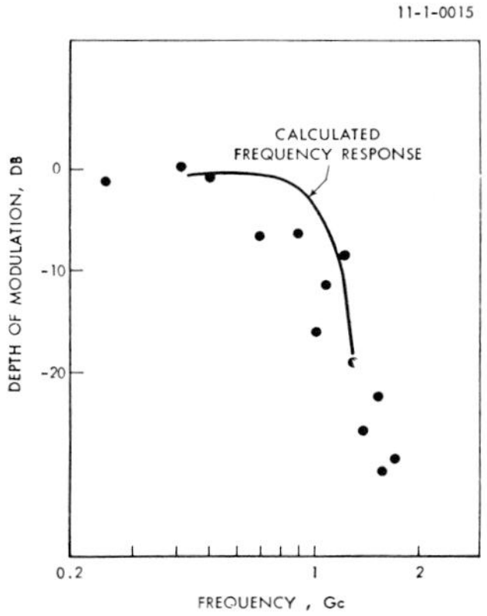

Fig. 4. Calculated and measured frequency response for a traveling-wave amplitude modulator.

[6] Peters, C. J., Further developments in wideband coherent light modulators, *1963 NEREM Record*, p 154.
[7] Kaminow, I. P., and J. Liu, Propagation characteristics of partially loaded two-conductor transmission line for broad-band light modulators, *Proc. IEEE*, vol 51, Jan 1963, pp 132–136.

Conclusion

KDP type amplitude modulators exhibiting gigacycle bandwidths and requiring modest drive power are feasible. The performance of these traveling-wave modulators in terms of the modulation bandwidth, the power requirements, and other performance characteristics, is directly determined by the material constants such as the index of refraction, dielectric constant, and electro-optic coefficient. Other properties of the electro-optic material such as the thermal index of refraction coefficient, although they enter indirectly, exert no less influence on the overall modulator performance. These secondary quantities to a large extent are unknown for several crystals in the KDP family.

Acknowledgment

R. Lucy, E. McGann, and G. Ratcliffe of this Laboratory have made significant contributions to the realization of the wideband modulator. Fruitful discussions with V. Fowler and C. Buhrer of General Telephone and Electronics Laboratory, Inc. are gratefully acknowledged.

Reprinted from *Proc. IEEE* **53**, 455–460 (1965).

0 to 3 GHz Traveling-Wave Electrooptic Modulator

***Abstract*—A report is given on the construction and testing of a traveling-wave electrooptic modulator that requires a nominal 5-watt drive power to obtain 30 percent amplitude modulation from 0 to 3-GHz. The modulator employs potassium-dihydrogen-arsenate crystals and has been tested at 6328 Å with CW drive power.**

This letter reports the construction and testing of a traveling-wave electrooptic modulator that requires a nominal 5-watt drive power to obtain 30 percent amplitude modulation from 0 to 3 GHz. The modulator was tested at 6328 Å using CW drive power.

The modulator consisted of a dielectrically loaded coaxial transmission line with a rectangular cross section as shown in Fig. 1 [1], [2]. The dielectric load was a chain of potassium-dihydrogen-arsenate (KDA) crystals. The electric field of the transmission line was parallel to the *c*-axis of the crystals and transverse to the direction of optical propagation. A half-wave plate separated the chain into two sections of equal length, having oppositely directed *c*-axis orientation. This technique, which has been discussed elsewhere, provides cancellation of natural birefringence, thermally induced birefringence, and to first order improves the field of view [3], [4].

A survey of materials in the potassium-dihydrogen-arsenate family led to the conclusion that KDA was the best available for this modulator technique considering loss tangent, magnitude of electrooptic coefficient, thermal birefringence sensitivity, and crystal chain length versus required drive power for 30 percent amplitude modulation.[1] A length of 16 cm was chosen; the crystals' square cross section was 2-mm per edge, a dimension compatible with the output beamwidth of a conventional 6328 Å laser.

The cross-sectional dimensions of the transmission line were determined experimentally by matching the microwave phase velocity to the optical [5]. A 3-dB reduction in modulated optical power occurs at a modulation frequency just above 3 GHz as a result of the transit-time effect [3]. The final dimensions checked closely with those determined by a computer solution of the microwave boundary value problem [6].

The size of the dielectric support of the center conductor was determined by making its transverse thermal conductance equal to that of the brass shims leading from the top of the crystal to the side walls. This provided good transverse thermal balance [3]. Longitudinal thermal unbalance occurs because of microwave standing waves in the modulator, which induces a birefringence [3]. The coupling tab between the coaxial connector and the center electrode was experimentally adjusted to minimize the VSWR.

The characteristic impedance of the line was 16 ohms. Terminated with a specially fabricated 16-ohm load, the VSWR was less than 2:1. In the worst case this VSWR caused a longitudinal thermal unbalance birefringence of about 15°/watt of drive power. This occurred only at frequencies where the standing-wave pattern was maximally asymmetric. Beam steering due to transverse thermal unbalance was unobservable with the transmitted beam thrown 300 feet onto a distant screen and with 5-watt CW drive power.

The extinction ratio was 5:1. This was determined by operating the modulator between parallel and then crossed polarizers with full modulation power. The unextinguished portion of the beam with crossed polarizers was comprised of two approximately equal components: the first was due to random scattering at the crystal interfaces, while the second was due to imperfect cancellation of the natural birefringence imparted by the crystal to slightly off-axis rays [4]. The optical transmission loss of the modulator was 4 dB.

Figure 2 shows the percent modulation for 5-watt drive power as determined by measurement of the shift in dc level of a photomultiplier output due to the application of modulation drive power [7]. Four measurements were taken for each point shown to eliminate the effects of birefringence induced by longitudinal thermal unbalance. Two signals,

Manuscript received November 28, 1966. The work reported here was supported by the U. S. Army Electronics Command, Ft. Monmouth, N. J., under Contract DA-28-043-AMC-01283(E).

[1] The survey did not include lithium niobate or tantalate. The modulator structure described is suitable for employment of these crystals.

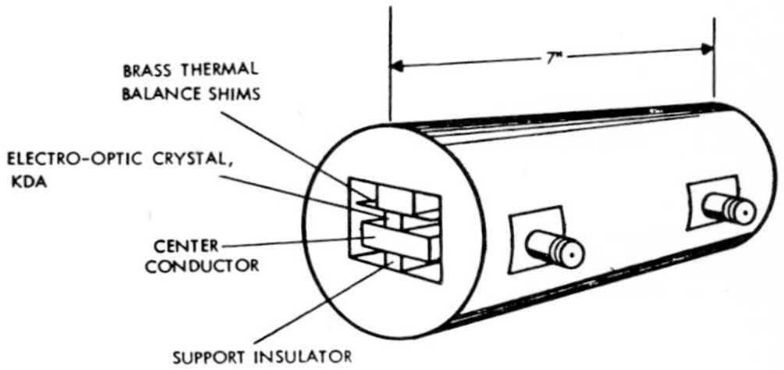

Fig. 1. Construction of the 0–3 GHz traveling-wave modulator.

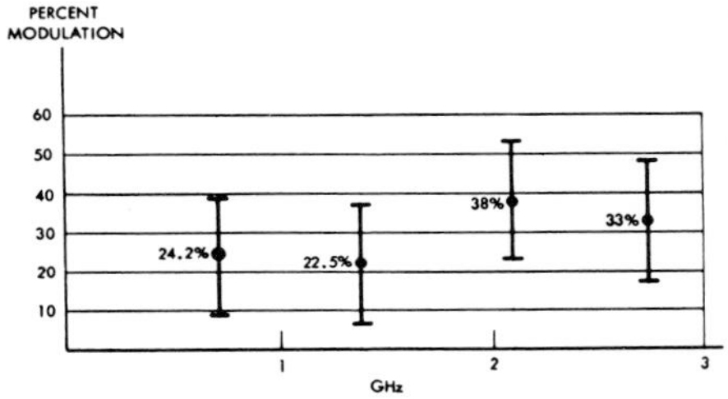

Fig. 2. Measured modulation at 5-watt drive power.

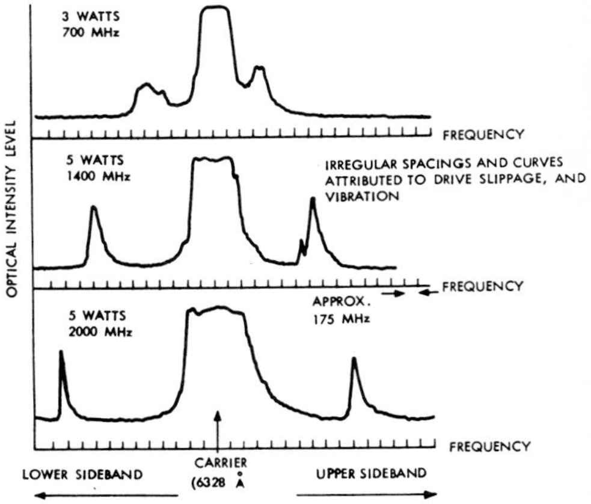

Fig. 3. Sidebands of 700, 1400, and 2000 MHz with traveling-wave modulator at 6328 Å, as observed at the output of a Fabry-Perot interferometer while tuned in frequency.

S_1^p and S_1^s, were observed for, respectively, a parallel and a crossed polarizer placed between the modulator and the photomultiplier. Two other signals S_2^p and S_2^s, were observed for, respectively, a parallel and a crossed polarizer placed between a $\lambda/4$ plate following the modulator to provide bias [3] and the photomultiplier. It can be shown that

$$S_1^p = k_1[1 + J_0(2\Gamma)\,\mathrm{Cos}\,2\zeta]$$

$$S_1^s = k_1[1 - J_0(2\Gamma)\,\mathrm{Cos}\,2\zeta]$$

$$S_2^p = k_2[1 + J_0(2\Gamma)\,\mathrm{Sin}\,2\zeta]$$

$$S_2^s = k_2[1 - J_0(2\Gamma)\,\mathrm{Sin}\,2\zeta]$$

where

k_1, k_2 = constants determined by detector efficiency
ζ = thermally induced birefingent phase shift
Γ = phase shift induced at modulation frequency.

The foregoing equations can be solved for Γ, and the percent modulation can thereby be determined from the measurements. The limit of experimental accuracy, shown in the data of Fig. 3, is approximately ± 50 percent. The numbers cited are the average of a large number of measurements at each operating frequency. To further corroborate the percent modulation data, measurements were taken using a scanning Fabry-Perot interferometer. A typical recording of 0.7, 1.4, and 2.0 GHz modulation sidebands is shown in Fig. 3. Sidebands extending to 4 GHz have been observed.

The effort reported here has demonstrated an optical modulator capable of achieving useful modulation percentage with a microwave bandwidth and a modest drive power requirement. The technique employed can be utilized with most electrooptic materials in the visible and the infrared.

ACKNOWLEDGMENT

The authors wish to thank W. J. Rattman and G. McDowell for assistance given during the latter period of this effort.

W. E. BICKNELL
B. K. YAP
C. J. PETERS
Electro-Optical Research Dept.
Applied Research Lab.
Sylvania Electric Products, Inc.
Waltham, Mass.

REFERENCES

[1] T. S. Chen, "Determination of the capacitance, inductance, and characteristic impedance of rectangular lines," *IRE Trans. on Microwave Theory and Techniques*, vol. MTT-8, pp. 510–519, September 1960.
[2] W. S. Metcalf, "Characteristic impedance of rectangular transmission lines," *Proc. IEE (London)*, vol. 112, pp. 2033–2039, November 1965.
[3] C. J. Peters, "Gigacycle-bandwidth coherent-light traveling-wave amplitude modulator," *Proc. IEEE*, vol. 53, pp. 455–460, May 1965.
[4] J. W. Evans, "The birefringent filter," *J. Opt. Soc. Am.*, vol. 39, pp. 229–242, March 1949.
[5] C. J. Peters, "Gigacycle bandwidth coherent light traveling-wave phase modulator," *Proc. IEEE*, vol. 51, pp. 147–153, January 1963.
[6] I. P. Kaminow and J. Liu, "Propagation characteristics of partially loaded two-conductor transmission line for broadband light modulators," *Proc. IEEE*, vol. 51, pp. 132–136, January 1963.
[7] I. P. Kaminow, "Microwave modulation of the electro-optic effect in KH_2PO_4," *Phys. Rev. Lett.*, vol. 6, pp. 528–530, May 15, 1961.

Reprinted from the PROCEEDINGS OF THE IEEE
VOL. 55, NO. 2, FEBRUARY, 1967
pp. 225-226

Reprinted by permission from IEEE JOURNAL OF QUANTUM ELECTRONICS
Vol. QE-5, No. 12, December 1969

Half-Octave Bandwidth Traveling-Wave *X*-Band Optical Phase Modulator

***Abstract*—Multiple interactions of optical and microwave fields in an electrooptical crystal have yielded low-power optical phase modulation over a 4.6-GHz bandwidth.**

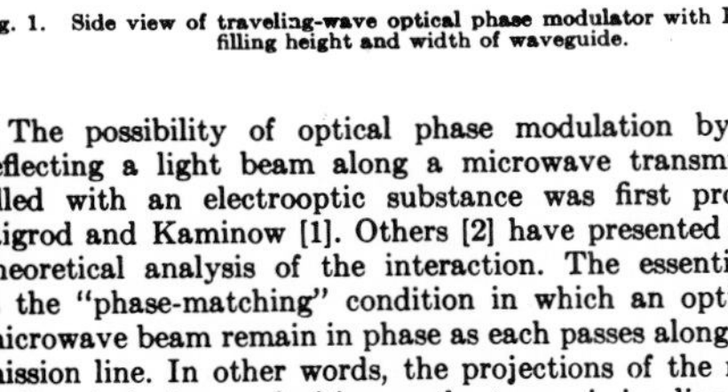

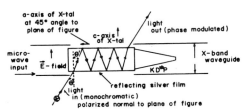

Fig. 1. Side view of traveling-wave optical phase modulator with KD*P crystal filling height and width of waveguide.

The possibility of optical phase modulation by multiply reflecting a light beam along a microwave transmission line filled with an electrooptic substance was first proposed by Rigrod and Kaminow [1]. Others [2] have presented a detailed theoretical analysis of the interaction. The essential feature is the "phase-matching" condition in which an optical and a microwave beam remain in phase as each passes along the transmission line. In other words, the projections of the microwave and optical phase velocities on the transmission-line axis must be equal. Since excessive microwave power is damaging to an electrooptical crystal, it is desirable to increase modulation index by lengthening the interaction path via a traveling-wave interaction rather than by increasing the incident microwave power.

Manuscript received July 30, 1969. This work was supported by the Air Force Office of Scientific Research, OAR, USAF, under Contract F44620-68-C-0017, Project THEMIS.

In the experiment described herein, an argon laser beam (0.5145 μ) was directed at about 20° to the optical axis of a KD*P (KD_2PO_4) crystal that was inserted in a slotted *X*-band waveguide. The optical beam was polarized at approximately 45° to the a axis of the crystal. The electric vector of the fundamental mode of the waveguide was parallel to the optic axis of the crystal and, hence, the instantaneous microwave field altered the optical beam velocity via the r_{63} electrooptic coefficient in KD*P. The sides of the crystal were plated with silver in order to reflect the light beam in "zig–zag" manner as depicted in Fig. 1. A truncated rectangular pyramid of KD*P was cemented onto the back surface of the modulator crystal. The bonding thickness was much less than an SHF wavelength. This was done to inhibit the excitation of standing waves in the modulator crystal. However, if there should be SHF waves traveling in the opposite direction in the modulator, they would impart a relatively small change in phase in the optical beam since they are unsynchronized with the phase of the optical beam. The angle of incidence was determined by the phase-match condition mentioned above. The angle of incidence θ is given by the following equation:

$$\theta = \sin^{-1} (\eta \sin \theta') = \sin^{-1} (v_m \eta^2 / c) \tag{1}$$

where θ and θ' are shown in Fig. 1, η is the optical index, and v_m is the microwave phase velocity for the particular waveguide structure and dielectric. For this experiment v_m was taken as 4.6×10^9 cm/s [3] and η as 1.5 [4]. For the sample used in this work, it was possible to obtain six successive reflections of the light beam and, hence, seven passes of the light through the crystal, as indicated in Fig. 1. The optical beamwidth was approximately 2 mm. In order to frequency-analyze the modulated optical beam, a thermally scanned Fabry–Perot interferometer [5] and a photomultiplier were positioned to receive the beam after it exited from the crystal.

Fig. 2 shows five separate scans of the interferometer for various frequencies covering a band of 4.6 GHz. The microwave power was square-wave-modulated at 1760 Hz. The output of the photomultiplier was directed into a phase-locked detector in order to suppress the central orders of the inter-

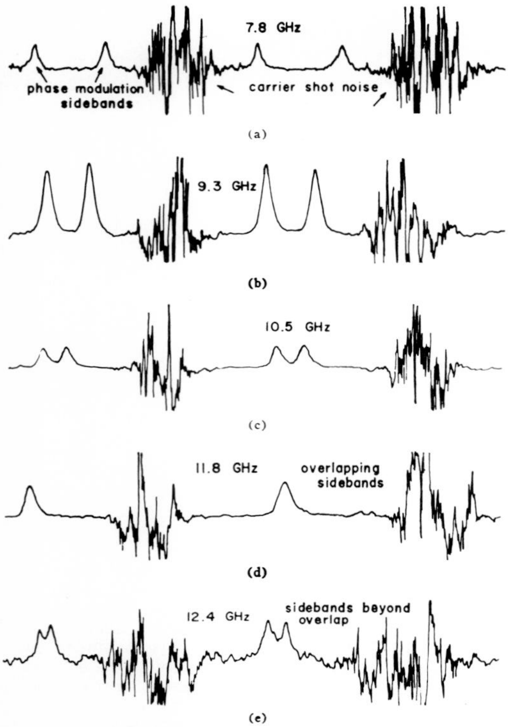

Fig. 2. Interferometer scans depicting sideband frequencies of phase-modulated light at various modulation frequencies. Frequency separation between successive noise clusters is equal to 23.9 GHz. Frequency meter readings of the modulation drive for the scans are as follows. (a) 7.8 GHz. (b) 9.3 GHz. (c) 10.5 GHz. (d) 11.8 GHz. (e) 12.4 GHz. Large noise excursions have been clipped for reproduction.

ferogram. The central orders appear in the form of shot-noise blips that are passed by the effective bandwidth of the phase-locked detector. Without the phase-lock detection and the chopped microwave source, the central orders "swamp" the side orders (sidebands) when the modulator is driven at low-power levels, as it was in this experiment. The free spectral range of the interferometer used was 23.9 GHz, which is the spacing between successive central orders in Fig. 2. Thus, the sideband structure seen in Fig. 2 is in excellent agreement with the modulation drive frequency denoted in each trace. The drive frequency was measured for each trace, using a resonance-type frequency meter. The signal-to-noise level is seen to be frequency dependent. This is easily explained by the fact that the output power of the X-13 klystron ($\sim$200 mW) used was frequency dependent. Also, the microwave absorption in the crystal exhibits a frequency dependence.

Thus, low microwave power, ultrawide-bandwidth optical phase modulation has been demonstrated utilizing a traveling-wave interaction. Amplitude modulation could be accomplished in a similar system by arranging the $\boldsymbol{a}$ axis or $\boldsymbol{b}$ axis of the crystal normal to the plane of incidence of the optical beam and parallel to the $\boldsymbol{E}$ vector and by placing a polarizer rotated to extinction (no microwave field) in the path of the outgoing optical beam.

Acknowledgment

The author wishes to thank Profs. W. G. Mayer and W. J. Thaler for helpful discussions regarding this work.

D. C. Auth[1]
Dept. of Physics
Georgetown University
Washington, D. C. 20007

References

[1] W. W. Rigrod and I. P. Kaminow, "Wide-band microwave light modulation," *Proc. IEEE*, vol. 51, pp. 137–140, January 1963.
[2] M. DiDomenico and L. K. Anderson, "Broadband electro-optic traveling-wave light modulators," *Bell Sys. Tech. J.*, vol. 42, pp. 2621–2678, November 1963.
[3] D. C. Auth, W. G. Mayer, and W. J. Thaler, "A light diffraction technique for measuring dielectric constants at microwave frequencies," *Proc. IEEE* (Letters), vol. 57, p. 96, January 1969.
[4] T. C. Lee, J. D. Heaps, and F. M. Schmidt, "A KD_2PO_4 light beam deflector," *Proc. IEEE* (Letters), vol. 56, pp. 1628–1629, September 1968.
[5] D. C. Auth, "Thermal scanning of a Fabry-Perot interferometer," *Phys. Letters*, vol. 27A, p. 536, September 1968.

[1] Now with the Department of Electrical Engineering, University of Washington, Seattle, Wash.

Reprinted from

VOLUME 16, NUMBER 11 APPLIED PHYSICS LETTERS 1 JUNE 1970

A 964-GHz TRAVELING-WAVE ELECTRO-OPTIC LIGHT MODULATOR

I. P. Kaminow, T. J. Bridges, and M. A. Pollack

Bell Telephone Laboratories, Holmdel, New Jersey 07733

(Received 18 March 1970; in final form 16 April 1970)

A 0.633-μm laser has been modulated at 964 GHz (311 μm) and 891 GHz (337 μm) by a novel phase-matched $LiNbO_3$ electro-optic modulator driven by an HCN laser. The performance of the modulator agrees with calculations based on the radio-frequency electro-optic coefficient. Similar experiments with a CdS modulator were unsuccessful presumably because of the generation of photocarriers.

A cw HCN laser has been employed to drive a continuous traveling-wave $LiNbO_3$ electro-optic light modulator at 964 GHz (311 μm) and at 891 GHz (337 μm). The modulating and carrier laser beams propagate along directions that make an angle chosen to satisfy the phase-matching condition, in a simple and novel internal reflection geometry. Approximately 10^{-5} of the power in a 0.633-μ carrier is converted into each sideband for each watt of far-infrared modulating power. The performance agrees within experimental uncertainty with calculations based on the radio-frequency (rf) (65 MHz) electro-optic coefficient. This invariance is expected because the lowest-frequency lattice resonance having appropriate symmetry[1] occurs at 7500 GHz (250 cm^{-1}), well above 965 GHz. The modulator is especially suitable for precision spectroscopic and metrological applications[2] because of the large frequency separation between carrier and sidebands. which can be measured very accurately by mixing the far-infrared (FIR) laser with harmonics of rf standards.[3]

Utilizing the r_{33} electro-optic coefficient in $LiNbO_3$, i.e., both the visible carrier and FIR modulating waves polarized along the c axis, the phase modulation index is[4]

$$\eta = (\pi n_3^3 r_{33}/\lambda_c)\int E_m(l)\,dl \qquad (1)$$

with n_3 as the extraordinary refractive index at carrier wavelength λ_c, E_m as the peak modulating field, and l as the path of the carrier along which the integral is taken. The ratio R of power in each first sideband to power in the carrier for a phase-modulated signal is

$$R = J_1^2(\eta)/J_0^2(\eta) \approx \tfrac{1}{4}\eta^2 \qquad (2)$$

for small η, with $J_n(\eta)$ as the nth-order Bessel function. The sideband spectrum is illustrated in Fig. 1(a).

Phase velocities of the interacting waves must be matched over the path l specified in (1) for each sideband frequency $\omega_\pm$ separately,

$$\vec{k}_\pm = \vec{k}_c \pm \vec{k}_m, \quad \omega_\pm = \omega_c \pm \omega_m, \qquad (3)$$

where $\vec{k}$ is the wave vector. If the angle between $\vec{k}_0$ and $\vec{k}_m$ is $\lambda_\pm$ for each sideband, as in Fig. 1(b), then[5]

$$\cos\gamma_\pm = (n_3/\epsilon_3^{1/2})\{1 \pm [(\epsilon_3 - n_3^2)/2n_3^2](\omega_m/\omega_c)\}$$

$$\approx n_3/\epsilon_3^{1/2} = \cos\gamma, \qquad (4)$$

for ω_m/ω_c small, with ϵ_3 the dielectric constant along the c axis at ω_m, and $\gamma \approx \gamma_\pm$. Taking[4] $\epsilon_3 = 27$ and $n_3 = 2.20$ yields $\gamma = 65°$ and $(\gamma_- - \gamma_+) = 0.51°$. If the matching condition is not exactly satisfied, then (1) is reduced by a $(\sin x/x)$ factor[6] that has its first zero when the angular deviation is

$$\delta\gamma = \pm\lambda_m/l_T(\epsilon_3 - n_3^2)^{1/2} \qquad (5)$$

For total path length $l_T = 2$ mm, as in our case, $\delta\gamma \approx \pm 2$. In our experimental configuration, the FIR modulating beam is incident normally on a $LiNbO_3$ slab of thickness t, where $t^{-1} \approx \alpha_3$ and α_3 is the FIR absorption coefficient for fields polarized along c. If γ is less than the angle for total internal reflection β ($\sin\beta = n_3^{-1}$) the carrier may be incident on the same face as the modulating beam. But if $\gamma > \beta$, as for $LiNbO_3$, the internal reflection configuration in Fig. 2 is particularly convenient. Here $t = 0.86$ mm and $w = 3.68$ mm.

The optical carrier is provided by a small (~10 mW) He-Ne laser operating at 0.633 μm. A 10-cm lens focuses the beam into the crystal. Fine tuning of the matching angle is achieved by

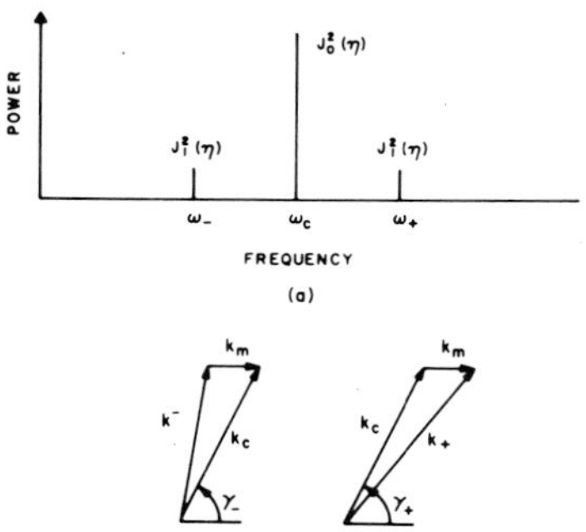

FIG. 1. (a) Sideband structure. (b) Wave-vector matching.

mirror displacement S shown in Fig. 2. A double monochromator, cooled S-20 photomultiplier, and lock-in amplifier detect the optical beam. The sidebands are observed with the reference chopper at A and the carrier with the chopper at B. Sideband ratio R is measured by inserting calibrated attenuators into the 0.633-μm beam and η is determined from (2). The FIR beam is generated by a 3-m-long cw HCN laser capable of producing about $\frac{1}{2}$ W at either 337 or 311 μm in the fundamental transverse mode and a single longitudinal mode. It is focussed onto the crystal by a 20-cm lens. A 10-dB attenuator is introduced at the output of the HCN laser to isolate it from crystal and lens reflections. The waist diameter D measured with a scanning slit is 1.9 mm between

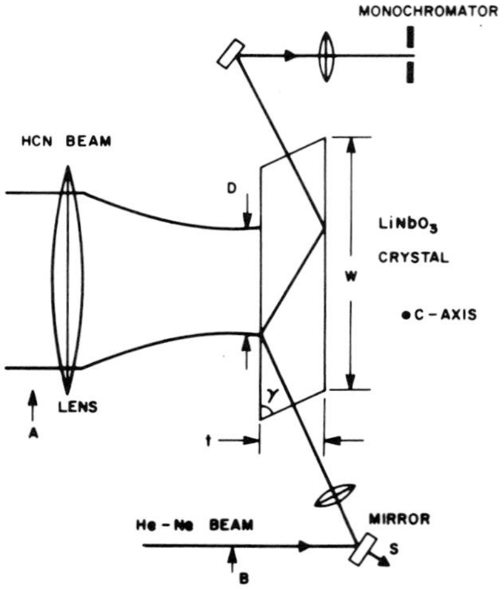

FIG. 2. Internal reflection modulator configuration (schematic drawing).

half-power points, which is slightly greater than the projection of the 0.633-μm beam path onto the face of the crystal.

The phase-matched modulation index and sideband ratio can be calculated from the distribution of $E_m(l)$ along the optical path. For a fundamental Gaussian beam propagating along the z axis, the field at the waist varies as $\exp[-(r/w_0)^2]$ in the radial direction, with $w_0 = 1.6$ mm corresponding to the measured half-power diameter D. The field decays as $\exp(-\frac{1}{2}\alpha_3 z)$, with $\alpha_3 = 11$ cm^{-1} (Ref. 7). Because of surface reflections, the modulating power P entering the crystal is TP_{IN}, with T=0.54 and P_{IN} is the incident power. The field at $z = 0$, $x = 0$ is

$$E_m(0) = (4z_0 TP_{IN}/\pi\epsilon_3^{1/2} w_0^2)^{1/2}, \tag{6}$$

where $z_0 = 377\ \Omega$. According to (6), $E_m(0) = 440P_{IN}^{1/2}$ V/m with P_{IN} in watts. Since $\alpha_3 l = 0.95$, multiple reflections can be neglected. Note that adjacent segments of the optical beam path are not modulated because the matching condition is not satisfied. After some manipulation the integral in (1) becomes $9.6\times10^{-4}\ E_m(0)$ V. For comparison, the optical path length l_T is 20×10^{-4} m. Then, with the rf electro-optic coefficient[8] $r_{33} = 31\times10^{-12}$ m/V, the calculated η and R are

$$\eta = 7.0\times10^{-3} P_{IN}^{1/2} (\text{rad}), \tag{7}$$

$$R = 1.2\times10^{-5} P_{IN}.$$

Repeated sideband ratio measurements with $P_{IN} \approx 0.1$ W give

$$R = (0.7\pm0.3)\times10^{-5} P_{IN} \tag{8}$$

at either 964 or 891 GHz. The good agreement confirms the invariance of r_{33} up to 964 GHz. The chief experimental uncertainties arise from measurement of P_{IN}(~ 50%) with an Eppley thermopile having a reflection coefficient of 90% at 337 μm, and from measurement of optical attenuation at 0.633 μm (~ 20%). The angles calculated in (4) and (5) were experimentally found to be $\gamma = 63°$, $\gamma_- - \gamma_+ = 0.45°$, and $\delta\gamma = 1°$. These are internal angles that have been corrected for refraction at the surface. The observed γ, which is significantly smaller than the calculated value, implies $\epsilon_3 \approx 24$ if $n_3 \doteq 2.2$.

Operating characteristics of the device at other carrier and modulation frequencies can be determined by considering the wavelength dependence in (1) as well as dispersion in α_3, ϵ_3, and n_3.

Calculations indicate that a modulator with efficiency comparable to $LiNbO_3$ can be made using CdS at a matching angle of 34.5°. However, no modulation was observed with an experimental CdS modulator, presumably due to generation of photocarriers by the 0.633-μm beam. It is estimated from a linear extrapolation of low light level photoconductivity data provided by the crystal supplier (Harshaw) that the resistivity in the neighborhood of a focused (4×10^{-3} cm diameter) 15-mW beam is reduced from 10^5 Ω-cm to ~10^{-3} Ω-cm, and the absorption coefficient is raised to ~ 10^4 cm^{-1}. Photocarrier production can be reduced by operating farther from the band edge and/or using undoped CdS.

We are grateful to R.H. Stolen for measuring the infrared absorption coefficients of our samples, and to E.G. Burkhardt for assistance in development of the HCN laser.

[1]I. P. Kaminow and W. D. Johnston, Jr., Phys. Rev. 160, 519 (1967).

[2]J. L. Hall, R. L. Barger, P. L. Bender, H. S. Boyne, J. E. Faller, and J. Ward, Electron Technology (Warsaw) 2, (1969); Z. Bay and G. G. Luther, Appl. Phys. Letters 13, 303 (1968).

[3]L. O. Hocker, A. Javan, and D. Ramachandra Rao, Appl. Phys. Letters 10, 147 (1967).

[4]I. P. Kaminow and E. H. Turner, Proc. IEEE 54, 1374 (1966).

[5]W. W. Rigrod and I. P. Kaminow, Proc. IEEE 51, 137 (1963).

[6]I. P. Kaminow and Julia Liu, Proc. IEEE 51, 132 (1963).

[7]Values measured on our samples by R. H. Stolen at 337μ, 296 °K: $LiNbO_3$, $\alpha_3 = 11.2$ cm^{-1}, $\alpha_1 = 20.3$ cm^{-1}; CdS, $\alpha_3 = 2.3$ cm^{-1}, $\alpha_1 = 2.9$ cm^{-1}. For $LiNbO_3$ see also D. R. Bosomworth, Appl. Phys. Letters 9, 330 (1966).

[8]E. H. Turner, Appl. Phys. Letters 8, 303 (1966).

Reprinted from *Opt. Commun.* **5**, 374-379 (1972).

TRAVELLING WAVE ELECTRO-OPTIC MODULATORS

G. WHITE and G.M. CHIN
Bell Telephone Laboratories, Holmdel, New Jersey 07733, USA

Received 23 May 1972

The performance of travelling wave electro-optic modulators is considered. Analyses are made of the characteristics of these modulators in both the time and frequency domains. These analyses are used in the design of a 1.5 GHz modulator for high speed optical modulation. It is shown that even at these high bandwidths it is not necessary to resort to velocity compensation of the electrical and light signals.

1. Introduction

Light modulation using the Pockels' effect, which is exhibited by a number of electro-optic crystals, is well established. Pockels' effect type modulators have been developed in a number of forms including, the untuned lumped element [1], tuned cavity [2], and travelling wave type [3]. All of these realizations exhibit certain disadvantages including low modulation efficiency, narrow bandwidth or complex construction. The travelling wave type however, possesses a number of advantages for baseband operation. Theoretically, large bandwidths are obtainable with this type of modulator with velocity compensation of the electrical and light signals. Such compensation requires that techniques be adopted to either decrease the velocity of the light signal [4] or increase the velocity of the electrical signal [5]. The first technique presents some difficult fabrication problems while the latter involves a loss of modulation power due to the modulating field being partially distributed in nonactive material. For modest bandwidths (≈ 1 Gbit $\sec^{-1}$), however, velocity compensation is not necessary and many of these disadvantages are avoided. This paper considers the characteristics and limitations of these modulators, specifically, using $LiTaO_3$ as the dielectric crystal, and it is shown how designs may be realized to produce a modulator characteristic impedance that is well matched to the impedance levels of high speed driving circuits so that efficient interfacing is obtained over a broad modulation frequency band.

Bandwidth limitations in travelling wave modulators result from the differential transit times. These effects are analyzed in this paper and it is also shown how the effect of electrical attenuation, along the length of the modulator, modifies these results. Design results are summarized and the experimental characteristics of a particular modulator are presented.

2. Transit time effects in travelling wave electro-optic modulators

The modulator structure under consideration is of the form of a parallel plate transmission line with the electro-optic material as the dielectric. If the characteristic impedance is matched to that of the driving circuit impedance and the dielectric dispersion is negligible, electrically, the modulator appears as a broadband, real impedance, matched structure; optically, the electro-optic response is limited by the transit time effect. This effect may be analyzed as follows.

2.1. *Time domain analysis*

Consider a rectangular pulse of width τ, height $1/\tau$, which is allowed to propagate along the conductors of the parallel plate modulators, of length L, in the same direction as that of the light beam. In this situation, the electrical pulse is travelling at a velocity v_S, and the light signal is travelling at a velocity v_l. For $v_l > v_S$, it can readily be shown that the induced phase retardation of the exiting light beam has a finite rise and fall rectangular form. Since the time required for the pulse to completely travel through the crystal, t_S, is

$$t_S = L/v_S + \tau$$

and the length dl, that the light signal will travel in the same interval of a time is

$$dl = (L/v_S + \tau)\, v_l . \quad (1)$$

Then, the portion of the light signal interacting with the pulse is

$$(L/v_S + \tau)\, v_l - L \quad (2)$$

and the time of interaction T_i is

$$T_i = \frac{(L/v_S + \tau)\, v_l + L}{v_l} = \frac{L}{v_S} - \frac{L}{v_l} + \tau . \quad (3)$$

Now, the phase retardation magnitude, Γ, is determined as follows:

After time τ, the electrical pulse has completely entered the modulator. A point of light entering the modulator at this time will experience a voltage $1/\tau$, until it passes the front end of the electrical pulse. The phase retardation is cummulative along the interactive length, d, of the modulator so that the phase retardation for that point of light is,

$$\Gamma = (\pi/V_0 L)\,(1/\tau)\,(d) , \quad (4)$$

where V_0 is the half wave voltage of the modulator. But, the interactive length, d, is

$$d = \frac{\tau}{1/v_S - 1/v_l} \quad (5)$$

and, therefore,

$$\Gamma = \frac{\pi}{V_0 L\,(1/v_S - 1/v_l)} = \frac{\pi}{V_0 T} , \quad (6)$$

where $T = L(1/v_S - 1/v_l)$.

Now, if we let the pulse width $\tau \to 0$, the input function tends to an impulse function, and the resulting impulse response $\Gamma_i\,(t)$ will be of rectangular form, i.e.,

$$\Gamma_i\,(t) = (\pi/V_0 T)\;[U(t) - U(t-T)] , \quad (7)$$

where $U(t)$ is the unit step function. The step function response is obtained simply as the integral of the impulse response function. In this case, the rise time of the travelling wave modulator is,

$$t_r = L(1/v_S - 1/v_l) \quad (8)$$

$$= (L/c)\,[(\epsilon_r)^{1/2} - n] , \quad (9)$$

where c is the velocity of light, ϵ_r is relative dielectric permittivity and n is the index of refraction.

2.2. *Frequency domain analysis*

The frequency response of the modulator can readily be found by Fourier transformation of the impulse response function (7) which has the form

$$\Gamma(\omega) = (2\pi/V_0 T\omega)\,\sin(\tfrac{1}{2}\omega T) . \quad (10)$$

This is of the familiar sin ω/ω form where a 3dB bandwidth can be defined at $\omega_{3dB} = 2.8/T$.

2.3. *Attenuation of electrical signal in modulator*

Loss of electrical modulation power, along the length of the modulator crystal, is frequently observed in practical devices. This loss results in a reduction in magnitude of the induced phase retardation since the electrical field strength is not constant along the entire modulator length. Assume that the voltage attenuation along the length of the modulator crystal has the form $\exp(-\alpha_1 l)$, when α_1 is observed to be essentially frequency independent in the range considered. The impulse response is then of the form,

$$\Gamma(t) = (\pi/V_0 T)\,\exp(-\alpha_2 t)\,[U(t) - U(t-T)] \quad (11)$$

$$= (\pi/V_0 T)\,\{\exp(-\alpha_2 t)\,U(t)$$

$$- \exp(-\alpha_2 T)\exp[-\alpha_2\,(t-T)]U(t-T)\} , \quad (12)$$

where

$$\alpha_2 = \frac{\alpha_1}{(1/v_S - 1/v_l)}. \tag{13}$$

The initial value of phase retardance will be equal to the zero electrical attenuation case. This is due to the initial value being induced at the beginning of the crystal, before attenuation takes place. As the modulating waveform traverses the modulator its amplitude is decreased due to attenuation. Concomitantly, the magnitude of the induced phase retardation decreases with the same attenuation factor, since phase retardation is a linear function of applied voltage. The resulting frequency domain equation is obtained simply from the Fourier inversion of eq. (12), i.e.,

$$\Gamma(\omega) = \frac{\pi}{V_0 T}\left(\frac{\exp\,[-\mathrm{i}\tan^{-1}(\omega/\alpha_2)]}{(\alpha_2^2 + \omega^2)^{1/2}} - \exp(-\alpha_2 T)\frac{\exp\{-\mathrm{i}[\tan^{-1}(\omega/\alpha_2) - T\omega]\}}{(\alpha_2^2+\omega^2)^{1/2}}\right) \tag{14}$$

This modified form of the phase retardation spectrum will result in an effective reduction in the modulator half wave voltage. For the case where the electrical power loss is one half, the effective reduction in modulation at half wave voltage is found, from eq. (14), to be 85 percent of the lossless case. More importantly, the form of eq. (14) indicates that, unlike the lossless case, the phase spectrum is nonlinear. This will result in frequency dispersion of the output waveform.

3. Modulator design process

The electrical design of the modulator is characterized by the bandwidth, modulation power and characteristic impedance. With the travelling wave modulator, the bandwidth, resulting from the transit time limitation is determined by the length of the modulator and the light and electrical signal velocity differential; characteristic impedance is determined by the crystal cross sectional aspect ratio and the relative permittivity; modulation power is a function of aspect ratio, half wave potential, optical frequency and depth of modulation.

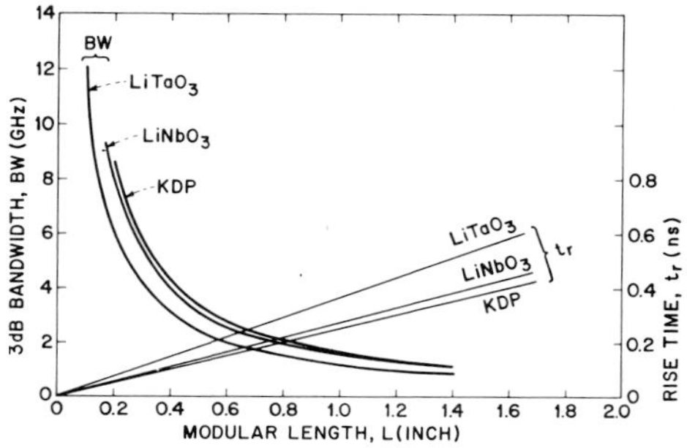

Fig. 1. Modulator bandwidth and risetime as a function of aspect ratio.

The bandwidth of the electro-optic modulator, defined at the 3dB point, is obtained directly from eq. (10). The step function response time is obtained directly from eq. (9). Both characteristics are independent of optical frequency, being determined solely by the transit time differential, T; these modulator characteristics are shown in fig. 1 for $LiTaO_3$, $LiNbO_3$ and KDP.

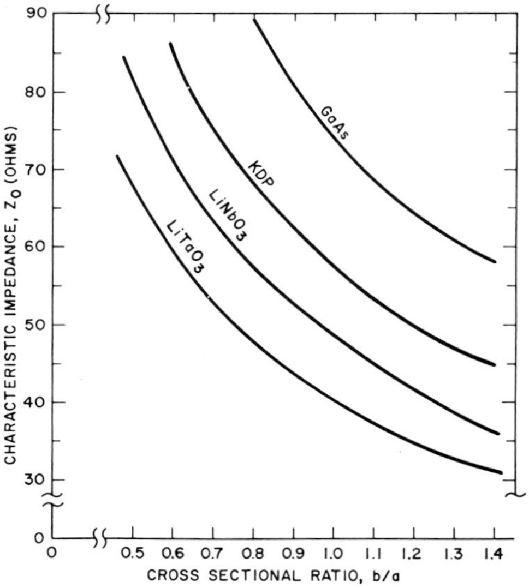

Fig. 2. Characteristic impedance as a function of cross-sectional ratio.

376

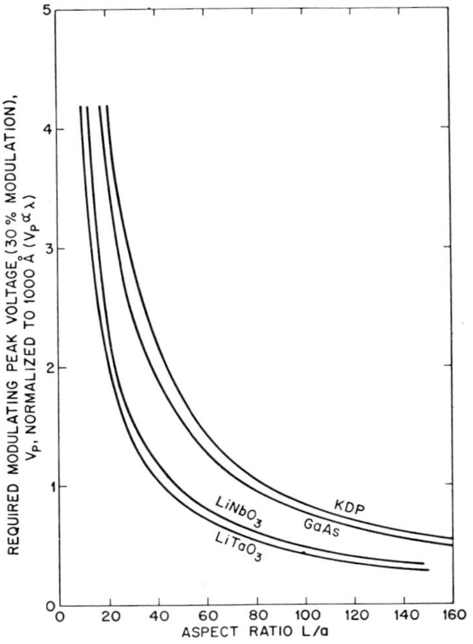

Fig. 3. Peak modulation potential as function of aspect ratio.

Characteristic impedance is readily calculated in terms of the sectional inductance [6] and capacitance. The results of these calculations are given in fig. 2 for various modulator materials. These results represent approximate values since the effects of electric field fringing are not included. The modulation power requirement is intimately associated with many of the modulator characteristics including aspect ratio, half wave potential, optical frequency and depth of modulation. In linear modulation systems 30% depth of modulation is the approximate maximum modulation depth. Beyond this point the strong nonlinear effects of the cosine transfer function become apparent [7]. Fig. 3 presents the peak modulation potential requirement for this depth of modulation as a function of the modulator parameters.

As a particular example of these design procedures, consider the following modulator requirements,

bandwidth = 2 GHz;
impedance, $Z_0 = 40\ \Omega$;
modulation power (30%), $P = 150$ mW;
material, $LiTaO_3$;
optical wavelength, 496 nm.

From fig. 1, we have, for 2 GHz bandwidth, $L = 600$ mils. From fig. 3 for $P = 150$ mW ($V_p = 3.47$ V), $L/a = 60$, that is $a = 10$ mils for $L = 600$ mils and from fig. 2, for $Z_0 = 40\ \Omega$, $b/a = 1.0$ or $b = 10$ mils.

Using these design parameters, the performance of an actual travelling wave modulator was evaluated. This modulator was fabricated with electrodes of chromium, gold and paladium on opposite faces of the crystal which was embedded in a microstrip mount as shown in fig. 4. The mounting is with a low temperature solder which provides effective damping of piezoelectric resonances [8].

4. Performance characteristics

The characteristic impedance from time domain reflectometry measurements was approximately 33 Ω as compared to the calculated value of 40 Ω. This difference may be accounted for by the fringing of the electric field, which has been neglected in the calculation. Measurements were conducted in a 50 Ω system and, while the modulator rod exhibited a deviation from this impedance, no significant standing waves were observed as a result of this mismatch. Measurements were made from 400 MHz to 2.5 GHz by inserting the modulator into a 50 Ω microstrip transmission line; only a constant, frequency independent, 1.4 dB attenuation was observed in the electrical signal.

The frequency response of the modulator was measured by applying a modulating voltage to the modulator structure and the exiting voltage, after it had traversed the crystal, was monitored by a sampling oscilloscope. The modulated light output was detected by a silicon photodiode in a coaxial mount. The silicon photodiode in the coaxial mount had a response time constant of 40 psec [9]. The voltage across the crystal was maintained at 3 V peak. The induced changes of temperature due to modulation signal heating caused some observable degradation in modulation depth; these changes were negated by adjustments of the optical compensator. This problem can be eliminated by a temperature self-compensation technique [8].

The optical beam was provided by an argon laser operated at a single frequency of 496 Å with a beam

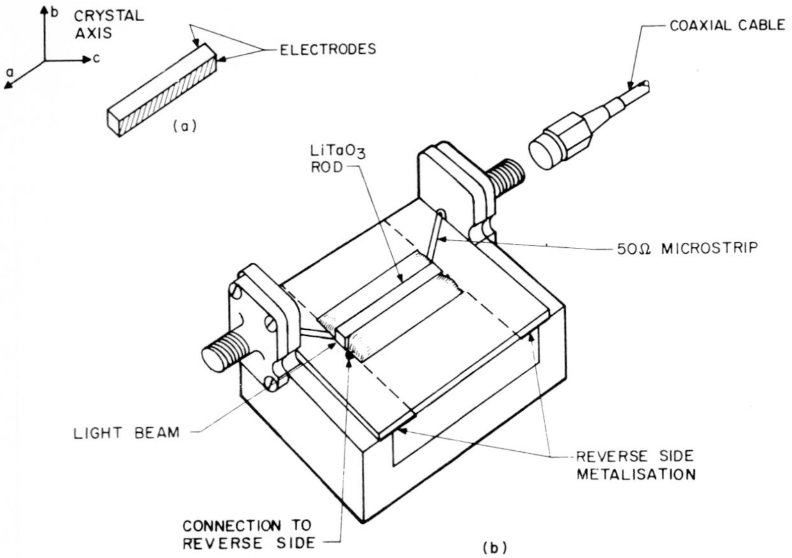

Fig. 4. Travelling wave modulator embedded in microstrip line mount.

power of approximately 43 mW. Fig. 5a shows the typical electro-optic output waveforms from the photodiode as well as the modulation signal exiting from the modulator at a frequency of 1.6 GHz. 30% modulation was obtained with 3 V peak modulating potential. Fig. 6 shows the photodiode output voltage versus modulation frequency. The 3 dB bandwidth is approximately 1.5 GHz.

In the time domain measurement, a 200 psec rise time pulse provided by a step recovery diode is allowed to propagate through the modulator. The upper trace in fig. 5 shows the shape of the applied voltage while the lower trace shows the electro-optic output wave shape. The rise time of the electro-optic response is approximately 400 psec. This response time is in agreement with the calculated value obtained via a convo-

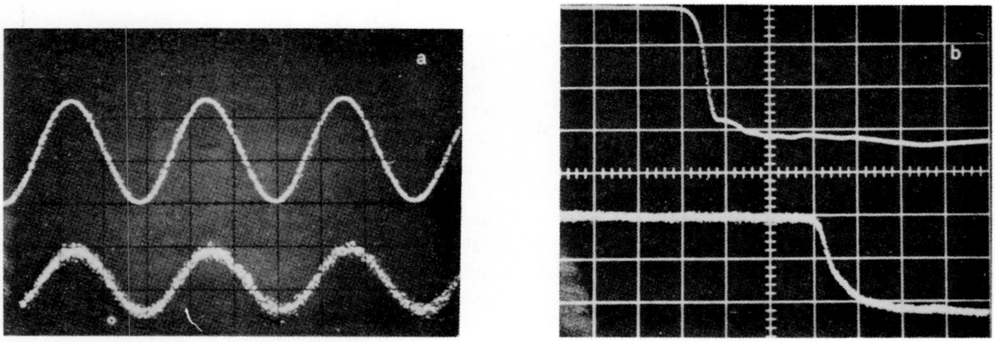

Fig. 5. (a) Typical electro-optic response at 1.6 GHz. (b) Electro-optic pulse response (horizontal, 500 psec/cm). In both (a) and (b) the upper curve is the electrical signal, 2V/div., and the lower curve is the electro-optic output, 20 mV/div.

378

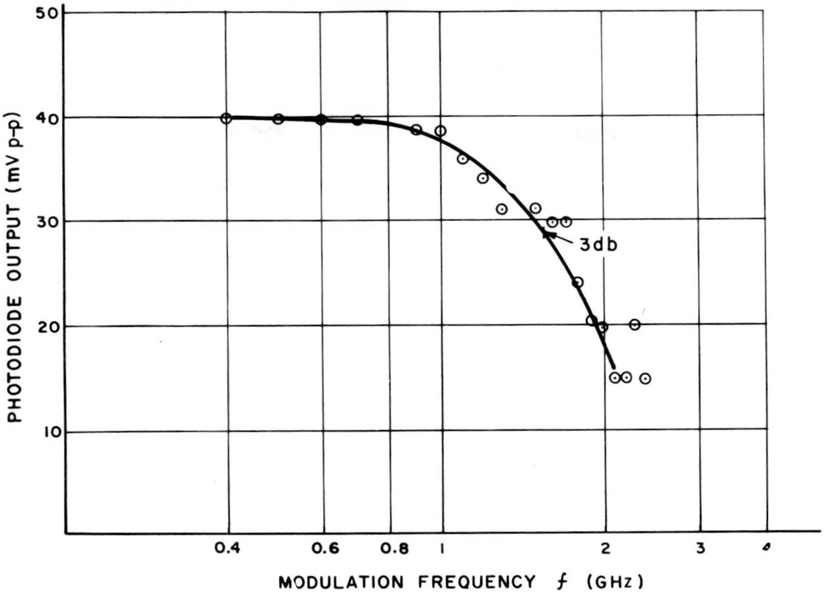

Fig. 6. Frequency response of modulator in the range 400 MHz to 2 GHz.

lution of the impulse response of eq. (7) and the input waveform of the step recovery diode.

5. Conclusions

The performance characteristics of travelling wave electro-optic modulators have been considered. The analysis of the performance in both the time and frequency domains has permitted a number of design aids to be presented. These aids provide substantial agreement with actual modulator performance at above 1 GHz. It is clear that for such bandwidths, velocity compensation of the electrical and optical signals is not necessary and extremely efficient matching of impedance levels is afforded. This matching relaxes considerably the interfacing requirements of the high speed electronic driving circuits with the optical components.

Acknowledgement

The authors are indebted to M.R. Biazzo for the fabrication of the modulator crystal and mounts.

References

[1] R.T. Denton, T.S. Kinsel and F.S. Chen, Proc. IEEE Letters 54 (1966) 1472.
[2] I.P. Kaminow, Phys. Rev. Letters 6 (1961) 528.
[3] M. Didomenico Jr. and L.K. Anderson, Bell System Tech. J. 27 (1963) 2621.
[4] I.P. Kaminow and J. Liu, Proc. IEEE 51 (1963) 132.
[5] C.J. Peters, Proc. IEEE 53 (1965) 455.
[6] W.F. Grover, Inductance calculations working formulas and tables (Dover Publications, New York).
[7] G. White, Bell System Tech. J. 50 (1971) 2607.
[8] M.R. Biazzo, Appl. Opt. 10 (1971) 1016.
[9] H. Melchior, private communication.

5. Frequency Shifters and Pulse Compressor

Reprinted from *Appl. Phys. Lett.* **1**, 46–49 (1962).

OPTICAL FREQUENCY SHIFTING BY ELECTRO-OPTIC EFFECT

C. F. Buhrer, D. Baird, and E. M. Conwell
General Telephone and Electronics Laboratories, Inc.
Bayside 60, N. Y.

(Received August 27, 1962)

We have shown theoretically that the frequency of a light beam can be shifted with very little loss in intensity by use of the transverse Pockels effect in a crystal of suitable symmetry. The principle has been used to produce shifts of 1000 and 1500 cycles in light from a sodium lamp and a helium-neon gas maser by means of a cubic zinc sulfide crystal. The existence of the shifts was demonstrated by producing the two shifted frequencies simultaneously and showing beats in the resulting light intensity at the difference frequency. Such shifts were produced earlier in a different way by the use of a pair of potassium dihydrogen phosphate crystals.[1] The present technique has the advantage that no harmonics are generated and that, except for light losses by reflection or absorption in the crystal, all the incident light can be shifted to the new frequency as compared with a theoretical maximum of about 50% for the other technique. As is true of the other technique, it should be capable, with minor modifications, of producing shifts well into the microwave range.

The optical characteristics of a birefringent crystal are conveniently described with the use of an ellipsoidal surface, the indicatrix, given by[2]

$$\frac{x^2}{n_1^2}+\frac{y^2}{n_2^2}+\frac{z^2}{n_3^2}+\frac{2yz}{n_4^2}+\frac{2zx}{n_5^2}+\frac{2xy}{n_6^2}=1\ , \qquad (1)$$

where x, y, and z are coordinate axes in the crystal. The properties of the indicatrix are such that the major and minor axes of its central section (an ellipse) normal to a given direction are the allowed polarization directions for light propagating in the given direction through the crystal. The lengths of the axes are numerically twice the refractive indices for the corresponding polarization directions. In terms of the coefficients in (1), the linear electro-optic, or Pockels, effect is described by

$$n_i^{-2}=(n_i^{-2})_{E=0}+\sum_{j=1}^{3} r_{ij}E_j\ , \qquad (2)$$

where the E_j are the electric field components and the r_{ij} the electro-optic coefficients.

Consider that we have light traveling along a 3-fold axis, to be taken as the z axis, in an electro-optic crystal. By symmetry, in the absence of an electric field the central section of the indicatrix normal to the 3-fold axis is circular, and there is no birefringence. On application of an electric field in the plane perpendicular to this axis, with components $E_x = E_m \cos\alpha$, $E_y = E_m \sin\alpha$, the section becomes elliptical. Symmetry considerations show[2] that, for the specified orientation,

$$\begin{aligned} r_{12} &= r_{61} = -r_{22}\ ; \\ r_{21} &= r_{62} = -r_{11}\ . \end{aligned} \qquad (3)$$

With these relations we may write the equation of the indicatrix section in the $z = 0$ plane as

$$\begin{aligned} &[(1/n_0^2)+(r_{11}E_x - r_{22}E_y)]x^2 \\ &\quad + [(1/n_0^2)+(-r_{11}E_x + r_{22}E_y)]y^2 \\ &\quad + 2[-r_{22}E_x - r_{11}E_y]xy = 1\ , \end{aligned} \qquad (4)$$

where n_0 is the refractive index in the absence of electric field. To write (4) in the principal axis system we must rotate the axes an angle θ given by

$$\begin{aligned} \theta = (1/2)\ \text{arc sin}\ [&-(r_{22}/\bar{r})\cos\alpha \\ &-(r_{11}/\bar{r})\sin\alpha] = -(1/2)(\alpha+\Phi)\ , \end{aligned} \qquad (5)$$

where $\bar{r} = \sqrt{r_{11}^2 + r_{22}^2}$, $\Phi = \text{arc sin}\ r_{22}/\bar{r}$. The fixed angle Φ, independent of the field direction, occurs because of the choice of the coordinate system for which the matrix r_{ij} was written. In the principal axis system the equation of the ellipse is

$$[(1/n_0^2)+\bar{r}E_m]x'^2 + [(1/n_0^2)-\bar{r}E_m]y'^2 = 1. \qquad (6)$$

If the electric field were a rotating one, with $\alpha = \omega_m t$, it is seen from (5) that the ellipse would rotate in the opposite sense to that of the field with an angular velocity $\omega_m/2$. It is this behavior, which results from the three-fold rotational symmetry, that is basic for frequency shifting by the technique described here.

The retardation Γ, in radians, of light with the slow direction of polarization relative to light with the fast direction, after traversing a thickness d of crystal is $2\pi d$ times the reciprocal of the free-space wavelength λ and times the difference in the indices of refraction. Since $\bar{r}E_m$ is small in practice, we obtain from (6), to a very good approximation,

$$\Gamma \simeq 2\pi d n_0^3 \bar{r} E_m/\lambda\ . \qquad (7)$$

Depending only on the magnitude of the electric field, this would be independent of time in a rotating field.

Consider now what happens when circularly polarized light travels through an electro-optic crystal along a three-fold axis with a rotating electric field applied in the plane perpendicular to the three-fold axis. Assume that the electric vector of the incident light is given by

$$A_x = A\cos\omega t,\quad A_y = A\sin\omega t\ , \qquad (8)$$

corresponding to a left-handed rotation. Inside the crystal the allowed polarization directions are x' and y'. If the transit time through the crystal is small compared to $2\pi/\omega_m$, we may write for the light emerging from the crystal

$$\begin{aligned} A_{x'} &= A\cos(\omega t - \theta + \Gamma/2)\ , \\ A_{y'} &= A\sin(\omega t - \theta - \Gamma/2)\ , \end{aligned} \qquad (9)$$

47

where Γ is given by (7). When these are expressed with respect to the original stationary axes, we find, after some trigonometry,

$$A_x = A \cos(\Gamma/2) \cos \omega t$$
$$- A \sin(\Gamma/2) \sin\{(\omega + \omega_m)t + \Phi\},$$
$$A_y = A \cos(\Gamma/2) \sin \omega t$$
$$- A \sin(\Gamma/2) \cos\{(\omega + \omega_m)t + \Phi\}, \qquad (10)$$

where (5) has been used to eliminate θ. The first terms in A_x and A_y correspond to a left-circularly polarized vibration at the original frequency with an amplitude $A \cos \Gamma/2$. The second terms in A_x and A_y correspond to a right-circularly polarized vibration at the angular frequency $\omega + \omega_m$ with amplitude $A \sin \Gamma/2$. It is seen that for $\Gamma = \pi$ complete conversion of the incident light to $\omega + \omega_m$ takes place. It is also noteworthy that for small Γ, less than 30° or so, the amount of $\omega + \omega_m$ generated is linear in Γ, and therefore linear in the electric field intensity.

In the preceding discussion the modulating electric field and the incident light polarization were assumed to rotate in the same direction. If the direction of either rotation were reversed, the frequency $\omega - \omega_m$ would be obtained.

Crystals of the proper symmetry – that is, having a 3-fold rotation axis and nonvanishing linear electro-optic effect – are found in classes 23 and $\bar{4}3m$ of the cubic system, $\bar{6}$ and $\bar{6}m2$ of the hexagonal system, and 3, 32 and $3m$ of the trigonal system. In the cubic system the electro-optic effect is usually described in terms of the coefficient r_{41} referred to cubic axes. This coefficient is $(\sqrt{6}/2)\,\bar{r}$. For the hexagonal and trigonal systems the axes are normally chosen as above.

We have demonstrated the operation predicted above using cubic zinc sulfide, which is in class $\bar{4}3m$. Two different samples cut from optical-quality regions of sphalerite specimens were used. One sample was a 3-mm cube, the other a bar 5-mm thick and 8.5-mm long. The end faces, which were (111) planes, were polished. Pairs of electrodes on the other four faces were fed with modulating signals of 2000 V peak amplitude, separated $\pi/2$ radians in phase, to provide a rotating electric field in the (111) plane. Both a sodium lamp and a helium-neon gas laser were used successfully as light sources. Light from either source was sent through a left-circular polarizer, through the crystal along a (111) axis, and then through a right-circular analyzer so that only the shifted frequency could emerge. This light was detected by a multiplier phototube, the output of which was displayed on an oscilloscope. Polarizer and analyzer were first adjusted so that no light went through the combination. Insertion of the zinc sulfide crystal resulted in a small amount of light emerging from the analyzer, perhaps because of scattering in the crystal. Figure 1 shows oscillograms under three conditions of operation. The top trace represents the modulating

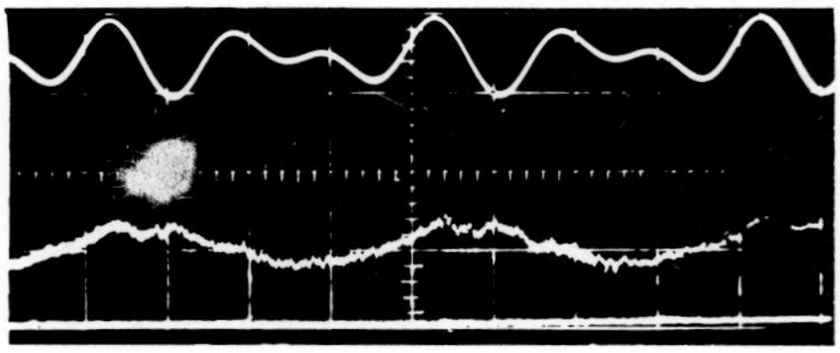

b

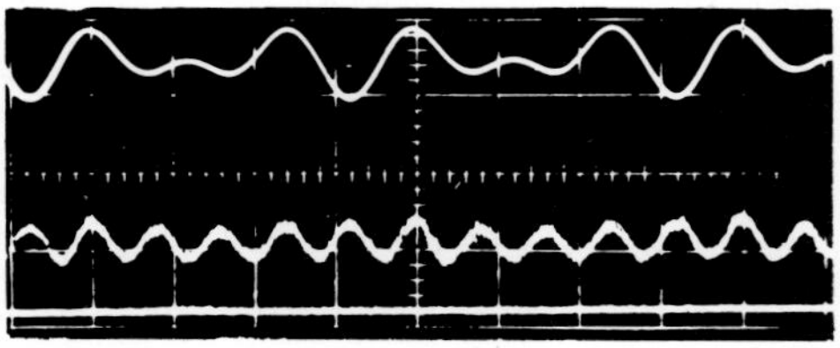

c

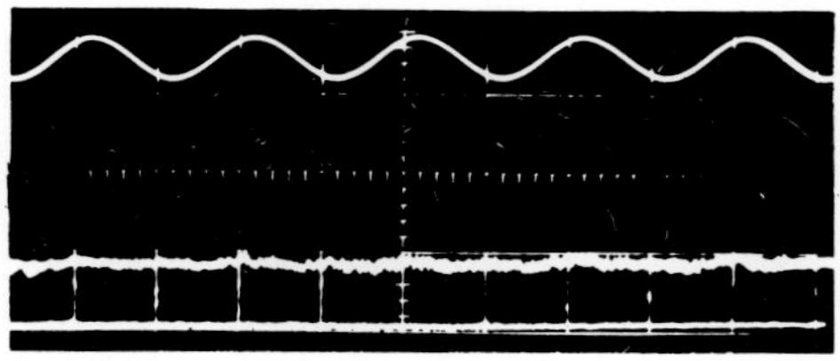

a

Fig. 1. Oscillograms showing modulating voltages and resulting photomultiplier output.

48

voltage, while the middle and bottom traces represent the photomultiplier output with and without incident light. In 1*a* the modulating voltage had a frequency of 1,000 cycles, and an increase in output proportional to the voltage is observed. In 1*b* the modulating signal consisted of 1,000- and 1,500-cycle voltage superimposed so that frequencies of $\omega/2\pi$ + 1,000 and $\omega/2\pi$ + 1,500 cycles were produced. Beats at a frequency of 500 cycles are observed in the photomultiplier output. In 1*c* the polarity of one of the voltages was changed so that angular frequencies $\omega/2\pi$ + 1,000 cycles and $\omega/2\pi$ − 1,500 cycles were produced. The beats are seen to have a frequency of 2,500 cycles.

The value of $\bar{r}$ measured for the large crystal was 1.55×10^{-7} cm/kV, in fair agreement with the value of Namba.[3] For an applied voltage of 2 kV, Γ calculated from (7) for the Na lamp wavelength is $\pi/4$, which corresponds to 15% conversion of the light intensity to the displaced frequency. For complete conversion with this crystal a peak voltage of 8 kV would be necessary. Smaller voltage would, of course, suffice for longer and thinner crystals.

Thanks are due Prof. H. Winchell of Yale University for supplying one of the sphalerite specimens.

[1]C. Buhrer, V. Fowler, and L. Bloom, *Proc. I.R.E.*, (in press).

[2]J. F. Nye, *Physical Properties of Crystals*, University Press, Oxford, 1960.

[3]S. Namba, *J. Opt. Soc. Am.*, **51**, 76 (1961).

IEEE JOURNAL OF QUANTUM ELECTRONICS, VOL. QE-4, NO. 8, AUGUST 1968

Optical Frequency Shifting of a Mode-Locked Laser Beam

MICHEL A. DUGUAY AND JOHN W. HANSEN

Abstract—**An optical frequency shifter making use of the electro-optic effect in $LiNbO_3$ was built to shift the Fourier spectrum of a mode-locked He–Ne laser; the shift was continuously adjustable from −45 GHz to +45 GHz about the central optical frequency of 473.61 THz. Shifted Fourier spectra recorded with a scanning Fabry–Perot interferometer were found to be in excellent agreement with theory.**

Introduction

THE desirability of tunable laser beams has long been recognized. Such devices would be very useful in high-resolution spectroscopy, multiple resonance experiments, and photochemistry, for example. We describe here a device which has proved capable of shifting the Fourier spectrum of the output beam of a mode-locked He–Ne laser beam over a range of ±45 GHz, about the central optical frequency 473.61 THz. The total scan—90 GHz—is still modest on the optical scale, but clearly represents an unsurpassed bandwidth on the microwave scale. Moreover, the success of this experiment points to the possibility of shifts of several THz within the near future, i.e., shifts large enough to change the color of laser beams.

Theory

The operation of the device [1] is most simply explained on the basis of a Doppler effect. An analysis of the device in terms of sidebands in the frequency domain has been given by Garrett and Duguay [2]. Normally one would associate the notion of Doppler shift with moving sources or observers. More generally, however, a Doppler shift arises from a time-varying *optical path length*. This will occur, even with stationary source and observer, provided the light traverses a medium whose refractive index is varying with time [3], [4].

In our experiment, short (≈0.35 ns) light pulses generated by a He–Ne laser, are passed through an electrooptic crystal whose refractive index is modulated by a sinusoidal RF electric field. The frequency of the RF field is a harmonic of the $c/2L$ repetition frequency of the mode-locked laser and is phase-locked to it (c is the speed of light and L is the effective length of the laser cavity). The RF phase is adjusted so that as the light pulses traverse the crystal, the refractive index is decreasing almost linearly with time (see Fig. 1). Since the optical path length is decreasing linearly with time, the effect at the observation point is the same as would result from a uniform motion of the source towards the observer, viz., a Doppler up-shift of the optical frequency. A down-shift is obtained by changing

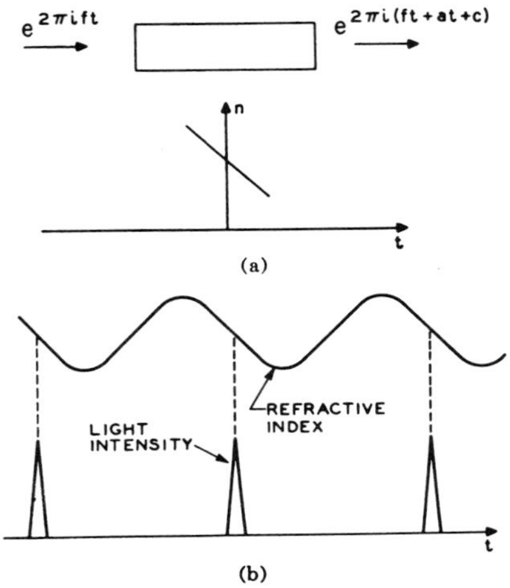

Fig. 1. (a) The refractive index n of the modulator crystal decreases linearly with time. A continuous wave which enters the crystal at frequency f emerges at an up-shifted frequency $f + a$. (b) In the experiment, the refractive index actually changes sinusoidally with time. Plotted on the same time scale is the intensity of light produced by the laser.

the RF phase by 180°. The amount of shift can be continuously varied by adjusting the value of the RF electric field.

Let us assume that the RF field modulates the refractive index n according to

$$n = n_0 - \Delta n \sin \omega t, \tag{1}$$

where n_0 and Δn are constants and ω is the RF angular frequency.

For a crystal of length d, the optical path length p for a portion of the light pulse entering the crystal at time $t - T$ and exiting at time $t + T$, is given by

$$p(t) = \int_{t-T}^{t+T} \frac{d}{2T}(n_0 - \Delta n \sin \omega t')\, dt', \tag{2}$$

$$p(t) = n_0 d - d\, \Delta n \left(\frac{\sin \omega T}{\omega T}\right) \sin \omega t, \tag{3}$$

where T is the transit time through *half* the crystal. Let ν be the central optical frequency of the mode-locked laser. The instantaneous Doppler shift $s(t)$ is then

$$s(t) = -\frac{1}{c}\left(\frac{dp}{dt}\right)\nu = \frac{\omega \nu\, d\, \Delta n}{c}\left(\frac{\sin \omega T}{\omega T}\right) \cos \omega t. \tag{4}$$

If the light pulses are very short compared to the RF period and cross the midpoint of the crystal at times

Manuscript received January 30, 1968; revised April 25, 1968.
The authors are with Bell Telephone Laboratories, Inc., Murray Hill, N. J.

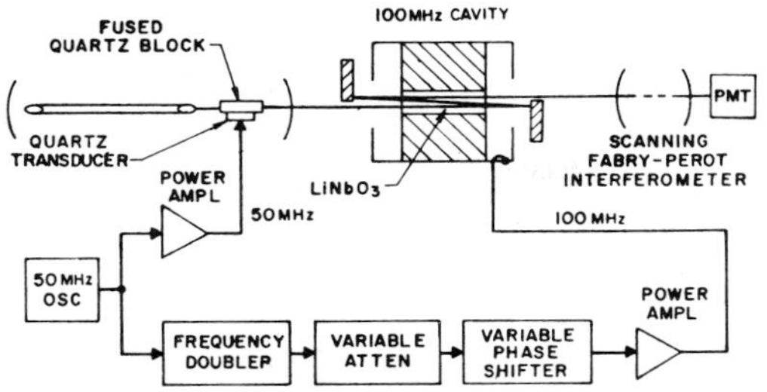

Fig. 2. The experimental arrangement showing the mode-locked laser, and 100-MHz RF cavity with the modulator crystal. Flat mirrors outside the cavity are used to fold the laser beam to produce multiple passes through the modulator.

$\omega t = 0, \pm 2\pi, \pm 4\pi, \ldots$ then cos ωt may be approximated over the duration of the pulse by unity and all the light is up-shifted by the maximum amount

$$S = \frac{\omega \nu\, d\, \Delta n}{c}\left(\frac{\sin \omega T}{\omega T}\right). \qquad (5)$$

Note that for transit times short compared to the RF period, the factor between parentheses in (5) is nearly unity.

Experimental Technique

The experimental setup is shown in Fig. 2. A 6328-Å He–Ne laser 1.5 m long was mode-locked by means of an acoustic modulator, as in the work of Hargrove, Fork, and Pollack [5]. A 10-MHz x-cut quartz transducer was bonded to a rectangular block of fused quartz, set at the Brewster angle. It proved necessary to reduce the acoustical Q of the block by sticking a piece of adhesive tape on the surface opposite the transducer. High acoustical Q's led to excessive temperature dependence of the phase of the acoustical drive, and hence of the phase of the light pulses. The transducer was driven at 50 MHz to induce mode-locking at the $c/2L$ light pulse repetition frequency of 100 MHz. These pulses were detected with an avalanche photodiode and displayed on a sampling oscilloscope.

The electrooptic crystal was a slab-shaped single-domain crystal of lithium metaniobate [6] of dimensions 2.7 × 11 × 31 mm. The c axis of the crystal was normal to the 11 × 31-mm surfaces upon which chromium–gold electrodes were evaporated. Antireflection coatings were evaporated on the entrance and exit faces (2.7 × 11 mm) of the crystal. The crystal was placed in the high electric field region of a reentrant cavity tuned to 100 MHz and having an unloaded Q of about 900. The Q of the cavity loaded by the crystal was about 600, implying that the crystal Q was $\approx$1800.

Power at 100 MHz was inductively coupled into the cavity; it was derived by frequency doubling and amplification from the same oscillator which was used to mode-lock the He–Ne laser. The RF field applied to the $LiNbO_3$ crystal was thus phase-locked to the train of light pulses. A variable delay line was used to adjust the phase of the RF field.

The He–Ne beam was plane-polarized so that its electric field vector was directed parallel to the c axis of the lithium-niobate crystal; this was also the direction of the RF electric field. The appropriate electrooptic coefficient is then r_{33} (equal to 3.08×10^{-9} cm/V, [7]) and we have

$$\Delta n = -n_e^3 r_{33} \frac{E}{2} = -1.64 \times 10^{-8} E, \qquad (6)$$

where n_e, the extraordinary refractive index, is equal to 2.20 at $\lambda = 6328$ Å, [8], and E is the amplitude of the RF electric field.

The optical mode spectra (Fourier spectra) were observed with a conventional scanning Fabry–Perot interferometer, the output of which was detected by a photomultiplier and displayed on an oscilloscope.

Experimental Results

When the RF electric field was adjusted to the maximum value allowed by the electronics, a shift of 4.8 GHz was observed. The Fourier spectra of the unshifted laser beam and the up-shifted beam are shown in Fig. 3. The spectrum of the mode-locked laser is roughly Gaussian in shape with a full width at half-height of 1.5 GHz corresponding in the time domain to Gaussian-shaped pulses, 0.30 ns at half-height. The intermode spacing is 100 MHz, the $c/2L$ frequency. The spectrum is centered at an optical frequency of 473.61 THz. As can be seen in Fig. 3 the spectrum of the up-shifted beam is identical in shape with that of the unshifted beam, in agreement with theory [2].

Two small dielectric mirrors were positioned about 1 cm away from the ends of the crystal as shown in Fig. 2; this allowed the laser beam to make several passes through the crystal, thereby leading to larger shifts. With 11 passes, shifts as large as ±45 GHz were recorded. Up-shifts and down-shifts by 39 GHz are shown in Fig. 4. Note that the free spectral range of the interferometer is 26.5 GHz in Fig. 4, so that a given peak is shifted by *one range and one half*, not just half a range as might appear from the figure. By varying the RF electric field amplitude from 0 to its maximum value, one could "follow" the peaks as they moved along the frequency scale, and therefore make sure that the shift was not in error by a multiple of 26.5 GHz.

Note that the shift for 11 passes (45 GHz) is not simply 11 times the single pass shift (4.8 GHz) because of the (sin $\omega T/\omega T$) factor in (5). This factor was 0.83 for 11 passes corresponding to a total transit time $2T$ equal to 2.9 ns.

This factor could have been reduced to essentially unity by replacing the left-hand small dielectric mirror in Fig. 2 by a curved mirror 1.5 m away. This way, a given light pulse would make a double pass through the crystal, go to the curved mirror and return (properly refocused) to the crystal exactly one RF period later; the Doppler shift on successive double passes would be maximum, the (sin $\omega T/\omega T$) factor in (5) being equal to 0.994.

At the maximum RF voltage the crystal was dissipating about 50 watts of RF power. To avoid heating effects the RF was applied with a maximum duty cycle of about 20

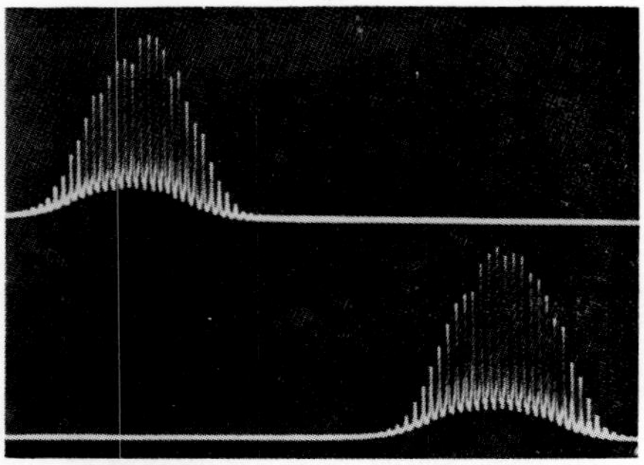

Fig. 3. Detected output of the scanning Fabry–Perot interferometer. The upper trace shows the 1.5-GHz-wide unshifted spectrum, centered at an optical frequency of 473.61 THz. The lower trace shows the spectrum up-shifted by 4.8 GHz, after one pass through the modulator.

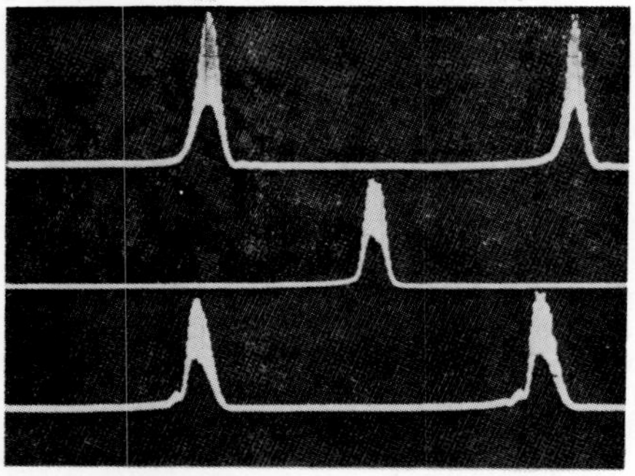

Fig. 4. Mode spectra with 9 passes through the modulator, and the interferometer set for a free spectral range of 26.5 GHz. The center trace shows the unshifted spectrum, the upper trace a down-shift of 39 GHz and the lower trace an up-shift of 39 GHz. Note that the shift is $1\frac{1}{2}$, not $\frac{1}{2}$, free spectral ranges. One may also see satellites associated with the shifted peaks.

percent, so that the average power dissipation was ≈ 10 watts in the crystal.

The RF power required to achieve a shift of 4.8 GHz in one pass need not be 50 watts if the crystal dimensions are optimized as in light modulators (see Kaminow and Turner, reference [12]. When this is done, one finds that the RF power required is given [9] by

$$\text{Power} = \eta^2 \frac{f}{Q} \times \text{constant},$$

where f is the RF frequency (here 100 MHz), Q is the quality factor of the circuit (here 600), η is the modulation index and is equal to the shift in units of f (here $\eta = 48$), and the constant for the present orientation of $LiNbO_3$ at 6328 Å is ≈ 2 mW/MHz. In conventional light modulators η is ~ 1. The factor η^2 is therefore quite large here by comparison. However, in the frequency shifter, bandwidth is not desired and is kept small (f/Q is ≈ 0.16 MHz in our experiment). The power requirement for an optimum geometry and a shift of 4.8 GHz in a single pass is then

$$\text{Power} = 48^2 \times (0.16\ \text{MHz}) \times (2\text{mW/MHz}) = 0.74\ \text{watts}. \quad (7)$$

For multiple passes one either increases the lateral dimension of the crystal, as was done here, or one uses many successive crystals with proper focusing at each stage. The result is that the power is multiplied by the number of passes.

Note that the power required is at a fixed frequency; such power is much more easily available than the broadband power required in light modulators.[1]

Satellite Peaks

In Fig. 4, one will notice a small satellite peak appearing to the low-frequency side of the up-shifted spectrum and to the high-frequency side of the down-shifted one. This is due to the slight departure of $\cos \omega t$ from unity in (2) for the wing portions of the light pulses ($t \sim \Delta t$, where Δt is the full width of the pulses at half-height); or equivalently, to the departure of the sine wave in (1) from a straight line at the time when the pulses traverse the crystal (see Fig. 1). For very large shifts, more satellite peaks would appear as predicted by the phase-modulation theory [2]. The theory shows that shifts of the order of the cube of the number of modes locked together times the mode spacing are possible before strong distortions of the output Fourier spectrum appear.

To see how this comes about, let us expand the expression for the instantaneous shift in powers of ωt; using (4) and (5) we have

$$s_1(t) = S_1 \cos \omega t$$

$$s_1(t) = S_1\left[1 - \frac{(\omega t)^2}{2} + \frac{(\omega t)^4}{4!} - \cdots\right]. \quad (8)$$

In the present experiment ωt for wing portions of the light pulses was

$$\omega t \sim \omega \Delta t = 2\pi \times 10^8\ \text{seconds} \times 0.3 \times 10^{-9}\ \text{seconds} = 1.9 \times 10^{-1} \quad (9)$$

so that the $(\omega t)^2/2$ factor in (8) was of the order of 2 percent, and all the higher order terms were negligible. The $(\omega t)^2$ factor causes energy in the wing portions of the pulse to be shifted by a smaller amount than energy in the central portion, the difference being

$$S_1 - s_1(\Delta t) = S_1 \frac{(\omega \Delta t)^2}{2}. \quad (10)$$

This difference becomes of the order of the laser beam linewidth for shifts large enough so that

$$S_1 \frac{(\omega \Delta t)^2}{2} \sim \frac{1}{\Delta t} \quad (11)$$

[1] Although the function of a frequency shifter is quite different from that of a phase modulator, it is interesting that they are identical in physical construction, and they both shift the instantaneous frequency of a light beam, a pulsed beam in one case, a CW beam in the other.

or

$$S_1 \sim \frac{2}{\omega^2 \Delta t^3} = \frac{f}{2\pi^2 (f\Delta t)^3}. \qquad (12)$$

When the RF frequency f is equal to the mode-locked laser repetition frequency $c/2L$, the number N of modes between the half-power points of the Fourier spectrum is

$$N = \frac{0.44}{f\Delta t}. \qquad (13)$$

Using this relation in (12) we find that for shifts

$$S_1 \sim 0.6\, N^3 f, \qquad (14)$$

distortions of the output Fourier spectrum will appear, in agreement with [2]. In our experiment at $f = 100$ MHz, N is about 15 so that distortions of the output Fourier spectrum are expected for shifts of the order of

$$S_1 \sim 200 \text{ GHz}. \qquad (15)$$

These distortions of the original line shape do not constitute, however, a serious limitation of the optical frequency shifter. For it is possible to virtually eliminate these distortions by passing the beam through a second electro-optic crystal driven at a harmonic of f, the frequency applied to the first crystal.[2] This second crystal would be driven at frequency mf (m = integer ≥ 2) in such a way as to produce an instantaneous shift given by

$$s_2(t) = -S_2 \cos m\omega t. \qquad (16)$$

Expanding (16) and adding to (8) we find that the total shift produced by the two crystals would be

$$s(t) = s_1(t) + s_2(t) = S_1 - S_2 - (S_1 - m^2 S_2)\frac{(\omega t)^2}{2} + (S_1 - m^4 S_2)\frac{(\omega t)^4}{4!} - \cdots . \qquad (17)$$

If the amplitude of the second shifter is adjusted so that

$$S_2 = \frac{S_1}{m^2} \qquad (18)$$

then, (17) reduces to

$$s(t) = S_1\left[\left(1 - \frac{1}{m^2}\right) + (1 - m^2)\frac{(\omega t)^4}{4!} - \cdots\right]. \qquad (19)$$

The same reasoning which led to (14) can again be applied here. We find that shifts would now have to be of the order of

$$S_1 \sim \frac{0.9}{m^2 - 1} N^5 f, \qquad (20)$$

in order for distortions due to the $(\omega t)^4$ term to become significant. In the present experiment, taking $m = 3$, this would mean shifts of the order of 10 THz.

[2] The use of an additional cavity to improve the quality of the shift has also been suggested independently by M. R. Schroeder.

Outlook

Clearly the present experiment only demonstrates the feasibility of significant optical frequency shifts by the Doppler effect in electrooptic crystals; much larger shifts could be obtained if desired. The easiest way to increase the shift is to make the laser beam go through the crystal a larger number of times. In the present experiment, the presence of poorly damped acoustic waves, piezoelectrically generated, caused light-intensity losses of about 10 percent per pass, which imposed a limit on the total number of passes. Proper design of the crystal holder could probably have eliminated those.

The use of higher RF voltages and better electrooptic crystals [10], [11] will also lead to larger shifts. For a given RF voltage and a given crystal, it is possible to increase the shift by using higher RF frequencies. The upper limit on the frequency is set by the width of the pulses [12] (through N) and by the amount of distortion on the output spectrum which can be tolerated. As was shown above the use of a second crystal would substantially increase this limit.

The mode-locked Nd : YA1G laser [13], [14] can produce pulses about 30 ps wide at 1.06 μ and $\approx$20 ps in the green at 0.53 μ by second harmonic generation. Since these pulses are more than 10 times shorter than the He–Ne pulses (0.3 ns), RF frequencies in excess of 1 GHz could be used for Doppler shifting. Shifts in excess of 500 GHz should be readily available in a Doppler shifter having the same parameters as the present one, except for the higher RF frequency. With the improvements suggested above, shifts of several THz appear feasible in the near future. Such shifts would be detectable by the eye as color changes.

Acknowledgment

The authors wish to express their gratitude to Dr. K. B. Jefferts for many suggestions, and to Dr. C. G. B. Garrett for stimulating discussions and encouragement throughout the course of this work. In addition, we should like to thank Dr. K. Nassau, who supplied the modulator crystal, and Dr. W. T. Lynch, who supplied the photodiode.

References

[1] M. A. Duguay, L. E. Hargrove, and K. B. Jefferts, "Optical frequency translation of mode-locked laser pulses," *Appl. Phys. Letters*, vol. 9, p. 287, 1966.

[2] C. G. B. Garrett and M. A. Duguay, "Theory of the optical frequency translator," *Appl. Phys. Letters*, vol. 9, p. 374, 1966.

[3] The effect has been previously used by L. Grodzins and E. A. Phillips, *Phys. Rev.*, vol. 124, p. 774, 1961, to shift the Fe^{57} 14 keV X-ray line, and by F. P. Küpper and E. Fünfer who shifted the frequency of a giant ruby laser pulse using the Kerr effect in nitrobenzene.

[4] For an alternate approach to electrooptic frequency shifting, see the very elegant work of C. F. Buhrer, D. Baird, and E. M. Conwell, *Appl. Phys. Letters*, vol. 1, p. 46, 1962.

[5] L. E. Hargrove, R. L. Fork, and M. A. Pollack "Locking of He–Ne laser modes induced by synchronous intracavity modulation," *Appl. Phys. Letters*, vol. 5, p. 4, 1964.

[6] K. Nassau, H. J. Levinstein, and G. M. Loiacono, "Ferroelectric lithium niobate," pts. 1 and 2, *J. Phys. Chem. Solids*, vol. 27, pp. 983 and 989, 1966.

[7] E. H. Turner, "High-frequency electro-optic coefficients of lithium niobate," *Appl. Phys. Letters*, vol. 8, p. 303, 1966.

[8] G. D. Boyd, Robert C. Miller, K. Nassau, W. L. Bond, and A. Savage, "$LiNbO_3$: an efficient phase matchable nonlinear optical material," *Appl. Phys. Letters*, vol. 5, p. 234, 1964.

[9] I. P. Kaminow and E. H. Turner, "Electro-optic light modulators," *Appl. Opt.*, vol. 5, pp. 1612–1628, October 1966.
[10] P. V. Lenzo, E. G. Spencer, and A. A. Ballman, "Electro-optic coefficients of ferroelectric strontium barium niobate," *Appl. Phys. Letters*, vol. 11, p. 23, 1967.
[11] J. E. Geusic, H. J. Levinstein, J. J. Rubin, S. Singh and L. G. Van Uitert, "The nonlinear optical properties of $Ba_2Na_2Nb_5O_{15}$," *Appl. Phys. Letters*, vol. 11, p. 269, 1967.
[12] Note that the width of the pulses can be reduced by optical pulse compression using the Doppler shifter. See "Compression of optical pulses" by J. A. Giordmaine, M. A. Duguay, and J. W. Hansen, *IEEE J. Quantum Electronics*, vol. QE-4, pp. 252-255, May 1968.
[13] M. DiDomenico, Jr., J. E. Geusic, H. M. Marcos, and R. G. Smith, "Generation of ultrashort optical pulses by mode-locking the YAIG : Nd laser," *Appl. Phys. Letters*, vol. 8, p. 180, 1966.
[14] J. E. Geusic, private communication. See also "Observation of picosecond pulses from a Nd : YAG laser" by M. Bass and D. Woodward (preprint), who measured pulses ~19 ps long in a self-locked Nd : YAG laser.

Reprinted from IEEE JOURNAL OF *QUANTUM ELECTRONICS*
Vol. QE-4, Number 8, August 1968
Pp. 477-481

Reprinted by permission from
IEEE JOURNAL OF QUANTUM ELECTRONICS
Vol. QE-7, No. 9, September 1971

Rotating-Waveplate Optical-Frequency Shifting in Lithium Niobate

JAMES P. CAMPBELL, SENIOR MEMBER, IEEE, AND WILLIAM H. STEIER, MEMBER, IEEE

***Abstract*—A rotating-waveplate optical frequency shifter using lithium niobate ($LiNbO_3$) has been constructed and fully evaluated. The experimental modulator frequency shifts the incoming 6328-Å light by 110 MHz, requires 15 W of drive power, and has an inherent 12-MHz bandwidth. The output beam has high spectral purity with very little power in unwanted sidebands and closely matches the TEM_{00} mode of the input beam. An analysis of the effects of electrical and optical maladjustments on modulator performance shows only moderate requirements on optical and electrical alignment. Heating due to the absorbed drive power slightly degrades the modulator in agreement with a temperature analysis of the modulator. An increase in insertion loss due to diffraction of the light by acoustic waves in the $LiNbO_3$ crystal was observed.**

Introduction

THE principal of using a rotating half-wave plate as a frequency shifter is well known. Devices based on it are in use at microwave frequencies [1] and at optical frequencies [2]. Buhrer *et al.* [3] first proposed the possibility of optical frequency shifting by rotation of an applied electric field in an electrooptic crystal with a threefold axis. To be frequency shifted the optical beam must be circularly polarized and directed along the threefold axis of the crystal. With no field applied, the crystal exhibits no birefringence and the emergent beam is unaffected. When the applied field has the proper half-wave amplitude and rotates in a plane normal to the threefold axis, a rotating half-wave plate is induced in the crystal. The emergent beam has its optical frequency shifted and its sense of polarization reversed. The frequency shift is equal to the rotation rate of the applied field.

An early implementation of the rotating-field modulator [4] at audio drive frequencies was hampered by the poor optical quality of the natural zinc sulfide crystals used. Tandem phase modulators, which approximate the action of the rotating-field modulator, have been demonstrated at audio frequencies [5], [6] and at microwave frequencies [7]. These modulators can use high-quality KDP crystals, which lack a threefold axis. However, they produce undesired frequency components in the output optical beam. These components inherently restrict conversion efficiency to 50 percent or less. Microwave-drive-frequency versions of the true rotating-field modulator have been operated [8], [9] with special provisions to handle the transit-time problems that arise at these frequencies. In these cases, operation at the half-wave condition, which eliminates the undesired input optical frequency from the output beam, was not possible because of a combination of weak electrooptic effects in the crystals used and inability to generate sufficiently large microwave fields in the crystals.

Manuscript received April 9, 1971; revised May 21, 1971. This work was supported by the Joint Services Electronics Program through the Air Force Office of Scientific Research, under Grant AFOSR-69-1622-B, and by Northrop Corporate Laboratories, Northrop Corporation, Hawthorne, Calif. This paper was based on a Ph.D. dissertation submitted by J. P. Campbell to the University of Southern California, Los Angeles.
J. P. Campbell was with the Aircraft Division of Northrop Corporation, Hawthorne, Calif. He is now with the Aerospace Corporation, El Segundo, Calif.
W. H. Steier is with the Department of Electrical Engineering, University of Southern California, Los Angeles, Calif.

The present experimental and theoretical investigation of a rotating-field modulator was prompted by the recent availability of large high-quality crystals of lithium niobate ($LiNbO_3$) [10]. This material has the required threefold-symmetry axis and a much stronger electrooptic effect than crystals used in earlier embodiments of the modulator. A drive frequency of 110 MHz was chosen; this frequency is somewhat below the region where transit-time effects become troublesome. This paper reports the first complete evaluation of a true rotating-field electrooptic frequency shifter using a high-quality electrooptic crystal.

Because a uniformly rotating applied field ideally results in a single, new frequency in the output beam, the rotating-field modulator has been referred to by earlier workers as a single-sideband suppressed-carrier (SSBSC) modulator. However, if the applied field contains several frequency components, its spectral content is not preserved in the output optical beam. Instead, a variety of new intermodulation terms arise because of the particular nonlinear relationship between the output waveform and the applied field vector. By contrast, an SSBSC modulator simply shifts the spectrum of the baseband information signal to a new spectral region.

Potential applications of the electrooptic frequency shifter include frequency-shift keying in a digital communication system and analog frequency modulation by applying a constant-amplitude, frequency-modulated subcarrier to the driving circuits of the electrooptic crystal. The frequency shifter can also be used to provide a tunable optical-frequency local oscillator in a coherent optical receiver and to implement the phase-mapping technique described by Crane [2].

An alternative to the rotating-field frequency shifter in the applications mentioned is the acoustooptic frequency shifter [11]. The acoustooptic device appears to require only about 1 W of drive power. Its chief drawback is that the output optical beam is deflected by an amount proportional to the imposed frequency shift.

Description of the Modulator

As sketched in Fig. 1, the modulator contains a $1 \times 1 \times 20$-mm $LiNbO_3$ crystal bonded to a copper heat sink. Stripes of silver paint on three of the rectangular crystal surfaces act as three electrodes; the heat sink serves as a fourth electrode. Drive-frequency signals from the power oscillator are applied directly to one pair of opposing electrodes and, with a 90-deg phase shift, to the other such pair. This gives the desired rotating electric field inside the crystal. The experimental modulator is designed for operation near 100 MHz. This frequency is low enough that variations in the driving field along the length of the crystal are negligible, but high enough to avoid dimensional acoustic mode resonances.

The optical beam, which is directed along the longitudinal axis (c axis) of the $LiNbO_3$ rod, is folded back on itself by a mirror for a second pass through the crystal. It can be shown [2] that the phase retardation for a given induced birefringence is thus doubled. As a result, the peak-voltage requirement is halved and the power dissipation is reduced by a factor of four.

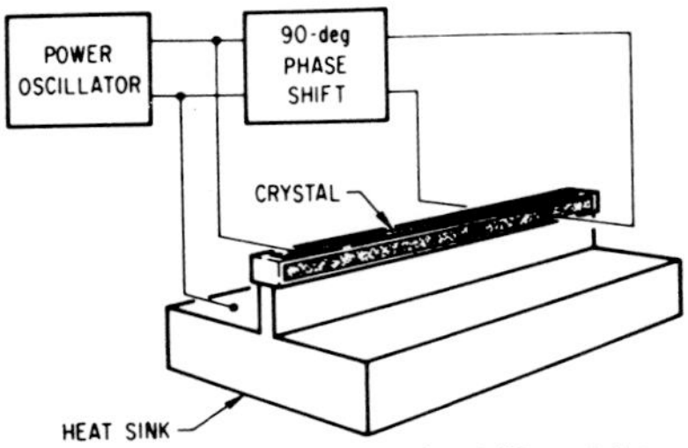

Fig. 1. Configuration of rotating-field modulator.

Power Requirement and Inherent Bandwidth

The drive-frequency power required to achieve complete conversion to the shifted frequency is given by

$$P = 2\tfrac{1}{2}(V_\pi^2)/R, \tag{1}$$

where V_π is the voltage required to produce half-wave phase retardation and R is the effective parallel resistance of the crystal, as determined by the crystal bulk and surface losses. The initial factor of two accounts for the two pairs of electrodes. The half-wave voltage is related to crystal parameters by [10]

$$V_\pi = \lambda d/(2n_0^3 r_{22} L). \tag{2}$$

The ordinary refractive index n_0 of lithium niobate is 2.29 and the electrooptic coefficient r_{22} is 3.4×10^{-12} m/V. The crystal width d is 1.0 mm and the effective length L (for double-pass operation) is 40 mm. An optical wavelength λ of 632.8 nm was used. Substitution of these numerical values into (2) gives a half-wave voltage of 194 V. The measured value of parallel resistance R at 110 MHz is 2000 Ω, giving an estimated drive-power requirement of 19 W.

As discussed by Kaminov and Turner [12], there is an inherent bandwidth for a modulator matched to a voltage generator through an ideal transformer and this bandwidth is determined by the impedance of the crystal. Let the modulator bandwidth B be the frequency range within which the square of the voltage across a pair of electrodes falls below its center-frequency value by less than a factor of 2. This bandwidth is given by

$$B = 1/(\pi RC), \tag{3}$$

where C is the parallel capacitance of the crystal. The measured value of C is about 13 pF, which gives an inherent bandwidth of 12 MHz. A greater bandwidth can be obtained at the expense of additional drive power (1.6 W/MHz) by shunting the crystal resistance R with additional resistance.

Beam Geometry and Field Configuration

In the experimental modulator the waist size of the TEM_{00}-mode beam from the He–Ne source is adjusted by appropriately placed lenses. The waist size is thus made very nearly optimum (0.12 mm in diameter) for passing through a crystal of this length [13]; it is located approximately at the folding mirror. The beam diameter at the input/output face of the crystal is then about 0.14 mm, facilitating alignment within the 1.0-mm end-face dimension.

Fig. 2 shows the size of the beam relative to the crystal cross section and gives qualitative sketches of the electric field distributions at two different times during the drive-frequency cycle. It is evident that the field is not uniform in regions away from the crystal's central axis. However, it is necessary to satisfy the requirement for a constant-amplitude uniformly rotating field only in the central region occupied by the beam.

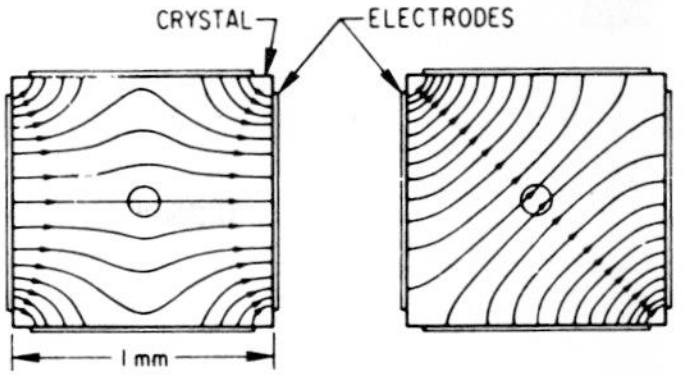

Fig. 2. Crystal cross sections showing approximate electric-field distributions when top and bottom electrodes are at zero potential (left) and $\frac{1}{8}$ modulation period later (right). The small circle is the e^{-2} intensity contour of the beam.

Heat Removal

The modulator crystal is bonded to a narrow ridge on the copper heat sink with silver-filled epoxy of high thermal and electrical conductivity. Removal of heat only from the bottom surface of the crystal results in internal temperature variation, the temperature increasing with vertical distance from the bottom surface. Ignoring end effects and applying boundary conditions that imply no heat removal from the crystal except via the heat sink, the heat-flow equation [14] can be solved to find the equilibrium temperature distribution within the crystal

$$T(x) = T_0 + (H/2k)(2dx - x^2). \tag{4}$$

The temperature T is (in this simplified analysis) a function only of x, the vertical distance from the bottom surface. The heat energy H generated per unit time per unit volume is assumed to be uniform throughout the crystal; k is the thermal conductivity, d is the vertical dimension of the crystal, and T_0 is the heat-sink temperature.

The effect of this temperature variation should be a vertical deflection upward and a defocusing of the output beam since the ordinary index of $LiNbO_3$ increases with increasing temperature [15]. Since r_{22} is almost independent of temperature up to about 100°C [16], this temperature gradient should affect the modulator performance only if it strains the crystal.

EXPERIMENTS

Static Response of the Crystal

Among the preliminary tests of the $LiNbO_3$ crystal were observations of the interference figures produced by placing the crystal between orthogonal circular polarizers and illuminating it with diverging monochromatic light [17]. Ideally, the interference figure (looking along the threefold axis) is circularly symmetric in the absence of an applied field. When a field is applied, the figure is distorted as shown in Fig. 3. The axes of symmetry of the distorted figure correspond to the privileged directions of the induced birefringence. The photographs show how the induced birefringent plate rotates through 90 deg as the applied field rotates through 180 deg. This behavior is fundamental to the operation of the modulator.

In another preliminary test, with the crystal again between orthogonal circular polarizers, a collimated monochromatic beam was passed along the crystal threefold axis. The variation of transmitted intensity with applied field showed the expected sine-squared behavior. However, the best extinction occurred not with zero applied field but with 50 V applied to one pair of electrodes. This was attributed to a residual strain in the crystal; consequently, provision was made to apply a dc bias of up to 50 V to that pair of electrodes during the modulation experiments.

Apparatus

Fig. 4 shows the arrangement used to operate and evaluate the modulator. The quarter-wave plate Q produces circular polarization in the crystal input beam. After passing through the crystal, the beam is reflected by mirror M_1 back through the crystal to the beam splitter. A portion of the beam is then reflected through an auxiliary lens L_2 into the scanning-mirror interferometer. The scanning-mirror interferometer (SMI), similar to those described by Herriott [18], and by Fork *et al.* [19], has a free spectral range of 250 MHz and a bandwidth (resolution) of a few megahertz.

The modulator is operated on a pulsed basis under the control of the pulser. The pulse used to switch on the power oscillator is also used to trigger the horizontal sweep of the oscilloscope. This, in turn, begins the motion of the scanning mirror in the SMI. The sweep rate is adjusted so that the SMI sweeps out its full frequency range during one pulse of modulator operation. Thus, a display of intensity versus optical frequency over a 250-MHz range appears on the oscilloscope during each pulse.

Each pair of electrodes is fed by an impedance transformer containing a pair of inductively coupled single-tuned resonant circuits. A variable-length coaxial line

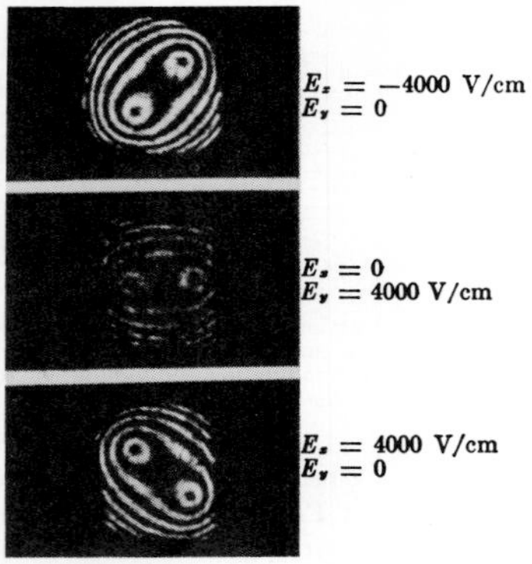

Fig. 3. Interference figures in lithium niobate with various applied electric fields. The z axis is vertical.

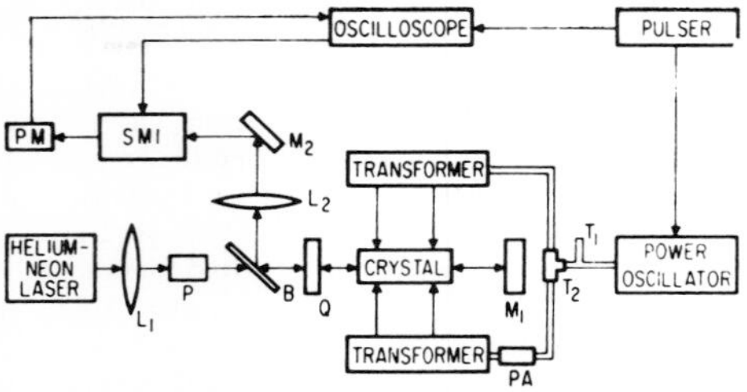

Fig. 4. Schematic of the experimental apparatus. L_1 represents the beam-forming optics and L_2 the refocusing lens; M_1 represents the retroreflective mirror and M_2 the folding mirror; P is the polarizing prism, B the beam splitter, Q the quarter-wave plate, T_1 the stub tuner, T_2 the coaxial tee, SMI the scanning-mirror interferometer, PM the photomultiplier detector, and PA the phase adjuster.

serves as a phase shifter to adjust the relative phase between the driving voltages.

Rotating-Field Action

Fig. 5 shows photographs of the SMI display at various oscillator power settings. The drive power is expressed as a percent of the power required to achieve the half-wave condition. The horizontal scale is frequency (about 28 MHz/maj div) and the vertical scale is relative intensity. At zero drive power (modulator turned off), a single "spike" appears, representing the single longitudinal mode output of the He–Ne laser at the carrier frequency. As the drive power increases, the carrier intensity diminishes and a sideband appears (to the right in the photographs), representing the shifted frequency. The sideband is displaced from the carrier by the drive frequency, 110 MHz. At the half-wave condition (100-percent drive power), the sideband intensity is maximized, and the carrier intensity falls to essentially zero. In the figure, the sideband intensity appears to be greater than that of the original carrier only because of the polarization selectivity of the beam splitter. (With a further increase in drive power, the carrier is observed to reappear, while the sideband intensity is reduced.) These variations in carrier and sideband intensities agree with theory.

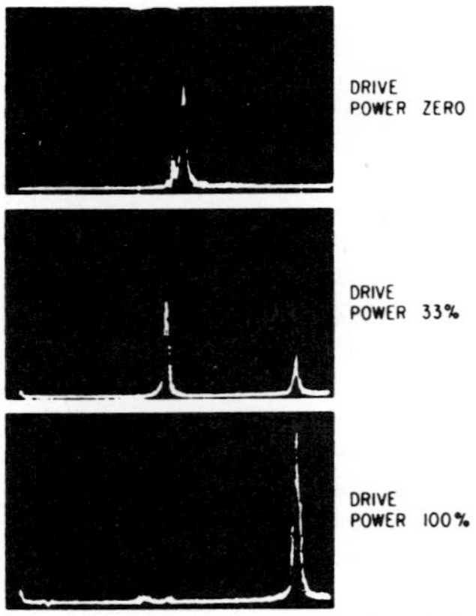

Fig. 5. Variations in carrier and sideband intensities with drive power.

The minor peaks appearing in some of the SMI photographs deserve comment. At the extreme left, the adjacent mode of the SMI cavity produces a second image of the sideband. This occurs because the sweep covers slightly more than the 250-MHz free spectral range of the SMI. At 100-percent drive power, a small peak appears to the left of the residual carrier. This also is due to an adjacent SMI mode that produces an image of a second-order sideband (i.e., a sideband shifted by 220 MHz). A primary-mode image of this component can be seen in Fig. 6, which is a composite of two SMI-display photographs. The laser frequency was readjusted between photographs. Therefore, in the composite, the frequency scale extends for about 250 MHz to each side of the sideband. Various frequencies of interest are labeled, including that of the opposite sideband, which is well suppressed in this case.

A further verification of rotating-field action was based on the relation between the sense of electric-field rotation in the crystal and the frequency shift imposed on the light beam. In the rotating-field modulator, reversing the direction of field rotation would change an upshift in frequency to a downshift. The direction of field rotation was reversed simply by reversing the connections to one pair of crystal electrodes. The result is shown in Fig. 7; reversal of field rotation moves the sideband from one side of the carrier to the other.

Spectral Purity

The relative intensities of the various frequency components in the modulator output beam were measured by visual observation and photography of the SMI display.

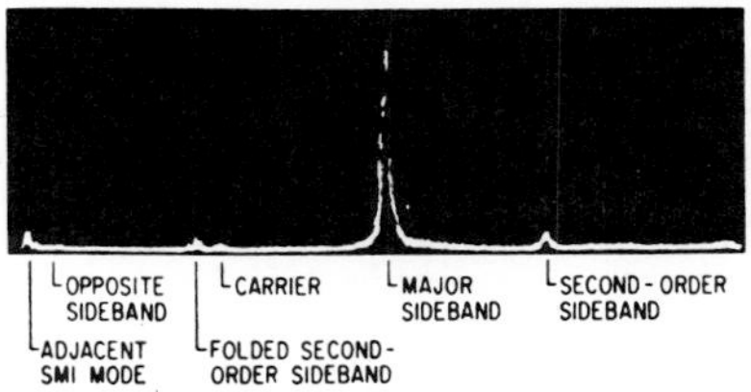

Fig. 6. Composite photograph of the SMI display showing modulator output intensity versus frequency.

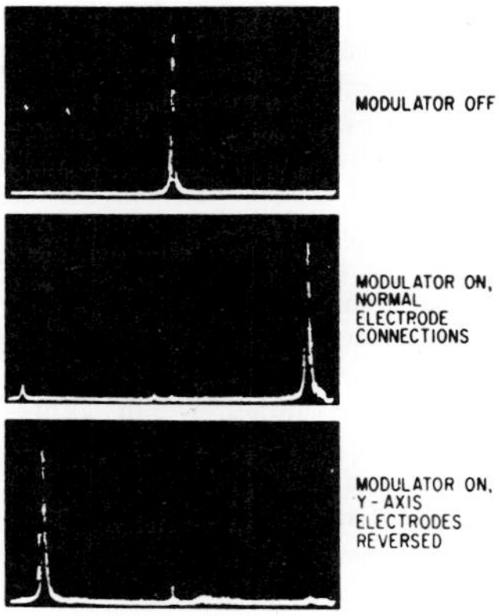

Fig. 7. The effect of reversing field rotation.

The modulator is conveniently characterized by suppression ratios, i.e., the ratio of the desired sideband to the residual carrier or to the undesired opposite sideband. The carrier suppression ratio could routinely be made 50:1. With careful adjustment of crystal position and orientation and of the variables of the radio-frequency circuits, it could be made to exceed 100:1. Similarly, suppression ratios for the opposite sideband were routinely 100:1 and exceeded 200:1 with careful adjustments. The superior suppression of the opposite sideband is not surprising since it depends chiefly on achieving the proper balance between the two driving signals. The carrier suppression depends, in addition, on maintaining precisely the half-wave signal amplitude. (A circular-polarization filter can be used to remove residual carrier from the output beam, but this is wasteful of optical power compared to carrier suppression in the modulator itself.)

The largest spurious-frequency component in the experimental modulator output is a second-order sideband shifted from the carrier by twice the drive frequency. The suppression ratio for this component is about 50:1 and is relatively insensitive to optical and radio-frequency adjustments. The intensity of this second-order sideband increases more or less in proportion to that of the first-order sideband; it is polarized in the same sense as the first-order sideband.

An analysis described later indicates that the probable source of the second-order sideband in the same polarization sense as the first-order sideband is an incorrect dc bias. This is borne out by the observation that the second-order sideband decreases as the bias is raised from zero to 50 V, the maximum attainable with the apparatus.

The spectral content (given in percentages) of the modulator output can be summarized as follows: desired sideband—96, opposite sideband—0.5, residual carrier—1, second-order sideband—0.5, opposite second-order sideband—0.5.

Acoustooptic Effects and Conversion Efficiency

It became evident early in the experimental program that a significant fraction of the light entering the modulator was being lost through interaction with acoustic waves in the crystal. The gratinglike behavior of the acoustic waves diverts a portion of the light into well-defined directions away from the main beam. The acoustic-wave velocities implied by the observed effects were found to agree with published values [10] for acoustic waves traveling normal to the threefold axis in $LiNbO_3$. The acoustic wavelengths involved ranged from 35–60 μm.

The acoustic waves are generated in the presence of time-varying applied fields by gradients in the field amplitude and by the discontinuities in material properties at the crystal boundaries [20]. It was found that acoustooptic losses could be significantly reduced by narrowing the electrodes (from 0.8 to 0.3 mm) and by increasing the drive frequency (from 60 to 110 MHz). In the final configuration of the experimental modulator the optical power loss attributable to acoustooptic interactions was 35 percent.

The overall conversion efficiency of the modulator is the ratio of the desired sideband power in the modulator output beam to the power in the input beam. In our case, the efficiency was limited to about 54 percent by the acoustooptic effect, the crystal surface reflections, and the power appearing in unwanted sidebands. This efficiency could be increased by antireflection coatings on the crystal end faces and by a reduction of the acoustooptic loss. One possible arrangement would involve moving the electrodes away from the crystal surfaces to reduce the electric field gradients inside the crystal. To conserve power it would be necessary to fill the space between the crystal and the electrodes with a dielectric material whose permittivity approximately matches that of the crystal. Otherwise the electric field inside the crystal would be a small fraction of that outside.

Power Requirement and Bandwidth

The modulator was operated over a wide range of duty ratios up to 25 percent. The pulse power required to achieve the half-wave condition was 15 W, slightly less than the predicted 19 W.

Carrier and opposite-sideband suppression ratios, which decrease rapidly as the applied voltage departs from the half-wave value, were observed to fall to one-half their center-frequency values at frequencies separated by about 1 MHz. On the basis of impedance measurements the bandwidth at the input port of the coaxial "tee" (see Fig. 4) was found to be 2.5 MHz. This is smaller than the inherent modulator bandwidth of 12 MHz because no attempt was made to preserve the full bandwidth in the matching circuitry. In principle, the driving circuits can be designed to achieve the full 12 MHz capability of the modulator, or an even greater bandwidth, at the expense of additional drive power.

Optical Output Beam Pattern

The measured optical output beam pattern at the desired sideband frequency was very close to the TEM_{00} Gaussian mode of the input beam; slight distortions suggested interference fringes. These distortions persisted when the modulator crystal was removed and can therefore be attributed to other optical elements. No observable beam distortion was caused by the modulator.

Thermal Effects

Most measurements were made with the modulator operating at a 0.5 percent duty ratio, which is low enough to prevent any measurable heating of the crystal. At higher duty ratios, enough radio-frequency power was absorbed to deflect and defocus the beam, producing a slight deterioration in modulator performance, as expected. At a 20-percent duty ratio, the highest attempted on a continuous basis, the equilibrium temperature reached on the heat sink ridge just below the crystal was 97°C, as measured by a thermocouple. (Note that no special measures were taken to remove heat from the heat sink.) Observation of the crystal interference figure showed slight distortions due to crystal strain at this temperature.

The observed upward beam deflections ranged from 2 mrad at a 7-percent duty ratio to 5 mrad at 20-percent duty ratio. The expected magnitude of the beam deflection can be calculated [21] from (4) and from Hobden and Warner's empirical expression [15] for the temperature dependence of refractive index in $LiNbO_3$. For operation of the modulator at a 20-percent duty ratio, with a power dissipation of 3 W and a variation in internal crystal temperature from about 100°C (measured at the heat-sink ridge) to an estimated 124°C at the upper surface, the predicted beam deflection is 2.5 mrad. In view of the approximations made, this value is in acceptable agreement with the observed deflection of 5 mrad.

A gradual degradation in modulator performance, as measured by carrier and opposite-sideband suppression ratios, was observed as the operating temperature increased. Even at 100°C, however, modulator performance remained reasonably good, with carrier and opposite-sideband suppression ratios of 15:1. Since the r_{22} electro-optic coefficient in $LiNbO_3$ is nearly constant at temperatures ranging from 20 to 100°C, the performance loss probably resulted from thermally induced strain and asymmetry in the crystal. Consistent with (4), the output-beam pattern was observed to broaden at high duty ratios.

It should be possible to greatly reduce the beam deflection and performance loss by arranging symmetrical heat removal. This might be done, for example, by providing a combination heat sink and electrode on each of the four sides of the crystal.

Effects of Modulator Maladjustments

A theoretical evaluation was made of the effects on modulator performance of various departures from ideal conditions. The good performance of the experimental modulator indicated that attention could be restricted to relatively small imperfections. The analysis was simplified by the small cross section of the beam relative to that of the crystal, which justified the assumption of electric-field uniformity over the beam cross section. The analysis resulted in expressions for the relative intensities of various undesired frequency components arising in the modulator output beam in terms of a parameter δ, the extent of maladjustment.

These results are summarized in Table I. For each type of modulator maladjustment, the table lists the relative intensities of the desired sideband at a frequency $(\omega + \omega_m)$ and of undesired components at the carrier frequency ω, at first- and second-order sideband frequencies on both sides of the carrier, and at the third-order sideband frequency nearest the desired sideband. Components more widely separated from the carrier are small compared to those listed. In each case, the output-beam components are identified as having either the same polarization as the carrier C or that of the desired sideband S. Only the dominant terms are listed explicitly in the table. An X in Table I indicates that a component exists at that frequency with an amplitude proportional to a higher power of the error. No entry indicates that the particular maladjustment produces no output-beam component at that frequency.

The first case given in Table I is the ideal case, in which the only output component is the desired sideband. The next six cases involve various electric-field maladjustments. These results were obtained by substituting the applicable field components into the following expressions [22] for the carrier- and sideband-polarized output beam amplitudes A_c and A_s:

$$A_c = \cos(\pi E/2)e^{i\omega t},$$

$$A_s = \sin(\pi E/2)(E_y + iE_x)(1/E)e^{i\omega t}. \qquad (5)$$

Here, E represents the magnitude of the applied electric field relative to its half-wave value; E_x and E_y are similarly normalized field components along the x and y axes of the crystal. As usual, the real parts of A_c and A_s are the physical quantities. In the ideal case, E_x is $\sin \omega_m t$ and E_y is $\cos \omega_m t$, where ω_m is the drive frequency. Then A_c vanishes and A_s is $\exp[i(\omega + \omega_m)t]$, as expected.

TABLE I

RELATIVE AMPLITUDES OF OUTPUT-BEAM COMPONENTS FOR VARIOUS MODULATOR MALADJUSTMENTS

Maladjustment	Applied Fields X Component	Applied Fields Y Component	Polarization*	$\omega - 2\omega_m$	$\omega - \omega_m$	ω	$\omega + \omega_m$	$\omega + 2\omega_m$	$\omega + 3\omega_m$
None (ideal case)	$\sin \omega_m t$	$\cos \omega_m t$	C						
			S				1		
Field-magnitude error	$(1 - \delta) \sin \omega_m t$	$(1 - \delta) \cos \omega_m t$	C			$\pi \delta/2$			
			S				1		
Amplitude imbalance	$(1 + \delta) \sin \omega_m t$	$\cos \omega_m t$	C	$\pi \delta/8$		$\pi \delta/4$		$\pi \delta/8$	
			S		$\delta/4$		1		$\delta/4$
Phase imbalance	$\sin (\omega_m t + \delta)$	$\cos \omega_m t$	C	$\pi \delta/8$				$\pi \delta/8$	
			S		$\delta/4$		$1 + i \delta/2$		$\delta/4$
Second harmonic in drive field	$\sin \omega_m t + \delta \sin 2 \omega_m t$	$\cos \omega_m t + \delta \cos 2 \omega_m t$	C		$\pi \delta/4$		$\pi \delta/4$		X
			S	X	X	$\delta/2$	1	$\delta/2$	X
Dc bias in drive field	$\sin \omega_m t$	$\delta + \cos \omega_m t$	C		$\pi \delta/4$		$\pi \delta/4$		X
			S	X	X	$\delta/2$	1	$\delta/2$	X
Electrodes not parallel to crystal axis ($E_z = \sin \delta \cos \omega_m t$)	$\sin \omega_m t$	$\cos \delta \cos \omega_m t$	C	$\pi \delta^2/16$		$\pi \delta^2/8$		$\pi \delta^2/16$	
			S		$\delta^2/8$		1		$\delta^2/8$
Reverse-polarized component of relative amplitude δ in input beam	same as ideal case		C		δ				
			S				1		
Light beam at an angle δ relative to the crystal axis ($\delta \leq 1$ mrad)	same as ideal case		C	$\pi r \delta/4$				$\pi r \delta/4$	
			S		$r \delta$		$1; r \delta/2$		$r \delta/2$

* C—carrier polarization; S—desired sideband polarization.

When one of the electric field maladjustments is present, the factors $\cos (\pi E/2)$ and $\sin (\pi E/2)$ become time dependent except in the simple case of a field-magnitude error and will thus give rise to new frequency components. In addition to this amplitude modulation, the term $[(E_y + iE_x)(1/E)]$ will manifest the irregularities (wobbling) in the formerly uniform electric-field rotation. This corresponds to phase modulation and also results in new frequencies.

The last two cases in Table I refer to optical maladjustments. The first of these is a reverse-polarized component in the input beam, which simply gives a downshifted sideband of corresponding intensity. The final case is a misalignment of the optical beam. The retardation suffered by a misaligned beam varies as the induced-birefringence axes rotate, giving rise once again to spurious frequency components in the output beam. The analysis in this case involves calculation of the intersection of the crystal's index ellipsoid with a plane normal to the beam direction, as described by Mason [23]. For misalignments greater than about 1 mrad, the natural birefringence of the crystal overpowers the effect of the relatively weak electrooptically induced birefringence and modulator performance degrades rapidly. This behavior is consistent with experimental observations. For misalignments of less than 1 mrad, the electrooptical effects dominate and introduce the spurious frequencies indicated in Table I. The quantity r appearing in this case is the ratio r_{43}/r_{22} of two of the electrooptic coefficients of the crystal. The desired sideband contains a component of amplitude $r\delta/2$, whose phase depends on the direction of misalignment relative to the crystal's transverse axis.

The results given in Table I show that the rotating-field modulator is not unduly sensitive to the various maladjustments that may be encountered in a practical device. This bears out the experimental observation that good spectral purity in the output beam can be achieved with straightforward electrical and optical adjustments.

SUMMARY

An electrooptic frequency shifter has been constructed and evaluated. The characteristics and performance of the experimental double-pass modulator are summarized in Table II. Theoretical analysis has shown that modulator performance is relatively insensitive to small maladjustments in the driving fields and in optical alignment. The chief problems associated with the modulator were diffraction of optical power by acoustic waves in the crystal, which caused a loss of about 35 percent of the optical power, and slight deflection (a few milliradians) of the optical beam by temperature gradients in the crystal at duty ratios exceeding 5 percent. It should be possible to reduce these problems by reducing electric-field gradients in the crystal and by providing symmetric heat removal from the crystal, respectively.

Two major conclusions are drawn from this investigation. First, a rotating-field electrooptic modulator using $LiNbO_3$ can produce a frequency-shifted output of high spectral purity with only moderate requirements on optical and electrical alignment. Second, insertion loss caused by acoustooptic effects in the crystal may limit

TABLE II
SUMMARY OF EXPERIMENTAL MODULATOR CHARACTERISTICS AND PERFORMANCE

Crystal	Lithium niobate, *C* cut
Crystal dimensions	$1 \times 1 \times 20$ mm
Optical wavelength	632.8 nm
Drive frequency	110 MHz
Drive power required at drive frequency	15 W
Carrier and opposite-sideband suppression	100:1
Spurious-frequency power in output beam	4 percent
Conversion efficiency	54 percent
Bandwidth	12 MHz (crystal only) 2.5 MHz (at power-divider input)
Output-beam pattern	TEM_{00} mode[a]
Maximum duty ratio	20 percent
Operating temperature at maximum duty ratio	97°C

[a] Rippled by multiple-reflection interference fringes not attributed to the modulator.

the present form of the modulator in applications in which optical power is at a premium.

ACKNOWLEDGMENT

Generous loans of equipment were made by Dr. W. K. Pratt and Dr. H. L. Stover of the University of Southern California and by the Aircraft Division of the Northrop Corporation. Valuable technical assistance was provided by E. D. Garlinger, H. R. Owen, and M. K. Mannes. The Engineering Shop of the University of Southern California fabricated the scanning-mirror interferometer.

REFERENCES

[1] A. G. Fox, "An adjustable wave-guide phase changer," *Proc. IRE*, vol. 35, Dec, 1947, pp. 1489–1498.
[2] R. Crane, "Interference phase measurement," *Appl. Opt.*, vol. 8, Mar. 1969, pp. 538–542.
[3] C. F. Buhrer, D. H. Baird, and E. M. Conwell, "Optical frequency shifting by electro-optic effect," *App. Phys. Lett.*, vol. 1, Oct. 1962, pp. 46–49.
[4] C. F. Buhrer, L. R. Bloom, and D. H. Baird, "Electro-optic modulation with cubic crystals," *Appl. Opt.*, vol. 2, Aug. 1963, pp. 839–846.
[5] C. F. Buhrer, V. J. Fowler, and L. R. Bloom, "Single sideband suppressed-carrier modulation of coherent light beams," *Proc. IRE* (Corresp.), vol. 50, Aug. 1962, pp. 1827–1828.
[6] C. J. Peters, "Optical frequency translator using two phase modulators in tandem," *Appl. Opt.*, vol. 4, July 1965, pp. 857–861.
[7] C. F. Buhrer, "Single sideband microwave light modulation," *Proc. IEEE* (Corresp.), vol. 52, Aug. 1964, pp. 969–970.
[8] ——, "Wide-band eletcro-optic light modulation utilizing an asynchronous traveling-wave interaction," *Appl. Opt.*, vol. 4, May 1965, pp. 545–550.
[9] P. Page and H. Pursey, "Tunable single sideband electro-optic ring modulator," *Opto-Electron.*, vol. 2, Jan. 1970, pp. 1–4.
[10] E. G. Spencer, P. V. Lenzo, and A. A. Ballman, "Dielectric materials for electrooptic, elastooptic and ultrasonic device applications," *Proc. IEEE*, vol. 55, Dec. 1967, pp. 2074–2108.
[11] H. Z. Cummins and N. Knable, "Single sideband modulation of coherent light by Bragg reflection from acoustical waves," *Proc. IEEE* (Corresp.), vol. 51, Sept. 1963, p. 1246.
[12] I. P. Kaminov and E. H. Turner, "Electrooptic light modulators," *Appl. Opt.*, vol. 5, Oct. 1966, pp. 1612–1628.
[13] H. Kogelnik and T. Li, "Laser beams and resonators," *Appl. Opt.*, vol. 5, Oct. 1966, pp. 1550–1567.
[14] J. Irving and N. Mullineux, *Mathematics in Physics and Engineering*. New York: Academic Press, 1959, p. 832.
[15] M. V. Hobden and J. Warner, "The temperature dependence of the refractive indices of pure lithium niobate," *Phys. Lett.*, vol. 22, Aug. 1966, pp. 243–244.
[16] J. D. Zook, D. Chen, and G. N. Otto, "Temperature dependence and model of the electro-optic effect in $LiNbO_3$," *Appl. Phys. Lett.*, vol. 11, Sept. 1967, pp. 159–161.
[17] H. Fay, "Electro-optic modulation of light propagating near the optic axis in $LiNbO_3$," *J. Opt. Soc. Amer.*, vol. 59, Nov. 1969, pp. 1399–1404.
[18] D. R. Herriott, "Spherical-mirror oscillating interferometer," *Appl. Opt.*, vol. 2, Aug. 1963, pp. 865–866.
[19] R. L. Fork, D. R. Herriott, and H. Kogelnik, "A scanning spherical mirror interferometer for spectral analysis of laser radiation," *Appl. Opt.*, vol. 3, Dec. 1964, pp. 1471–1484.
[20] E. H. Jacobsen, "Sources of sound in piezoelectric crystals," *J. Acoust. Soc. Amer.*, vol. 32, Aug. 1960, pp. 949–953.
[21] V. J. Fowler, C. F. Buhrer, and L. R. Bloom, "Electro-optic light beam deflector," *Proc. IEEE* (Corresp.), vol. 52, Feb. 1964, pp. 193–194.
[22] W. K. Pratt, *Laser Communication Systems*. New York: Wiley, 1969, p. 84.
[23] W. P. Mason, "Optical properties and the electro-optic and photoelastic effects in crystals expressed in tensor form," *Bell Syst. Tech. J.*, vol. 29, Apr. 1950, pp. 161–188.

Reprinted from
Volume 14, Number 1 APPLIED PHYSICS LETTERS 1 January 1969

COMPRESSION OF PULSES FROM A MODE-LOCKED He-Ne LASER

M. A. Duguay and *J. W. Hansen*
Bell Telephone Laboratories, Inc.
Murray Hill, New Jersey 07974
(Received 7 October 1968)

Pulses of 500-psec duration, emitted by a mode-locked He–Ne laser, have been electro-optically frequency swept and then compressed to 270 psec by multiple reflections from an interferometer proposed by Gires and Tournois.

We wish to report in this letter the compression of pulses from a mode-locked He–Ne laser. The technique used here is expected to be generally applicable to the compression of pulses ranging in widths from a few nanoseconds to a few picoseconds. The use of a novel dispersive structure, introduced in 1964 by Gires and Tournois,[1] was essential to the success of the present experiment.

The basic principle of the compression technique[2] is that used in the chirp radar.[3] The compression is accomplished in two steps. First, a linear optical frequency sweep is applied to the pulse,[2] which is then said to be "chirped." An extreme example of a chirped pulse would be one with a blue leading edge, a yellow peak and a red trailing edge. (We shall call this pulse down-chirped because the frequency goes down with time.) The second step is to send this chirped pulse through a dispersive element where the group velocity or group delay varies linearly with optical frequency. This element introduces a differential delay between the blue and red parts of the pulse in such a way that the red lagging edge of a down-chirped pulse catches up with its blue leading edge. When this happens the pulse has been compressed to its minimum width $\sim(\Delta f)^{-1}$ where Δf is the magnitude of the frequency sweep.

In Ref. 2 the lagging edge of a pulse from a mode-locked He–Ne laser was made redder than the leading edge by Δf = 6 GHz, and it was calculated that the suggested dispersive element, bromobenzene, would have had to be of impractical length, in this case, to achieve the available compression factor of 4.

The work of Gires and Tournois[1] was recently brought to our attention[4] and we set up the dispersive structure proposed by them to compress chirped pulses. Their structure, shown in Fig. 1, consists essentially of a pair of dielectric-coated flat mirrors, spaced *d* mm apart, and aligned parallel to one another as in a Fabry–Perot interferometer (left, Fig. 1). Unlike in a Fabry–Perot, the mirrors have unequal reflectivities; one is highly reflecting (99.8% here, ideally it should be 100%), the other one has only 32% reflectivity. A third mirror, on the right in Fig. 1, allows the laser beam to be reflected several times from the pair of flat mirrors; that mirror is slightly curved (10-m radius) to prevent excessive diffraction of

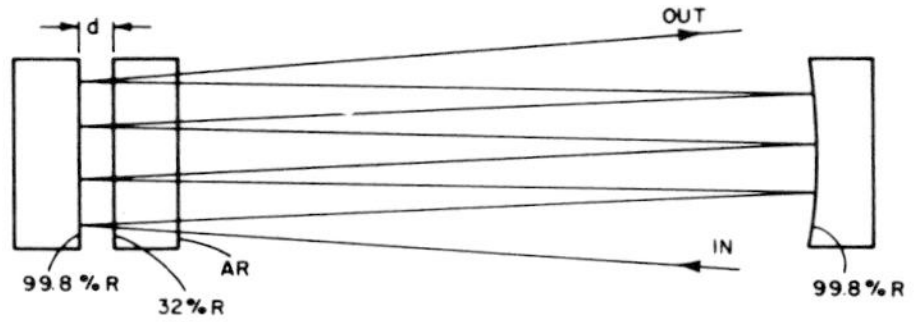

Fig. 1. Dispersive structure proposed by Gires and Tournois to compress chirped light pulses. The pair of flat mirrors (left) constitute an interferometer with strongly dispersive but lossless reflectivity characteristics. The curved (10-m radius) mirror is 80 cm to the right.

the beam. As one tunes the spacing of a Fabry–Perot interferometer the transmission, reflectivity, and dispersion (or phase delay) curves go through resonances. The striking features of the interferometer of Gires and Tournois is that the reflectivity remains very nearly constant and high (ideally 100%) through the resonances, but the phase delay curve still maintains its resonant behavior. Therefore near a resonance, one has high dispersion, but very low loss, in reflection. A different dispersive structure has been used recently by Treacy[5] who found the 4-psec pulses from a mode-locked Nd:glass laser to be naturally FM modulated. Treacy obtained compression effects by using a pair of gratings as a dispersive element.

In our experiment, pulses 500 psec long, 10 nsec apart, from a He–Ne laser mode-locked by a neon cell,[6] were passed through a $LiNbO_3$ phase modulator or Doppler shifter,[7,8] driven by a 100-MHz rf wave and operated in the chirp mode.[2] The spectrum of the laser output, observed with a scanning Fabry–Perot interferometer, was roughly Gaussian-shaped, with 1.5-GHz full width at half-maximum (FWHM). After passage through the Doppler shifter the pulses, now chirped, had a spectral width of 2.8-GHz but were unaltered in the time domain. The pulses were reflected four times from the Gires–Tournois interferometer as shown in Fig. 1. A fast photodiode with a risetime of ~ 150 psec and a Hewlett–Packard sampling oscilloscope with a 28-psec risetime were used to display the pulse waveforms. The results are shown in Fig. 2. There, the shape of

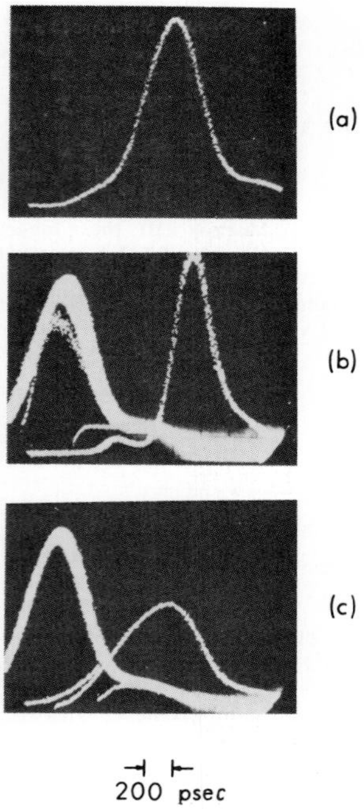

Fig. 2. Photographs of sampling oscilloscope traces showing the pulse shapes that result from different tunings of the Gires–Tournois interferometer (GTI); (a) input pulse, not chirped (rf off), reflected off-resonance, FWHM = 500 psec; (b) GTI tuned to one side of a resonance, the right trace shows a compressed pulse, FWHM = 310 psec, the left trace is for an unchirped pulse (rf off); (c) GTI tuned to opposite side of the resonance, the right trace shows an expanded pulse, FWHM = 700 psec, left trace is for rf off.

the pulses emerging from the Gires–Tournois interferometer (GTI) are shown for three different tunings of the spacing d, near the value d = 10 mm. In Fig. 2(a), the interferometer is tuned off resonance and the rf is off on the Doppler shifter; in this case the dispersion is negligible and one sees the unaltered incident pulse, which has a 500-psec FWHM in this experiment. In part (b) of Fig. 2 the interferometer is tuned halfway up a resonance. The left-hand trace shows the output pulse when the rf is off in the Doppler shifter, which is 90% of the time, accounting for the heavier trace. The middle trace shows the pulse when the rf is on (10% duty cycle): the pulse appears to be 310 psec at half-height. The chirped pulses have been compressed. In Fig. 2(c), the interferometer is tuned on the opposite side of the resonance; there the sign of the dispersion curve does not match the sign of the frequency sweep and the chirped pulses (middle trace) are expanded to 700 psec. By changing the rf phase by 180°, we could reverse the sign of the sweep and change from pulse compression to pulse expansion on a given side of a resonance.

If the detector risetime of 150 psec is unfolded from the measured width of 310 psec, one obtains 270 psec for the full width at half-height of the compressed pulse. The original pulse has therefore been compressed by a factor of 1.85, which is also equal to the ratio of the input and output spectral widths. The error on all measurements was ±5%. The peak of the compressed pulse would exceed the peak of the unchirped pulse by a bigger factor (ideally 1.85) than appears in Fig. 2(b) if it had not been for losses in the Doppler shifter, when the rf was turned on, caused by acoustic diffraction effects[8]; these reduced the peak height by ≈ 35%.

Much larger compression ratios are possible with this technique.[1,2] When the magnitude of the frequency sweep is increased, the GTI spacing d has to be decreased to maintain the proper dispersion characteristic over the increased optical frequency interval.[1] At the same time the number of reflections has to be increased to achieve full compression. In the present experiment larger frequency sweeps were possible (up to 10 GHz). However, the small acceptance angle of the GTI (~ 3 mrad) and diffraction effects combined to prevent the use of more than 5 reflections on the small size (1.9-cm-diam) mirrors used in the GTI. The use of larger mirrors (5–10-cm-diam) in a geometry of the type suitable for optical delay lines[9] would allow a large number of reflections, and therefore large compression ratios.

Another possibility is to cascade pulse compressors (modulator/+ GTI). With a compression ratio of, say, 2 per stage, the over-all ratio after n stages is 2^n.

We are grateful to Dr. J. A. Giordmaine for stimulating discussions and material help, and to Dr. Robert C. Miller for useful comments on the manuscript. We also thank Dr. H. Melchior who kindly made available to us the fast photodiode and sampling oscilloscope.

[1] F. Gires and P. Tournois, Compt. Rend. 258, 6112 (June 1964).

[2] J. A. Giordmaine, M. A. Duguay, and J. W. Hansen, IEEE J. Quant. Electron. **QE-4**, 252 (1968).

[3] J. R. Klauder, A. C. Price, S. Darlington, and W. J. Albersheim, Bell System Tech. J. 39, 745 (1960).

[4] We are grateful to F. Gires for informing us of his previous work through J. A. Giordmaine.

[5] E. B. Treacy, Phys. Letters **28A**, 34 (1968).

[6] A. G. Fox, S. E. Schwartz, and P. W. Smith, Appl. Phys. Letters **12**, 371 (1968).

[7] M. A. Duguay, L. E. Hargrove, and K. B. Jefferts, Appl. Phys. Letters **9**, 287 (1966).

[8] M. A. Duguay and J. W. Hansen, IEEE J. Quant. Electron. **QE-4**, 477 (1968).

[9] D. R. Heriott and M. J. Schulte, Appl. Opt. 4, 883 (1965).

6. Guided Wave Materials and Modulators

Reduced Modulator Drive-Power Requirements for 10.6-μ Guided Waves

W. B. GANDRUD

Abstract—**It is shown that a reduction of more than an order of magnitude in electrooptic modulator drive power requirements should be possible at 10.6 μ by the use of a dielectric slab waveguide, despite the dimensional limitations imposed by electrode absorption.**

The need for improved modulation efficiency at 10.6 μ is widely recognized [1]. The purpose of this correspondence is to examine the possible impovement in electrooptic modulation obtainable if guided waves are used to overcome the limitations imposed by diffraction.

Kaminow and Turner [2], [3] have shown that for negligible parallel-circuit capacitance and conductance, the drive power required by the electrooptic modulator of Fig. 1 obeys

$$P \propto ad/l. \tag{1}$$

If the wave to be modulated is not guided, diffraction of the Gaussian beam imposes the limit [2]

$$a^2/l,\ d^2/l \geq 4\lambda_0/n_1\pi = 4.1\ \mu(\text{GaAs, } 10.6\ \mu). \tag{2}$$

This limit, which prevents a and d from being less than $\approx$1 mm, could be avoided by using a dielectric slab waveguide [4] as a modulator. The consequences of evanescent wave absorption by the metal electrodes must be considered, however.

Because of the complex conductivity and extremely small skin depths encountered at frequencies $\approx 10^{13}$ Hz, the microwave frequency methods [5] of calculating loss in metallic walls will not be used. Instead, we resolve the wave with propagation constant β in the guide into two criss-crossing plane waves [6] whose angle of incidence on the metal walls is θ (see Fig. 2). For simplicity, we make the problem one dimensional by assuming $a \gg d$. If λ_0 is the free space wavelength, θ is given by [6]

$$\sin\theta = \lambda_0\beta/2\pi n_1. \tag{3}$$

Solving for the modes of the guide and inserting the resulting β into (3) yields

$$\cos\theta = (m+1)\lambda_0/2n_1 d, \qquad m = 0, 1, 2, 3, \cdots \tag{4}$$

Since Goos–Hanchen shifts are generally negligible at metallic boundaries [7], the wave travels a distance $d \tan\theta$ along the guide between reflections. If the fraction of power absorbed in one reflection is $A_{12}(\theta)$, then the attenuation coefficient in nepers per unit length of the guide will be [8]

$$\alpha = A_{12}(\theta)/d\tan\theta. \tag{5}$$

$A_{12}(\theta)$ may be calculated from the formulas of Born and Wolf [9], using the complex refractive indices measured at $\lambda_0 = 10\ \mu$. For all combinations of metals and dielectrics examined, it was found that

$$n_1^2 \sin^2\theta/n_2^2(\kappa_2^2 - 1) < 0.1$$

at 10 μ. When this quantity is much less than 1, Born and Wolf's [9] u_2 and v_2 become n_2 and $n_2\kappa_2$, respectively. We then

Manuscript received August 6, 1971.
The author is with Bell Telephone Laboratories, Inc., Whippany, N. J. 07981.

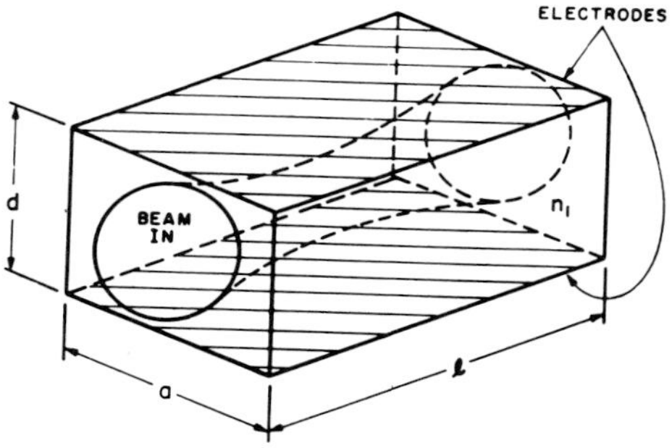

Fig. 1. Modulator geometry for both guided and nonguided waves.

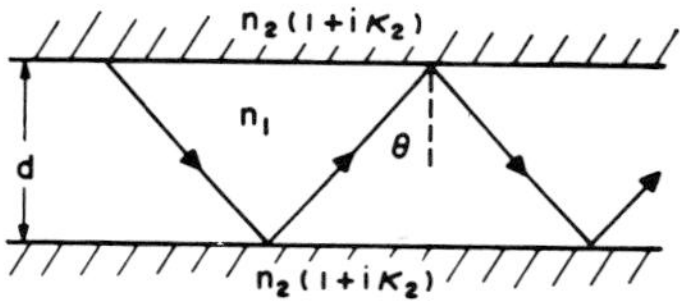

Fig. 2. Resolution of propagating mode into criss-crossing plane waves.

have, in the notation of Fig. 2 and [9],

$$A_{12}(\theta) = 1 - \rho_{12}^2$$

$$\cong \begin{cases} \dfrac{4n_1n_2\cos\theta}{(n_1\cos\theta + n_2)^2 + n_2^2\kappa_2^2} & \text{(TE)} \\[2ex] \dfrac{4n_1n_2\cos\theta}{(n_2\cos\theta + n_1)^2 + n_2^2\kappa_2^2\cos\theta} & \text{(TM)} \end{cases} \tag{6}$$

Both of these expressions are zero for $\theta = 90°$, but $A_{12}(\theta)$ increases much faster [10] for the TM wave than for the TE wave as θ becomes less than 90°, hence TM modes will involve more loss than TE modes. From (5) and (6), the attenuation approaches zero as $\theta \to 90°$. From (4), this is accomplished by choosing the TE_0 mode in an overmoded guide (i.e., $\lambda_0/2n_1d \ll 1$). In this approximation, (4)–(6) give

$$\alpha \cong \lambda_0^2/d^3 n_1 n_2(\kappa_2^2 + 1)\cdot(TE_0). \tag{7}$$

The functional dependences here are the same as those obtained by the microwave frequency method. Assuming a maximum tolerable α of 0.1 cm^{-1} (0.43 dB/cm), (7) can be solved for d. It is seen in Table I that the minimum usable d is about 20 μ.

A value of $\alpha = 0.1$ cm^{-1} imposes an upper limit of $\approx$ 5 cm on l. Since the wave is not guided in the a dimension, (2) applies to a, giving

$$a \geq [(4.1\ \mu)(5\ \text{cm})]^{1/2} = 450\ \mu.$$

Then

$$ad/l = (450\ \mu)(20\ \mu)/(5\ \text{cm}) = 0.18\ \mu.$$

Comparing this with the diffraction-limited value of 4.1 μ (2),

TABLE I

VALUES OF d FROM (7) FOR VARIOUS METALS[a] ON GaAs ($n_1 = 3.3$), ASSUMING $\alpha = 0.1\ \text{cm}^{-1}$

Electrode	$n_2(10\ \mu)$	$-n_2\kappa_2(10\ \mu)$	Reference	d (7)
Ag	10.7	69.0	[11]	20 μ
Au	7.4	53.4	[11]	21
Cu	12.6	64.3	[11]	22
Al	25.4	67.3	[11]	26
In	23.8	51.7	[12]	29
Pt	12.3	36.8	[13]	30
Cr	11.0	22.8	[13]	39

[a] The definition of refractive index used in $n_2(1 + i\kappa_2)$.

the reduction in drive power resulting from guiding is seen to be a factor of 4.1/0.18 = 23.

Coupling losses would be encountered with both types of modulators. As mentioned in [2], lossless coupling into the nonguided modulator requires a safety factor of ≈ 3, i.e., some nine times more drive power than for the ideal case assumed here. For the waveguide modulator, a high-index prism coupler with a theoretical maximum efficiency [6] of 81 percent could be used.

Guiding in the a as well as the d dimension of Fig. 1 would result in another factor ≈ 20 reduction in drive power. This would, however, require a fabrication technique (such as ion bombardment [14]) whose effectiveness has not yet been demonstrated at 10μ.

Polished slabs of single-crystal Ge approximately 20 mm by 3 mm by 20 μ may be prepared by standard lapping techniques [15]. Chang and Loh [16] have coupled 10.6-μ radiation into a deposited polycrystalline Ge film. They also suggest the use of an additional dieletric layer to reduce the field at the electrode, thus making possible somewhat smaller values of d, and hence P. In addition, one might consider other geometrical configurations than the one shown in Fig. 1.

In conclusion, it has been shown that significant reduction in electrooptic modulator drive power requirements should be possible by waveguiding at 10.6 μ, despite the dimensional limitations imposed by electrode absorption.

ACKNOWLEDGMENT

This work is the outgrowth of many stimulating discussions with R. L. Abrams.

REFERENCES

[1] D. M. Henderson and R. L. Abrams, "A comparison of acoustooptic and electrooptic modulators at 10.6μ," *Opt. Commun.*, vol. 2, pp. 223–226, Oct. 1970, and references therein.

[2] I. P. Kaminow and E. H. Turner, "Electrooptic light modulators," *Proc. IEEE*, vol. 54, pp. 1374–1390, Oct. 1966.

[3] I. P. Kaminow, "Measurements of the electrooptic effect in CdS, ZnTe, and GaAs at 10.6 μ," *IEEE J. Quantum Electron.*, vol. QE-4, pp. 23–26, Jan. 1968.

[4] J. E. Goell and R. D. Standley, "Integrated optical circuits," *Proc. IEEE*, vol. 58, pp. 1504–1512, Oct. 1970, and references therein.

[5] R. E. Collin, *Field Theory of Guided Waves.* New York: McGraw-Hill, 1960, sec. 5.3.

[6] P. K. Tien and R. Ulrich, "Theory of prism-film coupler and thin-film light guides," *J. Opt. Soc. Amer.*, vol. 60, pp. 1325–1337, Oct. 1970.

[7] H. K. V. Lotsch, "Reflection and refraction of a beam of light at a plane interface," *J. Opt. Soc. Amer.*, vol. 58, pp. 551–561, Apr. 1968.

[8] This approach was used by C. C. Eaglesfield, "Optical pipeline: A tentative assessment," *Proc. Inst. Elec. Eng.* (London), vol. B109, pp. 26–32, Jan. 1962.

[9] M. Born and E. Wolf, *Principles of Optics.* Oxford, England: Pergamon Press, 1965, 3rd ed., sec. 13.4.1.

[10] See e.g., G. Hass, *Applied Optics and Optical Engineering*, R. Kingslake, Ed. New York: Academic Press, vol. 3, 1965, p. 318.

[11] *Ibid*, pp. 316–317.

[12] G. P. Motulevich and A. A. Shubin, "Determination of the microscopic characteristics of indium from its infrared optical constants and electrical conductivity," *Sov. Phys.—JETP*, vol. 17, pp. 33–36, July 1963.

[13] A. P. Lenham and D. M. Treherne, "Optical constants of transition metals in the infrared," *J. Opt. Soc. Amer.*, vol. 56, pp. 1137–1138, Aug. 1966.

[14] E. R. Schineller, R. Flam, and D. Wilmot, "Optical waveguides formed by proton irradiation of fused silica," *J. Opt. Soc. Amer.*, vol. 58, pp. 1171–1176, Sept. 1968.

[15] R. L. Abrams, private communication.

[16] W. S. C. Chang and K. W. Loh, "Guided-wave propagation at 10.6 μ," *J. Opt. Soc. Amer.* (Abstract), vol. 61, p. 677, May 1971, also *Appl. Opt.*, vol. 10, pp. 2361–2362, Oct. 1971.

Reprinted by permission from
IEEE JOURNAL OF QUANTUM ELECTRONICS
Vol. QE-7, No. 12, December 1971

Reprinted from JOURNAL OF APPLIED PHYSICS, Vol. 39, No. 7, 3426–3434, June 1968

Printed in U. S. A.

Reverse-Biased Gallium Phosphide Diodes as High-Frequency Light Modulators

F. K. REINHART
Bell Telephone Laboratories, Incorporated, Murray Hill, New Jersey
(Received 12 January 1968)

Reverse-biased gallium phosphide diodes have been successfully operated as high-frequency intensity and phase modulators of light at room temperature. The high-frequency modulation is fundamentally limited by the series resistance and the capacitance of the diodes. Cutoff frequencies as high as 7 GHz have been measured. Diode capacitance, typically less than ·7 pF at the operating point, and driver impedance determine the broad-band characteristic. Intensity modulation measurements have been performed up to 500 MHz. The power consumption per MHz bandwidth for 40% intensity modulation was 2.7 mW for a diode only 0.7 mm long. A diode of 1.5 mm length used as a phase modulator needed only 1.5 mW of power per MHz bandwidth for a modulation index of 1 rad at a wavelength of 0.633 μ. This latter value corresponds to an intensity modulation depth of over 80%.

I. INTRODUCTION

The properties of GaP diodes as light modulators have been studied. It was shown earlier[1] that light guided along the depletion layer of reverse-biased GaP diodes experiences a linear electro-optic effect. Sizable phase shifts can be obtained by changing the reverse bias by only a few volts. Depending on the orientation of the light polarization with respect to the junction field, the diodes act as phase modulators or as polarization modulators. The polarization modulation is easily converted into intensity modulation by standard techniques. A phase-modulation index of 2.2 rad has been achieved at an optical wavelength of 0.633 μ. Intensity modulation has been studied up to 500 MHz. All GaP diode modulators studied thus far are very short. Therefore, there are no significant transit time effects, and the diodes can be considered as lumped modulators into the GHz range. It appears that the frequency limitation of the modulators is caused by the intrinsic series resistance and the junction capacitance. These two quantities determine to a large extent the power consumption and the voltage distribution of the diodes. It will be very important to minimize the power dissipation of the diode not only to obtain a good modulation efficiency but also to prevent heating effects from limiting the frequency range of the diodes.

In Secs. II and III, the fabrication procedure, the equivalent circuit, and the power dissipation of the diodes are discussed. In Sec. IV the important optical properties of the diodes are given. Sections V and VI deal with the intensity modulation and the phase modulation, respectively. A summary and conclusions are given in Sec. VII.

II. DIODE FABRICATION

The GaP used for fabrication of the diodes was made by slow cooling of a GaP-enriched Ga solution.[2] The raw material, n-type platelets, doped with Te in the range 10^{17}–10^{18} cm^{-3}, was carefully inspected and selected for least strain and good optical and electrical homogeneity. The junction was usually obtained by Zn diffusion into an almost scratch-free polished Ga face, the $(\bar{1}\bar{1}1)$ plane, at temperatures between 700° and 800°C.[3] The depth of diffusion ranged from 25 μ to 40 μ for the various diodes. The diffused bars were then provided with Ohmic contacts, and two faces were polished parallel to a $\{1\bar{1}0\}$ plane. If the bar showed a satisfactory electro-optic effect, the capacitance of the diode was reduced by cutting strip-mesas. The width of a strip-mesa was usually between 50 μ to 80 μ. The locations of the strip-mesas were chosen so as to eliminate low-voltage microplasmas. In this way the reverse breakdown voltages of the mesa diodes were always increased, typically by a few volts. It is believed that the cutting operation gets rid of the worst material defects in the junction region. Whether those defects are already present in the material or whether they are caused by the handling and the diffusion is not yet established. The cutting operation is an especially important step in order to reduce the device capacitance and to increase the reverse breakdown voltage which makes larger modulation depths possible. The mesa diodes were then mounted into a coaxial package.[4] Finally the diodes were provided with SiO antireflective coatings which reduced the reflection losses to less than 0.5% at $\lambda=0.633$ μ.[5]

III. ELECTRICAL PROPERTIES

Capacitance and conductance measurements as a function of bias have been performed in the frequency range from 1 to 100 MHz with a Boonton Electronics admittance bridge model 33A-S11. The accuracy in this frequency range is better than $\pm 2.5\%$ for the capacitance values and better than $\pm 4\%$ for the conductance values. The equivalent circuit of diode impedances measured by the bridge is shown in Fig. 1(a). The frequency dependence of the obtained data very often indicates that the equivalent circuit can be better

[1] D. F. Nelson and F. K. Reinhart, Appl. Phys. Letters **5**, 148 (1964).
[2] D. G. Thomas, M. Gershonzon, and F. A. Trumbore, Phys. Rev. **133**, A269 (1964).
[3] P. W. Foy (private communication).
[4] E. Dickten (private communication).
[5] J. J. Schott (private communication).

TABLE I. Capacitance data of diode KC7–1BB.

A. Measured capacitance as a function of bias and frequency. Values in parenthesis are calculated from frequency independent parameters given in B.

f	100 kHz		1 MHz		10 MHz		100 MHz	
Bias (V)	G_p (μmho)	C_p (pF)	G_p (μmho)	C_p (pF)	G_p (μmho)	C_p (pF)	G_p (μmho)	C_p (pF)
0	0.3 (0.28)	40.99 (41.0)	27.2 (28.1)	39.95 (40.2)	658 (668)	22.24 (22.1)	2270 (2300)	16.34 (16.2)
10	0.09	19.31	6.7	19.15	358	14.39	1181	8.21
20	0.4 (0.038)	15.1 (15.1)	4.3 (3.8)	15.07 (15.1)	264 (261)	13.37 (12.3)	1030 (1027)	6.59 (6.37)
28	0.9	13.2	3.6	13.27	219	11.01	976	5.88

B. Frequency-independent parameters calculated from values of Table I.A assuming equivalent circuit according to Fig. 1(b).

Bias (V)	R_1 (Ω)	C_1 (pF)	R_2 (kΩ)	C_2 (pF)	C_1/C_2 (1)
0	14.0	16.4	1.10	24.6	0.667
20	14.5	6.2	1.21	8.9	0.697

described as a parallel connection of two voltage-dependent capacitances each in series with a constant resistance as shown in Fig. 1(b). This relatively complicated equivalent circuit reflects the fact that the diode mesa is often not properly isolated from the rest of the diffused layer. The equivalent circuit of Fig. 1(b) leads to a measured low-frequency capacitance of $C_p = C_1 + C_2$. At sufficiently high frequencies when $\omega R_2 C_2 > 1$ and $\omega R_1 C_1 \ll 1$, one gets $C_p \approx C_1$. Some of the measured capacitance data as a function of bias voltage and frequency are shown in Table I.A. At any given bias a strong frequency dependence is noted; hence, the equivalent circuit of Fig. 1(a) is inadequate. With the data of Table I.A, the equivalent, frequency-independent circuit parameters according to Fig. 1(b) have been determined for two bias values and are shown in Table I.B. The frequency dependence of C_p and G_p calculated from these circuit parameters is given in parenthesis in Table I.A. There is good agreement with the originally measured data. The only significant discrepancy appears at very low frequencies in the G_p data because the dc impedance which is predominantly determined by surface leakage has been neglected on purpose. As one can see from Table I.B, the deduced series resistances are constant within the error limit and the capacitances are only voltage dependent. Since the mesa cutting was done on a homogeneous bar, one might expect the ratio of the capacitances C_1/C_2 to be almost independent of bias voltage and this is supported by Table I.B. Additional capacitance measurements have been made with a slotted coaxial line to frequencies as high as 1.2 GHz. Adaptor and line inhomogeneities have contributed some significant measurement errors particularly in the case of large capacitances. It is expected that the errors at 1.2 GHz do not exceed 20% for capacitance values smaller than 20 pF. At lower frequencies, e.g., 500 MHz the errors are believed to be less than 10% when using the slotted-line technique. The high-frequency measurements support the equivalent circuit of Fig. 1(b) derived from the low-frequency measurements.

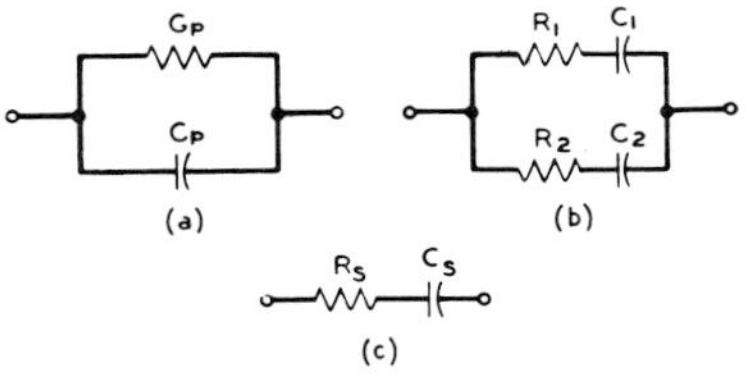

FIG. 1. Equivalent circuits. (a) Parallel circuit as obtained from capacitance bridge measurements. (b) Equivalent circuit of a diode with an incompletely isolated mesa (KC7–1BB). (c) Equivalent series circuit of a properly isolated mesa diode (KC46–CA).

A diode with a properly isolated mesa can be described by the equivalent circuit shown in Fig. 1(c). The series resistance as a function of bias voltage for such a diode is shown in Table II. As in the previous case, the series resistance can be considered as constant within the stated accuracy. The agreement of the capacitance values at any measured bias point is good.

The impedance of diode KC46-CA related to a characteristic line impedance of 50 Ω is shown in the Smith chart of Fig. 2. The impedance points lie on constant resistance circles at any frequency. This fact clearly demonstrates that the impedance of this diode can be

TABLE II. Capacitance and series resistance of diode KC46-CA as a function of bias and frequency. The series resistance is independent of bias within the measuring accuracy.

f	1 MHz	100 MHz		500 MHz	
Bias (V)	C (pF)	R_s (Ω)	C_s (pF)	R_s (Ω)	C_s (pF)
0	17.53	8.64	17.42	7.2	17.3
2	13.11	8.56	13.05	7.4	12.9
4	11.16	8.53	11.09	7.5	11.0
8	9.15	8.58	9.12	7.6	9.0
16	7.30	8.36	7.26	7.7	7.2
27	6.08	8.32	6.06	7.9	6.0

described adequately by an equivalent circuit according to Fig. 1(c). It appears that the series resistance at 1.2 GHz is considerably lower than for the other frequencies. Since the difference is believed to be outside the error limit, it is suggested that the reduction of the effective series resistance is caused by the elimination of some excess contact resistance at very high frequencies. Ohmic tin contacts on n-type GaP very often show some small additional contact resistance that is probably caused by the formation of a transition layer between the GaP and the tin.[4] The frequency data presented here suggest that the diode impedance can be understood in terms of the usual p-n junction depletion layer, the series resistance caused by the spreading resistance in the bulk material and the additional contact resistance.

The electric field of the junctions studied so far is parallel to the [111] direction. For this orientation, a direct piezoelectric resonance is only excited for acoustic wavelengths about twice the depletion layer width since only longitudinal acoustic waves along the [111] direction are generated.[6] Acoustic resonance frequencies are estimated to lie in the frequency range from about 2 GHz to 12 GHz. Depending on the mechanical coupling, deviations from the previously discussed frequency dependence of the diode impedance are then expected. The absence of any piezoelectric resonance in the frequency band studied here is anticipated to give a very smooth electro-optic effect over a frequency band extending from dc up into the GHz region.

Knowing the diode impedance as a function of frequency, we can determine the power consumption of a diode, P_d, if the voltage across the junction capacitor is known. In the case of a sinusoidally varying voltage with a peak value V and an angular frequency ω, one obtains in the case of the simple series circuit [Fig. 1(c)]

$$P_d = \tfrac{1}{2}\omega^2 R_s C^2 V^2. \qquad (1)$$

The capacitance C stands for an appropriately chosen average value because for a given large voltage swing the diode capacitance cannot be considered as a constant. The amount of the deviation from the small-signal capacitance C_{dc} at the dc-bias point V_{dc} depends on the junction characteristic and the parameter v defined as

$$v = V/(V_0 - V_{dc}), \qquad (2)$$

where V_0 is the built-in potential. The voltage across the junction cannot exceed V_0 when driven into forward bias, therefore we have $v \leq 1$.

An estimate of the nonlinear capacitance effect has been made by assuming a sinusoidally varying junction voltage and calculating the power dissipation of the distorted diode current in the series resistance. This estimate will be fairly accurate, if $\omega(R_0 + R_s)C \ll 1$, where R_0 stands for the source resistance of the driving generator.

In the case of an abrupt junction, the maximum deviation occurs at $v = 1$ with $C/C_{dc} = \sqrt{2}$. For $v < 0.76$ the capacitance correction is less than 10% and for $v < 0.3$ even less than 1%. The linearly graded junctions lead to much smaller corrections, namely, only 16% for $v = 1$.

The harmonic distortion of the current leads via $R_0 + R_s$ to voltage distortions across the junction capacitor and hence to an unwanted nonlinear light modulation. Since the harmonic distortion goes along with excessive power consumption, it will be desirable to reduce the parameter v by choosing a bias point as

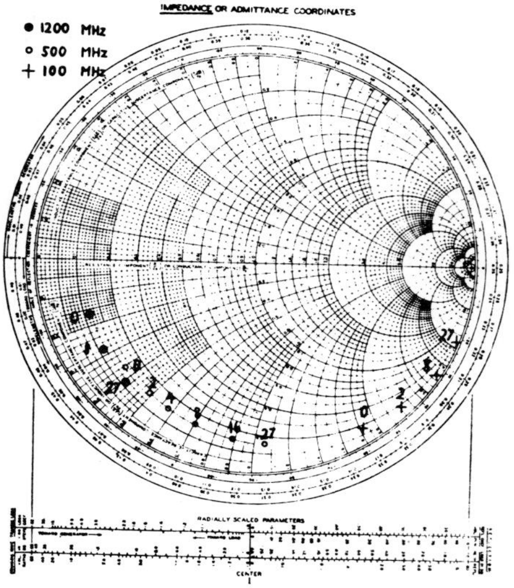

FIG. 2. Normalized impedance of the diode KC46-CA as a function of bias and frequency. Normalization impedance is 50 Ω. The reverse-bias voltage is given by the numbers.

[6] D. L. White, IRE UE-9, 21 (1962).

TABLE III. Coefficients α_i ($i=1, 2, 3$) of the electro-optic effect for the three principal orientations of the electric field.

	$E \parallel [111]$ direction $E_x=E_y=E_z=E/\sqrt{3}$	$E \parallel [110]$ direction $E_x=E_y=E/\sqrt{2}$ $E_z=0$	$E \parallel [001]$ direction $E_x=E_y=0$ $E_z=E$
α_1	$1/2\sqrt{3}$	$\frac{1}{2}$	$-\frac{1}{2}$
α_2	$1/2\sqrt{3}$	$-\frac{1}{2}$	$\frac{1}{2}$
α_3	$-1/\sqrt{3}$	0	0
Principal axis 1	in (111) plane	in $(\bar{1}10)$ plane, $-45°$ with [110] direction	$\parallel$ [110] direction
Principal axis 2	in (111) plane	in $(\bar{1}10)$ plane, $+45°$ with [110] direction	$\parallel$ $[\bar{1}10]$ direction
Principal axis 3	$\parallel$ [111] direction	$\parallel$ $[\bar{1}10]$ direction	$\parallel$ [001] direction

close to the reverse-bias breakdown as possible. From this point of view linearly graded diodes with large reverse breakdown voltages are desirable.

The power dissipation of the diodes should be minimized in order to maximize the modulation efficiency and to eliminate the need for special cooling without which the diode might burn out. (The burnout power level of a diode in a coaxial mount is several hundred milliwatts.) The minimization of P_d was discussed elsewhere.[7] The performance of the diode modulator can be best characterized by the power P_0 that is necessary to obtain a certain modulation depth per unit bandwidth Δf. Equation (1) is then rewritten as

$$P_d = P_0 \Delta f. \tag{3}$$

It is understood that optimum performance is obtained in a matched circuit with a bandwidth

$$\Delta f = \omega^2 R_s C/\pi. \tag{4}$$

From this we get the characteristic power

$$P_0 = (\pi/2) C V^2. \tag{5}$$

The characteristic power P_0 only depends on the capacitance of the diode and the voltage necessary for a desired modulation depth which expediently is chosen as 1 rad for a phase modulator. Good diodes will have $P_0 \leq 2\text{mW/MHz}\cdot\text{rad}^2$. If a larger bandwidth is required than the one given by Eq. (4), an appropriate impedance network is to be added. The additional power needed for the larger bandwidth can then be dissipated outside the diode. Therefore, the danger of frequency limitation imposed by the burnout power of the diode is reduced. Diodes whose strip mesas are not properly isolated generally have to absorb more power than those with a well isolated mesa. It is particularly for this reason that the latter are preferred.

IV. OPTICAL PROPERTIES

GaP is a cubic material with no center of symmetry. Therefore, its linear electro-optic effect can be described with only one constant, r_{41}. A good value for bulk material is $r_{41} = 0.97 \times 10^{-10}$ cm/V at a wavelength $\lambda = 0.633\ \mu$.[8] At this same wavelength the refractive index equals $n = 3.31$.[9] The induced birefringence due to an applied electric field E across a sample can be readily calculated for a given orientation. The induced phase shift φ_i that a plane light-wave propagating along a principal axis with its polarization parallel to another principal axis experiences by transversing a crystal of length l is given by

$$\varphi_i = (2\pi n/\lambda)(1 + \alpha_i n^2 r_{41} E) l. \tag{6}$$

The factor α_i depends on the orientation of the electric field and on the principal axis to which the subscript i refers. A few values of α_i are given in Table III for the three main orientations: $E \parallel [111]$, $E \parallel [110]$, and $E \parallel [001]$.[10] In order to get the most efficient phase modulator one has to pick the orientation that gives the largest α_i. Out of these orientations, the [111] direction is the best with the light polarization parallel to it. The most efficient polarization or intensity modulator can be found by looking for the largest difference of the phase shifts of any of two orthogonal polarization directions. Inspection of Table III shows that the best orientation in this case is the E field parallel to the [110] direction. Fortunately, there is no large difference in performance if an optimally oriented phase modulator is used as a polarization modulator and vice versa. In both cases, the power consumption for the not optimally oriented modulator type is $\frac{4}{3}$ of the optimally oriented one. Since good GaP is fairly readily available in thin (111) platelets, the [111] orientation of the electric field will generally be preferred over the [110] orientation.

The halfwave voltage for unit aspect ratio (crystal length equal to electrode spacing) of GaP is 9.0 **kV**. This halfwave voltage is almost four times larger than the value given for $LiTaO_3$. On the other hand, the radio frequency dielectric constant is about four times smaller than the one of $LiTaO_3$.[11] The power consump-

[7] F. K. Reinhart, D. F. Nelson, E. Dickten, and P. W. Foy, SSDRC Princeton, June (1965).

[8] D. F. Nelson and E. H. Turner, J. Appl. Phys. **39**, 3337 (1968).
[9] W. Bond, J. Appl. Phys. **36**, 1674 (1965).
[10] S. Namba, J. Opt. Soc. Am. **51**, 76 (1961).
[11] R. T. Denton, F. S. Chen, and A. A. Ballman, J. Appl. Phys. **38**, 1611 (1967).

tion per unit bandwidth of the $LiTaO_3$ modulator is expected to be approximately one fourth of a conventional bulk GaP modulator with the same aspect ratio. However, it will be evident from the experimental data given in the following sections that the GaP *diode* modulator can perform as well as a $LiTaO_3$ modulator. It is pointed out elsewhere[1,12] that the diode modulator shows a different dependence of the phase shift with wavelength and also with voltage than a bulk modulator.

Weakly doped GaP is transparent from $\lambda=0.55\ \mu$ out to $\lambda=12.5\ \mu$, where lattice absorption bands begin to play a role.[13] GaP doped in the range 10^{17}–10^{18} cm^{-3} has an absorption constant α of the order of 1 cm^{-1} at a wavelength $\lambda=0.633\ \mu$. It is believed that this small absorption is largely caused by free carriers. This absorption and the strong wavelength dependence of the phase shift might prevent successful operation of the junction modulators in the infrared. Measurements in the near infrared at $\lambda=1.15\ \mu$ have not indicated any excessive absorption.

The light transmission of diode KC46-CA has been determined to be as high as 85%. The amount not transmitted is partly lost by absorption and partly by scattering. If all the losses were to be attributed to absorption, one would obtain $\alpha\simeq2.3$ cm^{-1}. The scattering in this case is believed to be caused by small surface imperfections and possibly by submicroscopic precipitates within the GaP. Scattering can also be attributed to a nonplanar junction waveguide. However, it is believed that this latter cause is a minor one in the diodes studied here because significant scattering in the waveguide goes along with a poor electro-optic effect. The fabrication of long planar junction waveguides (>1 mm) has been found to be extremely difficult even when using the procedures described in Sec. II.

The phase shift in a given material can be maximized by maximizing the product El. The length l is limited by either absorption, transit time effects, or diffraction in the junction plane, whichever is more critical. The electric field E can be maximized without increasing the applied voltage over a desired value only by confining the beam size in the direction of the field to a value that is as small as possible. A limitation will occur when the field strength reaches the breakdown limit. The GaP junction modulator has a dielectric profile in the junction region that allows it to act as a dielectric waveguide. This dielectric waveguide acts to confine a beam in the high-field region as desired. Unfortunately the cause of the dielectric profile is not understood yet and hence no optimization procedure for this feature of the diode modulator can be given.

In order to demonstrate the effect of the junction waveguide on the intensity distribution, a He–Ne laser beam was focused on the entrance face of the diode. The spot size of the beam was about 6 μ in diameter. An enlarged image of the exit face was obtained with a second objective the numerical aperture of which was 0.38. This aperture is sufficiently large for providing a good image quality at a magnification of 150. The intensity trace of the beam in the image plane of the exit face of the diode after passing through the homogeneous bulk n-region of the diode is shown in Fig. 3 by the solid line. The trace is essentially Gaussian. [Note: The ripple originated in the laser beam and not in the optical system.] The intensity traces for the beam coupled into the junction waveguide are shown in Fig. 3 for two bias voltages, traces a and b. The beam polarization is parallel to the electric field that is oriented along the [111] direction. The traces a and b are not Gaussian. Furthermore, the two peak values are substantially higher than before. The width of the traces also depends on the bias voltage. There is no significant voltage-dependent absorption involved, because the integrated beam power is the same within 5% for the two cases. The difference might be caused by a change of the coupling efficiency due to the change of the boundary conditions with voltage.[14] At this time,

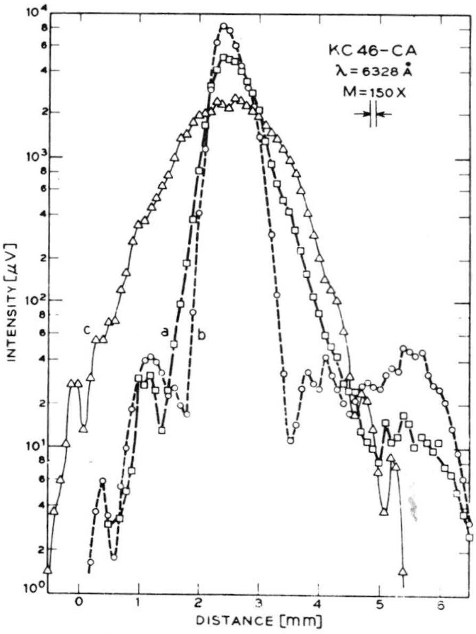

FIG. 3. Intensity trace across image of exit face of diode KC46-CA with light guided along junction [a: no bias applied, b: 28 V reverse bias] and with light passing through the bulk n region c.

[12] F. K. Reinhart, D. F. Nelson, and J. McKenna (unpublished).

[13] D. Kleinman, and W. G. Spitzer, Phys. Rev. **118**, 110 (1960).

[14] J. McKenna, Bell System Tech. J. **46**, 1491 (1967) and a following paper.

the real cause of the significant difference of the peak values and slopes at 0 V and 28 V reverse bias as shown by curves a and b, respectively, is not completely understood. The originally proposed models[12,15] give only qualitatively correct answers. Further work aimed at a quantitative understanding of this effect is planned.

From a practical point of view the dependence of the intensity trace on voltage is highly undesirable, because it may cause degradation in a light transmission system. It should be added that the intensity trace for the polarization direction in the (111) plane depends considerably less on bias voltage. This, however, goes qualitatively along with a considerably smaller electro-optic effect (see Table III). The fact that the intensities of the two principal polarizations experience such different voltage dependences[12] might make it fairly difficult in the case of intensity modulation to reshape the beam in a satisfactory way, if large changes of the modulator voltage are needed.

The junctions give guiding only in one direction. From this it follows that a focused beam will spread within the plane of the junction. The spreading angle is dependent on the effective numerical aperture of the objective used to couple the light into the junction region. Since the focusing of the beam is diffraction limited, the spread of the beam cannot be made arbitrarily small. Thus, the length of the diode might be unduly limited for a desired, minimized, strip-mesa width in order to minimize the capacitance, unless corrective measures are taken, e.g., by means of an appropriately designed astigmatism of the lens system. Estimates suggest that a mesa width of 25 μ and a diode length of 2 mm should not lead to excessive losses caused by diffuse scattering at the surface. A diode of this dimension will be more difficult to align than a diode used in this work which has a mesa width of approximately 60 μ and a length of 1.5 mm. The alignment of this latter diode with astigmatism-free objectives is relatively easy.

Figure 3 demonstrates that the waveguide effect is significant. No accurate figure can be given of the actual fraction of the intensity of the light that is not guided. One only can take the light in the low-intensity ripple in the curves a and b of Fig. 3 to be nonguided light. It is not clear how much nonguided light is covered up by the guided portion. The intensity measurements presented here can be used for establishing a lower limit on the amount of the light held in the waveguide. They suggest that at least 70% of the transmitted light is guided. Originally a value of 90% was determined by means of a different technique which, however, is less reliable.[7] This earlier determination is not very accurate but seems to come fairly close to the correct value because calculation of the coupling for a considerably less favorable input beam shape has shown that the guided light portion is about 90%.[14] More

[15] I. P. Kaminow, Appl. Phys. Letters 7, 123 (1965).

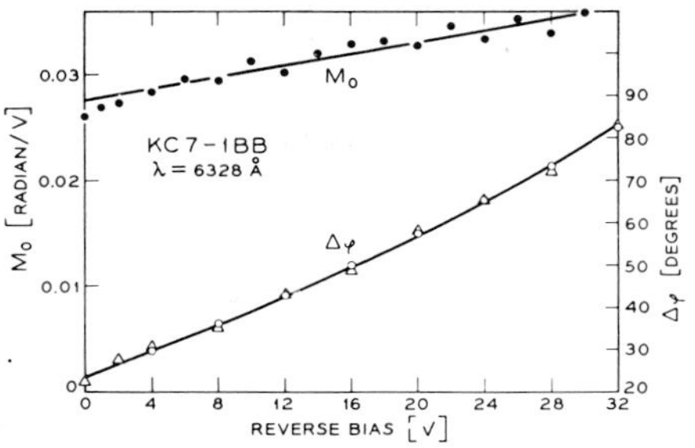

FIG. 4. Modulation depth per volt, m_0, and phase difference $\Delta\varphi$ as a function of reverse bias of diode KC7–1BB. Triangles (△) in $\Delta\varphi$ plot were directly measured with a Sénarmont compensator, whereas circles (○) were obtained by integrating the smoothed m_0 data. In order to obtain a fit, a constant strain of 20° was assumed.

work is planned in order to find better agreement between theory and experiment.

V. INTENSITY MODULATION

Measurements of the phase difference $\Delta\varphi$ as a function of bias voltage were made using an Ehringhaus or Sénarmont compensator. A single lowest-order transverse mode He–Ne laser beam was passed into the junction as described in the preceding section. The electric field of the diodes reported here is parallel to the [111] direction. The light polarization was at 45° to the junction field. The light transmitted through the diode was collected by means of a microscope objective, passed through a compensator and then through a polarizing filter which was crossed to the beam polarization. The transmitted beam intensity was detected with a photomultiplier.

The phase difference $\Delta\varphi$ vs reverse bias of diode KC7-1BB is shown by the triangles in Fig. 4. The diode is only 0.52 mm long. The maximum phase difference that can be obtained with a single pass is about 60° or about 1 rad peak to peak with 32 V applied. The phase difference is slightly superlinear with bias. The small-signal intensity modulation depth m at lower frequencies can be determined by measuring the light intensity excursion I due to an applied ac signal V and the average dc light intensity I_0 the polarization of which is adjusted with a compensator to yield a resulting circular dc polarization in the absence of a modulating signal. One obtains the modulation depth by the ratio $m=I/I_0$. In the small signal case ($m\ll 1$), the modulation depth per volt, m_0, can be expressed as $m_0=m/V$ or

$$m_0=\partial\Delta\varphi/\partial V, \tag{7}$$

with $\Delta\varphi$ expressed in radians.

A direct measurement of m_0 at 10 MHz as a function of bias is shown in Fig. 4. A small, approximately linear

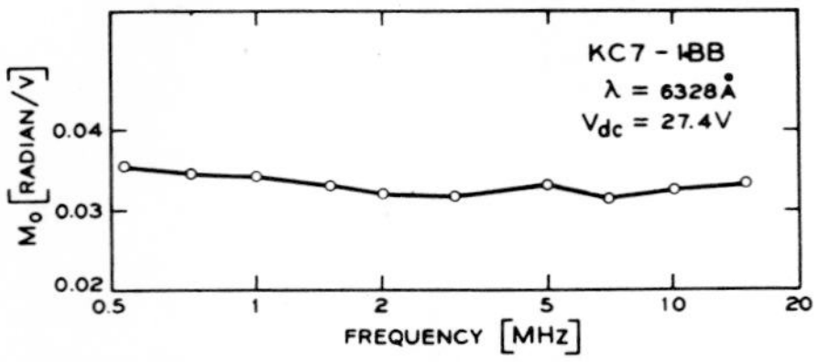

FIG. 5. Low-frequency data of the modulation depth per volt, m_0, of diode KC7-1BB at a reverse bias of 27.4 V.

increase of m_0 with reverse bias is obtained. The relative accuracy is estimated to be around 5%. The absolute error might be as high as 15%. If the slope of m_0 can be attributed to the linear electro-optic effect influencing the wave properties, a value for $r_{41} = 0.7 \times 10^{-10}$ cm/V is obtained from the slope. Such a value agrees fairly well with other recent data.[8] According to Eq. (7), the phase difference can be obtained from these data by integration. The integrated data are shown in Fig. 4 by the circles. Good agreement with the dc data (triangles obtained from compensation measurements) has been obtained by assuming a strain level of 20°.

Measurements of m_0 with the same technique were performed over a frequency band from 0.5 MHz to 15 MHz. The data shown in Fig. 5 were obtained at a fixed negative bias of 27.4 V. The slight frequency response is attributed to the broad-band circuitry rather than to the modulator.

The performance of diode KC7–1BB as a broad-band light intensity modulator was also checked at frequencies ranging from 250 to 500 MHz. The arrangement was essentially the same as in the previous experiments. Only the photomultiplier was replaced by a Si-avalanche photodiode which was working into a broad-band mixer having an input impedance $R_L = 50\ \Omega$. The power P_s of the Si diode delivered to the mixer was determined substitutionally. From this the peak current I was determined by $I = (2P_s/R_L)^{1/2}$. The average dc

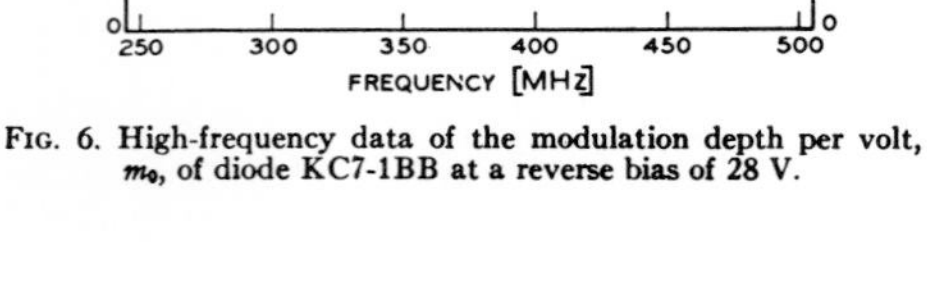

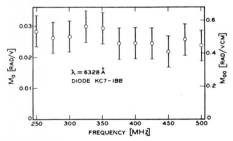

FIG. 6. High-frequency data of the modulation depth per volt, m_0, of diode KC7-1BB at a reverse bias of 28 V.

current I_0 for a net 90° phase difference was also measured. The modulation index was then determined as before. The voltage across the GaP diode was monitored with a calibrated slotted line. The values for m_0 and their error flags are given in Fig. 6. The considerable scattering of the measured points is expected from the measuring procedure. Furthermore, the high-frequency measurements seem to yield about 30% less modulation depth per volt than the low-frequency measurements. There is some experimental evidence that this small degradation of the modulator performance was at least partly due to errors in the optical alignment caused by the limited mechanical stability of the optical system. Within the quoted experimental error limits, however, the modulation index per volt appears to be constant from dc to at least 500 MHz. The performance limitation of the diode modulator is

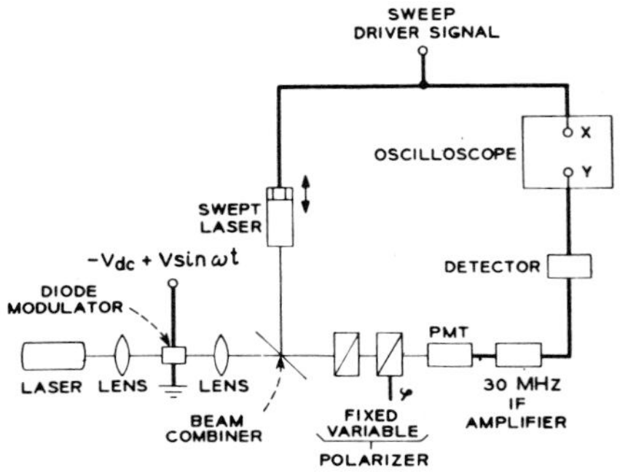

FIG. 7. Experimental arrangement used for the measurements of the phase modulation.

therefore predictable from its electrical circuit description.

Using diode KC7–1BB, an intensity modulation depth of 40% with a single light path was measured at 250 MHz with a driving power consumption of only 300 mW. The bandwidth was approximately 110 MHz. This is equivalent to a power consumption of 2.7 mW per MHz bandwidth for 40% intensity modulation depth. At 500 MHz the actual modulation depth could not be made that large because of the limited power capability of the diode. Measurements made at smaller (about 20%) modulation depths at this frequency indicated fair agreement with corresponding values at 250 MHz.

VI. PHASE MODULATION

The phase modulation of several diodes was measured at the He–Ne laser line λ = 6328 Å by means of a heterodyning technique described by Kaminow.[15] A schematic drawing of the experimental setup is given in Fig. 7.

The polarized laser beam was sent through the diode junction with its polarization plane parallel the [111] direction. of the electric field or perpendicular to it. The beam axis was chosen along the [110] direction as in the case for intensity modulation. The collected beam was combined with a second laser (local oscillator) the frequency of which was swept by means of a mirror mounted on a piezoelectric transducer. The combined beams were first passed through a fixed polarizer in order to secure a desired polarization orientation and then through a second polarizer for variable attenuation (indicated by φ). The two beams were allowed to beat with each other in a photomultiplier; the output of which was connected into a tuned 30 MHz IF amplifier. The output of the IF amplifier was rectified and displayed on an oscilloscope with the aid of the sweep signal applied to the transducer. The pattern on the

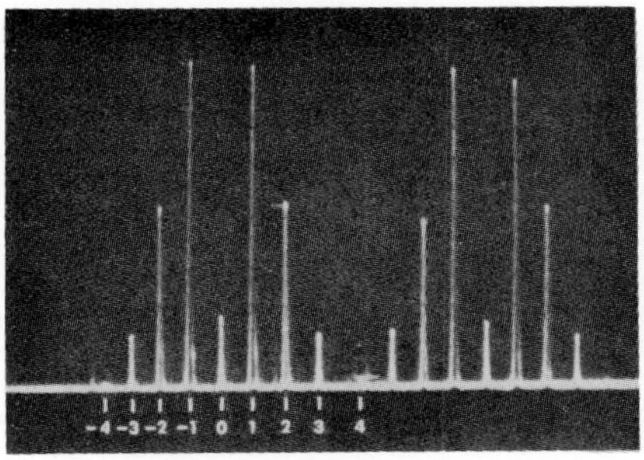

FIG. 8. Spectrum and image frequency spectrum of a laser beam modulated with a GaP diode to a depth of 2 rad. Modulation frequency 7.23 MHz. The numbers indicate the order of the sidebands created by the phase modulation.

oscilloscope shown by Fig. 8 displayed the frequency spectrum of the modulated laser beam over the swept frequency range twice, because an output at the IF amplifier occurs whenever the frequency difference is ± 30 MHz. The amplitude of the displayed spectrum was not linear. The modulation index was determined from the relative sideband strengths and by comparing them with the prediction of phase-modulation theory. In order to measure the relative sideband strengths, a known attenuation of the combined beams was introduced by adjusting the orientation of a second polarizing filter. The phase shift per volt with the polarization direction parallel to the electric field is referred to as $m_{0\|}$. The phase shift per volt for the other polarization direction is called $m_{0\perp}$.

Measurements of the values $m_{0\|}$ and $m_{0\perp}$ as a function of bias have been made on several diodes. The results of a typical diode with a length of 0.71 mm, KC46-CA, are shown in Figs. 9 and 10. The frequency

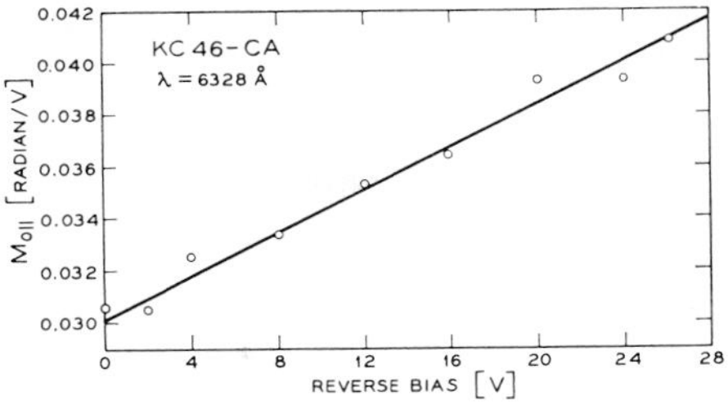

FIG. 9. Phase-modulation index per volt, $m_{0\|}$, as a function of bias of diode KC46-CA.

of the modulating signal was 14.5 MHz. As expected from Table III, the values for $m_{0\|}$ are larger than the ones for $m_{0\perp}$. A mild linear dependence on bias voltage is noted in both cases, but it is relatively larger for $m_{0\|}$ than for $m_{0\perp}$. With the previously mentioned model, the slopes of these curves are in good agreement with a value $r_{41}=0.7\times10^{-10}$ cm/V within an estimated uncertainty of 15%.

In this diode, a peak voltage of 14 V produces a modulation index of approximately $m=0.5$ rad for the optimum orientation. The power consumption for this modulation index is about 2.5 mW per MHz bandwidth. The obtainable modulation index is limited by the reverse breakdown of this diode which is $\simeq 28$ V. More modulation index would only be obtained for a multiple light pass through the diode. Capacitance measurements indicated that the bandwidth of a tuned matched circuit at 500 MHz would be about 200 MHz. A modulation index of 0.5 rad at a bandwidth of 200 MHz would require too much power dissipation for the diode if no special cooling was provided. It is to be noted however that this diode is not really optimized; otherwise the power consumption could be substantially lower.

The phase modulation of the electro-optic diode is also slightly nonlinear. The measurements suggest that the electro-optic distortion is quadratic. The second-

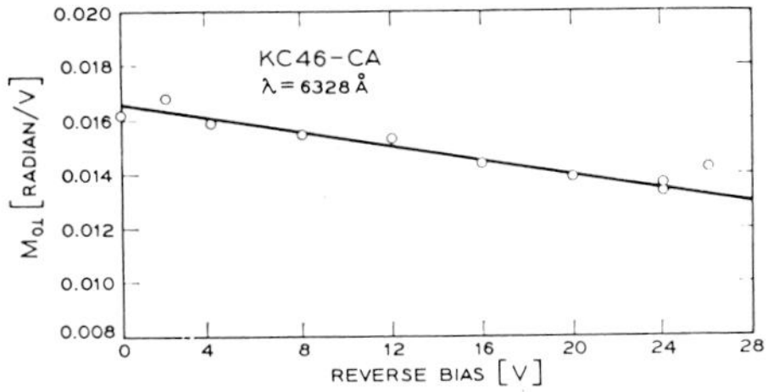

FIG. 10. Phase-modulation index per volt, $m_{0\perp}$, as a function of bias of diode KC46-CA.

harmonic distortion has been calculated from the experimental data. For the diode KC46-CA the maximum second-harmonic distortion amounts to 4% for $m=0.5$ rad. This distortion can only be minimized by reducing the drive voltage for a given modulation index. Such a reduction also yields the least power dissipation and the least distortion of the driving signal due to the nonlinear junction capacitance.

Phase-modulation experiments have been performed to frequencies as high as 200 MHz. Within the error limits which are estimated to be around 25%, no change of the modulation performance has been observed as a function of frequency.

A diode, KB80–1CB, of 1.5 mm length and a reverse breakdown voltage of 61 V was constructed. A peak voltage of 28 V produced a modulation index of 2 rad at a dc reverse bias of 32 V with the junction field parallel to the light polarization. The frequency spectrum of the modulated laser is shown in Fig. 8 at $m \simeq 2$ rad. The modulation frequency was 7.23 MHz. The frequency was chosen to be small so that there was no overlap of the image frequency spectrum. Note that at the modulation depth shown, the carrier frequency (0) is relatively small and that the magnitude of the third sideband is sizable. In the picture all sidebands up to and including the fourth can be observed. The amplitude and the frequency scale are not linear. The relative amplitudes as observed experimentally agreed fairly well with those calculated from the theory of the phase modulation. The separation of the spectra is twice the intermediate frequency (60 MHz). The cutoff frequency of this diode was 7 GHz. If it were used in a tuned circuit at 1 GHz, a bandwidth of about 300 MHz would result with a power consumption of 450 mW for a modulation index of 1 rad. For continuous modulation this power consumption is rather high but it might still be below the critical burnout power level. The optimum reverse biasing voltage for 1 rad modulation depth was near 48 V. A peak signal of only 12 V was necessary to obtain a modulation index of 1 rad. This corresponds to $m_{0||}=83$ mrad/V at $V_{dc}=-48$ V. Such a value compares fairly well to $m_{0||}=40$ mrad/V at $V_{dc}=-24$ V of diode KC46-CA which is only half as long. The capacitance at -48 V was measured at 100 MHz as 6.2 pF. The capacitance in the circuit was found to be not more than 6.7 pF. A power consumption of 1.5 mW was necessary in order to obtain 1 rad modulation index per 1 MHz of bandwidth. These values were deduced from measurements at14.5 MHz and at 51.5 MHz and agreed within 1 dB.

VII. CONCLUSIONS AND SUMMARY

The high modulation efficiency of the GaP diode light modulator is attributed to the high electric field in the junction region (10^5 V/cm) and to a waveguide which prevents the light from spreading out of the high-field region. The diode modulator appears to be equivalent to a bulk modulator with the width over which the field extends being about equal to the decay constant of the electric field vector of the light outside the waveguide region.

Some of the waveguide properties are dependent on the applied bias and hence lead to beam distortions and slightly nonlinear modulation characteristics. In the case of the phase modulation, the beam distortions are not expected to affect the modulator performance seriously because the phase fronts of the beam are not distorted in a strain-free diode modulator. Phase-front distortion can however result from strains.[16,17] The effects on amplitude modulation are larger because the peak intensities of the light components along the principal axis have a different voltage dependence. The quantitative aspects of this have not been studied in detail but they appear not to be serious especially in the case of pulse modulation.

The modulation experiments have shown that good results can be obtained by using high-quality lenses and a stable diode holder that allows precise adjustments of the diode position. The optical alignment of the modulator is relatively easy with such a positioner. It appears from this that the small size of the diode represents no obstacle to the use of this modulator.

A power of 1.5 mW for a phase-modulation index of 1 rad/MHz bandwidth has been measured on a diode 1.5 mm long. Converting this amount of phase modulation into intensity modulation, a modulation depth of 84% would result. It is expected that an improved modulator design will reduce the characteristic power to 0.5 mW/MHz·rad^2 without increasing the alignment problems too seriously.

ACKNOWLEDGMENTS

The author wishes to thank J. K. Galt, C. D. Thurmond, and D. F. Nelson for many stimulating discussions, F. A. Trumbore for providing the material, P. W. Foy and E. Dickten for preparing and assembling the diodes, W. T. Lynch for providing a Si-avalanche photodiode, and J. J. Schott for his technical assistance.

[16] D. F. Nelson and J. McKenna, J. Appl. Phys. **38**, 4057 (1967).

[17] J. McKenna and J. A. Morrison, Bell System Tech. J. **47**, (1968).

Efficient GaAs-$Al_xGa_{1-x}As$ Double-Heterostructure Light Modulators

F. K. Reinhart
Bell Telephone Laboratories, Murray Hill, New Jersey 07974

and

B. I. Miller
Bell Telephone Laboratories, Holmdel, New Jersey 07733
(Received 30 September 1971)

Properly designed GaAs-$Al_xGa_{1-x}As$ double heterostructures produce strong optical waveguides. The propagation constants of the waveguide modes can be readily modulated by the linear electro-optic effect. Measurements at a wavelength $\lambda = 1.153$ μm have yielded a phase modulation of 180° with −10 V applied bias to a device only 1 mm long. The power necessary to phase modulate light at $\lambda \approx 1$ μm by 1 rad is of the order of 0.1 mW per 1-MHz bandwidth. The power dissipation is very strongly dependent on wavelength. At present, the high-frequency modulation is limited by the series resistance and capacitance of the device. The highest cutoff frequency determined thus far, ≈ 4 GHz, is considerably lower than that calculated based on the geometry and material properties.

Significant phase modulation of visible light was achieved in reverse-biased GaP *p-n* junctions due to a naturally occurring optical dielectric waveguide and a sizable linear electro-optic or Pockels effect.[1] Similar effects are expected in cw laser-type GaAs-$Al_xGa_{1-x}As$ double heterostructures (DH) because of a very pronounced and controllable optical dielectric waveguide[2,3] coupled with a strong Pockels effect.[4] The optical waveguide of the DH structures may lead to a much tighter coupling of the optical field to the junction field than that characteristic of GaP *p-n* junctions. Since this interaction can be controlled in the DH structures, very strong phase modulation may result in the red and infrared portion of the spectrum.

The *p-n* junction of DH lasers usually occurs at one of the boundaries of the high-optical-dielectric-constant region (see Figs. 1 and 3 of Ref. 2). Under reverse bias the boundaries of the depletion layer move, respectively, further into the regions having the high and low optical dielectric constants, n_1^2 and n_2^2. The penetration depth of the depletion layer essentially depends on the doping profiles. The junction electric field E_j perturbs the optical-dielectric-constant profile via the Pockels effect. This perturbation is very small compared to the fractional-optical-dielectric-constant step, $\Delta = (n_1^2 - n_2^2)/n_1^2$, which is of the order of 0.1 for typical DH lasers.[3] Significant perturbations of the mode parameters will result only if the high-optical-field region coincides with the depletion layer. From this argument it follows that efficient interaction can be achieved by reducing the high-optical-dielectric-constant region having a width $2w$, and by having the depletion layer extend over $2w$. These conditions may also be obtained, in principle, with *p-i-n*, *p-i-p*, or *n-i-n* structures, where the *i* layer is essentially coincident with the high-optical-dielectric-constant layer.

The DH lasers or modulators were grown on a [100] substrate of *n*-GaAs by liquid-phase epitaxy.[5,6] The first and third layer consist of $Al_{0.3}Ga_{0.7}As$ of *n* and *p* type, respectively. Typical doping levels for these layers are $(1-5) \times 10^{17}$ cm^{-3}. The second layer is typically *n*- or *p*-type GaAs with doping levels ranging from 10^{16} to 10^{17} cm^{-3} as determined from junction-capacitance measurements. The growth of *i* layers by liquid-phase epitaxy appears quite feasible at present. We have obtained π-ν—type layers instead of *i* layers.

TABLE I. Characteristic data of a DH junction phase modulator.

	Calculated						Measured
	λ (μm)	w (μm)	C (pF)	Orientation [100]	[110]	[111]	Orientation [100]
P_O (mW/MHz rad^2)	1.153	0.203	14.0	0.22	0.22	0.16	...
(Phase modulation)	0.9	0.152	18.8	0.077	0.077	0.058	...
P_{OP} (mW/MHz rad^2)	1.153	0.203	14.0	0.22	0.055	0.073	0.21
	0.9	0.152	18.8	0.077	0.019	0.026	...
(Polarization modulation)							
	1.153	0.203	14.0	182	364	315	173
M_{00} (deg/V cm)	0.9	0.152	18.8	354	708	613	...

Appl. Phys. Lett., Vol. 20, No. 1, 1 January 1972

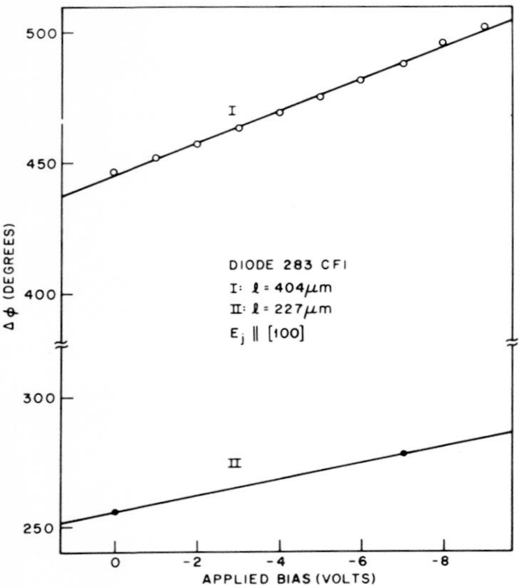

FIG. 1. Phase difference vs applied bias at $\lambda = 1.153$ μm for two lengths of the same diode.

In such structures depletion-layer widths up to 0.6 μm have been observed.

The presence of the junction electric field lowers the symmetry of the crystal, and thus the originally isotropic crystal becomes birefringent in the depletion-layer region and the resulting propagation constant is orientation dependent. The orthogonally polarized modes are excited by means of a focused linearly polarized light beam, the polarization of which is oriented at 45° to the junction electric field. The elliptically polarized light characterized by the phase difference $\Delta\varphi$, emerging from the exit face of the modulator, is collimated by a second lens and passed throught an Ehringhaus or Sénarmont compensator and polarizing filter arrangement. The polarization modulation is measured either visually with the aid of an ir converter or through a slit positioned at the real image of the exit face and a photomultiplier tube. In the latter case, a slit is desirable in order to discriminate against the continuum mode background.[1] The background can be reduced by proper excitation of the waveguide modes also. With the aid of oil immersion, up to 90% of the transmitted light has been excited as discrete waveguide modes. In order to obtain such a high-mode excitation efficiency, it is necessary to carefully match and align the incoming focused beam with respect to the waveguide. The adjustment of position vertical to the junction plane may be critical to about ± 0.1 μm.

In Fig. 1, $\Delta\varphi$ measurements are shown for a unit with $2w = 0.14 \pm 0.02$ μm and E_j parallel to the crystallographic [100] direction and with the light ($\lambda = 1.153$ μm) traveling along the [0$\bar{1}$1] direction. In order to determine $\Delta\varphi$ between the TE and TM modes on an absolute basis, the diode was measured in the same area before and after cleaving, hence for two different lengths (I) and (II). The ratio of the $\Delta\varphi$ values agrees with the length ratio well within the accuracy of measurement (± 5%). The large $\Delta\varphi$ value at $E_j \approx 0$, $\Delta\varphi_0$, is due to the inherent different propagation constants of the TE and TM modes in the waveguide apart from the effects of birefringence. From $\Delta\varphi$, the value present at full forward bias (no "junction field"), a fairly accurate determination of the effective Δ is obtained.[3] For this case a value of $\Delta = 0.094$ is deduced. It is noteworthy that such modulator devices may also be useful as simple static phase plates.

We have also studied the intensity distribution of the light across the real image of the exit face. The following results are quite remarkable: (i) The shape of the planar waveguide modes appears to be independent of the additional phase shifts imposed by the compensator; (ii) very high extinction ratios (up to 20 dB) have been found; and (iii) occasional focusing of the modes within the plane of the junction occurs. This latter fact would be very desirable from a device point of view, if it can be controlled.

It is customary to compare phase modulators by the power they consume in order to obtain 1 rad of phase modulation per 1 MHz of bandwidth.[4,7] Typical projected data for fundamental modes are compiled in Table I for various crystallographic orientations of E_j with λ as a parameter. For the calculation it was assumed that $2w$ is identical with the depletion-layer width. The values shown for phase modulation apply for $E_j \parallel$ [100] for the TE mode, $E_j \parallel$ [111] for the TM mode, and in the case of $E_j \parallel$ [110] to either of the modes.[1] The calculations were performed to obtain the least power per unit length of light travel similar to Ref. 8 yielding optimum values of w. A length, $l = 1$ mm, a width along the junction plane, $b = 50$ μm, and $\Delta = 0.1$ were assumed. Such dimensions are in the range of what can be readily obtained and handled. In order to use such narrow modulators the exciting beam has to be astigmatic.[9] With astigmatic beams the light interaction can, in principle, be made arbitrarily long. Using arguments similar to the ones in Ref. 4, it can be shown that the characteristic modulation power P_0 decreases with $l^{-1/2}$, if a simple focused Gaussian distribution of the light is assumed within the junction plane. However, the capacitance C of the device is proportional to $l^{3/2}$ for astigmatic Gaussian light distributions. This dependence contrasts to the diffraction-limited modulator.[4,10] From this it becomes obvious that light confinement in the junction plane is highly desirable because $P_0 \propto l^{-1}$. In addition, b can be chosen as narrow as a few micrometers.

In Table I we have also compiled the characteristic power P_{OP} in order to obtain a phase difference of 1 rad per 1-MHz bandwidth between the orthogonal modes and the corresponding characteristic phase difference per volt and per length, M_{00}. For the case of $E_j \parallel$ [100] and $\lambda = 1.153$ μm, the theoretical predictions have already been verified. It should be emphasized that polarization modulation is readily converted into intensity modulation, by an output polarizer and that 1 rad of polarization modulation corresponds to a linearized intensity modulation of 88%. We have constructed a modulator of $l = 1.04$ mm with a half-wave-voltage of only

10 V and an extinction ratio approaching 20 dB. If the modulator is used in a double-pass fashion, an additional reduction of power by a factor of 2 is possible.

The high-frequency performance of electrical-junction modulators has been discussed in detail in Ref. 7. The situation is expected to be quite similar in DH junction modulators. The series-resistance cutoff frequency f_c and the bandwidth limitation due to the burn-out power level are expected to be higher in DH modulators than in the GaP diodes. Capacitance measurements of DH modulators yielded $f_c \approx 4$ GHz. It is expected that this value can be improved significantly by applying better contacts.

In conclusion, the DH modulator proves to be a phase, polarization, or intensity modulator for the infrared portion of the spectrum of unparalleled efficiency. An even better modulator performance is expected in the red portion of the spectrum by adequately adjusting the Al content of the layers.

We wish to thank R. C. Miller for continuous encouragement, and J. J. Schott, R. Capik, and P. W. Foy for their technical assistance.

[1] F. K. Reinhart, D. F. Nelson, and J. McKenna, Phys. Rev. 177, 1208 (1969).
[2] I. Hayashi, M. B. Panish, and F. K. Reinhart, J. Appl. Phys. 42, 1929 (1971).
[3] F. K. Reinhart, I. Hayashi, and M. B. Panish, J. Appl. Phys. 42, 4466 (1971).
[4] I. P. Kaminow and E. H. Turner, Proc. IEEE 54, 1374 (1966).
[5] M. B. Panish, S. Sumski, and I. Hayashi, Met. Trans. 2, 795 (1971).
[6] B. I. Miller, J. E. Ripper, J. C. Dymant, E. Pinkas, and M. B. Panish, Appl. Phys. Letters 18, 403 (1971).
[7] F. K. Reinhart, J. Appl. Phys. 39, 3426 (1968).
[8] W. G. Oldham and Ali Bahraman, IEEE J. Quantum Electron. QE-3, 278 (1967).
[9] Beams emerging from GaAs lasers are naturally astigmatic. Gaussian beams from gas lasers such as used in the present investigation are readily made astigmatic by introducing a cylindrical lens of suitable focal length at an appropriate place in the incident light beam.
[10] R. T. Denton, F. S. Chen, and A. A. Ballman, J. Appl. Phys. 38, 1511 (1967).

OPTICAL GUIDING AND ELECTRO-OPTIC MODULATION IN GaAs EPITAXIAL LAYERS*

David HALL, Amnon YARIV and Elsa GARMIRE

Division of Engineering and Applied Science, California Institute of Technology, Pasadena, California 91109, USA

Received 2 April 1970

Single mode TE or TM propagation is demonstrated in an optical waveguide consisting of a high resistivity semiconductor (GaAs) layer ($\approx 10\ \mu$) which is sandwiched between a metal film and a lower resistivity semiconductor. A reverse bias applied to the metal-semiconductor Schottky barrier causes an electro-optic retardation (or, in general, phase variation) which can be used for modulation purposes. Amplitude modulation with a "half-voltage" $V_{1/2} = 84$ volts is demonstrated at $\lambda_0 = 1.15\ \mu$ with a sample 2.4 mm long.

The recent availability of ultra-pure semiconductors such as GaAs with very few free carriers makes possible for the first time optical waveguiding and modulation in semiconductor epitaxial layers. These devices have a number of practical advantages over previous optical waveguides. Electro-optic modulation of the waveguided light is performed with ease at voltages a hundred times smaller than in bulk modulators and with little loss. Infrared applications of such devices now become practical.

Dielectric discontinuities or gradients associated with different doping regions in semiconductors can propagate optical modes. Such waveguiding in GaAs p–n junctions has been observed [1,2] and analyzed [3,4], and electro-optic phase modulation of these modes in GaP p–n junctions has been demonstrated [5]. Dramatically better performance is possible with epitaxial layers because very much larger homogeneous samples can easily be grown. The optical properties of epilayer waveguides are controlled by varying the doping and thickness of the epilayer and substrate. This is possible because they do not exhibit the unexplained built-in refractive index of p–n junctions [6]. Epilayers have much better optical quality than the thin films of ZnO and ZnS on glass substrate which provide a waveguide when used with a special light input coupler [7]. An advantage of the semiconducting substrate is that it becomes the conducting base required for light modulation.

* This research was supported by the Office of Naval Research.

In this paper we describe optical propagation and modulation in an optical waveguide which is illustrated in fig. 1. It consists of a metal – nearly intrinsic semiconductor – doped semiconductor, layered structure. In our experiment

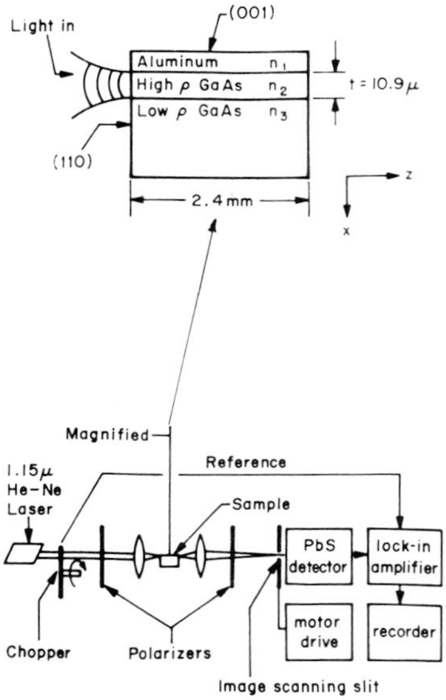

Fig. 1. Bottom: Experimental setup.
Top: Enlarged view of the sample.

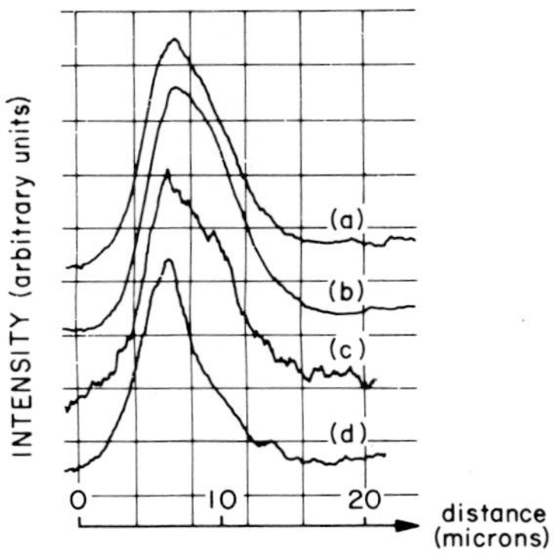

Fig. 2. Intensity plots of the lowest order modes
(a) TE mode. The input beam is lowered (in the sense of fig. 1) 5 microns in the x direction from its position in (b).
(b) TE mode. The input beam is centered on the high ρ region.
(c) TE mode. The input beam is raised 5 microns.
(d) TM mode, centered.

an epitaxial layer ($t = 10.9\ \mu$) of high resistivity ($n \approx 10^{15} cm^{-3}$) GaAs was grown on a more heavily doped ($n \approx 10^{17} cm^{-3}$) substrate. The heavier doping lowers the index of refraction so that $n_3 < n_2$ and optical waveguiding is possible*.

To demonstrate the existence of waveguiding, we focussed a 1.15 μ He–Ne laser beam on a cleaved input face of the sample. A magnified image of the output face was scanned with a moving slit and the transmitted intensity was recorded as a function of position. The setup is sketched in fig. 1 with the data shown in fig. 2. Typically 2/3 or more of the light energy was concentrated in the epilayer with a peak intensity fifty times brighter than when the light was not waveguided through the epilayer. Large changes of the input beam position in the x direction are seen to have a negligible effect on the shape of the intensity profile, although changing the amount of energy coupled in. This suggests strongly that we are exciting substantially a single mode. TM or TE optical waveguide modes were excited by choosing the input laser polarization to $E \parallel x$ and $E \parallel y$, respectively.

The application of a reverse bias voltage V to the Schottky surface barrier gives rise to a region with a strong electric field ($\parallel$ to x) within the epitaxial layer. For the crystal orientation used in our experiment we expect an electro-optic retardation of the form (see, for example, ref. [8])

$$\Gamma_{xy} = (\beta_{TM} - \beta_{TE})l = \frac{\pi l n_2^3 r_{41} \eta}{\lambda_0 t} V. \qquad (1)$$

Here βl is the phase change in the waveguide, r_{41} is the electro-optic coefficient of GaAs, and η is the ratio of the guide retardation to that in the bulk. If the guided wave is sufficiently far above cut-off and if the thickness of the Schottky barrier approaches t, then $\eta \to 1$. The "half-voltage" of the guide (the voltage causing $\Gamma_{xy} = \pi$) is thus

$$V_{1/2} = \frac{\lambda_0}{\eta\, n_2^3\, r_{41}} \frac{t}{l}. \qquad (2)$$

Using $n_2^3 r_{41} = 59 \times 10^{-12}$ m/V, $\eta = 1$, $t = 10.9\ \mu$, $\lambda_0 = 1.15\ \mu$ and $l = 2.4$ mm, eq. (2) gives $V_{1/2} = 88$ V.

The retardation characteristics of the guide were checked by placing it between crossed polarizers and measuring the transmittance as a function of applied voltage. The data shown in fig. 3 are in fair agreement with a theoretical plot

$$\frac{I}{I_0} = \sin^2\left[\left(\frac{\pi}{2}\right)\left(\frac{V - 12}{84}\right)\right] \qquad (3)$$

indicating a "half-voltage" of 84 volts to be compared to the calculated value of $V_{1/2} = 88$ volts. The 12 volts offset is due to the combination of the well-known built-in voltage and residual (zero field) birefringence.

In this waveguide the propagating fields for TE modes are

$$E_y \propto \exp(\alpha^{(1)}_{TE} x - i\beta_{TE} z) \qquad \text{Region 1}$$

$$E_y \propto \sin(h_{TE} x - \phi_{TE}) \exp(-i\beta_{TE} z) \qquad \text{Region 2}$$

$$E_y \propto \exp[-\alpha^{(3)}_{TE}(x - t) - i\beta_{TE} z] \qquad \text{Region 3}$$

For TM modes E_y is replaced by $H_y = E_x$. Using these fields in Maxwell's equations plus the appropriate boundary conditions yields the propagation constants $\alpha^{(1)}$, $\alpha^{(3)}$, h, and β as well as ϕ. For high, but finite metal conductivity, both the TM and TE waves exhibit a waveguide cut-off

* The experimental data is consistent with an index discontinuity of $4 \times 10^{-4} < n_2 - n_3 < 8 \times 10^{-4}$.

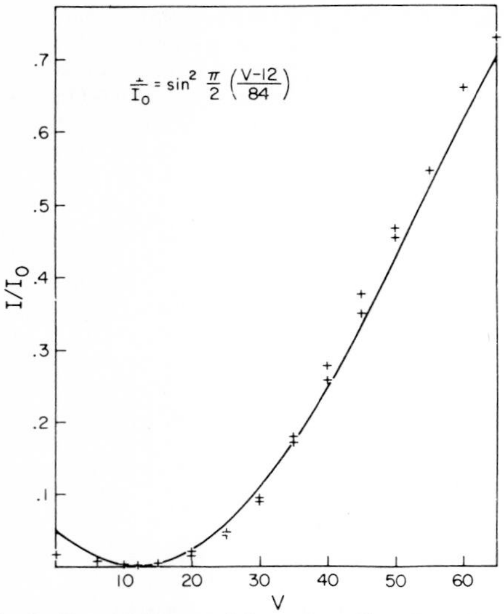

Fig. 3. Transmittance of the waveguide, placed between crossed polarizers, as a function of the applied reverse voltage.

condition and values of fields which are small at the metallic interface. It is interesting to note that infinite conductivity would yield $\phi_{TE} = 0$ and $\phi_{TM} = \pi/2$, in which case the TM intensity would peak at the metal.

The lowest order propagation modes exist alone when

$$\frac{\pi}{2} < \left(\frac{2\pi}{\lambda_o}\right) t \left(n_2^2 - n_3^2\right)^{1/2} < \frac{3\pi}{2}. \qquad (4)$$

In the sample used here (4) yields $10^{-4} < n_2 - n_3 < 9 \times 10^{-4}$. This is in agreement with the refractive index difference estimated from the free carrier contribution in the epilayer of 2.2×10^{-4}. Experimental confirmation of cut-off was obtained from the fact that an epilayer with fewer free carriers and an estimated $n_2 - n_3 = 0.22 \times 10^{-4}$ did not waveguide.

The TE and TM attenuation constants were estimated using an index of refraction for the Al film of $n \approx 1 - 10i$. The corresponding attenuation distances (to 1/3 in field) are $L_{TE} \approx 30$ cm and $L_{TM} \approx 3$ cm. The larger TM attenuation is due to a deeper penetration into the metal. Since waveguiding introduces small loss into the light beam and GaAs is transparent at 10.6 μ, epilayers should be particularly useful as modulators for CO_2 laser light.

In practice, region 3 can be replaced with any other material whose index $n_3 < n_2$. Only region 2 need be electro-optic. We also noticed that the guiding properties are hardly affected by the removal of the Al film. This is due to the large index discontinuity at the air-semiconductor interface. This suggests that a variety of functions such as coupling, guiding, and modulation can be performed sequentially on a single substrate with metal electrodes applied selectively to certain regions where modulation is to be performed.

Special thanks for their helpful experimental suggestions go to A. Shuskus, W. Oshinsky and J. Konarski of the United Aircraft Research Laboratories in East Hartford, Connecticut. Also, the competent technical assistance of D. Armstrong and useful discussions with D. Vahey are gratefully acknowledged.

REFERENCES

[1] A. Yariv and R. C. C. Leite, Appl. Phys. Letters 2 (1963) 55.
[2] W. L. Bond, B. C. Cohen, R. C. Leite and A. Yariv, Appl. Phys. Letters 2 (1963) 57.
[3] W. W. Anderson, IEEE J. Quantum Electron. QE-1 (1965) 228.
[4] W. G. Oldham and A. Bahraman, IEEE J. Quantum Electron. QE-3 (1967) 278.
[5] D. F. Nelson and F. K. Reinhart, Appl. Phys. Letters 5 (1964) 148.
[6] F. K. Reinhart, D. F. Nelson and J. McKenna, Phys. Rev. 177 (1969) 1208.
[7] P. K. Tien, R. Ulrich and R. J. Martin, Appl. Phys. Letters 14 (1969) 291.
[8] A. Yariv, Quantum electronics (Wiley, New York, 1967) p. 310.

Reprinted from

VOLUME 17, NUMBER 3 APPLIED PHYSICS LETTERS 1 AUGUST 1970

OBSERVATION OF PROPAGATION CUTOFF AND ITS CONTROL IN THIN OPTICAL WAVEGUIDES*

David Hall, Amnon Yariv, and Elsa Garmire

Division of Engineering and Applied Science, California Institute of Technology, Pasadena, California 91109

(Received 8 June 1970; in final form 15 June 1970)

The first observation of optical cutoff in thin-film waveguides is reported. The waveguides consist of thin ($\sim 10\mu$) epitaxial layers of high-resistivity GaAs deposited on lower-resistivity GaAs substrates. The optical cutoff is controlled through the electro-optic effect by applying an electric field across the epitaxial layer.

Guiding and electro-optic modulation of light in thin epitaxial semiconductor films has recently been demonstrated.[1] In this paper we report the first observation and control of optical cutoff in such waveguides.

The optical waveguide consists of a GaAs high-resistivity epitaxial layer ($\sim 12\ \mu$) sandwiched between a metal film and lower-resistivity GaAs substrate as shown in Fig. 1. The existence of confined modes is due to a discontinuity Δn of the index of refraction at the epitaxial layer–substrate interface.[1]

The theory describing the propagation of modes in this structure can be adapted from that of the symmetric dielectric waveguide.[2] The symmetric guide can support, in general, two types of modes: *TE* waves where $\vec{E}$ is parallel to y, and *TM* waves in which $\vec{E}$ is parallel to x. The existence of a conducting plane (metal film) at $x=0$, however, limits the *TE* and *TM* modes in our case, to those possessing odd symmetry about $x=0$. These can be written as

$$E_y(TE) \propto \sin(hx)\exp(-i\beta z),$$
$$H_y(TM) \propto \sin(hx)\exp(-i\beta z), \quad |x| < t \tag{1}$$

$$E_y(TE) \propto \exp[-p(x-t) - i\beta z],$$
$$H_y(TM) \propto \exp[-p(x-t) - i\beta z], \quad |x| > t. \tag{2}$$

The lowest-order TE_1 and TM_1 (the numerical subscript gives the number of zero crossings in the interval $|x| < t$) modes can exist only if the condition

$$(2n_0\Delta n)(2\pi t/\lambda_0)^2 > (\pi/2)^2 \tag{3}$$

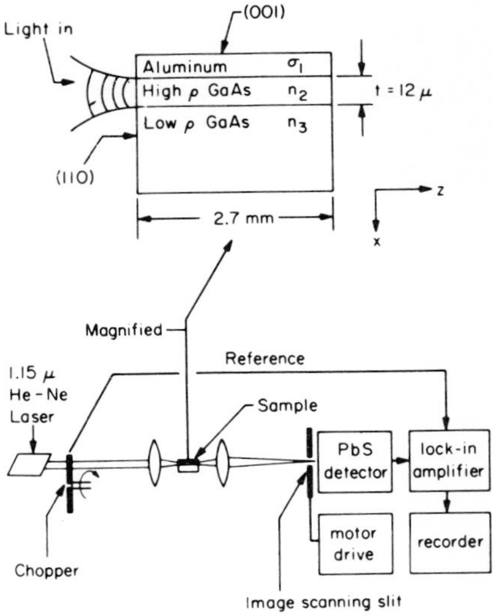

FIG. 1. The experimental setup.

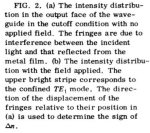

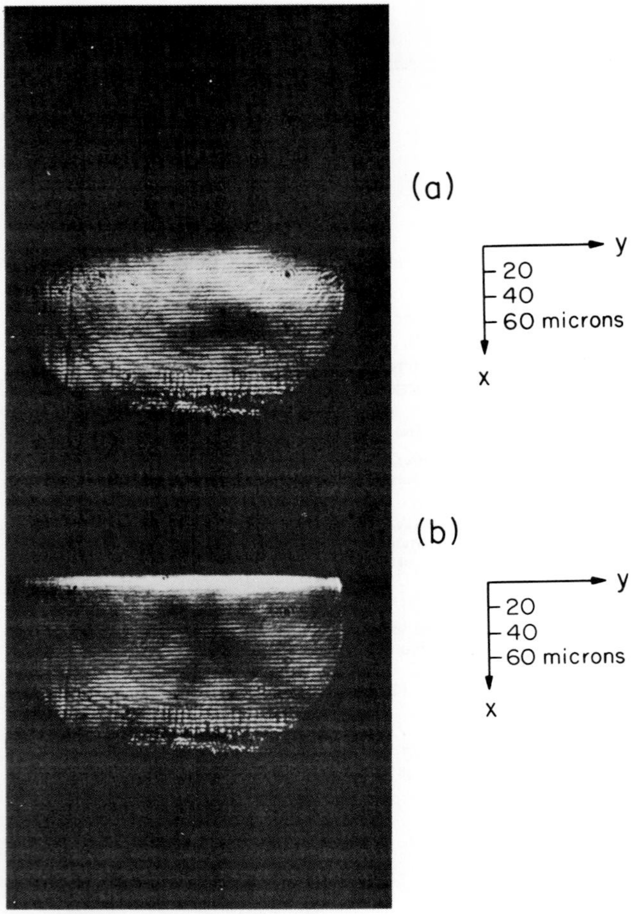

FIG. 2. (a) The intensity distribution in the output face of the waveguide in the cutoff condition with no applied field. The fringes are due to interference between the incident light and that reflected from the metal film. (b) The intensity distribution with the field applied. The upper bright stripe corresponds to the confined TE_1 mode. The direction of the displacement of the fringes relative to their position in (a) is used to determine the sign of Δn.

is satisfied. When the sign of the inequality in (3) is reversed, the field intensity increases with x so that confined propagation does not exist. This condition is referred to as cutoff.

The index discontinuity Δn at the interface $x = t$ is due, in our experiment, to two mechanisms. The first is the dependence of the index on the doping level. This discontinuity, which we denote as $\Delta n_{\text{chemical}}$, is known to lead to mode confinement in p-n junctions.[3,4] In our guide $\Delta N \approx 2\times 10^{16}$ cm^{-3} and we estimate $\Delta n_{\text{chemical}} \sim 10^{-4}$. The second contribution is due to the linear electro-optic effect in GaAs and is proportional to the reverse bias V applied to the metal-semiconductor junction. For the crystal orientation shown in Fig. 1 the electro-optic contribution to the index of a wave polarized along y is

$$\Delta n = n_0^3 r_{41} E_x/2,$$

and is zero for waves polarized along x.[5] We can consequently, write condition (3) for confined propagation as

$$\Delta n_{\text{chemical}} + \frac{n_0^3 r_{41} V}{2t} > \frac{1}{32 n_0}\left(\frac{\lambda_0}{t}\right)^2, \tag{4}$$

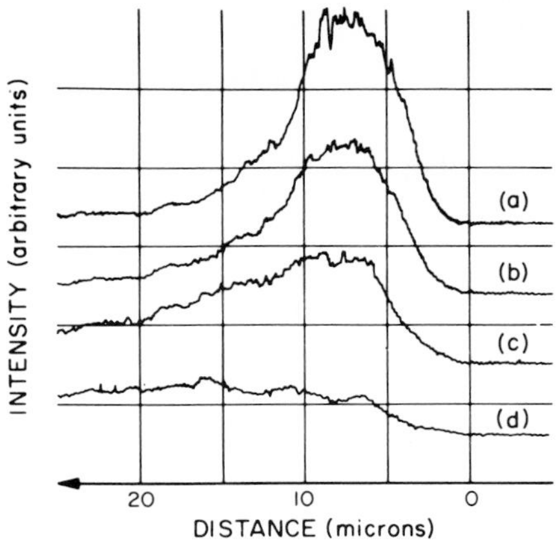

FIG. 3. The intensity distribution of the TE_1 mode measured with applied voltages of (a) 130, (b) 100, (c) 70, and (d) 0 V.

for the *TE* mode and as

$$\Delta n_{\text{chemical}} > (1/32n_0)(\lambda_0/t)^2, \quad (5)$$

in the case of the *TM* wave. r_{41} is the electro-optic coefficient of GaAs and the applied voltage is $V = E_x t$.

The doping level of the substrate ($N \sim 2 \times 10^{16}$ cm^{-3}) and the thickness $t = 12\ \mu$ were chosen in our experiment so that at $\lambda_0 = 1.15\ \mu$ condition (5) was not fulfilled and no confined modes can exist. The application of a voltage V increases Δn by adding, as indicated in (4), an electro-optic contribution making it possible for a confined *TE* wave to exist. A magnified image of the output face of the crystal with and without an applied bias ($V = 130$ V) is shown in Fig. 2. The existence of a confined mode with the voltage on is clearly evident. In addition, we made the following observations: (1) When the optical polarization is rotated by 90° ($\vec{E} \parallel x$) so as to excite a *TM* wave, no confined mode exists with or without an applied field. This is consistent with the fact that there is no electro-optic contribution to Δn in the case of the *TM* wave. (2) By changing the crystal orientation we can reverse the sign (see caption under Fig. 2) of the electro-optic contribution to Δn as "seen" by the *TE* mode from (+) to (−). When this is done the application of a voltage does not lead to a confined mode in agreement with (4).

The gradual onset of confinement with increasing voltage is shown by the intensity profile plots in Fig. 3. The dependence of the guided intensity on the applied voltage can be used for modulation purposes.

In summary: The phenomena of propagation cutoff in thin optical waveguides is demonstrated. A continuous electro-optic control of the cutoff condition is used to demonstrate its effect on the intensity distribution of the dominant *TE* mode.

The authors wish to thank A. Shuskus and W. Oshinsky of United Aircraft Research Laboratories in East Hartford, Conn. for supplying the GaAs samples.

---

*Research supported by the Office of Naval Research and by the Advanced Research Projects Agency through the Army Research Office, Durham, N. C.

[1]D. Hall, A. Yariv, and E. Garmire, Opt. Commun. May 1970 (to be published).

[2]See, for example, R. E. Collin *Field Theory of Guided Waves* (McGraw-Hill Book Co., New York, 1960).

[3]A. Yariv and R. C. C. Leite, Appl. Phys. Letters 2, 55 (1963). Also W. L. Bond, B. G. Cohen, R. C. C. Leite, and A. Yariv, *ibid* 2, 57 (1963).

[4]D. F. Nelson and F. K. Reinhart, Appl. Phys. Letters 5, 148 (1964).

[5]S. Namba, J. Opt. Soc. Am. 51, 76 (1961).

Reprinted from *Appl. Phys. Lett.* **21**, 307-309 (1972).

Interdigital electro-optic thin-film modulator

John N. Polky and Jay H. Harris
Department of Electrical Engineering, University of Washington, Seattle, Washington 98195
(Received 15 June 1972; in final form 3 August 1972)

An integrated optical modulator is presented that achieved 50% depth of modulation. A double-ended coupling prism allowed nitrobenzene to be used as the waveguide material. Also, an approximate theory of operation is developed.

An integrated modulator for thin-film waveguides is described. Unlike the crystalline devices described by others,[1,2] our structure uses nitrobenzene as the active waveguide material. Amplitude modulation of an optical guided mode is obtained by Bragg diffraction from periodic index variations in the guiding layer. Three major improvements over the device in Ref. 3 include unclad metal electrodes, a double-ended input-output prism, and increased modulation efficiency.

An illustration of the integrated modulator is shown in Fig. 1. Interdigital copper electrodes 1 μ thick were

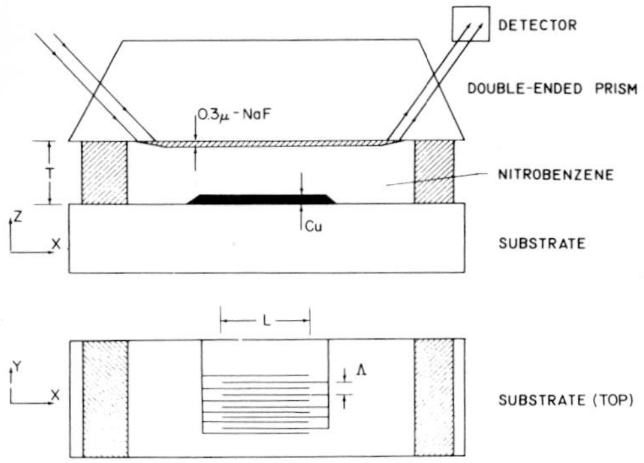

FIG. 1. Illustration of the thin-film modulator system used for the experiment. Guided modes propagate in the thin film of nitrobenzene while interdigital copper electrodes provide the modulating field. Shaded areas indicate sodium fluoride material.

evaporated onto a microscope slide substrate of refractive index 1.52. The electrodes had a period Λ and an active length L. In addition, NaF spacers ($T = 7\ \mu$) were evaporated onto either end of the microslide to support an input-output prism. Nitrobenzene ($n = 1.55$) was used to fill the void between the prism and substrate and served as the electro-optic material. Preliminary calculations and observations indicated that cladding of the interdigital electrodes was not essential for the indicated guide thickness. For copper, the average attenuation of TE waves was computed to be 0.5 dB/cm.

A *double-ended* prism coupler was designed to provide a one-piece input-output device and to confine the nitrobenzene in a continuous guiding layer. The prism was cut from a piece of polished flint glass ($n = 1.73$), and a 0.3-μ layer of sodium fluoride ($n = 1.32$) was deposited onto the coupling face. A 2-mm taper at either end of the NaF layer provided a variable tunneling[4] region for coupling of a 0.6328-μ laser beam.

A device was constructed with the dimensions $L = 0.5$ cm and $\Lambda = 24\ \mu$ (Fig. 1). Coherent light was mechanically chopped at 1000 Hz and coupled into the waveguide. Simultaneously, a 200-V 8000-Hz signal was applied across the interdigital electrodes. The output beam was detected with a PIN photodiode, and the resulting intensity was displayed on an oscilloscope. A photograph of the scope display is shown in Fig. 2, from which we can see that an approximately 50% modulation of the input signal was accomplished.

The modulation apparent in Fig. 2 was caused by a periodic perturbation in the mode index that resulted in diffraction of the incident wave. To examine the nature of diffraction in the structure, it is useful to express the spatially varying mode index in the grating region as

$$n_w = \bar{n}_w + \Delta n_s(y) + \Delta n_t(y, t), \tag{1}$$

where Δn_s and Δn_t are the static and temporal changes, respectively, and $\bar{n}_w$ is the average mode index.

The static mode index change, Δn_s, is caused by the physical presence of the electrodes. To estimate the value Δn_s, we divide the waveguide into two regions of interest: Region (1) is the waveguide cross section over an electrode, and region (2) is the area between a pair of electrodes. For a hypothetical waveguide composed entirely of either cross section, a wave index can be calculated. Approximating Δn_s by a sinusoidal function with peak values obtained by separate calculation, we write

$$\Delta n_s \approx |n_w^{(1)} - n_w^{(2)}| \sin(\kappa y)/2, \tag{2}$$

where $\kappa = 2\pi/\Lambda$, Λ is the grating wavelength, and the superscripts identify each region.

The temporal variation of the mode index (Δn_t) is provided by the electric field of the grating electrodes when a voltage is applied. Using a linear approximation for the potential variation between each electrode, a solution of the Laplace equation can be found. Under this approximation, the potential function in the plane of the electrode is trapezoid shaped with peak-to-peak value V. The first space harmonic is then

$$\Phi \approx V(8/\pi^2)\cos(\kappa y/2)\exp(-\kappa z/2), \tag{3}$$

where V is the voltage applied across the electrodes and z is the distance away from the plane of the electrodes. Taking the gradient of Φ, the electric field becomes

$$\bar{E} \approx \tfrac{1}{2}V\kappa(8/\pi^2)\exp(-\kappa z/2)[\sin(\kappa y/2)\hat{y} + \cos(\kappa y/2)\hat{z}]. \tag{4}$$

The modal index change Δn_t can be approximately determined by again considering two cross-sectional regions. Keeping in mind that the Kerr effect depends on the relative orientation of the optical electric field and the optic axis, the peak electro-optically induced index change in the nitrobenzene for TE incident waves in regions (1) and (2) is

$$\Delta n_2^{(1)} = \lambda K[(V/\Lambda)(8/\pi)]^2 \exp(-\kappa z), \qquad \text{region (1)} \tag{5}$$

$$\Delta n_2^{(2)} = 2\lambda K[(V/\Lambda)(8/\pi)]^2 \exp(-\kappa z), \qquad \text{region (2)} \tag{5a}$$

where K ($= 3.6 \times 10^{-12}$) is the Kerr constant,[5] and λ is the optical wavelength. Note that the index change in the

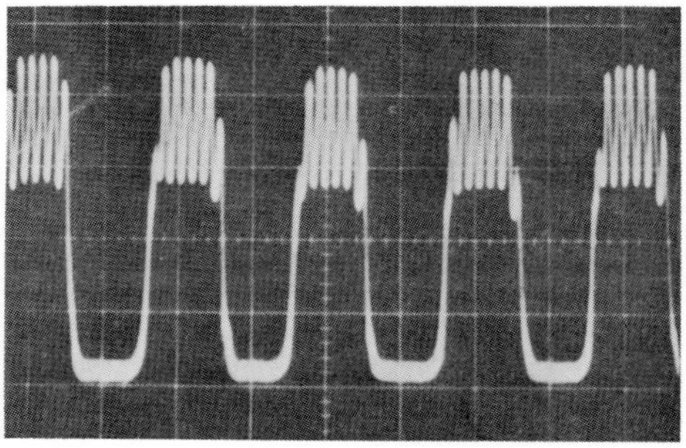

FIG. 2. Photograph of the real time intensity of the electro-optic modulator output. A mechanical chopper (1000 Hz) was used to turn the input light on and off. Approximately 50% depth of modulation occurred.

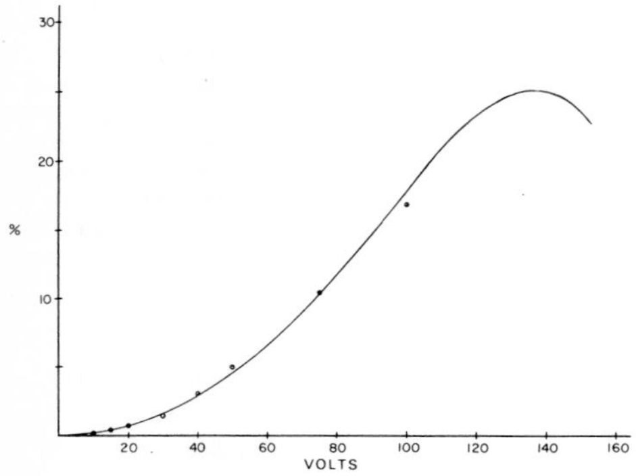

FIG. 3. Plot of percent modulation versus input voltage. The solid line is the theoretical estimate, and the dots are experimental points.

nitrobenzene decays rapidly with distance from the electrodes. The value of wave index change $|\Delta n_t|$ in each cross section can be estimated by solving the approximate eigenvalue equation of an inhomogeneous dielectric waveguide for TE waves, viz.,

$$\tan^{-1}\left(\frac{u_1}{iu_2(z_1)}\right) + \tan^{-1}\left(\frac{u_3}{iu_2(z_2)}\right) - \int_{z_1}^{z_2} u_2(z)\,dz = m\pi,$$

$$m = 0, 1, 2, \ldots . \tag{6}$$

Equation (6) is derived by assuming a WKB solution for the boundary value problem. The parameters of Eq. (6) are

$$u_i = (2\pi/\lambda_0)(n_i^2 - n_w^2)^{1/2}, \quad i = 1, 2, 3 \tag{7}$$

where n_i is the refractive index of each material layer and n_w is the wave refractive index. Since only n_2 is a function of z, the limits of integration extend across the guiding layer. Expanding u_2 [Eq. (7)] to first order in Δn_2, a wave index change may be obtained for each region. Expressing $\Delta n_t(y, t)$ as a sinusoid with peak-to-peak value $|\Delta n_t^{(1)} - \Delta n_t^{(2)}|$, the temporal wave index variation can be approximated by

$$\Delta n_t \approx \frac{\lambda K n_2}{2\kappa}\left(\frac{V}{\Lambda}\frac{8}{\pi}\right)^2 \left| \frac{1 - \exp(-\kappa t_2)}{t_2 n_w^{(2)}} - \frac{1 - \exp(-\kappa t_1)}{2 t_1 n_w^{(1)}} \right|$$

$$\times \sin(\kappa y)\cos^2(\omega t), \tag{8}$$

where t_1 and t_2 are the film thicknesses in regions (1) and (2), respectively.

The Bragg solution for diffraction of a plane wave can be approximately applied to the guided waves of our device. Following previous discussions of this problem,[3,6] the intensity of the undiffracted beam is

$$I_0 = \cos^2[\tfrac{1}{2}k_0 L(|\Delta n_s| + |\Delta n_t|\cos^2\omega t)], \tag{9}$$

where $k_0 = 2\pi/\lambda_0$, L is the grating length, and ω is the modulation frequency. A series expansion of Eq. (9) reveals frequency components at 0, 2ω, 4ω, etc., and, using Eqs. (8) and (9), we can estimate the degree of modulation for the 2ω component. The configuration of Fig. 1 was used with $L = 1.9$ mm, $\Lambda = 12\ \mu$, and $\omega = 1000$ Hz. First, I_0 was measured with no voltage applied to the device, then the percent modulation was observed versus input voltage. Figure 3 indicates a fair agreement between theory and experiment.

For bandwidth and power-consumption calculations, the modulator may be represented by a resistor and capacitor in parallel. At a frequency of 10 kHz, these parameters were found to be $c = 8.6$ pF and $R = 2.1$ MΩ. Assuming a 50-Ω source, the projected bandwidth is 2 GHz. Furthermore, for a 100-V signal the power consumption is approximately 5 mW. Previous studies of the dielectric properties of nitrobenzene[7] have shown that the Kerr constant begins degrading around 1–3 GHz, while the power absorption increases rapidly near 500 MHz. Therefore, a practical integrated device would be limited to around 500 MHz when nitrobenzene is used. The modulator will function in the gigahertz range; however, the large power consumption could cause thermal degradation of the modulation process. The obvious solution to the problem of high-frequency modulation in optical waveguides appears to be crystalline thin films. On the other hand, one difficulty might be the unwanted generation of acoustic waves in the crystalline integrated device.

An improved integrated modulator with an efficiency of 50% has been presented. Also, the effective use of an electro-optic liquid waveguide has been made possible through the design of a double-ended prism-coupling device. A further improvement of this type modulator should make possible the use of lower signal voltages and higher modulating frequencies.

[1] J. F. St. Ledger and E. A. Ash, Electron. Letters 4, (No. 6) (1968).
[2] J. M. Hammer, Appl. Phys. Letters 18, 147 (1971).
[3] D. P. GiaRusso and J. H. Harris, Appl. Opt. 10, 2786L (1971).
[4] J. H. Harris and R. Shubert, IEEE Trans. Microwave Theory Tech. **MTT-14**, 269 (1971).
[5] *American Institute of Physics Handbook*, edited by D. E. Gray (McGraw-Hill, New York, 1963), p. 6-187.
[6] W. R. Klein and B. D. Cook, IEEE Trans. Sonics Ultrasonics **SU-4**, 123 (1967).
[7] G. L. Clark, J. Chem. Phys. 25, 125 (1956).

Reprinted from *Appl. Phys. Lett.* **21** 87-88 (1972).

Optical waveguiding in proton-implanted GaAs†

E. Garmire, H. Stoll, and A. Yariv
California Institute of Technology, Pasadena, California 91109
R.G. Hunsperger
Hughes Research Laboratories, Malibu, California 90265
(Received 29 March 1972)

We have produced optical waveguides in n-type GaAs by implantation with 300-keV protons. The guiding is shown to be due to the elimination of charge carriers from the implanted region. Annealing of the waveguide leads to very large reductions in the 1.15-μ guided-wave absorption.

Optical guiding has been observed previously[1] in proton-implanted fused silica. Our own interest in fabricating active integrated optics components in semiconductors led us to explore the effect of proton bombardment in GaAs. We found that polished n-type GaAs crystals implanted with 300-keV protons form effective waveguides for light of 1.15-μ wavelength.

Proton bombardment in GaAs is known to produce compensation of both n- and p-type materials.[2] This compensated layer has a thickness of ~1 μ for each 100-keV proton energy.[3] The implanted region, which has a much smaller free-carrier concentration than the substrate, possesses a smaller plasma contribution to the refractive index. Thus its optical dielectric constant exceeds that of the substrate by

$$\Delta\epsilon = \frac{(N_s - N_c)e^2}{m^* \omega^2}, \qquad (1)$$

where N_s and N_c are the carrier densities in the substrate and in the compensated region, respectively. m^* and e are the effective mass and charge of the carriers and ω is the radian optical frequency. If the implanted layer is to support confined optical mode propagation, the condition

$$\frac{\Delta\epsilon}{\epsilon_0} > \left(\frac{\lambda_0}{4t}\right)^2 \qquad (2)$$

has to be satisfied, where t is the thickness of the implanted layer and λ_0 is the wavelength in vacuum. Combining this with (1) leads to a condition for guiding,

$$N_s - N_c > \frac{\pi^2 c_0^2 m^* \epsilon_0}{4e^2 t^2}, \qquad (3)$$

where c_0 is the velocity of light in vacuum. For effective compensation, $N_s \gg N_c$ and (3) becomes a condition for the minimum substrate carrier concentration necessary for guiding. We note that condition (3) is independent of the optical wavelength. This circumstance is due to the dependence $\Delta\epsilon \propto \omega^{-2}$ of the plasma effect.

In our experiment 300-keV protons were implanted with doses $\approx 10^{15}/\text{cm}^2$ into polished (100) or (111) faces of n-type GaAs. The thickness of the compensated layer was 3 μ, measured both from capacitance data and with a scanning electron microscope. The optical waveguiding profile was determined with the setup in Fig. 1. The method of coupling light into and out of the cleaved faces of the waveguide was similar to that used in Ref. 4. A vibrating mirror galvanometer was used to scan the image past the (fixed) detector slit thereby making it possible to obtain an instantaneous and continuous display of the output intensity profile on an oscilloscope. Typical light profiles are shown in Fig. 2.

Using $t = 3$ μ in condition (3) gives $N_s = 6\times10^{17}$ cm^{-3} as the minimum substrate concentration for confined optical propagation. We observed strong guiding in samples with $N_s = 2\times10^{18}$ cm^{-3}, weak guiding in samples with $N_s = 6\times10^{17}$ cm^{-3}, and no guiding with $N_s = 4\times10^{17}$ cm^{-3}. These results are consistent with the plasma model for the dielectric constant difference.

The propagating mode attenuation was determined from the dependence of the output-input ratio of the mode power on the length of the guide. This procedure also yields the input coupling efficiency. With light focusing into the front cleaved surface of the waveguide, as much

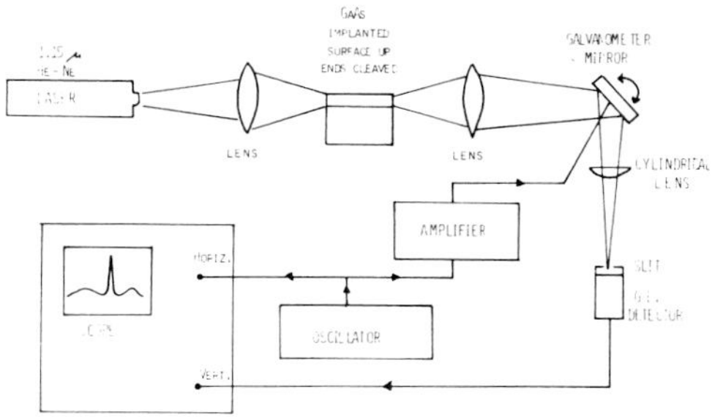

FIG. 1. Experimental apparatus.

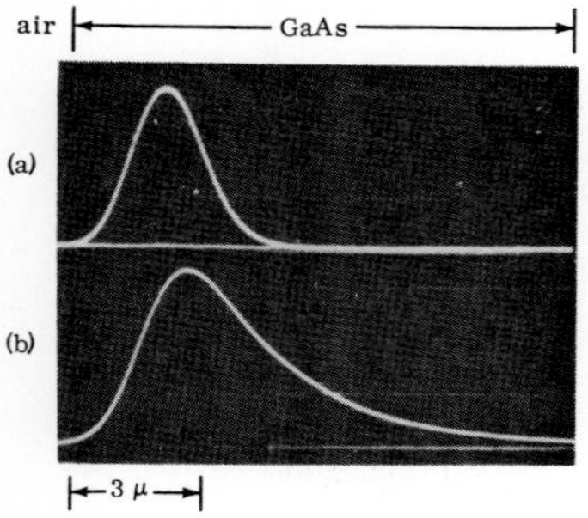

FIG. 2. Mode profiles: (a) Substrate: $6 \times 10^{18}/cm^3$; dose: $2 \times 10^{15}/cm^2$; anneal temperature: 500 °C. (b) Substrate: $2 \times 10^{18}/cm^3$; dose: $3 \times 10^{14}/cm^2$; anneal temperature: 500 °C.

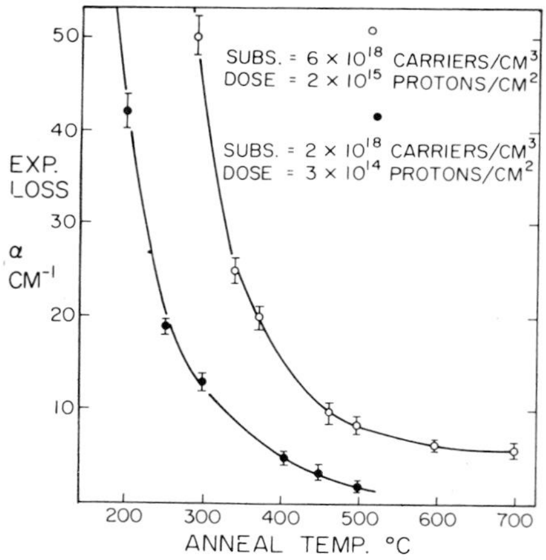

FIG. 3. Measurements of exponential power loss constant as a function of anneal temperature.

as 40% of the laser power was coupled into the guiding modes.

The proton bombardment causes a very large attenuation of the guided modes. This is possibly due to absorption involving the deep traps which are believed to be responsible for the compensation. Two have been identified at 0.4 and 0.8 eV above the valence band edge.[5] These losses can be substantially reduced by proper annealing (in flowing gas, typically for 30 min). Figure 3 shows the dependence of the mode power loss constant α on the annealing temperature. Reducing the proton dose to the minimum required for compensation should lead to a reduction of α below the value of 2 cm^{-1}, which is the lowest value to date.

Annealing above 500 °C was performed with a SiO_2 cap on the sample to prevent dissociation of GaAs. The cap was removed in HF prior to the guiding experiments. Excellent Schottky barriers were made on implanted layers which had been annealed to 700 °C, with back-bias voltages as large as 20 V and very low leakage current. Before annealing, the resistive layer allowed considerable current flow although the breakdown voltage was ~150 V. The annealed implanted waveguides should function as useful electro-optic modulators for guided light.[6]

The optical waveguiding properties of implanted layers should complement the rapidly growing body of electrical and backscattering measurements in implanted regions. If the compensated region has many fewer carriers than the substrate ($N_c \ll N_s$), the exact shape of the compensation profile does not affect the refractive-index profile. However, when the dose is decreased, or the anneal temperature is raised until $N_c \approx N_s$, measurements of waveguide properties can provide useful information.

The already demonstrated ability to obtain type conversion with ion implantation[7] and our demonstration of reasonably low-loss waveguiding in proton-implanted GaAs suggest that implantation may be a useful technique for fabricating more complex integrated optical circuits incorporating light emitting diodes (or lasers), waveguides, and detectors. Another set of interesting possibilities is suggested by the demonstration of converting GaAs into $Ga_xAl_{1-x}As$ by Al^+ implantation.[8]

[†]Research at California Institute of Technology supported by the National Science Foundation.

[1]E. R. Schineller, R. P. Flam, and D.W. Wilmot, J. Opt. Soc. Am. 58, 1171 (1968).
[2]E. Wohlleben and W. Beck, Z. Naturforsch. 21a, 1057 (1966).
[3]A. G. Foyt, W. T. Lindley, C. M. Wolfe, and J. P. Donnelly, Solid-State Electron. 12, 209 (1969).
[4]D. Hall, A. Yariv, and E. Garmire, Appl. Phys. Letters 17, 127 (1970).
[5]B. R. Pruniaux, J. C. North, and G. L. Miller in *Ion Implantation in Semiconductors*, edited by I. Ruge and J. Graul (Springer-Verlag, Berlin, 1971), p. 212.
[6]D. Hall, A. Yariv, and E. Garmire, Opt. Commun. 1, 403 (1970).
[7]R. G. Hunsperger and O. J. Marsh, Met. Trans. 1, 603 (1970).
[8]R. G. Hunsperger and O. J. Marsh, Appl. Phys. Letters 19, 327 (1971).

Reprinted from *Appl. Phys. Lett.* **21**, 95-98 (1972).

Fabrication of single-crystal semiconductor optical waveguides by solid-state diffusion

H.F. Taylor, W.E. Martin, D.B. Hall, and V.N. Smiley
Naval Electronics Laboratory Center, San Diego, California 92152
(Received 14 February 1972; in final form 26 April 1972)

Optical surface waveguides have been fabricated by diffusing selenium into single-crystal CdS substrates to produce graded-composition CdS_xSe_{1-x} crystals. Planar guides which confine a beam in one dimension and guides produced by masked diffusion capable of two-dimensional beam confinement have been obtained. Evidence of guiding of light from a HeNe laser is provided by photographs and by measurements of spatial intensity profiles. Losses are estimated to be 10—15 dB/cm for one-dimensional guides and 30—40 dB/cm for two-dimensional guides.

Much of the experimental effort in the area of integrated optical circuits has been directed towards the production of thin-film dielectric waveguides. Planar optical surface waveguides in amorphous or polycrystalline materials have been fabricated by depositing a layer of higher refractive index on a lower-index glass substrate and by increasing the refractive index in the vicinity of the surface of a glass substrate.[1] Waveguiding has also been observed in the depletion layer of epitaxially grown[2,3] and diffusion-doped[4] single-crystal semiconductors.

The use of solid-state diffusion to produce composition gradients in compound semiconductor single crystals is an alternative approach to the fabrication of miniature optical waveguides. The diffusion process can produce large refractive index changes in large-area crystals. Selective masking of substrates could make possible the production of desired waveguide patterns. By using semiconductor materials with favorable electro-optic, acousto-optic, photoconductive, and nonlinear optical properties, it may be possible to produce components such as modulators, detectors, switches, and frequency converters within a diffused waveguide matrix. The use of luminescent or lasing semiconductor materials as substrates could allow optical sources or amplifiers to be incorporated into the waveguide structure.

The results of an experimental investigation of the diffusion of selenium into CdS single crystals as a method for fabricating optical waveguides are reported in this letter.

Two previous studies of the diffusion of selenium into CdS have been reported. Handelman and Kaiser[5] have estimated a diffusion rate at 800 °C by visual observation of the depth of change of crystal color as a function of diffusion time. Woodbury and Hall[6] have used radioactive tracer techniques to determine diffusion constants over the range of temperatures from 650 to 1000 °C.

The diffusion process produces a graded mixed CdS_xSe_{1-x} crystal, in which the selenium mole fraction decreases towards the interior.[5] The refractive indices for ordinary and extraordinary rays at a given wavelength are monotonically decreasing functions of x in the CdS_xSe_{1-x} system.[7] Therefore, the refractive index decreases towards the interior in the diffused crystal, as required for a surface waveguide.

The CdS substrates used in the present experiment were commercial crystals grown by the Piper-Polich method and polished to a smoothness of one-fiftieth of an optical wavelength. The crystals were oriented so that the optic axis was normal to the surface upon which the waveguide was to be fabricated. The diffusion process consisted of heating the host crystal in an atmosphere of sulfur and selenium. A quartz tube containing a CdS substrate, sulfur, selenium, and CdS powder (added to

TABLE I. Parameters for diffusion runs. Comparison of calculated and observed diffusion depths.

Run No.	t (h)	T (°C)	m_S/V (mg/cm^3)	m_{Se}/V (mg/cm^3)	d_0 (μm)	d_c (μm)
1	40	600	1.10	3.7	2.5	2.4
2	24	700	1.08	2.7	3.6	5.2
3	6.5	700	1.15	4.2	3.2	2.7

reduce thermal etching of the substrate during diffusion) was connected to a diffusion pump and sealed at a pressure of 5×10^{-7} Torr. The diffusion furnace had a temperature gradient of less than 1 °C over the length of the diffusion tube, and fluctuations in the mean temperature of less than 2 °C. Table I gives diffusion time t, temperature T, and ratio of diffusant mass to ampoule volume m/V for three waveguide diffusion runs.

Each diffused crystal was examined with a microscope under white-light illumination to estimate the depth to which a change in color relative to that of the bulk crystal could be discerned. Table I compares these observed diffusion depths d_0 with diffusion depths d_c calculated from the relation $d_c = (\lambda_1^2 t)^{1/2}$, where λ_1^2 is a diffusion constant determined empirically by Woodbury and Hall.[6] Sulfur pressures were higher and selenium pressures much lower in the Woodbury and Hall experiments than in the present work; nevertheless, agreement between observed and calculated diffusion depths is rather good.

The surface composition of diffused crystals was determined from measurements of their photoluminescence spectra at 77 °K. The wavelength λ_f of the intensity peak of the broad edge-emission band was correlated with crystal composition.[8] Table II gives values of λ_f observed for the waveguides and compares the sulfur mole fraction x_f estimated from these fluorescence data with values x_c calculated from the equilibrium relation[5]

$$x = K_{CdSe} p_{S_2}^{1/2} / (K_{CdSe} p_{S_2}^{1/2} + K_{CdS} p_{Se_2}^{1/2}), \quad (1)$$

where K_{CdSe} and K_{CdS} are equilibrium constants for the dissociation of CdSe and CdS, and p_{Se_2} and p_{S_2} are diatomic gas partial pressures. The partial pressures were calculated from the m/V data of Table I using polymer equilibrium constants reported by Berkowitz and Marquart[9] for sulfur and deduced from data of Berkowitz and Chupka[10] and of Brooks[11] for selenium. Values of K_{CdS} were taken from the data of Goldfinger and Jeunehomme,[12] as were the values of K_{CdSe} used to calculate the first value of x_c in Table II. Data of Korneeva *et al.*[13] for K_{CdSe} were used to calculate the second value of x_c given in Table II. Even though the diffusion process was not allowed to reach total equilibrium in the bulk crystal in the present experiment, surface compositions determined from photoluminescence studies were close to those calculated from (1).

To investigate waveguiding, light from a HeNe laser was focused onto the polished edge of a diffused crystal with a microscope objective. The diameter of the focused spot was about 3 μm. The incident beam propagated in a direction parallel to the plane of the waveguide. A magnified image of the near-field output from the opposite edge of the crystal was viewed with the aid of a second objective. Figure 1 is a photograph of

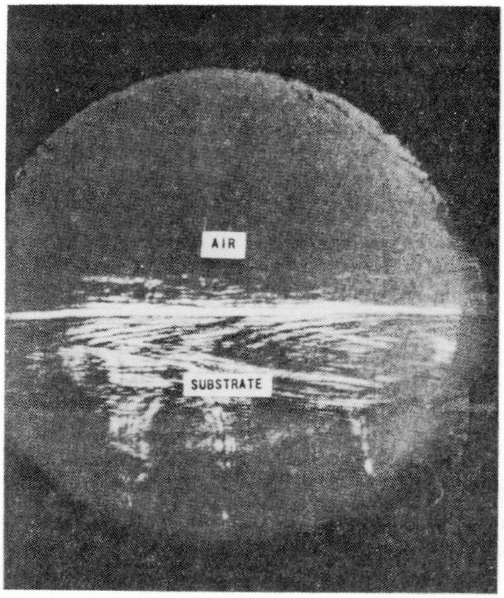

FIG. 1. Photograph of light from a HeNe laser transmitted through a 3-mm length of diffused waveguide.

the magnified near-field pattern of the light transmitted by a planar waveguide produced in run No. 1. The beam has spread by diffraction in a direction parallel to the surface of the crystal (horizontal direction in the photograph), but is confined by the waveguide in the direction orthogonal to the surface. A more quantitative determination of the near-field intensity variation was obtained by scanning a magnified image of the waveguide aperture with a moving slit coupled to an optical detector.[3] Figure 2 shows a transmitted-intensity—vs—position profile for this waveguide.

The sulfur mole fraction at the surface of this waveguide was estimated from fluorescence data to be 0.84. Data correlating refractive index with composition in CdS_xSe_{1-x} crystals[7] were used to deduce that the 6328-Å refractive index at the surface of this waveguide was 2.52 for ordinary rays and 2.54 for extraordinary rays, an increase of 2.4% over the values $n_0 = 2.46$ and $n_e = 2.48$ in bulk CdS. The number of guided modes was estimated by obtaining solutions to the wave equation

TABLE II. Values of waveguide surface composition determined from fluorescence measurements compared with values calculated from Eq. (1).

Run No.	λ_f (Å)	x_f	p_{S_2} (atm)	p_{Se_2} (atm)	x_c [a]	x_c [b]
1	5750	0.84	0.30	0.14	0.74	0.85
2	5770	0.83	0.68	0.37	0.76	0.86
3	5750	0.84	0.71	0.45	0.74	0.85

[a] K_{CdSe} from data of Goldfinger and Jeunehomme (Ref. 12).
[b] K_{CdSe} from data of Korneeva *et al.* (Ref. 13).

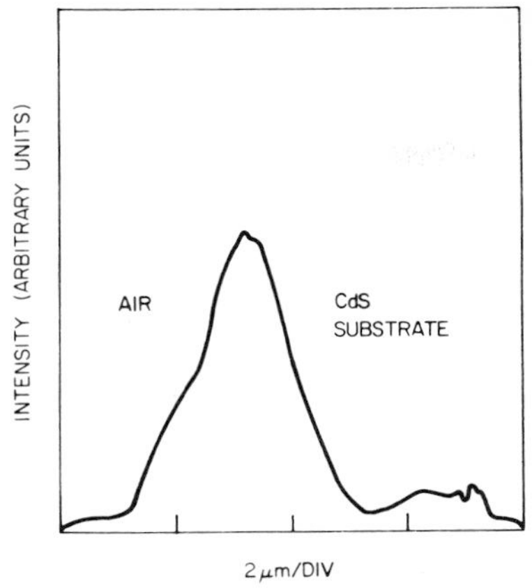

FIG. 2. Near-field intensity vs position profile for the one-dimensional waveguide (resolution ≈ ½ μm). The coordinate axis is normal to the surface of the crystal which defines the plane of the waveguide.

under the assumption that the refractive index varies linearly from the value at the surface to the value in pure CdS over a distance of 2.5 μm, the observed diffusion depth. These calculations indicate that the waveguide should support three TE and three TM guided modes.

Waveguides which confine a beam in two dimensions have been produced by masked diffusions. A 0.5-μm-thick film of SiO was vacuum deposited on the surface of a CdS substrate which was shadowed by a glass fiber 50 or 200 μm in diameter. A subsequent treatment in an oxygen atmosphere converted the SiO to SiO_x, with $1 < x \leq 2$. Microscopic examination after diffusion revealed that the color of the unmasked portion of the crystal had changed with respect to the surrounding material. A further indication that the mask had performed properly was given by visual examination of the photoluminescence of the crystal at 77 °K. A yellow strip of luminescence corresponding to the unmasked region contrasted with the blue-green emission from the surrounding crystal.

Light from a HeNe laser was coupled into these guides in the manner described earlier for one-dimensional guides. Figure 3 is a photograph of the magnified near-field pattern of the light transmitted by two different waveguides produced by masked diffusion during run No. 1.

Losses in the waveguides were estimated from measurements of the intensity of scattered light emerging from the waveguide as a function of distance along the propagation path.[14] Losses were 10–15 dB/cm in one-dimensional guides and 30–40 dB/cm in guides produced by masked diffusion (two-dimensional guides).

In conclusion, optical waveguides have been fabricated by diffusing selenium into single-crystal CdS substrates

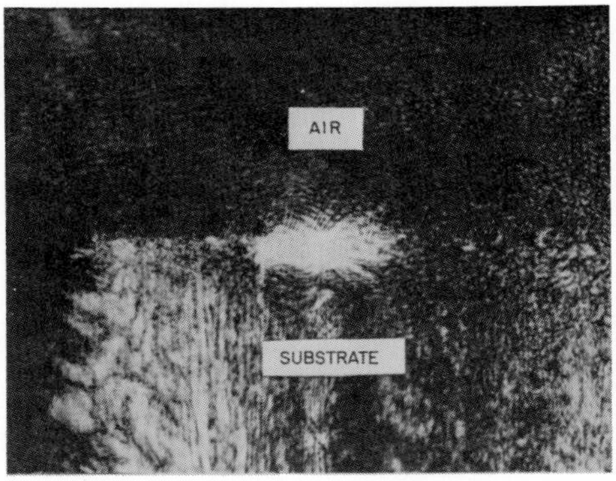

(a)

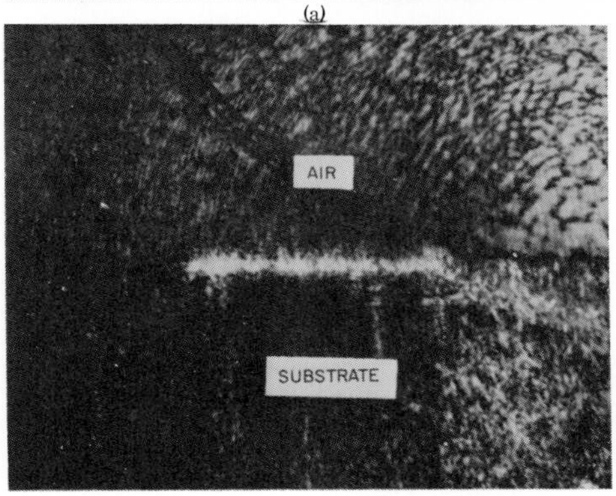

(b)

FIG. 3. Photographs of light from a HeNe laser transmitted through a 1-mm length of two different waveguides produced by masked diffusion. (a) guide width = 50 μm. (b) guide width = 200 μm.

to produce graded-composition CdS_xSe_{1-x} crystals. These surface waveguides should be more amenable to the new techniques[1] for coupling light into guides than are interior waveguides produced in semiconductors by impurity diffusion or epitaxy.

The fractional changes in refractive index of 2.4% reported here are an order of magnitude greater than in single-crystal semiconductor waveguides fabricated by diffusion,[4,15] and are comparable to the largest changes produced by epitaxy.[2] Large index differences will be needed in optical circuits which require close beam confinement[16] and small bending radii.[17]

Two-dimensional beam confinement, which is required for many of the components suggested for integrated optical circuits,[18] has previously been obtained in glass,[14] in photoresist,[19] in organic materials,[20] and in amorphous or polycrystalline Ta_2O_5.[21] To our knowledge, the two-dimensional guides reported in this letter are the first produced in single-crystal semiconductors.

[1]See P.K. Tien, Appl. Opt. 10, 2395 (1971), and references cited therein.

[2]I. Hayashi, M.B. Panish, and F.K. Reinhart, J. Appl. Phys. 42, 1929 (1971).
[3]D. Hall, A. Yariv, and E. Garmire, Appl. Phys. Letters 17, 127 (1970).
[4]F.K. Reinhart, D.F. Nelson, and J. McKenna, Phys. Rev. 177, 1208 (1969).
[5]E.T. Handelman and W. Kaiser, J. Appl. Phys. 35, 3519 (1964).
[6]H.H. Woodbury and R.B. Hall, Phys. Rev. 157, 641 (1967).
[7]M.P. Lisitsa, L.F. Gudymenko, V.N. Malinko, and S.F. Terekhova, Phys. Status Solidi 31, 389 (1969).
[8]H.F. Taylor, V.N. Smiley, W.E. Martin, and S.S. Pawka, Phys. Rev. B 5, 1467 (1972).
[9]J. Berkowitz and J.R. Marquart, J. Chem. Phys. 39, 275 (1965).
[10]J. Berkowitz and W.A. Chupka, J. Chem. Phys. 48, 5743 (1968).
[11]L.S. Brooks, J. Am. Chem. Soc. 74, 227 (1952).
[12]P. Goldfinger and M. Jeunehomme, Trans. Faraday Soc. 59, 2851 (1963).
[13]I.V. Korneeva, V.V. Sokolov, and A.V. Novoselova, Zh. Neorgan. Khim. 5, 241 (1960) [Russ. J. Inorg. Chem. 5, 117 (1960)].
[14]J.E. Goell and R.D. Standley, Bell System Tech. J. 48, 3445 (1969).
[15]D.F. Nelson and F.K. Reinhart, Appl. Phys. Letters 5, 148 (1964).
[16]E.A.J. Marcatili, Bell System Tech. J. 48, 2071 (1969).
[17]E.A.J. Marcatili, Bell System Tech. J. 48, 2103 (1969).
[18]S.E. Miller, Bell System Tech. J. 48, 2059 (1969).
[19]H.W. Weber, R. Ulrich, E.A. Chandross, and W.J. Tomlinson, Appl. Phys. Letters 20, 143 (1972).
[20]R. Ulrich, H.P. Weber, E.A. Chandross, W.J. Tomlinson, and E.A. Franke, Appl. Phys. Letters 20, 213 (1972).
[21]D.H. Hensler, J.D. Cuthbert, R.J. Martin, and P.K. Tien, Appl. Opt. 10, 1037 (1971).

Reprinted from *Appl. Phys. Lett.* **21**, 183-185 (1972).

Epitaxial electro-optic mixed-crystal $(NH_4)_x K_{1-x} H_2PO_4$ film waveguide

V. Ramaswamy
Bell Telephone Laboratories, Crawford Hill Laboratory, Holmdel, New Jersey 07733
(Received 17 April 1972)

Observation of optical guidance in an epitaxial mixed-crystal film $(NH_4)_xK_{1-x}H_2PO_4$ grown on a (100) KDP substrate is reported. The film thickness was ~38 μ. The ordinary and extraordinary indices of the film for $x=0.07$ at 589.3 nm were $n_{fo}=1.5105$ and $n_{fe}=1.4695$. The difference in corresponding indices between the film and the substrate was 10^{-3}. When the film waveguide was excited by a Gaussian He-Ne laser beam, the distribution of energy across the output face of the crystal confirmed one-dimensional guiding in the epitaxial film.

Recently, the need for homogeneous electro-optic thin films has been reiterated as the necessary first step toward the development of modulators and other desired thin-film components for use with integrated optics.[1] Yariv[2] has suggested the use of a gallium aluminum arsenide film on a similar substrate with a higher concentration of aluminum, utilizing the technology of heterojunction injection lasers.[3] Tien[4] has suggested the possibility of using gallium aluminum phosphide epitaxial films, based on the fact that the lattice constants of these materials match very closely (to less than 0.01 Å), and the atomic radii of Ga and Al are very nearly the same. Since all of the materials considered belong to the cubic point group $\bar{4}3m$, only one lattice constant and one index have to be considered. Motivated by the desire to obtain a low-loss electro-optic film waveguide, we have successfully grown epitaxial layers of homogeneous mixed-crystal electro-optic films formed from various proportions of ammonium dihydrogen phosphate (ADP) and potassium dihydrogen phosphate (KDP) on KDP substrates. The lattice parameters and ordinary and extraordinary indices of ADP and KDP at 25 °C are given in Table I.

While the lattice parameters a_0 of ADP and KDP match closely, the values for c_0 differ considerably, and thus severe strains are to be expected with higher ammonium concentrations and thicker films. However, the optical quality of the mixed-crystal films was remarkably good for small thicknesses (5–75 μ). In this brief letter, we report the observation of guidance in such films.

The KDP substrate was a 2.8-mm-square rod approximately 1.5 cm long with its broad surface parallel to the (100) plane and its axis along the *c* axis of the crystal. Figure 1 shows the unpolished (001) surface, with an epitaxial growth of about 40 μ on the four sides (100), viewed through a Leitz microscope at 16× magnification. Since the film-substrate boundary was not easily visible, one end of the crystal was illuminated with white light at the four corners so that the guiding film became visible in contrast to the substrate. Both the front and the back surfaces as well as the top film were polished using a renewable soft beeswax lap impregnated with 0.3-μ Al_2O_3 powder and lightweight lubricating oil.[5] After polishing, the thickness of the guiding film was about 38 μ. The measured values of the ordinary and extraordinary indices of the film at 589.3 nm were $n_{fo}=1.5105$ and $n_{fe}=1.4695$, which resulted in $\Delta n_o=0.001$ and $\Delta n_e=0.0011$. This corresponds to a value of $x=0.07$ in the $(NH_4)_xK_{1-x}H_2PO_4$ mixed crystal. X-ray diffraction patterns from the thick-film surface indicated that a single-crystal layer had been grown and that its orientation corresponded to that of the (100) KDP substrate.

The guiding film was excited directly by using a TEM_{00} He-Ne laser special care was taken in obtaining as nearly a Gaussian distribution as possible by proper irising of the beam in the laser cavity). The beam was modulated mechanically using an 800-Hz vibrating reed inside the cavity. The beam was focused on the film by a long-working-range microscope objective (Zeiss UD 20) with a measured numerical aperture (NA) of 0.38.

FIG. 1. (001) surface of the KDP substrate with an epitaxial growth of about 40 μ on the four sides (001). Magnification 16×.

TABLE I. Lattice parameters and ordinary and extraordinary indices of ADP and KDP at 25 °C.

Crystal (Group $\bar{4}2m$)	a_0 (Å)	c_0 (Å)	n_o (λ= 589.3 nm)	n_e
ADP[a]	7.5006	7.5490	1.5242	1.4787
KDP[b]	7.4529	6.9751	1.5095	1.4684

[a] V.T. Deshponde and A.A. Khan, Acta Cryst. **16**, 936 (1963); I.V. Gardner, Natl. Bur. Std. Test No. TP-110 613, 1947 (unpublished).

[b] T.R. Sliker and S.R. Burlage, J. Appl. Phys. **34**, 1837 (1963); A.N. Winchell and H. Winchell, *The Microscopical Characters of Artificial Inorganic Substrates: Optical Properties of Artificial Minerals*, 3rd ed. (Academic, New York, 1964), pp. 186—187.

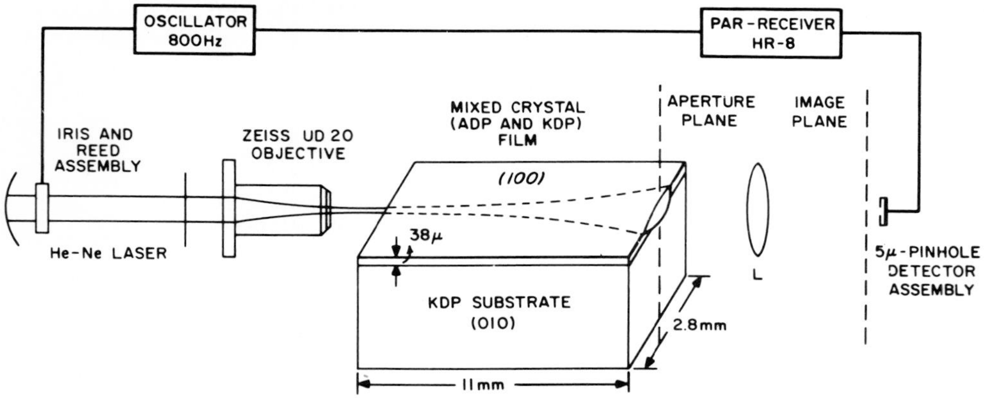

FIG. 2. Experimental setup.

The NA of the asymmetrical air-film-substrate geometry is decided by the ordinary indices[6] of the film (n_{fo}) and the substrate (n_{so}) and is given by NA $= (2n_{so}\Delta n_o)^{1/2}$, which in our case was 0.055. Since the beam did not fill the entire aperture of the objective, the effective NA closely matched that of the guide. For a Gaussian beam of width $w \approx 1.2$ mm at the entrance of the objective, the measured value of the NA was 0.053, and therefore all the allowable higher-order modes were excited in the film. It was necessary to avoid any substrate modes which would interfere with guided modes at the output. Figure 2 illustrates the setup used to excite the film.

Due to one-dimensional guidance, the input beam was confined only in the direction perpendicular to the film plane. Figure 3 shows a photograph of the output beam at the end of the crystal when viewed directly with a Leitz microscope at 18× magnification. The near-field pattern was rather difficult to measure, and it was also difficult to obtain the energy distribution in the guide from the far-field diffraction pattern. Therefore, the output face of the crystal was imaged on a ground-glass screen by a large-diameter convex lens. The position of the lens and the screen was adjusted to provide a lateral magnification of 2. The screen was then replaced by a 5-μ iris attached to a solar cell, and the entire assembly was moved across the image plane of the aperture with the help of a micropositioner. The output of the solar cell was fed into a PAR HR-8 phase-sensitive receiver (Fig. 2) which also was provided with a reference signal from the reed oscillator. The energy profile is shown in Fig. 4. As can be seen from the figure, energy was essentially confined to the film. The ordinary index of the substrate differs from that of the guiding film only by 10^{-3}, whereas the index difference between the air and film is large. Therefore, the amount of the guided ener-

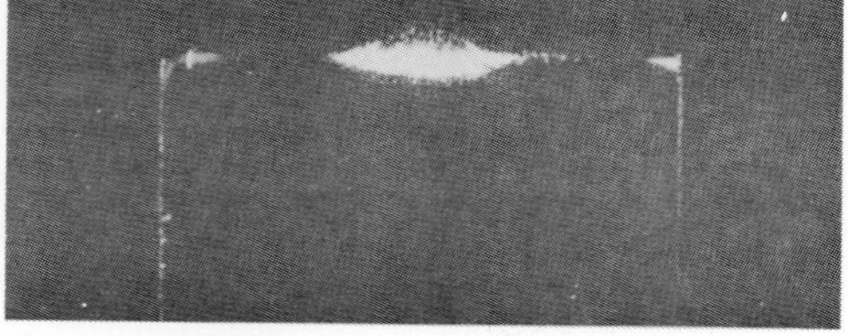

FIG. 3. Photograph of the output face of the crystal with the input beam confined in the direction perpendicular to the film plane. Magnification 18×.

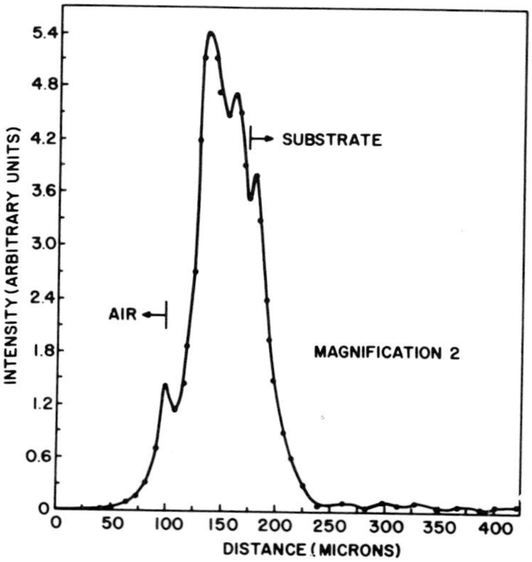

FIG. 4. Energy distribution in the image plane of the output face of the crystal, confirming one-dimensional guidance in the film.

gy in the air cladding region was quite small when compared with that in the substrate. Excluding the reflectance losses suffered at the air-film interfaces, the total losses (combined absorption and scattering losses less than 0.5 dB/cm) in the film were too small to be directly measurable without an elaborate setup. However, the films described here, grown in (100) planes, are not directly suitable for electro-optic experiments. The growth properties in other orientations are under investigation.

In conclusion, we have grown epitaxial layers of mixed (ADP and KDP) crystal films and demonstrated optical guidance with negligible absorption losses.

It is a pleasure to acknowledge the technical assistance of M.D. Divino, and helpful discussions with R. Goldstein of Lasermetrics and with E.A.J. Marcatili and A.R. Tynes of Bell Laboratories.

---

[1]P.K. Tien, Appl. Opt. **10**, 2395 (1971).

[2]A. Yariv, *Topical Meeting on Integrated Optics—Guided Waves, Materials, and Devices, Las Vegas, Nevada*, 1972, *Digest of Technical Papers* (Optical Society of America, Washington, D. C., 1972).

[3]H. Kressel, H. Nelson, and F.Z. Harorglo, J. Appl. Phys. **41**, 2019 (1970).

[4]P.K. Tien in Ref. 2.

[5]V. Ramaswamy and M.D. Divino, Rev. Sci. Instr. (to be published).

[6]Since the longitudinal E field component of the TM modes is small, this approximation is reasonably valid.

Low-loss epitaxial ZnO optical waveguides*

J.M. Hammer, D.J. Channin, M.T. Duffy, and J.P Wittke
RCA Laboratories, Princeton, New Jersey 08540
(Received 30 June 1972; in final form 10 August 1972)

Optical waveguide losses below 5 dB/cm have been measured on single-crystal epitaxial ZnO films grown on Al_2O_3. These films promise to be useful in a variety of active integrated optic applications. Comparison of the details of loss measurements with carrier density and mobility measurements gives information on possible loss mechanisms.

We have measured the optical waveguide properties of single-crystal ZnO films epitaxially deposited on Al_2O_3 substrates. Waveguide losses less than 5 dB/cm at 6328 Å have been observed. These may be compared to losses greater than 20 dB/cm reported for sputtered ZnO films.[1]

ZnO is an interesting optical waveguide material because it is transparent from 0.4 to 2 μm, exhibits the Pöckels electro-optic effect, is piezoelectric, has sizable nonlinear polarizability coefficients, and can be doped to be an excellent photoconductor. Thus, using a low-loss ZnO waveguide, it should be possible to perform a variety of active operations on guided light such as have been proposed for integrated optical systems.[2]

Single-crystal ZnO films can be grown on Al_2O_3 (sapphire) substrates by close-spaced chemical vapor transport.[3] The heated (750–850 °C) substrate is suspended close to a heated (800–900 °C) ZnO powder source in a flow of hydrogen gas. The growth rate is sensitive to the exact temperatures chosen. The epitaxial relation between film and substrate pertaining to this study is such that the $(11\bar{2}0)$ planes and $[0001]$ directions of ZnO are parallel to the $(01\bar{1}2)$ planes and $[0\bar{1}11]$ directions of the sapphire, respectively. Thus, the c axis of hexagonal ZnO grown on $(01\bar{1}2)$-oriented Al_2O_3 lies in the plane of the film.

The as-deposited films are semiconducting n type, with resistivity in the 1- to 10-Ωcm range. The waveguides described below were not compensated although it is possible to compensate these films by diffusion with lithium or sodium to have resistivities up to 10^8 Ωcm. X-ray studies of the grown films show sharp Bragg diffraction peaks typical of hexagonal single crystals.

We report on measurements on two samples. Sample A was grown at a rate of 1.3 μm/min, has a Hall mobility of 31 cm^2/V sec, and a carrier concentration of $3\times10^{17}/cm^3$. Sample B was grown at a rate of 0.25 μm/min, has a Hall mobility of 35 cm^2/V sec, and a carrier concentration of $7.5\times10^{16}/cm^3$. We note that mobilities as high as 90 cm^2/V sec have been measured on some samples. The samples were polished with chromium oxide before use as waveguides. After polishing, sample A was 4 μm and sample B was 10 μm thick. X-ray studies of the films after polishing showed no change in crystal characteristics, as compared to studies taken prior to polishing.

Scanning electron micrographs of the two samples taken after polishing are shown in Fig. 1. The higher degree of gross surface defects in sample A as compared to sample B is apparent and, as will be seen, is correlated to the waveguide loss.

Laser light was coupled into the film using a strontium titanate prism coupler.[4] The attenuation is determined by measuring the intensity of light scattered out of the

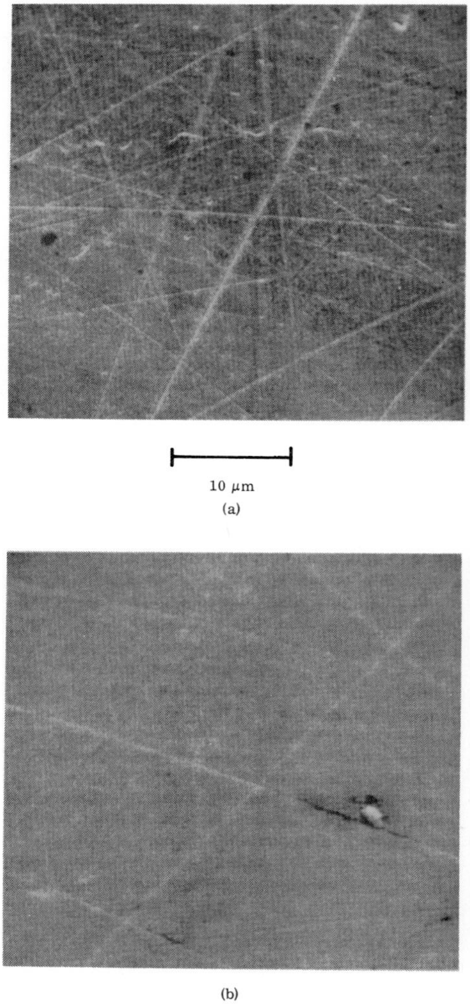

FIG. 1. Scanning electron micrographs of polished epitaxial ZnO films: (a) sample A; (b) sample B.

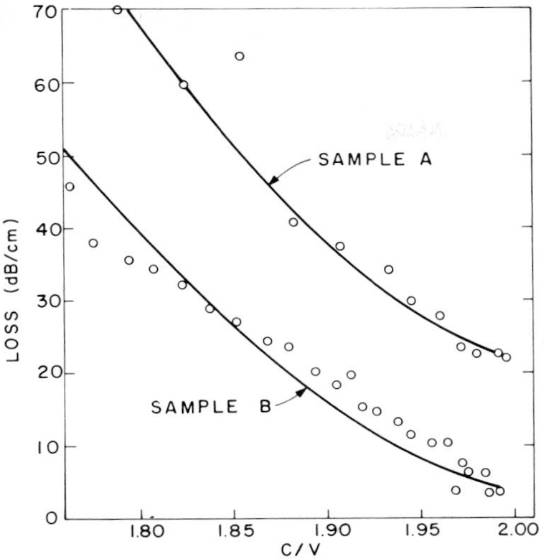

FIG. 2. Loss for TE modes measured at 6328 Å as a function of waveguide effective index. Fitted curves represent bulk and surface scattering. c/v approaches the bulk crystal value of 1.99 for the lowest mode (TE_0).

film as a function of downstream position. A fiber optic probe is used to pick up the scattered light. The slope of a linear fit to a plot of the logarithm of scattered intensity vs probe position gives the loss per unit length.

Because the samples are relatively thick, a number of modes can be independently excited. For any given mode the effective waveguide index (c/v) can be determined from the coupling angle and prism parameters.

Plots of loss as a function of effective index of refraction at 6328 Å are shown in Fig. 2. Each point represents the data for a particular mode. The curves are obtained following the analysis of Tien, [1] which gives

$$\text{loss} = A/\sin\theta + B(\cos\theta)^3/\sin\theta, \qquad (1)$$
$$\sin\theta = (1/n_f)(c/v).$$

n_f is the film index and A and B are fitted scattering strengths. The first term gives the effect of bulk scattering for a thick guide. This term is the principal contributor to the loss in low-order modes (high c/v) and is nearly independent of c/v. The second term gives the effect of surface scattering. For thick guides, this term approaches zero for low-order modes and increases rapidly with increasing mode number. Thus, this analysis enables us to separate the effects of bulk and surface scattering.

Note that the lowest observed loss at 6328 Å is 4.0 dB for the TE_0 mode of sample B. The strong increase in loss with mode indicates that surface scattering will play an important and perhaps dominant role in thinner waveguides of this system. Thus, the importance of surface treatment of the sapphire prior to epitaxial deposition and of the condition of the final ZnO surface is apparent.

The variation of waveguide loss with wavelength gives a measure of the range over which the films are useful and information about the loss mechanisms. The results of measurements of the loss in the TE_1 mode as a function of wavelength are shown in Fig. 3. Lines of He-Se, He-Ne, and Nd:YAG lasers covering the range from 0.4605 to 1.06 μm were used. On the basis of the mode theory, the TE_1 mode loss is almost entirely due to bulk attenuation for both samples. Thus, the thickness should not influence the loss in this mode for the two samples studied. As can be seen, the data for sample B are reasonably well fitted by a line proportional to λ^{-4}. This is the wavelength dependence of Rayleigh scattering and suggests that the loss is due to scattering by bulk inhomogeneities with characteristic dimensions small compared to λ. The loss in sample A departs significantly from the λ^{-4} law at long wavelengths.

Although a detailed study of the origin of loss in these guides is still in progress, it is interesting to attempt a tentative identification of the relationship between the bulk loss and some film parameters. At the outset we note that the plasma wavelength, 62 μm, of the carrier electrons is too long and the band-edge wavelength

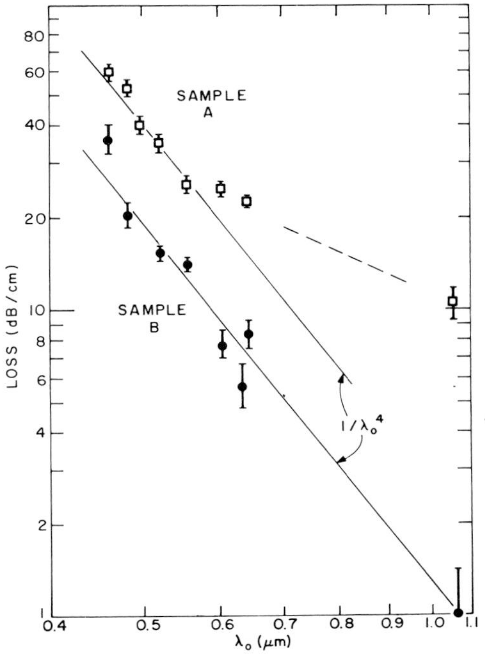

FIG. 3. Loss measured for TE_1 mode as a function of optical wavelength λ_0. Lines represent wavelength dependence of Rayleigh scattering.

(0.4 μm) too short to affect these measurements. From Fig. 1, the higher-loss sample A has a substantially rougher surface than the lower-loss sample B. Sample A was grown at a faster rate and has four times the carrier concentration of sample B. Both samples, however, have almost the same Hall mobility. The optical loss is thus correlated with the carrier concentration and surface condition but not with the mobility. These observations imply that the optical scattering process does not strongly scatter the electrons. A possible source of optical scattering centers with dimensions small compared to λ is an excess of zinc ions associated with the carrier concentration. The large-scale surface roughness seen in sample A appears to extend deeply into the film and may account for the observed departure from the Rayleigh law at long wavelengths in this sample.

We may conclude that epitaxial ZnO films grown on sapphire may provide a useful medium for many integrated optic applications. The loss in these films can be relatively low, and improvements, as different surface treatment and growth conditions are more fully explored, may be expected. Finally, the study of optical waveguide loss appears to provide a sensitive probe of defects in epitaxial thin films.

---

*Work partially supported by Wright-Patterson Air Force Base, Avionics Laboratory, Dayton, Ohio.

[1]P.K. Tien, Appl. Opt. 10, 2395 (1971).
[2]Stewart E. Miller, Bell System Tech. J. 48, 2059 (1969).
[3]G. Galli and J.E. Coker, Appl. Phys. Letters 16, 439 (1970).
[4]P.K. Tien, R. Ulrich, and R.J. Martin, Appl. Phys. Letters 14, 291 (1969).

Reprinted from *Appl. Phys. Lett.* **21**, 358-360 (1972).

Optical waveguiding layers in $LiNbO_3$ and $LiTaO_3$

I.P. Kaminow
Crawford Hill Laboratory, Bell Telephone Laboratories, Holmdel, New Jersey 07733

J.R. Carruthers
Bell Telephone Laboratories, Murray Hill, New Jersey 07974

(Received 2 January 1973)

Positive refractive-index layers in $LiNbO_3$ and $LiTaO_3$ have been produced by a novel out-diffusion technique. The index profiles for a variety of conditions are measured directly with an interference microscope. Low-loss optical waveguiding on the surface of these crystals has been observed.

The growing interest in fiber optical communications systems as well as the prospect of making efficient inexpensive optical devices have stimulated activity in integrated optics.[1] The importance of modulators, switches, and deflectors for these applications has led to the investigation of methods for producing a waveguiding layer (having a higher refractive index than its surroundings) in electro-,[2–6] acousto-,[2] and magneto-optic[7] crystals. The methods studied include in-diffusion,[2] ion-implantation,[6] and epitaxial growth.[3–5,7] However, a low-loss optical guide in a crystal of high electrical resistivity (to allow the application of modulating fields) suitable for use in an efficient electro- or acousto-optic modulator has not yet been reported. We have developed a novel and simple out-diffusion technique for achieving thin positive index layers in $LiNbO_3$ or $LiTaO_3$, which are among the best available electro- and acousto-optic materials, without degrading the original surface.

Both $LiNbO_3$ and $LiTaO_3$ can crystallize in a slightly nonstoichiometric form, $(Li_2O)_\nu(M_2O_5)_{1-\nu}$, where $M = Nb$ or Ta and ν ranges between 0.48 and 0.50.[8] (Attempts to produce crystals with ν outside the specified range result in the precipitation of a second phase.) It is known that in $LiNbO_3$,[9] and probably in $LiTaO_3$[10] as well, that the ordinary index n_o is independent of ν, but within the allowed range the extraordinary index n_e increases approximately linearly as ν decreases. For $LiNbO_3$,[8] $dn_e/d\nu = -1.63$, and for $LiTaO_3$,[11] $dn_e/d\nu = -0.85$. Hence, reducing ν at the surface should result in an optical guiding layer. In principle, either M_2O_5 could be diffused into the surface or Li_2O could be preferentially diffused out to achieve a guiding layer. The smaller size of Li compared to M suggests that Li will diffuse more readily than M. Also, the nonstoichiometric range of $\nu < 0.5$ suggests that Li is not as strongly bonded to the lattice as M. The Li bond is the more ionic and weaker, while the M bond is the more covalent and stronger.[12,13] Hence, it is reasonable to expect that if Li_2MO_3 is heated sufficiently in vacuum, then excess Li_2O will diffused through the surfaces. Our experiments support this hypothesis.

A poled $LiNbO_3$ crystal (I-2), obtained from Isomet, with dimensions of $15\times2\times5$ mm along the a, b, and c crystal axes, respectively, was placed in a Mettler Thermogravimetric microbalance. This instrument allows the weight of the sample to be monitored while it is heated in vacuum. The sample was held at $T = 1100$ °C and 6×10^{-6} Torr for $t = 21$ h, during which time a weight loss W of ~180 μg was recorded. In order to remove any discoloration of the crystal, air was then admitted while the sample was maintained at 1100 °C for 2 h. Another crystal (I-3) was similarly treated at 1100 °C for 64 h and experienced a weight loss of 480 μg, while a third sample (I-5) treated at 1100 °C for 135 h experienced a weight loss of 620 μg. The samples were clear, colorless, and well polished before and after treatment. Quoted absolute weight losses are uncertain to +100 and −0 μg because of initial transients in the electrobalance during the heating cycle. Continuous monitoring in the steady state indicates a large initial rate of weight loss, crudely approximating the law $W \approx t^{1/2}$ expected for a diffusion process.

Refractive-index profiles normal to the surfaces were measured with a Leitz interference microscope. With this instrument interference fringes, in polarized light, can be observed with a resolution of ~2 μm. Interferograms through the (a, c) face of (I-2) are shown in Fig. 1. The edge in Fig. 1(a) is normal to the c axis, and the light (Hg lamp) is an ordinary wave. Only a very small ordinary index change Δn_o is observed. The index change Δn is given by $\Delta n = p\lambda/d$, where p is the number of fringes by which the interference pattern in the graded

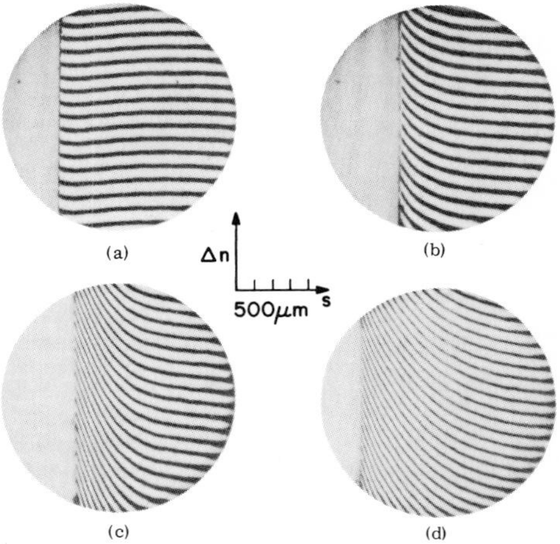

FIG. 1. Interferograms: (a) ordinary wave, diffusion along c, I-2; (b) extraordinary wave, diffusion along c, I-2; (c) extraordinary wave, diffusion normal to c, I-2; (d) extraordinary wave, diffusion normal to c, I-3.

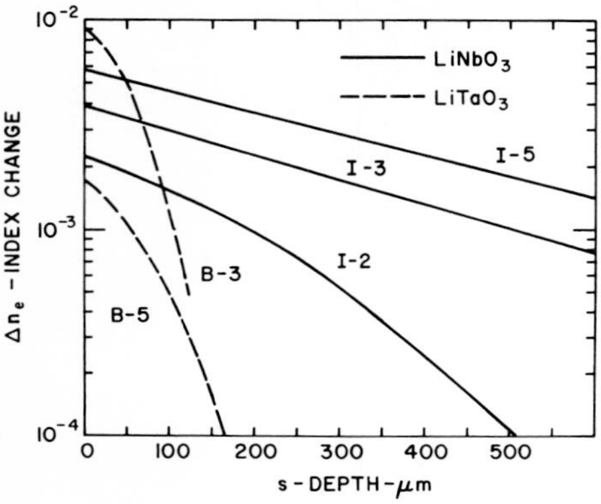

FIG. 2. Experimental index profiles in $LiNbO_3$ and $LiTaO_3$ for diffusion normal to c.

region is shifted from the unperturbed pattern, λ is the wavelength (0.546 μm), and d is the sample thickness (2000 μm). The fringe shift depicts the index profile directly. A substantial positive index change is observed with extraordinary light as in Fig. 1(b), where the edge again is normal to the c axis corresponding to out-diffusion along the c axis. The extraordinary index change is greater in Fig. 1(c), where the edge is parallel to the c axis corresponding to out-diffusion normal to the c axis. The interferogram of Fig. 1(d) illustrates the still greater out-diffusion experienced by (I-3) under observation conditions comparable to those in Fig. 1(c) for (I-2).

Experimental index profiles for diffusion normal to the c axis are plotted in Fig. 2. The curves are well represented by an empirical expression involving the complementary error function[14]

$$\Delta n_e = A\,\mathrm{erfc}(s/B), \tag{1}$$

where s is the depth below the surface, A is a function of t and T, $B=(Dt)^{1/2}$, and D is the diffusion constant, which is an exponential function of T. The constants for I-2, for example, are $A=2.2\times10^{-3}$, $B=360$ μm, $D=4.2\times10^{-9}$ cm²/sec for diffusion normal to c; and $A=1\times10^{-3}$, $B=210$ μm, $D=1.5\times10^{-9}$ cm²/sec for diffusion along c. Experimentally, we find $A\approx t^{1/2}$.

The weight losses calculated from (1) and $dn_e/d\nu$ on the assumption of Li_2O evaporation only are 25, 70, and 120 μg for specimens I-2, I-3, and I-5, respectively. As these values are considerably less than the measured losses, other components must contribute to W. Since the diffusion coefficient of oxygen in $LiNbO_3$ [15] is 10^{-10} cm²/sec at 1100 °C, which is comparable with D values quoted above, these losses may include oxygen evolution with concomitant $Nb^{5+}\rightarrow Nb^{4+}$ reduction. Both Li_2O and oxygen losses have been previously reported for $LiNbO_3$ heated in a vacuum.[16] Losses due to NbO_2 are not expected to be significant at 1100 °C since the vapor pressure of pure NbO_2 [17] is only 10^{-5} that of pure Li_2O.[18]

A refractive-index gradient of form (1) will guide light near the surface $s=0$ when A is positive. It can be shown[19] that the number of guided modes, q, is given approximately by

$$q\approx(B/\lambda)(2\pi n_e A)^{1/2} \tag{2}$$

for q large. The refractive indices of $LiNbO_3$ measured at $\lambda=0.633$ μm are $n_e=2.214$ and $n_o=2.294$. The three samples described above support many modes; e.g., for I-3 with diffusion normal to c, $q\approx198$.

Guiding can[1,20] be demonstrated with the prism coupler arrangement shown in Fig. 3, where crystals are oriented with a, b, and c along z, x, and y, respectively, and the incident beam is polarized as an extraordinary (TE) wave. A bright streak appears along the surface when θ is adjusted near an angle θ_0 slightly less than the critical angle. There is no observable decay in the strength of the scattered light over the 1-cm length of the streak, which suggests that the loss is $\lesssim 1$ dB/cm. The mode radiates from the end of the guide, producing a far-field pattern narrow in the y direction but elongated in the x direction. Measurement of the beam angle α provides an estimate for the extent h of the field in the x direction in the guide: $h\approx\lambda/\alpha$. For I-3, $h\approx10$ μm, which indicates that the optical energy for the modes being coupled is confined to the neighborhood of maximum Δn_e near $s=0$.

An output prism coupler produces a well-defined spot at $\theta'=\theta_0$ when $\theta=\theta_0$. A faint "m-line"[20] passes through the spot, indicating only minor scattering into degenerate modes propagating in other directions in the plane. Waveguiding, as demonstrated by the coupled-out spot, exists over a range of angles $\Delta\theta_0$. Calculation shows that $\Delta\theta_0$ for each sample corresponds to a range of waveguide propagation constants[1,20] $\Delta\beta$ given approximately by $2\pi A/\lambda$. Thus, the waveguide supports a large number of unresolved modes. In order to produce guides that support only a few low-order modes, the product $A^{1/2}B$ must be reduced by adjustment of t and T.

The melting and Curie temperatures, T_m and T_c, of $LiNbO_3$ are functions of ν; T_m is about 1238 °C and $1100 < T_c < 1180$ °C for $0.48<\nu<0.50$.[8] The dc linear electro-optic coefficient, r_c, of the bulk crystals was found to be the same before and after treatment, confirming that the crystals are not depoled by the out-diffusion process at $T<T_c$.

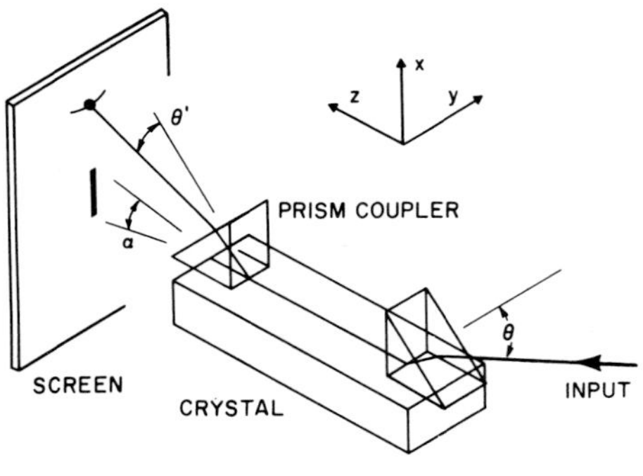

FIG. 3. Optical waveguiding apparatus.

Guiding layers of excellent quality were also observed in $LiTaO_3$. Although $LiTaO_3$ and $LiNbO_3$ are isomorphic, T_m for the former is 1650 °C and $T_c \approx 600$ °C. Out-diffusion at 600 °C is too slow to be of interest, and samples were treated at higher temperatures. The treated samples were found to be depoled and, although guiding was not affected, they must be repoled in order to be useful in electro- or acousto-optic applications.

The index profiles for diffusion normal to c in two $LiTaO_3$ crystals grown by Ballman are shown in Fig. 2. One crystal (B-5) was treated at ~1150 °C for ~3 h and the other (B-3) at 1400 °C for 20 min. The diffusion parameters for B-5 are $A = 1.7\times10^{-3}$, $B = 130$ μm, $D = 4\times10^{-9}$ cm²/sec; and for B-3, $A = 9\times10^{-3}$, $B = 106$ μm, $D = 25\times10^{-9}$ cm²sec. Thus, A and D increase rapidly with T. Since $A^{1/2}B$ is smaller for these samples than for the $LiNbO_3$ samples, q is smaller. Indeed several discrete modes can be observed with the output prism coupler.

The authors are grateful to J.G. Bergman for helpful discussions, and to A.A. Ballman for providing the $LiTaO_3$ crystals.

[1] P.K. Tien, Appl. Opt. 10, 2345 (1971).
[2] W.E. Martin and D.B. Hall, Appl. Phys. Lett. 21, 325 (1972).
[3] V. Ramaswamy, Appl. Phys. Lett. 21, 183 (1972).
[4] J.M. Hammer, D.J. Channin, M.T. Duffy, and J.P. Wittke, Appl. Phys. Lett. 21, 358 (1972).
[5] D. Hall, A. Yariv, and E. Garmire, Opt. Commun. 1, 403 (1970).
[6] E. Garmire, H. Stoll, A. Yariv, and R.G. Hunsperger, Appl. Phys. Lett. 21, 87 (1972).
[7] P.K. Tien, R.J. Martin, S.L. Blank, S.H. Wemple, and L.J. Varnerin, Appl. Phys. Lett. 21, 207 (1972).
[8] J.R. Carruthers, G.E. Peterson, M. Grasso, and P.M. Bridenbaugh, J. Appl. Phys. 42, 1846 (1971).
[9] J.G. Bergman, A. Ashkin, A.A. Ballman, J.M. Dziedzic, H.J. Levinstein, and R.G. Smith, Appl. Phys. Lett. 12, 92 (1968).
[10] A.A. Ballman, H.J. Levinstein, C.D. Capio, and H. Brown, J. Am. Ceram. Soc. 50, 657 (1967).
[11] R.L. Barns and J.R. Carruthers, J. Appl. Crystallogr. 3, 395 (1970).
[12] G.E. Peterson and P.M. Bridenbaugh, J. Chem. Phys. 48, 3402 (1968).
[13] M.E. Lines, Phys. Rev. B 2, 698 (1970).
[14] J. Crank, *Mathematics of Diffusion* (Oxford U.P., New York, 1956).
[15] P.J. Jorgensen and R.W. Bartlett, J. Phys. Chem. Solids 30, 2639 (1969).
[16] M.M. Pinaeva-Strelina and I.A. Dmitrieu, Inorg. Mater. 2, 1248 (1966).
[17] A. Schukarev, G.A. Semenov, and K.E. Frantseva, Russ. J. Inorg. Chem. 11, 129 (1966).
[18] A.N. Nesmeyanov and L.P. Belykh, Russ. J. Phys. Chem. 34, 399 (1960).
[19] E.A.J. Marcatili (private communication); D. Marcuse (private communication).
[20] P.K. Tien and R. Ulrich, J. Opt. Soc. Am. 60, 1325 (1970).

Reprinted from *Appl. Phys. Lett.* **21**, 326-328 (1973).

Thin-film $LiNbO_3$ electro-optic light modulator

I.P. Kaminow
Bell Telephone Laboratories, Crawford Hill Laboratory, Holmdel, New Jersey 07733

J.R. Carruthers
Bell Telephone Laboratories, Holmdel, New Jersey 07733

E.H. Turner
Bell Telephone Laboratories, Murray Hill, New Jersey 07974

L.W. Stulz
Bell Telephone Laboratories, Crawford Hill Laboratory, Holmdel, New Jersey 07733
(Received 27 February 1973)

An out-diffused planar optical waveguide in $LiNbO_3$ has been used to produce an efficient broad-band electro-optic phase modulator. The ratio of modulation index η and voltage is $0.13\ V^{-1}$, the maximum base bandwidth with 50-Ω load is 3.2 GHz, and the modulating power per unit bandwidth for $\eta = 1$ rad is 0.2 mW/MHz.

An out-diffusion technique for producing optical waveguiding layers on $LiNbO_3$ and $LiTaO_3$ was developed recently[1] with the intention of constructing active thin-film devices. The diffusion of Li_2O from the surface produces a layer with reduced Li/Nb or Li/Ta ratio and consequent increased extraordinary refractive index. We have now demonstrated the utility of these layers by building and testing an efficient wide-band $LiNbO_3$ phase modulator whose characteristics can be satisfactorily accounted for by the bulk electro-optic coefficient of $LiNbO_3$.

The power per unit bandwidth, $P/\Delta f$, required to drive a *bulk* modulator rod of length L and square cross section d^2 is proportional[2] to d^2/L. The minimum value of this factor is determined by diffraction of the laser beam passing through the modulator crystal. With the beam focused so that the waist occurs at the center of the rod, the minimum value for d^2/L is $4\lambda/n\pi$, where λ is the optical wavelength and n is the refractive index. For this minimum condition, the power density at the edges of the aperture is less than $1/e^2$ times the power density at the center of the aperture. In order to alleviate the alignment problem, modulators are usually designed with a safety factor[2] S such that

$$d^2/L = S^2(4\lambda/n\pi), \tag{1}$$

with

$$S \gtrsim 3.$$

In a *planar* waveguide, there is no beam spreading normal to the plane, but diffraction in the plane still limits electrode spacing according to (1). However, since alignment is simpler and reflections from crystal surfaces are not a problem, one may employ the minimum value $S \approx 1$ in the planar structure.

We have used the simple modulator structure illustrated in Fig. 1: a $LiNbO_3$ planar waveguide with aluminum electrodes evaporated on the surface, and input and output rutile prism couplers. The out-diffused crystal has dimensions of $15 \times 2 \times 5$ mm along the a, b, and c crystal axes, respectively, and is one described earlier[1] and designated I-3. The extraordinary index profile is given by

$$\Delta n_e = A\,\mathrm{erfc}(-x/B), \quad x < 0 \tag{2}$$

where $-x$ is the depth below the surface, $A = 4 \times 10^{-3}$, and $B = 530\ \mu m$. The guide, which can support ~198 modes, is excited in TE modes via the input coupler by a 0.633-μm laser polarized along the crystal c axis.

The electrodes were formed photolithographically with dimensions chosen so that

$$b^2/L = S^2(4\lambda/n_e\pi), \tag{3}$$

where b is the electrode spacing and $S \approx 1$. The extraordinary index, n_e, measured on our sample at 0.633 μm is 2.214.

As indicated in Fig. 2, the width of the electrodes, a, is chosen so that $a \approx b$. The capacitance C for a coplanar condenser with $a = b$ on a uniaxial crystal like $LiNbO_3$ having dielectric constants[3] $K_a = 43$ and and $K_c = 28$ along the a and c axes, respectively, is given approximately by[4]

$$C = \epsilon_0[1 + (K_a K_c)^{1/2}]L. \tag{4}$$

(The dielectric constants do vary somewhat with Li/Nb ratio.[5])

The modulating field components just below the surface of the crystal are

$$E_x(0, y) = 0 \quad \text{and} \quad E_y(0, y) = V/b, \quad |y| < b/2 \tag{5}$$

where V is the voltage between electrodes. The E_y component decreases with depth at least as fast as[4] $\exp(x/x_0)$,

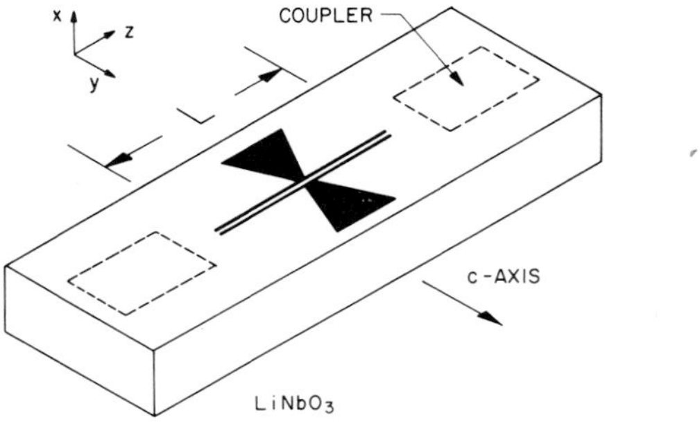

FIG. 1. Thin-film $LiNbO_3$ electro-optic phase modulator.

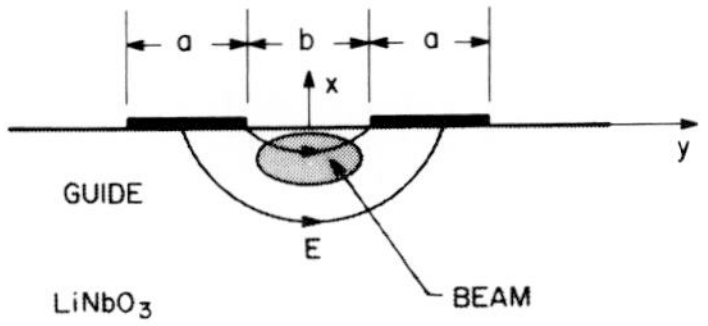

FIG. 2. Coplanar electrodes on $LiNbO_3$ guiding layer.

where

$$x_0 = (K_a/K_c)^{1/2}(2b/\pi). \tag{6}$$

For most effective use of the modulating field, the penetration depth of the optical beam should be comparable with x_0. The finished electrode dimensions were $L = 6.2$ mm, $a = 44$ μm, and $b = 57$ μm, yielding $S = 1.2$, $x_0 = 45$ μm, and $C = 2.0$ pF. The measured capacitance at 50 MHz was ~3 pF.

If a load resistance R is placed in parallel with C and the combination is driven by a matched voltage generator with impedance R, the base bandwidth is given by[2]

$$\Delta f = (\pi RC)^{-1}. \tag{7}$$

For $R = 50$ Ω and the calculated $C = 2$ pF, the maximum bandwidth is $\Delta f = 3.2$ GHz. Transit-time limitations[2] are above 3.2 GHz for $L = 6.2$ mm.

For the crystal c axis oriented along y, the phase modulation index is

$$\eta = \pi n_e^3 r_{33} \overline{E}_y L/\lambda, \tag{8}$$

where r_{33} is the electro-optic coefficient and $\overline{E}_y = uV/b$ is the effective modulating field. The factor u is a number less than unity that takes account of the fact that E_y varies across the beam. Taking[3] $r_{33} = 31 \times 10^{-12}$ m/V, we calculate $\eta/V = 0.18u$ V^{-1}. (It has been shown[5] previously that r_{33} is independent of the Li/Nb ratio in bulk crystals.)

The modulation index can be measured by using the heterodyne system[6] illustrated in Fig. 3. The stabilized He-Ne lasers (Spectra Physics Model 119) oscillate in only one longitudinal mode because of their restricted lengths. The local-oscillator laser can be swept over a 500-MHz range without appreciable variation in amplitude by varying the mirror spacing. The spectrum of the modulated carrier laser mixes with the local oscillator in a photodiode; the photocurrent is passed through a 70-MHz-i.f. amplifier and is detected and displayed on a oscilloscope. The ratio of sideband to carrier amplitudes is $J_1(\eta)/J_0(\eta)$, where J_n is the nth-order Bessel function. The amplitude ratio is measured with the aid of calibrated optical attenuators placed in front of the local oscillator, and η is calculated from the result. The use of input and output prisms, rather than focusing the beam into and out of the edges of the layer, ensures that only guided light is detected.

In the experiment, a General Radio oscillator feeds a miniature 50-Ω coaxial cable leading to a panel connector adjacent to the modulator crystal. Thin gold wires from the connector connect the voltage to the electrodes on the crystal. The capacitance of connector, leads, and electrodes measured at the connector is ~4 pF. In order to obtain a correct reading of V at high frequency, it is necessary to place the voltmeter probe (Hewlett Packard Model 11096A) in direct contact with the electrodes.

The measurements yield $\eta/V = 0.13$ V^{-1}, constant to within 10% over the available measuring range of the apparatus, 50—500 MHz. The voltage was also varied from 0.7 to 7 V without altering η/V. The measured and calculated values of η/V agree if the effective field factor u is set equal to 0.7, which is reasonably close to unity. Thus, we (a) confirm that the beam passes cleanly between the electrodes in the $x = 0$ plane and does not penetrate much deeper than x_0, (b) justify the assumption that the electro-optic coefficients in the guiding layer and bulk crystal are practically the same, and (c) demonstrate experimentally a base bandwidth at least as great as 500 MHz.

The observed value of u may seem surprisingly close to unity in view of the fact that the penetration of the modulating field is approximately $x_0 = 45$ μm while the thickness of the guiding layer is approximately $B = 530$ μm. The likely explanation is that, by adjusting the input angle to the prism coupler for maximum modulation, we selectively excite only the shallow low-order modes.[7] The experimental error in the measurement of η/V is probably less than 15%. The peak voltage required to obtain $\eta = 1$ rad is 7.7 V. The corresponding power $P = V^2/2R$ consumed in the 50-Ω load is 590 mW, and, for $\Delta f = 3.2$ GHz, $P/\Delta f = 0.19$ mW/MHz. If we use the capacitance measured at the connector rather than the calculated C, Δf will be halved and $P/\Delta f$ doubled.

In order to improve $P/\Delta f$, the optical beam and modulating fields must be confined to smaller cross sections over their interaction length. Optical confinement in the $y = 0$ plane can be improved by reducing the out-diffusion time and/or temperature in order to reduce the layer thickness.[1] Other schemes are being considered that will guide the optical beam in the $x = 0$ plane in order to eliminate diffraction effects; then b^2/L may be reduced indefinitely. In order to use the modulating field most effectively, the modulating field distribution should be tailored to just overlap the optical beam; for the closely

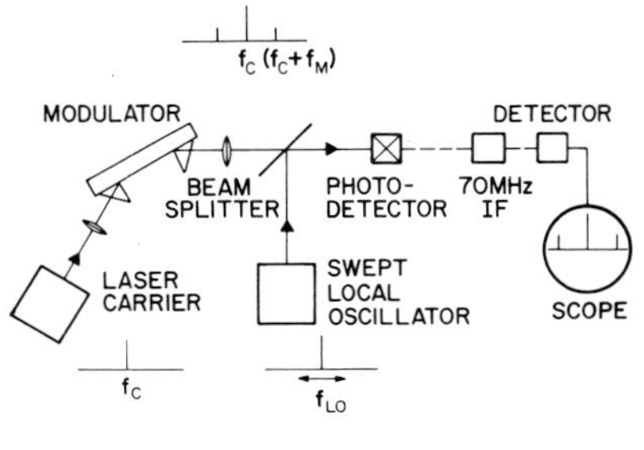

FIG. 3. Apparatus for heterodyne measurement of the phase modulation index.

confined optical beam, this can be achieved by reducing the electrode spacing.

In some applications, amplitude or pulse modulation is preferred to phase or frequency modulation. The former mode of operation may be achieved in a number of ways by reorienting the crystal and/or restructuring the electrodes.[8] The feasibility of these approaches is being studied.

The authors are grateful to R.V. Schmidt and J.R. Perucca for their help in making the electrodes.

[1]I. P. Kaminow and J.R. Carruthers, Appl. Phys. Lett. **22**, 326 (1973).
[2]I. P. Kaminow and E.H. Turner, Proc. IEEE **54**, 1374 (1966).
[3]I. P. Kaminow and E.H. Turner, in *Handbook of Lasers*, edited by R.J. Pressley (Chemical Rubber Co., Cleveland, Ohio, 1971).
[4]H. Engan, IEEE Trans. Electron Devices **ED-16**, 1014 (1969).
[5]E.H. Turner, F.R. Nash, and P.M. Bridenbaugh, J. Appl. Phys. **41**, 5278 (1970).
[6]I. P. Kaminow, Appl. Phys. Lett. **7**, 123 (1965); Appl. Phys. Lett. **8**, 54 (1966).
[7]D. Marcuse (unpublished).
[8]See, for example, M.A.R.P. de Barros and M.G.F. Wilson, Proc. Inst. Electr. Eng. **119**, 807 (1972).

Reprinted from *Appl. Phys. Lett.* **22**, 540-542 (1973).

Pulse amplitude modulation of a CO_2 laser in an electro-optic thin-film waveguide*

P.K. Cheo

United Aircraft Research Laboratories, East Hartford, Connecticut 06108

(Received 28 August 1972; in final form 21 December 1972)

Beam steering of a 10.6-μm guided-wave mode in an electro-optic GaAs thin-film waveguide is observed. The deflection angle increases linearly with increasing voltage and interaction length. A switching time of about 60 nsec has been obtained and is limited by the detector response. This technique has been used to obtain more than 12% amplitude modulation of a CO_2 laser by applying only 50 V to an ~ 20-μm-thick GaAs thin-film waveguide having a total interaction length of 0.5 cm.

The power required[1] to modulate a Gaussian beam by using a bulk electro-optic crystal having an optimum configuration is proportional to λ^3, where λ is the laser wavelength. At longer laser wavelengths, conventional modulator devices are very inefficient. For this reason, the use of the most efficient 10.6-μm CO_2 laser as a wide-band communication source has been severely limited. In an attempt to overcome this difficulty, we have studied[2] in detail the use of GaAs epitaxial thin-film waveguides which offer a promising means of obtaining an over 1-GHz [3] modulation bandwidth for the 10.6-μm laser system at a very low rf power level. The use of a GaAs thin film to modulate the 1.15-μm He-Ne laser has previously been reported.[4,5] This letter describes a different technique for obtaining very efficient amplitude modulation of a CO_2 laser in an electro-optic GaAs epitaxial thin-film waveguide by beam steering of a 10.6-μm guided-wave mode. A switching time of about 60 nsec has been measured, and it is a response limited by the ir photodiode element (PbSnTe Raytheon ir 101) used in our experimental setup. A 1.1-mrad angular shift of the guided-wave mode away from the electro-optically active region in the plane of the thin film has been obtained by applying a peak voltage pulse, V_p, of 50 V to an ~ 20-μm-thick GaAs thin-film waveguide having a total interaction length, l, of 0.5 cm. This angular shift increases linearly with increasing V_p and l. With this technique it is not only possible to obtain amplitude modulation of a laser beam or to generate short laser pulses at high repetition rates, but also to provide rapid switching or deflection of a laser beam for optical storage and signal processing at a rate much faster than the transit-time-limited acousto-optic thin-film waveguide devices.[6]

The waveguide modulator used in this experiment is shown in Fig. 1. It consisted of a high-resistivity ($\rho \geq 10^5$ Ω cm) GaAs thin film epitaxially grown on a heavily doped ($N = 1.6 \times 10^{18}$ cm^{-3}) substrate. The index difference Δn between the active thin film and the low-resistivity substrate for the 10.6-μm radiation is about 0.3. For input and output coupling, two phase gratings[7] having 3×3-mm aperture size, periodicity $\Lambda \simeq 3.5$ μm, and 1.2-μm depth of groove have been fabricated in this epilayer. They are so oriented that the guided-wave mode of various orders can be excited and propagated along the (011) direction. A 0.5-cm-long and 1.5-mm-wide Schottky barrier electrode was fabricated in between these two grating couplers and was used to sustain a high electric field strength along the (001) axis at a right angle to the direction of propagation. The measured capacitance was 25 pF. The measured film thickness, t, at several points along the interaction length by the Schottky barrier measurements[8] varied from 18 to 21 μm over a length of 0.5 cm.

This waveguide modulator was placed on a rotating platform so that the angle of incidence, θ, could be adjusted to excite a desired guided-wave mode. A linearly polarized CO_2 laser having a beam width $\omega \simeq 0.3$ mm was incident on the input grating coupler. A liquid-nitrogen-cooled PbSnTe photodiode having an aperture of 0.0018 cm^2 is located about 10 cm away from the output grating coupler. Figure 2 shows the peak radiation pattern transmitted through the film as a function of θ. These peaks occur at angles which correspond well with the calculated[2] values for various TE modes, as indicated in Fig. 2. Polarization of these modes has been analyzed with a wire-grid polarizer. By setting θ at 12°, we have measured the radiation pattern by scanning the detector element across the output grating coupler in the plane of incidence. The results are plotted in Fig. 3, as represented by the solid curve. These results indicate that other TE modes with lower intensity are also present in the guide. The occurrence of other order modes is attributed to mode conversion[9] as a result of scattering from imperfections of the waveguide used in this experiment.

When a negative square-top voltage pulse, as shown by the upper trace of Fig. 4(a), was applied to the Schottky barrier electrode, a light pulse was detected by the PbSnTe photodiode located about 10 cm away from the output grating coupler, as shown by the lower trace of Fig. 4(a). This light pulse disappears when either the

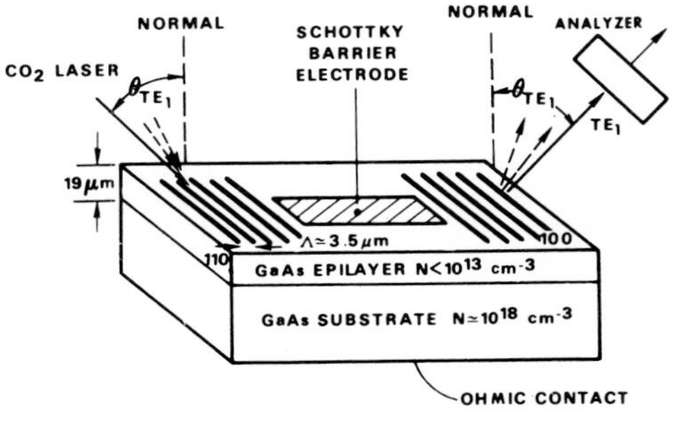

FIG. 1. GaAs thin-film modulator for the 10.6-μm CO_2 laser. The active length is 0.5 cm.

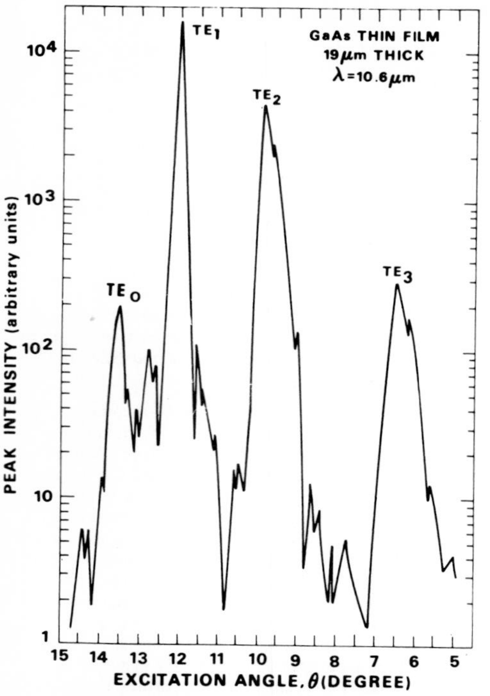

FIG. 2. Peak transmission vs the angle of incidence measured from the film normal. The periodicity of the gratings is 3.5 μm. The calculated β/k values for the TE_0, TE_1, TE_2, and TE_3 modes are 3.267, 3.239, 3.194, and 3.125, respectively.

output grating coupler is blocked or the voltage pulse is removed from the Schottky barrier electrode. The voltage pulse, which has a rise time less than 10 nsec, was measured by an FET probe with a 40-dB attenuator at the Schottky barrier electrode. The rise time of the modulated laser pulse is ~60 nsec (10–90%), a response limited essentially by the response of the ir detector used in our experiment. Figure 4(b) shows a train of short negative-going pulses which appear only when voltage pulses are applied, as shown by the upper trace of Fig. 4(b). The chopped light pulse, L_c, having a pulse width of ~3.5 msec, represents the unmodulated TE_1 mode intensity transmitted through the waveguide. The intensity of the modulated laser pulses, L_m, was found to increase linearly with increasing V_p and l.

At $V_p = 50$ V and $\theta = 12°$, we have measured L_m as a function of detector position, which was varied by scanning the detector element in the plane of incidence. The results, as shown by the dotted curve in Fig. 3, indicate that other modes have also been modulated by the applied electric field in a way similar to that observed for the TE_1 mode. These results along with the polarization analysis of the modulated laser pulses rule out a mode conversion process[10,11]—i.e., $TE_i \to TE_j$, $TE_i \to TM_i$—as a possible mechanism responsible for the decrease of laser power in the presence of an electric field. Further investigation reveals that the negative-going pulse does not represent a loss of laser power; in fact, it corresponds to a beam steering of the guided TE_1 mode in the plane of the thin film. By moving the detector element in the direction perpendicular to the plane of incidence, we observed that the amplitude of the modulated laser pulse changes from a negative to a positive value with respect to the chopped laser pulse, as shown in Fig. 5. Simultaneous measurements of L_c and L_m as a function of detector displacement along a line perpendicular to the plane of incidence are plotted in Fig. 6. The results show that the modulated beam is shifted away from the electro-optically active region by an angle $\alpha \simeq 1.1$ mrad for $V_p = 50$ V, and $l = 0.5$ cm. It was observed that the pulse amplitude of the modulated light is greatest when the guided-wave mode is propagating along the edge of the Schottky barrier electrode. The electro-optic change in refractive index for light propagating along the (011) direction is

$$\Delta n_{EO} = -\tfrac{1}{2} n^3 r_{41} V/t, \tag{1}$$

where n, r_{41}, and t are the refractive index, electro-optic coefficient, and the thickness of the guiding film, respectively. The difference in refractive index between the active and nonactive region of the guiding film can cause the observed beam-steering effect as a result of reconstruction of the wave front of two plane waves having a slight phase difference, $\Delta\Gamma = 2\pi l \Delta n_{EO}/\lambda$, propagating along the edge of the electrode. Based on this model we can qualitatively estimate the angle of deflec-

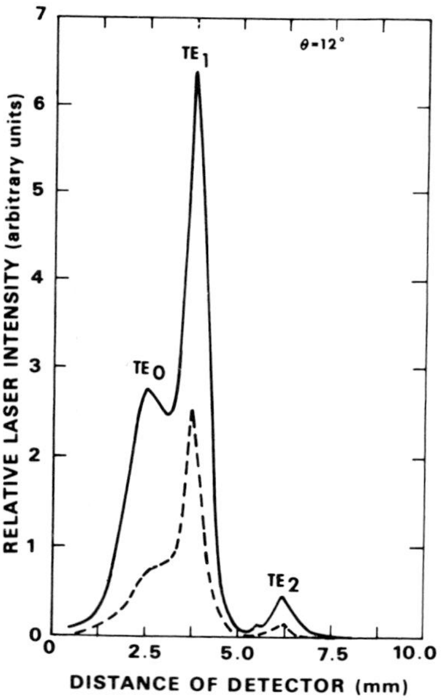

FIG. 3. Unmodulated and modulated laser intensity vs the distance of detector scan in the plane of incidence. Detector is located about 8.5 cm away from the output grating coupler. The distance increases as detector moves toward the normal.

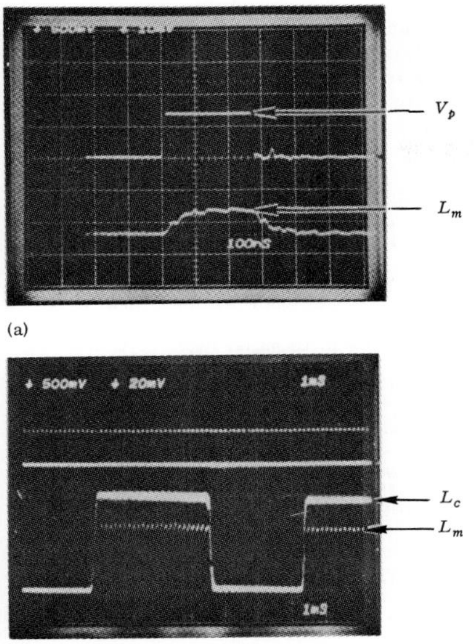

(a)

(b)

FIG. 4. (a) Waveforms of the voltage (upper trace) and the modulated laser (lower trace) pulses. (b) Waveforms of the voltage (upper trace) and the modulated and the unmodulated laser (lower trace) pulses.

tion α by the expression

$$\alpha \simeq (l/\omega_0)\Delta n_{EO}, \tag{2}$$

where ω_0 is the beam width of the guided mode. For $V = 50$ V, $l = 0.5$ cm, $t = 20$ μm, and $\omega_0 = 0.3$ mm, Eq. (2) gives a deflection angle $\alpha \simeq 1$ mrad, which is in good agreement with our measurements. To measure the depth of modulation, we first collect nearly all the transmitted power P_t with the help of a $f/1$ germanium lens by matching the detector aperture with the radiation coupled out of the output grating. When voltage is applied, a decrease in the detector output which corresponds to a maximum modulated signal P_m is obtained. The measured P_m/P_t ratio is about 12.8% at $V_p = 50$ V. By choosing $l = 1$ cm and $t = 10$ μm, we estimate that a 50% depth of modulation can be achieved by applying 50 V to this thin-film modulator. It should be emphasized that the observed phenomenon is by no means unique to this particular device. In fact, three thin-film modulators have been built, and they all exhibit the same modulation characteristics. Most of the data presented here are based on one device which has a grating as the output coupler and allows us to analyze its output characteristics in greater detail. Experiments are still in progress to optimize the device configuration in order to improve the efficiency and to provide a better understanding of the mechanism.

The advantage of the above described device over the conventional bulk modulator is obvious. More can be gained by using such a device to modulate lasers at

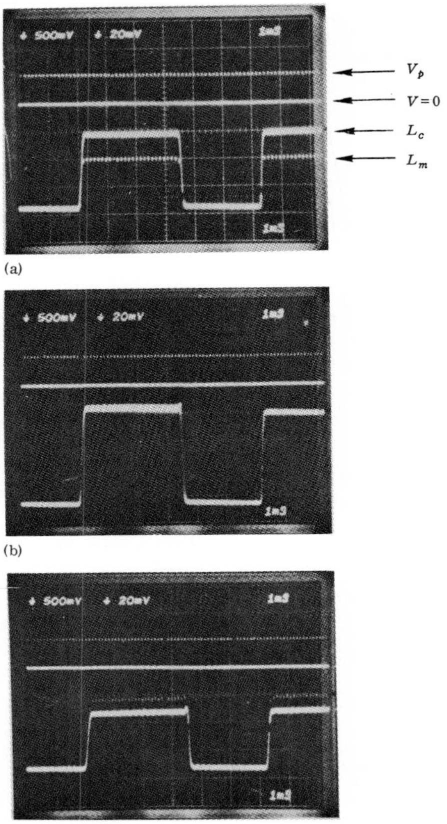

(a)

(b)

(c)

FIG. 5. Sequence of events showing the characteristics of the modulated laser pulses as the detector element scans across the transmitted laser beam profile. (a) Detector is located to the right of beam center, (b) near the beam center, and (c) to the left of beam center.

shorter wavelengths. The improvement factor is expected to be proportional to $1/\lambda^2$. At shorter wavelengths, one not only gains a better resolution but also a higher field strength by using a thinner waveguide. The present modulation scheme is much more simple and convenient than the conventional phase or polarization modulation via thin film,[5] where either a heterodyne receiver or a simultaneous excitation of two orthogonal modes (TE and TM) in a guide is required. In comparison with the scheme that utilizes the waveguide cutoff,[4] our preliminary results indicate that the efficiency of our present scheme is more than two orders of magnitude greater than that obtainable from a waveguide device operating near its cutoff.

The author wishes to thank J. Swindal for making gratings by photolithographic techniques, and W. Glueck for

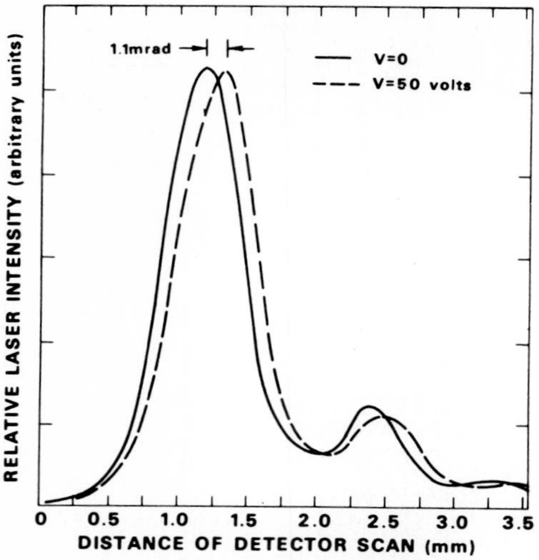

FIG. 6. Simultaneous measurements of the modulated and the unmodulated laser pulses as a function of detector position.

technical assistance in experiments. He also wishes to thank Dr. C. Buczek, Dr. M. Gilden, and Dr. A. Stein of United Aircraft Research Laboratories and Dr. W. L. Knecht of the Air Force Avionics Laboratory for stimulating discussions.

---

*Work supported in part by the Air Force Avionics Laboratory and by the Office of Naval Research.

[1]I. P. Kaminow and E. H. Turner, Proc. IEEE 54, 1374 (1966).
[2]P. K. Cheo, J. M. Berak, W. Oshinsky, and J. L. Swindal, Appl. Opt. (to be published).
[3]T. J. Bridges, T. Y. Chang, and P. K. Cheo, Appl. Phys. Lett. 12, 297 (1968).
[4]D. Hall, A. Yariv, and E. Garmire, Appl. Phys. Lett. 17, 127 (1970).
[5]F. K. Reinhart and B. I. Miller, Appl. Phys. Lett. 20, 36 (1972).
[6]L. Kuhn, M. L. Dakss, P. K. Heidrich, and B. A. Scott, Appl. Phys. Lett. 17, 265 (1970).
[7]M. Dakss, L. Kuhn, P. F. Heidrich, and B. A. Scott, Appl. Phys. Lett. 16, 523 (1970).
[8]J. A. Copeland, IEEE Trans. Electron Devices ED-16, 445 (1969).
[9]D. Marcuse, Bell Syst. Tech. J. 48, 3187 (1969).
[10]M. Shah, J. D. Crow, and S. Wang, Appl. Phys. Lett. 20, 66 (1972).
[11]L. Kuhn, P. F. Heidrich, and E. G. Lean, Appl. Phys. Lett. 19, 428 (1971).

Reprinted from *Appl. Phys. Lett.* **22**, 241-244 (1973).

Reprinted from **APPLIED OPTICS**, Vol. 5, page 1675, October 1966

A Survey of Laser Beam Deflection Techniques

V. J. FOWLER AND J. SCHLAFER

Abstract—**Methods of high-resolution, high-speed, optical beam deflection and scanning are reviewed with respect to resolution and scanning frequency capabilities. A general description is given of external deflector devices in the categories of variable reflectors, variable refractors, birefringent deflectors, and interference deflectors. The different techniques are then evaluated on the basis of their application to high-speed, high-resolution, precision scanning applications.**

I. Introduction

DEVELOPMENT of methods of high-speed, high-resolution optical beam deflection have been stimulated by the advent of the laser with its intense, highly collimated beam of light. Potential applications for laser beam deflection techniques include: 1) acquisition scanning for optical radar; 2) line scanning of optical beams for film recording of video television or radar signals; 3) high-speed oscillography; 4) raster scanning of laser beams for video signal generation; 5) line scanning for laser beam television projection systems; 6) aperiodic scanning for laser symbol projection; and 7) laser beam scanning of optical memory devices for read-in, read-out, or erasure. These applications all require rapid deflection, low light loss, low optical-phase-front distortion, high deflection accuracy, and moderately large light-power-handling capability. Other important requirements, which vary widely with the applications, include magnitude of horizontal and vertical deflection, aperture diameter, bandwidth, drive voltage, optical wavelength range, degree of color registration, deflection linearity, deflection rate, and environmental factors.

This paper covers only those techniques for deflecting a narrow beam from a laser by a device external to the laser cavity. Interesting alternative possibilities [1]–[4] of using internal devices to control the direction of the light emitted by the laser will not be covered here. Furthermore, it will be assumed that in most cases the deflector is to be used to deflect a round beam of Gaussian transverse intensity distribution [5] (the so-called zero-order transverse mode TEM_{00} of the laser).

In the following sections reference will be made to deflector resolution, i.e., the number of resolvable positions, or spots, the deflected beam may assume [6]. Using the Rayleigh criterion a beam of half angle divergence θ deflected through an angle ϕ would exhibit a resolution of

$$N = \frac{\phi}{\theta} = \frac{\phi w}{\epsilon\lambda} \qquad (1)$$

where w is the beamwidth, λ the wavelength, and $\epsilon = 1$ for rectangular beam of uniform intensity, 1.22 for a circular beam of uniform intensity, and 1.27 for a beam with a Gaussian intensity distribution. The deflection angle ϕ may always be increased through the use of passive elements such as a telescope. However, the post deflection resolution is invariant.

The laser beam deflection techniques covered here are grouped into the following four categories: 1) variable

Manuscript received June 10, 1966.
The authors are with The Bayside Laboratory, General Telephone and Electronics Laboratories, Inc., Bayside, N. Y.

Present address of authors: General Telephone and Electronic Laboratories, Inc., Waltham, Massachusetts.

reflectors, 2) variable refractors, 3) birefringent deflection, and 4) interference deflection. The operating principles and general characteristics of various deflection methods in these categories are described in the following sections. The different techniques are compared in the concluding section.

II. Variable Reflectors

Possibly the earliest method used to deflect a light beam was a form of mechanical or electromechanical scan in which light was reflected from a rotating mirror. The best-known examples of this technique are the optical oscillograph and the high-speed rotating mirror streak camera. Most optical oscillographs utilize a single mirror attached to a coil and suspended in a steady magnetic field. Passing a current through the coil causes the mirror to twist on the suspension. Light reflected from the mirror surface will be scanned through twice the mirror rotation angle due to the doubling upon reflection. Systems of this type may be operated either below or above their resonant frequencies as direct responding or ballistic instruments. The former type have been made with a useful frequency range of 0–13 kHz and resolution of 200 spots [7]. The frequency response is limited by the moment of inertia of the mirror and coil in combination with the spring constant of the suspension. Use of a smaller mirror or a stiffer spring increases the resonance frequency for a given drive signal, but only at the expense of resolution.

Multifaceted rotating mirrors, as found in high-speed streak and framing cameras, form a group of reflection-type scanning devices which could be considered essentially single frequency. While the scan speed may be governed over a large range, it is not amenable to rapid variations. The unidirectional rotation of the mirror leads naturally to a sawtooth-type scanning action with one scan line for each mirror face. Maximum scanning rates are limited by the peripheral velocity of the mirror, i.e., its bursting speed, and distortion of the mirror surface due to the large centrifugal acceleration. For beryllium, a common mirror material, this maximum velocity, based on material strength, is usually taken to be 500 m/s. At these speeds, however, the mirror surface takes on a cylindrical distortion which must be corrected with suitable optics. Using the above figure for the limiting velocity, a hexagonal rotating mirror could be made to resolve 5000 spots at about 31 000 sawtooth scans per second if 10 percent of the scanning time is allowed for the retrace.

By making use of the resonances of a mechanical system, large motions can often be obtained with low drive power. This principle is exploited in the torsional vibrating scanner described by Dostal [8]. A mirror, attached to one of the tines of a torsional fork, rotates as the tines twist about their axes. The fork, when driven at resonance, imparts a large amplitude angular scanning motion to the mirror. Scan frequencies up to 1600 Hz for a 0.5×0.5 cm mirror moving through a 5° peak-to-peak scan angle have been achieved.

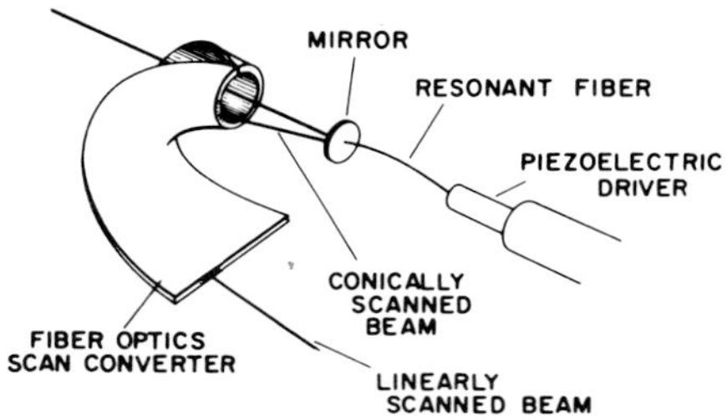

Fig. 1. Light scanned into a cone is converted to a linear scan through a fiber optics bundle.

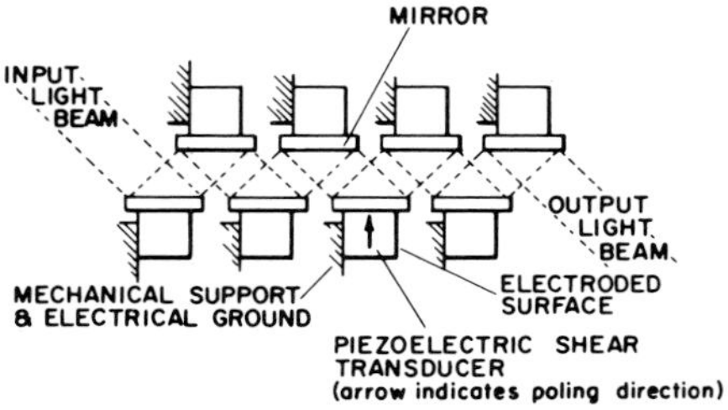

Fig. 2. A multiple reflection deflector uses shear-mode transducers to tilt the mirrors.

Another resonant device, Fig. 1, makes use of a fiber optics bundle to convert a conical scan to a linear scan [9], [10]. In this scheme a mirror, attached to the end of a thin quartz rod, is driven in a precessing motion by a piezoelectric transducer on the opposite end of the rod. Light reflected from the mirror is scanned into a cone which is focused on the ends of a circular fiber optic bundle. The other end of the bundle is flattened to form a line so that the emerging light scans across the line once for each cycle of the mirror. The device was designed for resonance at 15 750 Hz and a resolution of 700 spots.

Wide-band reflection scanning has been achieved by Schlafer and Fowler [11] using mirrors attached to piezoelectric shear transducers, as shown in Fig. 2. These transducers develop a shear strain in response to an electric field applied perpendicular to their poling direction. The induced shearing action causes the mirror to tilt through an angle proportional to the applied field. Multiple mirror structures are employed to increase the scan angle of the beam. With presently available piezoelectric materials, peak-to-peak angular motions of 0.05° for a single mirror are possible. The relative sizes of the mechanical components here again govern the bandwidth by determining the mechanical resonance frequency of the mirror-driver combination. Units with half-inch-square mirrors have been made to operate over a bandwidth from direct current to 17 kHz.

All of the reflection scanning techniques so far discussed lend themselves to multiple mirror configurations. Here the light beam is passed sequentially through a number of identical reflection scanners, moving in synchronism, to increase the scan angle and, thus, the resolution. This technique is particularly attractive when individual units are capable of only small-angle scanning as with the shear-element-driven mirror or the galvanometer and torsional fork scanners at higher frequencies. Mirrors can not be ganged indefinitely, however, because the input beam diameter must be reduced as the number of mirrors increases to prevent vignetting of the deflected beam by the edge of the last mirror. Eventually, the reduction in resolution due to the small beam diameter outweighs the advantages of extra mirrors. The optimum length of a multiple mirror structure to give maximum resolution is related to the mirror size and angular deflection per unit optical path length. This relation, alluded to in the Appendix, is

$$L_{\text{opt}} = W\sqrt{\frac{2}{3KW}}$$

$$N_{\max} = \frac{W}{\epsilon\lambda}\sqrt{(32/27)KW}$$

where L is the optical path length, W the input aperture, and KW the deflection per unit optical path length. It is shown in the Appendix that N may be increased by a factor of $\sqrt{2}$ if the light is focused through the deflecting structure such that the focal point lies (3/2) L from the input aperture.

III. Variable Refractors

Both of the basic refraction phenomena, refraction at a dielectric interface and refraction by an index gradient, have been used in deflection schemes. The first of these has been most often utilized in the form of a prism of variable refractive index. A light beam traversing the prism is deviated by an amount depending upon the prism shape, orientation, and refractive index. Chen et al. [12] have found that the resolution available from an isosceles-shaped prism is maximum when the beam passes through at the minimum deviation angle. The resolution is given as

$$N = \Delta n \frac{l}{\epsilon\lambda}\left(\frac{w}{W}\right), \tag{2}$$

where Δn is the induced change in refractive index, l the base length of the prism, and w/W the ratio of the beamwidth to input aperture of the prism.

Refraction also takes place when a gradient of index exists in the propagation media perpendicular to the wavefront normal. If this is a linear gradient the wavefront remains planar (for small refraction angles) and the ray trajectory is bent in the direction of the gradient. This process is depicted in Fig. 3. The angle of the ray after propagating a distance L is given, to a good approximation, by [13]

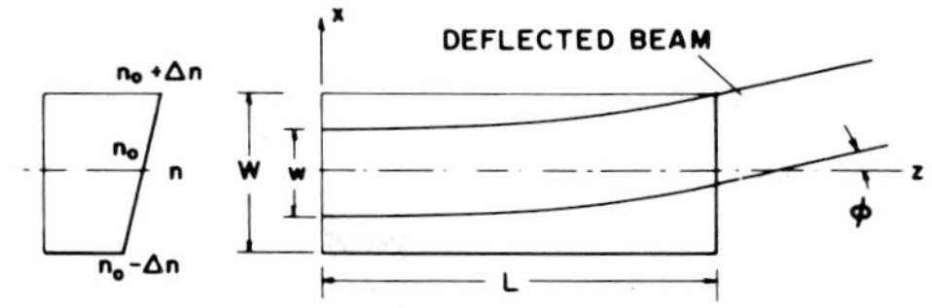

Fig. 3. A beam of light passing through a media with an index gradient normal to the propagation direction is refracted in the direction of the gradient.

$$\phi = L\frac{dn}{dx}\,. \tag{3}$$

Using this result, and referring to Fig. 3, the resolution may be found from (1) to be

$$N = 2\Delta n(L/\epsilon\lambda)(w/W). \tag{4}$$

In both the case of the prism and the refractive index gradient the factor w/W may be made nearly unity if L is small. In most cases, however, Δn will be small, and it may be advantageous to make L large. This can be done in the prism by directly increasing the base length or by cascading prisms [12]. As L is increased the deflection of the beam inside the device becomes appreciable, and vignetting at the output aperture restricts the beamwidth to less than the zero deflection full aperture W. A point is finally reached, in trading beamwidth for optical path length, for which the resolution is maximum.

This condition is analogous to the resolution optimization problem mentioned above for multiple mirror systems and is treated in the Appendix.

Several approaches have been used to achieve the variation of refractive index necessary for a refractive deflector. Chen et al. [12], [14], and Haas, Johannes, and Cholet [15] have used the quadratic electrooptic effect in prisms of potassium tantalate niobate (KTN) and $BaTiO_3$. While these materials are capable of index changes of the order of $\Delta n = 5(10)^{-3}$, their full potential resolution has not yet been realized due to the poor optical quality of available crystals. Other electrooptic materials, such as deuterated potassium dihydrogen phosphate (KD*P), have smaller effects ($\Delta n \cong 10^{-4}$) but are more nearly perfect optically. These materials can be expected to perform at frequencies extending into the microwave range [14], [15], however, power considerations and heating effects will limit their practical use to about 10^6 Hz.

By passing current through a prism of CdS, Kalibjian et al. [17] have obtained deflection utilizing the temperature-induced shift of the absorption edge. A similar effect has been employed by Liu and Walters [18] to produce

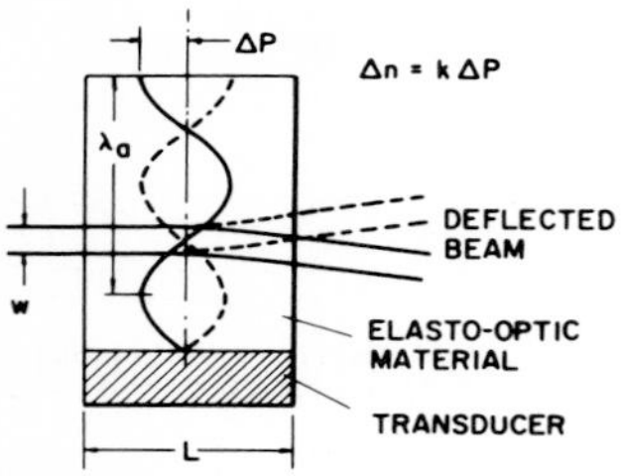

Fig. 4. The variation of refractive index with pressure *P* is used in an acoustic standing-wave cell to form index gradients.

linear index gradients in rectangular samples of GaAs. Although substantial changes of index may be obtained by this method, response times are generally slow and power dissipation in the crystal is a problem. It has been proposed that the shift in absorption edge with electric field (Franz-Keldysh effect) be utilized for rapid beam deflection [19].

Linear refractive index gradients have been produced electrooptically by Fowler, Buhrer, and Bloom [13] using electrodes shaped to produce a quadratic field in a bar of KDP. It may also be possible to produce substantial index gradients in certain materials through uneven optical pumping [20].

Acoustic waves propagating in a transparent medium give rise to sinusoidal index variations through the elasto-optic effect. Over portions of these sine waves the index gradient may be considered linear and used for deflection. Figure 4 shows a light beam traversing an ultrasonic deflection cell at the node of an acoustic standing wave. Traveling- and standing-wave versions of this technique have been demonstrated by a number of investigators [21]–[25]. Because the optical aperture is limited to a small fraction of the acoustic wavelength λ_a, resolution depends primarily on being able to obtain large changes of index at realistic pressures. Resonant structures such as these are necessarily narrow band, but scanning frequencies may extend to the megahertz region [23].

IV. Birefringent Deflection

The generalized birefringent deflection cell consists of a polarization modulation element in conjunction with a birefringent polarization discriminator. In operation, the polarization state of the incoming light beam is varied by the modulator, and this variation is converted by the discriminator to an angular or linear displacement of the beam. The most popular embodiment of this principle has been the digital deflector wherein the modulator acts as a polarization switch. Two distinct beams are derived in the birefringent discriminator, corresponding to the ordinary and extraordinary rays, as the polarization is switched between two orthogonal states. This is illustrated

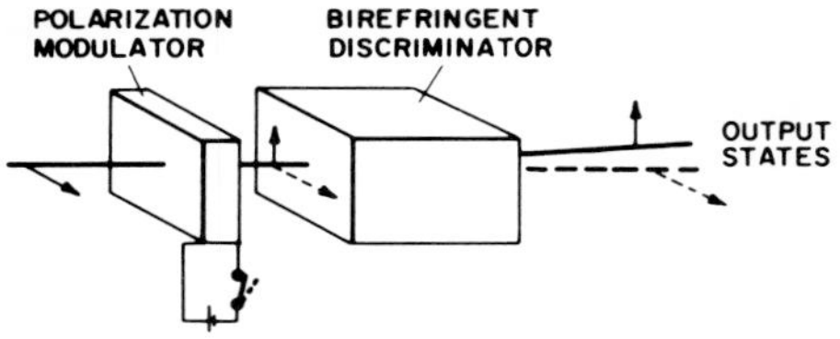

Fig. 5. Binary birefringent deflector uses the modulator as a polarization switch.

in Fig. 5. Binary cells of this type may be cascaded *n* times to obtain 2^n distinct beam positions at the output.

For rapid switching the polarization modulator is normally an electrooptic cell, with an electrically controllable birefringence, arranged to produce either 0° or 90° rotation of the plane of polarization, depending upon the applied signal. Birefringent calcite crystals have been used as polarization discriminators by Kulcke et al. [26], [27], Nelson [28], and Schmidt [29], while Tabor [30] and Soref and McMahon [31] have proposed Wollaston prisms for this purpose.

By using cascaded binary cells of this type to give a two-dimensional array, resolutions of greater than 10^6 seem practical with present technology. Lee and Moskowitz [32] have analyzed the feasibility of even higher resolution systems with respect to optical tolerances and signal-to-noise characteristics. Scanning rates are determined by the switching speeds and switching rates of the individual polarization switches. The scanning rate is ultimately limited by the power dissipation in the electro-optic crystals and is set at about 10^6 deflections/second for presently available materials.

Other schemes for birefringent deflection employ conical refraction [33]–[35] or optical activity [35] for the discriminating function. In this technique the polarization modulator is made to scan continuously through all linear polarization states which are then separated spatially in the discriminator. With either conical refraction or optical activity approximately two resolvable positions are available from each discriminator element. If these elements are cascaded and interspersed with passive polarizers (only one modulator is needed), resolution can be multiplied as before; however, only at the expense of light intensity. Although this system offers the advantage over the digital technique of lower power requirements, light loss soon becomes intolerable.

V. Interference Deflection

Through the use of multiple-beam interference effects, scanning devices may be built which require a change in optical path length of only one wavelength to scan through all of the resolvable positions. In the previously described techniques the same variation in the active element would yield one resolution position.

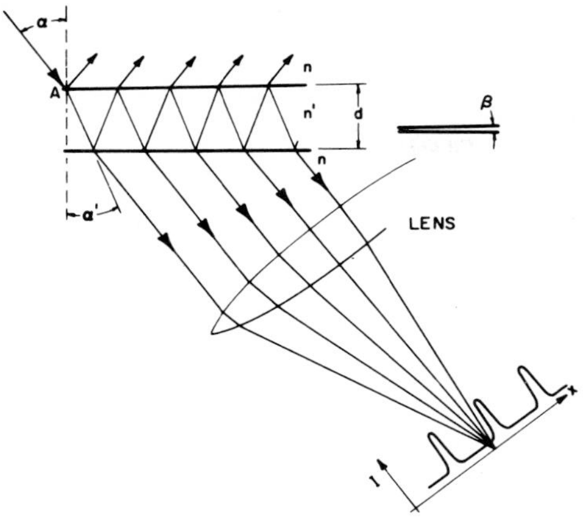

Fig. 6. Multiple beams from a two mirror interferometer, with wedge angle β, combine to form a fringe system which may be scanned laterally.

In the interference deflection method the beam to be scanned is incident on a set of nearly parallel mirrors which form an interferometer, as shown in Fig. 6. Those rays which are transmitted after multiple reflections are collected by a lens and focused on a screen. The phase relations of the transmitted beams are such that they interfere to give a set of narrow fringes on the screen whose intensity distribution is proportional to [36]

$$I \sim \frac{1}{1 + F \sin \delta/2}, \tag{5}$$

where $\delta = 4\pi(d+\beta x)n' \cos \alpha'/\lambda$ and F is the finesse of the system.

If β is adjusted such that one fringe appears in the field, a change in phase of one-half wavelength in the cavity, i.e., δ changes by 2π, will cause this fringe to be scanned across the field. This phase change can be brought about through variation of the cavity length d or the refractive index n'.

The resolution for such a deflection system is determined by the ratio of the fringe width to fringe space or the finesse

$$N = \frac{\pi\sqrt{R}}{1 - R}, \tag{6}$$

where R is the reflectivity of the mirrors.

It is pointed out by Buck and Holland [37] that scanning rates will ultimately be limited by the time needed to re-establish the field in the cavity after deflecting to a new position. In their arrangement α is zero and the fringe system is localized at the output mirror. Since, for resolutions exceeding $N=200$, the total light in the fringe drops below 1 percent of the incident light, they suggest that the input mirror also serve as one mirror of a laser cavity.

Korpel [38] has overcome this problem by bringing the light into the cavity through an aperture in the mirror at A and adjusting α so that the beam remains in the cavity after the first reflection. In this way one of the mirrors may be made totally reflecting and, neglecting absorption, all of the power may be extracted in the fringe system.

Interference phenomena also play a role in electrooptic grating [39] and acoustic grating [40] deflection systems. This type of deflector is described in detail elsewhere in this issue.

VI. Comparison of Deflection Techniques

All of the deflection techniques described in this paper utilize some method for avoiding light loss (e.g., multiple dielectric coated mirrors, Brewster angle refraction, Bragg angle diffraction, anti-reflection film, and transparent electrodes). These methods can all be made quite effective so that, in principle, there is no reason to reject any of the techniques on the basis of light loss. Furthermore, by using identical deflection devices in tandem, one can sometimes obtain increased deflection resolution with a higher, but still acceptable, loss.

Phase front distortion must be reduced to negligible values for all components used in a high-resolution deflection system. In principle, all of the deflection techniques described in this paper can provide nearly diffraction-limited performance. In practice, however, optical distortion is at present a problem with: a) electrooptic refractors using new high-sensitivity materials, such as KTN; b) refractors at high frequencies for which dielectric losses heat the refractive medium nonuniformly; c) acoustic standing-wave refractors utilizing sinusoidal standing waves.

All of the deflection techniques can be made to operate over wide optical wavelength ranges, but with varying degrees of color separation. Only the variable reflectors have zero optical dispersion and deflection sensitivities which are independent of the wavelength. This is an important advantage for multicolor projection system applications, since it is much easier to align undeflected beams and pass them through a single beam deflector than to register separately scanned beams.

For many applications the deflection must be an accurately prescribed function of the deflection signal voltage. There are two ways of achieving accurate deflection: a) using a deflection technique which provides adequate precision and stability, and b) forcing the required precision by using an imprecise deflector with a precise and stable deflection sensor in a closed-loop automatic deflection control servomechanism. Deflection sensing can be accomplished by passing the deflected beam through a beam splitter so that a small portion is reflected to the side into an accurate deflection sensor, such as an image dissector or a split-field ratio photodetector.

Direct-drive reflectors and refractors based on electrooptic or piezoelectric effects generally suffer from nonlinearities and strong temperature dependence. To some extent both of these weaknesses can be overcome by processing the input signal so that the applied electrical charge is proportional to the deflection signal voltage. This is effective because both the electrooptic change of refractive index and the piezoelectric shear strain are proportional to the induced polarization to an accuracy of about 0.25 percent, at least an order of magnitude better than the proportionality to the deflection voltage. Another way to get around nonlinearities, where accurate sinusoidal deflection is applicable, is to operate the deflector at a strong acoustic resonance, taking care that the harmonics are not also resonant.

Among the techniques mentioned in this paper, only the tandem birefringent light switch and the acoustic grating provide deflection angles which are directly related to the applied deflection signal and independent of drive signal nonlinearity, frequency distortion, and heating effects. These techniques are also applicable over a wide frequency range, making them well suited to random-access deflection applications. At present, however, material inefficiencies at high switching rates and high acoustic frequencies are a major problem with these devices.

For many applications a triggered sawtooth waveform is needed with high resolution, a high repetition rate, and short retrace time. The direct approach is to use a wide-band deflector, such as a piezoelectrically driven mirror structure or an electrooptic refractor, driven by a sawtooth waveform. However, driven mirror structures made small enough to provide adequate bandwidth have limited resolution and, in addition, the steep retrace waveform induces a strong acoustic ringing. Electrooptic refractors can be made nearly free of ringing, but the resolution is even lower. Ballistic scanners, such as a moving coil mirror drive operated above the lowest mechanical resonant frequency, can be made with increased aperture. Much of the advantage, however, is lost by the fact that a ballistic scanner responds to the integral of the signal, and thus the peak deflection decreases at higher frequencies.

Rotating mirrors or prisms also offer a direct means for achieving periodic sawtooth scans, but each trace cannot be triggered separately and, therefore, synchronization to an external time base requires good phase and frequency stability of both the deflector and the external time base. Indirect sawtooth scanning based on the use of resonant sinusoidal drives and optical scan conversion is subject to this same limitation. Where optical scan conversion is used to achieve a linear scan of a modulated beam with a nonlinear scan motion, one has the alternative of using electrical scan conversion of the modulation signal to accommodate the nonlinear scan. This eliminates the synchronization problem, but the varying scan rate gives rise to objectional variations in average brightness across the scan line, although this could be compensated by appropriate intensity modulation of the beam.

Triggered high-resolution fast sawtooth scans can also be achieved with a swept-frequency acoustic grating. This method can provide separate triggering of each scan line and is free of the acoustic resonance problems of the previously mentioned direct scanning methods. Unlike the mirror devices, however, it cannot be used to scan a single multicolor beam because of the large variation of deflection sensitivity with wavelength.

No one of the deflection techniques described in this paper is presently best suited for a majority of applications, and even the best choices for particular applications have serious intrinsic and practical limitations. However, this field is quite new, and the increasing interest in the problems of optical deflection will undoubtedly lead to the development of improved deflection techniques and materials.

Appendix

Distributed Deflection Systems

In many deflection techniques the deflection is distributed along the light path in a continuous or quasi-continuous (e.g., multiple reflection) fashion such as in Fig. 3. Since the resolution is proportional to the product of the beamwidth, and the accumulated deflection angle ϕ, it is natural to make w and the optical path length L as large as possible. However, these parameters cannot be increased arbitrarily since the deflection of the beam within the device itself will eventually cause it to strike the edge of the exit aperture. This situation may be improved somewhat by deflecting a converging beam, as in Fig. 7, allowing greater beam swing at the exit aperture.

If the largest attainable deflection per unit optical path length is specified, there exists an optimum relation between the deflector size and beam convergence for which resolution is maximized. This relation is found, with the help of Fig. 7, as follows.

If $\phi(z)$ is the angle which any ray makes with the z-axis then

$$\frac{dx}{dz} = \phi(z) \tag{7}$$

using the small angle approximation.

It is assumed that a constant deflection per unit length K exists such that

$$\frac{d\phi(z)}{dz} = K, \tag{8}$$

giving

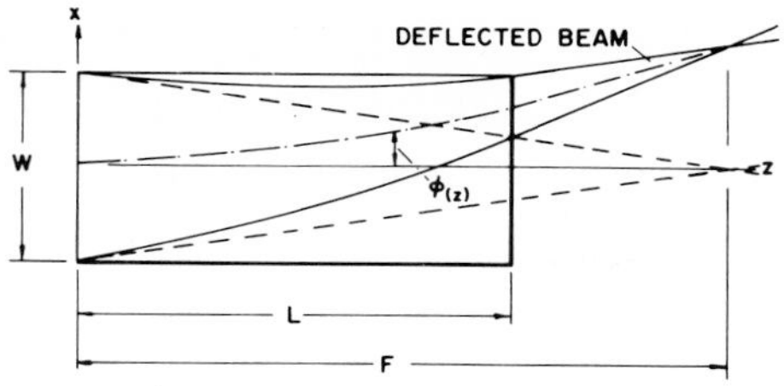

Fig. 7. Distributed deflection of a focused beam. Dashed lines indicate undeflected rays.

$$\phi(z) = Kz + \phi_i \tag{9}$$

where ϕ_i is the entrance angle of the ray.

When the extreme (top) ray undergoes greatest deflection it just grazes the exit aperture at $z = L$. At this plane the above equations predict

$$\phi_{(L)} = KL + \phi_i = -\phi_i,$$

or

$$L = \frac{-2\phi_i}{K} = \frac{W}{KF}. \tag{10}$$

where, again, the small angle approximation has been taken and F is defined in Fig. 7. This is the maximum value L may assume once the other parameters have been specified.

The incremental resolution expression for a beam of half angle divergence $\theta = \epsilon\lambda/w$, being deflected bilaterally through an angle $\pm d\phi$, may be written from (1) and (8)

$$dN = \frac{2d\phi}{\theta} = \frac{2w_{(z)}}{\epsilon\lambda} d\phi$$

$$= \frac{2w_{(z)}}{\epsilon\lambda} Kdz. \tag{11}$$

Here $w_{(z)} = (F - z)W/F$ is the width of the beam subject to a deflection $d\phi$. The overall resolution is determined from the accumulated deflection angle beamwidth product through the deflector, found by integrating (11) over the maximum length $L = W/KF$

$$N = \frac{W^2}{F}\left(1 - \frac{W}{2KF^2}\right) \tag{12}$$

Equation (12) may now be maximized with respect to F to give

$$N_{\max} = \frac{W}{\epsilon\lambda}\sqrt{\frac{32}{27}KW}$$

$$L_{\text{opt}} = W\sqrt{\frac{2}{3KW}} = \frac{2}{3}F. \tag{13}$$

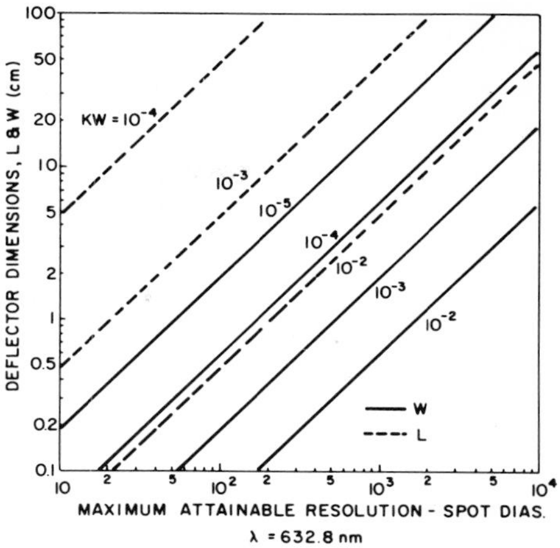

Fig. 8. Dimensions L (dashed) and W (solid) of a distributed deflector as a function of resolution for the parameter KW.

A similar result may be derived for collimated light yielding values for $N_{\max}$ and L_{opt} which are smaller by $1/\sqrt{2}$. For most refractive configurations $KW = 2\Delta n$ and is independent of the deflector dimensions. Figure 8 is a plot of (13) which shows how large W and L must become to achieve a given resolution N with a given maximum value of the parameter KW. Normally, a value is specified for N and the corresponding optimum deflector dimensions are read on the ordinate for a particular value of KW.

References

[1] R. V. Pole, R. A. Myers, and J. Nuñez, "Bidirectional electrically switched laser," *Appl. Opt.*, vol. 4, pp. 119–121, January 1965.

[2] R. V. Pole, R. A. Myers, W. Wieder, and E. S. Barrekette, "Laser deflection and scanning," in *Optical and Electro-optical Information Processing*, J. T. Tippett et al. Eds. Cambridge, Mass.: M.I.T. Press, 1965, ch. 21.

[3] E. S. Kohn and V. J. Fowler, "An internally scanned laser," presented at the 1966 Internat'l Quantum Electronics Conference, Phoenix, Ariz.

[4] R. A. Meyers, R. V. Pole, and J. Nuñez, "Laser deflection with the conjugate plano-concentric resonator," *Appl. Opt.*, vol. 4, pp. 140–141, January 1965.

[5] H. Kogelnik and T. Li, "Laser beams and resonators," this issue.

[6] J. G. Skinner, "Comment on light beam deflectors," *Appl. Opt.*, vol. 3, p. 1504, December 1964.

[7] Bulletin 7365, Consolidated Electrodynamics Corporation, Monrovia, Calif.

[8] F. Dostal, "The fork as a scanner: a new twist," *Electronic Communicator*, vol. 1, pp. 4–5, January 1966.

[9] C. M. Alsabrook, "A multicolor laser display," *18th Annual National Aerospace Electronics Conference*, pp. 325–331, May 1966.

[10] C. E. Baker and A. D. Rugari, "The laser display," *1965 Proc. Society for Information Display, 6th Nat'l Symp. on Information Display*, p. 85.

[11] J. Schlafer and V. J. Fowler, "A precision, high speed, optical beam steerer," presented at the 1965 Internat'l Electron Devices Meeting.
[12] F. S. Chen, J. E. Geusic, S. K. Kurtz, J. G. Skinner, and S. H. Wemple, "Light modulation and beam deflection with potassium tantalate-niobate crystals," *J. Appl. Phys.*, vol. 37, pp. 388–398, January 1966.
[13] V. J. Fowler, C. F. Buhrer, and L. R. Bloom, "Electro-optic light beam deflector," *Proc. IEEE* (*Correspondence*), vol. 52, pp. 193–194, February 1964.
[14] F. S. Chen, J. E. Geusic, S. K. Kurtz, J. G. Skinner, and S. H. Wemple, "The use of Perovskite paraelectrics in beam deflectors and light modulators," *Proc. IEEE* (*Correspondence*), vol. 52, pp. 1258–1259, October 1964.
[15] W. Haas, R. Johannes, and P. Cholet, "Light beam deflection using the Kerr effect in single crystal prisms of $BaTiO_3$," *Appl. Opt.*, vol. 3, pp. 988–989, August 1964.
[16] I. P. Kaminow, "Microwave modulation of the electro-optic effect in KH_2PO_4," *Phys. Rev. Lett.*, vol. 6, pp. 528–530, May 15, 1961.
[17] R. Kalibjian, T. Huen, C. Maninger, and J. Yee, "Laser deflection modulation in a CdS prism," *Proc. IEEE* (*Correspondence*), vol. 53, p. 539, May 1965.
[18] S. G. Liu and W. L. Walters, "Optical beam deflection by pulsed temperature gradients in bulk GaAs," *Proc. IEEE* (*Correspondence*), vol. 53, pp. 522–523, May 1965.
[19] K. W. Boer, "Franz-Keldysh effect for appreciable deflection of light beams," *Physica Status Solidi*, vol. 8, pp. K179–K180, 1965.
[20] U. J. Schmidt, "The problems of light beam deflection at high frequencies," *Proc. Symp. on Optical Processing of Information*, D. K. Pollack et al., Eds. Baltimore, Md.: Spartan, 1963, pp. 98–103.
[21] A. J. Giarola and T. R. Billeter, "Electroacoustic deflection of a coherent light beam," *Proc. IEEE* (*Correspondence*), vol. 51, pp. 1150–1151, August 1963.
[22] R. Lipnick, A. Reich, and G. A. Schoen, "Nonmechanical scanning of light using acoustic waves," *Proc. IEEE* (*Correspondence*), vol. 52, pp. 853–854, July 1964.
[23] R. Lipnick, A. Reich, and G. A. Schoen, "Nonmechanical scanning of light in one and two dimensions," *Proc. IEEE* (*Correspondence*), vol. 53, p. 321, March 1965.
[24] H. G. Aas and R. K. Erf, "Application of ultrasonic standing waves to the generation of optical beam scanning," *J. Acous. Soc. Am.*, vol. 36, pp. 1906–1913, October 1964.
[25] C. D. LaFond, "Optical imaging unit shown feasible," *Missiles and Rockets*, pp. 32–39, June 7, 1965.
[26] W. Kulcke, T. J. Harris, K. Kosanke, and E. Max, "A fast, digital-indexed light deflector," *IBM J.*, vol. 8, pp. 64–67, January 1964.
[27] W. Kulcke, K. Kosanke, E. Max, H. Fleisher, and T. J. Harris, "Convergent beam digital light deflector," *Optical and Electro-optical Information Processing*, J. T. Tippett et al., Eds. Cambridge, Mass.: M.I.T. Press, ch. 23, 1965.
[28] T. J. Nelson, "Digital light deflection," *Bell Sys. Tech. J.*, vol. 43, pp. 821–845, May 1964.
[29] U. J. Schmidt, "A high speed digital light beam deflector," *Phys. Lett.*, vol. 12, pp. 205–206, October 1964.
[30] W. J. Tabor, "The use of Wollaston prisms for a high-capacity digital light deflector," *Bell Sys. Tech. J.*, vol. 43, pp. 1153–1154, May 1964.
[31] R. A. Soref and D. H. McMahon, "Optical design of Wollaston-prism digital light deflectors," *Appl. Opt.*, vol. 5, pp. 425–434, March 1966.
[32] R. K. Lee, Jr. and F. Moskowitz, "Transmission and self-generated noise characteristics of polarization scanned digital optical systems," *Appl. Opt.*, vol. 3, pp. 1305–1310, November 1964.
[33] A. Bromley, "High-power light flux resulting from bunching of light wave packets," *Appl. Phys. Lett.*, vol. 5, pp. 210–212, November 1964.
[34] R. Burns, "On the possibility of using conical refraction phenomena for laser beam steering," *Appl. Opt.*, vol. 3, pp. 1505–1506, December 1964.
[35] W. Haas and R. Johannes, "Light beam scanning using conical refraction and optical activity," *Appl. Opt.*, vol. 5, pp. 1088–1089, June 1966.
[36] M. Born and E. Wolf, *Principles of Optics*, 2nd ed. New York: MacMillan, 1964, ch. 7.
[37] W. E. Buck and T. E. Holland, "Optical beam deflector," *Appl. Phys. Letts.*, vol. 8, pp. 198–199, April 1966.
[38] A. Korpel, "Phased array type scanning of a laser beam," *Proc. IEEE* (*Correspondence*), vol. 53, pp. 1666–1667, October 1965.
[39] M. G. Cohen and E. I. Gordon, "Electro-optic [$KTa_xNb_{1-x}O_3$ (KTN)] grating for light beam modulation and deflection," *Appl. Physics Lett.*, vol. 5, pp. 181–182, May 1964.
[40] A. Korpel, R. Adler, P. Desmares, and T. M. Smith, "An ultrasonic light deflection system," *IEEE J. of Quantum Electronics* (*Correspondence*), pp. 60–61, April 1965.

NANOSECOND BASEBAND OPTICAL-DIFFRACTION MODULATOR

Indexing terms: Electro-optical effects, Optical modulation, Modulators, Thin-film circuits

Latest measurements on an electro-optic diffraction modulator show optical-pulse risetimes of 1·5 ns with a drive of only 25 V and 6 nJ per pulse. The modulator lends itself to integration into thin-film optical circuits and is insensitive to temperature variations. Means of improving the performance still further are available.

This letter presents the latest results of a diffraction-type laser modulator which has been previously described.[1] Optical-pulse risetimes of 1·5 ns are obtained with a drive voltage of around 25 V, leading to a low drive-pulse energy requirement. The present design requires 6 nJ per pulse; this design is not optimised, and considerable improvement in performance will be attainable. A further important feature is the insensitivity to temperature variations. The construction lends itself to inclusion in thin-film planar optical circuits.

The basic arrangement is shown in Fig. 1. The lithium-niobate crystal is 0·15 × 5 × 10 mm. An interdigital electrode structure, with a 300 μm pitch, deposited by photolithography provides the spatially periodic electric field E_z which changes the refractive index of the crystal for light travelling in the y direction and polarised in the z direction. It should be noted that application of E_z does not rotate the index ellipsoid, and thus the light retains its z polarisation while passing through the crystal.

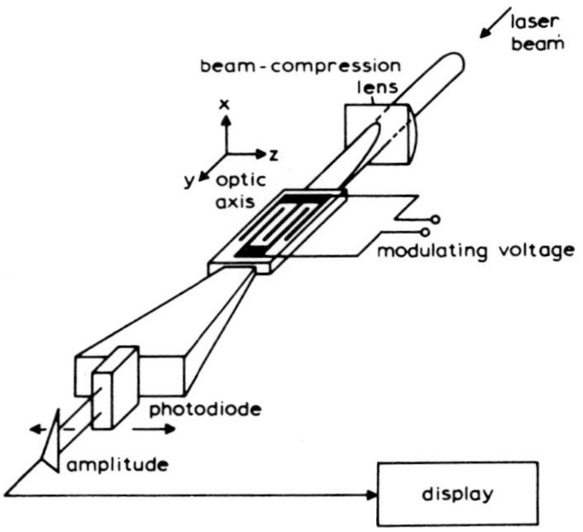

Fig. 1 *Experimental arrangement*

The electric field E_z produces a spatially periodic variation of refractive index in the z direction, causing the light to be diffracted into orders, the first occurring at an angle $\theta = \lambda/p$, where λ is the wavelength of light and p is the electrode pitch. With a helium-neon laser and the present pitch, $\theta = 2$ mrad. The diffracted beams are resolved easily by a photodiode placed 1 m from the modulator. Fig. 2 shows measured diffraction patterns for two values of applied modulating voltage: zero voltage (curve *a*) and 25 V (curve *b*), which gives an extinction ratio of 25 dB.

It is assumed, as a first approximation, that the emergent beam has constant amplitude but a sinusoidally corrugated phase front. It is then easy to calculate the intensity of the beam in the far-field region, using simple linear-array theory. The intensity on the axis is given simply by $J_0^2(\alpha V)$ where J_0 is the zero-order Bessel function of the first kind, α is a constant and V is the modulating voltage. Measurements of beam intensity against voltage V confirm this up to the first extinction, after which the measured intensity is less than the theoretical value. Reflection losses (which could be reduced by blooming) from the faces of the crystal account for a measured insertion loss of 1·5 dB.

Linear intensity modulation of the laser beam is obtained by biasing the modulating voltage to the linear part of the $J_0^2(\alpha V)$ curve. Measurements at 5 kHz show that 5·2 V r.m.s. with a bias of 12·5 V, produces 65% intensity modulation with 3% total harmonic distortion measured at the output of a photodiode. Measurements at 100 MHz give similar results.

Pulse modulation is obtained with 25 V pulses applied to the electrodes. Fig. 3 shows a measured optical-pulse risetime of 1·5 ns. At present, we are limited by speed of both the driving and detection circuits. The transit time (0·1 ns) through the crystal will, of course, provide a limit to the performance. There are, presumably, losses associated with the excitation of acoustic waves, but they are small enough not to have any observable effect on the pulse shape.

The pulsed performance is improved by applying d.c. bias. For example, if 5 V bias is applied, only 20 V drive is needed to extinguish the beam on the axis, and the required energy per pulse is reduced from 6 nJ to 4 nJ. This improvement is

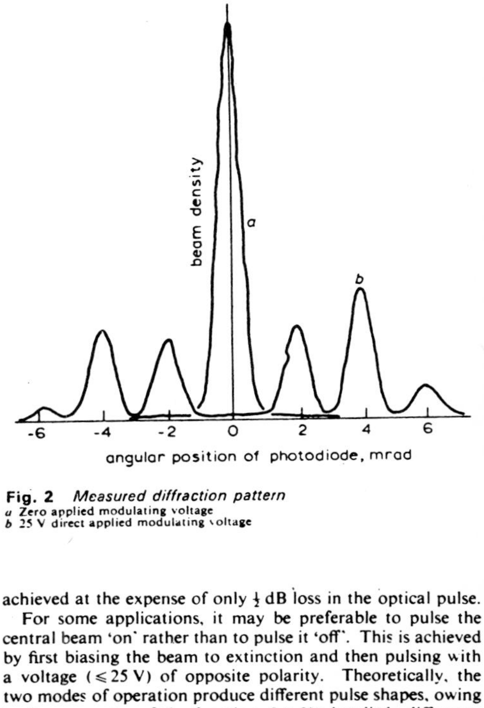

Fig. 2 *Measured diffraction pattern*
a Zero applied modulating voltage
b 25 V direct applied modulating voltage

achieved at the expense of only ½ dB loss in the optical pulse.

For some applications, it may be preferable to pulse the central beam 'on' rather than to pulse it 'off'. This is achieved by first biasing the beam to extinction and then pulsing with a voltage (≤ 25 V) of opposite polarity. Theoretically, the two modes of operation produce different pulse shapes, owing to the assymetry of the function $J_0(\alpha V)$, but little difference is observed experimentally.

Variations in temperature have only a small effect on the modulator; the electro-optic coefficients themselves vary only slightly with temperature.[2] Measurements show that the extinction ratio (measured at d.c.) varies by only ± 1 dB about the nominal 25 dB as the temperature is raised 10 K above ambient.

The present pitch could be drastically reduced, and it is instructive to consider its effect on the performance. The beam-diffraction angle would be increased, the electric field would penetrate less into the crystal, so that the laser beam would have to travel much nearer to the electrodes. In the extreme case, this could be effected by so reducing the thickness of the crystal that it behaves as a thin-film waveguide.[3, 4]

More important still is that the required voltage is reduced and that the capacitance per unit pitch is unaltered. Thus, if the number of pitches per beamwidth remains constant, the required energy is reduced. A modest reduction in pitch of one half would reduce the present required energy per pulse from 6 nJ to 1·5 nJ.

Work is continuing on this type of device and full details will be published elsewhere.

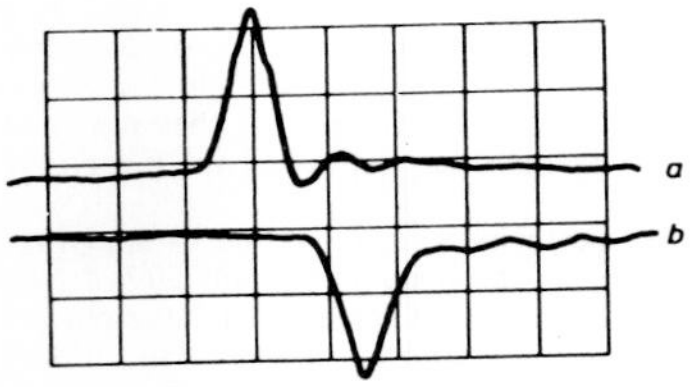

Fig. 3 *Pulse waveforms*
a Modulating pulse at electrodes. Vectical scale: 10 V /division
b Optical pulse at output of amplifier
Horizontal scale: 5 ns /division

Acknowledgments: The authors wish to thank Prof. E. A. Ash for stimulating discussions and the UK Science Research Council for financial support. M. A. R. P. de Barros is the recipient of a Calouste Gulbenkian Fellowship.

M. A. R. P. DE BARROS
M. G. F. WILSON

28th April 1971

Department of Electronic & Electrical Engineering
University College London
Torrington Place, London WC1, England

References

1 ST. LEDGER, J. F., and ASH, E. A.: 'Laser-beam modulation using grating diffraction effects', *Electron. Lett.*, 1968, **4**, pp. 99–100
2 LANDOLT-BORNSTEIN: 'Numerical data and functional relationships in science and technology—Group III, Vol. 2' (Springer, 1969)
3 TIEN, P. K., ULRICH, R., and MARTIN, R. J.: 'Modes of propagating light waves in thin deposited semiconductor films', *Appl. Phys. Lett.*, 1969, **14**, pp. 291–294
4 DAKSS, M. L., KUHN, L., HEIDRICH, P. F., and SCOTT, B. A.: 'Grating coupler for efficient excitation of optical guided waves in thin films', *ibid.*, 1970, **16**, pp. 523–525

Note: More details are given in M.A.R.P. de Barros and M.G.F. Wilson, High-speed electro-optic diffraction modulator for baseband operation, *Proc. IEE* (*London*) **119**, 807–814 (1972).

Reprinted from *Electron. Lett.* **7**, 267 (1971).

DIGITAL ELECTRO-OPTIC GRATING DEFLECTOR AND MODULATOR

J. M. Hammer
RCA Laboratories, Princeton, New Jersey 08540
(Received 22 October 1970)

A new method of laser light deflection and modulation based on diffraction by electro-optic phase gratings has been demonstrated. The method is applicable to thin-film light guides, requires relatively low power for high-speed operation, and is capable of high diffraction efficiency.

A novel method of producing laser light deflection and modulation has been demonstrated. The method uses simple conducting electrode patterns deposited on thin slabs or films of electro-optic crystals to produce voltage-controlled optical phase or polarization gratings. This approach yields high diffraction efficiency and modulation depth with modest power consumption and is readily adapted to deflect and modulate light traveling in thin-film optical wave guides.[1] In addition, a separate electrode pattern may be provided for each output light position to obtain digital control.

The experimental arrangement is shown in Fig. 1. A z-cut [001] $LiNbO_3$ [2] wafer is provided with columns of electrodes on the top surface and a ground plane on the bottom. The elements of a single column are connected by a common bus. Voltage applied between a single column and the ground plane produces the grating characteristic of that column. The y periodic electric field causes periodic variation in refractive index for a sheet of light traveling in the x direction. The z polarization component of the light encounters a simple periodic phase change. Thus, light is diffracted into grating orders along the y direction. The diffracted light is a sheet in the same plane as the undiffracted light.

For the case of rectangular electrodes spaced so that $a = d/2 = t$ (see Fig. 1) the index variation in the y direction will be that of a "square wave" near the upper surface. Near the ground plane the index will be uniform. In the mid-plane, the in-

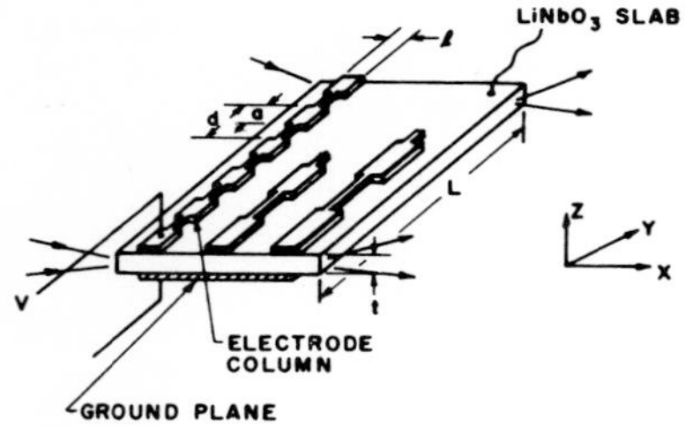

FIG. 1. Digital electro-optic grating. Three electrode columns are shown. Light travels along the x axis. Application of voltage to one of the columns diffracts the light parallel to the y direction. The intensities of the various diffraction orders are characteristic of the periodicity of the particular column and of the magnitude of the voltage.

dex variation will approximate a sinusoidal function. By solving for the fields for each of these regions and taking a linear average of intensities, the relative far-field intensity variation of the grating orders is estimated by Eq. (1), [3]

$$I/I_0 = \begin{cases} \frac{1}{3}\{1 + [J_0(\phi)]^2 + (1+\cos\phi)/2\}; & n = 0 \\ \frac{1}{3}\{[J_n(\phi)]^2 + 2(1-\cos\phi)/n^2\pi^2\}; & n = 1, 3, 5, \cdots, \\ \frac{1}{3}[J_n(\phi)]^2; & n = 2, 4, 6, \cdots \end{cases} \tag{1}$$

where ϕ is the relative phase shift produced by the electro-optic effect. For a transverse linear electro-optic material with half-wave voltage $V_{\lambda/2}$ and applied voltage V,

$$\phi = \pi(l/t)(V/V_{\lambda/2}). \tag{2}$$

In broadband pulse operation it is difficult to match the load to the generator. Thus, the reactive power P is a realistic measure of the required operating power. Near-optimum conditions are obtained when $\phi = \pi$. Here $V = (t/l)V_{\lambda/2}$ and the reactive power may be shown to be

$$P = \epsilon_0\epsilon_r(Lt/4l)V_{\lambda/2}^2 f. \tag{3}$$

ϵ_r is the relative dielectric constant, ϵ_0 is the permittivity of space, L is the length of the optical aperture in the y direction, and f is the average pulse repetition rate. As a comparison, the voltage required to obtain N spots with a conventional isoceles electro-optic prism[4] deflector is $V_{\lambda/2}$ and the power is

$$(3/2)^{1/2}\,\epsilon_0\epsilon_r tN^2V_{\lambda/2}^2 f.$$

This represents a voltage increase by a factor of l/t over the grating. Also, the prism power requirements increase as N^2 while the grating power is independent of N.

148

Each angular position desired will be produced by a particular grating column. For instance the three columns shown in Fig. 1 each have a different grating space and thus provide three independent deflection angles. Similarly, N columns each with a different grating space would be required to obtain N positions. In order that each deflection position be resolved, the finest grating space d must be equal to or smaller than $d = L/N$ and the other spaces increased in suitable increments.

Measurements were made on an electro-optic grating with dimensions $d = 3\times10^{-4}$ m, $a = t = d/2$, $L = 5\times10^{-3}$ m, and $l/t = 3.67$. The gold electrodes were deposited on a z-cut $LiNbO_3$ wafer. The edges parallel to the zy plane were optically polished. 6328-Å light from a He-Ne laser was focused through the wafer with a cylindrical lens. The emergent light was brought to a focus by a second cylindrical lens followed by a 1-m focal length spherical lens. A 60-cycle ac voltage was used to avoid electron trap effects.[5] Recorder plots of the intensity of the far-field pattern were obtained using a moveable 4-μ slit and detector. A typical recording is shown in Fig. 2. As would be expected from $d = L/N$, 16 spots with half-widths equal to those shown can be fitted in the distance between the zero and first orders. The measured and estimated [Eq. (1)] intensities of the zero, first, and second orders are plotted against voltage in Fig. 3. There is fair agreement between the measured and estimated intensity. Approximately 17% of the incident light is placed in each lobe of the first order at 600 V. The zero order is reduced by 60% at 600 V and 74% at 800 V.

Under pulsed operation, light-pulse rise times of less than 10 nsec are observed and seem to be

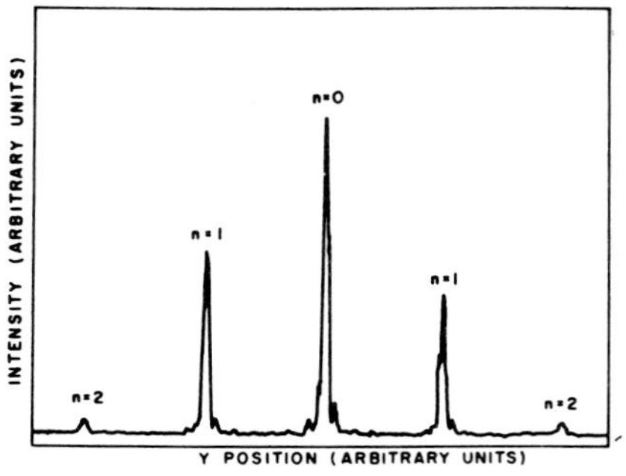

FIG. 2. Recorder tracing of the intensity of the focused far-field pattern. A 4-μ slit is moved parallel to the y direction to map out the pattern.

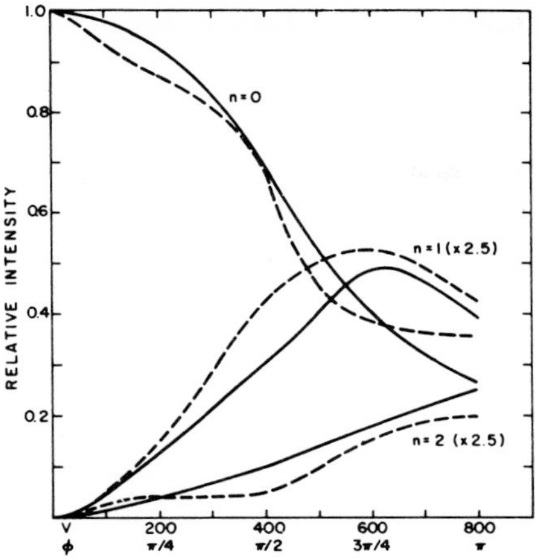

FIG. 3. Relative intensity of the orders $n=0$, 1, and 2 as a function of voltage and phase shift. The phase shift is calculated from Eq. (2) using $V_{\lambda/2}=2.94\times10^3$ V (Ref 2). Solid line—measured value. Dashed line—values estimated with Eq. (1).

limited by the rise time of the applied voltage. The reactive power is calculated to be 0.73 W for 10^6 Hz average pulse repetition rate.

The digital electro-optic grating thus is useful for both light deflection and modulation. The observed zero-order modulation depth of 64% and first-order intensity are limited by the fringing fields in the particular geometry studied. Reducing the thickness t to that of thin-film wave guides (~1 μm) would result in a lessening of the fringe fields and an approximately two orders of magnitude reduction in power. While operation of this device on a waveguide mode has not yet been experimentally shown, there is no theoretical reason to expect it to fail. In addition, the similar effect of diffraction of waveguide modes by acoustic waves has been shown.[6]

If the length l (in the x direction) is increased, a thick grating mode of operation is obtained. Here 100% of the light may be diffracted into first order by operating in a Bragg regime while the power required is reduced by a factor proportional to t/l.

Thus, a new method of laser light deflection and modulation based on diffraction by electro-optic phase gratings has been demonstrated. The method appears to be applicable to both plane-wave and thin-film waveguide transmission, requires relatively little power for high-speed operation, and is capable of high diffraction efficiency.

The author wishes to thank J. Minville for assistance in preparing the gratings.

[1]P. K. Tien, R. Ulrich, and R. J. Martin, Appl. Phys. Letters 14, 291 (1969).

[2]E. H. Turner, Appl. Phys. Letters 8, 303 (1966); P. Y. Lenzo, E. G. Spencer, and K. Nassau, J. Opt. Soc. Am. 56, 633 (1966).

[3]Max Born and Emil Wolf, *Principles of Optics* (MacMillan, London, 1964), 2nd ed., pp. 401-405.

[4]V. J. Fowler and J. Schlafer, Proc. IEEE 54, 1437 (1966).

[5]F. S. Chen, J. Appl. Phys. 38, 3418 (1967).

[6]L. Kuhn, M. L. Dakss, P. F. Heidrich, and B. A. Scott, Appl. Phys. Letters 17, 265 (1970).

Reprinted from **APPLIED OPTICS**, Vol. 11, page 613, March 1972

Optical Beam Steering Using a Multichannel Lithium Tantalate Crystal

R. A. Meyer

A multichannel phase modulator is described which employs the electrooptic properties of lithium tantalate to achieve phase modulation. The modulator's speed and 2π voltage are compatible with high speed microelectronics. The beam steering properties of this one-dimensional optical phased array antenna are described, and the beam steering results for a forty-six-channel modulator are given.

I. Introduction

The signal processing capabilities of an optical phased array have stimulated the search for high speed, two-dimensional optical light modulators. An acoustooptic array[1] and a membrane light modulator[2] have been described previously. In the past, the high voltages required for 2π phase modulation have limited the use of electrooptic crystals. This paper describes a multichannel lithium tantalate phase modulator whose speed and 2π voltage are compatible with high speed microelectronics. The beam steering results for this one-dimensional optical phased array are given.

II. Multichannel Lithium Tantalate Phase Modulator

A diagram of the multichannel lithium tantalate phase modulator is shown in Fig. 1. The crystal is cut and polished such that the surfaces are perpendicular to the $\hat{X}_1$, $\hat{X}_2$, $\hat{X}_3$ axes (corresponding to the a, b, c axes of the crystal). The bottom surface of the crystal (perpendicular to the $\hat{X}_3$ axis) is coated with a thin layer of chromium–gold which acts as a common electrical ground. This surface is then bonded to a brass block whose thermal expansion coefficients are approximately equal to those of lithium tantalate such that strain is not induced in the crystal due to thermal expansion. The brass block also acts as a mechanical clamp to inhibit changes in the crystal refractive indices due to the piezoelectric and photoelastic effects.[3] A thin layer of chromium–gold is deposited on the top surface of the crystal and etched into forty-six parallel electrodes that are 0.2 mm wide and on 0.5-mm centers. These electrodes are parallel to the $\hat{X}_2$ axis of the crystal.

The author is with Johns Hopkins University, Applied Physics Laboratory, Silver Spring, Maryland 20910.

Received 4 October 1971.

The electrooptic properties of single domain lithium tantalate have been well documented.[4] Lithium tantalate is uniaxial and remains uniaxial (without a rotation of the principal axes) when an electric field is applied parallel to the $\hat{X}_3$ axis.[5] Coherent light polarized parallel to either the $\hat{X}_1$ or $\hat{X}_3$ axes and propagating along the $\hat{X}_2$ axis will remain linearly polarized as an electric field is applied that is parallel to the $\hat{X}_3$ axis. The crystal exhibits birefringence (both natural and induced), and therefore light that is not polarized parallel to the $\hat{X}_1$ or $\hat{X}_3$ axis will in general become elliptically polarized.

When a voltage is applied to one of the electrodes of the phase modulator described above, the electric field under the central area of the electrode is approximately parallel to the $\hat{X}_3$ axis. Assuming that the field is uniform, the light that propagates under the electrode will be retarded in phase (due to the electrooptic effect) by an amount,

$$_3\Delta\phi_3 \doteq (-\pi l_2 n_3{}^3 r_{33} V_3)/\lambda l_3 \qquad (1)$$

for light polarized parallel to the $\hat{X}_3$ axis, and

$$_1\Delta\phi_3 \doteq (-\pi l_2 n_1{}^3 r_{13} V_3)/\lambda l_3 \qquad (2)$$

for light polarized parallel to the $\hat{X}_1$ axis, where

l_2 = the length of the crystal in the $\hat{X}_2$ direction (1.5 mm),
l_3 = the thickness of the crystal in the $\hat{X}_3$ direction (0.10 mm),
n_3 = the natural index of refraction for light polarized parallel to the $\hat{X}_3$ axis (2.180),
n_1 = the natural index of refraction for light polarized parallel to the $\hat{X}_1$ axis (2.175),
r_{33} = a linear electrooptic coefficient (3.0×10^{-9} cm/V),
r_{13} = a linear electrooptic coefficient (6.9×10^{-10} cm/V),
λ = the wavelength of the illuminating beam (6328 Å), and
V_3 = the voltage applied to the electrode.

From these equations it can be seen that the voltage required for 2π phase modulation is dependent on the length to thickness ratio (l_2/l_3) of the modulator ele-

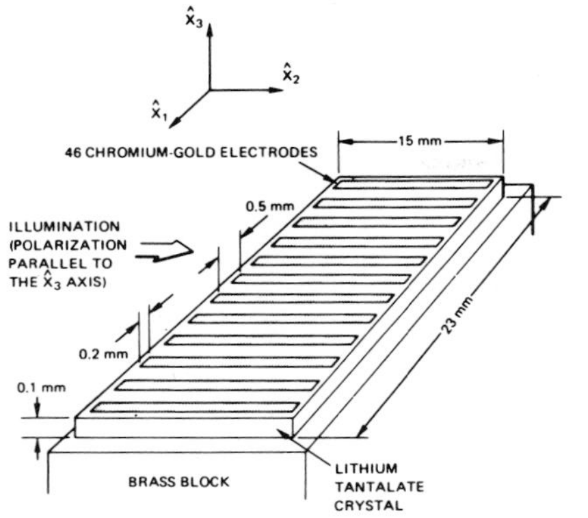

Fig. 1. Multichannel lithium tantalate phase modulator.

ments. For the present modulator dimensions, approximately 27 V are required for a complete 2π phase modulation when the light is polarized parallel to the $\hat{X}_3$ axis, and approximately 120 V are required when the light is polarized parallel to the $\hat{X}_1$ axis. To be within the voltage range of high speed transistor electronics, the illuminating polarization of the crystal modulator was chosen to be parallel to the $\hat{X}_3$ axis.

The electric field distribution is nonuniform and also not parallel to the $\hat{X}_3$ axis at positions that are not near the central area under the electrodes due to the electric field fringing effects. Therefore, light that propagates along these parts of the crystal will not be uniformly phase modulated and also will become elliptically polarized. A mask is used to block the light from all but the central areas under the electrodes. The present mask consists of a linear array of 100-μ square apertures located on the same centers as the electrodes.

The relative dielectric constant (ϵ_r) along the $\hat{X}_3$ axis for lithium tantalate is 43 (see Ref. 4), and therefore the effective capacitance of the elements (which limits the frequency response of the modulator) is approximately 10 pF.

Measurements on the masked modulator indicate that approximately 32 V are required for 2π phase modulation and that the modulation follows a linear voltage law.

With no voltages applied to the crystal electrodes, phase distortion of an illuminating plane wave has been observed at the output surface of the crystal. This phase distortion (caused by nonuniformities in the crystal) can be compensated by applying appropriate voltages to the modulator electrodes.

III. Beam Steering Properties of the Optical Phased Array

The beam steering properties of a phased array radar antenna have been discussed extensively in the literature.[6] Also, an optical phased array has been described based on the membrane light modulator.[2] Basically, when a linear phase slope is impressed across a phased array antenna, the far field pattern (or beam) of the antenna is steered away from the broadside position.

The lithium tantalate phase modulator can be considered as an optical phased array antenna. By applying appropriate voltages to the different electrodes, a linear phase slope can be obtained across the array, and the optical beam of this optical antenna can be steered.

When a linear periodic array of isotropic radiators of the same amplitude and phase is located in the front focal plane of a perfect lens (Fig. 2), the spatial Fourier transform (or antenna pattern) of the array exists in the back focal plane of the lens and is described by the following equation:

$$U_a(\xi,\eta) = A\,\frac{\sin[(M\pi\Delta X\xi)/\lambda f]}{\sin[(\pi\Delta X\xi)/\lambda f]}, \tag{3}$$

where

$U_a(\xi,\eta)$ = the complex light distribution in the Fourier transform plane (which is independent of η for a one-dimensional array of isotropic radiators),
M = the number of point radiators,
ΔX = the spacing between the point radiators,
f = the focal length of the lens, and
λ = the wavelength of the illumination.

This equation describes a periodic linear array of grating lobes (in the ξ direction) whose widths (from the peak to the first zero) are

$$\Delta\xi = \lambda f/M\Delta X. \tag{4}$$

A grating lobe peak occurs whenever

$$\xi_P = K\lambda f/\Delta X, \tag{5}$$

where $K = 0, \pm 1, \pm 2. \ldots$ Using the Rayleigh resolution criteria (that the peak of one beam be in the null of an adjacent beam), there are M resolvable beam positions between the grating lobes.

Due to the finite size of the crystal elements (100 μ square), Eq. (3) must be multiplied by an element pattern to describe the transform pattern of the masked crystal modulator. Assuming a uniform phase across

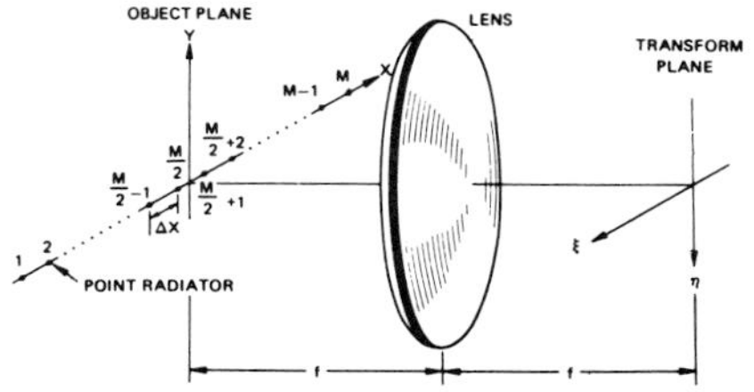

Fig. 2. Linear array of point radiators in the front focal plane of a lens.

the modulator elements, this element pattern is described by

$$U_e(\xi,\eta) = ab\left[\frac{\sin(\pi a\xi/\lambda f)}{(\pi a\xi/\lambda f)}\right]\left[\frac{\sin(\pi b\eta/\lambda f)}{(\pi b\eta/\lambda f)}\right], \tag{6}$$

where

a = the width of the element in the X direction, and
b = the width of the element in the Y direction.
(For the present mask, $a = b = 100\ \mu$.)

When a linear phase slope of p complete phase cycles are impressed across the crystal array ($\phi_m = 2\pi mp/M$), the transform pattern for the masked lithium tantalate phase modulator is described by

$$U(\xi,\eta) = Aa^2\left[\frac{\sin(\pi a\xi/\lambda f)}{(\pi a\xi/\lambda f)}\right]\left[\frac{\sin(\pi a\eta/\lambda f)}{(\pi a\eta/\lambda f)}\right] \times \left[\frac{\sin[(M\pi\Delta X\xi)/\lambda f - \pi/p]}{\sin[(\pi\Delta X\xi)/\lambda f - \pi/Mp]}\right]. \tag{7}$$

The grating lobe peaks now occur at

$$\xi_P = [K + (p/M)](\lambda f/\Delta X), \tag{8}$$

where $K = 0, \pm 1, \pm 2 \ldots$ Therefore, the peaks have been steered along the ξ axis by an amount equal to $p(\lambda f/M\Delta X)$.

IV. Optical Beam Steering Results

A schematic of the optical configuration for one-dimensional beam steering is shown in Fig. 3. A polarizer is used to cancel the depolarizing effects of the quartz-coated mirrors. A polarization rotator is used to align the polarization of the input beam parallel to the $\hat{X}_3$ axis of the crystal. Conventional collimating optics expand the beam to illuminate the crystal. The transmit mask is positioned within 100 μ of the output surface of the crystal by means of a three-axis translator. The output surface of the masked crystal is located in the front focal plane of the transform lens, and the spatial Fourier transform of the array exists in the back focal plane (transform plane). The light intensity in the transform pattern is read by a scanning mirror readout system. The mirror scans a projected image of the transform past a slit in front of the photomultiplier such that the current out of the photomultiplier as a function of time corresponds to the light intensity in the transform plane as a function of the distance along the scan. The photomultiplier output is displayed on an oscilloscope.

A block diagram of the electronics used for driving

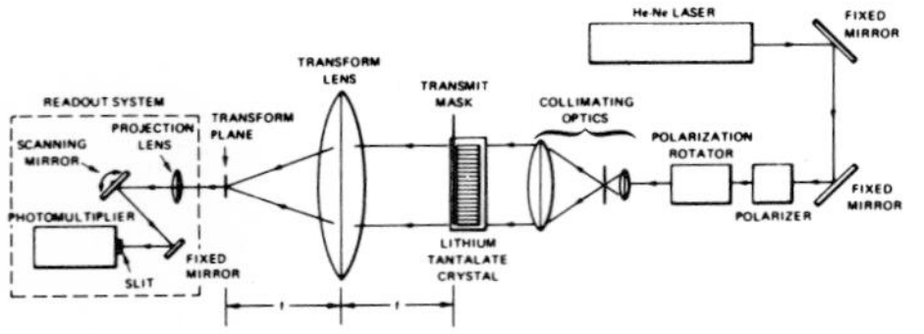

Fig. 3. Schematic of the optical configuration.

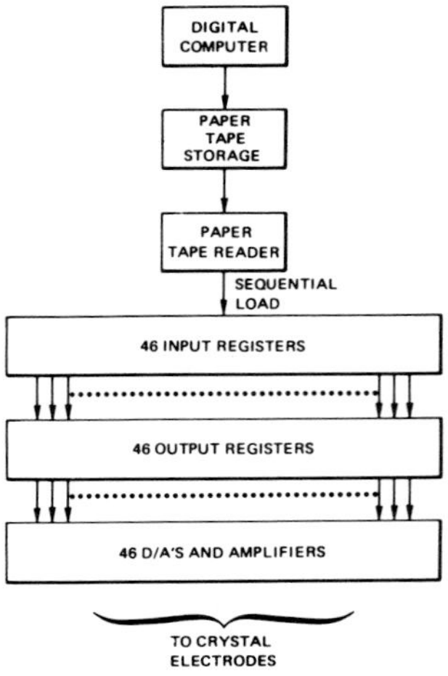

Fig. 4. Block diagram of the electronics.

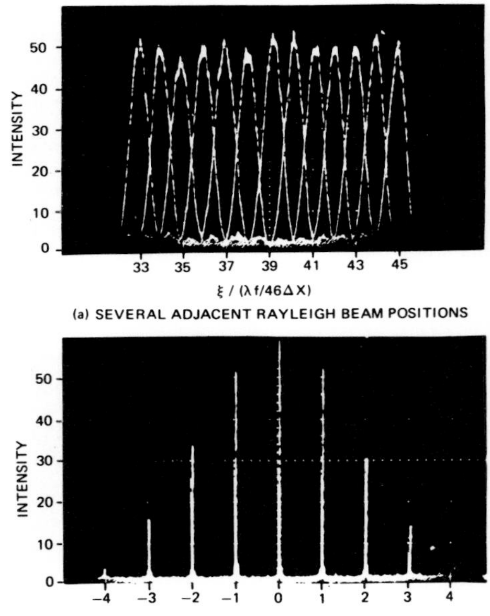

(a) SEVERAL ADJACENT RAYLEIGH BEAM POSITIONS

(b) GRATING LOBE STRUCTURE

Fig. 5. One-dimensional optical beam steering results using the multichannel lithium tantalate phase modulator.

the crystal is shown in Fig. 4. For a given beam position, the appropriate voltages (including the phase compensation discussed in Sec. II) for each element of the crystal array are calculated on a digital computer (modulo 2π phase) and stored on paper tape. The voltage words are sequentially read from the paper tape into the forty-six input registers (one register per crystal element). Once all the values for one beam position have been loaded, they are transferred in parallel to the storage registers which are tied directly to digital-to-analog converters, amplifiers, and the crystal electrodes.

Some experimental results are shown in Fig. 5. Since the crystal has forty-six independent elements ($M = 46$), there are forty-six Rayleigh beam positions between the grating lobes. The top figure shows several adjacent Rayleigh beam positions superimposed on one picture. The width of the lobes obey Eq. (4), and the intensity at the crossing point for two adjacent beam positions satisfies Eq. (7). The bottom picture shows the grating lobe structure. The variation in the grating lobe intensities is due to the element pattern. From Eq. (7), there are nine grating lobes under the main lobe of the element pattern. The distance between the grating lobes represents the distance the beam can be steered unambiguously.

V. Conclusions

A forty-six channel lithium tantalate phase modulator has been developed. Using phased array beam steering techniques, this optical phased array antenna has been used to perform one-dimensional optical beam steering.

The author would like to acknowledge J. B. Garrison who initiated the Applied Physics Laboratory's venture into optical signal processing and also J. L. Queen and D. G. Grant who have sustained the program since its inception. Also due credit are A. Finkel and D. N. Qualkinbush for their technical support. The crystal modulator was fabricated for the Applied Physics Laboratory by the Isomet Corporation, Palisades Park, New Jersey. This work was supported by the Navy under ORD-034C2.

References

1. L. B. Lambert, M. Arm, and A. Aimette, in *Optical and Electro-Optical Information Processing* (MIT, Cambridge, Mass., 1965).
2. D. G. Grant, R. A. Meyer, and D. N. Qualkinbush, "An Optical Phased Array Beam Steering Technique," *Proceedings of the Technical Program, Electro-Optical Systems Design Conference—1971 East* (Industrial and Scientific Conference Management, Inc. 1971).
3. J. F. Nye, *Physical Properties of Crystals* (Oxford U. P., Oxford, England, 1964), p. 244.
4. P. V. Lenzo, E. H. Turner, E. G. Spencer, and A. A. Ballman, Appl. Phys. Lett. **8**, 81 (1966).
5. P. V. Lenzo, E. G. Spencer, and K. Nassau, J. Opt. Soc. Am. **56**, 633 (1966).
6. T. C. Cheston and J. Frank, *Radar Handbook*, M. I. Skolnik, Ed. (McGraw-Hill, New York, 1970).

8. Optical Damage

Reprinted from JOURNAL OF APPLIED PHYSICS, Vol. 40, No. 8, 3389–3396, July 1969

Optically Induced Change of Refractive Indices in $LiNbO_3$ and $LiTaO_3$

F. S. CHEN
Bell Telephone Laboratories, Incorporated, Murray Hill, New Jersey 07974
(Received 4 November 1968; in final form 3 February 1969)

Local changes of indices of refraction observed in poled single crystals of ferroelectric $LiNbO_3$ and $LiTaO_3$ when illuminated by focused light have been studied. The extraordinary index of refraction was observed to decrease as much as 10^{-3} with a focused Ar laser light of 20 mW intensity as $\lambda = 0.488\ \mu$, while the change of ordinary index was much smaller. The effect is attributed to the drifting of photoexcited electrons out of the illuminated region followed by their retrapping near the beam periphery. The space-charge field between these retrapped electrons and the positive ionized centers in the illuminated region causes the observed change of refractive indices via the electro-optic effect of the samples.

I. INTRODUCTION

A local inhomogeneity of the indices of refraction has been observed in a few ferroelectric single crystals when they were illuminated by laser light.[1–2] In $LiNbO_3$ the extraordinary index of refraction in the illuminated region decreases as much as 10^{-3}. This causes the light to diverge making the use of these crystals as electro-optic modulators, acousto-optic modulators, and second-harmonic generators impractical. Part of the optically induced change of the indices of refraction gradually fades in a few hours but the remaining part stays essentially unchanged for days when the light is removed unless the crystal is heated to over 170°C. This later part has been referred to as an integrating component,[1,3] and this will be the subject of this paper.

It is here proposed that the effect often referred to as "optical damage" is due to the drifting of photoexcited electrons out of the illuminated region followed by their retrapping near the beam periphery. The space-charge field between these retrapped electrons and the positive ionized centers in the illuminated region then causes the observed inhomogeneity of refractive indices via the linear electro-optic effect of the samples. Persistent space-charge fields caused by the displacement of photoexcited charges and their subsequent localization in deep traps were previously observed in nonferroelectric materials.[4–5] In the next section, some of the observations and measurements made on the optically induced changes of indices of refraction will be discussed. This will be followed by a section describing a model to interpret these observations and further experiments made to clarify the proposed model. A brief discussion of an alternate model will be presented.

II. BASIC EXPERIMENTAL OBSERVATIONS

The experiments on optically induced changes of refractive indices were performed at room temperature on poled single crystals of ferroelectric $LiNbO_3$ and

[1] A. Ashkin, G. D. Boyd, J. M. Dziedzic, R. G. Smith, A. A. Ballman, H. J. Levinstein, and K. Nassau, Appl. Phys. Lett. 9, 72 (1966).
[2] F. S. Chen, J. Appl. Phys. 38, 3418 (1967).
[3] A. Ashkin, B. Tell, and J. M. Dziedzic, IEEE J. Quantum Electron. 3, 400 (1967).
[4] A. G. Chynoweth, Amer. J. Phys. 20, 218 (1952).
[5] H. Kallmann and B. Rosenberg, Phys. Rev. 97, 1596 (1955); J. R. Freeman, H. P. Kallmann, and M. Silver, Rev. Mod. Phys. 33, 553 (1961).

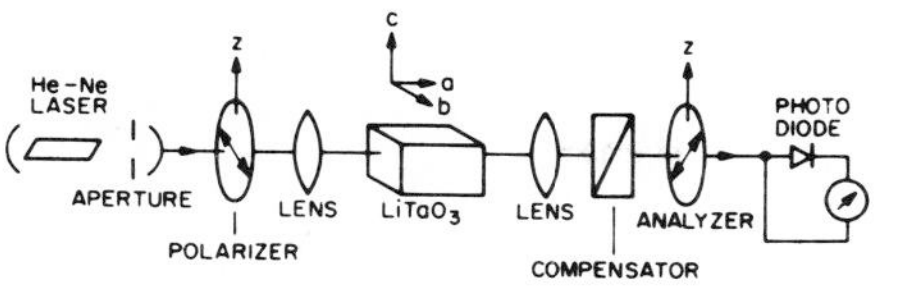

FIG. 1. Experimental setup for probing the optically induced changes of refractive indices.

$LiTaO_3$. Both crystals belong to the same point group $3m$, have large linear electro-optic effects,[6–7] have large spontaneous polarizations (71 and 50 $\mu C/cm$,[2,8] respectively), and have similar optically induced changes of refractive indices. Since some success has been achieved to make samples of $LiTaO_3$ less susceptible to optically induced index change by annealing them near Curie temperature with an electric field applied along the c axis,[9] most of the measurements reported here were performed on $LiNbO_3$ which is more susceptible to these induced index changes. It is not clear why $LiTaO_3$ responds better to the annealing treatment than $LiNbO_3$. Samples of $LiNbO_3$ used in the experiments absorbed light typically less than 20%/cm at $\lambda=0.488\ \mu$ and a few percent per centimeter at $\lambda=0.63\ \mu$.[10] The sample was illuminated by a laser beam whose direction of propagation was normal to the c axis. Only part of the surface of the crystal was illuminated. The optically induced changes of refractive indices were observed not to depend on whether the c faces were electroded or not. Either a 0.633-μ He–Ne laser with an output power of 20 mW or a 0.488-μ Ar-ion laser with an output power up to 400 mW was used to optically induce refractive index changes in the samples. In probing the induced refractive index changes the lasers were operated at much lower power. The following observations were made:

(1) During illumination of the sample with a high intensity light, linearly polarized with the plane of polarization at 45° from the c axis of the sample, it was found that the light transmitted through the sample (about 1-cm long) was split into three beams, displaced from each other along the c axis. The central beam which was not displaced was found to be an ordinary ray, while the two outer beams were extraordinary rays. This demonstrated that the optically induced changes reduced the extraordinary index of refraction most and the ordinary index of refraction least.

(2) No induced change of indices was observed when the sample was illuminated by a 0.5-W YAIG:Nd laser ($\lambda=1.064\ \mu$) focused to 0.1-mm diam. The same sample showed an index change when illuminated by a He–Ne laser ($\lambda=0.63\ \mu$) or by an Ar laser ($\lambda=0.488\ \mu$) of 1 mW focused to the same diameter. Generally shorter wavelength light would induce the index change more readily than longer wavelength light.

(3) The induced index change could be erased by heating the sample to approximately 170°C or by illuminating the sample with a mercury discharge lamp. The latter effect is related to the observation made by Ashkin *et al.*[1] that an index change in a small illuminated spot was effectively erased by a large-diameter beam which created its own large area of induced index change.

(4) The spatial distribution of the optically induced change of the indices of refraction was probed in the following way (Fig. 1). A poled sample of $LiTaO_3$ was cut into a rectangular rod 2.5 mm×2.5 mm×1.25 cm with the long dimension along the crystallographic a axis (also the light path). The sample was held at temperature 40°±0.05°C and along with a Babinet–Soleil compensator was positioned between a pair of crossed polarizers. A He–Ne laser (output≈20 mW, $\lambda=0.63\ \mu$) focused to approximately 0.2-mm diam was used to induce an index change. By reducing the diameter of an aperture inside the laser cavity, the laser power was reduced to 1 mW and the beam diameter to 0.03 mm. The laser intensity was further reduced by a neutral density filter, and this reduced intensity light was used to probe the index change caused by the high power and large diameter light beam. Before the intense laser illumination, the birefringence (n_e-n_o), where n_e and n_o are the extraordinary and ordinary indices of refraction, respectively, was probed with low-intensity beam and the compensator by translating the sample orthogonal to the light propagation. Then the high power laser was used to induce index

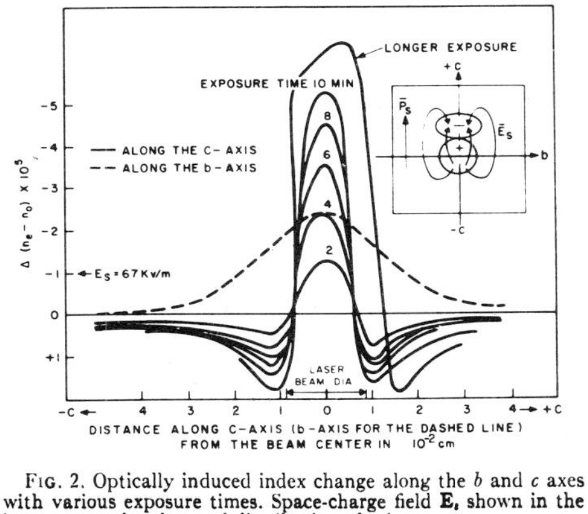

FIG. 2. Optically induced index change along the b and c axes with various exposure times. Space-charge field $\mathbf{E}_s$ shown in the inset causes the observed distribution of $\Delta(n_e-n_o)$.

---

[6] P. V. Lenzo, E. H. Turner, E. G. Spencer, and A. A. Ballman, Appl. Phys. Lett. **8**, 81 (1966).
[7] E. H. Turner, Appl. Phys. Lett. **8**, 303 (1966).
[8] S. H. Wemple, M. DiDomenico, Jr., and I. Camlibel, Appl. Phys. Lett. **12**, 209 (1968).
[9] H. J. Levinstein, A. A. Ballman, R. T. Denton, A. Ashkin, and J. M. Dziedzic, J. Appl. Phys. **38**, 3101 (1967).
[10] K. Nassau, in *Ferroelectricity*, E. F. Weller, Ed. (Elsevier Publishing Company, Inc., Amsterdam, 1967).

changes in the sample for a specified period of time and $(n_e - n_o)$ was probed again. The change in birefringence, $\Delta(n_e - n_o)$, observed was attributed to the intense laser illumination. The readings of $\Delta(n_e - n_o)$ were reproducible within a few percent. Since n_o was little affected, $\Delta(n_e - n_o)$ was approximately the same as the change in n_e, i.e., Δn_e. The spatial variation of $\Delta(n_e - n_o)$ along the c axis for various total exposure times is shown in Fig. 2. $\Delta(n_e - n_o)$ along the b axis and passing through the center of the beam is also shown for an exposure time of 4 min. One notices that $\Delta(n_e - n_o)$ along the c axis reverses sign near the beam edge, while it remains negative along the b axis. The induced index change was observed to be almost confined within the beam diameter. Due to the linear electro-optic effect of $LiNbO_3$ and $LiTaO_3$, the spatial distribution of $\Delta(n_e - n_o)$ along and perpendicular to the c axis can be linearly related to the electric field distribution. One notices that it is similar to the distribution of space-charge field in optically damaged KTN[2] where it has been shown that the retrapping of photoexcited carriers near the illuminated region was the cause of observed effect. As the exposure time to intense light was further increased, $\Delta(n_e - n_o)$ along the c axis showed asymmetry about the laser beam. The magnitude of $\Delta(n_e - n_o)$ near the positive c side of beam edge became somewhat greater compared to the negative c side and also $\Delta(n_e - n_o)$ along the c axis reversed its sign at the point away from the beam edge on the $+c$ side as indicated in Fig. 2. This is consistent with the observation made by Ashkin *et al.*[1] that the laser beam diverges more toward the negative c side. $\Delta(n_e - n_o)$ eventually increased further with longer exposure times and subsequently reached a steady state.

(5) $\Delta(n_e - n_o)$ as a function of laser power and exposure time was measured on a thin plate of $LiNbO_3$. The optical path (along the a axis) was typically between 0.25 and 0.5 mm. Samples with short optical path were chosen to reduce the divergence of laser light caused by the induced index change and also to make

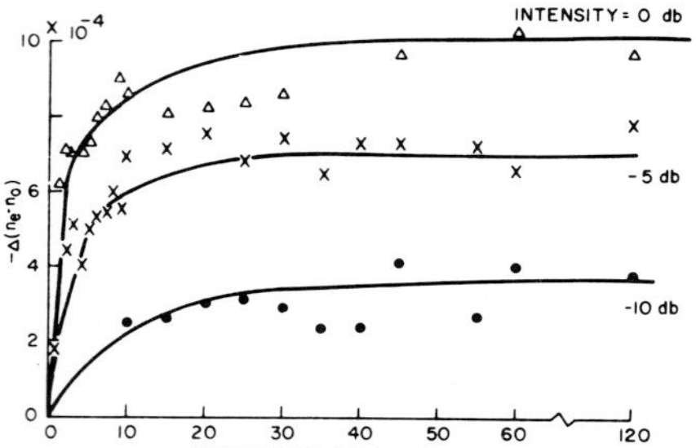

FIG. 3. $\Delta(n_e - n_o)$ of $LiNbO_3$ sample vs exposure times at different levels of Ar laser illumination ($\lambda = 0.488\ \mu$). The light was focused to approximately 10^{-2} cm in diameter. 0 dB = 20 mW.

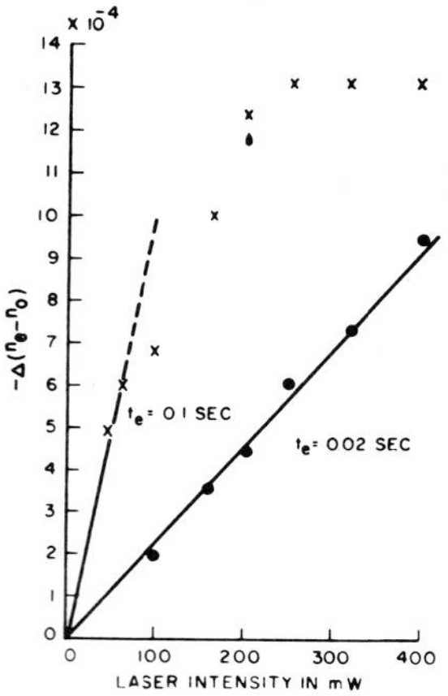

FIG. 4. $\Delta(n_e - n_o)$ of $LiNbO_3$ sample vs illuminating laser intensity for exposure times of 0.02 and 0.1 sec. The beam diameter was approximately 10^{-2} cm.

the phase difference between the extraordinary and ordinary rays less than 2π rad to avoid confusion in interpreting the compensator readings. The light from an Ar laser ($\lambda = 0.488\ \mu$, 20 mW) focused to approximately 0.1 mm in diameter was incident normal to the plate to induce refractive index changes. The spots under illumination with different intensity and exposure times were separated from each other by 0.5 mm. The maximum of $\Delta(n_e - n_o)$ which appeared near the center of the illuminated region was measured using a polarized microscope with a reduced intensity He–Ne laser (10 μW and 1-mm beam diameter) illumination. The illumination by the reduced intensity He–Ne laser could be left on for several hours without further change in refractive indices of the sample. The accuracy of reading $\Delta(n_e - n_o)$ was approximately within $\pm 15\%$. Figure 3 shows $\Delta(n_e - n_o)$ vs exposure times for different power levels. The induced refractive index change reached its steady-state value in 1 sec when the laser intensity was 20 mW (0 dB) and the steady-state value of $\Delta(n_e - n_o)$, $\Delta(n_e - n_o)_s$ increased with the laser intensity. $\Delta(n_e - n_o)$ vs power with fixed exposure times is shown in Fig. 4. The induced refractive index changes increased linearly with power up to 400 mW with an exposure time of 0.02 sec, but it saturated at 200 mW with an exposure time of 0.1 sec. In the range where $\Delta(n_e - n_o)$ vs laser intensity is linear, one notices that $\Delta(n_e - n_o)$ is proportional to the product of laser intensity and exposure times. Figure 5 shows $\Delta(n_e - n_o)_s$ vs power with an exposure time (2 min) long enough to insure that the index change reached its steady state. Although more data were necessary to determine the exact dependence of $\Delta(n_e - n_o)_s$ on power, Fig. 5 shows that $\Delta(n_e - n_o)_s$ increased approximately as the square

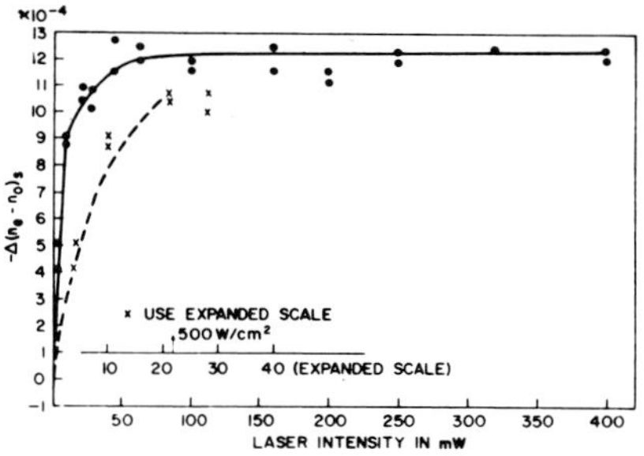

FIG. 5. Steady-state $\Delta(n_e-n_o)$ of $LiNbO_3$ sample vs illuminating laser intensity for 2 min exposure. The beam diameter was approximately 10^{-2} cm. The dashed curve is $-\Delta(n_e-n_o)=2.5\times10^{-4}$ (intensity in milliwatts)$^{1/2}$.

root of power until 20 mW. Then it remained unchanged with further increase in power.

III. PROPOSED MODEL AND CLARIFYING EXPERIMENTS

A simple model is proposed which explains most of the observations mentioned in the preceding section. Although this model assumes an internal field of not well understood origin, the model does explain most of the experimental data. Additional experiments which were performed to further document the assumption of an internal field will be discussed. A mathematical analysis of the model was made to explain the observed relationships between $\Delta(n_e-n_o)$, the laser intensity, and the exposure times. Additional support of this model was found during the study of volume, holographic storage using the optically induced refractive index changes. An alternative to the proposed model will also be discussed and its deficiencies pointed out.

A. Proposed Model

Let us assume that there are two types of electron traps before light illumination. Traps of the first type are initially filled and neutral, and they provide electrons by photoexcitation. Traps of the second type are initially empty and can capture electrons. Let us also assume that there is an internal electric field in the direction from the positive end of spontaneous polarization of the sample to the negative end. Then the photoexcited electrons drift toward the positive end of the spontaneous polarization leaving behind positive charges of ionized trap centers. The photoexcited charges will be retrapped and reexcited out of the traps until they eventually drift out of the illuminated region and are finally retrapped there. Since there is no photoexcitation outside the illuminated region and, for deep traps, the thermal excitation is too weak to reexcite charges out of the traps, the negative charges stay trapped there. The space-charge field $\mathbf{E}_s$ thus created between the trapped electrons and the positive ionized centers causes the observed spatial variation of the indices of refraction via the electro-optic effect of the sample. Further since $LiNbO_3$ and $LiTaO_3$ show linear electro-optic effect [i.e., an external field applied in the direction of spontaneous polarization, $\mathbf{P}_s$, of the samples decreases (n_e-n_o) linearly and a field applied opposite to $\mathbf{P}_s$ increases (n_e-n_o) linearly], the observed spatial variation of $\Delta(n_e-n_o)$ is linearly related to the spatial distribution of electric field. A spatial distribution of trapped electrons and positive ionized centers which gives rise to the observed spatial distribution of refractive index changes is shown in the inset of Fig. 2. The region illuminated by laser beam is shown as a circle with its center at the origin of the b and c axes. One sees that the space-charge field shown in Fig. 2 is in the right direction to decrease $\Delta(n_e-n_o)$ near the beam spot and hence diverges the laser beam. Also it is consistent with the observation that $\Delta(n_e-n_o)$ along the c axis reverses sign near the beam edge but it remains negative along the b axis. The sign of the drifting charges is negative since the space-charge field [and hence the magnitude of $\Delta(n_e-n_o)$] is larger (for long exposure times) near the positive c side of the beam edge. The induced index change exhibits mainly in the distortion of extraordinary index because the field induced change (electro-optic effect) of extraordinary index is larger than the change of ordinary index by approximately a factor of four when the field is along the c axis.[6–7]

The model explains the observed spatial distribution of optically induced refractive index changes. To account for $\Delta(n_e-n_o)=10^{-3}$ via the electro-optic effect, a space-charge field of 6.7×10^4 V/cm must be assumed. The density of photoexcited electrons required to produce such a field can be estimated as follows: Assume two cylinders of diameter 0.1 mm (the beam diameter used to obtain the data shown in Fig. 5) are in contact and one of them is charged uniformly with positive charges while the other is charged with negative charges. Then the electron density must be approximately $4\times10^{14}/cm^3$ if the field at the contact is to be 6.7×10^4 V/cm. The density of electrons involved is rather small since the density of trap centers can vary from about 10^{12} cm^{-3} in some of the purest crystals to as high as 10^{19} cm^{-3} in highly imperfect crystals.

Erasing of the induced refractive index changes by flooding the sample with uv light or by heating can be explained in the following way. By flooding the sample with a large-diameter light from a uv source, the trapped charges outside the boundary of the originally illuminated region as well as the charges in the unionized trap centers are photoexcited. They drift out of the region flooded by ultraviolet, are retrapped at the periphery of uv beam, and thus create a new large area of index changes. The index change in the small originally illuminated region is effectively erased because the trapped charges outside of its boundary are removed. By heating the sample above 170°C, the trapped charges are thermally excited to the conduction band and, at the same time, it is possible that the internal field approaches zero. The optically induced index changes disappear because the conduction electrons drift back to the illuminated region and they neutralize the positive ionized centers.

Let us now consider how the steady-state $\Delta(n_e-n_o)$ might be approached. With light illumination, initially filled traps in the illuminated region release electrons by photoexcitation. The ionized traps can now capture electrons and hence the rate of recapturing electrons increases. The rate of recapturing the photoexcited electrons eventually exceeds the rate of electrons drifting out of the illuminated region and hence $\Delta(n_e-n_o)$ approaches a steady state.

It was observed that the induced refractive index changes increased faster with the same light intensity after the sample was annealed in an oxygen deficient environment to increase the number of oxygen vacancies.[11] This observation suggests that oxygen vacancies might be one of the sources of electron traps involved in the induced refractive index changes.

B. Mathematical Analysis of the Model

Let us now examine what the model predicts for the dependence of $\Delta(n_e-n_o)$ on illuminating light intensity and exposure time and compare it with the experimental dependence shown in Figs. 3–5.

Assume that there exists a conduction band to which electrons can be raised via photoexcitation from the traps and that at room temperature electrons can be released from the traps only by photoexcitation. Since we assume an internal field along the c axis, the electrons also move only along the c axis. We slao assume that there is an electron trap level of density $N_t(\text{cm}^{-3})$ in the bandgap and $N_t'(\text{cm}^{-3})$ of the traps were initially filled while $N_t-N_t'\equiv\Delta N$ were initially empty.

We further assume that part of the photoexcited electrons at some point inside the illuminated region are quickly recaptured by traps and the remaining free electrons drift toward the boundary of illuminated region. However, they drop into the traps and are reexcited out of the traps several times more before they are eventually removed from the illuminated region. The time they take to move out of the illuminated region increases as the trapping of electrons becomes significant since these drifting electrons increasingly spend more time in the traps. The repeated retrapping of free electrons will be taken into account by defining a rate at which electrons are removed from the illuminated region as n/t_n where n is the density of free electrons in cm^{-3} and t_n is the average transit time of electrons across the diameter L of the illuminating light, i.e.,

$$t_n=L/2\mu^*E, \tag{1}$$

where μ^* is the drift mobility. If no trapping processes are involved, μ^* as defined by Bube[12] will be the same as the microscopic mobility μ which free carriers would have. As the trapping of free carriers becomes significant, μ^* will become smaller than μ by a factor equal to the time spent in the conduction band between traps, divided by the time required to escape from a trap on the average. In Eq. (1), E is the drift field which can be expressed as

$$E=E_i-E_s, \tag{2}$$

where E_i is the internal field in the crystal and E_s is the space-charge field between the electrons trapped at the beam periphery and the positive ionized trap centers at the illuminated region. E_s is the field which induces the index change in the sample via electro-optic effect.

The rate of photoexcitation f for weak absorption can be expressed as[13]

$$f=\eta Ikn_t\equiv AIn_t,$$

where η is the number of electrons released from the traps per unit energy of the absorbed radiation, I is the flux density (W/cm^2) of the incident radiation, kn_t is the absorption constant, n_t is the density of filled traps, and $A\equiv\eta k$. Then the equations describing the free electron density $n(\text{cm}^{-3})$ and the trapped electron density $n_t(\text{cm}^{-3})$ inside the illuminated region can be expressed as

$$\partial n/\partial t=AIn_t-n(N_t-n_t)B-n/t_n \tag{3}$$

$$\partial n_t/\partial t=-AIn_t+n(N_t-n_t)B, \tag{4}$$

where $B=vS$, v is the thermal velocity of free electrons, and S is the electron capture cross section of the empty traps. We assume that there is no spatial variation of the quantities defined so far (i.e., they are already averaged in space). Equation (3) states that the rate of increase in free carriers in the illuminated region is equal to the rate of photoexcitation, minus the rate of retrapping, minus the rate at which electrons are removed from the illuminated region.

The electrons which drift out of the illuminated region are assumed to stay retrapped at the proximity of the region. The number of electrons per cm^2 moved out of the region after an exposure time t_e is

$$N(t_e)=\int_0^{t_e}\frac{Ln}{t_n}\,dt. \tag{5}$$

[11] F. S. Chen, J. T. LaMacchia, and D. B. Fraser, Appl. Phys. Lett. **13**, 223 (1968).

[12] R. H. Bube, *Photoconductivity of Solids* (John Wiley & Sons, Inc., 1960), Chap. 3.

[13] Reference 12, Chap. 6.

Since $LiNbO_3$ and $LiTaO_3$ exhibit linear electro-optic effects, one can express

$$\Delta(n_e - n_o) \propto E_s \propto N. \qquad (6)$$

During the early stage of laser illumination, the trap states are mostly filled. Thus if we neglect the retrapping term in Eqs. (3) and (4) and take t_n as constant in time ($t_n \approx L/2\mu E_i$), we obtain from Eqs. (3)–(5),

$$N(t_e) = N_t'L - [N_t'L/(AIt_n - 1)] \times [AIt_n \exp(-t_e/t_n) - \exp(-AIt_e)]. \qquad (7)$$

Here it was assumed that at $t=0$, $n=0$, and $n_t = N_t'$. For the case where $AI \ll 1/t_n$, and $t_e > t_n$, Eq. (7) becomes

$$N(t_e) \approx LN_t'[1 - \exp(-AIt_e)] \approx LN_t'AIt_e. \qquad (8)$$

Equation (8) shows that the induced change of indices is proportional to the energy density of illuminating light initially [below saturation of $\Delta(n_e - n_o)$]. This was observed experimentally as shown in Fig. 4.

As the illumination continues, more traps will be ionized and hence the rate of retrapping will increase. The induced change of indices will increase with a much reduced rate when the rate of retrapping exceeds the rate at which electrons drift out of the illuminated region, i.e.,

$$B(N_t - n_t) \gtrsim 1/t_n = C[I/(N_t - n_t)], \qquad (9)$$

where $C \equiv \mu E\eta k/LvS$. Equation (9) was obtained by combining Eq. (1) with the following equation:

$$\mu^* = [\eta kI/vS(N_t - n_t)]\mu. \qquad (10)$$

Equation (10) in turn was obtained by modifying the relation[12] between μ^* and μ for thermal retrapping, although here it is assumed that trapped electrons can be released primarily by photoexcitation. The apparent steady state observed at reduced light intensity (Fig. 3) can be explained by the greatly reduced rate at which electrons drift out of the illuminated region and a weak thermal reexcitation of trapped electrons at the proximity of the region. Thermal reexcitation of trapped electrons reduces the magnitude of $\Delta(n_e - n_o)$ and this has been neglected in the analysis. Thus if Eq. (9) is taken as the condition for the onset of steady state, then, since $L(N_t' - n_t) = L(N_t - n_t - \Delta N)$ is approximately equal to the total number of electrons per cm^2 which have moved out of the illuminated region at steady state, i.e., $L(N_t' - n_t) \approx N(t_e = \infty)$, one obtains from Eqs. (6) and (9),

$$\Delta(n_e - n_o)_s \propto L(N_t' - n_t) \approx [(CI/B)^{1/2} - \Delta N]L. \qquad (11)$$

Equation (11) is valid only when $(CI/B)^{1/2} > \Delta N$. From Fig. 5 it is seen that for $I < 500$ W/cm^2 the dependence predicted by (11) is approximately observed. For larger values of I, $\Delta(n_e - n_o)_s$ no longer increases with $I^{1/2}$ because the magnitude of the space-charge field approaches the internal field and hence the net drift field E approaches zero. It is also possible that $\Delta(n_e - n_o)_s$ remain unchanged for larger values of I due to the complete ionization of the initially filled traps.

Although the approximate analysis presented could explain the observed dependence of $\Delta(n_e - n_o)$ on the light energy density and $\Delta(n_e - n_o)_s$ on I, a further refinement of the model taking into account the spatial as well as the temporal dependence of n and n_t would be desirable.

C. Further Experiments Related to the Internal Field

The proposed model of optically induced refractive index changes assumes the presence of an internal electric field $\mathbf{E}_i$ antiparallel to the spontaneous polarization. This field is the cause of photoexcited electrons drifting out of the illuminated region. Further experiments related to the internal field will be discussed.

The speed with which the index changes take place increases, for a given density of optical power, with the drift field because of the shorter transit time of photoexcited electrons across the illuminated region. Thus one should be able to vary the speed of index changes by applying an electric field. Indeed it has been observed that the index changes progressed faster when a field was applied parallel to $\mathbf{E}_i$ so as to increase the drift field than when a field was applied antiparallel to $\mathbf{E}_i$. This observation is another evidence for the proposed model. Another experiment to test the model would be to apply an external electric field larger than $\mathbf{E}_i$ and antiparallel to it during the light illumination. Then the photoexcited electrons would drift toward the negative c side of the sample. This would create a space-charge field in the direction to increase the extraordinary index locally, in contrast to the reduced extraordinary index observed when no external field was applied during light illumination. Experimentally this was not possible since only 8 kV/cm, which was too small compared to $\mathbf{E}_i$ ($\approx$70 kV/cm), could be applied to the sample without risking breakdown of the sample.

Some insight into the presence of and the role played by the internal field in the optically "damagable" sample can be obtained with properly treated samples of $LiTaO_3$ which showed no optically induced index changes,[9] (possibly the internal field was removed by the treatment). These samples show no change in $(n_e - n_o)$ when illuminated if no field is applied. However, $(n_e - n_o)$ near the illuminated region could be increased or decreased by applying an external field parallel to or antiparallel to the spontaneous polarization of these samples during the light illumination, and it showed a similar spatial distribution shown in Fig. 2.

It has been suggested that the pyroelectric field created by heating due to absorption of the illuminating

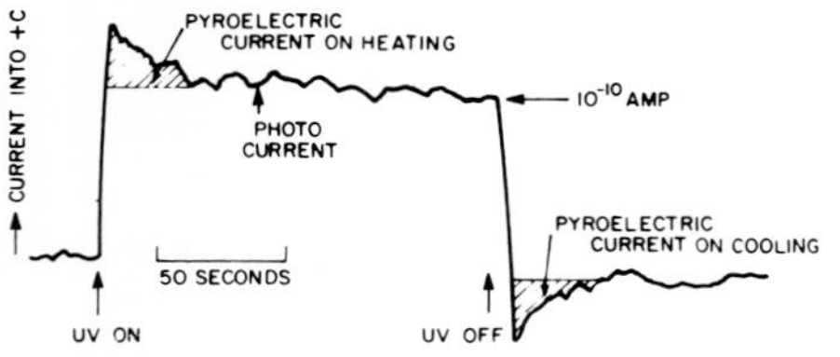

FIG. 6. Current flow into the c faces of $LiNbO_3$ vs time with uv illumination.

light might be the origin of the internal drift field. Noting that both for $LiNbO_3$ and $LiTaO_3$, $dP_s/dT<0$ where T is the temperature, the pyroelectric field would have an opposite sign to the assumed internal field. This observation excludes the pyroelectric field as the possible origin of internal drift field assumed in the proposed model.

It has been observed by Chynoweth[14] and Miller and Savage[15] that electric fields exist in the interior of single crystals of $BaTiO_3$ above their Curie temperature. The origin of the field was attributed to the space-charge layers at the surfaces.[14] It is conceivable that the internal drift field assumed in our model of index change might have its origin similar to that observed in $BaTiO_3$. The following experiment was performed on a poled single crystal of $LiNbO_3$ to detect the presence of internal field and to determine its direction with respect to the spontaneous polarization of the sample. An electrometer was connected between a pair of silver paste electrodes on the c faces of the sample: The a faces were illuminated with uv light from a mercury discharge lamp. Care was taken to mask the electrodes from uv illumination to prevent a possible emission of electrons from the metal electrodes into the crystal.[16] The current flow as the uv light was turned on and off is shown in Fig. 6. The transient component of the current which decayed in about 20 sec as the uv light was turned on and off is the pyroelectric current. The steady component of the current while uv light was on is due to the drifting of photoexcited carriers under the influence of an internal field. The presence of the internal field was thus demonstrated by this experiment. From the direction of the current flow, we conclude that the internal electric field must be in the direction opposite to $\mathbf{P}_s$. Although the magnitude of the internal field in poled $LiNbO_3$ as well as its origin could not be determined, its presence was proved and its direction was shown to agree with the direction of internal field assumed in explaining the mechanism of optically induced index change. Illumination of the same sample with Ar laser ($\lambda=0.488\ \mu$) showed a much smaller steady photocurrent although the current flow vs time was similar to the one shown in Fig. 6.

[14] A. G. Chynoweth, Phys. Rev. **102**, 705 (1956).
[15] R. C. Miller and A. Savage, J. Appl. Phys. **30**, 808 (1959).
[16] R. Williams and R. H. Bube, J. Appl. Phys. **31**, 968 (1960).

D. Observations Made on Holographic Storage in $LiNbO_3$

Further support of the proposed model of optically induced refractive index changes came from studies utilizing these effects for phase only, volume holographic storage.[11] During these studies interference fringes were formed by two plane waves. When the c axis of the sample was oriented parallel to the fringes as shown in Fig. 7(a), the proposed model predicts that no appreciable phase grating is expected since the photoexcited electrons migrate toward the positive c end and are retrapped near the beam periphery. Consequently, space-charge fields normal to the fringes are not created and an appreciable phase grating cannot be recorded. On the other hand, with the c axis normal to the fringes as shown in Fig. 7(b), large index changes in the fringes can be induced to form an appreciable phase grating. Indeed experimentally we observed more than 40% diffraction efficiency when the fringes were recorded normal to the c axis and less than 1% when the fringes were parallel to the c axis.

Another support of the proposed model was demonstrated during the reconstruction of images from holograms recorded in these crystals. When the polarization of the reading beam was extraordinary, the diffraction efficiency of the recorded phase grating was approximately ten times higher than when the reading beam was ordinary. This constitutes a strong support of optically induced index changes via the electro-optic effect since the diffraction efficiency depends on $\sin^2\Delta n$ and the electro-optic coefficient for the extraordinary ray $n_e^3r_{33}$ is 3–4 times as large as the coefficients for the ordinary ray $n_o^3r_{13}$.

E. An Alternate Model Considered

Let us consider briefly another model which has been suggested to explain the optically induced index changes. In this model we assume that the samples

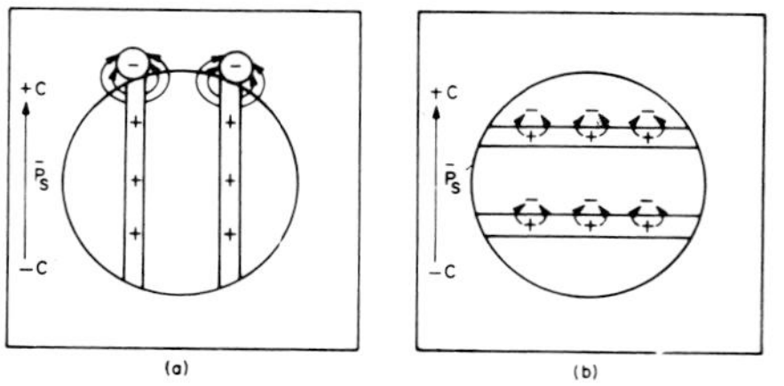

FIG. 7. Spatial distribution of space charges and their fields in the interference fringes. Only two fringes are shown. (a) When the fringes are parallel to the c axis, and (b) when the fringes are normal to the c axis.

have negligible diffusion coefficients perpendicular to the c axis; the photoexcited carriers then diffuse out of the illuminated region toward $+c$ and $-c$ and are retrapped at the beam periphery. Since there is a decrease of the density of trapped electrons in the illuminated region and an increase of trapped electron density at the beam periphery, there would be changes in refractive indices due to changes in optical absorption through Kramers–Kronig relations. This model can explain the spatial distribution of $\Delta(n_e-n_o)$ shown in Fig. 2 except its asymmetry along the c axis at a long exposure time. This model was soon discarded because the spatial distribution of $\Delta(n_e-n_o)$ did not change with an external field of 8 kV/cm applied along the c axis during laser illumination. This field should dominate the carrier diffusion, modify the charge distribution, and therefore modify the spatial distribution of $\Delta(n_e-n_o)$ in this model. Difficulties with this model are also encountered with the large observed $\Delta n_e(\approx 10^{-3})$ while the change in absorption is small.

IV. CONCLUSIONS

A simple model is described to explain the following aspects of the optically induced refractive index changes observed in poled ferroelectric crystals of $LiNbO_3$ and $LiTaO_3$:

(1) The spatial distribution of the refractive index changes near the illuminated region.

(2) The induced changes in extraordinary index is larger than the ordinary index.

(3) The index changes before they reach steady states are proportional to the energy density of illuminating light.

(4) The index changes at steady states increase with the flux density of light initially and then they saturate at about 10^{-3} with further increase in the density of light flux.

Based on this model, one can also explain the observation made during the experiments on holographic storage in these crystals that a strong phase grating could be recorded only when the interference fringes were transverse to the c axis. The model assumed the presence of an internal electric field antiparallel to the spontaneous polarization. The field was assumed to be approximately 70 kV/cm in order to account for the refractive index changes of 10^{-3} observed in $LiNbO_3$. The presence of the internal field and its direction were confirmed by observing the flow of photocurrent when the samples were illuminated by uv light, but its origin is not understood. Further study on the presence of an internal field in imperfect ferroelectric crystals is needed. It is interesting to note that the high permittivity observed in fine-grained $BaTiO_3$ can also be explained by assuming the existence of an internal electric field of the direction and magnitude mentioned earlier.[17]

The optically induced index changes are detrimental to application of these crystals in optical harmonic generators, modulators, and acousto-optic deflectors; however, they have interesting applications in storing memory[18] and pure phase, volume holograms.[11]

ACKNOWLEDGMENTS

I wish to thank J. E. Geusic for his continuous encouragement during this work. Many discussions with R. T. Denton, M. DiDomenico, R. G. Smith, and S. H. Wemple and the assistance of R. P. Morris and T. C. Rich are gratefully acknowledged. I would also like to thank A. A. Ballman and K. Nassau for supplying some of the samples used in the experiments.

---

[17] A. K. Goswami, L. E. Cross, and W. R. Buessem, J. Phys. Soc. Japan **24**, 279 (1968).

[18] F. S. Chen, R. T. Denton, K. Nassau, and A. A. Ballman, Proc. IEEE **56**, 782 (1968).

Reprinted from "Laser Induced Damage in Optical Materials" (A. J. Glass and A. H. Guenther, eds.) pp. 15–26. Nat. Bur. Stand. Spec. Publ. 372, 1972

Optical Index Damage in Electrooptic Crystals

A. M. GLASS, G. E. PETERSON, AND T. J. NEGRAN

Bell Laboratories
Murray Hill, New Jersey

Optically induced refractive index changes which occur at low incident power densities (< 1 KW/cm²) in many electrooptic crystals have severely limited the application of these materials in the visible spectrum. Following a brief historical review of the subject, we discuss the recent advances in the understanding of the physical mechanisms involved, progress in reducing the damage susceptibility, and in enhancing the effect for holographic applications.

Particular attention is paid to $LiNbO_3$ and $LiTaO_3$ crystals. Optical and EPR studies of these materials have demonstrated that Fe^{2+} impurity ions present in nominally pure material are responsible for the index damage. The effects of stoichiometry variation, heat treatment, impurity and color center content, X-irradiation of crystals and the kinetics of the index damage process are accounted for by Fe^{2+}–Fe^{3+} reactions.

By careful control of crystal growth and stabilization of the Fe^{3+} impurity ion state, $LiNbO_3$ and $LiTaO_3$ crystals with greatly improved damage resistance have been prepared.

Key Words: Holographic measurements, laser induced index change, optical memories, reversible low power damage.

1. INTRODUCTION

Laser induced refractive index changes occur in many electrooptic crystals. The index change distorts the wavefront of a transmitted optical beam and provides a serious limitation of the use of these potentially useful materials for nonlinear optical applications. For this reason it is usually referred to as laser damage, but it differs from the catastrophic damage which generally occurs at much higher power densities in that the index change is reversible. Following a brief historical review of the subject, recent progress in understanding the origin and mechanism of the index change is described. While index damage has been observed in several important materials including $LiNbO_3$ [1,2],[1] $LiTaO_3$ [2], KTN [3], $BaTiO_3$ [4], $Sr_{1-x}Ba_xNb_2O_6$ [5] and CdS [6] primary attention will be focused on $LiNbO_3$ and $LiTaO_3$ since we have studied these more extensively than the others. Methods of controlling the susceptibility of crystals to the index

[1] Figures in brackets indicate the literature references at the end of this paper.

damage, both from the point of view of minimizing the effect for nonlinear optical applications and maximizing the effect for optical memory applications are described.

2. HISTORICAL REVIEW

In his early studies of laser induced index changes, Chen [7] accounted for his results by the drift of photoexcited electrons outside the illuminated region of the crystal where they are subsequently trapped. Chen proposed that the resulting space charge field gave rise to the index change via the electrooptic effect. Bleaching of the index change is possible either by illuminating the entire crystal with the same light that created the index change or by heating the crystal, both of which result in reactivation of the trapped electrons which return to their original sites. In the case of cubic materials such as KTN an external applied field is required to observe index damage, but in the pyroelectric crystals no external field is necessary.

Chen's model had the following requirements:

1. A source of photoexcited carriers of concentration $> 10^{15}\ \mathrm{cm}^{-3}$.
2. Suitable trapping sites.
3. A permanent internal field of $\sim 10^5$ V/cm.
4. A crystal resistivity sufficiently high that the space charge fields remained for extended periods (weeks).

A considerable amount of work followed on the identification of the defects responsible for the damage. Reduction of $LiNbO_3$ and $LiTaO_3$ was found to increase the effect [7], while the field annealing of these crystals at $\sim 600°$C reduced the effect [8]. The latter effect was subsequently associated with OH^- impurity ions (or protons) drifting into the crystals from the atmosphere [9]. Defects associated with off-stoichiometry [10] of $LiNbO_3$ and $LiTaO_3$, such as oxygen vacancies [7,11] and stacking faults [12] were also suggested as possible trapping sites.

The large spontaneous internal field required by Chen's model was difficult to account for, since it was of the wrong sign to be due to the pyroelectric effect and was too large to be due to surface effects. However, Johnston [12] pointed out that no initial internal field is required for the damage process. Optical excitation of a pyroelectric crystal gives rise to a macroscopic polarization change in the illuminated region and the divergence of this polarization acts as a source for an electric field. Furthermore, the equilibrium requirement that the total electric field $E_{\mathrm{tot}} = 0$ means only that $\nabla \cdot P = (\varepsilon - 1)\rho$, where ρ is the space charge density and ε is the dielectric constant, so it is possible, in a pyroelectric crystal to have a spatial variation of polarization without a corresponding variation of field. This polarization gives an index change via the electrooptic effect. In this way Johnston showed that the distribution of trapped carriers resulting from the diffusion of conduction electrons, skewed by electric field due to $\nabla \cdot P$ was able to account for all the details of Chen's observations (which Chen's model could not) without the introduction of any fields before or after illumination of the crystal. This also removed requirement #4 of Chen's model.

The purpose of our work was to identify the defects involved so that some control over the optical damage process may be possible. Early experiments on the effects of heat treatment, oxidation and reduction, stoichiometry and field annealing were not reproducible and it was not until our discovery [13] of the importance of iron contamination of nominally undoped material in the damage process that the confusion was removed.

3. QUANTITATIVE MEASUREMENT OF INDEX DAMAGE

There are two basic techniques for the measurement of index damage. One is to write in the index change with a focused green or blue laser and to measure the birefringence change with a red probe beam which does not affect the damage. One such arrangement is shown in Fig. 1. The crystal polar axis is normal to the incident beams and 45° to the polariser axis. If the transmission of the Pockel's cell arrangement is initially set at zero with the compensator then the birefringence Δn induced by the 5145 Å argon laser gives rise to a transmission

$$T = \sin^2(\pi/\lambda) \int_0^d \Delta n_x dx \tag{1}$$

where d is the crystal thickness. Since most of the birefringence is induced over the near field distance of the focal spot an approximate measure of Δn is obtained. The sensitivity of this technique is limited by the crystals extinction ratio and typically $\Delta n > 10^{-5}$ can be measured. This technique gives a direct measure of the usefulness of a crystal for nonlinear applications and enables the use of high power densities in the write beam. It

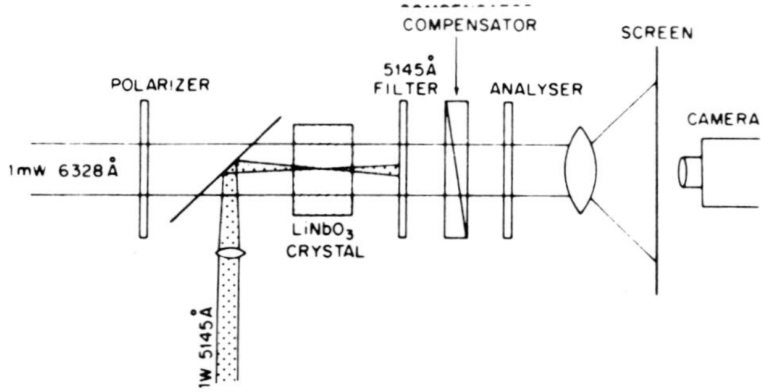

Fig. 1. Apparatus for measuring and photographing the birefringence change induced at the focus of a 5145 Å argon laser beam.

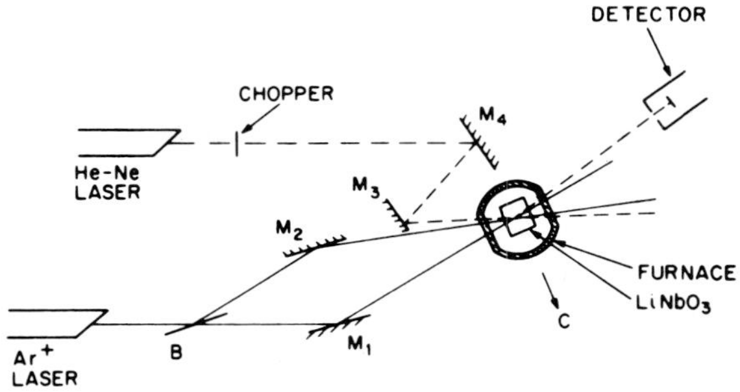

Fig. 2. Holographic technique for measuring laser induced index changes. B is a beam splitter and the M_i are mirrors.

suffers from the disadvantage that thermally induced birefringence changes may be larger than the laser damage and confuses some measurements. The holographic technique [4,14] provides a more accurate method for quantitative measurement of the index (not birefringence as before) change and the kinetics of the process. Two plane waves intersect in the crystal at an angle θ as shown in Fig. 2 and the interference pattern forms an elementary hologram because of the induced index change. The diffraction efficiency of the grating [15]

$$\eta = \sin^2(\pi \Delta n d/\lambda)\cos\theta \tag{2}$$

where here Δn is the modulation amplitude of the index change and d is the interaction length which in our case is the crystal thickness. The minimum index change which can be measured is limited by scattering from defects and typically $\Delta n > 10^{-7}$ can be measured. This greater apparent sensitivity is offset by the fact that much lower power densities must be used. Thermal effects are unimportant, but vibration effects become important. Thus the holographic technique was used for its greater flexibility and accuracy throughout most of this work, while the focused beam technique was used when higher power densities were necessary, or unpoled (multidomain) crystals were examined. For measurement of damage susceptibility the 5145 Å writing beams were σ polarized with a power density $\sim 1\ \text{W/cm}^2$ while the 6328 Å read beam was π polarized, the c axis of the crystal being normal to the grating planes. This measures Δn_3. Other polarizations and crystal orientations were used to study the damage mechanism as discussed later.

4. EARLY EXPERIMENTS

Crystals obtained from different sources grown from melts of the same stoichiometry varied widely in their damage susceptibility. Even crystals from the same source, same stoichiometry and same heat treatment varied

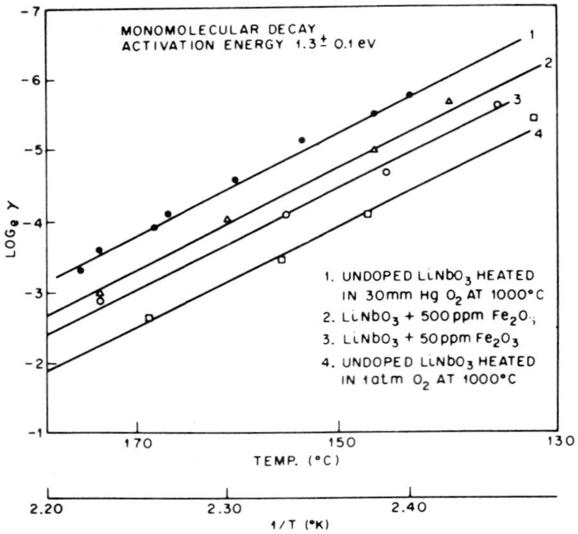

Fig. 3. A plot of the thermal decay constant γ defined by $\Delta n = \Delta n_0 \exp -\gamma t$, against the reciprocal absolute temperature for 1) undoped $LiNbO_3$ heated in 0.04 atm. O_2 at 1000°C 2) as grown $LiNbO_3$ + 0.05% Fe_2O_3 3) as grown $LiNbO_3$ + 0.005% Fe_2O_3 4) undoped $LiNbO_3$ heated at 1 atm O_2 at 1000°C.

greatly from one to another. Variation of crystal stoichiometry from a Li/Nb ratio in the melt of 44% to 54% had no observable effect on index damage, which seemed to remove the possibility of stoichiometric defects as the origin of damage. Studies of the thermal bleaching kinetics showed that at each temperature the index decays were exponential (monomolecular) with a single activation energy of 1.2 ± 0.1 eV for all crystals regardless of damage susceptibility, although the entropy of activation was found to vary somewhat from one crystal to another and depended on heat treatment. The results are summarized in Fig. 3. Both the thermal and optical bleaching kinetics were independent of the spatial frequency of the index variation.

All crystals annealed in oxygen at 1000°C damaged less than crystals annealed in oxygen partial pressures of 100 mm Hg, but at lower oxygen partial pressures there was no further increase in damage susceptibility. A typical result is shown in Fig. 4. This seemed to eliminate oxygen vacancies as the origin of damage and point to impurities, or other charge compensating defects. OH^- ion impurities were observed to enter crystals during field annealing in air, with a general reduction in damage [8], but these OH ions could be subsequently removed by annealing crystals in oxygen without any corresponding increase in damage. OH^- ion content was in all

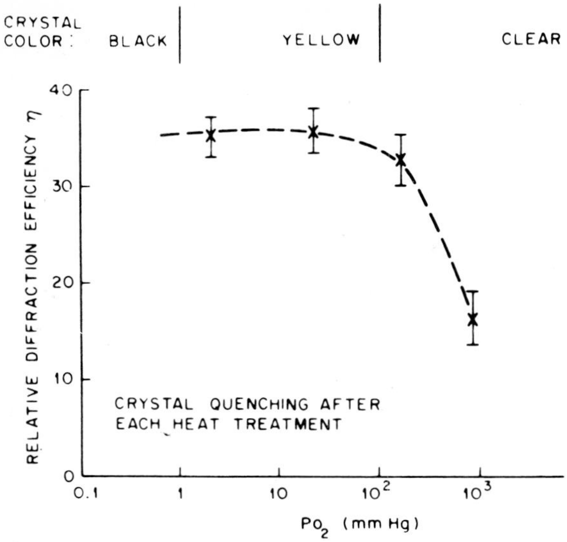

Fig. 4. Relative diffraction efficiency of a typical $LiNbO_3$ crystal after heat treatments in various oxygen partial pressures. Crystals were quenched from 1000°C.

cases measured by the absorption at $\sim$3470 cm^{-1}. Crystals were analyzed and found to contain several impurities, but doping with these impurities gave no measurable increase in damage. Long term field annealing and heat treatments often gave erratic and irreproducible results. No optical luminescence associated with damage and no laser induced epr signals (10 GHz) were found. Any photoconductivity was masked by the pyroelectric effect [16].

While all this data to some extent characterized the index damage process, and eliminated a few possible defects as the origin of the damage, little progress toward identification of the active centers was achieved.

5. *IRON CONTAMINATION*

510 MHz epr equipment was set up to study impurities in $LiNbO_3$. This equipment was well suited for the study of ferroelectrics both because of the large volume of crystal which could be contained in the cavity and because large fractional modulation of the magnetic field is possible. This is useful for studying the broad paramagnetic resonances in these materials when g broadening is suspected.

In all nominally undoped crystals it was found that the Fe^{3+} resonance line at $g = 6$ when $H \perp c$ and $g = 2$ when $H \parallel c$ dominated the spectrum [17], the impurity concentration varying from 10 to 100 parts per million in different crystals. A typical epr spectrum is shown in Fig. 5. Earlier spectroscopic analysis had not revealed the presence of these impurities due to interference from niobium lines but these impurities have now been identified by more careful analysis [18] and results are consistent with the epr data.

The damageability of crystals was found to correlate well with the iron impurity concentration, in fact, crystals doped with 0.05 wt% Fe_2O_3 were found to be far more susceptible to index damage than any other crystals examined. By analysis of $LiNbO_3$ at each stage of the powder preparation and crystal growth process it was found that most of the contamination of undoped crystals came from the ceramics used as furnace tubes of crucible insulation [17]. By taking care to avoid any contact or proximity of heavily contaminated materials with the $LiNbO_3$ at high temperatures crystals as pure as the starting materials (1 to 2 parts per million) were prepared. These crystals showed lower damage than any of the crystals we had studied. Comparison of the holographic diffraction efficiencies of newly poled crystals with different iron content, rapidly cooled from 1100°C is shown in the first row of Table 1. *Valence Change* of iron in $LiNbO_3$ occurs readily with suitable heat treatment. Almost complete conversion of Fe^{2+} to Fe^{3+} is possible by heating crystals in oxygen at 600°C for two days. Even crystals doped with 0.05 wt% iron were perfectly clear after this treatment and the absorption spectrum is shown in Fig. 6. Rapid cooling of crystals following an anneal in oxygen for a few minutes at 1000°C always gave a high Fe^{2+}

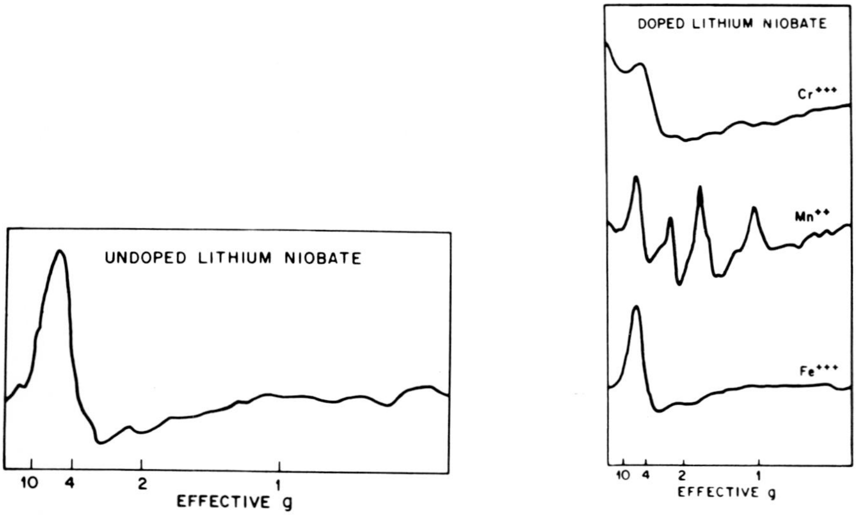

Fig. 5. E.P.R. spectrum of an undoped $LiNbO_3$ crystal (ground to a powder) compared with $LiNbO_3$ powder doped with Cr^{3+}, Mn^{2+}, and Fe^{3+} impurities.

concentration owing to the very small energy difference between the Fe^{2+} and Fe^{3+} states in the crystal. The crystal spectrum following this treatment is shown in Fig. 6—crystals appeared quite brown. Heating crystals in lower oxygen partial pressures gave increased Fe^{2+} and almost complete conversion to the Fe^{2+} state was obtained by heating crystals in nitrogen—after which the crystals appeared black.

TABLE 1
Diffraction efficiencies (%) of $LiNbO_3$ crystals, 0.2 cm thick, after various heat treatments. The low Fe crystals are the highest purity crystals obtained by careful crystal growth.

Treatment	Undoped	0.05 % Fe_2O_3	low Fe #1	low Fe #2
Poled from 1150°C and quenched	0.20	95[a]	0.019	0.010
Annealed for 75 hr at 600°C	0.021	1.0	0.0039	not detected
Field annealed at 600°C for 15 min with 5 mA/cm²	0.007	[b]	0.0004	"

[a] This was the maximum diffraction efficiency observed. An efficiency of 50% was still obtained with this crystal thinned down to 0.02 cm.
[b] This crystal had very uneven Fe^{2+} distribution.

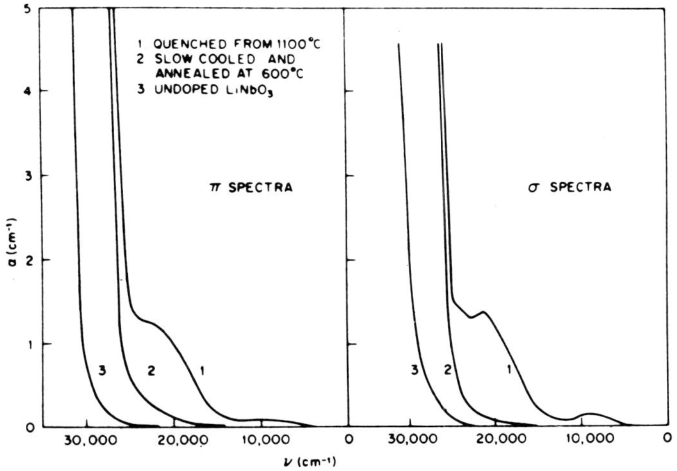

Fig. 6. Optical absorption spectra of iron doped $LiNbO_3$(0.05% Fe_2O_3), 1) after quenching from 1100°C 2) after slow cooling and annealing at 600°C compared with 3) undoped $LiNbO_3$ for both π and σ polarizations.

While measurement of the Fe^{3+} content was possible with epr, identification of the Fe^{2+} state was made on the basis of the optical spectra. The absorption band at 1.1 μm seen in the brown crystals is characteristic of Fe^{2+} ions in octahedral coordination [19]. Since there are no allowed cyrstal field transitions of the Fe^{3+} ion this spectrum is clear until the charge transfer band 0.4 μm.

The susceptibility of crystals to index damage was found to depend only on the Fe^{2+} concentration of crystals. (The holographic diffraction efficiency depends on approximately the square of the Fe^{2+} concentration.) Diffraction efficiencies of oxidized crystals are shown in the second row of Table 1 where it is seen that the damage is considerably lower than the quenched crystals in the first row. In order to increase the damage resistance of crystals still further attempts were made to completely stabilize the Fe^{3+} by the addition of colorless impurities of different valence such as Ti^{4+}, W^{6+}, Mg^{2+}, and Al^{3+} ions. None of these attempts were successful however. Since it is not known which sites the Fe ions occupy, nor what the charge compensating mechanisms are, the failure of these attempts has no special meaning.

Crystals heated in oxygen pressures below 100 mTorr appear black. Thin wafers of these crystals actually have a deep blue color. These reduced crystals have a much higher electrical conductivity than clear crystals. A spectrum of a thin wafer is shown in Fig. 7. The absorption band centered

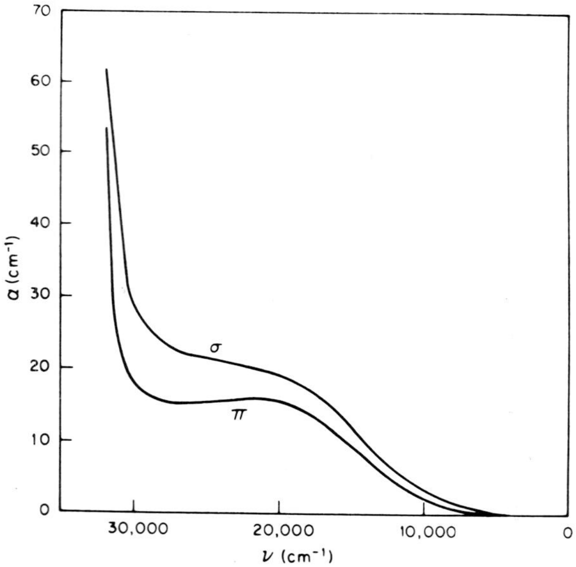

Fig. 7. Optical absorption spectra of $LiNbO_3$ after reduction in a nitrogen atmosphere at 1000°C for 10 minutes. The crystal appeared deep blue.

at about 0.5 μm (20,000 cm^{-1}) is characteristic of Nb^{4+} ions [19] and is not associated with the Fe content of crystals. These ions act as donors (the conduction band of $LiNbO_3$ being Nb^{5+} d_ε orbitals [20]) thereby increasing the crystal conductivity. *Field annealing* of iron-doped crystals results in a visible concentration gradient of Fe^{2+} ions in the crystals, the higher concentration being near the negative electrode. EPR measurements show a slightly higher Fe^{3+} concentration near this electrode also. The results indicate that these impurities carry an effective positive charge (possibly substituting for Li^+ ions) and drift toward the negative electrode. OH^- ions (or H^+ ions) enter the crystal from the positive electrode to compensate for the Fe ion current. The corresponding decrease in damageability of crystals is due to the decrease in Fe^{2+} content (Fe ions being pulled right out of the crystal) and not due to the increased OH^- ion content. If field annealing is performed in an atmosphere free of water vapor the Fe ion drift is not as effective since there is no compensation mechanism. The effect of field annealing crystals of various iron concentrations on the holographic diffraction efficiency is shown in the third row of Table 1. A further decrease of damageability is seen. Extended field annealing gave no further decrease in damage, possibly because of Fe impurities entering the crystal from the positive electrode (evaporated platinum) or because of iron impurities becoming immobile at crystal defects. Although no diffraction was observed from one of the low iron crystals after the field annealing, index damage was still evident at higher power densities using the focused beam technique.

All these experiments show the correlation of index damage with Fe^{2+} content of crystals and account for all the previously observed effects. The importance of the cooling rate and the contamination of crystals from furnace ceramics during poling and heat treatments account for the erratic behavior of our own early experiments. It is of prime importance to monitor the Fe concentration of crystals to understand their damage characteristics. All heat treatments and poling of crystals for these results were performed in furnaces sheathed with silica and high purity platinum electrodes and containers.

6. X-IRRADIATION

X-irradiation of crystals also makes them more susceptible to index damage. This is again due to valence changes of iron impurities due to the ionizing radiation, as demonstrated by optical and epr experiments. Crystals turn brown after irradiation, the absorption depth depending on the iron concentration and the spectrum is the same as the Fe^{2+} spectrum. (There is also some evidence of Nb reduction.) Annealing of crystals at about 150°C restores the crystal to its initial state. The activation energy for the thermal bleaching of the X-ray induced absorption is 1.3 ± 0.2 eV, much the same as that for the decay of the index damage, but the entropy of activation is smaller (decays occur nearer room temperature) and the decay appears to be bimolecular (retrapping of thermally activated carriers is important). The effects of γ irradiation on the damageability of crystals [21] also seem to be due to valence change of Fe ions from the induced absorption spectrum.

7. MECHANISM OF INDEX CHANGE

We now have strong evidence that Fe ions are the basis for the index damage. The Fe^{2+} ions are the source of photoelectrons via the reaction

$$Fe^{2+} + h\nu = Fe^{3+} + e \quad \text{(conduction)}. \tag{3}$$

These electrons (e) drift or diffuse out of the illuminated region where they can be trapped, possbily by Fe^{3+} ions via the reverse of reaction (3). This is indeed suggested by the similar wavelength dependence of the optical bleaching and writing processes. The index damage is then due to a spatial modulation of Fe^{2+} and Fe^{3+} ions. There is some assurance that the charge compensating defects of the iron impurities do not play a primary role in the damage process since other divalent and trivalent impurities have no noticeable effect in index damage and one might expect the charge compensating mechanism to be the same for some of these ions.

The broad absorption band observed around 0.5 μm in the Fe^{2+} ion spectrum must be due to charge transfer from Fe^{2+} ions to the conduction band [22]. Since comparison of Figs. 6 and 7 confirm that it is not due to reduced niobium. The shape of this band accounts for the wavelength dependence of optical damage.

There is no reason why other multivalent impurities such as Mn^{2+} – Mn^{3+} should not give rise to index damage by the same process. The apparent absence of any effect of these ions [23] in our experiments must either be due to the absence of a suitable charge transfer process at 5145 Å or masking by other optical absorption processes which do not give rise to conductivity. It appears that the set of conditions required for index damage is energetically favorable for Fe ions and other impurities have smaller effects which are not observable above the effects of residual iron impurities.

Once photoactivated electrons are in the conduction band they can move by drift or diffusion. Johnston [12] pointed out that both effects are important to account for the index changes observed by Chen [7], with diffusion being the more important for short exposures. In fact, one might expect that with increasing spatial frequency diffusion becomes more important since the concentration gradient of conduction electrons increases for a given optical intensity. In Fig. 8 we show a photograph of the birefringence induced by a focused beam of 5145 Å radiation in a $LiTaO_3$ crystal doped with iron. Similar results were obtained with $LiNbO_3$

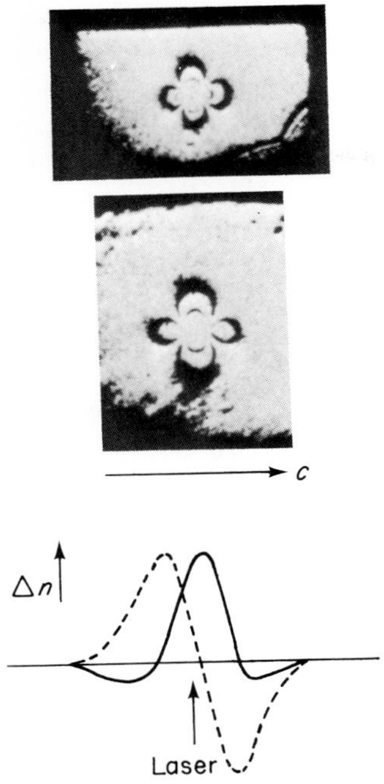

Fig. 8. Typical laser induced birefringence patterns in $LiTaO_3$: Fe (0.05%). The line drawing is a plot of the birefringence change along the *c* axis. The broken line is the birefringence change which would occur due to space charge fields due to diffused carriers.

crystals. The birefringence pattern is symmetrical about the focal point which indicates that drift effects are small and the redistribution of carriers is by diffusion. The results of Fig. 8 are qualitatively the same as Chen's results on undoped $LiNbO_3$ for short exposures. Recent work [24] suggests that diffusion is dominant for the higher spatial frequencies encountered in holographic storage, using γ irradiated $LiNbO_3$. The birefringence pattern of Fig. 8 also shows that the index change does not result from a space charge field (this would give the birefringence change shown by the broken line in Fig. 8) but from the polarization change associated with the redistribution of electrons. This result is expected since the conductivity of these $LiNbO_3$ crystals ($< 10^{14}$ ohm-cm) would relax the space charge fields in a few minutes or less. If higher resistivity crystals are available then space charge fields could play an important role for extended periods [25].

Johnston's model for the spatial variation of polarization requires that there be a significant difference between the dipole moment of unit cells containing Fe^{2+} ions and Fe^{3+} ions. The change in dipole moment of each impurity is additive, owing to the polar nature of the host, giving a macroscopic polarization change. Such changes of dipole moment $\Delta\mu$ upon optical excitation have been measured experimentally for the Cr^{3+} ion to be about 2.9 Debye in $LiNbO_3$ [26] and preliminary results for Fe^{2+} ions suggest a change $\Delta\mu$ of about 5 Debye. Using this value we can obtain a rough estimate of the quantum efficiency of the holographic writing process if other contributions to the macroscopic polarization change are neglected.

8. QUANTUM EFFICIENCY

The quantum efficiency q of the writing process in the case of laser induced index damage is the probability of the electron from an excited Fe^{2+} ion being trapped outside the laser beam and contributing to the index change. This will be a function of the spatial frequency written into the crystal since for the lower spatial frequencies the electrons have to travel further and the probability of being trapped within the illuminated region without contributing to the index change increases. Of course, in the limit of dc (uniform crystal illumination) no index change is recorded. This effect could account for the decreasing diffraction efficiency with increasing grating spacing observed in $BaTiO_3$ [4]. To estimate the quantum efficiency for a grating spacing of 1 μm we use the data of Fig. 9 where the diffraction efficiency η of 0.045 cm and 0.14 cm thick crystals of iron doped $LiNbO_3$ have been plotted as a function of time for various incident power densities. These crystals had an extinction coefficient of $\alpha = 1.4\ \text{cm}^{-1}$ at 5145 Å. The initial slope of the curve at short times for an incident power W of 0.9 W/cm is, for the thinner crystal,

$$(d\eta^{1/2}/dt) = 0.03\ \text{sec}^{-1} \qquad \text{or} \qquad (d\eta^{1/2}/dW) = 33 \times 10^{-7}\ \text{m}^2\,\text{J}^{-1}.$$

From Eq. (2) we calculate for $\eta \ll 1$

$$(d\eta^{1/2}/dW)_{t\to 0} = (\pi t/\lambda \cos\theta)(dn_3/dW)_{t\to 0} \sim 3 \times 10^3 (dn_3/dW)_{t\to 0}.$$

Since 1 Joule $\sim 4.5 \times 10^{18}$ photons at 5145 Å we have the index change per absorbed photon density N

$$dn_3/dN = (h\nu/\alpha)dn_3/dW = 17 \times 10^{-31}\ \text{m}^3/\text{photon}\,. \tag{4}$$

The same result is obtained for the thicker crystal in Fig. 9. Since the index change has electrooptic origin, for the configuration used

$$\Delta n_3 = \frac{n_3^3 r_{33} \Delta P_3}{2(\varepsilon_{33} - 1)} = \frac{n_3^3 r_{33} q N \Delta\mu}{2(\varepsilon_{33} - 1)} \tag{5}$$

where $\Delta\mu$ is the change in dipole moment associated with the Fe^{2+} to Fe^{3+} change. Using published values for n_3, ε_{33}, and r_{33} [28] and the preliminary value for $\Delta\mu \sim 5$ Debye we calculate from Eqs. 4 and 5 a quantum efficiency of 17%. It has been demonstrated that larger values of q may be obtained with an external applied field to increase the drift velocity of the excited carriers [27].

It must be emphasized that this calculation assumes that space charge fields, and contributions to ΔP_3 from sources other than the excited state

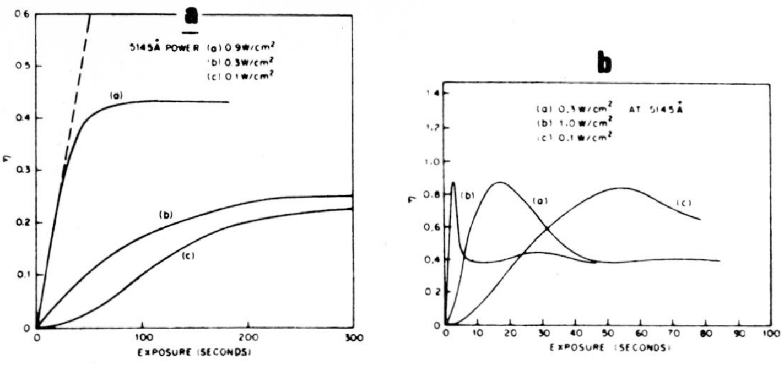

Fig. 9. Formation of elementary holograms as a function of exposure to 5145 Å radiation; a) is from a 0.045 cm thick crystal and b) is from a 0.14 cm thick crystal.

dipole, were unimportant. This assumption is almost certainly invalid—especially for short exposures, but the estimate does point out that this model provides a reasonable interpretation of the data.

Within these approximations it is also possible to estimate the Fe^{2+} ion concentration necessary to obtain the maximum observed diffraction efficiency in Fig. 9. From this data and Eq. 2 we calculate a maximum index change $\Delta n_{\max} \simeq 3 \times 10^{-4}$. Thus from Eq. 5 we estimate the maximum number of trapped electrons (using $\Delta\mu \sim 5$ Debye) to be about $3 \times 10^{25}\,\mathrm{m}^{-3}$. This is some three times greater than the total Fe concentration of the crystal. It is doubtful that $\Delta\mu$ can be increased to account for this discrepancy since the dipole moment of a $LiNbO_3$ unit is only 10 Debye, thus other contributions to the polarization—dipole induced polarization—are important. In view of the above assumptions this mechanism gives reasonable interpretation of the observations.

9. *PHOTOCHROMIC EFFECTS*

Evidence that the laser induced change has electrooptic origin is afforded by the polarization dependence of the diffraction efficiency of an elementary hologram [14]. If the hologram is written with the *c* axis normal to the grating planes, then the diffraction efficiencies of π and σ polarized read beams at 6328 Å are in the ratio 8.6:1 for $\eta \ll 1$. This is precisely what one expects from the ratio of electrooptic coefficients [28]:

$$\eta\pi/\eta\sigma \simeq (\Delta n_3/\Delta n_1)^2 = (n_3^3 r_{33}/n_1^3 r_{13})^2 = 8.4.$$

This result does not depend on the origin of the variation of P_3 since both space charge fields and excited state dipoles will both contribute to ΔP_3 such that $\nabla \cdot P_3 \neq 0$.

If, however, a hologram is written with the *c* axis parallel to the grating planes, then some information concerning the microscopic origin of $\nabla \cdot P_3$

can be obtained. The excited state dipole moment can only, by symmetry, give a variation in P_3, while space charge fields will give a variation in P_1 or P_2 only for this configuration. Thus in equilibrium $\nabla \cdot P = 0$ and no diffraction would be observed due to the electrooptic effect. If the crystal is not in equilibrium and there are net space charge fields due to trapped carriers (at times shorter than the relaxation time), then diffraction will be observed. When the crystal b axis is normal to the grating planes

$$\eta\pi = 0 \qquad \text{and} \qquad \eta\sigma = n_2^3 r_{22} \Delta P_2/(\varepsilon_2 - 1).$$

For the same space charge fields $\eta\sigma$ for this configuration should be about half of $\eta\sigma$ for the previous configuration. No diffraction is measured with this configuration at 6328 Å in our experiments suggesting that no space charge fields are present. However, when the 5145 Å laser is used as the read beam, then a diffraction efficiency of about 1% of $\eta\sigma$ for the previous configuration with the same exposure was observed in an iron doped $LiNbO_3$ crystal 1.5 mm thick. This difference for the two wavelengths was too great to be due to dispersion of r_{22}. A possible explanation of the result is photochromism. Since the basis for the index variation is the photochromic Fe^{2+}–Fe^{3+} reaction, an amplitude hologram is expected. The diffraction efficiency of such an elementary hologram is [15]

$$\eta = \exp -\left(\frac{2\alpha d}{\cos\theta} s h^2 \frac{\alpha d}{2\cos\theta}\right) \tag{6}$$

where α is the modulation amplitude of the absorption depth. To estimate the importance of this effect, we will assume that all Fe^{2+} ions possible contribute to the hologram, then for the 0.15 cm thick crystal, using $\alpha \simeq 1.4$ from Fig. 6 we find $\eta = 0.009$ with little dependence of the efficiency on the polarization of the read beam, due to the small dichroism. This estimate is considerably greater than the measured diffraction efficiency of 0.1% so the observed effect could indeed be due to photochromism.

10. $LiTaO_3$

Qualitatively the behavior of $LiNbO_3$ and $LiTaO_3$ is similar. There are, however, important quantitative differences. The index damage susceptibility of $LiTaO_3$ is much lower than $LiNbO_3$ for both undoped and iron-doped crystals by a factor of about 30. A comparison of the two materials is shown in Table 2. The data in this table was obtained using the focused beam technique of Fig. 1 with a 7-cm focal length lens. The incident power listed is the minimum power density necessary to just see transmission through the pockels cell due to the laser induced index change for the exposure times given. At these powers defocusing of the beam was also just observed. It was necessary to use this technique since high temperature heat treatments dipole $LiTaO_3$ (Curie temperature $\simeq$ 620°C) and repoling of course changes the crystal characteristics. The results of Table 2 give some semiquantitative idea of the damage susceptibility for comparing different crystals, but the absolute magnitudes depend on the spatial frequencies (focal length of the lens) and the exposure time. The $LiTaO_3$ crystals obtained from Crystal Technology Inc. had the highest damage resistance of all those studied after suitable heat treatments and field annealing, even though the Fe^{3+} content of these crystals was greater than 10 parts per million. The iron is almost entirely stabilized in the Fe^{3+} state.

A clue to the reason for the difference in damageability of $LiNbO_3$ and $LiTaO_3$ may be given by the absorption spectrum of Fig. 10. $LiTaO_3$: Fe^{2+} does not have the pronounced absorption band at about 0.5 μm which is present in $LiNbO_3$. The excitation of an electron from an Fe^{2+} ion to the conduction band may be less probable than excitation to a nonconducting state with 5145 Å radiation. This may be related to the fact that the Ta^{5+} ion is a great deal more difficult to reduce to Ta^{4+} than the equivalent Nb^{5+}–Nb^{4+} reaction. Ta^{4+} can only be obtained in sufficient concentration to color the crystal if crystals are heated in hydrogen at 1000°C, while Nb^{5+} reduces with much less severe treatment. Because of this property it is possible to obtain almost complete conversion of Fe^{3+} to Fe^{2+} in $LiTaO_3$ before the crystals turn black. It is interesting to see from Table 2 that the heavily reduced crystal seemed to damage less than the quenched crystal. This implies that the presence of Fe^{3+} ions as traps are essential to maximize the damage. It is also interesting to see that annealing $LiTaO_3$ crystals in air at 1400°C for several hours results in lower damage than crystals annealed at 1200°C for the same time. This treatment increases the oxidation state of the $LiTaO_3$ thereby increasing the Fe^{3+}/Fe^{3+} ratio. The improvement of the Crystal Technology crystal is presumably due to a variation of the crystal growth procedure.

TABLE 2
Peak intensity in W/cm² at the focus of a 5145 Å argon laser beam, necessary to just observe index damage during a 10 sec exposure

Crystal	Quenched from 1000°C	Slow cooled and field annealed[a]
$LiTaO_3$ annealed at 1200°C for 25 hr after growth	200	900
$LiTaO_3$ annealed at 1400°C for 25 hr after growth	600	3000
$LiTaO_3$: Crystal technology	1500	8000
$LiTaO_3$ + 0.05% Fe_2O_3	10	30
$LiTaO_3$ + 0.05% Fe_2O_3 (reduced in H_2 and annealed 15 minutes in N_2 at 1000°C)	25	—
$LiNbO_3$ low iron	40	300
$LiNbO_3$ + 0.05% Fe_2O_3	0.5	6

[a] Field annealed at 600°C for about 10 minutes with 5 mA/cm². This procedure poled $LiTaO_3$.

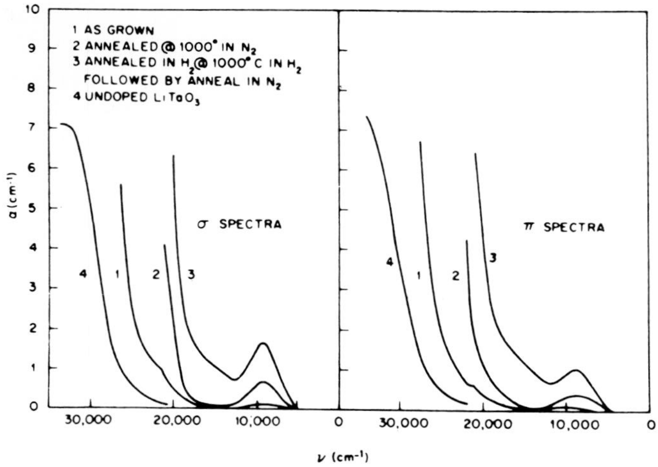

Fig. 10. Optical absorption spectra of iron doped $LiTaO_3(0.05\%Fe_2O_3)$ 1) as grown 2) after annealing at 1000°C N_2 3) after annealing in H_2 at 1000°C, compared with 4) undoped $LiTaO_3$, for π and σ polarizations.

11. APPLICATIONS OF LASER INDUCED INDEX DAMAGE

Laser induced index changes have been used as the basis of an erasable pure phase holographic memory [14] and may find future application in distributed feedback systems [29] and integrated optics. For these applications maximum writing sensitivity is required so that iron doped $LiNbO_3$ is particularly useful. By suitable doping, choice of crystal thickness and heat treatment, a compromise between optical absorption loss and writing sensitivity may be achieved for any application. We have been able to achieve holographic diffraction efficiencies of 50% using ~ 1 J/cm^2 of incident energy with $LiNbO_3$ + 0.05% Fe crystals 0.2 cm thick with ~30% absorption loss at 5145 Å. The angular selectivity

$$\Delta\theta = n\lambda/(2t \sin\theta) \tag{7}$$

of this crystal was about 1 mR for a grating spacing of 1 μm. With thicker crystals higher angular selectivity can be obtained, but without improvement in writing sensitivity since these crystals have to be oxidized somewhat to prevent excessive absorption loss. An advantage, in principle, of higher angular selectivity is that many holograms can be superimposed in the same volume of crystal and independently read out. However, it is not possible to erase one hologram without erasing all the others in the same volume. Furthermore, partial erasure occurs during readout, by optical bleaching since read and write wavelengths must be the same to avoid distortion in the thick crystals. Fixing holograms eliminates the problem of optical bleaching during reading but it also removes the versatile feature of optical erasability. Fixing holograms may be accomplished by any polarization relaxation process which compensates wholly or partially for the polarization variation in the crystal, then subsequent optical bleaching of the trapped electrons will leave a fixed hologram. Such procedures have been demonstrated for undoped $LiNbO_3$ [21,25] and $BaTiO_3$ [30]. The polarization relaxation process could be local polarization reversal [30], or other ionic rearrangement. For crystals not in equilibrium when there are space charge fields present, fixing could be accomplished by ionic conductivity to relax these fields [25]. Polarization relaxation requires only local changes while field relaxation requires ionic drift over macroscopic distance. Since there is no dependence of the thermal bleaching associated with the fixing on the spatial frequency of the index pattern in $LiNbO_3$, the former mechanism seems to be operative, consistent with earlier observations that space charge fields do not persist.

For some memory applications it may be advantageous to use thin crystals, heavily doped with iron to maximize the writing sensitivity, so that the angular selectivity is poor. Then readout may be performed with a longer wavelength radiation such that optical bleaching is not a problem. Second order distortion effects may be tolerable. We can see from Eqs. (2) and (7) that for writing with 5145 Å radiation and reading with 6328 Å we need $\Delta\theta > 50$ mR or crystal thickness $< 4 \times 10^{-2}$ cm. With this kind of system the holograms would not be superimposed but arranged in an array so that each can be spatially addressed. In this way single holograms can be erased.

12. DIFFUSION DOPING

To achieve such thin holograms of high sensitivity is relatively simple by diffusion doping of crystals. Heavily iron-doped layers about 25 μm (measured by the angular selectivity of an elementary hologram) can be diffused into $LiNbO_3$ in a few hours at 1100°C, while leaving the crystal in a single domain state. 1% diffraction efficiency could be obtained with 10 J/cm^2 incident energy or 3% with 60 J/cm^2 and less than 10% absorption loss at 5145 Å. This corresponds to a peak to peak index change of about 0.0025 without even focusing. The measured angular selectivity $\Delta\theta \simeq 100$ mR was sufficiently great that both diffracted beams, each side of the normal to the crystal surface, could be observed with normal incidence of the read beam.

13. CONCLUSIONS

The optically induced refractive changes in $LiNbO_3$ and $LiTaO_3$ have been reasonably well characterized and the basic mechanisms understood. Our measurements are consistent with the interpretation that only iron impurities contribute to the laser damage in these two materials, even though there is no fundamental reason why other impurities might not result in similar effects. The set of conditions necessary for index damage appears particularly favorable for iron impurities in $LiNbO_3$. It is known that the addition of iron increases the damageability of $Ba_2NaNb_5O_{15}$ [21] and $BaTiO_3$ [30] but at the present time it is not known whether this impurity is the only cause of damage in these materials. In the case of $BaTiO_3$ the situation is a little more complicated in that the addition of some impurities is accompanied by an increase in the electrooptic coefficients at room temperature so that increased damage susceptibility could be due to this effect rather than the direct effect of charge transfer from the impurities.

Solely by varying the Fe^{2+} concentration of $LiNbO_3$ and $LiTaO_3$ it has been possible to vary the laser induced index changes over about four orders of magnitude for the same exposure. It has only been possible to prepare $LiNbO_3$ and $LiTaO_3$ with resistance to index damage for incident powers less than 100 W/cm^2 and 10 KW/cm^2 respectively by careful control of crystal growth. Since the distribution coefficient of iron in $LiNbO_3$ is less than, but close to unity [16] zone refining is not expected to give great improvement. However, any improvement at all increases the usefulness of crystals both as electrooptic modulators, since increased powers can be used, and as parametric oscillators, since the temperature of operation can be decreased, thereby increasing the useful tuning range. Each order of magnitude decrease in damage susceptibility decreases the lowest possible operating temperature by 20°C.

The study of iron in $LiNbO_3$ and $Ba_2NaNb_5O_{15}$ has also led to progress in the understanding of self-focusing by two step absorption in these materials at high power densities [31]. In this context it is worth pointing out that the excited state dipole effect provides a direct index change in addition to thermal effects which may contribute to self-focusing.

14. ACKNOWLEDGMENTS

Throughout this work we have had the assistance and interest of many of our colleagues. In particular we would like to thank P. M. Bridenbaugh and A. A. Ballman for growing the crystals used in this work, Miss B. E. Prescott and Mrs. G. A. Pasteur for measuring the optical absorption spectra of our crystals and A. Carnevale for assistance with the epr measurements. Helpful discussions of unpublished work with D. L. Nash and F. Micheron, M. Clark and L. K. Anderson are gratefully acknowledged.

15. REFERENCES

1. Peterson, G. E., Ballman, A. A. Lenzo, P. V. and Bridenbaugh, P. M., *Appl. Phys. Lett.*, **5**, 62 (1964)
2. Ashkin, A., Boyd, G. D., Dziedzic, J. M., Smith, R. G., Ballman, A. A., Levinstein, H. J. and Nassau, K., *Appl. Phys. Lett.* **9**, 72 (1966).

3. Chen, F. S., J. *Appl. Phys.* **38,** 3418 (1967).
4. Townsend, R. L. and LaMacchia, J. T., J. *Appl. Phys.* **41,** 5188 (1970).
5. Thaxter, J. B., *Appl. Phys. Lett.* **15,** 210 (1969).
6. Ashkin, A., Tell, B. and Dziedzic, J. M., *IEEE J. Quantum Electron.* **3,** 400 (1967).
7. Chen, F. S., J. *Appl. Phys.* **40,** 3389 (1969).
8. Levinstein, H. J., Ballman, A. A., Denton, R. T., Ashkin, A. and Dziedzic, J. M., J. *Appl. Phys.* **38,** 3103 (1967).
9. Smith, R. G., Fraser, D. B., Denton, R. T. and Rich, T. C., *J. Appl. Phys.* **39,** 4600 (1968).
10. Peterson, G. E. and Carruthers, J. R., *Solid State Chem.* **1,** 98 (1969).
11. Jorgensen, P. J. and Bartlett, R. W., Tech. Rep. No. ONRAD686721, Stanford Research Institute (1969). Unpublished.
12. Johnston, Jr., W. D., J. *Appl. Phys.* **41,** 3279 (1970).
13. Peterson, G. E., Glass, A. M. and Negran, T. J., *Appl. Phys. Lett.* **19,** 130 (1971).
14. Chen, F. S., LaMacchia, J. T. and Fraser, D. B., *Appl. Phys. Lett.* **13,** 223 (1968).
15. Kogelnik, H., *Bell System Tech.* **48,** 2909 (1969).
16. *Phys. Stat. Sol.* (a) **9** 301 (1972). The optically excited current observed in this work appears to have pyroelectric origin—not photoconductivity as reported.
17. Peterson, G. E., Glass, A. M. and Carnevale, A., *J. Amer. Ceram. Soc.* **56,** 278 (1973).
18. Nash, D. L., submitted to *Appl. Optics.*
19. See for instance C. J. Ballhausen "Introduction to Ligand Field Theory" McGraw Hill Book, (New York, 1962).
20. DiDomenico, M., private communication.
21. Amodei, J. J., Phillips, W. and Staebler, D. L., *Appl. Optics* **11,** 390 (1972).
22. Clark, M. G., Di Salvo, F. J., Glass, A. M., and Peterson, G. E., *J. Chem. Phys.* Nov. (1973).
23. Ref. 21 reports small effects due to Mn and Cu impurities, but the Fe content of these crystals is not reported.
24. Staebler, D. L. and Amodei, J. J., *J. Appl. Phys.* **43,** 1042 (1972).
25. Resistivities of 10^{18} ohm cm have been reported for $LiNbO_3$ by Staebler, D. L. and Amodei, J. J., *Ferroelectrics* **3,** 107 (1972).
26. Glass, A. M. and Auston, D. H., *Optics Commun.* **5,** 45 (1972).
27. Staebler, D. L. and Amodei, J. J., *1972 Int. Quantum El. Conference, Montreal.*
28. Kaminow, I. P. and Turner, E. H., "Tables of Electrooptic Coefficients," Handbook of Lasers Chemical Rubber Co., 1971.
29. Kogelnik, H. and Shank, C. V., *J. Appl. Phys.* **43,** 2327 (1972).
30. Micheron, F. and Bismuth, G., *Int. Electrooptics Conference, 1972, Brighton, England.*
31. Shenke, D. P. and Smith, R. G., to be published.

9. Kerr Effect Devices

Microwave Modulation of Light Using the Kerr Effect*

D. F. Holshouser, H. Von Foerster, and G. L. Clark†
University of Illinois, Urbana, Illinois
(Received May 10, 1961)

Modulation of light at 3 and 6 kMc is achieved by applying a superimposed electrostatic and microwave field to a carbon-disulfide Kerr-cell which is incorporated within the high-electric-field region of a resonant cavity. The development of this light shutter requires the analysis of the Kerr effect under circumstances in which the transit time of light is appreciable. A Kerr cell whose length is such that the transit time of light is one-half the period of the modulating microwave field proves to have particular advantages over other designs. The light shutter is realized with a re-entrant microwave cavity with provision for the application of electrostatic as well as microwave fields. At about 26-kv dc and 10-kw pulsed 3-kMc ac power, the system modulates a light beam of several milliwatts radiant power up to 80%.

INTRODUCTION

Recent developments in the generation of coherent light have heightened interest in methods for the high-frequency modulation of light. While it appears that a small degree of modulation at microwave frequencies can be obtained by several techniques,[1] as yet large depths of modulation in this frequency range have been achieved only by the time-tested Kerr electro-optical effect.[2–4]

The realization of a Kerr cell shutter which modulates light at microwave frequencies poses several problems which are not present at low frequencies: (a) While the transit time of light through a Kerr cell of usual dimensions—i.e., a few centimeters—is negligible if the applied electric field oscillates with a low frequency, at microwave frequencies the transit time occupies an appreciable fraction of the period of the applied electric field; (b) the intense electric fields required to achieve significant light modulation are difficult to obtain at microwave frequencies; (c) bipolar liquids exhibiting high Kerr constants at low frequencies, e.g., nitrobenzene,[5] may become excessively lossy in microwave fields; and (d), since commercial light detectors cannot respond to microwave modulation, indirect methods for the measurement of amplitude and frequency of the modulated light are required.

The following paper presents an approach which circumvents these difficulties. First, expressions are derived which describe the behavior of a Kerr electro-optical shutter, taking into consideration finite transit time of the light passing through the system. It will be shown that two types of cells are of a particular advantage, namely, those for which the transit time is precisely one-half of the period of the applied electric field (π cell), and those for which it is only one-fourth of this period ($\frac{1}{2}\pi$ cell).

The requirements of high ac fields acting on the doubly refracting medium are met by incorporating the Kerr cell proper into the high field region of a cavity resonant at the frequency of the applied microwave field. An appreciable relaxation of these requirements is found in the π cell which is made operable by providing a certain amount of "dc bias" to the cell.

Due to the high electric field intensities obtained by this method it is now feasible to use birefringent media, as, e.g., carbon disulfide, which exhibit a comparably small Kerr constant, but absorb only a small fraction of the microwave power fed into the cavity.

Detection of the modulated light is accomplished by a phase interference technique in which the light beam traverses the cell twice.

Finally, details are presented of an experimental shutter system which provides up to 80% light modulation at and above frequencies of 3 kMc.

ANALYSIS

General Solution

As in the conventional Kerr cell shutter, the optical arrangement to be discussed is composed of doubly refracting elements placed between crossed polarizing elements which are oriented with axes at 45° with respect to the birefringent axis (Fig. 1). In this arrangement the light transmittance of the system is given by

$$\eta=\tfrac{1}{2}-\tfrac{1}{2}\cos\delta, \tag{1}$$

where δ is the total phase shift between the component of light with polarization coincident with the birefringent axis and the component whose polarization is perpendicular to this direction.

If, as in the arrangement shown in Fig. 1, the double refraction is the result of two optical elements, the Kerr cell producing a phase shift δ_E and a nonelectrical element producing a phase shift δ_{NE}, then the total double-refraction phase shift is given by the sum

$$\delta=\delta_{NE}+\delta_E. \tag{2}$$

* This work has been supported by the Air Force Office of Scientific Research.

† Presently at Space Technology Laboratories.

[1] P. S. Pershan, and N. Bloembergen, "Microwave modulation of light," Proceedings of Second Quantum Electronics Conference, Columbia University Press, New York (to be published).

[2] G. L. Clark, D. F. Holshouser, and H. M. Von Foerster, "The Kerr cell as an ultra-high frequency shutter," Tech. Rept. No. 1-1, Air Force contract, March, 1955.

[3] G. L. Clark, doctoral thesis, University of Illinois, Urbana, Illinois, 1957.

[4] D. F. Holshouser, doctoral thesis, University of Illinois, Urbana, Illinois, 1958.

[5] G. L. Clark, J. Chem. Phys. 25, 125–129 (1956).

The nonelectrical doubly refracting element, which might be a plate of glass under stress or a quarter-wave plate, is included in the system to achieve an adjustable parameter whose usefulness will become evident later.

If the electric field E, present within the Kerr cell, contains a frequency component so high that the amplitude of E changes appreciably during the transit of a photon through the cell, then the electrical double-refraction phase shift is given by the integral

$$\delta_E = 2\pi B \int_{-L/2}^{+L/2} E^2(s)ds, \qquad (3)$$

where B is the Kerr constant of the cell liquid, s is the distance along the light beam with the origin at the midpoint of the cell, and L is the length of the cell over which fields are present.

For this discussion it will be assumed that the Kerr constant B is the same for all frequencies of the modulating electric field and that the spectral range of the light beam is restricted so that the variation of B with light frequency may be neglected. For generality we shall consider the case where the electric field is composed of an electrostatic component and a single frequency microwave component, both uniform in space within the Kerr cell liquid, given by

$$E = E_0 + E_1 \sin\varphi_m \qquad (4)$$
$$\varphi_m = \omega_m t,$$

where ω_m is the angular microwave frequency and t is time.

In order to solve the integral in Eq. (3), it is desirable to transform it from a spatial to a temporal expression. This is done by recognizing that

$$ds = (c/n)dt = (c/n\omega_m)d\varphi_m, \qquad (5)$$

where c is the free space velocity of light and n is the index of refraction of the cell liquid. The limits of integration may be transformed according to

$$L = (c/\omega_m n)\Phi, \qquad (6)$$

where Φ, the "electrical length" of the cell, represents the change in phase of the microwave field during the transit of a photon through the cell of length L. For convenience, a normalizing parameter

$$A = (2\pi c B/n\omega_m)^{\frac{1}{2}}, \qquad (7)$$

and normalized dimensionless field components $\mathcal{E}_0$ and $\mathcal{E}_1$ are defined such that

$$\mathcal{E}_0 = AE_0 \qquad (8)$$

and

$$\mathcal{E}_1 = AE_1.$$

Using the expressions in Eqs. (4)–(8), Eq. (3) reduces to

$$\delta_E = \int_{\varphi-\frac{1}{2}\Phi}^{\varphi+\frac{1}{2}\Phi} (\mathcal{E}_0 + \mathcal{E}_1 \sin\varphi_m)^2 d\varphi_m, \qquad (9)$$

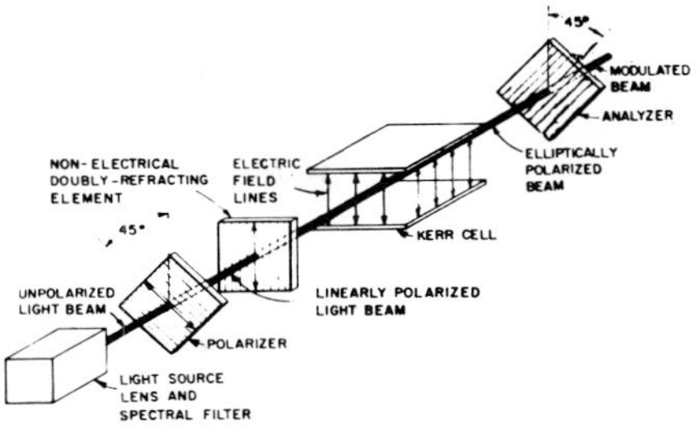

FIG. 1. Optical arrangement for Kerr cell light shutter.

where φ is the phase angle of the applied electric field at which the photon arrives at the midpoint of the cell. Equation (9) readily integrates to give as the solution

$$\delta_E = \Phi(\mathcal{E}_0^2 + \mathcal{E}_1^2) + 4\mathcal{E}_0\mathcal{E}_1 \sin\tfrac{1}{2}\Phi \sin\varphi - \tfrac{1}{2}\mathcal{E}_1^2 \sin\Phi \cos 2\varphi. \qquad (10)$$

This phase shift, added to the nonelectrical phase shift δ_{NE}, and substituted into Eq. (1), results in an expression for the light transmittance of the shutter as a function of the microwave field phase φ, with $\mathcal{E}_0$, $\mathcal{E}_1$, and δ_{NE} as operating parameters and Φ, the electrical length of the cell, as a design parameter. It can be readily seen that adjustment of these parameters can provide a great variety of light modulation waveforms. Even when the range of δ_E is restricted to values not exceeding 2π, either one, two, or four identical pulses of light can be obtained during each period of the applied microwave field; by increasing the field intensities to provide ranges of δ_E exceeding 2π, higher frequency (though nonidentical) light pulses may be achieved. Since experiment has shown that with carbon disulfide as the doubly refracting liquid and with microwave frequencies larger ranges of δ_E are difficult to achieve because of dielectric breakdown, this discussion is restricted to excursions of δ_E less than 2π.

A general discussion of Eq. (10) shows that certain choices of the parameters Φ and $\mathcal{E}_0$ have certain advantages over other possible choices, if it is desired to achieve greatest modulation with the smallest applied electric field intensities. Two cases of particular interest are the one where the electrical length of the cell $\Phi = \frac{1}{2}\pi$ and the superimposed dc field $\mathcal{E}_0 = 0$; and the other one where $\Phi = \pi$, but $\mathcal{E}_0 \neq 0$. In the $\frac{1}{2}\pi$-cell case the temporal variation of δ_E is twice the driving microwave frequency, ω_m, and in the π-cell case δ_E varies exactly with ω_m. These two cases are now discussed in more detail.

The $\frac{1}{2}\pi$ Cell

The total double-refraction phase shift δ, for $\Phi = \frac{1}{2}\pi$ and $\mathcal{E}_0 = 0$ is obtained from Eqs. (10) and (2) and may be expressed as the sum of a time-independent and an

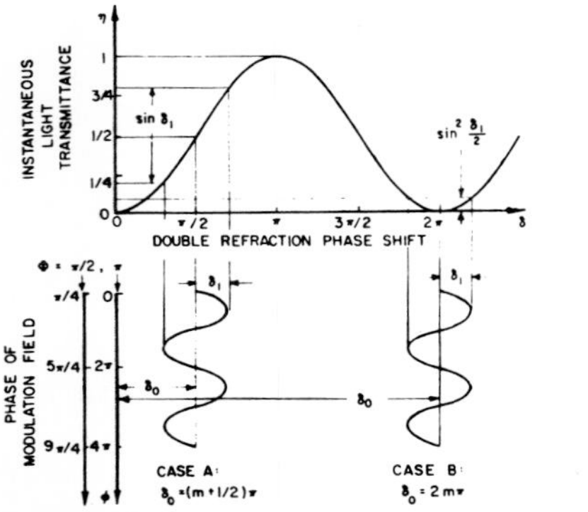

FIG. 2. Examples of light modulation for two operating modes (A) and (B) and for two choices of the electrical length of the Kerr cell: $\varphi=\frac{1}{2}\pi$ and $\varphi=\pi$.

oscillating term, i.e.,

$$\delta=\delta_0+\delta_1\cos 2\varphi, \tag{11}$$

where

$$\delta_0=\delta_{NE}+\tfrac{1}{4}\pi\mathcal{E}_1^2 \quad\text{and}\quad \delta_1=\tfrac{1}{2}\mathcal{E}_1^2.$$

There are two operating conditions of particular interest, both of which are schematically represented in Fig. 2. They are:

Case A, for which $\delta_0=\delta_{0A}=(m+\frac{1}{2})\pi$,

and

Case B, for which $\delta_0=\delta_{0B}=2m\pi$,

m representing any integer.

For case A, the light modulation is about the point for which $d\eta/d\delta$ is maximum so that the greatest range in light transmittance is achieved for a given field amplitude; the light modulation frequency is twice the driving microwave frequency. The range of shutter transmittance for this case is

$$\Delta\eta_A=\sin\tfrac{1}{2}\mathcal{E}_1^2.$$

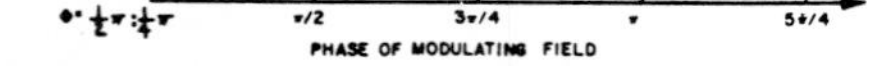

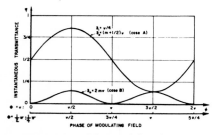

FIG. 3. Time variation of light transmission η for two Kerr cell lengths ($\varphi=\frac{1}{2}\pi$ and π) and two operating modes A and B.

In case B, the amplitude of light modulation is less, but the frequency is four times the driving modulating frequency. In this case the range of shutter transmittance is given by

$$\Delta\eta_B=\sin^2\tfrac{1}{4}\mathcal{E}_1^2.$$

Figure 3 shows examples of the modulation waveforms for the two cases.

The π Cell

For a cell whose length corresponds to $\Phi=\pi$, and to which is applied an electrostatic field as well as the microwave field, the total double-refraction phase shift δ can again be expressed as the sum of a time-independent and an oscillating term:

$$\delta=\delta_0+\delta_1\sin\varphi \tag{12}$$

where

$$\delta_0=\delta_{NE}+\pi\mathcal{E}_0^2+\tfrac{1}{2}\pi\mathcal{E}_1^2$$

and

$$\delta_1=4\mathcal{E}_0\mathcal{E}_1.$$

Figures 2 and 3, referred to earlier, also show modulation characteristics of the π cell. The two cases A and B, as described in the previous section, apply as well to the π cell.

For case A, the greater light modulation is obtained and the modulation frequency is equal to the driving microwave frequency. The range of shutter transmittance is

$$\Delta\eta_A=\sin 4\mathcal{E}_0\mathcal{E}_1.$$

For case B, the light modulation frequency is twice the driving microwave frequency, and

$$\Delta\eta_B=\sin^2 2\mathcal{E}_0\mathcal{E}_1.$$

It is to be noted that for the π cell no light modulation occurs when the electrostatic field vanishes. However, one has the opportunity to minimize the microwave field required by making the electrostatic field large.

Comparison of $\frac{1}{2}\pi$ Cells and π Cells

Suppose that dielectric breakdown within the Kerr cell is the factor which ultimately limits the amount of light modulation which can be obtained. If E_M is the

TABLE I. The comparison of π and $\frac{1}{2}\pi$ Kerr Cells with same peak total field E_M, and same light pulse frequency ω_p; ($\gamma=2\pi cBE_m^2/n\omega_p$).

Cell length L/λ_m	Φ Radians	Static field E_0	Microwave field E_1	Static double refraction δ_0/π	Range of transmittance $\Delta\eta$	Frequency ratio ω_m/ω_p
$\frac{1}{4}$	$\frac{1}{2}\pi$	0	E_M	$m+\frac{1}{2}$	$\sin\gamma$	$\frac{1}{2}$
				$2m$	$\sin^2\gamma$	$\frac{1}{4}$
$\frac{1}{2}$	π	$E_M/2$	$E_M/2$	$m+\frac{1}{2}$	$\sin\gamma$	1
				$2m$	$\sin^2\gamma$	$\frac{1}{2}$

peak instantaneous field that can be tolerated, it is of interest to find whether the $\frac{1}{2}\pi$ cell or the $\frac{1}{2}\pi$ cell provides the greater light modulation. Under these circumstances the amplitude of the microwave field for the $\frac{1}{2}\pi$ cell is E_M, with $E_0=0$, while for the π cell $E_0=E_1=\frac{1}{2}E_M$ gives the greatest modulation. Table I summarizes the modulation properties of the two cells.

A study of this table shows that the maximum modulation amplitudes are identical for the two cell lengths. The π cell has the advantage that lower microwave fields are required; the $\frac{1}{2}\pi$ cell requires lower driving microwave frequency for the same light-modulation amplitude and frequency.

Methods of Detection

Since there are no photosensitive devices which respond to light modulated at microwave frequencies, methods had to be devised for determining the modulation of light from measurements of average light transmittance. The simplest scheme is to measure the average light transmittance as a function of applied electric field. We have for the average light transmittance:

$$\bar{\eta}=\frac{1}{2\pi}\int_0^{2\pi}\eta(\varphi)d\varphi,$$

and thus, by combining either Eqs. (1) and (11), or Eqs. (1) and (12), one obtains

$$\bar{\eta}=\tfrac{1}{2}-\tfrac{1}{2}\cos\delta_0\cdot J_0(\delta_1), \qquad (13)$$

where J_0 is the zeroth-order Bessel function. If the field amplitudes E_0 and E_1 and the nonelectrical double-refraction phase shift δ_{NE} are known, this expression may be used to predict the average light transmittance of the light shutter. It is to be noted that Eq. (13) does not contain the modulation frequency.

A second method of detection which measures the light modulation frequency by phase interference is realized by a shutter arrangement as shown in Fig. 7. A single polarizing element is used and the light beam is reflected from a movable mirror to provide a second transit through the Kerr cell. For this arrangement the instantaneous light transmittance,

$$\eta_{\frac{1}{2}\pi}=\tfrac{1}{2}+\tfrac{1}{2}\cos2(\delta_0+\delta_1\cos\varphi_1\sin\varphi) \qquad (14a)$$

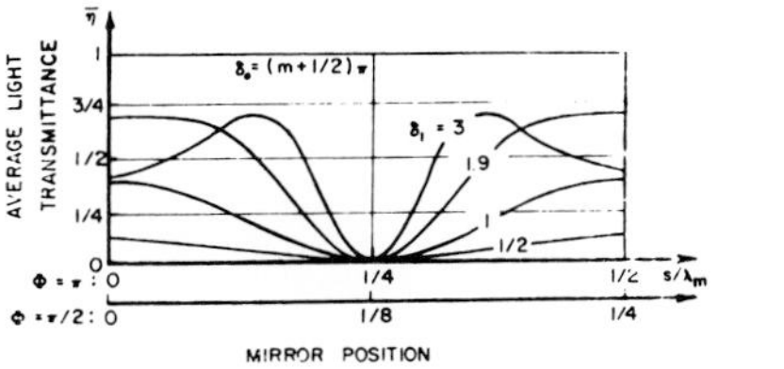

FIG. 4. Variation of average light transmission with mirror position for interference method of detection.

and

$$\eta_\pi=\tfrac{1}{2}+\tfrac{1}{2}\cos2(\delta_0+\delta_1\cos2\varphi_1\cos2\varphi) \qquad (14b)$$

for $\frac{1}{2}\pi$ and π cells, respectively, and φ_1 is the microwave phase shift while light travels the distance s from the cell midpoint to the movable mirror, and may be expressed in terms of the microwave wavelength λ_m by

$$\varphi_1=2\pi s/\lambda_m. \qquad (15)$$

The time average of light transittance for this system is found to be

$$\bar{\eta}=\tfrac{1}{2}+\tfrac{1}{2}\cos2\delta_0\cdot J_0[2\delta_1\cos(2\pi^2s/\Phi\lambda_m)]. \qquad (16)$$

Figure 4 is a graphical representation of Eq. (16) for a single value of δ_0 and several values of δ_1 and it is evident that, as the mirror is moved, appreciable changes in average light transmittance may be realized. The wavelength of the light modulation frequency is obtained by merely measuring the distance between mirror positions which produce minimum transmittance.

EXPERIMENTAL

Kerr Cavity

In order to minimize the microwave field requirements, the length chosen for the physical model was that corresponding to the π cell. To achieve the maximum microwave field intensity within the cell for a given microwave power input, the cell is incorporated into a resonant structure with provisions for superimposing the necessary electrostatic field. Figure 5 illustrates the basic structure of such a "Kerr cavity."

The high-electric-field region is in the central portion of the cavity and is filled with carbon-disulfide. Bubbles are eliminated and purity maintained in the liquid by continuous distillation. A light beam of cross section 2×4 mm is accommodated.

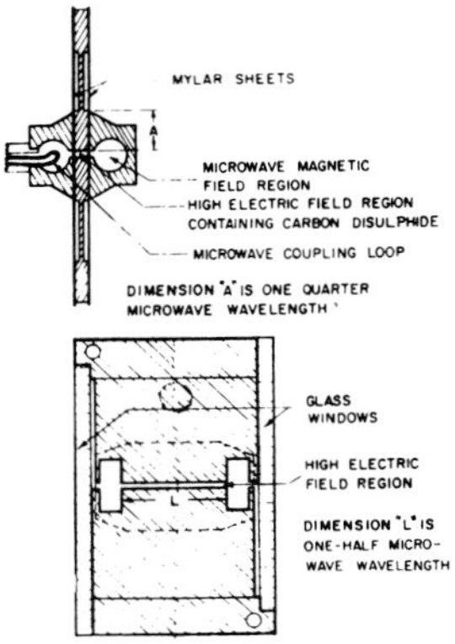

FIG. 5. Cross-sectional sketches of π Kerr cavity.

FIG. 6. Photograph of the Kerr cavity.

The magnetic microwave fields are largely confined to the region outside the electric field region, and microwave power is coupled into the cavity through a loop. The outer cavity sections are electrostatically isolated from the central section by $\frac{1}{4}$-mm-thick sheets of Mylar which also confine the carbon-disulfide. Quarter-wave transmission line segments provide an rf short between the outer and central sections.

The Kerr cavity assembly shown in the photograph of Fig. 6 is designed to be driven with 3-kMc-microwave power up to 15 kw and electrostatic potentials up to 40 kv. The microwave Q of the system lies between 150 and 500.

Detection

The phase interference method described earlier, involving the experimental arrangement shown in Fig. 7, has been used to determine the light modulation properties of the Kerr cavity just described. The light source is an Osram high-pressure mercury lamp. A low-frequency revolving light shutter is included in the system, in order to discern the effects of stray light and stray microwave fields. A photomultiplier connected to a preamplifier and oscilloscope detects the average light transmittance. The source of microwave power is a modified APS-2F radar transmitter generating 1-μsec pulses of microwave power at 120 pps.

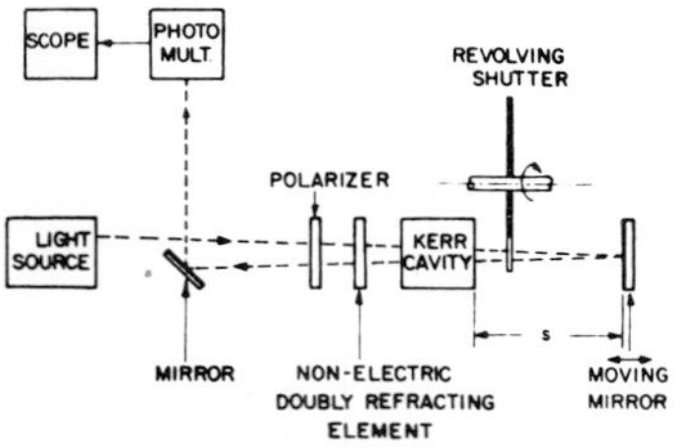

FIG. 7. Experimental arrangement for detection of microwave modulated light by interference.

Typical oscillograms of the photomultiplier output for several mirror positions are shown in Fig. 8. In each photograph the upper trace occurs with the mechanical shutter open, the lower trace with it closed. The pulses shown are approximately 1-μsec long and coincide with the driving microwave pulses.

Table II presents a set of experimental data for twenty-one mirror positions, covering more than two periods of variation of the average light transmittance. Due to nonuniform stress in the Kerr cavity windows and stray light, the minimum irradiance I_{10}, obtained by adjusting the electrostatic field, is appreciable for this particular set of data. Average light transmittance $\bar{\eta}$ was computed as the ratio of the increase of irradiance above the minimum level to the irradiance with no fields. Inspection of Table II shows that the observed maxima of the average light transmittance $\bar{\eta}$ are not equal, but linearly increasing with increasing mirror distance s. This inequality is believed due to nonuniformity in modulation of the light across the breadth of the beam. By applying a correction factor, linear with mirror positions, to the values for $\bar{\eta}$, the maxima are equalized yielding the values $\bar{\eta}^*$. These values are plotted in Fig. 9 (circles) together with values of $\bar{\eta}$ obtained from Eq. (16) (solid line).

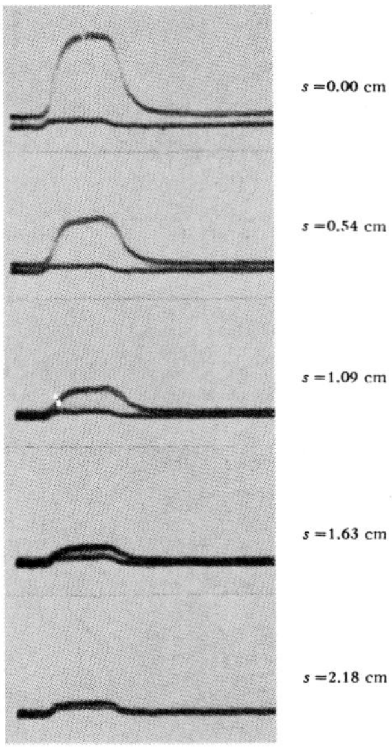

FIG. 8. Oscilloscope traces of photomultiplier outputs for several mirror positions.

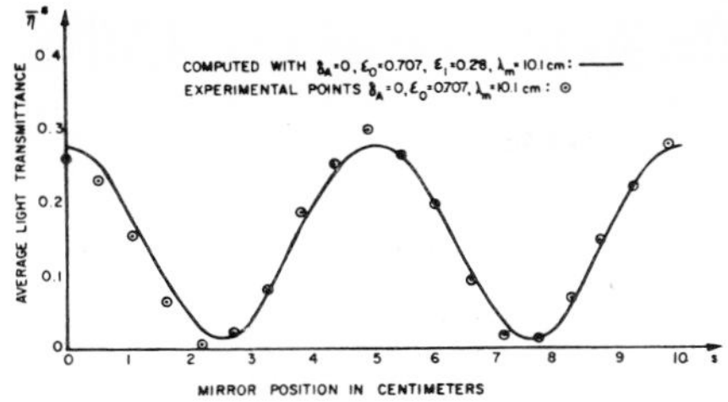

FIG. 9. Comparison of calculated curve with experimental data in phase interference experiment.

CONCLUSIONS

By comparing the points obtained from experiment and from Eq. (16), it can be safely concluded that the light is modulated at a frequency near 3 kMc ($\lambda_m \simeq 10$ cm) and that the normalized microwave field amplitude corresponds to approximately $\epsilon_1 = 0.28$. With the knowledge of the two field parameters ϵ_0 and ϵ_1 the operation of the Kerr cavity in the conventional shutter arrangement with a single transit of light is established through Eqs. (1) and (12). For the two modes of operation—case A and case B—as mentioned before the following results are obtained:

	δ_0	$\Delta\eta$	Light frequency	Pulse width picoseconds
Case A	$(m+\frac{1}{2})\pi$	0.71	3 kMc	170
Case B	$2m\pi$	0.15	6 kMc	80

Thus, large depths of modulation of light at microwave frequencies are obtainable with appropriate modifications of the classical Kerr cell. However, considerable microwave power is required. Since the dielectric losses of carbon disulfide appear to be low at 3 kMc, it is presumed that still shorter light pulses, possibly as short as 10 picoseconds, are realizable.

Note added in proof. Attention is called to the following publication: I. P. Kaminow, Phys. Rev. Letters **6**, 528 (1961).

TABLE II. Experimental data for phase interference experiment under conditions: $\delta_{NR}=0$, $E_0=26$ kv, $\lambda_m=10.1$ cm, approximately 10-kw pulsed microwave power, cavity Q of 180.

	Relative photomultiplier output with				
Relative mirror position (cm)	No. fields I_∞	dc field only I_{10}	combined fields I_{11}	$\bar{\eta}=\frac{I_{11}-I_{10}}{I_\infty}$	$\bar{\eta}^*$
0	132	37	64	0.20	0.25
0.54	132	37	61	0.19	0.23
1.09	114	32	46	0.13	0.15
1.63	97	27	32	0.05	0.06
2.18	94	26	26	0.01	0.01
2.72	90	25	27	0.02	0.02
3.27	90	25	31	0.07	0.08
3.81	92	26	41	0.17	0.18
4.36	90	25	46	0.24	0.25
4.90	89	25	51	0.29	0.30
5.45	86	24	47	0.27	0.26
6.00	88	24	42	0.20	0.19
6.54	88	24	33	0.10	0.09
7.09	91	25	27	0.02	0.02
7.63	89	25	26	0.02	0.01
8.18	90	25	32	0.08	0.07
8.72	89	25	40	0.18	0.14
9.27	90	25	50	0.28	0.22
9.82	94	26	60	0.36	0.28
10.35	93	26	58	0.35	0.25
10.90	91	25	52	0.30	0.21

Reprinted from JOURNAL OF THE OPTICAL SOCIETY OF AMERICA, Vol. 51, No. 12, 1360–1365, December, 1961
Printed in U. S. A.

Reprinted from APPLIED OPTICS, Vol. 5, page 1652, October 1966

Carbon Disulfide Traveling-Wave Kerr Cells

A. J. CHENOWETH, O. L. GADDY, AND D. F. HOLSHOUSER

Abstract—**Carbon disulfide has identical microwave and optical dielectric constants, as well as extremely low optical and microwave loss. These properties make it possible to construct long traveling-wave light modulators at microwave frequencies using the Kerr electrooptic effect induced in CS_2 by an electric field propagating on a TEM transmission line.**

Several experiments with traveling-wave Kerr cells consisting of resonant strip transmission lines immersed in CS_2 are described. A decrease in the microwave power required for modulation by a factor of two, by cooling the modulators to a temperature of $-55°C$, is demonstrated. Simultaneous modulation of light at two microwave frequencies by excitation of two of the longitudinal modes of the strip line resonator is also described. Relatively high efficiency modulation with long devices of this type is also reported. In these experiments, the microwave power required for large depths of modulation is reduced by almost two orders of magnitude compared to previously reported CS_2 light modulators, and is within less than a factor of two of the calculated power for cells up to 44 cm in length. For longer cells, increasingly larger than predicted powers are required.

Introduction

Carbon disulfide was used as the electrooptic material in Kerr cell devices for modulation of light at microwave frequencies as early as 1957 [1]. These early modulators were constructed so that the optical transit time was one-half of the period of the modulating frequency in order to reduce transit time effects, and these devices typically required several kilowatts of microwave power to achieve large depths of modulation [2], [3]. Microwave frequency light modulators using the linear electrooptic effect in solids have also been reported [4].

Although the Kerr effect in carbon disulfide is relatively weak compared to electrooptic effects in nitrobenzene and other materials, it is attractive as a material for microwave frequency light modulation for a number of reasons. This material has extremely low optical and microwave loss. The loss tangent is typically of the order of 10^{-4} at frequencies up through 15 Gc/s [5], [6], and optical attenuation is quite low in the visible and near infrared out to approximately 2 microns [7]. In addition, CS_2 is a nonpolar liquid with almost identical microwave and optical dielectric constants, which makes it extremely simple to construct low dispersion traveling-wave modulators using TEM transmission line structures. Finally, since the material is a readily available liquid, almost any length structure that is desired may be realized inexpensively. Recent work with carbon disulfide light modulators using traveling-wave structures has resulted in experimental modulators that require considerably less microwave power than earlier CS_2 devices. The results of these and other experiments will be reported in this paper.

Manuscript received May 19, 1966. This work was supported by the Air Force Office of Scientific Research under Grant AF-AFOSR 390-65.

The authors are with the Department of Electrical Engineering, University of Illinois, Urbana, Ill.

Description

In a traveling-wave Kerr cell filled with liquid carbon disulfide, a TEM transmission line may be used as the Kerr cell electrodes. A light beam propagating between the conductors of a transmission line immersed in liquid carbon disulfide travels at precisely the same velocity as a microwave signal traveling in the same direction on the line. The transverse electric field of the modulating signal, therefore, maintains velocity synchronism with the light. The light thus experiences a constant electrically induced birefringence as it traverses the entire length of the cell. Such a modulator is illustrated schematically in Fig. 1.

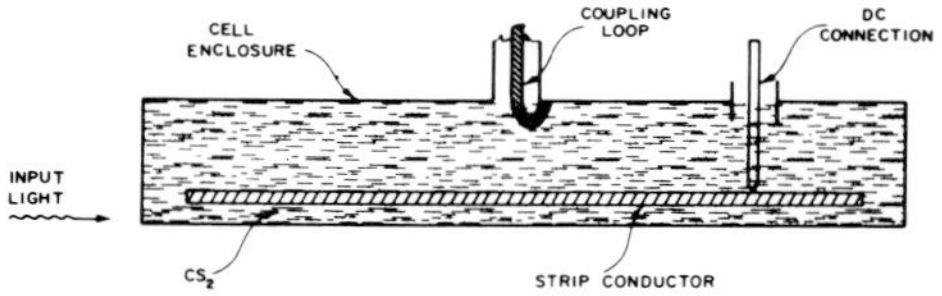

Fig. 1. Schematic drawing of a traveling-wave Kerr cell.

Here an enclosed strip transmission line immersed in carbon disulfide is made an integral number of one-half wavelengths long at the microwave modulating frequency and is effectively open-circuited at both ends. This transmission line system then becomes a longitudinal microwave resonator which can be excited by means of the inductive coupling loop shown on the drawing. The resulting electric field standing wave pattern between the conductors consists of equal amplitude forward and backward traveling waves. The light entering the optical window at one end travels in synchronism with one of the traveling microwave modulating waves and interacts with the induced birefringence over the entire length of the transmission line resonator. It will be shown later that interaction with the backward wave can be avoided.

Since the Kerr effect is quadratic with electric field, it is necessary to dc bias the cell in order to obtain nearly linear modulation at the same frequency as the modulating signal. This dc biasing is accomplished either by means of a thin probe directly connected to the strip conductor at one of the RF electric field minima or by high impedance resistors connected to the ends of the conductors in order to reduce the disturbance of the RF field distribution on the conductor.

Analysis of the Traveling-Wave Kerr Cell

As with the conventional Kerr cell, a birefringent phase shift between horizontal and vertical components of light is produced as it passes through the cell upon application of electric field. In general, this phase shift δ is given by

$$\delta = 2\pi B \int_{-L/2}^{L/2} E^2(z, t)dz \tag{1}$$

where B is the Kerr constant, L is the optical path length of the cell in the z direction, and $E(z, t)$ is the electric field between the electrodes in the cell.

In a traveling-wave Kerr cell, the electric field can consist of a dc term E_0 and two running waves of amplitude E_1 and E_2 varying at the modulation frequency ω and traveling in opposite directions.

$$E(z, t) = E_0 + E_1 \sin(\omega t - \beta z) + E_2 \sin(\omega t + \beta z) \tag{2}$$

where β is the phase constant of the line. The electric field seen by a phase front of light traveling with velocity ω/β is

$$E(z, \phi_0) = E_0 + E_1 \sin \phi_0 + E_2 \sin(\phi_0 + 2\beta z) \tag{3}$$

where ϕ_0 is the phase of the electric field at $z=0$. With this field, the birefringent phase shift becomes

$$\delta(\phi_0) = 2\pi BL\left\{E_0^2 + \frac{E_1^2}{2} + \frac{E_2^2}{2} + E_1E_2\frac{\sin \beta L}{\beta L} + 2E_0E_1\left[1 + \frac{E_2}{E_1}\frac{\sin \beta L}{\beta L}\right]\sin \phi_0 + \left[\frac{E_1^2}{2} - E_1E_2\frac{\sin \beta L}{\beta L} + E_2^2\frac{\sin 2\beta L}{2\beta L}\right]\cos 2\phi_0\right\}. \tag{4}$$

The birefringent phase shift thus consists of three components: a dc or constant phase shift term, a component varying at the modulation frequency ω, and a double frequency component.

The term of most interest, of course, is the second, i.e., the one varying at the fundamental frequency ω; and it is seen from (4) that the amplitude of this term is proportional to the product E_0E_1. Clearly, one may minimize the ac field requirement for the modulation by using as high a dc field as possible. Under most conditions, E_0 will be very much greater than E_1 or E_2 and (4) can be simplified to

$$\delta(\phi_0) \approx \delta_0 + \delta_m \sin \phi_0 \tag{5}$$

where

$$\delta_0 \approx 2\pi BLE_0^2 \tag{6}$$

and

$$\delta_m = 4\pi BLE_0E_1\left[1 + \frac{E_2}{E_1}\frac{\sin \beta L}{\beta L}\right] \tag{7}$$

Under these conditions, the double frequency variation of δ is negligible. Examination of (7) shows that the interaction of the backward wave with the light varies periodically with the length of the interaction, and becomes very small as the length becomes large. Also, if the electrode length is precisely an integral number of half-wavelengths at the modulation frequency, no interaction with the backward wave occurs at all. This is the case for the modulator shown in Fig. 1 where the transmission line forms a longitudinal resonator at the modulating frequency.

A terminated transmission line could also be used to establish the fields in a device of this type, and this would completely eliminate, or at least minimize, the backward wave. This type of operation increases the microwave power required to establish the necessary fields for significant depths of modulation; however, operation over a much larger bandwidth would be possible than in the resonant case. The modulation bandwidth possible with the resonant case is not insignificant, however. This results because this type of resonant system has an infinite number of resonant modes. The open-circuited line resonator of Fig. 1 is resonant at every frequency for which the line length L is an integral number of one-half wavelengths. These resonant frequencies are spaced in frequency by a factor of $c/2\sqrt{\epsilon_r}L$ where ϵ_r is the relative dielectric constant of the liquid and c is the free space velocity of light. Microwave subcarrier modulation signals could, therefore, be applied to the Kerr cell at each of these resonances. With a cell length of say 1 meter, the resonant frequencies would be spaced approximately every 100 Mc/s. If each of the resonances were driven with a subcarrier in the frequency range 100 to 10 000 Mc/s and if each subcarrier modulation bandwidth were 10 Mc/s, a total information bandwidth of 1000 Mc/s would be possible. In addition, two or more of these cells could be placed in tandem with the resonances staggered, providing additional bandwidth capability.

Modulation Power Requirements

An advantage of carbon disulfide as an electrooptic material for light modulators is its extremely low dielectric loss at microwave frequencies. The modulation power required, in most cases, results primarily from ohmic losses in the structure supporting the electric fields rather than dielectric losses. Since relatively high electric field intensities are needed to provide large depths of modulation in Kerr cells using carbon disulfide, ohmic losses can be a significant factor in microwave power dissipation.

Power required to produce a given electric field in the configuration illustrated in Fig. 1 can be easily estimated. In this case, E_1 and E_2 are equal, and the expression for the ac component of the standing wave electric field on the line becomes

$$E_{AC} = 2E_1 \sin \phi_0 \cos \beta z. \tag{8}$$

If this electric field is assumed to be confined to a region between two strip conductors of spacing a, width b, and length L in the z direction, the power dissipated in ohmic losses in the conductors P_c is given by

$$P_c = \frac{2R_s bL}{\eta^2} \tag{9}$$

where η is the intrinsic impedance of the medium between the conductors and R_s is the surface resistance of the conductors [8].

The dielectric loss P_d in the liquid carbon disulfide can also be calculated

$$P_d = \iiint \frac{\sigma_d E_{AC}{}^2}{2}\,dxdydz = \sigma_d baLE_1{}^2 \tag{10}$$

where σ_d is the effective conductivity of the dielectric at the modulating frequency as given by the loss tangent. These expressions for ohmic and dielectric loss ignore the losses introduced by fringing fields on the line. This increase in power dissipated can be accounted for by multiplying these expressions by a "fringing field factor" F which is the ratio of the measured capacitance per unit length to that calculated assuming no fringing fields. The total microwave power required is the sum of the ohmic and dielectric losses

$$P = \left[\sigma_d a + \frac{2R_s}{\eta^2}\right] FbLE_1{}^2. \tag{11}$$

For frequencies below 10 Gc/s, the ohmic loss term of (11) is the most predominant in CS_2 Kerr cells, and the two terms are equal at frequencies near 15 Gc/s for $a = 0.2$ cm.

Depth of Modulation

If the light entering the traveling-wave Kerr cell is polarized at an angle of 45° with respect to the direction of the electric field in the cell, the polarization of the output light beam is modulated at a microwave rate. Placing a polarizing filter at the output window of the cell converts this elliptically polarized light to intensity modulated light. If the output polarizing filter (analyzer) is crossed with respect to the polarization of the input light, the instantaneous transmittance of the system is given by

$$T(\delta) = \tfrac{1}{2} - \tfrac{1}{2}\cos\delta \tag{12}$$

where δ is given by (5).

When the dc field is adjusted for an average transmittance of 0.5, the depth of intensity modulation m is defined as

$$m = T_{\max} - T_{\min}. \tag{13}$$

The depth of modulation can then be expressed as

$$m = \sin\delta_m. \tag{14}$$

Using (7), (11), and (14), the microwave power required for a given depth of modulation is obtained, viz.:

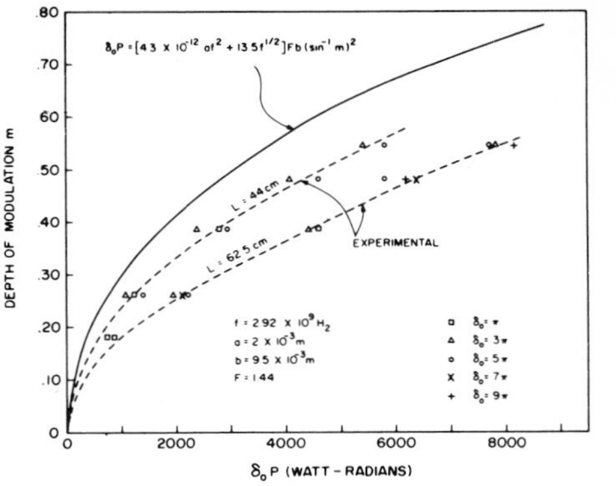

Fig. 2. Calculated and measured depth of modulation vs. power required for CS_2 traveling-wave Kerr cells at room temperature.

$$P = \left[\sigma_d a + \frac{2R_s}{\eta^2}\right] \frac{Fb(\sin^{-1} m)^2}{16\pi^2 B^2 LE_0{}^2}. \tag{15}$$

The power required for small depths of modulation, therefore, varies as m^2 and inversely with the square of the applied dc field. Also, the power is seen to vary inversely with the length of the device. Making the cell long and utilizing as high a dc field as possible, therefore, reduces the amount of microwave power required for a given depth of modulation.

Another interesting feature of this type of modulator, pointed out by the above relationship, is that the power required for modulation varies inversely as the square of the Kerr constant B. It is known that the magnitude of the Kerr constant for nonpolar liquids such as CS_2 varies inversely with absolute temperature of the liquid [9]. As a result of this, the power required for modulation varies as the square of the absolute temperature. This reduction in microwave power required by cooling the modulator has been observed and the results will be described below.

Knowing that (in MKS units) the permittivity and Kerr constant in CS_2 are, respectively,

$$\epsilon = 2.33 \times 10^{-11} \quad \text{and} \quad B = 3.2 \times 10^{-14};$$

that the loss tangent of CS_2 as a function of frequency f may be approximated [5] by

$$\tan\delta_L = 8\pi \times 10^{-15} f;$$

and that the surface resistance of the conductors may be expressed by

$$R_s = 2.5 \times 10^{-7}\sqrt{f},$$

appropriate substitutions may be made in (15) to yield a useful expression for the product of dc birefringence (radians) and required power (watts), viz.:

$$\delta_0 P = [4.6 \times 10^{-12}\, af^2 + 11.6\sqrt{f}] Fb(\sin^{-1} m)^2. \tag{16}$$

This expression is plotted in Fig. 2, together with experimental data to be discussed, for modulators of a particular geometry and frequency.

In testing this type of modulator, it is usually convenient to measure depth of modulation by measuring the change in average light or average transmittance $\overline{T}$ after first biasing the cell with dc to a minimum in the transmittance-phase shift relationship; that is at $\delta_0 = k\pi$, $k = 1, 2, 3, \cdots$. Application of the microwave modulating field then results in double frequency modulation; however, a change in average light transmittance also occurs. This change in average light can be measured and related to the depth of modulation one would obtain by shifting the operating point to $T = 0.5$ and applying the same amplitude microwave modulating electric field [3].

Experimental Results

Two types of experimental traveling-wave Kerr cell light modulators were constructed and tested. The first type consisted of a rectangular brass enclosure with an unbalanced strip line conductor held at a spacing of 2 mm from one of the walls by teflon insulators. The length of the strip conductor was 37 cm and was open-circuited at both ends making it 6 wavelengths long at a frequency of approximately 3 Gc/s. Double walled optical windows were sealed to end flanges which were sealed to flanges on the guide by means of teflon gaskets. This type of modulator was used in the low temperature experiments to be described below. A photograph of a similar device may be found in [5].

The second type of modulator consisted of a pair of balanced strip conductors of width 0.9 cm, held at a spacing of 2 mm by teflon insulators, and enclosed by a long glass tube. A cylindrical metal shield enclosed the tube providing RF shielding for the transmission line. Dc connections were made by means of high RF impedance resistors connected to the ends of each conductor, and the structure was excited with a coupling loop inserted into an indentation in the glass tube. Optical window assemblies were sealed to the glass tube with flanges and teflon gaskets. Figure 3 illustrates one of these Kerr cells.

In the experiments using these modulators, a He-Ne gas laser operating at 6328 Å served as the light source. A 0–30 kV dc power supply was used to apply the dc field to the Kerr cell electrodes, and a pulsed S-band magnetron and a triode cavity oscillator provided the microwave power for the experiments. The Kerr cells were filled with reagent grade carbon disulfide, no purification or distillation of the liquid used in these experiments was required. The depth of modulation produced for various values of microwave power input was measured under a number of conditions with both type modulators using the method discussed above.

The traveling-wave Kerr cell constructed with the rectangular metal enclosure was used to determine the effect of reducing the temperature of carbon disulfide on the Kerr constant and microwave power required for modulation. Measurements of power required for 50 percent modulation ($m = 0.5$) were first made at room temperature ($T = 20°C$) for two values of dc electric field E_0 which correspond to a dc birefringence δ_0 of π and 3π. The device was then placed in a hollow foamed plastic insulating enclosure, surrounded by dry ice, and allowed to come to temperature equilibrium at approximately $-55°C$. Measurements were again made of power required for 50 percent modulation with several values of applied dc field. The results of these measurements are shown in Table I for both temperatures, along with the calculated power for each condition as given by (18).

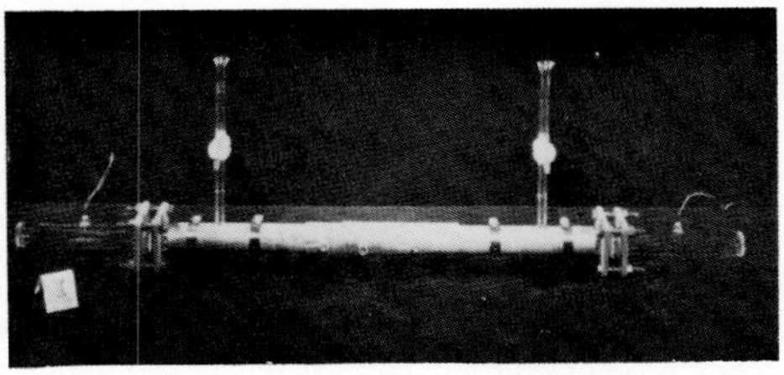

Fig. 3. Photograph of an experimental traveling-wave Kerr cell using a balanced strip line and a glass enclosure.

TABLE I

$T = 20°C$, $m = 0.5$

δ_0	E_0 (volts/meter)	Measured P (watts)	Calculated P (watts)
π	6×10^6	4800	775
3π	10^7	2100	258

$T = -55°C$, $m = 0.5$

δ_0	E_0 (volts/meter)	Measured P (watts)	Calculated P (watts)
π	4.4×10^6	3500	576
5π	1.08×10^7	800	115

It was pointed out above that the Kerr constant of nonpolar liquids such as CS_2 varies inversely with the absolute temperature. The ratio of the two temperatures in Table I is 1.35. Inspection of (18) shows that, at constant m and δ_0, the power required varies inversely with B, hence the power required at the low temperature should be reduced by the temperature ratio for the same δ_0, and the results shown in Table I agree with this within experimental error. Equation (15) indicates that, at constant E_0, the power required for a given depth of modulation varies inversely with B^2 and, therefore, should be proportional to T^2. The results shown in Table I also agree within experimental error. Reducing the temperature of the modulator to $-55°C$, therefore, lowers the power required for modulation by approximately a factor of two with constant E_0. In addition, it was found that higher dc fields could be safely applied to the device at low temperatures, further reducing power requirements. At reduced temperatures the breakdown field increased by at least 50 percent over the 1.0 to 1.5×10^7 volt-meter^{-1} observed at room temperature.

The measured and calculated power for this modulator differed by a factor of 6 to 8. This was due to power loss caused by applying the dc voltage to the strip conductor by means of a probe at a voltage minimum. Some RF power was consequently coupled out of the resonator, increasing the power requirement for modulation.

Much better agreement between measured and calculated power was obtained with the second type of experimental modulator. The dc field was applied to the ends of the pair of strip electrodes in these devices through resistors, virtually eliminating power loss at the dc connection point. Some experimental results with two of these modulators of length 44 and 62 cm at room temperature are shown plotted in Fig. 2, along with the calculated relationship between depth of modulation and power. The data shown represents several values of δ_0 (or E_0) for each modulator. For the 44 cm long modulator, the ratio of the measured to calculated power was consistently 1.5 and the same ratio for the 62.5 cm long device was 2.5. Experiments with a 100 cm long modulator resulted in measured power more than 50 times greater than the calculated power. The reason for this increasing discrepancy between measured and calculated power with increasing electrode length is not immediately apparent at this time. The effect, however, does appear to be similar to an effect that would be expected if the velocity of propagation of the light and microwave field differed by approximately 10 percent. Measurement of the optical index of refraction of the liquid with a Michelson interferometer, and the microwave phase velocity on the strip line resonator by a perturbation method, yield agreement between the two velocities within 1 percent. This effect is currently being investigated further.

Another experiment that was performed, using the glass enclosed traveling-wave Kerr cell modulators, was the simultaneous modulation of light at two microwave frequencies. Two independent microwave sources were used to excite the strip line resonator with two different coupling loops. The 44 cm cell was used in these experiments with resonances at 2.5 and 2.92 Gc/s. Depths of modulation were obtained which agreed closely with the theory, and very little coupling and interaction between two sources was observed. The calculated loaded Q for the modulators for each resonance in this frequency range is approximately 700.

Discussion of Results

Experiments in which CS_2 traveling-wave Kerr cells were operated at reduced temperatures have shown that significant reduction in microwave power required for modulation can be achieved in this manner. A decrease in the power required can be accomplished by increasing the Kerr constant as well as the dielectric strength of the liquid. Power reduction greater than a factor of two has been achieved by cooling the devices to a temperature of $-55°C$. Further reduction of temperature to slightly above the freezing point of CS_2 ($-110°C$) would be expected to result in even greater reduction in microwave power requirements.

Relatively long interaction length, high efficiency devices of this type have also been constructed and tested. With cells 44 cm long, 50 percent modulation has been achieved at 3 Gc/s with a microwave power of less than 190 watts and 18 percent modulation with only 48 watts. Extrapolation of these experimental results to lower depths of modulation indicate that 5 to 10 percent modulation should be possible with power levels of only a few watts on a continuous basis.

In addition, it has been shown that light modulation can simultaneously be achieved efficiently at two microwave frequencies with devices of this type by exciting the modulator at two of the strip line longitudinal resonances. Simultaneous modulation at more than two microwave frequencies should be possible with this type of modulator.

The traveling-wave carbon disulfide Kerr cells described above thus combine the advantages of resonant and traveling-wave devices by reduction of microwave power requirements, by utilizing long traveling wave structures while at the same time reducing the power requirements further by utilizing a resonant transmission line system. With this type of device it is possible to modulate light at many frequencies from the UHF to microwave region and modulation depths of a few percent should be possible on a CW basis with only a few watts of power.

Acknowledgment

The authors wish to acknowledge the invaluable assistance of A. B. Wilson, K. Kuehl, M. Watson, and E. Boose in the construction of the experimental devices reported in this paper.

References

[1] G. L. Clark, "The Kerr cell as a microwave frequency optical shutter," Ph.D. dissertation, University of Illinois, Urbana, 1957.
[2] D. F. Holshouser, "The time element in photoelectric emission," Ph.D. dissertation, University of Illinois, Urbana, 1958.
[3] D. F. Holshouser, H. Von Foerster, and G. L. Clark, "Microwave modulation of light using the Kerr effect," *J. Opt. Soc. Am.*, vol. 51, pp. 1360–1365, December 1961.
[4] I. P. Kaminow, "Microwave modulation of the electro-optic effect in KH_2PO_4," *Phys. Rev. Lett.*, vol. 6, no. 10, p. 528, 1961.
[5] O. L. Gaddy, D. F. Holshouser, and R. E. Stanfield, "Microwave and electro-optical properties of carbon disulfide," *1962 Proc. 3rd Internat'l Quantum Electronics Conf.*, pp. 1679–1686.
[6] D. H. Whiffen, "Measurements on the absorption of microwaves; Part IV, non-polar liquids," *Trans. Faraday Soc.*, vol. 46, pp. 124–130, February 1950.
[7] *Near Infrared Spectra.* Champaign, Ill.: Anderson Physical Lab. 1958.
[8] E. C. Jordan, *Electromagnetic Waves and Radiating Systems.* New York: Prentice-Hall, 1950.
[9] E. V. Condon and H. Odishaw, *Handbook of Physics.* New York: McGraw-Hill, 1958.

Reprinted from JOURNAL OF APPLIED PHYSICS, Vol. 37, No. 1, 388–398, January 1966

Light Modulation and Beam Deflection with Potassium Tantalate-Niobate Crystals

F. S. CHEN, J. E. GEUSIC, S. K. KURTZ, J. G. SKINNER, AND S. H. WEMPLE
Bell Telephone Laboratories, Incorporated, Murray Hill, New Jersey
(Received 18 June 1965; in final form 23 August 1965)

The dielectric and electro-optic properties of $KTa_xNb_{1-x}O_3$(KTN) are discussed from the point of view of the material's usefulness in light modulators and beam deflectors. It is shown that baseband light modulators with 200- to 300-Mc/sec bandwidths and analog deflectors with 200 to 300 resolvable spots are within the practical capabilities of this material.

INTRODUCTION

THE electro-optic properties of materials can be used to modulate, switch, or deflect light beams; however, the practical device utilization of electro-optics is severely limited by the smallness of the effects in most materials if reasonable drive voltages and drive powers are to be used. In this paper we report some experimental results for devices employing the ABO_3 perovskite potassium tantalate-niobate (KTN) as the electro-optic material. As reported previously,[1–3] crystals having a tantalum to niobium ratio of 0.65/0.35 have a very large quadratic electro-optic effect in the vicinity of room temperature.

In Sec. I the physical and electro-optic properties of KTN are summarized, and in Secs. II and III we present experimental results and design considerations for a baseband light modulator and an analog beam deflector utilizing KTN. The analog beam deflector makes use of a prism (or its equivalent) of KTN to scan a light beam spatially. Practical applications might include picture projection, optical computers, or pattern writing.

I. PHYSICAL PROPERTIES OF KTN

A. Dielectric Properties

In order to analyze electro-optic devices utilizing KTN as the active medium, it is important to understand its basic electrical and optical properties. Although a detailed discussion of these properties is outside the scope of this article, we shall summarize the relevant optical and electrical behavior in terms of a few well-known equations and constants.

Potassium tantalate-niobate is a solid solution of two perovskites, $KTaO_3$ and $KNbO_3$, which have very nearly the same unit cell size in their cubic phase ($KTaO_3$: $a_0=3.989$ Å,[4] $KNbO_3$: $a_0=4.021$ Å[5]), but quite different Curie temperatures ($KTaO_3$: $T_c\sim4$°K ±2K°,[6] $KNbO_3$: $T_c=698$°K[7]). Reisman and Banks[8] have shown that the volume per unit cell corrected to room temperature is constant to within $\sim1\%$ over the solid solution range $KTa_xNb_{1-x}O_3$ with $x=0$ to 1. Triebwasser[9] has studied the dielectric properties of this solid solution system and finds that the Curie temperature for the cubic to tetragonal transition varies nearly linearly over the same range. For $x=0.65$ the Curie temperature of KTN is $\cong10$°C, thus facilitating the operation of KTN electro-optic devices at room temperature.

The dielectric properties of a KTN with $x\cong0.66$ are shown in Fig. 1. Measurements were made with a 1615A General Radio capacitance bridge at 10 kc/sec with a field of 4 V/cm in a dry nitrogen atmosphere. The dielectric data shown in Fig. 1 obey a Curie–Weiss law

$$\kappa=C/(T-T_c) \qquad (1)$$

with

$$C=1.45\times10^5\text{°K}$$
$$T_c=271.0\text{°K}.$$

The Curie constant C, peak dielectric constant, and sharpness of the transition were all found to decrease

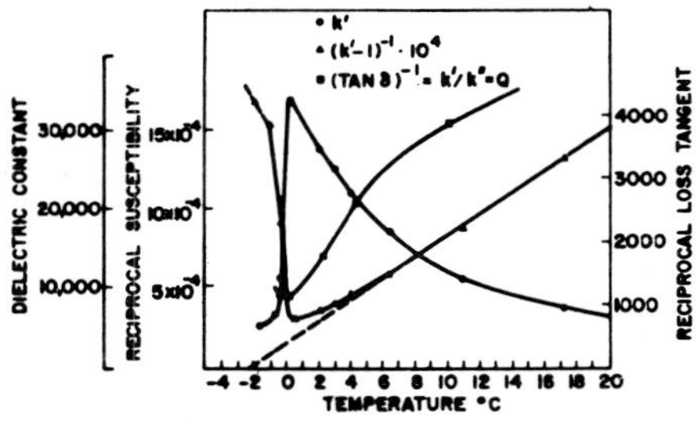

FIG. 1. Low field dielectric properties of KTN measured at 10 kc/sec.

[1] J. E. Geusic, S. K. Kurtz, T. J. Nelson, and S. H. Wemple, Appl. Phys. Letters **2**, 185 (1963).
[2] J. E. Geusic, S. K. Kurtz, L. G. Van Uitert, and S. H. Wemple, Appl. Phys. Letters **4**, 141 (1964).
[3] F. S. Chen, J. E. Geusic, S. K. Kurtz, J. G. Skinner, and S. H. Wemple, Proc. IEEE **52**, 1258 (1964).
[4] P. Vousden, Acta Cryst. **4**, 313 (1951).
[5] G. Shirane, R. Newnbaum, and R. Pepinsky, Phys. Rev. **96**, 581 (1954).
[6] S. H. Wemple, Phys. Rev. **137**, A1575 (1965). *Note:* The value of T_c for $KTaO_3$ reported by Wemple is significantly lower than that reported by Hulm *et al.* [J. K. Hulm, B. T. Matthias, and E. A. Long, Phys. Rev. **79**, 885 (1949)]. This is believed due to the higher purity of the crystals. No hysteresis loops were observed down to 2°K.
[7] S. Triebwasser, Phys. Rev. **101**, 993 (1956).
[8] A. Reisman and E. Banks, J. Am. Chem. Soc. **80**, 1877 (1958).
[9] S. Triebwasser, Phys. Rev. **114**, 63 (1959).

with increasing nonuniformity of composition. They were also found to be dependent on other factors of crystal quality such as internal strain, surface damage, and bulk resistivity. The higher values of the Curie constant and peak dielectric constant quoted here, as compared with those reported by Triebwasser, as well as the order of the transition, may be due to differences in these factors.

The phase transition is first order as evidenced by the very abrupt drop in dielectric constant at the phase transition by a factor of approximately four in about 0.5°K.[10] This conclusion for the sample shown in Fig. 1 is further strengthened by measurements of polarization P versus electric field E made with a Sawyer–Tower circuit at various temperatures above the phase transition. They show that the coefficient ξ of the fourth power term in Devonshire's[11] expansion of the free energy G

$$G \doteq [(T-T_c)/2\epsilon_0 C]P^2 + (\xi/4)P^4 + (\zeta/6)P^6 + \cdots \quad (2)$$

is negative. For a sample of KTN with a T_c of 302°K, the Devonshire coefficients have been obtained by fitting the P–E curves shown in Fig. 2 to the function

$$E = [(T-T_c)/\epsilon_0 C]P + \xi P^3 + \zeta P^5 \quad (3)$$

which is obtained from Eq. (2) by using the relation $E = \partial G/\partial P$. The results are

$$\xi \cong -6\times10^8 \text{ V}\times\text{m}^5/\text{C}^3$$
$$\zeta \cong +10^{11} \text{ V}\times\text{m}^9/\text{C}^5$$
$$C = 1.45\times10^5\,°\text{K}$$
$$T_c = 302.4°\text{K}.$$

The solid curves in Fig. 2 show good agreement with Eq. (3) over a wide range of temperature and electric field. The polarization data plotted in Fig. 2 were obtained by measuring the change in minimum deviation angle $\Delta\theta$ of a light beam passing through a KTN prism and relating this change to the induced change in refractive index Δn by the equation

$$\Delta n = \{[1-n^2\sin^2(\gamma/2)]^{1/2}/2\sin(\gamma/2)\}\Delta\theta,$$

where γ is the apex angle of the prism. The light beam was polarized parallel to the applied field and it was assumed that Δn is related to P^2 as given by Eq. (6b).

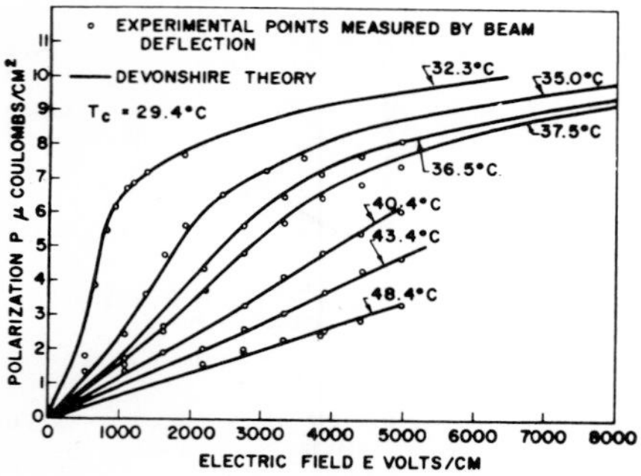

FIG. 2. High field dielectric properties of KTN.

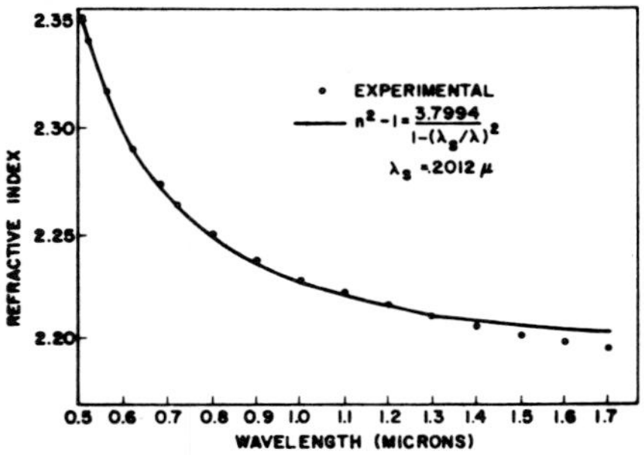

FIG. 3. Refractive index dispersion in zero field.

B. Optical and Electro-Optic Properties

Above its Curie point KTN is optically isotropic with a refractive index having the dispersion shown in Fig. 3. The refractive index at room temperature was measured from 0.5 to 2.37 μ by the minimum deviation method. The error in the refractive index values is estimated to be ±0.001. These data can be fitted to a single-term Sellmeier[12] dispersion formula in the visible region with $\lambda_s = 2012$ Å as shown in Fig. 3. Anomalous dispersion from the transverse optical modes[13] at 19, 51, and 700 μ makes a significant contribution beyond 1 μ, which can be taken into account by adding additional terms to the Sellmeier equation. The "optical" band gap of KTN is 3.1 eV,[14] and the crystals are transparent out to 6 μ where strong lattice absorption[15] sets in.

The electro-optic properties of KTN are characterized by three coefficients, g_{11}, g_{12}, and g_{44}, in accordance with the cubic centrosymmetric space group *Pm3m* of the ideal perovskite structure.[16] Since lattice polarization has been found to be the fundamental physical variable,[2,17,18] we have chosen to describe the expansion

[10] C. Kittel, Phys. Rev. **82**, 729 (1951).
[11] A. F. Devonshire, Phil. Mag. **40**, 1040 (1949); **42**, 1065 (1951).
[12] F. A. Jenkins and H. E. White, *Fundamentals of Optics* (McGraw-Hill Book Co., Inc., New York, 1950), Chap. 23, p. 469.
[13] A. S. Barker, Jr. (private communication).
[14] D. M. Dodd (private communication).
[15] A. S. Barker, Jr. (private communication).
[16] J. F. Nye, *Physical Properties of Crystals* (Oxford University Press, Oxford, England, 1960), Chap. 13, p. 24.
[17] W. Kanzig in *Solid State Physics*, edited by F. Seitz and D. Turnbull (Academic Press Inc., New York, 1957), Vol. 4, p. 89.
[18] R. C. Miller, Appl. Phys. Letters **5**, 17 (1964).

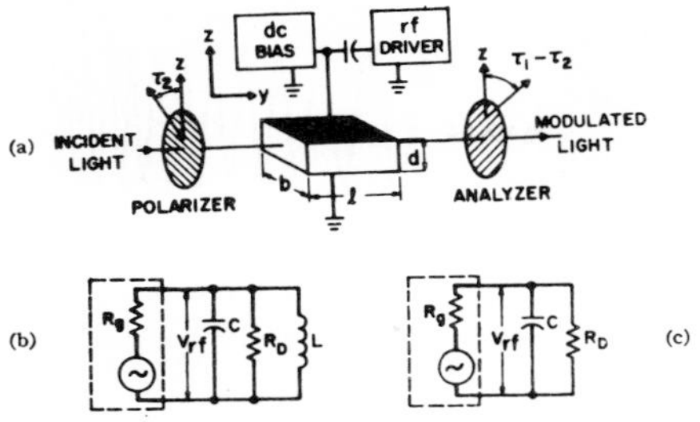

FIG. 4. KTN modulator configuration.

of the optical impermeability tensor β_{ij} (the reciprocal of the optical permeability tensor ϵ_{ij}) in terms of lattice polarization components P_i rather than electric field components.

$$\beta_{ij}(P)-\beta_{ij}(0)=\sum_{kl} g_{ijkl}P_kP_l. \quad (4)$$

The usual contraction of indices[16] and symmetry operations leads to the expressions

$$\beta_{11}=1/n^2+g_{11}P_x^2+g_{12}(P_y^2+P_z^2)$$
$$\beta_{22}=1/n^2+g_{11}P_y^2+g_{12}(P_x^2+P_z^2)$$
$$\beta_{33}=1/n^2+g_{11}P_z^2+g_{12}(P_x^2+P_y^2)$$
$$\beta_{13}=\beta_{31}=g_{44}P_xP_z$$
$$\beta_{23}=\beta_{32}=g_{44}P_yP_z$$
$$\beta_{12}=\beta_{21}=g_{44}P_xP_y,$$

where n is the refractive index in zero field.

The optical indicatrix is then described by the equation

$$\beta_{11}x^2+\beta_{22}y^2+\beta_{33}z^2+2\beta_{12}xy+2\beta_{13}xz+2\beta_{23}yz=1, \quad (5)$$

where x, y, z lie along the crystallographic cube axes. Using the general solution of Mason[19] for the birefringence seen by a wave of arbitrary wave normal, it can be shown, using the g_{ij} for KTN listed in Table I, that the maximum birefringence occurs for P in a [001] direction with the wave normal of the light beam perpendicular to P. In this case the crystal becomes negative uniaxial with the optic axis parallel to P and with the principal refractive indices given by

$$n_0(\equiv n_{\text{ordinary}})\cong n-(n^3/2)g_{12}P_z^2 \quad (6a)$$

$$n_e(\equiv n_{\text{extraordinary}})\cong n-(n^3/2)g_{11}P_z^2. \quad (6b)$$

TABLE I. Quadratic electro-optic coefficients (m^4/C^2) for several perovskites at 6328 Å. (For dispersion of $g_{11}-g_{12}$ in KTN see Ref. 2.)

$KTaO_3$[a]	$g_{11}-g_{12}=+0.16\ \pm0.01$
	$g_{44}=+0.12\ \pm0.01$
$KTa_{0.65}Nb_{0.35}O_3$[b]	$g_{11}-g_{12}=+0.174\pm0.01$
	$g_{11}=+0.136\pm0.01$
	$g_{12}=-0.038\pm0.01$
	$g_{44}=+0.147\pm0.01$
$SrTiO_3$[c]	$g_{11}-g_{12}=+0.14\ \pm0.01$
$BaTiO_3$[d]	$g_{11}-g_{12}=+0.13\ \pm0.02$

[a] 2° to 77°K, $T_c\sim4$°K, $n=2.24$.
[b] 285° to 310°K, $T_c\sim283$°K, $n=2.29$.
[c] 4.2° to 300°K, $n=2.38$.
[d] 408° to 433°K, $T_c\sim401$°K, $n=2.4$.

The electro-optic coefficients g_{ij} listed in Table I include a "secondary" contribution arising from electrostrictive strain which produces an elasto-optic deformation of the refractive index ellipsoid. This contribution is expected to drop off rapidly for frequencies substantially higher than the fundamental longitudinal acoustic mode of the sample (0.33 Mc·cm/sec). The "primary" electro-optic effect, on the other hand, is related to polar displacements within each unit cell, and the associated dispersion is given by the longest wavelength transverse polar mode of the crystal lattice. This frequency[13] lies in the 200–400 Gc/sec region.

It can be shown that the electrostrictive contribution to the g_{ij}'s can be written

$$g_{11}^*-g_{12}^*=(h_{11}-h_{12})(Q_{11}-Q_{12})(c_{11}-c_{12})$$
$$g_{44}^*=h_{44}Q_{44}c_{44}, \quad (7)$$

where h_{ij} are the stress-optic coefficients, Q_{ij} are the electrostrictive coefficients relating strain to polarization, and c_{ij} are the elastic coefficients. All of the above quantities are elements of fourth rank tensors so that the same index contractions apply as for the electro-optic coefficients.

If KTN is operated about a biasing polarization P_b in order to produce a low differential half-wave voltage, there may be an additional frequency dependence associated with piezoelectric clamping of the dielectric constant. This is due to the absence of a center of inversion symmetry in the biased crystal. Calculation of the ratio κ_c/κ_u, where κ_c and κ_u are the clamped and unclamped dielectric constants, respectively, can be accomplished using the Devonshire thermodynamic formalism. The result of this calculation is

$$\kappa_c/\kappa_u\cong(1+4\kappa_uc_{11}Q_{11}^2P_b^2\epsilon_0)^{-1}. \quad (8)$$

Substituting $\kappa_u=10^4$, $c_{11}=2.64\times10^{11}$ newton/m^2,[20] $Q_{11}\doteq0.04$ m^4/C^2, and $P_b=3\ \mu$C/cm^2, we obtain $\kappa_c/\kappa_u\doteq0.9$ for KTN.

Combining this result with Eq. (7) and preliminary measurements of the h_{ij}'s, Q_{ij}'s, and c_{ij}'s we estimate that the electro-optic effect should decrease by 20–50% in passing through the sample acoustic resonances when the sample is biased to 3 μC/cm^2. Measurements at 100 Mc/sec and 200 Mc/sec for a crystal biased to

[19] W. P. Mason, Bell System Tech. J. **29**, 161 (1950). *Note:* In Eq. (75) page 177 the term in $\beta_{12}\beta_{13}$ should be corrected to read

$$k_7=-4\beta_{12}\beta_{13}[\sin2\theta\sin\varphi(\cos^2\theta\cos^2\varphi+\sin^2\varphi)].$$

[20] T. B. Bateman (private communication).

$3\,\mu C/cm^2$ described in Sec. II show that the actual clamping effect is about 30%. A more complete discussion of clamping effects will be presented in a later publication.

II. MODULATORS UTILIZING KTN

A. Transfer Function and Half-Wave Voltage

Figure 4(a) schematically describes a possible configuration for a KTN modulator. The voltage is applied along one of the cube axes of KTN, which will be designated as the z axis. The light travels along the y direction. Let τ_1 be the angle between the axis of the polarizer and the analyzer and τ_2 be the angle between the z axis and the axis of the polarizer. Then the intensity of the light transmitted through the analyzer[21] is

$$\bar{I}=\bar{I}_0[\cos^2\tau_1-\sin 2(\tau_2-\tau_1)\sin 2\tau_2\sin^2(\Delta\Phi/2)], \quad (9)$$

where $\bar{I}_0$ is the incident light intensity and $\Delta\Phi$ is the phase difference between the extraordinary and ordinary ray after passing through the crystal of length l. From Eq. (6), $\Delta\Phi$ can be expressed as

$$\Delta\Phi=(2\pi l/\lambda)(n_0-n_e)=(\pi\, ln^3/\lambda)(g_{11}-g_{12})P_z^2, \quad (10)$$

where λ is the vacuum wavelength of the light. When the axis of the polarizer is along the z axis (i.e., $\tau_2=0$, or when $\tau_2-\tau_1=0$), $\bar{I}$ is independent of $\Delta\Phi$ and one obtains a phase modulator. For intensity modulation where maximum variation of $\bar{I}$ is desired for a given $\Delta\Phi$, we require $\tau_2=45°$ and $\tau_1=0°$ or 90°. We shall confine ourselves to intensity modulation with crossed polarizers ($\tau_1=90°$, $\tau_2=45°$) in which case the transfer function in Eq. (9) reduces to

$$\bar{I}=\bar{I}_0\sin^2(\Delta\Phi/2). \quad (11)$$

As the phase retardation $\Delta\Phi$ increases, the transmitted intensity $\bar{I}$ goes through successive minima when $\Delta\Phi$ corresponds to an even number of half-waves (i.e., $\Delta\Phi=m\pi$, m even integer) and successive maxima when $\Delta\Phi$ is an odd number of half-waves ($\Delta\Phi=m\pi$, m odd integer). Since $\Delta\Phi$ is proportional to P^2, the incremental change in polarization $\Delta P_{\pi b}$ between successive maxima and minima decreases with increasing phase retardation. Thus by biasing the KTN to a polarization P_b, by means of a dc electric field, the incremental half-wave voltage $\Delta V_{\pi b}$ required to produce $\Delta P_{\pi b}$ is substantially reduced. If we define $\epsilon_b=(\partial P/\partial E)_b$ as the small signal electrical permittivity at the bias point and assume that ϵ_b is constant over the increment $\Delta P_{\pi b}$, then it can be shown from Eq. (9) that the half-wave voltage in the biased condition is

$$\Delta V_{\pi b}=(\lambda/4a)(d/l)(1/P_b\epsilon_b), \quad (12)$$

where $a=(n^3/2)(g_{11}-g_{12})$.

An illustration of this reduction in half-wave voltage is shown in Fig. 5. In practice the bias polarization is set to a 50% transmission point ($m+1/2$ halfwaves) where the rf voltage needed to give 100% amplitude modulation is $\Delta V_{\pi b}/2$.

[21] F. D. Bloss, *An Introduction to Optical Crystallography* (Holt Rinehart and Winston, New York, 1961), p. 100.

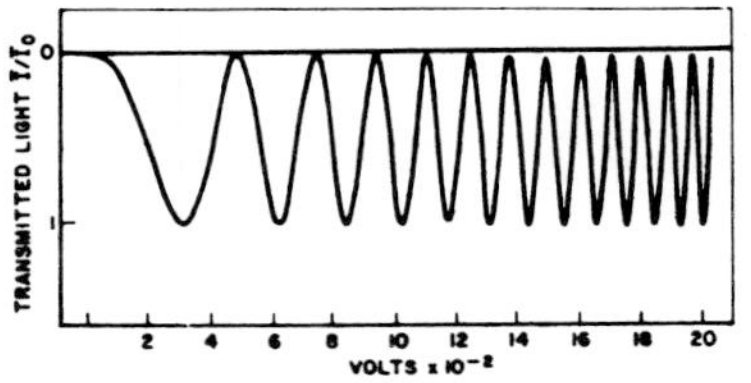

FIG. 5. Transmitted light as a function of applied voltage ($T-T_c\cong 20°C$, $d=3.3$ mm, $l=3.82$ mm).

B. Bandwidth and Modulating Power Requirements

The equivalent rf circuit of the driver and KTN crystal is shown in Figs. 4(b) and 4(c) for both resonant and baseband operation. The resistance R_D is related to the dielectric conductivity σ (=angular frequency ω times imaginary permittivity ϵ'') by the equation

$$R_D=d/\sigma A,$$

where A is the electrode area and d is the electrode separation of a rectangular sample. Defining the electrical quality factor Q as the ratio of the real to imaginary permittivity, we obtain $Q=\epsilon'/\epsilon''=R_D/X_c$. Since Q's are typically greater than a hundred, R_D can be neglected in calculating the bandwidth of the circuits in Figs. 4(b) and 4(c). (Heating caused by internal power dissipation in R_D cannot be neglected in modulator design and is discussed later in this section.) The bandwidth at the 3-dB power points for both circuits in this approximation is given by

$$\Delta\nu\cong 1/2\pi R_g C. \quad (13)$$

This lumped circuit analysis breaks down for modulation frequencies beyond 500 Mc/sec because the wavelength in the material approaches the sample dimensions.

In what follows we take the voltage V_g to be the peak-to-peak voltage developed across the sample at the 3-dB power points. From the preceding considerations the reactive power required for 100% modulation at the 3-dB point can then be expressed as

$$\mathcal{P}_r=\pi C_b\left(\frac{\Delta V_{\pi b}}{2}\right)^2\Delta\nu=\frac{\pi}{4}\left(\frac{\lambda}{4a}\right)^2\Delta\nu\left(\frac{bd}{l}\right)\left(\frac{1}{\epsilon_b P_b^2}\right), \quad (14)$$

where $C_b=\epsilon_b(bl/d)$ and we have substituted the expression for $\Delta V_{\pi b}$ given in Eq. (12). From this expression we see that the reactive power $\mathcal{P}_r$ decreases rapidly with increasing bias polarization. Eventually, however, dielectric saturation causes ϵ_b to decrease with

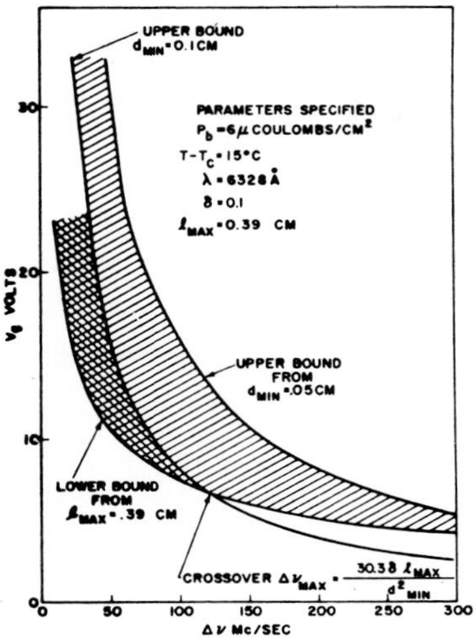

FIG. 6. Operating region of a broadband modulator as a function of driver voltage V_g.

the result that the reactive power exhibits a minimum as a function of increasing bias polarization. This minimum can be shown to occur at

$$P_b(\text{min power}) = (1/5\epsilon\zeta)^{1/4}. \tag{15}$$

For KTN this optimum bias polarization is approximately $6\ \mu C/cm^2$ for $\epsilon/\epsilon_0 = 10\,000$ (i.e., $T-T_c \cong 15°C$).

Having determined P_b we note from Eq. (14) that only the sample dimensions remain as variable parameters. Assuming that the maximum bandwidth for a given reactive power is desired, Eq. (14) requires minimum cross-sectional area *bd* and maximum modulator length *l*. In principle, the cross-sectional area for a single optical mode modulator can be reduced to less than 10^{-4} cm². Such small samples lead to fabrication difficulties and some compromise must be reached in practice.

There are several factors which combine to place an upper limit on the modulator length *l*. An analysis shows that the dimensionless parameter δ,

$$\delta = \left[\frac{2\pi a l}{\lambda} P_b^2\right] \frac{\Delta(T-T_c)}{T-T_c}, \tag{16}$$

is useful in determining the limitations on l due to imperfect ambient temperature control, temperature rise within the crystal resulting from dissipated power, and variations in the Curie temperature caused by chemical inhomogeneity, particularly nonuniformities in the Nb/Ta ratio. A simple physical interpretation of the parameter δ is that it represents the fractional change in transmission about a 50% transmission operating point. If we take $\delta = 0.1$, $\lambda = 6328$ Å, $T-T_c = 15°C$, $P_b = 6\ \mu C/cm^2$, and $\Delta(T-T_c) = 0.01°C$, we obtain $l_{max} \cong 0.39$ cm.

The specification of $\Delta(T-T_c)$ places limits on the three phenomena mentioned previously which contribute to $\Delta(T-T_c)$. Since the contributions of ambient temperature fluctuations and Curie temperature variations are independent of the design parameters, we shall discuss only the additional constraints on these design parameters imposed by internal heating.

We assume that the power $\mathcal{P}_r/Q$, where $\mathcal{P}_r$ is given by Eq. (14) and Q is the electrical quality factor, is dissipated uniformly throughout the modulator, and that thermal energy is removed by heat sinks located at the electroded faces. We can then substitute the resulting temperature distribution in Eq. (16) and integrate over the cross-sectional area. After some manipulation the following expression for the bandwidth can be obtained.

$$\Delta\nu = [2.56kQ(T-T_c)a\epsilon_b/\pi^2\lambda](l\delta/d^2), \tag{17}$$

where k is the thermal conductivity and Q is the electrical quality factor. Thus for a given δ_{max} (set by the permissable tolerance in the functioning of the modulator), given l_{max} {set by δ_{max} [see Eq. (16)]}, and given d_{min} (set by fabrication difficulties), there is an upper limit on the bandwidth. This is shown graphically in Fig. 6 for two values of d_{min}.

Using the foregoing analysis, the parameters for several different bandwidths have been calculated and are given in Table II. R_g is calculated from Eq. (13) using $C = \epsilon_b(bl/d)$. For three of the cases in Table II we have assumed heat sinks on the nonelectroded side faces. This permits operation at somewhat larger bandwidths, with only a slight increase in reactive power, while maintaining reasonable impedance levels.

From these results we conclude that baseband modulators with at least 300-Mc/sec bandwidth may be constructed using KTN provided material meeting the specifications of this section (particularly those on ΔT_c) become available.

Some experimental verification of the validity of the foregoing analysis up to 200 Mc/sec has been possible on carefully selected KTN samples and these data are given in Sec. D below.

TABLE II. Design parameters for KTN modulators.[a]

$\Delta\nu$ Mc/sec	d cm	b cm	l cm	$\mathcal{P}_r$ watts	$\mathcal{P}_d$ mW	V_g volts	V_{bias} volts	R_g ohms	Cooling
50	0.100	0.100	0.172	1.6	1.6	16	610	26.7	electrode
100	0.050	0.050	0.084	1.6	1.6	16	305	20.5	electrode
200	0.050	0.050	0.168	1.6	1.6	8	305	5.0	electrode
200	0.148	0.050	0.396	4.5	4.5	23.4	1000	15.0	side
300	0.148	0.050	0.396	4.5	4.5	15.2	1000	6.5	side
350	0.158	0.050	0.396	4.5	4.5	12.7	1000	4.7	side

[a] $P_b = 6\ \mu C/cm^2$, $T-T_c = 15°C$, $\lambda = 6328$ Å, $\delta = 0.1$, $Q = 1000$, $\Delta(T-T_c) = 0.01°C$, $k = 50$ mW/cm°C [R. Wolfe (private communication)].

C. Harmonic Distortion

In this section we treat the harmonic distortion produced by the nonlinearities in the transfer function described in Eqs. (9) and (10).

Let the total voltage applied to the sample be

$$V = V_b + (V_{rf}/2)\sin\omega t, \tag{18}$$

where V_b is the dc bias voltage and V_{rf} is the peak-to-peak modulating voltage at the angular frequency ω. If we assume that

$$\pi V_{rf}^2/16V_b \cdot \Delta V_{\pi b} \ll 1$$

then from Eqs. (10), (11), and (22) one obtains

$$\frac{\bar{I}}{I_0} = \tfrac{1}{2} + (-1)^m \left[\sum_{p=0}^{\infty} J_{2p+1}\left(\frac{\pi V_{rf}}{2\Delta V_{\pi b}}\right) \sin(2p+1)\omega t + \frac{\pi V_{rf}^2}{16 V_b \cdot \Delta V_{\pi b}} (1-\cos 2\omega t) \sum_{p=0}^{\infty} \beta J_{2p}\left(\frac{\pi V_{rf}}{2\Delta V_{\pi b}}\right) \cos 2p\omega t \right], \tag{19}$$

where $\beta = \frac{1}{2}$ for $p=0$ and $\beta=1$ otherwise, and the J's are the Bessel functions of the first kind. The J_{2p} terms are due to the quadratic nature of the electro-optic effect. These terms are negligible in practice since $V_b \gg V_{rf}$. When $V_{rf} = \Delta V_{\pi b}$ (100% intensity modulation), the intensity of the third harmonic is 12% of the fundamental. In order to keep the third harmonic to less than one percent of the fundamental, we must have $V_{rf} \leqq 0.306 \Delta V_{\pi b}$, i.e., the intensity modulation should not be more than 30% deep.

D. Measurements of the rf Response of KTN

Measurements of the dc and rf response of the induced birefringence of KTN were made on a sample of KTN of dimensions $b = d = 0.64$ mm and $l = 2.36$ mm having evaporated gold electrodes. The crystal terminated a short section of coaxial line through which the dc bias voltage and the modulating signal were applied. The holder was kept several degrees above room temperature and regulated to within ±0.3°C. A Philco microwave photodiode (type 4500) was used to detect the modulated light of wavelength $\lambda = 6328$ Å. The rf output of the diode was measured with a calibrated receiver. The rf voltage across the KTN was measured with a Hewlett–Packard vacuum tube voltmeter. Experimental accuracy was about ±10%. The light aperture in the KTN crystal was approximately 0.25 mm. The measured dc half-wave voltage was 15±2 V when the sample was biased to a measured phase retardation of 15π. An extinction ratio of only 50% was observed due to crystal inhomogeneities. The rf output voltage of the photodiode V_{out} vs the peak rf input voltage V_{rf} across the KTN at different frequencies up to 210 Mc/sec is shown in Fig. 7. In order to compensate for the small drifting of the output of the laser and the response of the photodiode, the dc bias of the photodiode was slightly adjusted to give the same V_{out} when $V_{rf} = 1.42$ V at different frequencies. From Eq. (19), when the receiver is tuned to the fundamental frequency, we expect

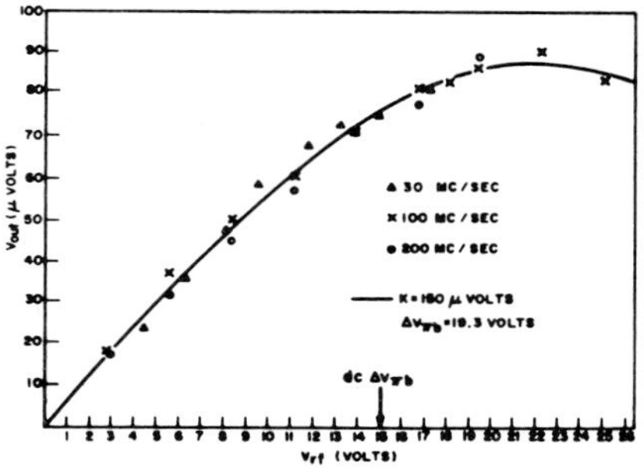

FIG. 7. Measurements of rf half-wave voltage.

$$V_{out} = K J_1(\pi V_{rf}/2\Delta V_{\pi b}), \tag{20}$$

where K is a constant. In Fig. 7 the diode output at the fundamental is plotted as a function of peak to peak drive voltage V_{rf} for 30, 100, and 200 Mc/sec. While there is some scatter in the points, they are consistent with Eq. (20), taking $K = 150\ \mu$V and $\Delta V_{\pi b} = 19.3$ V. This latter value is about 30% higher than the measured dc $\Delta V_{\pi b}$ of 15±1 V. Since the sample was biased to only 3 μC/cm^2, clamping on κ from Eq. (8) is expected to be around 10%. Clamping of the electro-optic coefficients $(g_{11} - g_{12})$ from Eq. (7) was estimated to be 20% to 40%. The observed 30% clamping effect is thus consistent with the discussion of Sec. I. The fundamental longitudinal thickness mode for this sample falls at 5.15 Mc/sec.

Before concluding this section, a brief discussion of several points is in order. The first point concerns resistivity and electrical contacts. The samples used in these measurements had resistivities in the vicinity of 10^{14} Ω-cm. Lower resistivities frequently found in "as-grown" samples of KTN give rise to contact difficulties when one wishes to maintain uniform polarization in the presence of a dc bias field. A discussion of the electrical transport properties and the types of contacts encountered will be given in a separate publication. The second point concerns the rather large nonuniformities in composition which occur during growth. The design analysis in the first part of this section indicated that variations of Curie temperature due to these inhomogeneities would have to be less than a few hundredths of a degree to achieve the desired 20-dB extinction. From optical observation of domain formation as a function of temperature, we have found that variations in Curie temperature over distances of several millimeters are typically several degrees. This severely

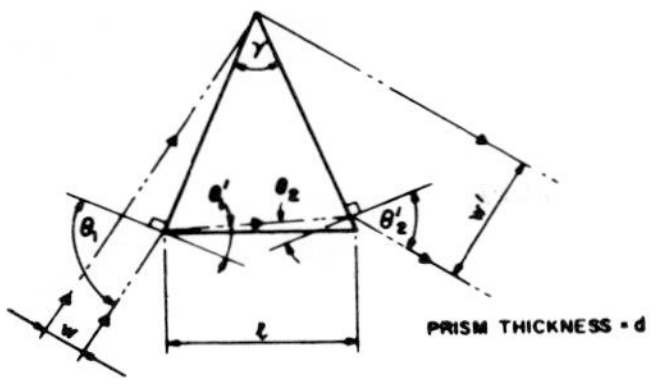

FIG. 8. Prism light beam deflector.

limits the light beam diameter which can be used. Various techniques for reducing this inhomogeneity are being investigated.

In conclusion of this section it can be said that the design analysis indicates that modulators with several hundred Mc/sec bandwidth are possible with low reactive and dissipated powers provided: (a) the material can be made sufficiently homogeneous (10–50 ppm uniformity in Ta/Nb ratio); (b) the temperature is controlled to within several hundredths of a degree; (c) the material can be made with resistivities of 10^{14} Ω·cm (or greater).

III. BEAM DEFLECTOR

A. Analog Beam Deflector

The induced change in the reference index of KTN can be used to deflect a light beam by employing prism-shaped elements of KTN across the path of the beam. The important requirement for a beam deflector is not a large deflection angle but a rather large number of resolvable spots. The shape of the prism and the orientation of the prism relative to the light beam should be arranged so as to maximize this number.

The diameter of a spot is determined by the divergence of the beam due to diffraction. If we assume a rectangular-shaped beam of width w' and wavelength λ, the half angle divergence $\delta\theta$ of the beam due to diffraction at the aperture is λ/w'. Using the Rayleigh criterion of resolution, the two spots are just resolved when the angular displacement of the beam $\Delta\theta$ equals $\delta\theta$, the number of resolvable spots R is given by

$$R=\Delta\theta/\delta\theta=\Delta\theta(w'/\lambda). \tag{21}$$

The value of R can be determined in the following manner. Assuming the entrance face of the prism is fully illuminated with a beam of width w, let w' be the width of the exit beam, γ be the prism angle, and l be the base length of the prism, we obtain from Fig. 8

$$w'=\frac{l}{2\sin(\gamma/2)}\cdot\frac{\cos\theta_1'}{\cos\theta_2}\cdot\cos\theta_2' \quad \text{for } \theta_1>\theta_m \tag{22}$$

and

$$w'=\frac{l}{2\sin(\gamma/2)}\cdot\cos\theta_2' \quad \text{for } \theta_1<\theta_m, \tag{23}$$

where θ_1 and θ_2 are the angles of incidence measured from the normal to the entrance and exit faces, respectively, θ_1' and θ_2' are the corresponding angles of refraction, and θ_m is the incident angle for minimum deviation of the beam. The change in the angular deflection $\Delta\theta$ of the beam for a given change in refractive index Δn is given by

$$\Delta\theta=(\sin\gamma/\cos\theta_1'\cos\theta_2')\Delta n. \tag{24}$$

It can be shown that the maximum value of R occurs at $\theta_1=\theta_m$ and is given by

$$R=\Delta n(l/\lambda). \tag{25}$$

We have observed values of Δn as large as 7×10^{-3} with KTN corresponding to a value of R of approximately $110\times l$(cm) for a wavelength of 6328 Å; therefore, two prisms, each with a length of 1 cm, can resolve 1.2×10^4 spots. If the beam has a circular cross section, R is decreased to $\Delta n(l/1.22\lambda)$ because of the increased diffraction angle of a circular beam.

We note that R in Eq. (25) is independent of the prism angle and depends only on the base length l of the prism. However, the value of γ must be less than $2\sin^{-1}(1/n)$ so that the beam is not totally internally reflected at the exit face of the prism. Since the refractive index of KTN at 6328 Å is 2.287, γ should be less than 52°.

A further consideration, with regard to the prism angle, is the reflection loss at the surfaces. The maximum induced change in the refractive index for a given applied field occurs when the plane of polarization of the light beam is parallel to the applied field. For this plane of polarization the reflection loss is a minimum when $\theta_1=0$; therefore the prism angle should be as small as possible, consistent with the size of the material available, to minimize reflection losses.

The deflector element can be made in a variety of shapes. By using a right angle prism, as shown in Fig. 9(b), the reflection loss at the first surface can be reduced for a particular plane of polarization. By the addition of a compensating prism, Fig. 9(c), the zero field deviation can be adjusted to any required value. If the compensating prism is in optical contact with the deflecting prism, the prism angle γ can be increased to $\sin^{-1}(n_c/n)$, where n_c is the refractive index of the compensating prism. A compensated prism can be

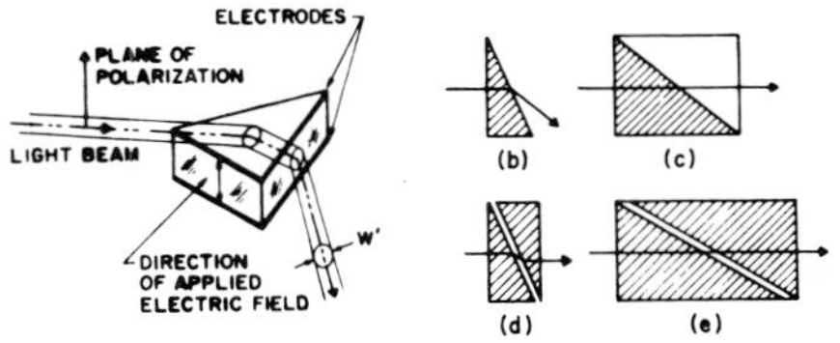

FIG. 9. Various prism geometries.

constructed from a single rectangular block of KTN with triangular electrodes; however, complications are introduced due to the fringing effect of the applied field extending into the compensating portion of the prism and also due to the gradient in electrostrictive strain at the electrode boundary.

The number of resolvable spots per unit length of deflector can be doubled by using two prisms in series, as shown in Fig. 9(d), in a "push-pull" method of operation. If the two prisms are separated by a material with a matching refractive index, to eliminate reflections at the interface, the prism angle and base length can be increased for a deflector of a given width. If the material between the two prisms is a half-wave plate, so as to rotate the plane of polarization of the light beam by 90°, the two deflector prisms share a common electrode and the value of R is increased to $(1-g_{12}/g_{11})\Delta n(l/\lambda)$ which equals $\Delta n(1.28l/\lambda)$. This arrangement is possible because the change in refractive index is positive or negative depending on the plane of polarization. [See Eq. (6).] In all cases the material between the two prisms must have a low dielectric constant to prevent fringing of the applied electric field from one prism to the other.

The typical experimental arrangement that we have employed consists of a single isosceles-shaped prism with the plane of polarization of the light beam parallel to the applied field and with the beam incident at the minimum deviation angle. The prism was contained within a temperature-controlled chamber. The deflection angle of the beam was measured with a Gaertner L114 goniometer. In order to measure the maximum change in refractive index with the minimum image distortion, it was necessary to use a light beam of approximately 0.06 cm in diameter. This was required because the KTN samples used in this experiment were not sufficiently homogeneous to use the full width of the prism.

Figure 10 shows the transmitted image through a KTN prism using a 0.05-cm-diam beam and a wavelength of 6328 Å. The prism had a base length of 0.38 cm, a thickness of 0.16 cm, and a prism angle of 46°. The effective prism length, which is determined by the beam diameter, is 0.087 cm. The expected beam divergence due to diffraction is 10.7 min of arc. The first diffraction ring is just visible on the upper photograph; the flare at the side of the pattern is due to a reflection from the glass walls of the prism chamber. The measured angular deflection of the beam was 34 min of arc which corresponds to an induced change in refractive index of 5.6×10^{-3}. The theoretical number of resolvable spots is $\Delta n(l/1.22\lambda)=6.4$, in agreement with the experimental result. The lower picture was produced by the same arrangement, including voltage, etc., as the upper picture but with increased optical attenuation in the beam. The different spot positions were obtained by increasing the voltage in increments. The increased optical attenuation enables the number of resolvable spots, based on the Rayleigh criterion, to be increased by about a factor of two because of the detection threshold of the film. The same result can be obtained with any other detector having a detection threshold.

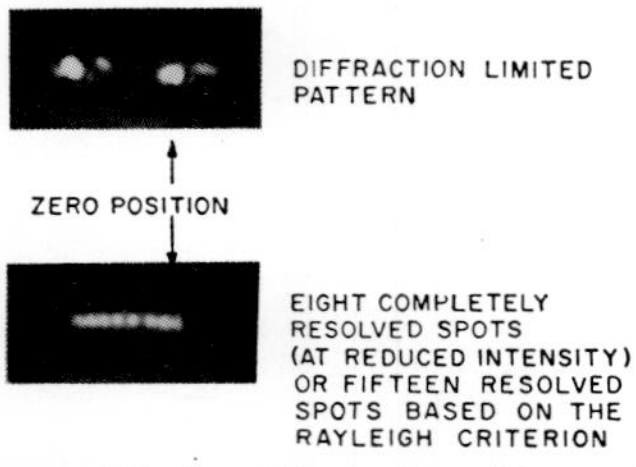

FIG. 10. Beam deflection of 34 min of arc with an applied field of 4970 V/cm. (Effective crystal length = 0.087 cm.)

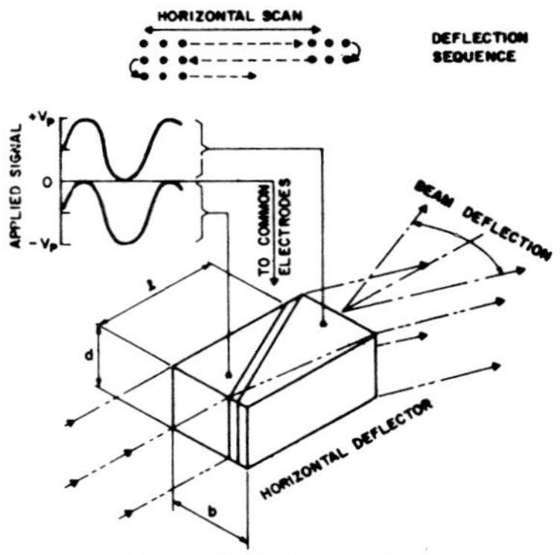

FIG. 11. Deflecting assembly.

B. Power and Dimensional Requirements for an Analog Beam Deflector

A typical beam deflector may be required to produce a two-dimensional array of spots, resolved by the Rayleigh criterion, in the sequential order shown in Fig. 11. We will consider the requirements for the horizontal deflector assembly. Let the assembly consist of two prisms operating in a push-pull with a peak to peak sine-wave voltage V_p being applied across each set of electrodes, with a negative dc bias $V_p/2$ being applied to one set of electrodes, and a positive dc bias $V_p/2$ being applied to the second set of electrodes. In Fig. 11 we assume that the beam incident on the horizontal deflector is parallel and has a square cross section of area $(d\times d)$.

We now wish to determine the voltage V_p, the dissipated power $\mathcal{P}_d$ and the dimensions of the horizontal deflector that are required to deflect the light beam over R resolvable spots per line at a rate of S

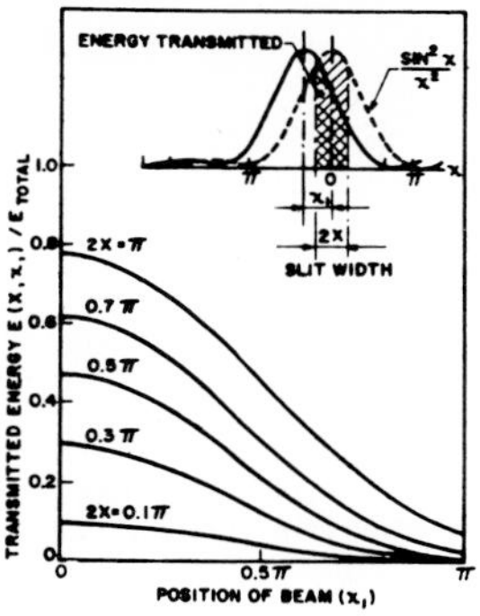

FIG. 12. Relative energy transmitted through the slit as a function of beam position x, for various slit-widths $2X$.

spots/sec. The frequency f of the deflecting voltage is $S/2R$. From the resolution requirement the length l of the deflector, using Eq. (29) and Eq. (6b) and remembering we have two prisms in series, is found to be

$$l=(R/2)\lambda/\Delta n=R\lambda/n^3 g_{11}P_b^2, \qquad (26)$$

where P_b is some reasonable value of polarization that can be produced in our electro-optic material. In Eq. (26) it was assumed that the light beam is polarized parallel to the electric field direction, which is also the [001] direction of the electro-optic material. To avoid reflections of the beam at the walls of the deflector it is necessary that the width b of the deflector be at least

$$b=d+lR\lambda/2d. \qquad (27)$$

Since no vertical deflection occurs in the horizontal deflector, the minimum required separation of the electrodes is d. The required voltage V_p is equal to $E\cdot d$ where E is obtained by inserting P_b into Eq. (3). Finally the power $\mathcal{P}_d$ dissipated in the modulator in scanning R spots at a rate S is given by

$$\mathcal{P}_d=G(bdl)(2\pi/Q)(S/2R), \qquad (28)$$

where G is the maximum stored energy per unit volume as obtained by setting $P=P_b$ in Eq. (3).

It is perhaps instructive to consider a specific example of a KTN deflector. Let us require that

$$R=300 \text{ spots/line},$$
$$S=10^6 \text{ spots/sec},$$
$$\lambda=6328 \text{ Å},$$
$$d=0.2 \text{ cm},$$

and employ the following values of $Q=10^3$, $\kappa=10^4$, and $P_b=8\ \mu\text{C/cm}^2$ which are reasonable for KTN. (This is the beginning of the saturation region of P versus E.) Applying these values in our discussion above, we then find that $l=1.83$ cm, $b=0.29$ cm, $V_p=1850$ V, and $\mathcal{P}_d=37$ mW.

The vertical deflection unit would have to be slightly larger than the horizontal unit to allow for the angular displacement of the beam. Also the vertical deflecting voltage would have to increase in steps to deflect the beam to the adjacent line and then repeat itself at a rate of S/R^2 cps, for a square array of spots. The power dissipation in the vertical deflector will depend on the vertical scan rate, but in general the dissipation will be less than that required for the horizontal deflector because of the low repetition rate of the applied voltage.

C. Beam Deflector Modulator

In Sec. II a form of intensity modulation was discussed that employed the induced relative phase retardation between two planes of polarization of the light beam. In this section we will consider the use of a beam deflector as an intensity modulator.

A beam deflecting system can be employed as an intensity modulator in one of two ways:

(a) by sweeping the beam across a suitably shaped aperture—a "deflector modulator," or

(b) by operating near the region of total internal reflection and sweeping through the critical angle—a "critical angle modulator."

1. Deflector Modulator

In a beam-deflection intensity modulator, a parallel beam of light is transmitted through a KTN prism and is focused onto a limiting aperture, such as a slit, that is located in front of an optical transmission line. The energy transmitted through the slit depends on the diffraction pattern that is formed at the slit, the location of the pattern relative to the slit, and the slitwidth. The shape of the diffraction pattern depends on the mode of propagation but for simplicity we will consider a one-dimensional problem in which the pattern is the far-field pattern of a slit illuminated with a plane wave.

The shape of the diffraction pattern is given by $\sin^2 x/x^2$, where $x=\pi\theta w'/\lambda$, w' is the beam width at the lens, θ is the angular displacement from the center of the pattern, and λ is the wavelength of the beam. When the beam is deflected to an angle $\Delta\theta$, the energy transmitted through the slit is

$$E(X,x_1)=C\int_{-X}^{X}\sin^2(x+x_1)/(x+x_1)^2 dx, \qquad (29)$$

where $x_1=\Delta\theta(\pi w'/\lambda)$, C is a constant, $2X$ is the width of the slit multiplied by $(\pi w'/\lambda f)$, and f is the focal length of the lens. The value of x_1 is proportional to $\Delta\theta$, hence to the square of the applied voltage; therefore, x_1 is proportional to the square of the modulating voltage V_m when there is no dc bias, and is proportional to V_m when the system is operated with a large dc bias. (See section on "Power and Dimensional Requirements for an Analog Beam Deflector.") It is of interest to note that in the case of the "deflector modulator" the intensity goes from maximum to minimum as the value of x_1 goes from 0 to π; this is equivalent to a full wave of retardation of the beam along the base of the prism. In the case of the modulator described in Sec. II, the phase shift required for an intensity change from maximum to minimum is a half-wave of retardation along the length of the rectangular block if we neglect the contribution due to g_{12}. Thus the base length of the prism must be twice as long as the rectangular block in order to go from maximum to minimum intensity with the same applied voltage; however, for a given cross section the total volume of material and the total power dissipated, etc., will be the same in each modulator.

Plots of $E(X,x_1)$ for various values of $2X$ are given in Fig. 12. The function $E(X,x_1)$ is the transfer function relating the transmitted energy and the induced beam deflection or the applied modulation voltage. In this respect it can be compared with the value of $\cos^2 x/2$ which is the transfer function for the modulator described in Sec. II. [Note: The function is $\cos^2 x/2$ or $\sin^2 x/2$ depending on the relative orientation of the polarizer and analyzer.]

In order to compare the linearity of the various transfer functions, including $\cos^2 x/2$, the curves were normalized at $x_1=0$ and replotted in Fig. 13 as the deviation $D(X,x_1)$ from a straight line; the straight line was chosen for each value of $2X$ so as to minimize the value of $D(X,x_1)$ over as large a region of x_1 as possible. The results for $0.1\pi<2X<\pi$ lie between the curves for $2X=0.1\pi$ and $2X=\pi$.

The results show that for certain values of $D(X,x_1)$ it is possible to operate over a larger value of x_1 with

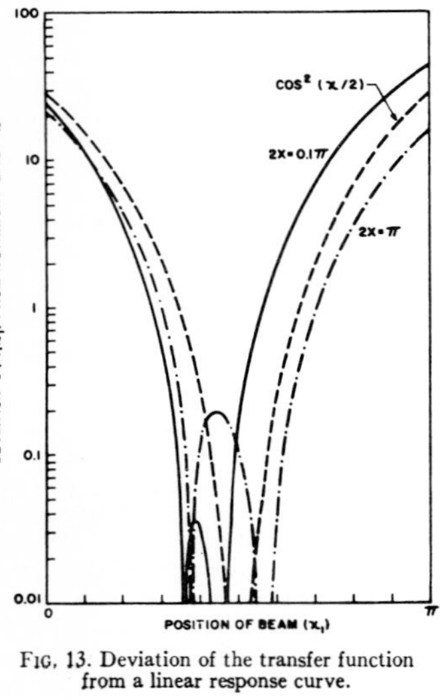

FIG. 13. Deviation of the transfer function from a linear response curve.

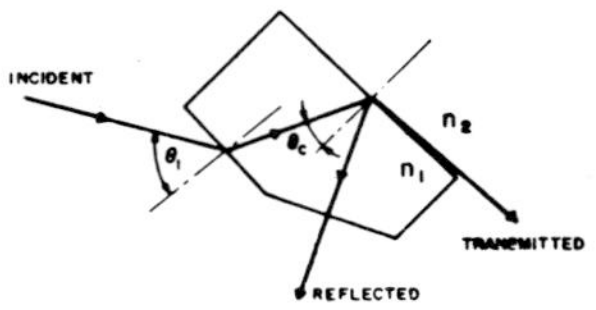

FIG. 14. Critical angle intensity modulator.

the "deflection modulator" than it is with the conventional modulator. It may be possible to improve the results for the "deflector modulator" by the use of an apodized slit (i.e., a limiting aperture in which the cut-off at the edges tails off gradually rather than being an abrupt cut-off). Calculations are being continued to evaluate the percentage of higher harmonics that are generated with the deflector modulator.

2. *Critical Angle Modulator*

A "critical angle modulator" operates in a region where the transmission through a given interface changes rapidly with changes of angle of incidence and with changes of the refractive index of the material. The critical angle θ_c is given by $\sin\theta_c=n_2/n_1$, where n_1 and n_2 are the refractive indices of the material on the incident and exit side of the surface, respectively. (See Fig. 14.)

The change in transmission for a given change in refractive index may be determined from the Fresnel equations. As an example, calculations for extreme values yield:

Plane of polarization	θ_1	$\Delta n \times 10^3$	R
Parallel to applied field	0°	11.5	83%
Parallel to applied field	90°	11.5	76%
Perpendicular to applied field	0°	3.2	58%
Perpendicular to applied field	90°	3.2	46%

where R decreases from 100% to the listed value for the given change in Δn.

When one considers that, with a modulator described in Sec. II of length 0.2 cm, an induced change in refractive index of 7.5×10^{-3} will change the transmitted intensity from a minimum to a maximum about fifty times, then it is obvious that the critical angle modulator using KTN has a very low efficiency and does not warrant further consideration at this point.

CONCLUSIONS

We have attempted to summarize in the present paper those dielectric and electro-optic properties of KTN which are relevant to its application in light modulators and analog beam deflectors. The results of our experiments and analysis indicate that light modulators with several hundred megacycles bandwidth should provide 100% modulation with dissipated powers of several milliwatts and reactive powers of a few watts. In addition an analog beam deflector capable of producing several hundred resolvable spots appears possible.

This performance which is indicated by our experimental results and analysis is dependent upon the availability of very high quality KTN crystal in which:

(a) the material is optically and electrically homogeneous with nonuniformities in Ta/Nb ratio less than 50 ppm;
(b) the resistivity is 10^{14} Ω·cm or greater.

ACKNOWLEDGMENTS

It is a pleasure to acknowledge the considerable help of W. A. Bonner and L. G. Van Uitert who grew all the KTN crystals[22] used in these investigations. We are also indebted to M. A. Karr, R. P. Morris, and H. W. Reinbold for their technical assistance during the course of these experiments.

[22] W. A. Bonner, E. F. Dearborn, and L. G. Van Uitert, Bull. Am. Ceramic Soc. 44, 9 (1965).

Reprinted from
Volume 15, Number 6 APPLIED PHYSICS LETTERS 15 September 1969

AN ULTRAFAST LIGHT GATE

M. A. Duguay and *J. W. Hansen*
Bell Telephone Laboratories, Inc.
Murray Hill, New Jersey 07974
(Received 2 July 1969)

A simple technique is described for gating light on and off on the picosecond time scale. The gate is built in much the same fashion as traditional Kerr cells, the difference lying in the use of powerful *optical* pulses rather than electrical pulses to induce a birefringence in various liquids. The direct observation of the exponential decay ($\tau = 32 \pm 6$ psec) of the birefringence induced in nitrobenzene shows that orientational effects are largely responsible for the refractive index changes induced by light in this liquid.

With the advent of lasers capable of producing powerful light pulses with durations of the order of 1 psec[1] or less,[2] many physical phenomena which take place on this ultrashort time scale have become potentially accessible to study. Since light is invariably used as a probe, it is imperative to develop means of controlling it or studying it on the corresponding time scale. It was shown by Mayer and Gires in 1964[3] that powerful *optical* pulses can be used in lieu of electrical pulses to induce a birefringence in liquids traditionally used in Kerr cells. In this letter, we describe the operation of an ultrafast gate, which is essentially a travelling-wave Kerr cell driven by ultrashort optical pulses.

We find the time response of the gate to be strongly affected by molecular relaxation times associated with the liquids used as dielectrics. In particular, we directly observe the exponential decay of the birefringence induced in nitrobenzene and measure its time constant to be 32 ± 6 psec. This observation indicates that a molecular orientational mechanism,[4] rather than an electronic[5,6] effect, dominates the optical Kerr effect in nitrobenzene, in contradiction to Ref. 6. When used in conjunction with sampling techniques,[7] the ultrafast gate should allow the direct viewing of weak, coherent or incoherent, light signals on a time scale of 10^{-12} sec or less. In particular, this would make possible the direct observation of the buildup time of fluorescent emission in various dyes and solids, and, therefore, lead to direct measurements of ultrashort relaxation times in these systems.

When a powerful plane-polarized optical field of peak amplitude E goes through an isotropic dielectric, it induces changes in the refractive index. These affect the propagation of a second weaker light beam, which may be used to probe the medium and which constitutes the signal to be gated in our experiment. The refractive index change $\delta n_{\parallel}$ for probe light polarized parallel to E in general differs from the index change $\delta n_{\perp}$ for light polarized normal to E; under steady-state conditions, the resulting birefringence varies with the field E according to[2,3,7]

$$\delta n_{\parallel} - \delta n_{\perp} = \tfrac{1}{2} n_{2B} E^2, \qquad (1)$$

where n_{2B} is an optical Kerr coefficient (usually quoted in electrostatic units) and E is in statvolts/cm. The corresponding differential phase retardation $\delta\varphi$ in a cell of length L cm is given by

$$\delta\varphi = \pi(L/\lambda)\, n_{2B}\, E^2, \qquad (2)$$

where λ is the signal wavelength (in cm) in vacuum, and $\delta\varphi$ is measured in radians. When the active liquid is placed between two crossed polarizers, the power transmission of the system is proportional to $\sin^2(\delta\varphi/2)$. A numerical example typical of our experiment with CS_2 is as follows: power density 100 MW/cm^2, corresponding $E = 910$ statvolts/cm, $n_{2B} = 2 \times 10^{-11}$ esu for probe light at $\lambda = 0.53 \times 10^{-4}$ cm (see Ref. 8), $L = 1$ cm, $\delta\varphi = 1$ rad, and transmission = 23%.

Equations (1) and (2) apply when the pulse duration is much longer than the relaxation time τ of the induced refractive index change. When this condition is not fulfilled, one must use the more general expression[9]

$$\delta n_{\parallel} - \delta n_{\perp} = \tfrac{1}{2} \frac{n_{2B}}{\tau} \int_{-\infty}^{t} E^2(t') \exp\left[(t'-t)/\tau\right] dt', \qquad (3)$$

which shows that τ sets a lower bound to the response time of the gate.

The experimental setup is shown in Fig. 1. Pulses at 1.06 μ, ~5 psec in duration,[1,2] were generated by a mode-locked Nd:glass laser Q-switched by a 70% transmitting solution of Eastman Kodak dye #9860 in dichloroethane. The infrared pulses, which may carry a power of the order of 100 MW over a beam area of 0.25 cm^2 and be plane polarized in the plane of Fig. 1, were passed through a 1-cm cell containing a liquid dielectric, where they induced a birefringence. The cell was placed between crossed polarizers P_1 and P_2, as in the usual Kerr cell. The axis of P_1 was 45° to the plane of the figure. Green light pulses were derived from the infrared ones by second-harmonic generation in a 2-cm KDP crystal and passed through the Kerr cell as shown. The crystal was deliberately mistuned so as to reduce the intensity of the green pulses to ~1% of the infrared. The green pulses did not, therefore, induce any appreciable birefringence in the liquid.

Delay elements D_1 and D_2 were used to vary the relative arrival times of the infrared and green

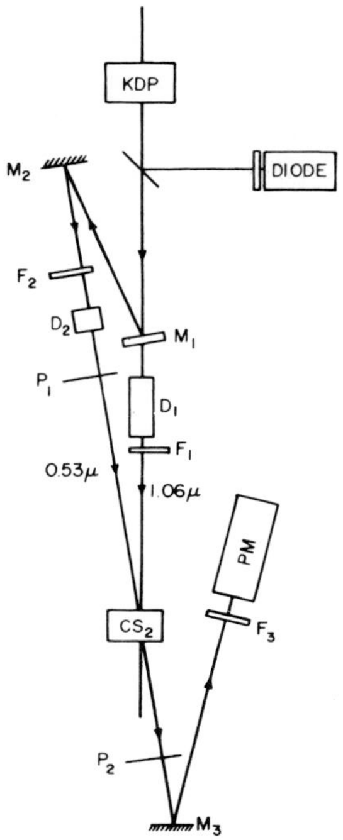

Fig. 1. Experimental setup for testing the ultrafast light gate. F_1, F_2, and F_3 are filters which allow only the indicated beams to follow the paths shown. M_1 is a beam-splitter, M_2 and M_3 are mirrors. P_1 and P_2 are crossed polarizers.

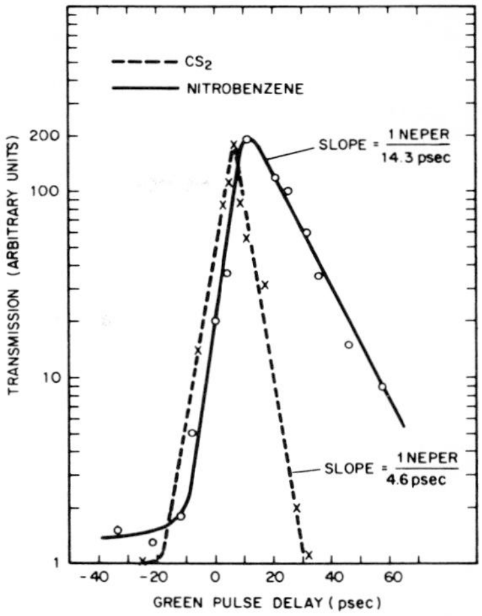

Fig. 2. Transmission curves obtained for CS_2 and nitrobenzene. The curves have been normalized to the same height for easier comparison. Each point is the average of ~6 measurements.

pulses at the Kerr cell. In this fashion the transmission of the gate (monitored by means of the photodiode and photomultiplier shown) could be probed as a function of time. One set of results for CS_2 and nitrobenzene is shown in Fig. 2. A sharp symmetrical curve ~8 psec wide at half-height is obtained for CS_2. For this run the transmission at the peak of the CS_2 curve was 10% (corrected for absorption in the Polaroid polarizers used). In other runs transmissions of up to 20% were recorded. Because the shape of the pulses used is complex[2] and at this time unknown, it is not possible to make an accurate comparison with theory and find from these data the value of the relaxation time τ in CS_2. If the effect we see is due to a field-induced reorientation of the CS_2 molecule, then according to Shapiro and Broida,[10] τ is 1.8 psec; if it is due to an electronic[5,6] distortion mechanism, then τ is expected to be $\sim 10^{-15}$ sec. In any case, we can regard the CS_2 curve in Fig. 2 as giving more or less the "prompt response" of the system.

The curve obtained with a 1-cm cell of nitrobenzene (Fig. 2) had a transmission of 1.4% at the maximum; it was scaled up in Fig. 2 for comparison with the CS_2 curve. The maximum is displaced towards longer delays, and an exponential tail clearly displays the effect of a relaxation time. For green pulse delays larger than 20 psec in Fig. 2, the value of $E^2(t)$ (power of the 1.06 μ pulse) is negligible. For $t > 20$ psec, one can approximate Eq. (3) by

$$\delta n_{\parallel} - \delta n_{\perp} = \tfrac{1}{2}\frac{n_2 B}{\tau} e^{-(t-20)/\tau} \times \int_{-\infty}^{t=20} E^2(t')\, e^{(t'-20)/\tau} dt', \qquad (4)$$

i.e., $\delta n_{\parallel} - \delta_{\perp} = \text{constant} \times e^{-(t-20)/\tau}$ for $t > 20$ psec.

The green probing pulses which arrive at these late times therefore see an exponentially decreasing birefringence. Because $\delta\varphi$ is small in our experiment, the transmission is proportional to the square of the birefringence, and we expect τ to be given by twice the logarithmic decrement of the tail in Fig. 2. The value obtained by averaging over three runs was 32 ± 6 psec. This value is to be compared with an indirectly measured value of 50 psec obtained by Starunov *et al.*[11] from the spectral width of the depolarized Rayleigh scattered light. Since 32 psec is a time characteristic of molecular reorientations, our observation provides further support[4,12] for the long held but recently disputed[6] belief that orientational effects dominate light-induced refractive index changes in nitrobenzene. We note, however, that the simultaneous presence of a fast but weaker electronic effect[5,6] is not excluded by our data.

In addition to carbon disulfide and nitrobenzene, we have studied methylene diiodide (CH_2I_2) which gave a curve identical to that of CS_2 but 10 times smaller, and dichloroethane which gave a curve approximately (our error bars were bigger) that of CS_2 but with a maximum 100 times smaller. This would imply an n_{2B} coefficient for dichloroethane ~10 times less than that of CS_2, i.e., $\sim 2\times 10^{-12}$ esu. We are investigating other materials with the hope of finding one which would have a large n_{2B} coefficient of electronic[5] origin, and, therefore, have a relaxation time of the order of 10^{-15} sec. With such a material the response time of the gate would be primarily limited by the group velocity mismatch between gating and gated pulses. This mismatch amounted to ~2 psec in the 1-cm CS_2 cell.

---

[1] J. A. Armstrong, Appl. Phys. Letters 10, 16 (1967); A. J. DeMaria, W. H. Glenn, M. J. Brienza, and M. E. Mack, Proc. IEEE **57**, 2 (1969).

[2] S. L. Shapiro and M. A. Duguay, Phys. Letters **28A**, 698 (1969).

[3] G. Mayer and F. Gires, Compt. Rend. **258**, 2039 (1964).

[4] C. C. Wang, Phys. Rev. **152**, 149 (1966).

[5] R. G. Brewer and C. H. Lee, Phys. Rev. Letters **21**, 267 (1968); R. G. Brewer and A. D. McLean, *ibid.* **21**, 271 (1968).

[6] A. P. Veduta and B. P. Kirsanov, Zh. Eksperim. i Teor. Fiz. **54**, 1374 (1968). [English transl.: Soviet Phys.—JETP **27**, 736 (1968)].

[7] J. M. L. Janssen, Philips Tech. Rev. **12**, 52 (1950); M. A. Duguay and J. W. Hansen, Appl. Phys. Letters **13**, 178 (1968).

[8] M. Paillette, Compt. Rend. **262B**, 264 (1966).

[9] R. A. Fisher, P. L. Kelley, and T. K. Gustafson, Appl. Phys. Letters **14**, 140 (1969).

[10] S. L. Shapiro and H. P. Broida, Phys. Rev. **154**, 129 (1967). See also I. L. Fabelinskii, Tr. Fiz. Inst. Akad. Nauk SSSR **9**, 183 (1958).

[11] V. S. Starunov, E. V. Tiganov, and I. L. Fabelinskii, Zh. Eksperim. i. Teor. Fiz. Pis'ma Redaktsiyu **4**, 262 (1966)[English transl.: Soviet Phys.—JETP Letters **4**, 176 (1966)].

[12] S. L. Shapiro, J. A. Giordmaine, and K. W. Wecht, Phys. Rev. Letters **19**, 1093 (1958).

194

10. Inverse Electrooptic Effect: Optical Rectification and Difference Frequency Mixing

Absolute Measurement of an Optical-Rectification Coefficient in Ammonium Dihydrogen Phosphate*

J. F. WARD†
The Harrison M. Randall Laboratory of Physics, University of Michigan, Ann Arbor, Michigan
(Received 17 September 1965)

A direct measurement of an optical-rectification coefficient in ammonium dihydrogen phosphate ($NH_4H_2PO_4$) is described. The result is $(X^0_{xyz}+X^0_{xzy})=(1.32\pm0.18)\times10^{-7}$ esu, at 6943 Å and 27°C. The 15% uncertainty represents an improvement by a factor of 20 over the previous absolute measurement of an optical rectification coefficient by Bass *et al*. The improved precision makes possible a more meaningful test of a theoretical relationship between the optical-rectification coefficients $\mathbf{X}^0$, and the linear electro-optic coefficient $\mathbf{X}^\omega$. This relationship, first pointed out by Armstrong *et al*. and studied in more detail by Ward and Franken, is $(X^0_{ijk}+X^0_{ikj})=\frac{1}{4}(X^\omega_{jik}+X^\omega_{kij})$. It is concluded that the present measurement, together with electro-optic data from the literature, is consistent with the validity of this relationship.

I. INTRODUCTION

OPTICAL rectification[1–5] is the production of a steady polarization $\mathbf{p}$ in a medium that is subjected to an optical, electromagnetic field. The magnitude of the polarization is proportional to the square of the optical-electric-field amplitude. The tensor coefficient for the process $\mathbf{X}^0$, is defined by

$$p_i^0=X^0_{ijk}E_j^\omega E_k^\omega\,, \tag{1}$$

where superscripts indicate relevant frequencies and the convention of summation over repeated indices is adopted. Theoretical arguments relating this coefficient to the linear electro-optic coefficient were first developed by Armstrong *et al.*[6] and in more detail by Ward and Franken.[7] The linear electro-optic effect may be described by an equation similar to Eq. (1):

$$p_j^\omega=X^\omega_{jik}E_i^0E_k^\omega\,, \tag{2}$$

and the relationship between the coefficients is

$$(X^0_{ijk}+X^0_{ikj})=\tfrac{1}{4}(X^\omega_{jik}+X^\omega_{kij})=\tfrac{1}{2}X^\omega_{jik}\,. \tag{3}$$

For crystals of class V_d such as ammonium dihydrogen phosphate ($NH_4H_2PO_4$) and potassium dihydrogen phosphate (KH_2PO_4), Eq. (3) reduces to two relationships

$$(X^0_{xyz}+X^0_{xzy})=\tfrac{1}{4}(X^\omega_{yxz}+X^\omega_{zxy})\,, \tag{4a}$$

and

$$(X^0_{zxy}+X^0_{zyx})=\tfrac{1}{4}(X^\omega_{xzy}+X^\omega_{yzx})\,. \tag{4b}$$

* This work was supported in part by the U. S. Atomic Energy Commission.

† Permanent address: Clarendon Laboratory, Oxford University, Oxford, England.

[1] M. Bass, P. A. Franken, J. F. Ward, and G. Weinreich, Phys. Rev. Letters **9**, 446 (1962).

[2] M. Bass, P. A. Franken, and J. F. Ward, Bull. Am. Phys. Soc. **8**, 624 (1963).

[3] M. Bass, Ph.D. thesis, University of Michigan, 1964 (unpublished).

[4] M. Subramanian, Ph.D. thesis, Purdue University, 1964 (unpublished).

[5] M. Bass, P. A. Franken, and J. F. Ward, Phys. Rev. **138**, A534 (1965).

[6] J. A. Armstrong, N. Bloembergen, J. Ducuing, and P. S. Pershan, Phys. Rev. **127**, 1918 (1962).

[7] J. F. Ward and P. A. Franken, Phys. Rev. **133**, A183 (1964).

The electro-optic coefficients for each of the crystals mentioned above are available in the literature. Bass *et al.*[5] have measured $(X^0_{zxy}+X^0_{zyx})$ in KH_2PO_4 to within a factor of 3, which large uncertainty arises mainly from the measurement of optical power. The result is consistent with Eq. (4b). Measurements of the variation of coefficients with temperature and relative measurements in various crystals[5] have indirectly supported the validity of Eq. (3).

The present work is concerned with a direct verification of Eq. (3) to improved precision. In particular, $(X^0_{xyz}+X^0_{xzy})$ in $NH_4H_2PO_4$ is measured to test Eq. (4a).

II. EXPERIMENTAL

The experimental arrangement is shown in Fig. 1. Light from a Q-switched ruby laser propagates through an $NH_4H_2PO_4$ crystal and into a calorimeter. The crystal forms the dielectric of a parallel plate capacitor across which a voltage is induced by the polarization set up in the crystal. The optical rectification coefficient is proportional to the time integral of this voltage divided by the optical energy measured by the calorimeter. The detailed relationship is derived in Sec. III.

1. Light Source

As the coefficient is small, a high-power light source is required. We have used a Q-switched ruby laser (LSI-Laser Systems Center LS 100). For run I a rotating prism Q switch was used to produce single pulses with energies 15–30 mJ and full width at half-intensity

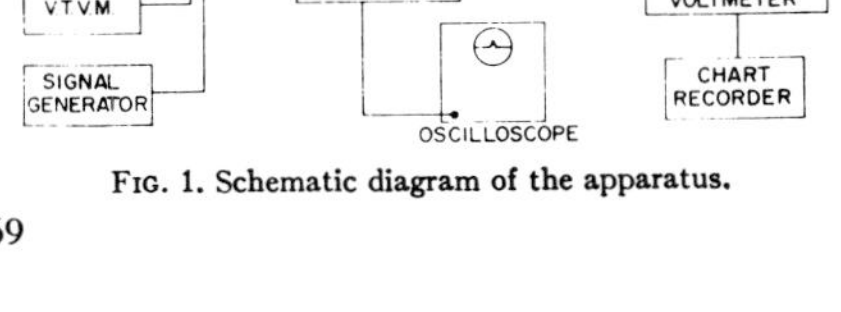

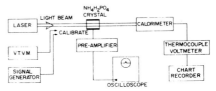

FIG. 1. Schematic diagram of the apparatus.

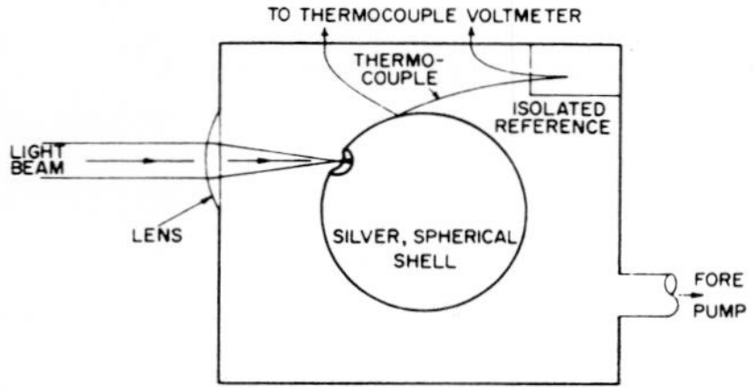

FIG. 2. Schematic diagram of the calorimeter designed and constructed by C. W. Bruce of the U. S. Air Force Weapons Laboratory.

25±5 nsec. For runs II, III, and IV a uranyl glass saturable filter was inserted within the laser cavity to produce single pulses with energies 50–110 mJ and full width at half-intensity 15±3 nsec.

2. Calorimeter

The calorimeter[8] which has been fundamental to the improved precision of this measurement was designed and constructed by Bruce of the U. S. Air Force Weapons Laboratory. Figure 2 indicates the design. The light is focused at the small entrance hole in a silver, spherical shell. The defocused beam hits the inside of the shell and is absorbed uniformly at the inner surface over many reflections. The rise in temperature is measured with a thermocouple whose emf is displayed on a chart recorder. Maximum voltage is recorded within 4 sec of the optical pulse and the decay-time constant is 2 min. These characteristics are achieved by minimizing the mass of the shell and thermally isolating it within an evacuated enclosure. Thermal loss is compensated by extrapolating the thermocouple voltage back to the time at which the optical pulse occurs. A more detailed description of the calorimeter is given in Ref. 8.

3. Crystal

The crystal geometry is shown in Fig. 3. This, and the choice of $NH_4H_2PO_4$, were dictated by the relatively large size of the optical rectification coefficient which is measured. Another advantage stems from the smallness of the piezoelectric coefficient d_{14}, which relates the voltage induced across the crystal capacitor to a strain in the direction of the light beam. This is relevant to the size of a piezoelectric signal which is seen after each light pulse. The signal is predominantly at the fundamental acoustic resonant frequency of the crystal (~60kcps) and, in the present case, its maximum amplitude is only a few percent of the peak optical-rectification signal. The phenomenon is interpreted[3] as being due to a small absorption of laser light by the crystal followed by impulsive thermal expansion. In previous work with KH_2PO_4,[3] the peak-to-peak piezoelectric signal was larger than the peak optical-rectification signal, and although the former increases more slowly than the latter it gave rise to a significant distortion of the optical-rectification signal. No significant distortion occurs in the present experiment.

Silver electrodes are painted directly on two crystal surfaces. In previous work[3,5] brass electrodes were held approximately 0.005 cm from the crystal surfaces to prevent laser light from striking the electrodes. This reduced a spurious signal, thought to arise from photoelectric emission from the electrodes, but introduced an uncertainty into the results because of the capacitance of the crystal-electrode gap. In the present work, the optical-rectification signal has been increased by the choice of crystal and geometry so that spurious signals are small in comparison and we prefer to eliminate the gap and the uncertainty arising from it.

The experiment is insensitive to geometrical alignment errors. The capacitor plates are oriented to within 1° with respect to the crystal axes. The direction of propagation of the light and the plane of polarization are aligned to within 3° with respect to the crystal axes. The combined error in the magnitude of the optical rectification coefficient from these sources is less than ½%.

4. Signal Detector

An equivalent circuit for the crystal considered as a generator is shown in Fig. 4. The open-circuit generator voltage is proportional to the instantaneous light intensity, the constant for the present crystal geometry being about 24 mV/MW. We have used optical pulses with peak power in the range 0.5–7 MW which result in peak optical-rectification signals of 12–170 mV. The method chosen for integrating this voltage over the pulse time is to display the voltage as faithfully as possible on an oscilloscope and to photograph, cut out, and weigh the area under the trace. The uncertainty introduced by this technique is small compared with other contributions to the uncertainty of the optical-rectification coefficient (see Sec. III).

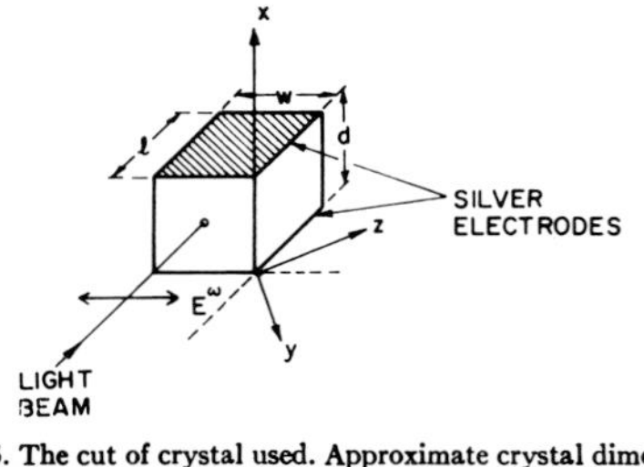

FIG. 3. The cut of crystal used. Approximate crystal dimensions are $w=d=1$ cm, $l=2$ cm. The light beam is in the yz plane at 45° to the y and z axes and the optical electric vector lies in the yz plane. Silver electrodes are painted on the two yz plane surfaces of the crystal.

[8] C. W. Bruce, U. S. Air Force Weapons Laboratory Technical Report No. 64-127, 1965 (unpublished).

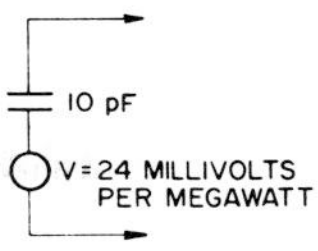

FIG. 4. Equivalent circuit of the crystal considered as a generator with voltage proportional to the power of the light beam in the crystal.

The detector response time is not negligible compared to times characteristic of the optical pulse, which necessitates a small ($<2\%$) correction that is now estimated. The detector response may be approximated by that of a low-pass RC circuit with $RC\equiv\tau$. The indicated voltage v is related to the true signal voltage V by

$$v+\tau(dv/dt)=V. \tag{5}$$

If the pulse lasts from $-t_0$ to $+t_0$ we have

$$v(-t_0)=V(-t_0)=V(+t_0)=0, \tag{6}$$

so that for a time of observation $T>t_0$

$$\int_{-t_0}^{T} v\,dt+\tau v(T)=\int_{-t_0}^{+t_0} V\,dt. \tag{7}$$

These terms are the observed integral, the error, and the required integral, respectively; so that a correction factor α may be defined by

$$\int_{-t_0}^{+t_0} V\,dt\equiv\alpha\int_{-t_0}^{T} v\,dt, \tag{8}$$

where

$$\alpha-1=\tau v(T)\Big/\int_{-t_0}^{T} v\,dt\approx\tau v(T)\Big/ t_0 v_{max}. \tag{9}$$

If the integration is extended until $v(T)$ is negligible, no error is introduced by the detector response. In practice, the integration is truncated at a time T such that $v(T)$ is about 2% of v_{max}. We approximate t_0 by the pulse full width at half-intensity. $\alpha-1$ is always less than 2% and is tabulated in Table I.

Another possible source of error in the integration procedure arises because the baseline of the optical-rectification trace is shifted downward during the pulse by about 10% of the signal amplitude. This is thought to be associated with the piezoelectric and photoelectric voltages discussed in Sec. II.3. The integration procedure is appropriate if the spurious signal increases linearly during the pulse and reasonable deviations from this are covered by the $\pm5\%$ error shown in Table IV.

TABLE I. Integration correction. τ is the detector rise time, t_0 the full width of the laser pulse at half-intensity, and α the integration correction factor.

Run	τ (nsec)	t_0 (nsec)	α
I	18	25±5	1.015±0.015
II, III, and IV	7	15±3	1.01 ±0.01

TABLE II. Summary of detector characteristics.

	Run	R_{in} (Ω)	C_{in} (pF)	R_{out} (Ω)	Gain	Rise time (nsec)
Preamplifier	I	100K	10	70	0.3	7
	II, III, and IV	100K	4	50	0.5	2
		Type		Sensitivity (mV/cm)		Rise time (nsec)
Oscilloscope	I	Tektronix 551 Type L Plug-in		5		16
	II, III, and IV	Tektronix 517		50		7

The detector consists of a transistorized, impedance-matching preamplifier located at the crystal and an oscilloscope. One detector was used for run I and another for runs II, III, and IV. Their characteristics are summarized in Table II.

A typical trace obtained during run II is shown in Fig. 5. The signal to noise ratio, excluding the change in baseline, is better than 100:1. The improvement over earlier work[5] is due to greater laser power, the choice of crystal, and improvements in geometry and electronics.

Direct, RC integration, using the Tektronix 551 oscilloscope and no preamplifier, is marginally possible with the most energetic light pulses used. The results are consistent with, but less precise than, those obtained with the apparatus and procedure described above.

5. Calibration of the Detector

A sinusoidal voltage from a signal generator is developed across a 50-Ω resistor in series with the crystal. It is clear from the equivalent circuit of the crystal generator (Fig. 4) that a signal injected in this way, directly simulates the open circuit optical rectification signal. A factor β which is the ratio of the voltage across the 50-Ω resistor to that indicated at the signal generator is established by measuring the former directly with a Hewlett-Packard type-410B vacuum-tube voltmeter. The frequency selected is in the low-frequency, flat-response region for the detector (10 Mc/sec for run I, 20 Mc/sec for runs II, III, and IV.) The reduced gain for the high-frequency components of the pulse does not introduce a significant uncertainty and is taken into account by the factor α discussed in Sec. II.4. Half-period areas are cut from a photograph of the oscillo-

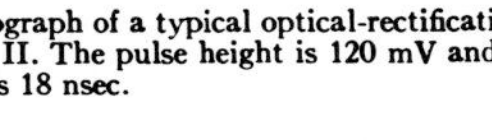

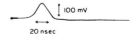

FIG. 5. Photograph of a typical optical-rectification oscilloscope trace from run II. The pulse height is 120 mV and the full width at half-height is 18 nsec.

TABLE III. Experimental data. The calorimeter thermocouple voltage W' (proportional to optical energy) and the mass of the photographed optical rectification trace $\int_{\text{pulse}} v\,dt$ in mg is shown for each pulse. The detector calibration and the integration correction α are discussed in Secs. II.5 and II.4, respectively. Pulses marked with an asterisk are rejected, as the laser has a tendency to produce double pulses under these conditions. The error quoted with the mean for each run of $\int_{\text{pulse}} V\,dt/W'$ is deduced from scatter within the run, whereas the error quoted with the weighted means includes contributions from the calibration and integration correction factors.

Run pulse	W' μV	$\int_{\text{pulse}} v\,dt$ (mg)	Calibration V nsec / mg	β	α	$\int_{\text{pulse}} V\,dt/W'$ in V nsec/μV	Run means	Weighted means	
I.1	0.248	8.7				3.07			
I.2	0.276	9.6	0.0863	1.00	1.015	3.05			
I.3	0.254	9.3	±0.0060	±0.07	±0.015	3.21	3.03	3.03	
I.4	0.171	5.9				3.02	±0.06	±0.31	
I.5	0.179	5.8				2.84			
II.1*	1.53	27.5				3.05*			
II.2*	1.67	25.3				2.57*			
II.3*	1.59	24.9				2.66*			
II.4*	1.38	23.6				2.91*			
II.5	1.06	19.2	0.180			3.08	3.14		3.13
II.6	1.06	18.95	±0.005			3.04	±0.05		±0.19
II.7	0.93	16.4				3.00		3.19	
II.8	0.96	18.4				3.26		±0.23	
II.9	0.92	17.2		0.93	1.01	3.18			
II.10	0.51	9.8		±0.06	±0.01	3.27			
III.1	0.613	18.0				3.52			
III.2	0.519	15.15	0.127			3.50	3.30		
III.3	0.621	16.8	±0.003			3.24	±0.13		
III.4	0.499	12.3				2.96			
IV.1*	1.53	25.7	0.169			2.68*			
IV.2*	1.51	26.85	±0.004			2.80*			

scope trace and weighed. This gives the mass corresponding to a known, time-integrated voltage which is the required calibration.

III. ANALYSIS OF DATA

We first derive an expression for the optical-rectification coefficient in terms of measured quantities. The large dc dielectric constant ϵ_z and the geometry of the crystal capacitor (capitance C) allow it to be treated, to a good approximation, as a section of an infinite parallel-plane capacitor so that

$$C=\epsilon_z wl/4\pi d\,, \tag{10}$$

where w, l, d, are crystal dimensions (see Fig. 3). In this approximation it can be shown[3] that the open-circuit voltage V induced across the capacitor is independent of the distribution of dipole moment within the crystal and is given by

$$V=p_z^0 Al/Cd\,, \tag{11}$$

where A is the cross-sectional area of the light beam.

Equation (1) restricted by the symmetry of the crystal yields

$$p_z^0=(X^0{}_{zyz}+X^0{}_{zzy})E_y{}^\omega E_z{}^\omega\,. \tag{12}$$

The optical power P within the crystal is given by

$$P=E_y{}^\omega E_z{}^\omega \times n_e cA/4\pi\,, \tag{13}$$

where c is the velocity of light and n_e is the extraordinary refractive index of the crystal. Equations (10), (11), (12), and (13) yield

$$(X^0{}_{zyz}+X^0{}_{zzy})=(c/16\pi^2)n_e\epsilon_z w(V/P)\,. \tag{14}$$

The energy W measured by the calorimeter is

$$W=\eta\int_{\text{pulse}} P\,dt\,, \tag{15}$$

so that

$$(X^0{}_{zyz}+X^0{}_{zzy})=\left(\frac{c}{16\pi^2}\right)n_e\epsilon_z w\eta\int_{\text{pulse}} V\,dt/W\,. \tag{16}$$

The factor η takes into account Fresnel reflection and scattering at the back surface of the crystal and reflection at the two surfaces of the calorimeter lens. The light reflected at the crystal surface contributes to optical rectification; all other scattered and reflected light is lost from the system. The fraction of the incident energy reflected at each lens surface is R' (taken as 5%,[8] the fraction reflected at the crystal surface is R (taken as 3.7%), and that scattered at the crystal surface is S (taken as 2.5±2.5%). With these assignments

$$\begin{aligned}\eta&=(1-R-S)(1-R')^2/(1+R)\\&=0.82\pm0.04\,.\end{aligned} \tag{17}$$

Each laser pulse produces a pair of data: the thermocouple voltage W' (proportional to the pulse energy), and the mass of the optical rectification trace (proportional to $\int_{\text{pulse}} v\,dt$). These data are shown in Table III together with calibration factors (Sec. II.5) and the integration correction factor α (Sec. II.4 and

Table I). Table III also shows values of $\int_{\text{pulse}} V\,dt/W'$ for each pulse, weighted means, and standard errors.

The pulses marked with an asterisk are rejected as, under these conditions, the laser has an intermittent tendency to produce a small second pulse carrying about 10% of the total energy. This is recorded by the calorimeter but is too late to be conveniently recorded on the optical-rectification trace.

The mean for each run is shown with standard error deduced from the scatter within the run. The standard errors of the weighted means include the uncertainties of calibration and of the integration correction. The over-all weighted average is

$$\int_{\text{pulse}} V\,dt/W' = 3.13 \pm 0.19\ V\ \text{nsec}/\mu\text{V}. \quad (18)$$

This value is shown in Fig. 6 together with the individual values, including the rejected pulses. It is seen from the figure that there is no evidence of variation with optical power except, as expected, in the double pulsing region. Nor are there significant differences between runs II and III, on the one hand, and run I, on the other, in which different apparatus are involved. This is also apparent from a comparison of the weighted means from Table III.

Equation (16) with data from Eq. (18) and Table IV yields the result

$$(X^0_{xyz} + X^0_{zxy}) = (1.32 \pm 0.18) \times 10^{-7}\ \text{esu}. \quad (19)$$

IV. LINEAR ELECTRO-OPTIC COEFFICIENT

The relationship between the electro-optic coefficient r_{41} given in the literature and the $\mathbf{X}^\omega$ of Eq. (4a) is[5]

$$(X^\omega_{yzx} + X^\omega_{zxy}) = -r_{41} n_e^2 n_0^2 / 2\pi. \quad (20)$$

There are three parameters which affect the magnitude of the linear electro-optic coefficient: temperature, the frequency of the low-frequency applied electric field, and the wavelength of the applied optical field.

The temperature dependence of $r_{41}(NH_4H_2PO_4)$ in the region of 20°C is taken as −0.25%/°C. This is the

TABLE IV. Factors and uncertainties relevant to the calculation of the optical-rectification coefficient.

Calorimeter thermocouple calibration	0.0975±0.0029 J/μV
Reflection-scattering factor η	0.82 ±0.04
Width of crystal w	0.95 ±0.01 cm
dc dielectric constant ϵ_z at 27°C[a]	56.4 ±0.1
Refractive indices n_0, n_e[b]	1.520, 1.476
Thermocouple voltmeter calibration	±2%
VTVM calibration (at ¾ full scale deflection)	±9%
Base line change	±5%
Geometrical alignment errors	<±0.5%

[a] R. Bechmann, *Piezoelectricity* (Her Majesty's Stationery Office, London, 1957), p. 246.
[b] F. Zernike, Jr., J. Opt. Soc. Am. 54, 1215 (1964).

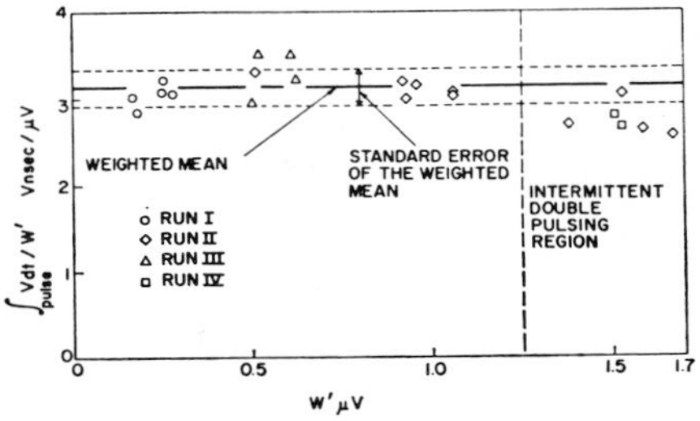

FIG. 6. The ratio of time-integrated optical-rectification signal to calorimeter thermocouple voltage (proportional to the optical-rectification coefficient) is plotted against calorimeter thermocouple voltage (proportional to optical energy) for each pulse. The weighted mean is also plotted. The high-energy pulses are rejected, as the laser has a tendency to emit a small second pulse under these conditions.

temperature dependence of the dielectric constant[9] ϵ_z and is appropriate because there is experimental and theoretical evidence to show that[10] $r_{mi}/(\epsilon_{ii}-1)$ or[3] $r_{mi}/(\epsilon_{ii}+2)$ is essentially temperature-independent. The numerical difference between these expressions is insignificant in the present case as ϵ_z is large.

If the frequency of the low-frequency applied field is small compared with the fundamental acoustic resonant frequency of the crystal (~50 kcps for crystals with 1-cm dimensions), then the *unclamped* coefficient r_{41}^T is measured. In the other limit the *clamped* coefficient r_{41}^S is measured. These are related by[11]

$$r_{41}^T = r_{41}^S + p_{44} d_{14}, \quad (21)$$

where[12] $p_{44} = -0.051$ is an elasto-optic coefficient and $d_{14} = -4.5 \times 10^{-8}$ esu is a piezoelectric coefficient, so that $r_{41}^T = r_{41}^S + 0.02 \times 10^{-7}$ esu.

Inference from data on $r_{63}(KH_2PO_4)$[13] and $r_{41}(NH_4H_2PO_4)$[14] indicates that between about 5500 and 6943 Å, $r_{41}(NH_4H_2PO_4)$ decreases by not more than 2% and we use 1±1%.

There are two values of $r_{41}(NH_4H_2PO_4)$ in the literature: Carpenter[11] finds that at 22°C and 5560 Å, $r_{41}^T = (6.25 \pm 0.10) \times 10^{-7}$ esu, and Ott and Sliker[14] find that at 21°C and 5460 Å, $r_{41}^T = (7.35 \pm 0.12) \times 10^{-7}$ esu. The discrepancy between these values is unexplained. The resulting estimates for r_{41}^S at 27°C and 6943 Å, which are relevant to the comparison with the optical rectification coefficient, are $(6.09 \pm 0.12) \times 10^{-7}$ esu and $(7.15 \pm 0.14) \times 10^{-7}$ esu, respectively. Using

[9] W. P. Mason, Phys. Rev. 69, 173 (1946).
[10] B. Zwicker and P. Sherrer, Helv. Phys. Acta 17, 346 (1944).
[11] R. O'B. Carpenter, J. Opt. Soc. Am. 40, 225 (1950).
[12] R. O'B. Carpenter, Ph.D. thesis, Harvard University, 1951 (unpublished), quoted by T. R. Sliker, Clevite Corporation Engineering Memorandum No. 64-10, 1964 (unpublished).
[13] D. A. Berlincourt, D. R. Curran, and H. Jaffe, *Physical Acoustics*, edited by W. P. Mason (Academic Press Inc., New York, 1964), Vol. I, Part A, p. 181.
[14] J. H. Ott and T. R. Sliker, J. Opt. Soc. Am. 54, 1442 (1964).

Eqs. (4a) and (20) gives the following predictions for the magnitude of the optical-rectification coefficient:

From Carpenter's electro-optic data,

$$(X^0_{xyz}+X^0_{xzy})=(1.22\pm0.023)\times10^{-7}\text{ esu}; \quad (22a)$$

and from Ott and Sliker's electro-optic data,

$$(X^0_{xyz}+X^0_{xzy})=(1.43\pm0.026)\times10^{-7}\text{ esu}. \quad (22b)$$

V. CONCLUSION

The measured magnitude of an optical-rectification coefficient in $NH_4H_2PO_4$ at 27°C and 6943 Å is

$$(X^0_{xyz}+X^0_{xzy})=(1.32\pm0.18)\times10^{-7}\text{ esu}.$$

The 15% uncertainty represents an improvement by a factor of 20 over the previous absolute measurement of an optical-rectification coefficient.[5]

The validity of the theoretical relationship, Eq. (3), between the optical-rectification and linear electro-optic coefficients may now be tested. Magnitudes of optical-rectification coefficients predicted from electro-optic data by Eq. (3), or more particularly, Eq. (4a), are as follows:

From Carpenter's electro-optic data,

$$(X^0_{xyz}+X^0_{xzy})_{\text{predicted}}=(1.22\pm0.023)\times10^{-7}\text{ esu};$$

and from Ott and Sliker's electro-optic data,

$$(X^0_{xyz}+X^0_{xzy})_{\text{predicted}}=(1.43\pm0.026)\times10^{-7}\text{ esu}.$$

The measured magnitude agrees with each of the predicted values to within experimental error. We conclude that these data are consistent with the validity of Eq. (3).

ACKNOWLEDGMENTS

It is a pleasure to thank P. Avizonis and C. W. Bruce of the U. S. Air Force Weapons Laboratory for the loan of their calorimeter, L. Cross of LSI-Laser Systems Center for advice on the modification of the laser, and P. A. Franken for many helpful discussions.

Reprinted from The Physical Review, Vol. 143, No. 2, 569–574, 11 March 1966
Printed in U. S. A.

Reprinted from *Appl. Phys. Lett.* **20**, 382-384 (1972).

Submillimeter Wave Generation by Difference-Frequency Mixing in GaAs

T.J. Bridges and A.R. Strnad
Bell Telephone Laboratories, Holmdel, New Jersey 07733
(Received 15 February 1972)

Non-phase-matched generation of 29.9 cm^{-1} is obtained by difference mixing of pulsed CO_2 laser radiation in room-temperature GaAs, with a detection signal-to-noise ratio of 10^3. Calculations show that comparable results could be obtained from 10 to 200 cm^{-1}.

Difference-frequency mixing of two coherent laser sources in a nonlinear material provides a method of generating radiation in the submillimeter region. The CO_2 gas laser is very appropriate for this application, since it combines high power output with many discrete oscillation frequencies in the range 900–1100 cm^{-1}. Possible differences between two such frequencies number several thousand, lying in the range ~1.5–150 cm^{-1}. An important advantage of gas lasers is the high spectral purity of the difference frequency.

A limited number of known nonlinear materials combine transparency for both CO_2 laser radiation and the generated submillimeter radiation. So far, InSb [1,2] and $InSb_{1-x}Bi_x$ [3] have been used to generate radiation near 100 cm^{-1}. These cubic (zinc-blende structure) semiconductors are optically isotropic and cannot be phase matched with birefringence. Phase matching was achieved by using anomalous dispersion,[1,3] or the magneto-optic effect.[2] Cooling to cryogenic temperatures was necessary to obtain these effects and to avoid high free-carrier absorption. Additionally, for the magneto-optic effect[2] a superconducting magnet was required.

In related work with the CO_2 laser,[4,5] difference frequencies between 1.7 and 2.8 cm^{-1} in the *millimeter* region were produced in room-temperature semi-insulating GaAs, another cubic semiconductor. We have now extended this work into the submillimeter region, generating output at 30 cm^{-1} in a GaAs crystal. Room-temperature operation is possible since absorption is small for both CO_2 laser and submillimeter radiation up to 100 cm^{-1}. Ashkin[6] has pointed out that although phase matching is not possible, coherence lengths are comparatively large, and reasonable amounts of submillimeter power may be generated. In work at 30 cm^{-1}, the present authors measured the coherence length ($\approx 0.70 \pm 0.01$ mm) by a wedge technique and found good

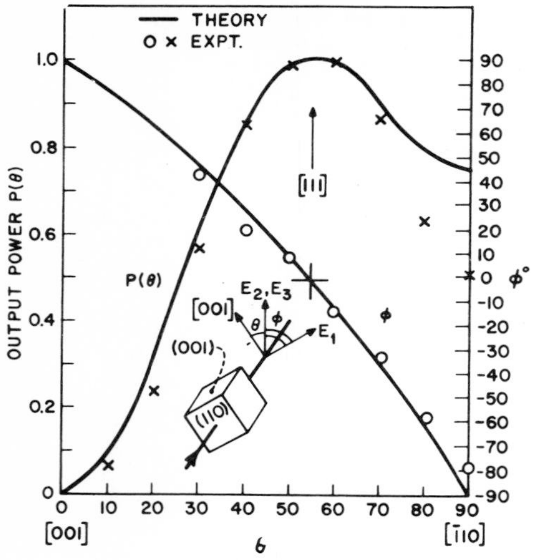

FIG. 1. Difference-frequency mixing as a function of crystal direction. $P(\theta)$ is power and ϕ is polarization angle of generated radiation. Normalized at [111] direction. E_1, E_2, E_3 are electric vectors at angular frequencies ω_1, ω_2, ω_3, respectively.

agreement with a calculated value. A parallel slice of crystal slightly less than one coherence length thick was then used to measure submillimeter output and its dependence on crystal orientation. Results compare reasonably well with theoretical predictions. Finally, we show theoretically that a useful signal could be obtained over the entire submillimeter region, from 10 to 250 cm^{-1}, using samples one coherence length thick.

Samples were prepared from single-crystal Cr-doped semi-insulating GaAs. The coherence-length wedge had one face in the (110) plane, with a thickness taper of 0.064 rad. Parallel samples were 0.51 mm thick and had faces in the (110) plane.

The two single-mode single-frequency CO_2 lasers were simultaneously[2] Q switched at 200 pulses/sec. By angular adjustment of a diffraction grating end reflector in each laser cavity, about 48 lines could be individually selected with frequencies[7] between 930 and 1082 cm^{-1}. Peak power of each laser was about 2 kW on the stronger lines with a pulse length of 250 nsec. The power could be reduced as desired by fixed attenuators. In the present experiment the two lasers were set to $P(18)$ and $R(20)$ of the 00°1–10°0 band, respectively, resulting in a difference frequency of 29.9 cm^{-1}. This frequency could be tuned in steps of ~0.48 cm^{-1} around 30 cm^{-1} by shifting both lasers together by one line per step. The two beams, combined in a beam splitter and linearly polarized in the same direction, were focused normally into the sample with a 12.5-cm-focal-length lens. Diffraction of the submillimeter radiation is the limiting factor in determining the beam size at the sample. The chosen beam size (radius ≈0.14 mm) was large enough to produce a 29.9-cm^{-1} beam with a confocal parameter equal to the crystal length. The geometry of the generation process was investigated by rotating the sample about the direction of propagation, allowing the electric vector of the laser radiation to be varied from the [001] through the [111] to the [110] direction. In the coherence-length measurement the electric vector of the laser radiation was maintained in the [111] direction, while the wedge was translated through the laser beam. Difference mixing could thus be obtained as a function of sample thickness.

The submillimeter radiation was measured with a liquid-He-cooled calibrated[8] InSb detector[9] and a boxcar integrator. A crystalline quartz filter strongly absorbed any transmitted laser power. Maximum possible amount of radiation was collected by a copper horn with its throat close to the sample. The horn reduced the far-field diffraction angle from ~120° to 40°, providing a considerably better match to the detector optics. Polarization characteristics were measured with a wire-grid polarizer. The horn was removed in this case since it possessed polarizing properties of its own.

The GaAs crystal belongs to the $\bar{4}3m$ symmetry class. From the appropriate nonlinear tensor,[10] the *electric* polarization in the dielectric at the difference frequency, and hence the generated power, may be calculated. Largest difference-frequency power $P([111])$ occurs when both electric vectors of the input radiation lie in the [111] direction. For collinear propagation in the [110] direction, the variation of the normalized generated difference-frequency power $P(\theta)$ and its angle of linear polarization ϕ, as the crystal is rotated, are given by

$$P_1(\theta)/P_1([111]) = \tfrac{3}{4}\sin^2\theta(3\cos^2\theta + 1), \qquad (1)$$

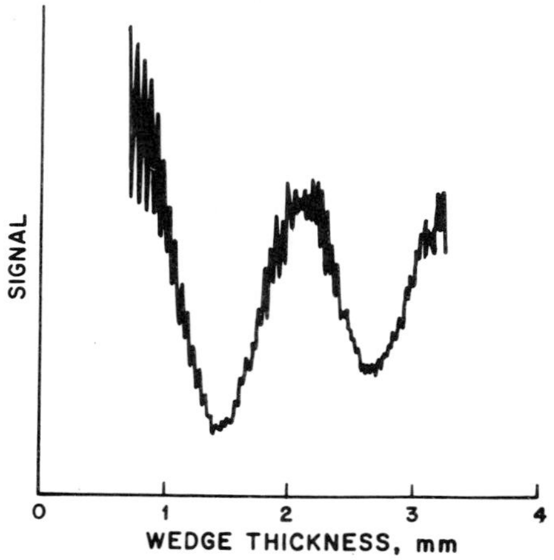

FIG. 2. Fringes produced by translating GaAs wedge through laser beam. Submillimeter output (29.9 cm^{-1}) vs wedge thickness at beam axis.

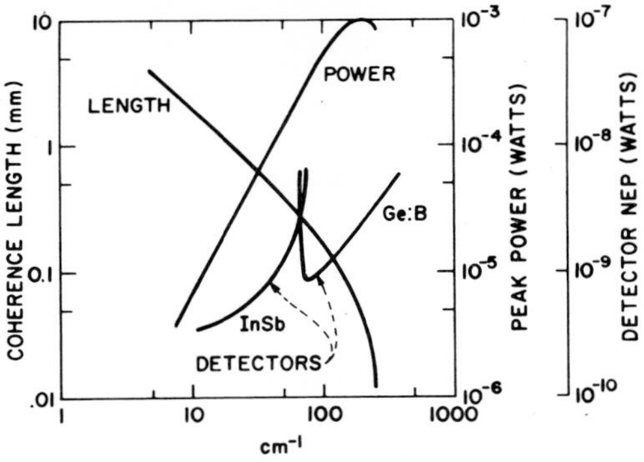

FIG. 3. Calculated output and coherence length vs frequency. Features above 150 cm^{-1} are due to dispersion close to lattice resonance. Value of d_{14} assumed constant. For detector conditions see Refs. 15 and 18.

$$\phi = \arctan \frac{3\cos^2\theta - 1}{3\sin\theta\cos\theta}, \qquad (2)$$

where θ and ϕ are defined in Fig. 1. For lowest-order-mode Gaussian beams (TEM_{00}) in the near field, the absolute value of $P_1([111])$ at angular frequency ω_1 is given in terms of the input powers P_2 and P_3 at angular frequencies ω_2 and ω_3, using mks units, by[11-13]

$$\frac{P_1([111])}{P_2P_3} = 2\overline{K}\left(\frac{\omega_1}{\omega_3}\right)^2 \frac{l^2}{w_2^2 + w_3^2} \frac{\sin^2\psi}{\psi^2}, \qquad (3)$$

where

$$\overline{K} = \left(\frac{\mu_0}{\epsilon_0}\right)^{1/2} \frac{(2d_{eff})^2\omega_3^2}{2\pi n_1 n_2 n_3 c^2}, \quad \omega_1 = \omega_3 - \omega_2,$$

and l is the interaction length, ω_2 and ω_3 are the beam radii of the Gaussian input beams, n_1, n_2, n_3 are the refractive indices at the respective frequencies, and $\psi = \pi l/2l_c$, where the coherence length $l_c = \pi/\Delta k$. The momentum mismatch Δk is given by $k_3 = k_1 + k_2 - \Delta k$, where k_1, k_2, k_3 are the propagation constants $n_1\omega_1/c$, etc. The effective nonlinear coefficient d_{eff} is given for the [111] direction by $2d_{14}/\sqrt{3}$,[4,14] where the appropriate d_{14} for the present process is the electro-optic[10] nonlinear coefficient ($d_{14} = 43\times10^{-12}$ m/V [14]). The submillimeter beam radius is given by[12] $1/w_1^2 = 1/w_2^2 + 1/w_3^2$.

Figure 1 shows a plot of Eqs. (1) and (2) together with our experimental results showing reasonable agreement between them. Discrepancies near $\theta = 0°$ and 90° are probably due to polarization sensitivity of detector optics. The maximum measured peak power was $(3.6 \pm 0.5)\times10^{-6}$ W for laser powers of 1.8 kW in each beam. This compares to a calculated value of 44×10^{-6} W from Eq. (3). Power loss due to surface reflection was allowed for, but resonance effects were neglected in this calculation. Some of the discrepancy in the measured power can be attributed to the large far-field diffraction angle of the submillimeter beam. At present, the collecting efficiency of the horn and detector is unknown. A signal-to-noise ratio of 1000 was obtained.[15]

The coherence length l_c is readily obtained from the data of Fig. 2 as the change in wedge thickness on the beam axis between adjacent fringe minima.[13] In the present case l_c is measured as 0.70 ± 0.01 mm which compares with the value of 0.665 mm calculated from refractive index data of Johnson *et al.*[16]

We have extended the calculations of coherence-length and submillimeter power output over a range of frequencies from 10 to 200 cm^{-1}. These results are shown in Fig. 3 and assume 1.8 kW of power in each incident beam focused[17] into a crystal one coherence length thick. The beam size is adjusted to generate a submillimeter beam with confocal parameter equal to the crystal thickness. A constant value of d_{14} is assumed. In view of the low loss of GaAs, resonance[11] might be expected to improve these values substantially. Since the usefulness of the generated power depends on detector sensitivity, the noise equivalent power of suitable fast detectors[18] is also shown, assuming appropriate bandwidth and integration times.[15] A signal-to-noise ratio varying from 10^4 to 10^6 to 1 over the band is predicted.

The above results show that difference mixing of CO_2 lasers with non-phase-matched GaAs can provide a useful submillimeter source from about 10 to 150 cm^{-1}. Isotope CO_2 lasers could extend this range to about 200 cm^{-1}.

The authors are grateful to A. Ashkin for suggesting the use of non-phase-matched difference mixing and to G.D. Boyd for many helpful discussions.

[1]F. Zernike, Phys. Rev. Letters 22, 931 (1969).
[2]N. Van Tran and C.K.N. Patel, Phys. Rev. Letters 22, 463 (1969); C.K.N. Patel and N. Van Tran, Appl. Phys. Letters 15, 189 (1969).
[3]N. Van Tran, A.R. Strnad, A.M. Jean-Louis, and G. Duraffourg, in *The Physics of Semimetals and Narrow Gap Semiconductors*, edited by D.L. Carter and R.T. Bates (Pergamon, New York, 1971), p. 231.
[4]T.Y. Chang, N. Van Tran, and C.K.N. Patel, Appl. Phys. Letters 13, 357 (1968).
[5]T.J. Bridges and T.Y. Chang, Phys. Rev. Letters 22, 811 (1969).
[6]A. Ashkin (private communication).
[7]T.Y. Chang, Opt. Commun. 2, 77 (1970).
[8]Calibrated using a HCN laser at 337-μm wavelength.
[9]M.A. Kinch and B.V. Rollin, Brit. J. Appl. Phys. 14, 672 (1963).
[10]I.P. Kaminow and E.H. Turner, Proc. IEEE 54, 1374 (1966). The electro-optic tensor r quoted in this reference is also appropriate to difference mixing where the difference frequency lies below, and the mixing frequencies lie above, the lattice resonances (see also Ref. 12). To convert to the equivalent nonlinear tensor d used in the present paper, see Ref. 11, Appendix 2.
[11]G.D. Boyd and D.A. Kleinman, J. Appl. Phys. 39, 3597 (1968), Eq. 5.17 (modified).
[12]G.D. Boyd and A. Ashkin, Phys. Rev. 146, 187 (1966).
[13]G.D. Boyd, H. Kasper, and J.H. McFee, IEEE J. Quantum Electron. QE-7, 563 (1971).
[14]G.D. Boyd, T.J. Bridges, M.A. Pollack, and E.H. Turner, Phys. Rev. Letters 26, 387 (1971).
[15]Detector bandwidth 10 MHz; aperture time 200 nsec, integration time 2.5 sec; boxcar signal-to-noise improvement ratio 30.
[16]C.J. Johnson, G.H. Sherman, and R. Weill, Appl. Opt. 8, 1667 (1969).
[17]Special precautions may be needed at the smaller spot sizes to prevent surface burning of the crystal.
[18]E.H. Putley, J. Sci. Instr. 43, 857 (1966).

11. Lattice Contribution to the Electrooptic Effect

Dispersion in the Nonlinear Susceptibility of GaP near the Reststrahl Band

W. L. Faust,* C. H. Henry, and R. H. Eick
Bell Telephone Laboratories, Murray Hill, New Jersey
(Received 25 April 1968)

This paper describes a continuation of earlier work, in which we reported measurements of the intensities of mixed frequencies from a 6328 Å beam and various infrared frequencies near the lattice reststrahl resonance, and in which we gave a theory for the dispersion of the nonlinear susceptibility which governs the mixing process near the reststrahl resonance. With more infrared frequencies, with data on the anti-Stokes side as well as on the Stokes side, and with improved techniques, we can now give a more meaningful comparison with theory. These new data provide additional confirmation of the theory for the dispersion of the nonlinear susceptibility. We also describe the apparatus more fully, and we demonstrate some incidental features of the mixing.

I. INTRODUCTION

In a previous paper[1] we demonstrated a strong resonance in the nonlinear susceptibility $d_{ijk}(\omega_S=\omega_L-\omega)$ governing mixing of 6328 Å light (ω_L) with various infrared frequencies (ω) near the reststrahl band, in GaP.[2] The nonzero elements (all equal) are denoted by d. We showed that the functional form for $|d|$ was

$$|d(\omega_S=\omega_L-\omega)|=|d_E\{1+C \times[1-(\omega/\omega_0)^2-i\omega\Gamma/\omega_0^2]^{-1}\}|, \quad (1)$$

where $C=-0.53\pm0.03$.[3] The constant C was determined experimentally by measuring the ratio of the intensities of the spontaneous Raman scattering from the transverse optical (TO) and from the longitudinal optical (LO) phonons.

Although the infrared laser ran on six distinct lines, and mixing was observed with each, experimental problems reduced us to four good data points on the Stokes side only. We have now been able to observe mixing with each of nine infrared frequencies, including one in the "gap" between ω_0 and ω_{LO}. We are able to display data at seven anti-Stokes and five Stokes frequencies, and our data are considered to be generally more reliable than those presented in the earlier paper. The experimental data fit the theory quite well. In Sec. II we give a more complete description of the experimental apparatus than that given in the earlier paper. In Sec. III we describe several polarization effects and other features of the frequency mixing. And in Sec. IV we present our new measurements of the nonlinear susceptibility. In an Appendix, we give an account of the calculation of the parameter C, more explicit than the treatment given in II.

II. APPARATUS

The optical portion of the apparatus is represented in Fig. 1. The infrared laser was operated on a continuous gas flow. O_2 and H_2 were mixed and admitted to give a total pressure of about 1 Torr. The bore was 35 mm, and the discharge length was roughly 360 cm (a Pyrex tube). One mirror was of gold, concave with a radius of 10 m. The other was a linear grid of aluminum, generated by photoresist techniques, on a silicon flat; it consisted of alternating 5-μ strips of aluminum and bare silicon. The grid functioned as a grating with the zeroth order only, in transmission and in reflection. For sufficiently long wavelengths and for the polarization with the E vector parallel to the grid lines, most of the energy is reflected.[4] The current was pulsed by discharge of a capacitor through a hydrogen thyratron, at a 360-pulse/sec pps rate. A typical pulse was a few hundred amperes at peak and about 10 μsec long. D. MacNair supplied us with special oxide cathodes suited to the oxidizing atmosphere.[5]

The infrared spectrometer used for monitoring individual lines and for relative power measurements was a simple $\frac{1}{4}$-m Bausch & Lomb unit with front-surface mirror optics, *not* in the Ebert geometry.[6] We used a standard Bausch & Lomb grating with approximately eight lines per millimeter, blazed at 112 μ. We took the net relative power of a line to be proportional to the sum of signal levels over all grating orders. (In fact, the highest order was always found to carry most of the power, which is consistent with the blaze angle.) The infrared detector was an Eppley Golay cell, used with a slow chopper and an HR-8 synchronous low-level volt-

* Present address: Departments of Physics and Electrical Engineering, The University of Southern Califronia, Los Angeles, Calif.

[1] W. L. Faust and C. H. Henry, Phys. Rev. Letters **17**, 1265 (1966), hereafter referred to as II.

[2] See also C. H. Henry and J. J. Hopfield, Phys. Rev. Letters **15**, 964 (1965), hereafter referred to as I.

[3] The definitions of ω_L, ω, ω_S, C, and d_E are adequately given in II. ω_0 is the natural resonance frequency of the optical lattice vibration in the absence of coupling to long-wavelength electromagnetic disturbances. The asymptotic TO frequency ω_{TO} for large-angle Raman scattering (large k-vector scattering) coincides with ω_0, which is 365 cm^{-1}. See Ref. 3 of I. The value of the damping constant Γ (as well as that of ω_0) is taken from infrared reflectivity data. The value taken for Γ is not critical; we have used $\Gamma=0.01\omega_0=3.65$ cm^{-1}.

[4] There is an extensive literature on such grid mirrors, ranging from exclusively mathematical treatises to discussions of application of wire grids in Fabry-Perot cavities. This is the first report, to our knowledge, of the use of grids prepared by photoresist methods, as laser mirrors.

[5] D. MacNair, Rev. Sci. Instr. **38**, 124 (1967).

[6] Such a geometry, for which all central rays describing the traversal of light through the system lie in one plane, seems to give spurious responses via paths for which the light strikes the grating more than once. The defect seems to be characteristic of a large-aperture instrument; and it was particularly noticeable in our application, where we have a number of discrete lines of widely varying intensity and over a wide wavelength range.

173 781

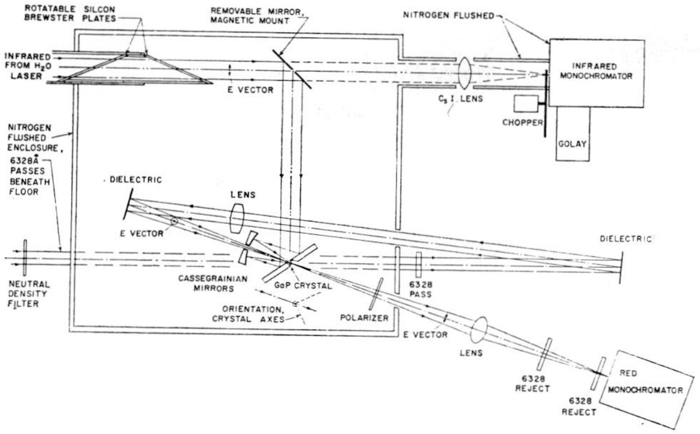

FIG. 1. Optical setup for study of mixing between 15 798 cm^{-1} (6328 Å—visible) and 182 to 428 cm^{-1} (23 to 55 μ—infrared) frequencies.

meter by Princeton Applied Research. We experienced a problem of nonlinear (and even negative-going) response to intense laser signals. We dealt with the problem by using attenuators, sheets of plastic and of Kleenex tissue calibrated on individual lines immediately before use. A Golay detector was chosen because it should have a constant sensitivity over a large wavelength range.

The 6328 Å laser had a bore tapered stepwise from 14 to 10 mm, a quartz tube. One mirror was very highly reflecting and had a radius of curvature of 10 m. The other was flat and transmitted 1% for output. Small magnets were used to suppress the 3.396 μ. The best gas fill was 0.06 Torr Ne, 0.35 Torr isotopic He^3 (fresh daily). It was found necessary to replace the quartz Brewster windows at intervals. We obtained about 200 mW in a spot diameter of 5 mm or less.

The visible spectrometer was a high-resolution Bausch & Lomb 2-m photographic unit, which we were also able to use with a photoelectric scanner for intensity measurements. The photoelectric detection was done with an S-20 photomultiplier (type FW 120, by ITT) with an integrated-circuit wideband amplifier (type PA 7600, by Philco) built into the base to obtain pulse levels well above the inductive pickup from the pulsed infrared laser. EG&G counting electronics were used to set a pulse detection threshold and for an acceptance gate over a time interval appropriate to the infrared pulse; counting was done with a Hewlitt Packard 50-MHz counter. The operation of counting synchronously with the infrared pulses (duty cycle $\approx$1:250) gave substantial noise reduction, $\approx\sqrt{250}$, since the principal noise was temporally continuous. This noise resulted from 6328 Å radiation scattered from optical surfaces, essentially as a wavelength-independent background; the photomultiplier dark current was smaller. An analogous improvement could presumably be made for the photographic technique by gating or chopping the 6328 Å beam. The facility for ready exchange between photographic and photoelectric detection was very useful. Survey work was done photographically, and detailed intensity measurements were taken photo-electrically.

The Cassegrainian optical system, giving essentially collinear illumination in the red and in the infrared, was chosen for reasons of phase matching, or maximization of the coherence volume.[7] For frequencies less than 307±1 cm^{-1}, no geometry gives phase matching; but collinear illumination comes closest (largest coherence volume). For frequencies between 307 cm^{-1} and ω_{TO} (365 cm^{-1}), there *is* an angle between beams which gives phase matching. Nevertheless, it was considered expedient not to attempt a variable geometry, but to do all work with the collinear arrangement. This *is* optimal for our greater infrared wavelengths, where the lines are rather weak, and it eliminates adjustments in the exit optics for different lines. *None* of the lines, then, was perfectly phase-matched; and the data-reduction process must account for the different coherence lengths. But this is inevitable for $\omega < 307$ cm^{-1}. The phase mismatch completely dominates the infrared absorption in determining the coherence length, for all but one of our infrared frequencies.[8] We are fortunate in that effects of finite crystal length do not appear, since the greatest infrared absorption length which occurs is several times less than the crystal length.

III. EFFECTS OBSERVED WITH LINEAR POLARIZERS AND ANALYZERS; OTHER FEATURES OF THE SCATTERING

The GaP surface upon which the collinear red and infrared beams were focused was chosen to have the crys-

[7] The radiated intensity is proportional to the square of a coherence length l_c. Two effects enter to limit l_c: absorption of the infrared light (by anharmonic coupling to acoustic modes) described by α, and wave vector mismatch Δk. Δk is the magnitude of the vector by which the input and output wave vectors fail to "add up"; the calculation of Δk is particularly simple in the present collinear geometry. The two effects add according to $l_c(\omega) = [(\Delta k(\omega))^2 + (\frac{1}{2}\alpha)^2]^{-1/2}$.

[8] The 375-cm^{-1} line, discussed further in Sec. IV.

tallographic orientation 110. The relation of the **k** vectors and the E vectors to the crystal axes is shown in Fig. 2(a); all three **k** vectors are perpendicular to the crystal surface. The mixed frequency light is radiated by a nonlinear polarization $P^{NL}=E_{ir}\cdot\mathbf{d}\cdot E_{6328}$. The thirdo-rder tensor d_{ijk}, a property of the cubic GaP crystal, has a zero for any two of i, j, k equal; and the nonzero elements have a common value. We have E_{6328} fixed in the $\hat{z}$ direction, along a principal cubic axis. From E_{ir} components directed as $-\hat{x}$ and $+\hat{y}$, we get P^{NL} components directed respectively as $-\hat{y}$ and $+\hat{x}$. Rotating an analyzer following the sample, we noted that the evident 6328 Å intensity and the rate of mixed-frequency quanta peaked just out of phase, that is, 90° apart; so the mixed-frequency light was indeed polarized as shown in Fig. 2(a). Figure 2(b) shows, on the lower two oscilloscope traces, the mixed-frequency quantum rate for the two analyzer positions.

Also, we employed an infrared polarizer to demonstrate that only the infrared component shown in Fig. 2(a) was effective. With a single plate of silicon at Brewster's angle serving as the polarizer (in transmission), we were unable to produce a satisfactory extinction. Conjecturing that the imperfect polarizer was responsible, we added a second plate. We were still able to produce only about a 10/1 ratio, rotating the two plates together. The theoretical performance of this polarizer is better than 100/1. We have not isolated the mechanism responsible for this effect.

These polarization experiments were performed with the 303.7-cm^{-1} line. We used a simple silicon flat instead of the grid-mirror, to give, presumably, an unpolarized output. The intensity measurements to determine $|d|$ as a function of ω (the principal effort of this experiment, see Sec. IV) were performed with the grid-mirror *and* the two-plate polarizer set for E_{ir} perpendicular to the $\hat{z}$ axis, in the beam immediately outside the infrared laser.

We note in Fig. 3 that the mixing signals appear to be of equal intensity on the Stokes and the anti-Stokes sides. The data displayed here are very early data, and

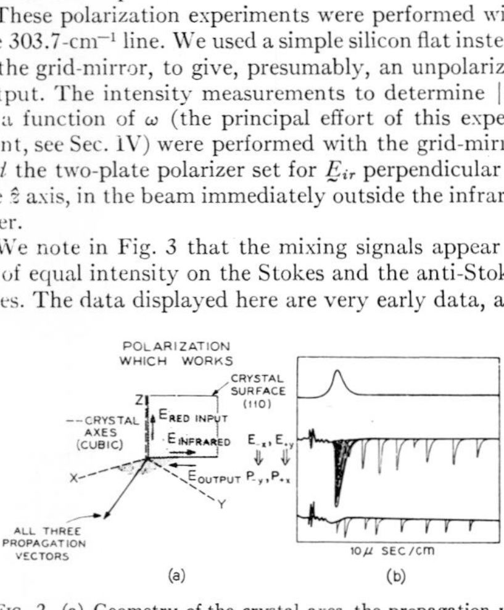

FIG. 2. (a) Geometry of the crystal axes, the propagation vectors, and the **E** vectors. The indicated components of the infrared **E** field are responsible for the respective components of $\mathbf{P}^{NL}$. $\mathbf{P}^{NL}$ then radiates the output, a transverse wave with $\mathbf{E}\|\mathbf{P}^{NL}$ and propagating in the forward $(+\hat{x}, +\hat{y})$ direction. (b) Upper trace is the infrared laser excitation current pulse. The other traces show photomultiplier output as a polarization analyzer following the sample is rotated $\|\ \hat{z}$ (center) and $\perp\hat{z}$ (bottom).

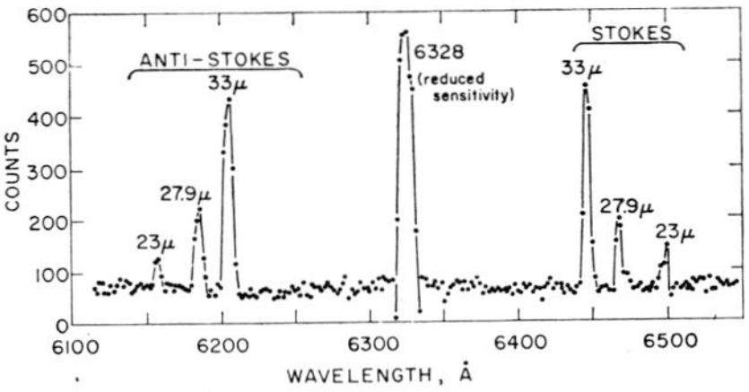

FIG. 3. Stokes and anti-Stokes mixed frequencies shown together to demonstrate the symmetry of the intensities. Gated electronics have suppressed signals other than those due to mixing.

there are several effects which have not been taken into account, but the figure serves for illustration. A more quantitative treatment of the question is given in Sec. IV.

Figure 4 gives densitometer traces of photographic plates from the anti-Stokes spectrum. The resolution is limited by the entrance slit width, 0.3 mm; this was the approximate 6328 Å spot size under $f/18$ focusing onto the spectrograph slit. The dispersion of the instrument is 3.87 Å/mm. The three unidentified lines toward the low-frequency side are probably grating ghosts. The other signals are identified as neon lines (fluorescence from the laser), frequency-mixing signals, and Raman scattering. The backward TO scattering (involving surface reflections) and the LO scattering are indicated. Forward TO Raman scattering produces the broad line appearing as a background near 6207 Å. For special reasons discussed in Sec. IV, an H_2O line at 375 cm^{-1} gives a mixing signal so weak that it does not appear on our photographic plates. With gated photoelectric detection, it is observed with a ratio of signal and background rates of about 3 to 1.

IV. RESONANCE OF THE NONLINEAR SUSCEPTIBILITY; NEW DATA

In Fig. 5 we display $|d|$ as a function of the infrared frequency in the neighborhood of the GaP reststrahl band (essentially Fig. 2 of II, but with additional data). The theoretical curves for $|d|$ and for the *linear* infrared susceptibility X are given for comparison.[1] The object here is to show that the data fit the theoretical shape; there is an experimentally undetermined over-all multiplier, corresponding, say, to the optical collection efficiency, which we adjust for best fit. On our log scale this is a matter of sliding the bold theoretical curve vertically. We might have chosen to assume the optical collection efficiency (or other equivalent parameter) to be constant only for the course of a single run over infrared frequencies, since there was more possibility of altered conditions between runs and especially for the distinction between Stokes and anti-Stokes runs. However, we find that the fit is essentially as good if we allow *no* relative normalization among the several runs. The

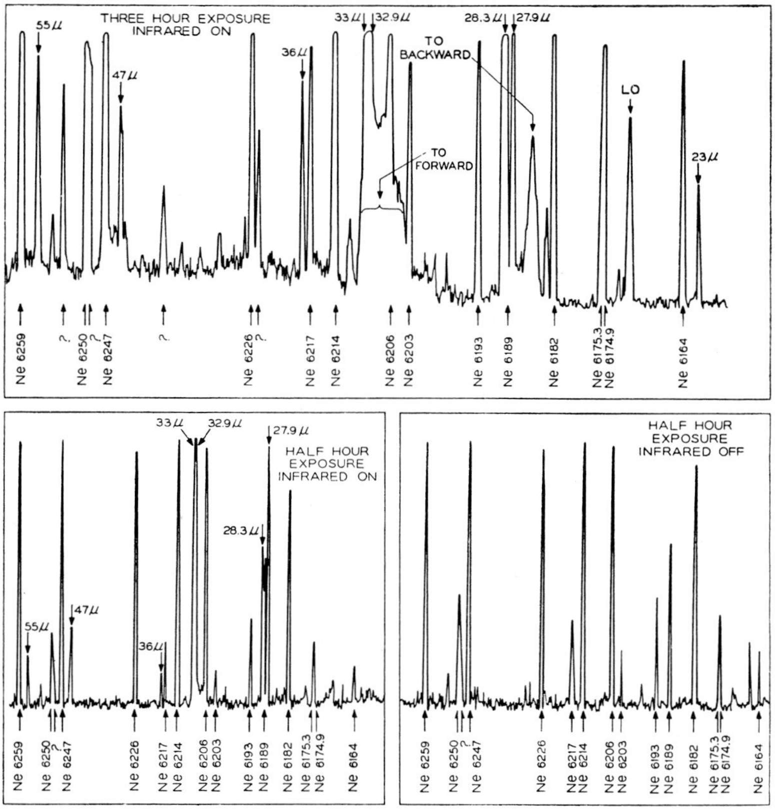

FIG. 4. Densitometer traces from photographic plates of the anti-Stokes spectrum. In II there is given a similar display for the Stokes side. The neon lines are due to spontaneous emission from the red laser, imperfectly rejected by the 6328 Å spike-pass filter. Lines identified by infrared wavelengths are due to mixing, and they disappear when the ir beam is blocked. "TO forward" and "backward" and "LO" are ordinary Raman scattering.

dominant problems are evidently random scatter and consistent departures from theory within individual runs, not normalization between runs. The implications are that the collection efficiency was stable between runs *and* that the $|d|$ for the Stokes side has essentially the same magnitude as well as the same shape as the $|d|$ for the anti-Stokes side. We can say that we are fitting five Stokes data points and seven anti-Stokes points with a single adjustable parameter.

We can anticipate as follows that essentially the same $|d|$ *should* govern Stokes and anti-Stokes radiation: The frequency-dependence of the two constants d_E and C in Eq. (1) has been investigated by Garrett,[9] who describes the nonlinearities of the crystal using a rather general model involving two anharmonic and anharmonically coupled oscillators. Garrett finds that the frequency dependence of C is negligible and that the constant d_E varies slowly with the frequency of the scattered light. d_E differs by at most 10% between our Stokes and our anti-Stokes frequencies. Since the scatter in our data is larger than 10%, this difference is not expected to be observable in our measured $|d|$, for the two sides.[10]

The data seem to suggest some systematic deviations from the theory, but the general agreement is quite

[9] C. G. B. Garrett (private communication).

[10] Frequency dependence of the grating efficiency and of the intensity radiated by a unit dipole have been ignored. All other evident corrections have been taken into account in the data-reduction process.

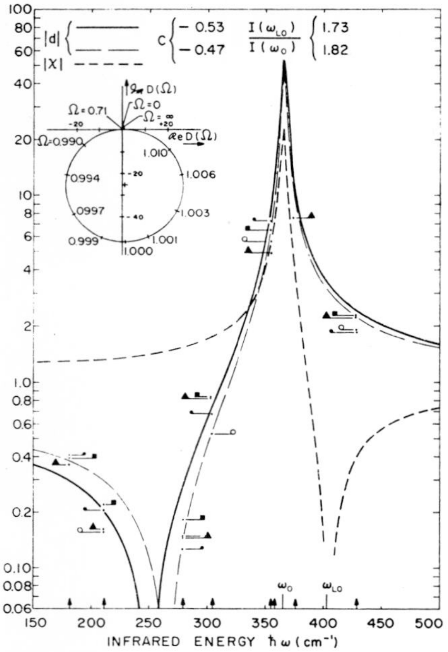

FIG. 5. The moduli of the linear and the nonlinear susceptibilities X and d versus infrared frequency. $C=-0.53$ is the value determined from the ratio $I(\omega_{LO})/I(\omega_0)=1.73\pm0.05$, observed in 90° Raman scattering (see II); the corresponding curve is a one-parameter (multiplicative) fit to the experimental $|d|$. $C=-0.47$ is the optimal value from a curve-fitting process; this corresponds to $I(\omega_{LO})/I(\omega_0)=1.82$. We hold $\Gamma=0.01\omega_0=3.65$ cm^{-1}. A larger $\Gamma\approx0.02\omega_0$ actually gives a somewhat better fit still. Triangles, etc., classify the data by runs. The unfilled and the filled symbols are, respectively, Stokes and anti-Stokes data points. The inset gives a complex plot of $D(\Omega)=1+C(1-\Omega^2-i\Omega\gamma)^{-1}$, the nonlinear analog of an Argand diagram.

good. A possible source of systematic experimental errors would be in the differing overlap with the 6328 Å spot for different spot patterns and sizes which the several infrared laser lines may have generated. This difficulty is probably not so severe as might at first be thought, since, in our experience, a laser medium well above threshold will generally seize upon enough modes of the resonator to fill out the area and the angular aperture of the tube (a wavelength-independent condition).

We must note one critical point which appears in the reduction of these data and of the data presented in II. The coherence lengths at various infrared frequencies are determined from the measured visible[11] and infrared[12] refractive indices. However, the dispersion from the initially available data did *not* correctly predict the frequency of forward *Raman scattering*, Stokes or anti-Stokes; and the coherence lengths implied were not consistent with our observed mixing intensities. In processing data for the previous paper, we assumed that the infrared data were in error; and we applied a uniform increment to the infrared refractive indices of +0.2374 (roughly 7% of the values of the index at our lower frequencies, away from the reststrahl band), to fit the observed frequency of forward Stokes TO *Raman scattering*. We then found reasonable agreement with theory for the Stokes and anti-Stokes *frequency-mixing intensities* (see Fig. 2 of II). The Raman and frequency-mixing experiments are quite sensitive to errors because they sense, loosely speaking, the *difference* between visible and infrared dispersion.

Barker[13] has recently reconsidered the treatment of the infrared refractive index. He has reanalyzed the infrared reflectivity, and he has studied the first-order Raman scattering line shapes. He finds that the data can be fitted only if ω_0, the resonant frequency of the lattice, and Γ, the lattice damping constant, are frequency-dependent. There is a certain range of choice of parameter values (frequencies, oscillator strengths, and damping), but generally the new infrared index values resemble our one-constant correction of +0.2374 applied to the older data. We have taken a choice of parameter values which gives very nearly the correct value of the frequency of forward Stokes TO *Raman scattering*, and we have again made a uniform additive correction (now only −0.0048) to produce the observed Raman frequency exactly. These are the values which we have used for the infrared refractive index (at the infrared laser frequencies), needed for calculation of coherence lengths in the *mixing experiment.*

The datum at 375 cm^{-1} is particularly interesting; the fit here constitutes a rather gratifying verification of the theory[7] of the coherence length:

$$l_c(\omega)=[(\Delta k(\omega))^2+(\tfrac{1}{2}\alpha)^2]^{-1/2}.$$

Whereas α is small for most of our frequencies, and Δk dominates, 375 cm^{-1} is contained in the region of high absorption and anomalous dispersion between ω_0(365 cm^{-1}) and ω_{LO}(403 cm^{-1}). Here $\frac{1}{2}\alpha=12\,400$ cm^{-1} and $\Delta k=8700$ cm^{-1}. The two terms are comparable, and the absorptive term is actually the larger. Despite the complications, the fit is essentially as good as for other frequencies; and the fit becomes substantially worse if either of the two terms is omitted. At 375 cm^{-1}, only 5.3% of the infrared energy penetrates the surface, and this energy is dissipated absorptively within a distance of 0.4 μ. On the other hand, $|d|$ is large; and we were able to take somewhat better than marginal measurements of intensity, in the face of noise.

$d(\omega_S=\omega_L\pm\omega)$ is, of course, a complex quantity, although we have experimental access only to $|d(\omega)|$; essentially the point is that the theory gives Eq. (1) *without* the modulus bars. Since we have agreement on $|d(\omega)|$, we are encouraged to believe that the theory

[11] D. F. Nelson (private communication).
[12] D. A. Kleinman and W. G. Spitzer, Phys. Rev. **118**, 110 (1960)
[13] A. S. Barker (private communication).

for $d(\omega)/d_E$ is correct for *phase*, as well. Accordingly, we have given, as an inset to Fig. 5, a complex plot versus Ω of $D(\Omega)=1+C(1-\Omega^2-i\Omega\gamma)^{-1}$, for $0\leq\Omega\leq\infty$, $C=-0.5$, $\gamma=0.01$; see Eq. (1). Note that (a) $D(-\Omega)=D^*(\Omega)$; (b) the poles are at $\frac{1}{2}[\pm(-\gamma^2+4)^{1/2}-i\gamma]\approx\{\pm1.0-i0.005\}$, in the *lower* half-plane because of the choice of sign of the damping term in Eq. (4) of II; this corresponds to the representation of $E(t)$ by $E_0e^{+i\omega t}$; (c) Re $D(\Omega)<0$ for $0.71\lesssim\Omega\lesssim1$; Re$D(\Omega)$ has *two* changes of sign; (d) $|D(\Omega)|$ has a minimum near $\Omega=(1+C)^{1/2}\approx0.71$, a very small value, but not an identical zero; (e) at the peak of $|D(\Omega)|$, $D(\Omega)$ is principally imaginary; (f) except where $|D(\Omega)-1|$ is small, $D(\Omega)$ is *very* well represented by a circle of radius $|C|/2\gamma=25$, centered at $1+iC/2\gamma=1-25i$. The approximate form is $D_{cir}(\Omega)=1+(C/2\gamma)(-\sin2\theta+i\cos2\theta+i)$, where $\Omega^2=1+\gamma\tan\theta$, and the range of θ is given by $-\frac{1}{2}\pi\approx\tan^{-1}(-100)=\tan^{-1}(-1/\gamma)\leq\theta\leq\frac{1}{2}\pi$.

V. CONCLUSION

Equation (1) gives correctly the dependence upon infrared frequency of $|d|$, the nonlinear susceptibility governing both Raman scattering and mixing of coherent beams in the visible and in the infrared, for the interesting region near the reststrahl band. We are encouraged to expect that in other materials, as well as in GaP, similar relations between Raman and mixing experiments will hold. The determination of C from an experimentally comparatively *simple* study of Raman scattering allows one to infer the frequency dependence (near the lattice resonance) of the nonlinear susceptibility governing mixing, parametric oscillation, etc.[14] Such processes are of substantial engineering interest, but *direct* mixing, etc., studies (such as the present experiment) require complex infrared and visible optical apparatus.

As we stated in the concluding remarks of II, "$\chi(\omega)$ and $d(\omega_S=\omega_L-\omega)$ are each a sum of two terms, a nonresonant term and a resonant term $\propto Q(\omega)/E(\omega)$. For $\omega<\omega_0$ these two terms contribute constructively to $\chi(\omega)$, but destructively to $d(\omega_S=\omega_L-\omega)$." For $\omega>\omega_0$, $Q(\omega)/E(\omega)$ takes the opposite sign,[15] with the opposite effects in χ and in d. See Fig. 5. In the case of χ, the observed behavior is to be expected on very general grounds. The nonresonant term is due to polarization of the electron clouds relative to the much heavier nuclei, while the resonant term is due to relative motion of the heavy positive ions and the heavy negative ions, taken as rigid bodies. In the static limit, we expect any two such mechanisms to give polarization in the same sense. For d, on the other hand, we are not able to construct a similar argument, nor *any* general argument. For some material other than GaP, we cannot rule out that d may exhibit a resonance of the same sense as that which occurs in general for χ, rather than one of the opposite sense.

ACKNOWLEDGMENTS

We wish to thank C. G. B. Garrett for much useful advice and encouragement in this work, A. S. Barker for communication of data on the linear infrared optical constants of GaP, prior to publication, D. MacNair for design and supply of cathodes suitable for use in the H_2O laser, Long Chi Lee for computer calculations, and M. H. L. Pryce and D. F. Nelson for profitable conversations.

APPENDIX

We have had some indication that the account of our calculation of the value of the constant C given in II was not sufficiently explicit; we will elaborate further. For general ω the Raman scattering is proportional to $|P^{NL}(\omega)|^2=|d_EE(\omega)+d_QQ(\omega)|^2$, where $E(\omega)$ and $Q(\omega)$ are governed by Eq. (4) of II (forced harmonic oscillator equation), and the amplitudes of E and Q are due to zero-point and thermal motion. For large k at $\omega\approx\omega_{TO}=\omega_0$, the wave is phononlike, with small E and large Q. Whereas the LO scattering is proportional to $|d_EE(\omega_{LO})+d_QQ(\omega_{LO})|^2$, the large-angle TO scattering is proportional to $|d_Q|^2|Q(\omega_0)|^2$, the E term being negligible. We take the ratio

$$
\begin{aligned}
|P^{NL}(\omega_{LO})|^2/|P^{NL}(\omega_0)|^2
&=|(d_E/d_Q)(E(\omega_{LO})/Q(\omega_{LO}))+1|^2\\
&\quad\times(|Q(\omega_{LO})|^2/|Q(\omega_0)|^2)\\
&=|(d_E/d_Q)(M/e_L)(\omega_0^2-\omega_{LO}^2-i\omega_{LO}\Gamma)+1|^2\\
&\quad\times|Q(\omega_{LO})|^2/|Q(\omega_0)|^2\\
&=|(1/C)(\omega_0^2-\omega_{LO}^2-i\omega_{LO}\Gamma)+1|^2\\
&\quad\times|Q(\omega_{LO})|^2/|Q(\omega_0)|^2.
\end{aligned}
$$

$Q(\omega_{LO})$ and $Q(\omega_0)$ obey homogeneous (*not* forced) harmonic oscillator equations:

$$M\ddot{Q}+M\omega_{LO}^2Q=0$$

and

$$M\ddot{Q}+M\omega_0^2Q=0,$$

respectively. The excitations obey Bose statistics, $n=[\exp(\hbar\omega\beta-1)]^{-1}$. $<Q^2(\omega)>_{av}=(\hbar/M\omega)(n+1)$, $(\hbar/M\omega)(n)$ for Stokes and anti-Stokes scattering, respectively. We find for the Stokes case

$$\langle Q^2(\omega_{LO})\rangle_{av}/\langle Q^2(\omega_0)\rangle_{av}=0.874.$$

Except for a small effect of frequency dependence ($<1\%$),[10] we have $|P^{NL}(\omega_{LO})|^2/|P^{NL}(\omega_0)|^2=I(\omega_{LO})/I(\omega_0)$; for the latter ratio we have the experimentally determined value 1.73 ± 0.05, in Stokes scattering. We now have sufficient information to calculate C, and we find $C=-0.53\pm0.03$ (but see Ref. 14 and Fig. 5 of this paper).

[14] The determination of C from the Raman scattering is, however, subject to an ambiguity associated with the solution of a quadratic equation; see Ref. 11 of II.

[15] The phase change at resonance characteristic of the response of a forced harmonic oscillator.

Reprinted from *Phys. Rev.* **173**, 781 (1968).

Contributions to Optical Nonlinearity in GaAs as Determined from Raman Scattering Efficiencies

W. D. Johnston, Jr., and I. P. Kaminow
Bell Telephone Laboratories, Holmdel, New Jersey 07733
(Received 2 July 1969)

Values for the electro-optic and second-harmonic-generation coefficients [r_{41} and d_{14}(SHG)] can be calculated from absolute spontaneous-Raman-scattering data alone. The ratio of electronic and lattice contributions to r_{41}, and the stimulated Raman gain coefficients for the LO and TO modes, may also be obtained. The technique is applied to GaAs and the value for r_{41} [$(1.5\pm0.1)\times10^{-12}$ m/V] agrees with direct measurements, while the value for d_{14}(SHG) [$(1.4\pm0.1)\times10^{-10}$ m/V] is within the range of some direct SHG measurements.

THE nonlinear optical properties of insulating crystals are derived from two sources: first, the perturbation of the optical polarizability by an electromagnetic field acting through a lattice displacement (lattice or deformation potential interaction); second, the perturbation of the optical polarizability produced by the direct action of the field on the electronic energy levels (nonlattice or electronic interaction).

In piezoelectric crystals with only one simultaneously Raman- and infrared-active mode of given symmetry type, measurement of the absolute scattering efficiencies for longitudinal and transverse modes S_L and S_T and the corresponding frequencies is sufficient to determine separately the lattice and electronic contributions, their ratio C, the electro-optic coefficient r_{ijk}, the nonlinear coefficient d_{kji}(SHG), and, with the measured linewidths 2Γ, the gain coefficients for stimulated Raman phonon or polariton scattering. The technique is applied to high-purity GaAs and the result is found to agree with previous measurements of r_{123} and C but contradicts an earlier second-harmonic-generation measurement of d_{123}(SHG). Several other techniques have been employed in the past to determine the absolute contributions of the lattice and nonlattice terms to electro-optic nonlinearity in $LiNbO_3$ [1] and GaAs [2] and the relative contributions in GaP [3] and ZnSe.[4]

In the case of semiconductors (where the macroscopic field may be regarded also as the "local" field), Loudon[5] has shown that both lattice and electronic interactions contribute to the Raman scattering efficiency for longitudinal modes (S_L) but that only the lattice interaction contributes to the scattering efficiency for transverse modes (S_T). It should be noted that what Loudon terms an electro-optic coefficient (z_{ijk}) is, in fact, only the electronic (nonlattice) contribution ($\xi_{ijk}/\epsilon_0 n^4$ in the notation of Refs. 1, 7, and 8) to the conventional electro-optic coefficient (r_{ijk}).[1] In ionic crystals where the Lorentz field is the appropriate local field,[6] the technique also applies, although some care must be taken to identify coefficients based on macroscopic parameters with microscopic interactions in a consistent fashion. When the crystal structure permits several simultaneously Raman- and infrared-active modes of the same symmetry (as in $LiNbO_3$), the present technique is complicated but determination of nonlinear coefficients from Raman data is possible in principle.[7]

We ignore plasmon and polariton effects (i.e., the plasma frequency is assumed much less than the TO frequency and the phonon wave vector is assumed much greater than the TO frequency divided by the velocity of light); then for crystals with zinc-blende structure the Raman efficiencies inside the medium are given by[1,5]

$$S_{L,T}=\sigma_{L,T}\rho^{-1}|d\alpha_{12}/dQ_3|^2{}_{L,T}, \tag{1}$$

with

$$\sigma_{L,T}=\frac{\hbar\omega_s^4(\bar{n}_{L,T}+1)ld\Omega}{32\pi^2\epsilon_0^2c^4\omega_{L,T}}, \tag{2}$$

where ρ is the reduced mass density, ω_T and ω_L the transverse and longitudinal mode frequencies, ω_s the Stokes frequency, $\bar{n}$ the Bose factor, l the scattering length, and $d\Omega$ the scattering solid angle.

The differential polarizability $d\alpha_{12}/dQ_3$ for the TO mode is $\partial\alpha_{12}/\partial Q_3\equiv\alpha_{123}$, and (introducing the notations of Refs. 1 and 2) for the LO mode, we have

$$\frac{d\alpha_{12}}{dQ_3}=\frac{\partial\alpha_{12}}{\partial Q_3}+\frac{\partial\alpha_{12}}{\partial E_3}\frac{\partial E_3}{\partial Q_3}$$
$$\equiv\alpha_{123}+\xi_{123}\beta_3^{-1}(\omega_L)\equiv\alpha_{123}[1-(aC)^{-1}], \tag{3}$$

[1] I. P. Kaminow and W. D. Johnston, Jr., Phys. Rev. **160**, 519 (1967); **178**, 1528(E) (1969).
[2] A. Mooradian and A. L. McWhorter, in *Proceedings of the International Conference on Light Scattering Spectra in Solids, New York University, 1968*, edited by G. B. Wright (Springer-Verlag, New York, 1969).
[3] W. L. Faust and C. H. Henry, Phys. Rev. Letters **17**, 1265 (1966).
[4] S. Ushioda, A. Pinczuk, W. Taylor, and E. Burstein, in *II-VI Semiconducting Compounds*, edited by D. G. Thomas (W. A. Benjamin, Inc., New York, 1967); R. C. C. Leite, T. C. Damen, and J. F. Scott, in *Proceedings of the International Conference on Light Scattering Spectra in Solids, New York University, 1968*, edited by G. B. Wright (Springer-Verlag, New York, 1969) (note the definition of C in these papers is the inverse of that used here).
[5] R. Loudon, Advan. Phys. **13**, 423 (1964); in *Proceedings of the International Conference on Light Scattering Spectra in Solids, New York University, 1968*, edited by G. B. Wright (Springer-Verlag, New York, 1969).
[6] H. Poulet, Ann. Phys. (Paris) **10**, 908 (1955).
[7] W. D. Johnston, Jr. (to be published).

TABLE I. Comparison of electro-optic, optical rectification, and SHG coefficients from analysis of Raman scattering with those obtained from direct measurement.

r_{41} (10^{-12} m/V)	d_{14}(SHG) (10^{-10} m/V)	d_{14}(OR) (10^{-10} m/V)	C
1.5±0.1	1.4±0.1	0.55±0.03	−0.59[a]
1.5±0.3	1.0±0.2	0.55±0.1	−0.46[b]
1.5±0.2[c]	...	...	...
...	1.9±0.9[d]	...	...
...	3.7±1.3[e]	...	...
...	...	1.04±0.17[f]	...
...	...	0.69±0.13[f]	...

[a] This paper. [b] See Ref. 2. [c] See Ref. 15. [d] See Ref. 16. [e] See Ref. 17. [f] See Ref. 18.

where, neglecting damping,

$$\beta_3(\omega)=\left[\frac{\epsilon_0 n_\infty^2}{a\rho\omega_T^2}\right]^{1/2}\frac{\omega_T^2}{\omega_T^2-\omega^2}, \tag{4}$$

$$a=\omega_T^2(\omega_L^2-\omega_T^2)^{-1}, \tag{5}$$

n_∞ is the high-frequency refractive index, and C is the ratio of lattice and electron contributions at $\omega=0$, i.e., $C=\alpha_{123}\beta_3(0)/\xi_{123}$. The electro-optic coefficient at modulating frequency $\omega\rightarrow 0$ is given by[8]

$$-\epsilon_0 n^4 r_{123}=\alpha_{123}\beta_3(0)+\xi_{123}$$
$$\equiv\alpha_{123}\beta_3(0)[1+C^{-1}], \tag{6}$$

with n the refractive index at the optical frequency, which may differ from n_∞ in Eq. (4).

Combining these equations to find the nonlinear coefficients in terms of measured quantities yields

$$C^{-1}=a[1\pm(\sigma_T S_L/\sigma_L S_T)^{1/2}], \tag{7}$$

$$r_{ijk}^2=S_T n_\infty^2(1+C^{-1})^2/\epsilon_0 n^8 a\omega_T^2\sigma_T, \tag{8}$$

$$\xi_{ijk}=-\epsilon_0 n^4 r_{ijk}/(1+C). \tag{9}$$

The electronic nonlinear coefficient is related to quantities defined elsewhere[9] by $\xi_{ijk}=4\epsilon_0 d_{kji}$(SHG) and $d_{123}\equiv d_{14}$, $r_{123}\equiv r_{63}=r_{41}$. The square root in (7) leads to a sign ambiguity that can be clarified as noted below. The scattering efficiencies and linewidths can be used to obtain phonon Raman gain coefficients[1,10] and, with C, polariton gain coefficients.[5,11]

A GaAs sample with edges along [100] axes having 3×10^{14} carriers/cm^3, a mobility of 5900 cm^2/V sec, and resistivity of 4 Ω cm was used in the experiments with 90° scattering geometry. After taking the geometry into account,[12] the efficiencies corresponding to α_{123} are

$$S_L/Ld\Omega=(2.3\pm0.2)\times10^{-6}\ \text{cm}^{-1}\ \text{sr}^{-1},$$
$$S_T/Ld\Omega=(1.5\pm0.2)\times10^{-6}\ \text{cm}^{-1}\ \text{sr}^{-1},$$
$$\omega_L=292\ \text{cm}^{-1},\quad \omega_T=269\ \text{cm}^{-1},$$
$$2\Gamma_L=1.6\ \text{cm}^{-1},\quad 2\Gamma_T=1.7\ \text{cm}^{-1}$$

for 1.06-μ excitation using measurement techniques described previously.[13] Because the plasma frequency is much less than ω_T, plasmons play no role.[2] From Eqs. (7)–(9), taking $n^2=12.1$ at 1.06 μ and $n_\infty^2=11.1$,[14] we calculate $r_{41}=(1.5\pm0.1)\times10^{-12}$ m/V, $C\equiv-0.59$, and d_{14}(SHG)$=(1.4\pm0.1)\times10^{-10}$ m/V. [In esu, $r_{41}=4.5\times10^{-8}$ and d_{14}(SHG)$=3.3\times10^{-7}$.]

The other solution is $r_{41}=30.75\times10^{-12}$ m/V, $C=+0.07$, and d_{14}(SHG)$=10.6\times10^{-10}$ m/V. A crude measurement of r_{41} or d_{14} serves to eliminate this solution. Alternatively, a qualitative inspection of Raman spectra for material with sufficient carrier density to permit observation of the plasmon–LO-phonon coupling[2] or of polariton spectra[4] would also suffice to eliminate this solution, which corresponds to constructive interference between the deformation potential and electronic nonlinearity terms.

The clamped electro-optic coefficient of semi-insulating GaAs has been measured directly by Turner[15] [$r_{41}=(1.5\pm0.15)\times10^{-12}$ m/V at 3.39 μ and 63 MHz] and is in good agreement with our first solution but not with the alternative solution. Our results for r_{41}, d_{14}(SHG), and C are in reasonable agreement with those of Mooradian and McWhorter obtained by a different technique.[2] Our value for d_{14}(SHG) agrees within experimental error with the (SHG) measurements of Wynne and Bloembergen[16] but disagrees with the value obtained by Patel.[17] The various values are compared in Table I, along with values for the optical rectification coefficient d_{14}(OR)$=\frac{1}{4}n^4 r_{41}$.[18] The nonlinear coefficients are expected to be only weakly wavelength-dependent for wavelengths greater than 1 μ, which is well removed from the band edge.[4,15]

The Raman phonon gain for a fundamental-mode 1.06-μ pump with confocal focusing in the crystal is calculated[10] to be 1.5%/W for a single pass. Although this gain is quite large by comparison with that of other solids,[19] our measurements on several GaAs

[8] I. P. Kaminow, in *Ferroelectricity*, edited by E. F. Weller (Elsevier Publishing Co., Amsterdam, 1967).

[9] G. D. Boyd and D. A. Kleinman, J. Appl. Phys. **39**, 359 (1968).

[10] G. D. Boyd, W. D. Johnston, Jr., and I. P. Kaminow, IEEE J. Quantum Electron. **QE5**, 203 (1969).

[11] C. H. Henry and C. G. B. Garrett, Phys. Rev. **171**, 1058 (1968).

[12] For $x(yz)y$ geometry, the observed LO and TO intensities must be multiplied by 2 to obtain (10), while for $x(yx)y$ the observed TO intensity may be used directly.

[13] W. D. Johnston, Jr., and I. P. Kaminow, Phys. Rev. **168**, 1045 (1968); **178**, 1528(E) (1969).

[14] B. O. Seraphin and H. E. Bennett (also M. Hass) in *Semiconductors and Semimetals*, edited by R. K. Willardson and A. C. Beer (Academic Press Inc., New York, 1967), Vol. 3.

[15] E. H. Turner (unpublished results); see also T. E. Walsh, RCA Rev. **27**, 323 (1966); E. H. Turner and I. P. Kaminow, J. Opt. Soc. Am. **5**, 3523 (1968).

[16] J. J. Wynne and N. Bloembergen, Phys. Rev., this issue, **188**, 1211 (1969).

[17] C. K. N. Patel, Phys. Rev. Letters **16**, 613 (1966).

[18] T. Y. Chang, N. VanTran, and C. K. N. Patel, Appl. Phys. Letters **13**, 357 (1968). The two values for d_{14}(OR) correspond to optical mixing measurements at difference frequencies of 53.5 and 54.3 GHz.

[19] W. D. Johnston, Jr., I. P. Kaminow, and J. G. Bergman, Jr. Appl. Phys. Letters **13**, 190 (1968).

samples at 1.06 μ indicate that the lowest absorption coefficient for currently available bulk material is $\sim$0.7 cm^{-1}, which makes these crystals unsuitable for Raman oscillator applications with the Nd-YAG laser.

The method described here is well suited to measurements of r_{ijk} on wurtzite or zinc-blende-type crystals with conductivity too large to sustain low-frequency modulating fields. It also provides more accurate measurements of ξ_{ijk} than present high-power-pulsed SHG measurements.

Reprinted from THE PHYSICAL REVIEW, Vol. 188, No. 3, 1209–1211, 15 December 1969
Printed in U. S. A.

Microwave Nonlinear Susceptibilities Due to Electronic and Ionic Anharmonicities in Acentric Crystals

G. D. Boyd, T. J. Bridges, M. A. Pollack, and E. H. Turner
Bell Telephone Laboratories, Holmdel, New Jersey 07733
(Received 16 December 1970)

A *microwave* nonlinear susceptibility analogous to the optical and electro-optical nonlinear susceptibilities is investigated in a number of acentric ferroelectric and semiconductor crystals. Contributions from ionic nonlinearities result in enormously larger nonlinear coefficients in some materials than any known for the optical or electro-optical effects. An interpretation is presented in terms of a relationship between the nonlinear coefficients and the electronic and ionic *linear* susceptibilities.

In this paper we correlate the little-studied microwave nonlinear susceptibility with the familiar optical and electro-optical nonlinear susceptibilities for three-frequency mixing. Our work includes the first measurement of the microwave nonlinear susceptibility coefficient[1] d^{m}, in a variety of acentric polar and nonpolar crystals (Table I). For some materials d^{m} exceeds the largest values of the optical nonlinear coefficient[2] d^{o} by many orders of magnitude. The much smaller differences between the electro-optic nonlinear coefficient[3] d^{eo} and d^{o} have been previously studied.[4,5] We interpret all these differences in terms of the values of the electronic and ionic linear susceptibilities, by means of a phenomenological model. We show how Kleinman's symmetry condition[6] for the d^{o} tensor coefficients also applies to d^{m} for some, but not all, materials. Finally we note that our macroscopic measure of nonlinearities is related to microscopic anharmonicities of the crystalline bonds and thus to other physical phenomena such as infrared absorption, pyroelectricity, and thermal expansion.

Optical nonlinearities (d^{o}) are purely electronic in origin since all frequencies are above the lattice mode frequencies. Values of d^{eo} and d^{m} differ from d^{o} because for d^{eo} one and for d^{m} all the frequencies lie below the optical lattice mode frequencies, so that ionic as well as electronic anharmonicities are present. The coefficient d^{m} is the most general of the various nonlinear coefficients in its dependence on these anharmonicities.

Miller[7] showed that d^{o} equals the product of linear susceptibility cubed (purely electronic in the optical region) and a frequency-independent, but somewhat material-dependent, parameter δ. Garrett[8] proposed a phenomenological model extending Miller's work to treat both electronic and ionic contributions to the nonlinear susceptibility. The nonlinear susceptibility is related to the linear electronic and ionic susceptibilities at each frequency by introducing four separate δ parameters. We interpret the listed values of d^{m}, d^{eo}, and d^{o} by a version of this theory.

Microwave nonlinearities have been reported before,[9-12] but primarily as a higher-order effect in the centric paraelectric state of ferroelectrics.[9,10] Limited measurements on acentric crystals[10-12] have been made but cannot be interpreted in terms of the coefficients discussed here.

Experimental technique.—The coefficient d^{m}, d^{eo}, or d^{o} is defined in mks units[2] by the relation between the induced-polarization-wave Fourier amplitude, $\mathcal{P}(\omega)$, and the electric-field Fourier amplitudes,[3,6] $E(\omega)$, as

$$\mathcal{P}_i(-\omega_3)=\epsilon_0 2d_{ijk}(-\omega_3,\omega_2,\omega_1)E_j(\omega_2)E_k(\omega_1), \quad (1)$$

where summation over repeated indices is implied. We adopt the convention (consistent with electro-optic usage) that the third index refers to the orientation of the modulating field. As defined in Eq. (1), the coefficient d^{o} is equivalent to the familiar optical second-harmonic-generation coefficient.[2] The factor of 2 in Eq. (1) arises because a mixing process rather than second-harmonic generation is being described. The third-rank tensor coefficient d_{ijk} differs from zero only in the acentric point groups, as does the piezoelectric coefficient.[13] Conservation of energy requires that $\omega_3=\omega_2+\omega_1$ and difference mixing occurs if $\omega_1\to-\omega_1$.

The determination of d^{m} is analogous to that used for electro-optic coefficients.[14] A 56-GHz carrier (ω_2) is mixed with a 100-MHz modulation field (ω_1) in the crystal, which fills a section of RG-98/U waveguide (0.376 cm×0.188 cm), except for a 0.05-cm gap at each side. To find a constant-strain (clamped) coefficient, ω_1 is high enough to avoid piezoelectric resonances. The modulation voltage is applied by metal electrodes to two opposing faces of the crystal. Normally

Table I. Nonlinear susceptibilities and related parameters. n, value appropriate to the measurement of d^o. ϵ, values taken from current literature. α, absorption coefficient, measured at $\lambda = 5.3$ mm in the waveguide. r, electro-optic coefficients [values and signs from I. P. Kaminow and E. H. Turner, in "Handbook of Lasers" (Chemical Rubber Co., Cleveland, Ohio, in press); see also E. H. Turner, to be published, for details of the sign determination]. d, given in mks units where $d(\text{mks}) = (4\pi/3)10^{-4}d(\text{cgs})$ and $d(\text{cgs})$ is defined as in Eq. (1) with $\epsilon_0 = 1$ (Ref. 3). d^o, signs from R. C. Miller and W. A. Nordland, Opt. Commun. 1, 400 (1970), and to be published. For KDP see W. A. Nordland, to be published. Except as noted, magnitudes are from (i) Ref. 2; (ii) J. Jerphagnon and S. K. Kurtz, Phys. Rev. B 1, 1739 (1970); (iii) G. E. Francois, Phys. Rev. 143, 597 (1966); and (iv) J. E. Bjorkholm and A. E. Siegman, Phys. Rev. 154, 851 (1967). d^{eo}, value of n in the original work was used, where possible, to convert to the electro-optic nonlinear susceptibility coefficient d^{eo}. d^m, absolute signs have not yet been determined. δ_{AB}, sign is that of d^m. Where d^{eo} contributes significantly to d^m, two possible values of δ_{AB} are given.

Material	Point Group	n	ϵ/ϵ_0	α cm^{-1}	χ^e	χ^i	r (10^{-12} m/V)	d^o (10^{-12} m/V)	d^{eo} (10^{-12} m/V)	d^m (10^{-12} m/V)	δ_D	δ_C	δ_{AB}	Measured d_{ijk}
$BaTiO_3$	4mm	2.29	57	1.7	4.25	52	+28	-6.8	-193	97,000	-0.08	-0.20	0.64	333
$LiTaO_3$	3m	2.14	40	1.0	3.58	35.4	+30.3	-20	-159	16,000	-0.44	-0.31	0.33	333
$LiNbO_3$	3m	2.16	25.5	0.48	3.66	20.8	+30.8	-40	-170	6,700	-0.82	-0.46	0.63	333
KH_2PO_4[a] (KDP)	$\bar{4}2m$	1.50 1.46	44 21	~0.9	1.24 1.13	41.8 18.9	-8.8	+0.48	+11	1,850[f]	+0.28	+0.36	0.053	123[f]
$NH_4H_2PO_4$[a] (ADP)	$\bar{4}2m$	1.51 1.47	58 14	~1.2	1.28 1.16	55.7 11.8	-5.5	±0.59	+7.2	970[f]	±0.31	+0.34 -0.40	0.024	123[f]
$LiIO_3$	6	1.72	6.53	0.4	1.96	3.58	+6.4	-4.3[b]	-14.5	±177	-0.57	-0.71	+2.7 -2.3	333
$NaNO_2$[c]	m2m	1.40	4.18	≲0.1	0.97	2.21	<0.9	0.12[d]	<0.9	36	0.12	-	2.3	333
ZnO	6mm	1.96	8.7	<0.05	2.84	4.91	+2.6	-7.2	-10.7	±176	-0.27	-0.08	+1.0 -0.9	333
CdS	6mm	2.35	9.25	0.15	4.53	3.72	-2.7	+31	+18	±127	+0.25	-0.18	+1.0 -1.4	333
CdTe	$\bar{4}3m$	2.66	9.4	≲0.1	6.07	2.3	-5.6	∓168	+73	±36	∓0.74	+2.7 -1.1	-0.8 -2.5	123
GaP	$\bar{4}3m$	2.95	10.75	0.1	7.70	2.05	-0.97	+78[e]	+20	±24	+0.16	-0.47	+0.1 -1.1	123
GaAs	$\bar{4}3m$	3.27	13.05	0.024	9.71	2.34	-1.5	+134[e]	+43	±51	+0.14	-0.41	+0.12 -1.4	123
Ag_3AsS_3	3m	2.52	21	~1.8	5.36	14.6	+0.9	-	-9	950	-	-	0.22	333

[a] Upper and lower values of n, ϵ, χ^e, and χ^i correspond to 1 and 3 axes, respectively.
[b] F. R. Nash, J. G. Bergman, G. D. Boyd, and E. H. Turner, J. Appl. Phys. 40, 5201 (1969).
[c] Polar 3 axis coincides with crystallographic b axis.
[d] K. Inoue, Jap. J. Appl. Phys. 9, 152 (1970).
[e] J. J. Wynne and N. Bloembergen, Phys. Rev. 188, 1211 (1969); also J. H. McFee, G. D. Boyd, and P. H. Schmidt, Appl. Phys. Lett. 17, 57 (1970).
[f] The listed value is the combination $\frac{1}{3}(2d_{231} + d_{123})$, which equals d_{123} if the Kleinman symmetry condition applies (see text). Account of double refraction requires that $\epsilon(\omega_3)$ in Eq. (2) be multiplied by $\cos^2\rho = (2\epsilon_{11} + \epsilon_{33})^2/3(2\epsilon_{11}^2 + \epsilon_{33}^2)$, where ρ is the double-refraction angle.

the electrodes are arranged so that $E(\omega_1)$ is parallel to $E(\omega_2)$, but some measurements in potassium dihydrogen phosphate (KDP) and ammonium dihydrogen phosphate (ADP) were also made with $E(\omega_1)$ perpendicular to $E(\omega_2)$. Only the sidebands ω_3 generated with $E(\omega_3)$ parallel to $E(\omega_2)$ could propagate in the unfilled waveguide. At 56 GHz the coherence length for these parallel fields is several centimeters even in birefringent crystals. Two independent tensor coefficients were measured in KDP and ADP and one in the other crystals. A tunable narrow-band heterodyne receiver and precision attenuator are used to measure the power ratio P_3/P_2 of the upper or lower sideband at ω_3 to the carrier at ω_2. The value of d^m is deduced from this ratio and the modulation voltage at ω_1. In these high-dielectric-constant materials it was assumed that P_2 and P_3 propagate entirely within the crystal and that the field $E(\omega_1)$ is adequately uniform, as shown by potential-model studies. Microwave resonances are accounted for by measuring P_3/P_2 vs ω_3 over several free spectral ranges of the crystal and then deducing the nonresonant value of the power ratio.

The power ratio is calculated from the polarization wave, the peak Fourier amplitude of which is given by $\mathcal{P}(-\omega_3)=\epsilon_0 2d_{\rm eff}E(\omega_2)E(\omega_1)$. The relationship of the effective[3] nonlinear coefficient $d_{\rm eff}$ to the tensor coefficients $d_{ijk}{}^{\rm m}(-\omega_3, \omega_2, \omega_1)$ depends on the point group and orientation of the crystal and fields. For point groups $\bar{4}2m$ and $\bar{4}3m$ the three parallel fields are chosen with equal angles to the three crystallographic axes and $d_{\rm eff}=(2/\sqrt{3})(2d_{231}+d_{123})/3$ and $(2/\sqrt{3})d_{123}$, respectively. The fields are parallel to [001] and $d_{\rm eff}=d_{333}$ for the other point groups. The side-band-to-carrier ratio is given by[15]

$$\frac{P_3}{P_2}\approx\left(\frac{k_3}{\beta_3}\right)^2\frac{\omega_3{}^2 d_{\rm eff}}{c^2\epsilon(\omega_3)}\left(\frac{l}{b}\right)^2 V_1{}^2, \tag{2}$$

where k_3 is the plane-wave propagation constant in the dielectric; β_3, the filled waveguide propagation constant; c, the velocity of light; $\epsilon(\omega_3)$, the dielectric constant for $E(\omega_3)$; l, the crystal length; b, the crystal thickness parallel to the electric field $E(\omega_1)$; and V_1, the modulating-voltage amplitude. As an example, $P_3/P_2=5\times10^{-6}$ at $\omega_3/2\pi=56$ GHz in $LiTaO_3$ with $l=1.0$ cm, $b=0.188$ cm, and $V_1=141$ V peak.

Interpretation of results. —Garrett suggests that $d_{ijk}(-\omega_3, \omega_2, \omega_1)$ can be generalized in terms of four Miller δ coefficients which are frequency independent and approximately equal in magnitude:

$$d(-\omega_3, \omega_2, \omega_1)=\chi_1{}^i\chi_2{}^i\chi_3{}^i\delta_A+\chi_1{}^i\chi_2{}^i\chi_3{}^e\delta_B+\chi_1{}^i\chi_2{}^e\chi_3{}^e\delta_C+\chi_1{}^e\chi_2{}^e\chi_3{}^e\delta_D. \tag{3}$$

The δ's can be related to coefficients of the crystal potential-energy terms cubic in the displacement of electrons and ions.[8] In Eq. (3) $\chi^e=n^2-1$ is the linear electronic susceptibility (n being the refractive index), $\chi^i+\chi^e=\epsilon/\epsilon_0-1$ (χ^i is the linear ionic susceptibility and ϵ the microwave dielectric constant), and subscripts indicate frequencies. The tensor nature of d and δ is not indicated. The large variation observed in d between materials is due to differences in values of χ's.

For $d^{\rm o}$ all $\chi_j{}^i=0$ and for $d^{\rm eo}$ only $\chi_1{}^i\neq0$. Consequently only the δ_D term is relevant for $d^{\rm o}$ while both δ_D and δ_C terms contribute to $d^{\rm eo}$. For $d^{\rm m}$ all terms contribute. Neglecting dispersion in χ^e (from the optical to the microwave region) and in χ^i, one obtains

$$d^{\rm o}=(\chi^e)^3\delta_D,\quad d^{\rm eo}-d^{\rm o}=\chi^i(\chi^e)^2\delta_C,\quad d^{\rm m}-d^{\rm eo}=(\chi^i)^2(\chi^i\delta_A+\chi^e\delta_B)=(\chi^i)^2(\chi^i+\chi^e)\delta_{AB}. \tag{4}$$

The quantity δ_{AB} is introduced since we cannot separate the contributions of δ_A and δ_B. Equation (4) enables one to derive δ_{AB}, δ_C, and δ_D (Table I) from $d^{\rm m}$, $d^{\rm eo}$, and $d^{\rm o}$. Akitt, Johnson, and Coleman[16] attempted to determine δ_B in CdTe from dispersion in $d^{\rm e}$ and $d^{\rm eo}$ data. Apart from this, values of δ_{AB} and δ_C have not been measured. For $\chi^i\gg\chi^e$ ($BaTiO_3$ through $NH_4H_2PO_4$), note that $\delta_{AB}\approx\delta_A$. The magnitudes of δ_D, δ_C, and δ_{AB} vary comparatively little, despite an extremely large range of d's. This is particularly impressive for materials with large χ^i. For a new material, using representative values of δ_{AB} and δ_C, one can predict $d^{\rm m}$ and $d^{\rm eo}$. For many materials, Levine[17] has calculated δ_D from bond parameters and he obtains good agreement with experiment. For the III-V compounds Flytzanis[5] has extended Levine's calculation to include ionic displacements and has calculated the ratio of $d^{\rm eo}/d^{\rm o}$, from which it is possible to derive δ_C/δ_D. Theoretical values of δ_A and δ_B have yet to be found.

Depending on the point group of the material there are a number of independent tensor coefficients d_{ijk}. Kleinman[6] shows that in the optical region where $\chi^e\gg\chi^i$, certain symmetries of $d^{\rm o}$ apply beyond those of the piezoelectric coefficients.[13] Similarly, in materials where $\chi^i\gg\chi^e$ it would be expected that the same conditions hold for $d^{\rm m}$. In KDP and ADP it would follow that $d_{231}{}^{\rm m}=d_{123}{}^{\rm m}$. A direct measurement of $d_{123}{}^{\rm m}$ was made in these materials with $E(\omega_1)$ perpendicular to $E(\omega_2)$ and $E(\omega_3)$. It was found that $d_{123}{}^{\rm m}=\frac{1}{3}(2d_{231}{}^{\rm m}+d_{123}{}^{\rm m})$ is obeyed for both materials, within experimental error, in agreement with the symmetry conditions. Where χ^i is not dominant then only two-index permutation (piezoelectric) symmetry will hold.

The δ's are closely related to the parameters describing other physical phenomena. For example, the pyroelectric coefficient has been derived in terms of parameters related to δ_A and δ_B.[8,18] Kleinman[19] has related the microscopic ionic anharmonicity of GaP by a local-field model to macroscopic quantities such as the strength and temperature shift of the infrared combination bands, the width of the fundamental lattice resonance, and the thermal expansion coefficient.[20] Our δ's are macroscopic parameters which can be similarly related to the microscopic ionic and electronic anharmonicities. A detailed comparison of our results with these phenomena has yet to be made.

We are indebted to many of our colleagues for help and advice with these materials: $BaTiO_3$, S. H. Wemple; GaP, L. C. Luther, R. H. Stolen, and H. W. Verleur; $LiTaO_3$, A. A. Ballman; $NaNO_2$, C. M. Hartwig (University of Southern California) for donating the crystal, and A. M. Glass; CdTe, J. E. Kiefer (Hughes Research Laboratories). We wish to thank D. A. Kleinman for many helpful discussions.

---

[1]The coefficient d^m ($= d^{\text{microwave}}$) describes nonlinear interactions at frequencies below the optic, but above the acoustic-resonance frequencies. This implies that d^m is the constant-strain or clamped value. The third-rank tensor nature of $d \equiv d_{ijk}$ is also implied, for all coefficients.

[2]R. Bechmann and S. K. Kurtz, in *Landolt-Bornstein: Zahlenwerte und Funktionen aus Naturwissenschaften und Technik. Gruppe III: Kristall- und Festkörperphysik*, edited by K.-H. Hellwege (Springer, Berlin, 1969), Vol. 2, p. 167; R. W. Minck, R. W. Terhune, and C. C. Wang. Proc. IEEE 54, 1357 (1966).

[3]$d_{ijk}^{eo}(-\omega_3, \omega_2, \omega_1) = -(n_i^2 n_j^2/4) r_{ijk}(\omega_2)$, where r_{ijk} is the electro-optic coefficient. See G. D. Boyd and D. A. Kleinman, J. Appl. Phys. 39, 3597 (1968), Appendix 2.

[4]I. P. Kaminow and W. D. Johnston, Jr., Phys. Rev. 160, 519 (1967); W. L. Faust, C. H. Henry, and R. H. Eick, Phys. Rev. 173, 781 (1968).

[5]C. Flytzanis, Phys. Rev. Lett. 23, 1336 (1969).

[6]D. A. Kleinman, Phys. Rev. 126, 1977 (1962).

[7]R. C. Miller, Appl. Phys. Lett. 5, 17 (1964).

[8]C. G. B. Garrett, J. Quantum Electron. 4, 70 (1968).

[9]M. DiDomenico, D. A. Johnson, and R. H. Pantell, J. Appl. Phys. 33, 1697 (1962); K. M. Johnson, J. Appl. Phys. 33, 2826 (1962).

[10]J. E. Geusic, S. K. Kurtz, T. J. Nelson, and S. H. Wemple, Appl. Phys. Lett. 2, 185 (1963).

[11]C. Wuensche, Z. Angew. Phys. 19, 501 (1965).

[12]I. V. Ivanov and N. A. Morozov, Fiz. Tverd. Tela 8, 3218 (1966) [Sov. Phys. Solid State 8, 2575 (1967)], and J. Phys. Soc. Jap., Suppl. 28, 53 (1970).

[13]J. F. Nye, *Physical Properties of Crystals* (Clarenden Press, Oxford, England, 1957).

[14]I. P. Kaminow, Appl. Phys. Lett. 7, 123 (1965), and 8, 54(E) (1966); I. P. Kaminow and E. H. Turner, Proc. IEEE 54, 1374 (1966).

[15]Equation (2) is equivalent (for $k_3 \approx \beta_3$) to $P_3/P_2 = J_1^2(\eta)/J_0^2(\eta) \approx \frac{1}{4}\eta^2$, characteristic of a phase-modulated signal (Ref. 14), where η is the phase-modulation index.

[16]D. P. Akitt, C. J. Johnson, and P. D. Coleman, J. Quantum Electron. 6, 496 (1970).

[17]B. F. Levine, Phys. Rev. Lett. 25, 440 (1970).

[18]R. A. Soref, J. Quantum Electron. 5, 126 (1969).

[19]D. A. Kleinman, Phys. Rev. 118, 118 (1960).

[20]C. Kittel *Introduction to Solid State Physics* (Wiley, New York, 1966), 3rd ed., p. 184, shows the relationship between the thermal expansion coefficient and the anharmonicity of the lattice.

12. Dispersion of the Electrooptic Effect near the Band Edge

Dispersion of optical and electro-optical coefficients in semiconductors

H. PURSEY and P. A. PAGE

Division of Molecular Science, National Physical Laboratory, Teddington, Middlesex
MS. received 3rd July 1969

Abstract. Simple models based on the free-electron approximation are developed to describe linear and non-linear optical absorption and dispersion in cubic semiconductors. The resulting formulae are programmed to enable numerical results to be obtained, and these are shown to be in good agreement with experiment.

1. Introduction

In a recently published paper (Pursey 1969, to be referred to as I) the authors describe some measurements of the linear electro-optic coefficient, or Pockels coefficient, near the absorption edge of the II–IV semiconducting compound zinc telluride. In an attempt to interpret the results, use was made of formulae derived by applying perturbation theory to a system with a ground state and a finite number of discrete excited states, by integrating the expressions with respect to frequency over ranges corresponding to the first and second conduction bands. Although the calculated dispersion curves were in good agreement with experiment, it was recognized at the time that the physical assumptions implicit in the calculations were unsatisfactory. In particular, replacing the summation over all states by an integration with respect to transition frequency is invalidated by the lack of a one-to-one correspondence between transition frequency and position in momentum space; furthermore, the procedure adopted in I required a knowledge of the frequency limits of a supposed 'window' in the ultra-violet absorption spectrum of zinc telluride. The existence of such a 'window' was reported by Mathur (1937), but there has been no subsequent confirmation of these results, and recent experiments carried out by the present authors using a vapour-grown thin film crystal of zinc telluride indicate total opacity throughout the ultra-violet range.

In the present treatment a relationship is assumed between energy and momentum, based on the free-electron model, so that the polarizability formulae can now be integrated with respect to a volume element in momentum space. It is then unnecessary to invoke experimental evidence concerning the nature of the excited states, since this follows from the usual treatment of a nearly-free electron in a periodic lattice.

2. Linear polarizability theory

We take as a starting point the standard expression for optical susceptibility at angular frequency ω:

$$\chi(\omega) = A \sum_n \frac{\langle x_{ng} \rangle^2}{\omega_{ng}^2 - \omega^2 - 2i\omega d_{ng}}, \tag{1}$$

where $\langle x_{ng} \rangle$ is the electronic transition moment between the ground state and nth excited state, ω_{ng} is the angular transition frequency, ω is the angular frequency at which χ is measured and d_{ng} is the linewidth of the transition. A is a constant of proportionality.

To apply this formula to semiconductors where discrete excited states are replaced by energy bands, each being expressed as a relation between energy E_n and momentum $\boldsymbol{k}_n$, we make the following assumptions.

(i) The transition moment can be regarded as a 'selection rule', namely that transitions can only take place vertically in reduced-zone k space, together with a factor proportional to $E_n^{1/2}$ representing density of states in the excited state. This follows from the orthogonal properties of Bloch-type wave functions which are analysed in some detail by Callaway (1964). Since the value of $\boldsymbol{k}_n$ corresponding to a ground state momentum $\boldsymbol{k}_g$ is given by

$$\boldsymbol{k}_n = \boldsymbol{k}_g - \boldsymbol{K}_n$$

where $\boldsymbol{K}_n$ is a vector corresponding to a lattice point in reciprocal space, it follows that $\langle x_{ng} \rangle^2$ may be replaced by E_n, and the summation over all states by an integration over the first Brillouin zone and a summation over all reciprocal lattice points.

(ii) Since $\langle x_{ng} \rangle^2$ will involve integrals over the space coordinates of Bloch-type functions, it must contain factors such as $1/l_1^2 l_2^2 l_3^2$, where l_1, l_2 and l_3 are the coordinates of the corresponding lattice point. Hence the contribution to the susceptibility from high-order bands will rapidly diminish as the order of the band increases, and a good approximation to the polarizability should be obtained by summing over bands derived from nearest- and next-nearest-neighbour reciprocal lattice points only.

(iii) The energy follows the free-electron model, and is therefore proportional to $|\boldsymbol{k}_n|^2$. Thus, $E_n \propto |\boldsymbol{k}_g - \boldsymbol{K}_n|^2$. Such a model will have no 'energy gap', and hence cannot correspond to a practical semiconductor. As an artifice to simulate an energy gap without undue mathematical complication we suppose the first Brillouin zone to be bounded by a sphere whose diameter is such that it falls short of the actual zone boundary in all directions. This effectively assumes the energy gap to be smallest along the direction of the nearest-neighbour points in reciprocal space.

With these assumptions, the expression for optical susceptibility may be written

$$\chi(\omega) = A \sum_n \int \frac{|\boldsymbol{k}_g - \boldsymbol{K}_n|^2 \, d\tau_g}{(\hbar/2m)^2 (|\boldsymbol{k}_g - \boldsymbol{K}_n|^2 - |\boldsymbol{k}_g|^2)^2 - (\omega^2 + 2i\omega d)} \tag{2}$$

the summation being taken over nearest- and next-nearest-neighbour points in reciprocal space.

We now consider the application of these ideas to a system such as zinc telluride discussed in I, which has a zinc blende-type space lattice and hence a reciprocal lattice which is body-centred cubic. The nearest neighbours in reciprocal space are therefore the eight body-centred points, followed by the six points of type (1, 0, 0).

To calculate the contribution to χ from the (1, 1, 1) points we take the [111] axis as the polar axis of a spherical coordinate system in which r, θ and ϕ have their usual meanings; in particular, θ is the angle between a ray vector r and the polar axis. When used as suffixes, r, θ and ϕ imply components of a vector along the respective direction. Let K_0 be the distance from the origin to the (1, 1, 1) reciprocal lattice points. Then the coordinates of $\boldsymbol{K}_{111}$ are

$$(\boldsymbol{K}_{111})_r = K_0 \cos\theta \qquad (\boldsymbol{K}_{111})_\theta = K_0 \sin\theta \qquad (\boldsymbol{K}_{111})_\phi = 0$$

while the coordinates of $\boldsymbol{k}_g$ are

$$(\boldsymbol{k}_g)_r = k_r \qquad (\boldsymbol{k}_g)_\theta = (\boldsymbol{k}_g)_\phi = 0.$$

It follows that

$$\begin{aligned} |\boldsymbol{k}_g - \boldsymbol{K}_{111}|^2 &= (k_r - K_0 \cos\theta)^2 + K_0^2 \sin^2\theta \\ &= k_r^2 + K_0^2 - 2k_r K_0 \cos\theta \end{aligned} \tag{3}$$

and

$$|\boldsymbol{k}_g - \boldsymbol{K}_{111}|^2 - |\boldsymbol{k}_g|^2 = K_0^2 - 2k_n K_0 \cos\theta. \tag{4}$$

Inserting these expressions in equation (2), and putting $(\hbar/2m)K_0^2 = \omega_z$, $2k_r/K_0 = r$ gives

$$\chi^{111}(\omega) = \frac{AK_0^5}{8\omega_z^2}\int \frac{(1 + \frac{1}{4}r^2 - r\cos\theta)\, r^2 \sin\theta \,\mathrm{d}r\,\mathrm{d}\theta\,\mathrm{d}\phi}{(1 - r\cos\theta)^2 - \{(\omega^2 + 2\mathrm{i}\omega d)/\omega_z^2\}} \tag{5}$$

as the contribution from each of the eight body-centred points.

A similar calculation for the contribution from each of the six (1, 0, 0) type points leads to

$$\chi^{100}(\omega) = \frac{3AK_0^5}{32\omega_z^2}\int \frac{(1 + \frac{3}{16}r^2 - \frac{1}{2}\sqrt{3}\, r\cos\theta)\, r^2\sin\theta\,\mathrm{d}r\,\mathrm{d}\theta\,\mathrm{d}\phi}{(1 - \frac{1}{2}\sqrt{3}\, r\cos\theta)^2 - \frac{9}{16}\{(\omega^2 + 2\mathrm{i}\omega d)/\omega_z^2\}} \tag{6}$$

the limits of integration in each case being

$$0 \leqslant \phi \leqslant 2\pi \qquad 0 \leqslant \theta \leqslant \pi \qquad 0 \leqslant r \leqslant a.$$

Now the absorption edge corresponds to zero value for the denominator of the integrand in the expression for $\chi^{111}(\omega)$ (equation (5)), along the polar axis $\theta = 0$, so that

$$(1 - a)^2 - \left(\frac{\omega_e}{\omega_z}\right)^2 = 0$$

whence

$$a = 1 - \frac{\omega_e}{\omega_z} \tag{7}$$

ω_e being the angular frequency at the absorption edge.

The integration with respect to ϕ is trivial. Writing

$$I(\alpha, \beta, \gamma) = \int_0^\pi \mathrm{d}\theta \int_0^a \mathrm{d}r\, \frac{(1 + \alpha r^2 - \beta r\cos\theta)\, r^2 \sin\theta}{(1 - \beta r\cos\theta)^2 - \gamma^2} \tag{8}$$

it follows that

$$\chi = C\left\{I\left(\frac{1}{4}, 1, \frac{\omega + \mathrm{i}d}{\omega_z}\right) + \frac{9}{16} I\left(\frac{3}{16}, \frac{\sqrt{3}}{2}, \frac{3}{4}\frac{\omega + \mathrm{i}d}{\omega_z}\right)\right\} \tag{9}$$

C being an undefined constant of proportionality.

Carrying out the integrations in (8) leads to

$$I = \frac{1}{2\beta^3}\{I_1(1 + \gamma) + I_1(1 - \gamma)\} + \frac{\alpha}{2\beta^5\gamma}\{I_2(1 - \gamma) - I_2(1 + \gamma)\} \tag{10}$$

where

$$I_1(u) = \int_{-\beta a}^{\beta a} x \ln(u + x)\,\mathrm{d}x$$

$$= u\beta a - \tfrac{1}{2}(u^2 - \beta^2 a^2)\ln\left(\frac{u + \beta a}{u - \beta a}\right) \tag{11}$$

and

$$I_2(u) = \int_{-\beta a}^{\beta a} x^3 \ln(u + x)\,\mathrm{d}x$$

$$= \tfrac{1}{2}u\beta a(u^2 + \beta^2 a^2) - \tfrac{1}{4}(u^4 - \beta^4 a^4)\ln\left(\frac{u + \beta a}{u - \beta a}\right). \tag{12}$$

Since γ, and hence u, is complex, the above expressions need to be separated into real and imaginary parts. The resulting formulae are complicated, but their derivation is straightforward in principle and details will not be given here. Finally, an ALGOL programme has been written which enables the real and imaginary parts of χ to be calculated as functions of the running variable ω and the three parameters C, ω_z and d, and then calculates from χ the refractive index and transmission factor, as described in I. The relevant formulae, quoted from I, are as follows:

$$\epsilon' = 1 + \mathrm{Re}\,\chi \qquad \epsilon'' = \mathrm{Im}\,\chi \tag{13}$$

ϵ' and ϵ'' being, respectively, the real and imaginary parts of the optical dielectric constant,

$$n^2 = \frac{\epsilon'}{2}\left[\left\{1 + \left(\frac{\epsilon''}{\epsilon'}\right)\right\}^{1/2} + 1\right] \tag{14}$$

$$k^2 = \frac{\epsilon'}{2}\left[\left\{1 - \left(\frac{\epsilon''}{\epsilon'}\right)\right\}^{1/2} - 1\right] \tag{15}$$

where n is the refractive index and k the optical absorption coefficient and finally

$$\tau = \exp\left(\frac{-2\pi k\delta}{\lambda}\right) \tag{16}$$

where τ is the transmission factor, δ the thickness of the crystal and λ the optical wavelength.

The theory is still too idealized for a meaningful evaluation of C, ω_z and d to be made in terms of measurable parameters, although the likely order of magnitude of ω_z and d can be assessed in the following way. Since $\omega_z = (\hbar/2m)\,K_0^2$, and K_0 is of order 10^{10} m^{-1} for a typical reciprocal lattice, it follows that ω_z is of order 5×10^{15} s^{-1} compared to 4×10^{15} s^{-1} for ω_e. Also, for a typical optical atomic transition we may expect a line-width of between 0·1 Å and 1·0 Å, compared with a transition wavelength of about 5000 Å.

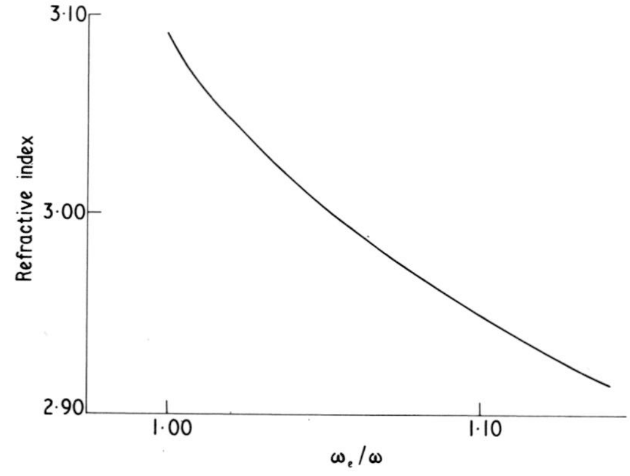

Figure 1. Frequency dependence of refractive index.

Thus, taking a normalized value of 100 for ω_e, as in I, we may anticipate a value between 40 and 400 for ω_z and between 0·002 and 0·02 for d. Trial and error shows that a good fit to experimental absorption and dispersion curves is obtained with $C = 12$, $\omega_z = 250$ and $d = 0{\cdot}006$, and these assignments are not in conflict with the above estimates. The corresponding curves of n and τ as functions of frequency are shown in figures 1 and 2.

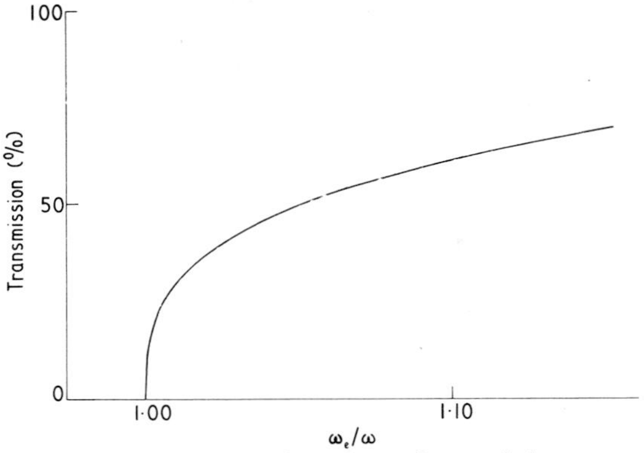

Figure 2. Frequency dependence of transmission.

3. Non-linear polarizability theory

Denoting the non-linear susceptibility by $\chi^{\rm nl}$, the expression corresponding to equation (1) is

$$\chi^{\rm nl}_{ijk} = A \sum_{n,n'} \{(\langle x_i \rangle_{nn'} \langle x_j \rangle_{ng} + \langle x_i \rangle_{ng} \langle x_j \rangle_{nn'}) \langle x_k \rangle_{n'g} A_{nn'} + \langle x_i \rangle_{ng} \langle x_j \rangle_{n'g} \langle x_k \rangle_{nn'} B_{nn'}\} \tag{17}$$

where

$$A_{nn'} = \frac{1}{\omega_{n'g}} \left(\frac{1}{\omega_{ng} + \omega + id} + \frac{1}{\omega_{ng} - \omega + id} \right)$$

$$B_{nn'} = \frac{1}{(\omega_{n'g} + \omega + id)(\omega_{ng} + \omega + id)} + \frac{1}{(\omega_{n'g} - \omega + id)(\omega_{ng} - \omega + id)}$$

(see Franken and Ward 1963).

In principle it would be quite possible to apply the method of analysis used above to this expression, but the presence of two frequency factors in the denominator of each term leads to a great increase in complexity. This arises from two sources, the first being the fact that to cover all possible combinations of excited states n and n' arising from nearest- and next-nearest-neighbour lattice points involves evaluating seven different integrals, after taking account of simplifications due to symmetry, instead of only two as in the case of linear susceptibility. Secondly, it is generally no longer possible to make the integrands independent of the ϕ coordinate, as was done by suitable choice of axes in the linear case, and evaluation of the resulting triple integral would be exceedingly tedious.

In order to avoid these difficulties a cruder model has been developed, based on one-dimensional periodic free-electron wave functions, which nevertheless shows the principles involved in calculating second-order polarizabilities, and gives reasonable agreement with experimental results. We accordingly treat the momentum as a scalar quantity, and take $K + k_{\rm g}$ as the momenta in the first and second excited states corresponding to ground state momentum $k_{\rm g}$. Integration is now over $k_{\rm g}$, and a term $k_{\rm g}^2$ is included in the numerator to represent the density of states in the lowest band; previously this was taken into account by a volume integral over the vector $\boldsymbol{k}_{\rm g}$. Corresponding to equation (2) we then have

$$\chi^{\rm nl} = A\{I_1(k_{\rm g}, \omega) + I_1(-k_{\rm g}, \omega) + I_1(k_{\rm g}, -\omega) + I_1(-k_{\rm g}, -\omega) + I_2(k_{\rm g}, \omega) + I_2(k_{\rm g}, -\omega)\} \tag{18}$$

where

$$I_1(k_g, \omega) = \int \frac{k_g^2 (K_0 - k_g)^2 (K_0 + k_g)^2 \, dk_g}{(\hbar/2m)\{(K_0 + k_g)^2 - k_g^2\}[(\hbar/2m)\{(K_0 - k_g)^2 - k_g^2\} + \omega + id]} \tag{19}$$

and

$$I_2(k_g, \omega) = \int \frac{k_g^2 (K_0 - k_g)^2 (K_0 + k_g)^2 \, dk_g}{[(\hbar/2m)\{(K_0 - k_g)^2 - k_g^2\} + \omega + id][(\hbar/2m)\{(K_0 + k_g)^2 - k_g^2\} + \omega + id]}. \tag{20}$$

Putting $x = k_g/K_0$, $\omega_z = (\hbar/2m) K_0^2$ and assuming $(1 - x^2)^2$ is constant over the range of integration leads to

$$\chi^{nl} = A \sum_{m=1}^{6} \int_0^{\frac{1}{2}(1-\omega_e/\omega_z)} \frac{x^2 \, dx}{(u_m + iv_m + 2x)(s_m + it_m - 2x)}, \tag{21}$$

the values of u, v, s and t being given in table 1.

Table 1

m	u	v	s	t
1	1	0	$1 + \frac{\omega}{\omega_z}$	$\frac{d}{\omega_z}$
2	$1 + \frac{\omega}{\omega_z}$	$\frac{d}{\omega_z}$	1	0
3	1	0	$1 - \frac{\omega}{\omega_z}$	$\frac{d}{\omega_z}$
4	$1 - \frac{\omega}{\omega_z}$	$\frac{d}{\omega_z}$	1	0
5	$1 + \frac{\omega}{\omega_z}$	$\frac{d}{\omega_z}$	$1 + \frac{\omega}{\omega_z}$	$\frac{d}{\omega_z}$
6	$1 - \frac{\omega}{\omega_z}$	$\frac{d}{\omega_z}$	$1 - \frac{\omega}{\omega_z}$	$\frac{d}{\omega_z}$

The integration of this function is straightforward, and a further ALGOL programme has been written to calculate the real part of χ^{nl} as a function of ω. Figure 3 shows the

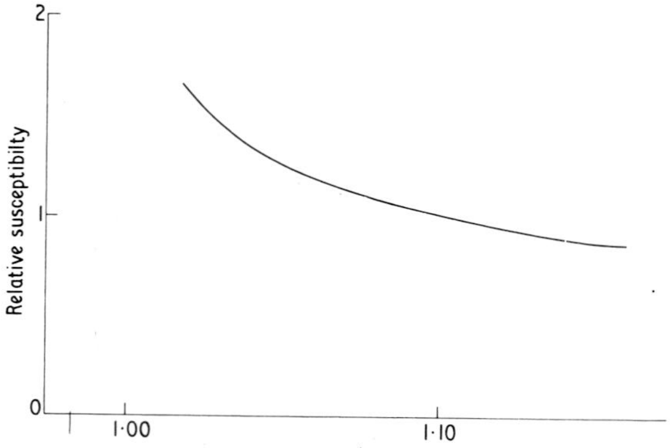

Figure 3. Frequency dependence of non-linear susceptibility.

dispersion curve obtained using the same values of ω_z and d as in the linear case. The general shape of the curve is in good agreement with the experimental data shown in I, although a better fit could in fact be obtained by choosing a higher value for ω_z. However, this is not of great physical significance bearing in mind the relative simplifications involved in the theory.

4. Conclusion

We have shown that a simple model, based on well-established physical principles, can be used to describe the broad features of linear and non-linear optical absorption and dispersion in semiconducting crystals of cubic symmetry. The next development would seem to entail the use of wave functions which take into account the periodic lattice potential, so that the energy gap would then be a direct consequence of the form of the wave functions. However, this would certainly lead to a formidable increase in mathematical complexity, which would in all probability be wholly disproportionate to the gain in physical understanding.

Acknowledgments

The authors would like to thank Mrs Anne Woolf for help in writing the ALGOL programme used to calculate the linear coefficients. This work forms part of the research programme of the Molecular Science Division of the National Physical Laboratory.

References

Franken, P. A., and Ward, J. F., 1963, *Rev. Mod. Phys.*, **35**, 23–9.
Callaway, J., 1964, *Energy Band Theory* (New York, London: Academic Press).
Mathur, L. L., 1937, *Indian J. Phys.*, **11**, 177–85.
Pursey, H., Page, P. A., and Musgrave, M. J. P., 1969, *J. Phys. C: Solid St. Phys.*, **2**, 1085–91.

Reprinted from:

JOURNAL OF APPLIED PHYSICS VOLUME 42, NUMBER 9 AUGUST 1971

Dispersion of Electro-Optic Effect in $BaTiO_3$ †

Alan R. Johnston

Jet Propulsion Laboratory, California Institute of Technology, Pasadena, California 91103

(Received 28 December 1970)

The dispersion of both the quadratic and linear electro-optic effects in flux-grown crystals of $BaTiO_3$ has been measured polarimetrically between 0.4 and 1.0 μ yielding $(g_{11}-g_{12})$ and $r_c = r_{33}-(n_a/n_c)^3 r_{13}$. A strong dispersion was found: $(g_{11}-g_{12})$ increases to double its long-wavelength limit at 0.4 μ. Both unclamped (low frequency) and clamped measurements were made. Birefringence and the principal indices were also determined. A two-oscillator Sellmeier model, in which one oscillator frequency is polarization dependent, was shown to represent closely all the data. The unclampled polarization potential, which specifies the magnitude of the oscillator frequency shift, was 3.9 eV $m^4 C^{-2}$, while its clamped value was one-third as large. Ultraviolet reflectivity calculated from the model assuming reasonable values of empirical damping agrees with the observations of Cardona and Gahwiller.

I. INTRODUCTION

In this paper we present experimental results on the dispersion of the electro-optic effect in single-crystal $BaTiO_3$, and compare them with a simple electron-oscillator model. We have previously described measurements of both the unclamped and clamped linear electro-optic effects,[1,2] as well as the experimental techniques used.[3] The present work extends these results to include the effect of varying the light wavelength.

We find that the two-frequency Sellmeier model first suggested by Di Domenico and Wemple[4] is able to tie together all the optical data with good agreement. Their model assumed two independent oscillator frequencies, one of which was assumed to shift quadratically with the lattice polarization. The frequencies corresponded to approximately 5 and 9 eV, the 5-eV oscillator being polarization dependent. Di Domenico and Wemple made a very thorough analysi of the linear and nonlinear optical properties of a number of materials containing an octahedral transition metal-oxygen building block. Their analysis included three crystal structures: the perovskites, the trigonal $LiNbO_3$ structure, and the "tungsten bronze" ferroelectrics. They were able to show that the linear and nonlinear optical properties can be explained in terms of the properties of the BO_6 building block alone, and that the differences observed between materials arise because of differences in crystal structure and in the low-frequency dielectric properties which couple the optical interaction with an external field.

The purpose of this paper is to examine in detail the dispersion of the optical properties in one of these materials—barium titanate ($BaTiO_3$)—and to show that the dispersions calculated from the Sellmeier model do agree with observation. We report the first direct measurements of the dependence of the electro-optic effects, both quadratic and linear, on light wavelength in $BaTiO_3$. Although the dispersion of the birefringence has been measured previously,[5–7] the dispersion of the electro-optic effect has not. The spontaneous birefringence in tetragonal $BaTiO_3$ was measured with a polarimeter between 0.4 and 2.0 μ, a larger range of wavelength than the earlier data covered. The refractive indices n_a and n_c were redetermined by the minimum-deviation method in the visible region. Our birefringence and indices differ somewhat from the earlier measurements.[5,7,8] The low-frequency quadratic electro-optic response was measured polarimetrically from 0.4 to 1.0 μ, and the linear electro-optic effect was determined over the same spectral range. The corresponding clamped values were also obtained.

The parameters of the two-frequency model were determined from this data. We find that if the long-wavelength approximation used by Di Domenico and Wemple is not made in calculating dispersions, improvement can be obtained in fitting the birefringence over the complete 0.4–2.0-μ-wavelength range. In addition, uv reflectivity predicted using reasonable assumed values for damping is in agreement with the results of Cardona[9] and Gahwiller.[10]

All our measurements were made using flux-grown crystals of $BaTiO_3$.[11] Wemple[12] has recently found that the absorption near the band edge in flux-grown $BaTiO_3$ is considerably larger than it is in melt-grown material. The flux-grown material has an absorption band centered near 3.2 eV not present in the melt-grown crystals. Impurity ions derived from the flux are thought to be responsible for the difference. This raises the question of whether the optical indices of the two types of material are comparable. However, we do not find large differences in the refractive index or birefringence. Some adjustment of the parameters of the model would be required in order to obtain a good fit for melt-grown crystals, but our conclusions would be the same for both types of material.

II. TWO-OSCILLATOR MODEL

In this section, we describe the two-frequency Sellmeier model which will be used to describe the optical index and the electro-optic effects. The notation of Di Domenico and Wemple[4] will be used. The optical index n is given by the expression

$$n^2 - 1 = \frac{S_\epsilon \lambda_\epsilon^2}{1 - \lambda_\epsilon^2/\lambda^2} + \frac{S_\gamma \lambda_\gamma^2}{1 - \lambda_\gamma^2/\lambda^2}. \tag{1}$$

The subscripts ϵ and γ refer to the two independent oscillators, the ϵ oscillator having the lower frequency. After Di Domenico and Wemple, we expect ϵ to be near 5 eV and γ near 9 eV. The quantities S_ϵ and S_γ, having the units of μ^{-2}, specify the oscillator strengths, and λ_ϵ and λ_γ give their wavelengths. We assume that λ_ϵ, the wavelength of the 5-eV oscillator, is shifted by a small amount $\Delta\lambda_\epsilon$ proportional to the square of the lattice polarization, while the other three parameters are constants. The ϵ oscillator can be thought of as representing the contribution of a single polarization-dependent band, while the γ oscillator is an average representing the effect in the transparent region of the remaining bands. Assuming the S_ϵ is polarization independent implies that the band which contributes to the ϵ oscillator is shifted in energy without an accompanying change in width.

We also assume that the polarization P that we are interested in is the sum of the ferroelectric polarization P_s and the field-induced polarization. The validity of this assumption has been established by a number of authors[13–15] who have pointed out that the linear electro-optic effect is equivalent to the quadratic effect observed above the Curie transition biased by the spontaneous polarization. For this assertion to be true, the basic quadratic shift in λ_ϵ must hold at least up to the value of the spontaneous polarization.

The polarization-induced shift in the ϵ oscillator is given by

$$\Delta\lambda_{\epsilon a} = -(\lambda_\epsilon^2/\lambda_0)\beta_{12}\, P_z^2, \tag{2}$$

$$\Delta\lambda_{\epsilon c} = -(\lambda_\epsilon^2/\lambda_0)\beta_{11}\, P_z^2. \tag{3}$$

The β_{ij} are Di Domenico's average polarization potentials, and the factor λ_0 merely puts β_{ij} in the units eV m^4 C^{-2}. The subscripts a and c refer to the orientation of the E vector of the light (i.e., n_a or n_c). For the symmetry of cubic $BaTiO_3$, a β_{44} also exists but will be only briefly mentioned. We discuss birefringence and polarimetric observations of electro-optic response, both of which involve only the difference $\beta_{11} - \beta_{12}$, so let us also define

$$\beta = \beta_{11} - \beta_{12}. \tag{4}$$

The polarization P_z is given by

$$P_z = P_s + \epsilon_0 (K_c - 1)\, E_c. \tag{5}$$

If there is no applied field, the birefringence $(n_a - n_c)$ may be calculated from (1)—(5). An expression giving the index change in terms of $\Delta\lambda_\epsilon$ is obtained by differentiating (1), and $\Delta\lambda_\epsilon$ is given for a or c polarized light by (2) or (3), respectively. Subtracting and introducing β with (4) yields an expression for the birefringence induced by the polarization P_z. Note that we have assumed the birefringence is small but have not required $\lambda \gg \lambda_\epsilon$.

The spontaneous birefringence is obtained if $E_c = 0$ and $P_z = P_s$ with the following result:

$$n_a - n_c = \frac{1}{n\lambda_0}\, \frac{S_\epsilon \lambda_\epsilon^3}{(1 - \lambda_\epsilon^2/\lambda^2)^2}\, \beta\, P_s^2. \tag{6}$$

Alternatively, if only an induced polarization exists [$P_s = 0$ in (5)], the quantity $g_{11} - g_{12}$ describing the quadratic electro-optic effect through the conventional definition

$$\Delta n = \tfrac{1}{2} n^3 (g_{11} - g_{12})\, P_z^2 \tag{7}$$

can similarly be derived. The result is

$$g_{11} - g_{12} = \frac{2\, S_\epsilon \lambda_\epsilon^3 \beta}{n^4 \lambda_0 (1 - \lambda_\epsilon^2/\lambda^2)^2}. \tag{8}$$

If both spontaneous and induced polarization are present, the linear electro-optic effect will be exhibited. Using the definitions

$$\Delta(n_a - n_c) = \tfrac{1}{2} n_c^3\, r_c E_c \tag{9}$$

and

$$r_c = r_{33} - (n_a/n_c)^3\, r_{13}, \tag{10}$$

we can calculate r_c:

$$r_c = \frac{4\, P_s \epsilon_0 (K_c - 1)\, S_\epsilon \lambda_\epsilon^3}{n\, n_c^3\, \lambda_0 (1 - \lambda_\epsilon^2/\lambda^2)^2}\, \beta. \tag{11}$$

Although—strictly speaking—the difference between n and n_c in the denominator of (11) is not significant, we use n_c^3 in order to be consistent with our use of n_c in calculating r_c from the experimental data.

It should be remembered that we are here considering the free (unclamped) condition, since we deal with the spontaneous birefringence and low-frequency electro-optic effects. Therefore, our values of the polarization potential β apply to the unclamped condition. Modifications must be made for the unclamped case, and will be discussed later. It happens that in $BaTiO_3$ the polarization potential β_{12} related to n_a is very small,[12] so we can identify n in Eq. (1) directly with n_a.

III. REFRACTIVE INDEX AND BIREFRINGENCE

The room-temperature birefringence was measured by placing a poled $BaTiO_3$ wafer between crossed polarizers, and noting the wavelengths λ_m of the maxima and minima of transmission. The polar axis of the crystal was oriented perpendicular to the light path and at 45° to the polarizer axis. The birefringence is then given by the expression

$$n_a - n_c = m\lambda_m/2t, \tag{12}$$

where m is the order of interference at λ_m and t is the geometrical thickness of the wafer.

In order to use this method, the value of the integer m corresponding to one of the λ_m must be determined

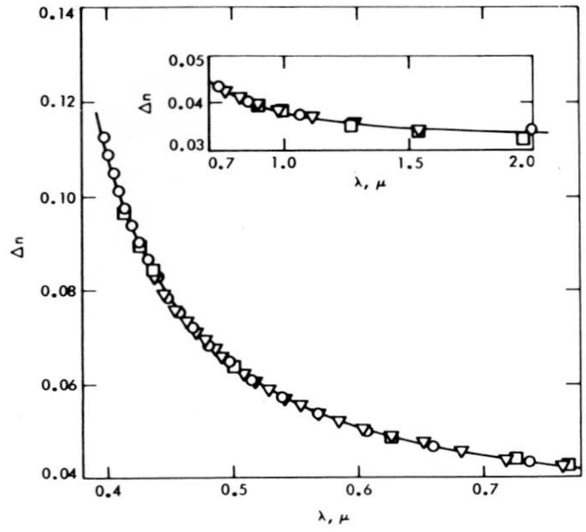

FIG. 1. Birefringence plotted vs wavelength. The points indicate the data observed on three samples of flux-grown $BaTiO_3$, while the curve was calculated using the parameters in Table I.

independently. Two methods were used, one being to lap one edge of a thin specimen as nearly as possible to a knife edge, and count fringes under a polarizing microscope; the other was to determine n_a and n_c and thus Δn by the minimum-deviation method. Such a determination of Δn is not as accurate as Eq. (12) but is adequate to determine m unambiguously. Both methods yielded the same result.

The resulting values for Δn are shown in Fig. 1 plotted as a function of wavelength. Data are shown for three samples. The accuracy was limited by the accuracy with which the thickness of each sample could be measured, approximately 1.5 μ. In plotting Fig. 1, the data for the thickest sample ($l = 178$ μ) are plotted directly, while for the thinner samples where the effect of uncertainty in thickness is much greater, the data were adjusted for a good match near 0.55 μ in order to show the dispersion more clearly. The required adjustment in terms of thickness was within the experimental error. The overall accuracy of the birefringence is estimated to be $\pm$ 2%.

We obtain $\Delta n = 0.056$ at the mercury green line 0.546 μ and 25 °C instead of Meyerhoffer's[7] widely quoted value of 0.072. Wemple, Di Domenico, and Camlibel[16] obtain $\Delta n = 0.061$ at 0.546 μ for melt-grown material. On reviewing the literature, we find the earlier measurements of Forsbergh[17] yielded 0.055 at 0.589 μ, a value 0.003 higher than our present one. Kay and Vousden[18] obtained $\Delta n = 0.058$ visually at an unspecified effective wavelength (0.55 μ?).

In order to check our technique, we made similar measurements using melt-grown $BaTiO_3$ samples[19] and compared the results with both those of Wemple *et al.* and ours obtained with flux-grown crystals. We found very close agreement between the data for our melt-grown samples and Wemple's. The birefringence is larger in melt-grown than in flux-grown material, but the difference could be explained by a 4% difference in the spontaneous polarization. The existence of such a difference is very reasonable, and is even suggested by comparing the data of Mertz[20] and Wemple.[16]

Referring back to Eq. (6), we expect $(n\Delta n)^{-1/2}$ to plot linearly against λ^{-2}, which we find to be the case in Fig. 2. If the analysis of Di Domenico and Wemple, which assumes $\lambda_\epsilon^2/\lambda^2 \ll 1$, is used over the range 0.4–2 μ, deviation of the data from the model is found. This deviation is removed by eliminating the long-wavelength approximation. From the slope and intercept in Fig. 3, we find $\lambda_\epsilon = 0.2799 \pm 0.003$ μ directly, and we can obtain the product βS_ϵ. The error attached to λ_ϵ is only that obtained from the mechanics of fitting the straight line found in Fig. 2. No evidence was found of an influence on the birefringence from lattice-mode dispersion in the infrared.

As mentioned previously, we also redetermined the refractive indices n_a and n_c for a flux-grown sample by the minimum-deviation method. An unusually thick (0.39-mm) butterfly wing was used, poled normal to the plane of the wafer. Plane surfaces with a suitable angle between them were worked on opposite edges and the light was passed through

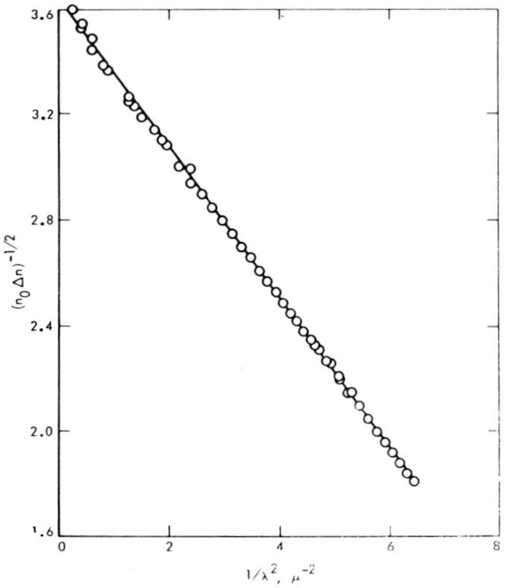

FIG. 2. Quantity $(n\Delta n)^{-1/2}$ vs $1/\lambda^2$, a plot from which λ_ϵ may be determined.

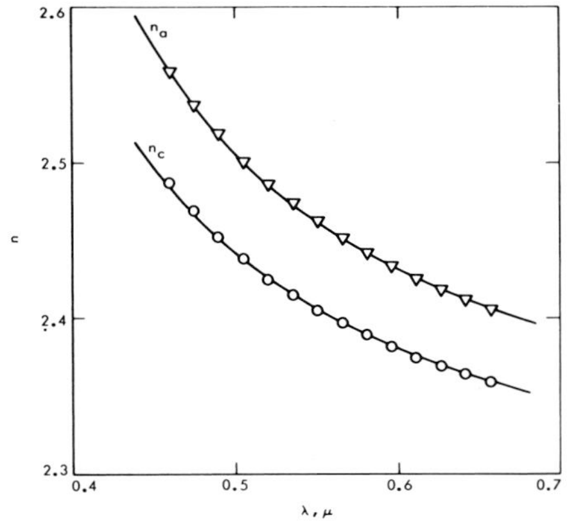

FIG. 3. Refractive index n_a and n_c vs λ for flux-grown $BaTiO_3$ obtained by the minimum-deviation method. The points are experimental; the solid curves are calculated.

parallel to the major (as-grown) faces of the wafer. The results are shown in Fig. 3. The ordinary index n_a agrees very closely with the measurements of Wemple *et al.*, while our n_c appears somewhat larger.

Shumate's[5] index values are lower than ours by 8%, a difference which is considerably larger than the expected experimental errors. The reason for this difference is not understood. Lawless and DeVries[8] obtained still smaller values for the principal indices by measuring the apparent thickness of a wafer with a microscope. However, their method is probably inherently less accurate.

Returning to Eq. (1) for the index ($n \approx n_a$), we can find the parameters S_ϵ and S_γ by fitting the n_a data in Fig. 3. It happens that the closeness of the fit is not sensitive to the choice of λ_γ, so $\lambda_\gamma = 0.1377\ \mu$ (9 eV) has been assumed, in order to be consistent with other data.[4]

The model parameters obtained by fitting $(n_a - n_c)$ and n_a as a function of wavelength are given in Table I. The solid lines in Figs. 1 and 3 were calculated using the parameters in Table I.

IV. QUADRATIC ELECTRO-OPTIC RESPONSE

The quantity $(g_{11} - g_{12})$ was measured as a function of light wavelength on three flux-grown samples using polarimetric techniques. The effect of clamping will be discussed below. The difference $(g_{11} - g_{12})$ relates the induced birefringence Δn to an applied electric field E according to the expression

$$\Delta n = \tfrac{1}{2} n^3 (g_{11} - g_{12})\, \epsilon_0^2\, (K_c - 1)^2\, E_c^2 . \qquad (13)$$

Here, n denotes the refractive index in the centro-symmetric state given by Eq. (1), ϵ_0 is the free-space permittivity, and K_c is the dielectric constant for a field applied along one of the principal axes. The variation between samples was too large to allow $(g_{11} - g_{12})$ to be calculated from the optical data with an average dielectric constant. The dielectric constant of each sample was measured with a capacity bridge after the sample was mounted at the temperature used for the optical measurements. An oven held the temperature constant near T_c + 10 °C. The effect of varying the temperature was checked, and $(g_{11} - g_{12})$ was found to be temperature independent, as it should be. The field was generated by a 250-Hz oscillator and amplifier combination having a zero dc average, thus eliminating the possibility of unwanted effects caused by the presence of a steady-state field. As a result, the induced birefringence varied at 500 Hz. Silver paste electrodes were used. A log-log plot of Δn vs E confirmed that a quadratic relationship between them [Eq. (13)] was followed.

The experimental results are shown in Fig. 4. Since we are interested in examining dispersion, the data have been adjusted to eliminate constant differences between samples, such as would be caused by errors in geometrical dimensions or the determination of dielectric constant of individual samples. Each value of $(g_{11} - g_{12})$ for an individual sample was multiplied by a factor which forced the experimental curve for that sample to pass through the average for all samples determined at 0.5461 μm. The factors were 5, 4, and 1% different from unity, and were within the experimental uncertainty in determining dimensions and dielectric constant.

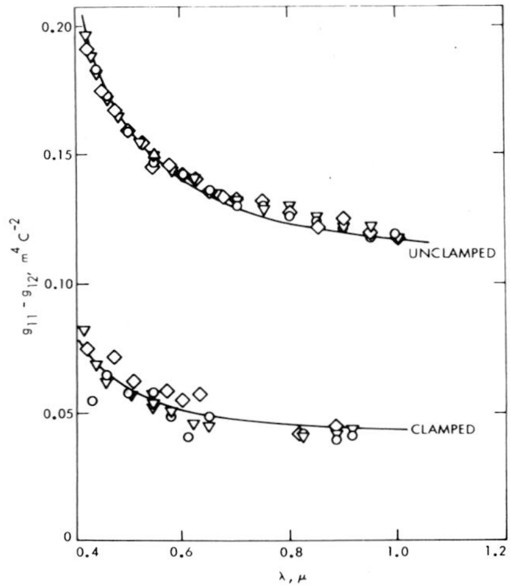

FIG. 4. Quadratic electro-optic response $(g_{11} - g_{12})$. The points are experimental; the solid line calculated. Both unclamped and clamped values are shown.

TABLE I. Parameters of the two-oscillator Sellmeier model as determined from the experimental data. The errors attached to the first three quantities are derived from the least-squares fit.

S_ϵ	$21.52 \pm 0.2\ \mu^{-2}$
λ_ϵ	$0.2799 \pm 0.003\ \mu$
S_γ	$137.7 \pm 1.0\ \mu^{-2}$
λ_γ	$0.1377\ \mu$ (9 eV assumed)
β (unclamped)	3.2 eV m^4 C^{-2} from birefringence
	3.9 eV m^4 C^{-2} from electro-optic effect
β (clamped)	1.5 eV m^4 C^{-2}

The solid line in Fig. 4 has been calculated using Eq. (8) assuming $\beta = 3.9$ eV m^4 C^{-2}. The agreement is quite satisfactory. The difference between $\beta = 3.2$ eV m^4 C^{-2} obtained from spontaneous birefringence and $\beta = 3.9$ eV m^4 C^{-2} needed to fit the electro-optic response is probably due to neglecting terms in P_ϵ^4 and higher powers in (2) and (3), which only become apparent at large polarizations.

V. LINEAR ELECTRO-OPTIC EFFECT

The linear electro-optic effect was also measured as a function of wavelength at room temperature (25 °C). The electric field was applied perpendicular to the light path and parallel to the polar axis of the sample. Flux-grown wafers poled with c parallel to their surfaces and electroded with silver paste on opposite edges were used. A 500-Hz sinusoidal applied field of the order of 1 kV/cm was used, but it was biased so that the swing was from zero to some positive value in order to avoid the possibility of depoling.

In the above geometry, a polarimetric measurement yields the combination r_c defined above in Eq. (10). The experimental unclamped r_c is plotted versus λ in Fig. 5. The curve represents the average for three samples normalized to $r_c = 1.06 \times 10^{-8}$ cm/V at $0.546\ \mu$. The extreme sample-to-sample variation before normalizing was ± 5%. The wavelength range was from $0.43\ \mu$ to $1.1\ \mu$m. The short-wavelength limit was a result of absorption in the sample, and the long-wavelength limit was imposed by the failing sensitivity of an S-1 photocathode.

A curve of r_c vs $\hat{\lambda}$ was calculated from the model [Eq. (11)] and is also shown in Fig. 5 labeled "theoretical unclamped". We have used $P_s = 0.25$ cm^{-2}, $K_c = 160$, and $\beta = 3.9$ eV m^4 C^{-2}. The agreement is good.

An analysis similar to the one used above to relate r_c to $(\beta_{11} - \beta_{12})$ can be used to relate r_{42} to the polarization potential β_{44}. If this is done, the expected dispersion of r_{42} is found to have the same form as that of r_c in contradiction with our earlier conclusion that r_{42} was independent of light wavelength.[21] We feel that the dispersion in r_{42} should be the same as in r_c, and that further experimental verification is desirable. The spontaneous birefringence must be known in order to calculate the experimental r_{42}, and, in our earlier paper, Meyerhoffer's birefringence was used. If the present Δn from Fig. 1 is used instead of Meyerhoffer's, some dispersion in r_{42} would have been found. However, the magnitude of the resulting dispersion would still be smaller than that of r_c. Our previously reported value[1] $r_{42} = 16.4 \times 10^{-8}$ cm/V at $0.546\ \mu$ becomes $r_{42} = 12.8 \times 10^{-8}$ cm/V if the present value of $\Delta n = 0.056$ is used to calculate r_{42} instead of $\Delta n = 0.072$.

VI. UV REFLECTIVITY

The results of the preceding sections should be consistent with the observed uv reflectivity. Although such a comparison is approximate because the Sellmeier model is intended for the transparent-wavelength region, it is possible to compute uv reflectivity if an empirical damping factor is assumed for each oscillator. With the introduction of the damping constants G_ϵ and G_λ, Eq. (1) becomes

$$n^2 = 1 + \frac{S_\epsilon \lambda_\epsilon^2}{1 - \lambda_\epsilon^2/\lambda^2 + 2iG_\epsilon \lambda_\epsilon/\lambda} + \frac{S_\gamma \lambda_\gamma^2}{1 - \lambda_\gamma^2/\lambda^2 + 2iG_\gamma \lambda_\gamma/\lambda}, \tag{14}$$

and the index n becomes complex. Equation (14) does not differ significantly from the original form [Eq. (1)] for wavelengths long enough ($\lambda \gtrsim 0.4\ \mu$) to be in the transparent region. The reflectivity at normal incidence is obtained from the expression

$$R = \left| \left(\frac{n-1}{n+1} \right)^2 \right|, \tag{15}$$

where n is the complex index from (14). Using the model parameters in Table I, which fit the visible refractive index, and assuming $G_\epsilon = 0.10$, $G_\gamma = 0.45$, we calculate the reflectivity shown in Fig. 6. The experimental results of Gahwiller[10] and Cardona[9] are also plotted in the graph. The damping factors were chosen for best fit. Reasonable agreement is ob-

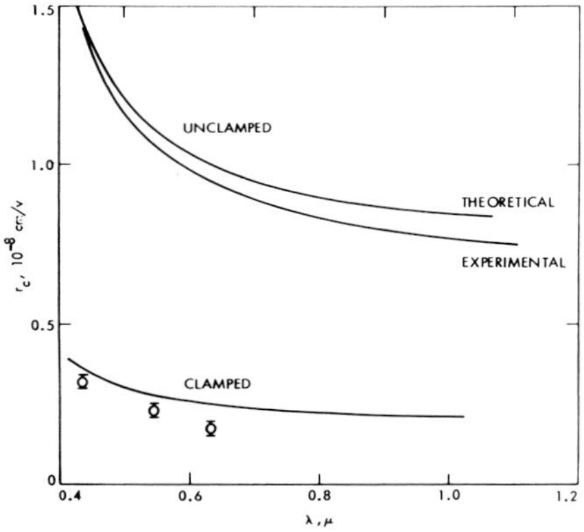

FIG. 5. Experimental $r_c = r_{33} - (n_a^3/n_c^3)\, r_{13}$ vs wavelength compared to the theoretical dispersion. Calculated and experimental clamped r_c are shown on the same plot.

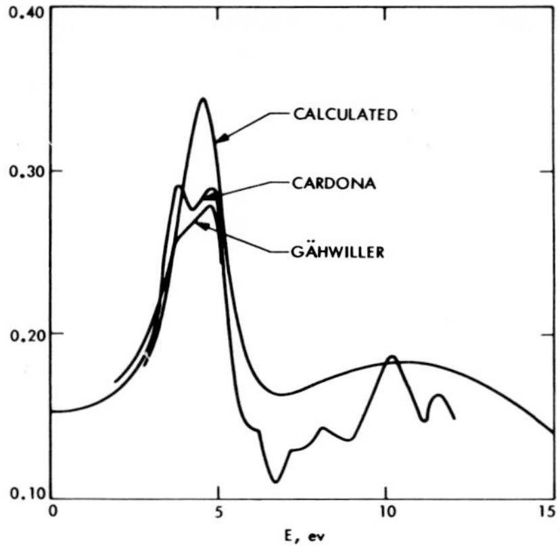

FIG. 6. Calculated uv reflectivity vs energy compared to measurements of Cardona and Gahwiller.

tained for both the height and width of each reflectivity peak, with one adjustable parameter.

Although empirical and approximate, this calculation shows that the oscillator picture of Table I is consistent with the uv reflectivity. The fairly narrow width (low damping) obtained for the ϵ oscillator also agrees with the conclusion that there is only one polarization-dependent transition.

The larger empirical damping constant assigned to the 9-eV peak may occur because the γ oscillator is really an average representing the combined effect of many widely spaced transitions ranging upward from 9 eV. It is also possible that some of the strength assigned to our 9-eV oscillator actually belongs to a transition in the 5-eV region that is independent of polarization. Dispersion in the visible region averages over all transitions and is not sensitive to detailed oscillator distributions, since even a single-oscillator formula will fit the refractive index itself fairly closely in any material. The important feature of our present model is that there is one transition near 5 eV that is polarization dependent, and that this transition must be taken into account separately in order to give the dispersion in the birefringence and electro-optic effects correctly.

VII. CLAMPING

We will now examine the adjustments which must be made to model in order to treat the effect of clamping. If the applied field changes rapidly compared to the mechanical resonance of the sample, inertial forces constrain the lattice to its unperturbed geometry. Even though ions within a unit cell may move with respect to one another in developing a lattice polarization, the unit cell itself must remain fixed. This is a different situation than holds for the unclamped condition, where the unit cell must distort in response to an applied field in such a way that no net force is applied to it. Since the ions involved in the polarization-dependent band structure find themselves in a somewhat different environment, it is reasonable to expect that the clamped effective polarization potential, which we will designate β^c, is somewhat different than the unclamped value β.

Experimental values for the clamped quadratic electro-optic effect $(g_{11}-g_{12})^c$ are plotted in Fig. 4 as a function of wavelength. These data are directly comparable with the unclamped data shown in the same figure, having been obtained from the same samples. The previously described pulse technique[2,3] was used in the measurement. It was again necessary to measure the dielectric constant of each sample with a laboratory bridge at 100 kHz at the same temperature at which the optical measurements were made in order to calculate $(g_{11}-g_{12})^c$ accurately. Clamping in the paraelectric dielectric constant was assumed to be negligible.[2]

The clamped effect can be calculated from the model by replacing the unclamped β in Eq. (8) with its clamped value β^c. The form of the expected dispersion remains unchanged. The calculated $g_{11}-g_{12}$ is also shown in Fig. 4. We find $\beta^c = 1.5$ eV m^4 C^{-2}—approximately one-third the unclamped β—for best fit. fit. The measured and calculated dispersion agree within the experimental accuracy.

The corresponding situation in the linear electro-optic effect is not quite as straightforward. Substitution of β^c for β in (11) is questionable because the linear effect is proportional to the cross product $P_s\Delta P$ from (5), and P_s is not clamped. However, assuming that β^c does not depend on lattice strain avoids the difficulty. To show that this is true, let us first arbitrarily assume that both the spontaneous polarization and the induced polarization are clamped. For example, suppose that a total polarization $P=P_s+\Delta P$ is instantaneously applied; then the clamped value of r_c is clearly obtained by substituting β_c for β in Eq. (11). If the small change in the ϵ oscillator energy upon which the optical properties depend is ΔE, then we have

$$\Delta E_{\text{clamped}} = \beta^c P^2{}_{\text{clamped}} = \beta^c\,(P_s+\Delta P)_{\text{clamped}}, \qquad (16)$$

which becomes

$$\Delta E_{\text{clamped}} = (\beta^c P_s^2 + 2\,\beta^c P_s\,\Delta P)_{\text{clamped}} \qquad (17)$$

to first-order ΔP. It is the last term, $2\beta^c P_s\Delta P$, that yields the linear electro-optic effect as before. If we now imagine that the lattice is allowed to distort in such a way that a strain identical to the zero-field spontaneous strain results, the actual conditions existing in the clamped linear effect will be obtained. If this strain is allowed to occur at constant polarization, the value of P_s does not change, but it now can be interpreted as the actual spontaneous polarization instead of a suddenly applied step. Therefore, if the clamped polarization potential is independent of changes in the lattice strain of the type associated with P_s, and occurring at constant polarization, substitution of β^c for β in Eq. (11) gives the clamped r_c correctly.

Measured values of r_c (clamped) at three wavelengths are shown in Fig. 5. The experimental accuracy was reduced because of limited light flux through the small useful area available in our samples. The magnitude is from our earlier measurement[2] at 0.546 μ, and the values at the other wavelengths were obtained relative to 0.546 μ. The value $\beta^c = 1.5$ eV $m^4 C^{-2}$ found in the clamped quadratic electro-optic effect was used to obtain the calculated curve.

Both the linear and quadratic clamped electro-optic effects are consistent with the model, with only the effective polarization potential β being modified in order to take into account clamping. The experimental accuracy is not sufficient to establish independently whether in fact only the ϵ oscillator is involved.

VIII. CONCLUSIONS

The measurements of refractive index, birefringence, and electro-optic constants in $BaTiO_3$ which have been described above can be summarized by the two-oscillator model using the parameters given in Table I. All the data are in agreement with it. The same model is valid under the clamped condition, except that the effective polarization potential is reduced to one-third of its unclamped value.

We measure a birefringence at 0.546 μ of 0.056, close to the value of 0.061 obtained by Wemple[16] for melt-grown samples and in disagreement with the widely quoted value[7] of 0.072. The difference in optical index between the flux-grown and the melt-grown types of $BaTiO_3$ single crystal is small, and is felt to be due to a small difference in spontaneous polarization between the two types of material rather than a direct influence of the impurities present in the flux-grown material on its index. The absorption near 0.4 μ is much stronger in flux-grown material,[12] but if the resultant effect on the optical index is estimated using dispersion theory, it is found to be negligible.

The assumption that only the ϵ (5-eV) oscillator frequency is polarization dependent is supported by a detailed examination of the birefringence. A maximum of ~10% of the observed Δn can be assigned to the γ (9-eV) oscillator before a significant degradation occurs in the data fit. The field-dependent ϵ (5-eV) oscillator is considerably weaker than the γ oscillator, being responsible for approximately one-third of the total optical frequency susceptibility. Qualitative agreement with uv reflectivity is obtained assuming a lightly damped 5-eV transition.

These observations confirm that a single polarization-dependent transition near 5 eV or possibly a group of closely spaced transitions is responsible for the observed electro-optic effects.

†This paper presents the results of one phase of research performed at the Jet Propulsion Laboratory, California Institute of Technology, sponsored by the National Aeronautics and Space Administration, under Contract No. NAS 7-100.

[1]A. R. Johnston and J. M. Weingart, J. Opt. Soc. Am. 55, 828 (1965).
[2]Alan R. Johnston, Appl. Phys. Letters 7, 195 (1965).
[3]Alan R. Johnston, Appl. Opt. 8, 1837 (1969).
[4]M. Di Domenico, Jr. and S. H. Wemple, J. Appl. Phys. 40, 720 (1969).
[5]M. S. Shumate, Appl. Opt. 5, 327 (1966).
[6]L. E. Cross, M. M. Nicolson, B. Zlotnicki, and R. Whiddington, Nature 165, 440 (1950).
[7]D. Meyerhoffer, Phys. Rev. 112, 413 (1958).
[8]W. N. Lawless and R. C. DeVries, J. Appl. Phys. 35, 2638 (1964).
[9]Manuel Cardona, Phys. Rev. 140, A651 (1965).
[10]C. Gahwiller, Solid State Commun. 5, 65 (1967).
[11]Obtained from Harwhaw Chemical Co., Cleveland, Ohio.
[12]S. H. Wemple, Phys. Rev. B 1, 193 (1970).
[13]S. K. Kurtz and F. N. H. Robinson, Appl. Phys. Letters 10, 62 (1967).
[14]S. H. Wemple, M. Di Domenico, Jr., and I. Camlibel, Appl. Phys. Letters 12, 209 (1968); Gerald Burns and A. W. Smith, J. Quantum Electron. QE-4, 584 (1968).
[15]T. Nakamura and A. R. Johnston, J. Phys. Soc. Japan Suppl. 28, 82 (1970).
[16]S. H. Wemple, M. Di Domenico, and I. Camlibel, J. Phys. Chem. Solids 29, 1797 (1968).
[17]P. W. Forsbergh, Jr., Phys. Rev. 76, 1187 (1949).
[18]H. F. Kay and P. Vousden, Phil. Mag. 40, 1019 (1949).
[19]Obtained from A. Linz, Laboratory for Insulation Research, MIT, Cambridge, Mass.
[20]W. J. Mertz, Phys. Rev. 91, 513 (1953).
[21]A. R. Johnston, J. Quantum Electron. QE-4, 334 (1968).

AUTHOR INDEX

SUBJECT INDEX